ANNUAL REVIEW OF
PLANT PHYSIOLOGY

ANNUAL REVIEW OF PLANT PHYSIOLOGY

WINSLOW R. BRIGGS, *Editor*
Carnegie Institution of Washington, Stanford, California

PAUL B. GREEN, *Associate Editor*
Stanford University

RUSSELL L. JONES, *Associate Editor*
University of California, Berkeley

VOLUME 29

1978

ANNUAL REVIEWS INC.   4139 EL CAMINO WAY   PALO ALTO, CALIFORNIA 94306

ANNUAL REVIEWS INC.
Palo Alto, California, USA

REPRINTS The conspicuous number aligned in the margin with the title of each article in this volume is a key for use in ordering reprints. Available reprints are priced at the uniform rate of $1.00 each postpaid. The minimum acceptable reprint order is 10 reprints and/or $10.00 prepaid. A quantity discount is available.

International Standard Serial Number: 0066–4294
International Standard Book Number: 0-8243-0629-5
Library of Congress Catalog Card Number: A51-1660

Annual Reviews Inc. and the Editors of its publications assume no responsibility for the statements expressed by the contributors to this Review.

PRINTED AND BOUND IN THE UNITED STATES OF AMERICA

PREFACE

The reader who regularly uses the cumulative index of the *Annual Review of Plant Physiology* is perhaps aware that during the past ten years or so, two categories have become very large. The first of these is "Development," which has increasingly become a catch-all for a wide range of different kinds of reviews that touch on development; the second is "Special Topics." The discerning reader may have noticed that these two categories have been serving increasingly as convenient repositories for chapters that did not fit appropriately elsewhere. The reader may also have noted that most articles dealing with nucleic acids and protein synthesis were in the inappropriate category of "Nitrogen Metabolism."

The Editorial Committee this year completely revised its outline of organization in a manner designed to reflect more closely the various areas of research which the *Annual Review of Plant Physiology* covers. Although the new organization is as artificial as the old, it has the advantage that developmental articles are placed in far better perspective, and the category of "Special Topics" can be completely eliminated! Because the outline with its various subdivisions (not shown in entirety in the cumulative index) serves as a guide for the Editorial Committee to help insure that they keep in mind the broadest possible sweep of current research in plant physiology when topics and authors are considered for future volumes, we hope the new outline will prove more useful than the old.

Members of the Editorial Committee are grateful to George Cheniae for his five years of service on the Editorial Committee, and to Elaine Tobin, who was a guest at the Committee meeting this year. They also welcome Maarten Chrispeels, who begins his five-year term on the Committee this year. There is another change, not in personnel but rather in title, which the Committee heartily endorses. Jean Heavener, who has worked with our Review for the past ten years, now has the title of Production Editor, a title which reflects much more accurately the careful and demanding work she does on each volume.

WINSLOW R. BRIGGS, EDITOR

Annual Review of Plant Physiology
Volume 29, 1978

CONTENTS

POPULATION AND ENVIRONMENT

ANNUAL REVIEWS INC. is a nonprofit corporation established to promote the advancement of the sciences. Beginning in 1932 with the *Annual Review of Biochemistry,* the Company has pursued as its principal function the publication of high quality, reasonably priced Annual Review volumes. The volumes are organized by Editors and Editorial Committees who invite qualified authors to contribute critical articles reviewing significant developments within each major discipline.

Annual Reviews Inc. is administered by a Board of Directors whose members serve without compensation.

Annual Reviews are published in the following sciences: Anthropology, Astronomy and Astrophysics, Biochemistry, Biophysics and Bioengineering, Earth and Planetary Sciences, Ecology and Systematics, Energy, Entomology, Fluid Mechanics, Genetics, Materials Science, Medicine, Microbiology, Neuroscience, Nuclear Science, Pharmacology and Toxicology, Physical Chemistry, Physiology, Phytopathology, Plant Physiology, Psychology, and Sociology. In addition, two special volumes have been published by Annual Reviews Inc.: *History of Entomology* (1973) and *The Excitement and Fascination of Science* (1965).

Photograph by Debra Biale

Jacob Biale

Ann. Rev. Plant Physiol. 1978. 29:1–23

ON THE INTERFACE
OF HORTICULTURE
AND PLANT PHYSIOLOGY[1]

❖7642

Jacob B. Biale

Biology Department, University of California, Los Angeles, California 90024

CONTENTS

[1]Abbreviations used in this chapter: ABA, abscisic acid; IAA, indoleacetic acid; NAA, naphthalene acetic acid; 2,4-D, 2,4-dichlorophenoxyacetic acid; GA, gibberellin; GA_3, gibberellic acid; Ethrel, 2-chloroethanephosphonic acid; Amo-1618, 4-hydroxyl-5-isopropyl-2-methylphenyl trimethyl ammonium chloride 1-piperidine carboxylate; B-9 or Alar, 1,1-dimethylamino succinamic acid; CCC, 2-chloroethyl trimethyl ammonium chloride; Phosphon, 2,4-dichlorobenzyl tributyl phosphonium chloride.

1

0066-4294/78/0601-0001$01.00

To My Family

PREFACE

The extension of the invitation by the editorial committee of the *Annual Review of Plant Physiology* to prepare this introductory chapter is a distinct honor; to live up to the challenge is no easy task. In contemplating a subject to be covered, I searched for a topic that has not been in my mind for some time. I felt that I could discuss the relationship between plant physiology and horticulture with some degree of detachment as it is now 15 years since my transfer from the College of Agriculture to the College of Letters and Science. The advantages of taking a look as an outsider may be counteracted by insufficient insight on my part into problems encountered recently by investigators in horticulture.

The choice of the term "Interface" was intended to narrow down the discussion to fields in which there is no sharp demarcation line between horticulture and plant physiology. I shall use the term "horticulture" to designate that body of knowledge concerned with understanding the behavior and culture predominantly of trees bearing consumable fruit. Studies with fruits borne by annual plants, vines, or shrubs have also contributed considerably to certain "Interface" topics and they, too, will enter into the total picture. In some quarters the term horticulture also includes trees, shrubs, and flowering plants used by society for ornamental purposes.

The realization that basic knowledge is necessary to explain and advance the operations of gardening goes back to Hale's *Vegetable Staticks*. In a treatise on "The Theory and Practice of Horticulture" (London, 1840), John Lindley stressed the need of physiological principles on which to base horticultural practices. It was almost a century before sufficient knowledge in plant physiology and in other disciplines, such as soil science, entomology, plant pathology, and genetics, was accumulated to furnish a basis for better understanding and for improvement of practices in fruit culture.

The dependence of the advancements in horticulture upon plant physiology and the interactions between these two fields can be clearly seen in the pages of the *Annual Review of Plant Physiology* since its inception in 1950. The earlier volumes placed emphasis on mineral nutrition, growth substances, carbon assimilation, respiration, and water relations. Within the framework of these fields a number of reviewers from agricultural institutions contributed topics dealing with nutrient deficiencies, salt uptake, soil moisture, foliar applications of fertilizer, dormancy in trees, growth substances in horticulture, and postharvest physiology of fruits and vegetables. With greater stress on biochemical aspects of plant physiology, the reviews delved deeper into mechanisms of action, formation of biologically important substances, the nature of the major plant processes, and metabolic pathways.

Special sections in the series devoted to development, environmental physiology, and special topics continue to cover subjects directly applicable to research in agriculture including horticulture.

In the first part of this discussion I wish to cite two important fields of physiological horticulture, indicating underlying ideas for experimental approach. As part of one of the quoted studies, a tribute is included to two late teachers and colleagues of mine who personified an effective approach to the integration between basic and applied science. In the second part of this presentation, the more personal section, emphasis is placed on the training desirable for work on "Interface" problems. In addition, I hope that drawing some thoughts from my own field of research points to the attractiveness of being engaged in a field in which there is no distinct demarcation line between the basic and the "bread-and-butter" problems.

FACING UP TO COMPLEXITIES IN HORTICULTURAL RESEARCH

During the end of the third decade and the beginning of the fourth, while I was enrolled as an undergraduate student in the College of Agriculture of the University of California, certain studies with fruit trees, which were in progress at that time, exerted considerable influence on the approach to research in physiological horticulture.

The Problem

The fruit industries of certain districts in California, as well as in other states and countries, were faced with physiological disorders that caused drastic cuts into yields of both deciduous and evergreen orchards. These disorders were known as "little leaf" on peaches and other stone fruits, as "rosette" on apples and pecans, and as "mottle leaf" on citrus. In citrus the mottle leaf syndrome is characterized by yellow streaks between the veins, while the veins themselves retain chlorophyll. In the other species the symptom manifests itself in the spring by the opening of tufts or rosettes of leaves that are very small, frequently no more than 5% of the normal leaf area. When it was recognized that the causal agent was neither fungal nor bacterial, the attention was directed to a possible nutritional deficiency.

Interdisciplinary Approach

The problem was undertaken by W. H. Chandler, professor of pomology, D. R. Hoagland, professor of plant nutrition, and P. L. Hibbard, analytical chemist. They decided that the effort should be spread out through many localities rather than concentrating on one spot, thus assuring a better chance of success on some of the many plots under treatment. Massive applications of fertilizer were ineffective except for one site which had a sandy soil with low fixing power for applied inorganic chemicals. In that plot, recovery of peach trees from little leaf was observed when large amounts of commercial grade ferrous sulfate were applied, but not when the chemically pure compound was used. Analysis showed considerable quantities of zinc in the commercial $FeSO_4$. Heavy applications of zinc sulfate worked only in orchards of one district with a special light soil. After a series of experiments in more than 50 sites throughout the state of California the conclusion was reached that the most effective and universal cure could be obtained from foliage sprays and in some cases from zinc nails driven into the wood or from zinc powder plugged into tree trunks and allowed to be carried to the foliage by the transpiration stream. It turned out that zinc deficiency was the cause for the several disorders occurring in a number of horticultural species listed above. In greenhouse experiments with sand culture it was possible to reproduce the disorder and to cure it by supplying low levels of zinc. Subsequent biochemical studies led to a tentative conclusion that the role of Zn is that of a cofactor in the synthesis of the amino acid tryptophane, the precursor of auxin. I do not know whether these biochemical studies were substantiated, whether auxin application was tried to correct the disorder, or whether the levels of the auxin were found to be low in the foliage of little leaf or mottle leaf. Answers to these questions are less revelant here than the implications of the work under consideration.

Take-Home Lessons

The studies with little leaf and mottle leaf made a very important contribution in solving a pressing problem, and at the same time they are indicative of the benefits derived from interaction between different disciplines.

The concurrent pursuit of nutritional requirements by the Division of Plant Nutrition was helpful in focusing attention on possible need for micronutrients by the tree. The laboratory effort with rapidly growing plants to show that certain elements are required in minute quantities demanded a high degree of purification of chemicals and the use of special laboratory apparatus free of any contamination. Realizing these demands, the laboratory investigator might have concluded that there must be in the soil sufficient impurities of such elements as B, Mn, Cu, Mo, and Zn to make it highly dubious to be able to demonstrate that these elements were deficient in trees. Some investigators with interest in pure science might have argued also that the understanding of basic processes of plant responses is essential prior to any attack on problems of an applied nature. The cooperators on this project did not adopt this philosophy, realizing full well that the trees would die before the mechanisms of plant processes were unraveled. They felt that complete understanding of the responses is not necessary for carrying out field trials and that answers to perplexing problems in a relatively short time are feasible even with long-lived fruit trees.

How to conduct the tests under orchard conditions was another important lesson derived from the zinc studies. Serious doubts were cast on the orchard fertilizer experiments in which large tracts of land were divided into plots and the effects of additions of each element or combination of elements were tested. With trees the experimental error is large because few can be planted per acre and uniform acreage is not too abundant. A greater degree of uniformity can be expected in deep rather than shallow soils because of better development of the root system in the soil with greater depth. Trees with an extensive root system on one plot may absorb more nutrient even if it is present in lower concentration than do trees on another plot with restricted roots. Under such conditions soil analysis would not tell the story, while deficiency symptoms are more reliable in indicating the need of supplying the unavailable nutrient. A grower may not wish to delay in applying fertilizer until the deficiency is manifested because yield and quality could be affected prior to the appearance of deficiency symptoms. In many cases the need for a particular nutrient can be demonstrated by leaf analysis for the element in question. Foliar analysis is certainly useful where a nutrient is in excess or where it is definitely deficient. As more knowledge is gained on physiological responses the horticulturist will be able to rely on the leaf to tell him about the needs of the tree.

Great and Humble Men of Science

I have chosen to discuss the zinc deficiency work not only because of the merit of this study for the subject under discussion but also because of my reverence for the two cooperators of this project: William H. Chandler (1878–1970) and Dennis R. Hoagland (1884–1949). I valued them as inspiring teachers and I continued to maintain close contact with them long after my student days in Berkeley. The impact of these men on a generation of students and on scholarship in their respective fields, coupled with their qualities as human beings, deserves special consideration.

Chandler was unique as a scientist, administrator, man of ideas, and man of character. There is no question in my mind that he earned to the fullest the title of horticultural scientist. He had the ability, the insight, and the experience of integrating the anatomical features, the functions, and the responses to the environment of fruit trees. In his books on both deciduous and evergreen orchards he succeeded in systematizing horticultural knowledge, but at the same time he questioned horticulture as an independent discipline as he questioned the existence of an independent science of agriculture. A research man, in his opinion, to be effective in horticulture must have thorough training in botany, chemistry, and plant physiology. When a student was preparing to do horticultural research, Chandler would recommend that he take a minimum number of courses in horticulture, since the practical aspects can be picked up later on the job. At the same time he felt that work with rapidly growing grasses cannot take the place of tests and observations of trees in the orchard. Neither can laboratory results be transposed into recommendations for practice without field trials. Frequently the problems of the farm do not seem to be closely related to available scientific principles; neither can one wait for a system of knowledge to evolve complete enough to supply answers to all farm problems. In such situations the farm adviser has fulfilled a crucial role. He brings field problems to the attention of the experiment station man, helps him in setting up trials, evaluating results, studying limitations, and drawing up conditions for restudy. In his personal discussions and in his speeches, Chandler advocated extra caution in interpreting data from field tests because of the inherent complexities involved in working with trees. To him the outstanding virtues of a good experimenter are curiosity, diligence, patience, tentativeness, and integrity in reporting his observations.

Chandler himself was a patient man and a man of sturdy character; his sturdiness seemed to come from the trees he worked with. He was an humble man, but not a timid one. He tended to see the good in people, but he did not mince any words when he noticed abnormal selfishness and capriciousness. Egocentrism, excessive ambition, self interest, and lack of sharing of credit among academic people irritated him particularly. He felt that for everyone in the institutions of higher learning who considers himself important and indispensable there are hundreds on the outside who could do as well had they been given the opportunity for education. He referred to these people as the dormant buds and he stated that the "emblem of his faith was the tree and its system of dormant buds." He hoped that man would cultivate his desire for prestige somewhat less and instead develop his group instincts and acquire a greater appreciation of his heritage and cultural values of life.

It is no surprise that the cooperation between Chandler and Hoagland was so successful. They both shared the philosophy of harmonious interaction between the applied and basic in agricultural research. They also had similar broad outlooks on university and world affairs. They were both men of unusual personal qualities which inspired their associates and students. While they were both aware of the complexities of plant-soil interrelationships, their research trends and research programs differed considerably except for the cooperative zinc problem. Chandler had chosen to stand by his trees despite the long years required for results and the cumbersome nature of his experimental material. Hoagland went in the direction of adapting more simplified systems in order to gain insight into mechanisms of ion accumulation by plant cells. The selective action in absorbing certain ions such as potassium against the concentration gradient fascinated him. He came to the conclusion that problems of this kind must be studied in a less complex medium than the soil, and therefore designed a suitable culture medium known to this day in plant physiological laboratories everywhere as the "Hoagland solution." He also realized that in order to obtain reproducible results it is essential to use relatively simple systems such as *Nitella* or isolated roots and constant environmental conditions. Together with A. R. Davis, he designed two plant chambers for the control of temperature, humidity, and light intensity. This equipment was probably one of the first phytotrons introduced to work with plants. Hoagland was very much admired by members of his department and by the faculty of the university as well as by plant physiologists everywhere. Despite his preoccupation with many departmental and campus duties, he found time for students and staff. Whenever I went to Berkeley I knew that I would be welcome in his office. Conversations were always lengthy and on many subjects; he always asked about the wellbeing of his friend Chandler. Hoagland, who was ailing in the last years of his life, would remark repeatedly that Chandler was wise in selecting good genes. If Hoagland was lacking in genes for physical health, he made up for this lack with a brilliant mind and a generous heart.

CHEMICAL REGULATION IN PHYSIOLOGY AND HORTICULTURE

The curiosity of plant physiologists about unilaterally illuminated coleoptiles turning toward the light and about horizontally placed roots bending downward has resulted in discoveries with a far-reaching impact on horticulture as well as on plant physiology. I wonder whether the horticulturist of 50 years ago realized the full significance of Went's successful isolation in agar blocks of minute amounts of a substance which moved from the tip downward in the oat coleoptile and caused cell stretching. It took less than a decade from the time of that discovery for investigators in horticulture to embark on research and use of IAA and synthetic auxins on a variety of responses in fruit trees. With the introduction of a number of other naturally occurring as well as synthetic growth-regulating substances, new opportunities have opened up to look for agents with specific functions and for actions of combinations of regulators. The field of chemical regulation of flower and fruit development selected here for demonstrating the interrelation of horticulture and plant physiology is of particular relevance to investigators whose aim is improvement in yields and quality of fruit crops.

Flower Bud Differentiation

The chemical regulation of floral initiation has been studied directly by the application of naturally occurring or synthetic substances and indirectly by the use of growth retardants which effect the levels of the endogenous regulators. The results of these studies are variable and the conclusions are complicated by interactions and changes in the nutritional status of the tree.

A spectacular result with flowering of pineapple and of other bromeliads was achieved with external application of NAA, 2,4-D, ethylene, and Ethrel. Ethylene is the product of Ethrel decomposition and is probably produced also as a result of auxin application. Flowering success with ethylene was reported also for apples and mangos, but not for other species. In some plants cytokinins were observed to promote flowering and in others a combination of benzyladenine and one of the gibberellins was more effective than either one alone. The promotion of floral initiation by GA_3 is well established for rosette plants with a long-day photoperiod, but gibberellins act as inhibitors of flowering in most woody dicotyledons.

The role of gibberellins in the control of vegetative and reproductive development has been the subject of several studies by Anton Lang and associates. In brief, gibberellins appear to have different effects at different concentrations. By the use of morphactins such as CCC, B-9, and Amo-1618 it has been possible to lower the content of endogenous GA_3 to a level suitable for flower initiation. The idea was advanced that flower formation is suppressed above a certain maximal level of GA. As to the endogenous controlling mechanism, it is not known what takes the place of the morphactins. Conceivably, abscisin occurring universally might turn the switch on GA synthesis. Another possibility is a dynamic equilibrium between the various gibberellins, each with a different specific function. Whichever the case may be, interactions play an important role whether between different forms of one group or between different groups of regulating substances. Some of the workers in this field ascribe an ultimate flowering role to florigen, postulated from photoperiodic studies as a substance produced in induced leaves and capable of moving through a graft union to a noninduced branch. The attempts to isolate and identify florigen met with little success.

In light of these complexities the work of the horticulturist has to be largely empirical as he explores the various treatments suggested by the laboratory people.

Normally the fruit investigator is not faced with problems of floral initiation. Failure to produce sufficient flowers for a good yield is rarely a problem in the highly selective clones of orchard species. The control of time of flowering to avoid spring frosts or other hazards is probably of greater importance, especially in deciduous orchards. Under these conditions flower buds are formed in mid- to late summer following the flush of growth and remain dormant until the next spring. The concern in this case, especially in warmer climates, is that there should be enough days at temperatures below 6–8°C to break the rest and allow for abundant and uniform bud opening. In evergreen trees, differentiation of flowers takes place from apical meristems terminally or at axils of leaves of current season's shoots or, as in deciduous trees, from shoots formed in the previous year. In both cases day length does not appear to play a role in the reproductive process. Flower formation in fruit clones can be influenced indirectly by nutrition. Insufficient flowers may be produced when the nitrogen deficiency is so severe that small leaves with low chlorophyll content are formed. Another cause, though less likely, for reduced flowering is when a great excess of nitrogen results in succulent growth. Micronutrient deficiencies could affect flowering, but only when the deficiency is uncommonly severe. The horticultural literature tends to stress the relationship between nitrogen level and carbohydrate accumulation as a factor in flowering. On this point there may be a meeting of minds with plant physiologists who postulate that the role of the endogenous growth regulators is to mobilize the photosynthates from the leaves.

The Control of Fruit Set and Growth

To insure a proper fruit set in relation to foliage surface and to make certain that the fruits develop to maturity is of special concern to the horticulturist. Plant physiologists within agricultural organizations have contributed significantly to the clarification of the role of growth substances produced during pollination, fertilization, and seed development. Some of the most notable contributions were made by J. P. Nitsch, L. C. Luckwil, and J. C. Crane. A brief summary of their findings and of others will serve as background for drawing a few general conclusions and implications.

Fruit set commences with pollination, thus supplying a stimulus to the ovarian wall in the form of auxin or auxin-like substances and possibly also in the form of GA or GA-like substances. The stimulus which continues with syngamy, the fusion of male nucleus with the egg cell, is ascribed to these substances as well. The action of pollination and fertilization in bringing about cell expansion in the tissue of the ovary wall can be replaced in some but not all species by external applications of growth-regulating substances. Parthenocarpic fruits were set by auxin in tomatoes and in strawberries, while in stone and pome fruits, in blueberries and in cranberries, only gibberellins were effective. In cherry a combination of the two substances was required. Either cytokinin or GA_3 was responsible for setting seedless grapes. In Calimyrna figs the role of pollen was replaced by an auxin-like chemical, 4-amino-3,5,6-trichloropicolinic acid, as well as GA and cytokinin. Both growth substances and growth retardants were found to increase yield in several species. Apricots responded to auxins but not to GA, the level of which is high in this fruit. GA_3 was effective in pears and in cranberries. Alar, CCC, and phosphon, as well as ABA applications, resulted in increased crops of grapes and tomatoes. Apparently the level of cytokinins was raised by the use of growth retardants. A spectacular increase in the rate of growth of figs and consequent acceleration of maturity was attained by use of ethylene, Ethrel, and by high concentrations of auxin, resulting in ethylene production by the tissue.

In order to translate the effects of external applications into mechanism of action, analyses were made of the various substances at several stages of fruit development. In apple seeds and pericarp tissue, known and unknown auxins as well as GA_4 and GA_7 were identified. In the banana, cytokinin-like and gibberellin-like substances in addition to IAA were discovered. A special non-indolic auxin was reported in citrus fruits. The content of growth substances is always much higher in the seed than in the mesocarp, but when changes in concentration were followed in relation to growth of the entire fruit no correlations were observed. In some cases it was shown that peaks in growth substance content coincided with peaks of nucellus or endosperm or embryo development. In general, the fluctuations in auxins or gibberellins do not correspond to trends in the rate of growth of the mesocarp.

As to the role of endogenous growth substances, the most widely held theory is that they fulfill a mobilization function. By maintaining relatively high levels of the regulators in the seed a sink for products of photosynthesis is established between the reproductive organs and the vegetative tissue. This theory does not explain the need for a variety of substances and the reason for widely differing chemical structures. Neither does it explain the differences among different fruits in response to applications.

Hormonal Effects in Mature Fruit

The complex problems arising from interactions and antagonisms between different growth-regulating substances can be clearly demonstrated in the studies dealing with fruit maturation. Horticulturists have used auxins, growth retardants and other substances to control abscission and to prevent premature fruit drop. In some instances, advanced maturity and ripening were ascribed to treatment, while, in fact, delay in harvesting could have made the difference. There was also the possibility that sufficient substance penetrated the abscising zone to prevent fruit drop, while permeation into the bulky fruit tissue was too slow to have an effect. By infiltrating thick banana slices (McGlasson and associates) with IAA or 2,4-D it was shown that ripening was delayed, while ethylene production and respiration were stimulated by treatment. Similarly, C. Frenkel and associates, working with intact pears, found that auxin can restrain the ethylene action. Infiltrating the tissue with the antiauxin p-chlorophenoxyisobutyric acid promoted ripening and reduced ethylene production, though it is not clear whether the level of ethylene was below the threshold concentration shown to be required for inducing the processes leading to ripening. An attempt to eliminate the ethylene action was made by placing antiauxin-infiltrated fruit under low pressure of 0.1 atmosphere; ripening was not retarded under this condition. In other studies it was found that auxin pretreatment delayed both normal and ethylene-induced ripening. As ripening commences there appear isozymes of peroxidase and IAA oxidase, suggesting that conceivably degradation products of auxin play a role in the process. The overall picture that emerges is that the auxin level in the fruit must be reduced and IAA oxidation products formed before the action of ethylene can be manifested. However, before this controlling role can be ascribed to auxin, it is necessary to obtain changes in the endogenous levels of the phytohormone.

Reports were made that GA also counteracts ethylene effects. This is based mostly on the retention of chlorophyll by treatment with GA as is the case in citrus peel. Some significant delays in ripening by GA were observed in stone fruits, especially in sweet cherries. In the case of apricots, cytokinins such as benzyladenine as well as GA treatment delayed color changes. The delay in chlorophyll destruction in oranges by cytokinin was ascribed either to the maintenance of GA levels or the retardation of the build-up in abscisic acid or ABA-like substances.

ABA levels have been investigated in apples and pears with a well-defined pattern of respiration related to ripening, the climacteric, as well as in nonclimacteric fruits such as citrus, grapes, and strawberries. In both cases endogenous levels of ABA increased preceding and during ripening. External applications of ABA accelerated the onset of ripening, and treatments which hastened senescence increased the level of ABA in the tissue. Some fruits exhibit a shift of sensitivity to ethylene during an advanced developmental stage when an increase in ABA concentration takes place. ABA was found to stimulate ethylene production in tissue slices. As a result of these studies the question arises of the nature of the ABA-ethylene relationship with respect to fruit ripening. Is it possible that ABA alone can be the triggering agent or is there a requirement for both substances coupled with disappearance of auxin and appearance of IAA oxidation products? The control of fruit ripening appears to involve complex hormonal interactions.

The State of the Art

The studies in my laboratory were not in the field of growth substances except the work on ethylene before it was recognized as a regulator. In order to systematize in my own mind the state of knowledge in this field, I made an attempt to select some of the major horticultural applications and relate them to one or more physiological roles. The tabulation presented here is a rough approximation. I am confident that there must be somewhere in the literature a more complete and more precise presentation of this kind. The inclusion of the effects of interactions would be of added importance. From the standpoint of the horticulturist, the classification of the numerous synthetic substances could be highly useful. This task would be quite difficult because of the great number of papers on growth regulators that have appeared in the horticultural literature and that have dominated the meetings of horticultural societies. The tendency to test each substance for a variety of activities as well as for yield and quality leaves one with the impression that the applications are more of an art than a science. This state of affairs is not surprising inasmuch as the plant physiologists and biochemists have not as yet unraveled the mechanism of action of the regulating substances at the cellular and at the tissue level.

Table 1   Some physiological roles and horticultural applications of growth regulators

Regulator	Physiological role	Horticultural application
Auxin	Cell elongation Tropisms Apical dominance	Rooting of cuttings Fruit set Tissue culture Abscission control

Gibberellin	Stem growth
	Flower formation in long-day
	  plants
	Enzyme induction
	Enhancement and retardation
	  of senescence
		Breaking dormancy
		Fruit growth
		Ripening retardation

Cytokinin	Cell division Inhibition of elongation Bud differentiation Regulation of foliar senescence	Delay of senescence Vegetative propagation Callus culture

Ethylene	Inhibition of cell elongation
	Diageotropism
	Suppression of bud growth
	Stimulation of formation of
	  abscission layer
		Fruit ripening
		Flower induction
		Leaf, flower, and fruit
		  shedding

Abscisic acid	Dormancy factor Inhibitor of seed germination Role in fruit abscission	Prolongation of dormancy in woody species

ABA, as the last of the growth substances discovered, has been credited with the regulatory role in several phenomena such as dormancy, abscission, ripening, and senescence. The control of these processes was ascribed previously to ethylene. The appearance of new substances results in increasing search for interactions and for mode of action. Kende and Gardner reviewed recently the literature on binding sites and came to the conclusion that "no single receptor protein for any of the plant hormones has yet been isolated." The search for receptors has been motivated by the situation in the animal field. It is possible that the plant regulators do not have the high degree of specificity of animal hormones. Conceivably, the mechanism of action involves a dynamic interrelationship between two or more of the regulators in which the balance between endogenous levels plays a role.

EMERGING RESEARCH FRONTIERS

Control of Basic Processes

The worldwide crisis in energy and in water supply is demanding drastic changes in orchard practices as well as in growing field crops. Research in all branches of agriculture will be increasingly directed toward utilization of atmospheric nitrogen as the fertilizers manufactured by energy from petroleum become too costly. In some vegetables and in ornamental horticulture notable success has been achieved in establishing symbiotic relationships between roots and nitrogen fixing microorganisms. We are far removed from accomplishing this with fruit trees. The development of new cultivars with this capability may hinge on achievements in modern methods of hybridization at the cellular level. There will be increasing demand for varieties requiring minimal quantities of water per unit dry matter produced. Transpirational losses can be reduced by antitranspirants and by regulation of stomatal opening, but care has to be exercised not to lower the photosynthetic efficiency. In horticulture the utilization of special substances for controlling transpiration, photosynthesis, and photorespiration will have as its goal not only economic use of water but also regularity of bearing behavior, increased yields, and improved fruit quality. For rational experimentation along this line more basic knowledge is needed on the mode of action of activators and inhibitors in plant processes.

Crop Regeneration and Improvement

The advances in plant cell and tissue culture coupled with the great strides in molecular genetics promise a bright outlook for the development of new varieties and new hybrids with an array of highly desirable agricultural traits. The dream may materialize when cultivars will be able to fix atmospheric nitrogen, have a high degree of resistance to drought, salinity, and disease, and produce a crop of high quality and high yield under a wide range of environmental conditions. There are many requirements for this achievement, but notable success has already been attained in the field of vegetative propagation. The principles of development of clones are well established and are universally applicable to all plants. Commercial production by rapid clonal propagation is now widely used in foliage plants, woody ornamentals, flowering plants, etc. The tissue culture method has been adapted also for the production of pathogen-free clones.

For crop improvement by cell culture the following stepwise procedure will be required: 1. growth of somatic and haploid cells, 2. isolation and culture of protoplasts, 3. intra- and intergeneric hybridization by protoplast fusion, 4. selection of desirable variants, and 5. vegetative regeneration of plants. For this technique to be successful in crop improvement certain conditions must be met. A well-developed tissue culture method is essential, and the modified trait has to find expression in the culture. Once an effective system is selected for the identification of the variant, it must be established that it is capable of regenerating and transmitting the desirable trait. Thus far, the first critical limitation for crop plants is the development of the tissue culture techniques. The analysis of the agronomic or horticultural trait under consideration at the cellular level presents another serious problem. Yield and quality are the usual goals of the horticulturist, but these phenotypes are highly complex end products of a series of biological processes and reactions. It would be helpful if use could be made of assays involving intermediary steps. For fruit trees the time saving factor is of special significance. A great deal of biochemical work involving metabolic pathways will have to be done to relate key reactions to horticultural goals.

Old Problem—New Approach

Some of the perplexing horticultural problems may be solved through studies at the cellular and subcellular level. I doubt whether the workers with apple scald or other chilling injury disorders back in the third or fourth decade of this century dreamed that the structure of cellular membranes might hold the key to this phenomenology. Chilling injuries are nonpathogenic disorders affecting horticultural produce at low temperatures, but not so low as to cause freezing of the tissue. The critical temperatures below which symptoms of physiological disorder appear may be as high as 12°C for the banana, 10°C for the lemon, 5–6°C for avocado, and 4°C for certain varieties of apple. The symptoms show up as spotting, discoloration, necrosis, and pitting on the skin of fruits. Surface cells collapse and the tissue becomes susceptible to invasion by decay organisms. Abnormal ripening follows chilling injury.

A great deal of physiological and chemical work has been done on this problem, but only recently a promising new approach was undertaken. Comparisons were made on the oxidation rates at different temperatures of mitochondria prepared from healthy tissue of both chilling sensitive and chilling resistant materials (Lyons and Raison). The results were presented as changes of Arrhenius activation energies plotted against temperature. In mitochondrial oxidations from chilling-resistant tissue the activation energy was constant over the entire range of temperature. On the other hand, in chilling sensitive material there was a break in the Arrhenius value at the temperature at which chilling occurs. The oxidative pattern was correlated with a physical phase transition in membranes from liquid-crystalline to solid-gel structure. This transition is considered to be responsible for conformational changes in the membrane-bound oxidative enzymes. An analysis of lipid composition revealed that the phospholipids from chilling-sensitive species had a tendency toward a higher ratio of saturated to unsaturated fatty acids. If this proves to be the case, the question arises whether it is possible to modify the composition and thus alter the response to temperature.

TRAINING FOR INTERFACE TEACHING AND RESEARCH

An Immigrant in California

My arrival in the USA from Poland was during the year prior to the stock market crash, but it took some time before I felt the impact of that event and never to the extent that the millions of unemployed did. To me America meant freedom and opportunity. When I mastered English sufficiently well to read novels, I enjoyed Louis Adamic's "Laughing in the Jungle" and "A Country Full of Nice People," which gave a fascinating insight into immigrant life in those years. But before I was privileged with this type of enjoyment I had to face up to the problem of language.

Since the fall semester had already started, I was taken directly from the transcontinental train to the campus in Berekeley. I was immediately confronted by a special examination in English for foreigners. The examining professor disclosed to my aunt what was totally obvious to me: I did not know any English. He said he would pass me because otherwise I could not register. My next problem was to decide which courses to take without the knowledge of the language of instruction.

Upon the advice of some fellow students, I enrolled in analytic geometry, scientific German, general botany, and Subject A (English). Mathematics had been a favorite subject with me in high school; therefore I had no difficulty following the symbols and solving the problems. Neither was there a serious problem with reading scientific passages in German, since I had studied the language for several years. The dilemma was to convince others that I understood what I was reading. The rest of the class experienced no difficulty in expressing themselves in English once they could understand the German. A sympathetic teacher excused me from class participation and trusted my competency. The story with botany was more complex. I had to take the introductory course as it was required for other courses. The evidence of the struggle is on all the pages of my copy of the textbook by Holman and Robbins. Nearly every sentence was translated into Polish, but that was of little help in following Professor Holman's lectures. The consequence was grim one day when I came to class and sensed an atmosphere different than usual. Everybody grabbed a paper and started writing without exhibiting the slightest surprise that an examination was taking place. I did not even make any attempt, whereupon I was called in by Holman who tried to talk to me in German. He excused me from examinations and instead suggested that I write two term papers. With the European notion of what a scholarly paper should be, I spent long hours in the small library of the botany department, removed the dust from the books by Sachs, Pfeffer, etc, and produced two papers entitled "Photosynthesis" and "Sexual reproduction of flowering plants." These papers more than fulfilled the requirement.

By the end of the fall semester of 1928, my English was sufficiently good to leave me free to contemplate the purpose and course of my training in agriculture. My goal in coming to California was to become a farmer, and later to join a cooperative settlement (kibutz) in Palestine and help establish a national home for the Jewish people. The studies in the agricultural curriculum in Berkeley did not hold out much promise to transform a city boy into a man of the soil. David Appleman, whom I met shortly after my arrival and who has been one of my closest friends to this day, tried to convince me that mathematics, chemistry, and physics are essential for training in agriculture. This made me dubious about continuing in Berkeley. About this time I discovered that Davis offered the kind of course that appeared to suit my purpose.

The Nondegree Program

The two-year course at Davis was designed to teach a wide variety of farm practices. You could learn how to plant, prune, raise chickens, use the tractor, and, if you could muster up the courage, arrange a date between a bull and a cow. There was little reference to principles, and use of books was kept to a minimum. Entrance requirements were very lax so as to make it possible for the sons (and rarely daughters) of farmers to enjoy college life. Since nearly all of the students came from farms, they did not need to learn the art of farming. I believe that later in life they would have valued their college years more had they learned to appreciate a book, analyze a play, or gain insight into the history of their country and of other countries. For anyone preparing to run the family farm or to manage a commercial orchard, courses in economics, chemistry, and biology might have been more beneficial for facing up to problems that could not be predicted a priori than learning the art of farming.

As for myself, I certainly did not belong there, though in later years administrative officers of the nondegree course cited my academic career as evidence of success for the program. Soon I came to the realization that I was learning very little about the principles of agriculture and the acquisition of farming practices was negligible. This state of affairs was brought home to me during the first winter recess when, following a full semester's course on pruning, I fancied myself an expert in this art and looked for a job. When I declared proudly to the man in the employment office in Sacramento that I came with experience from Davis, he promptly rejected me with: "We don't want college boys." I did succeed in landing a job pruning peaches that paid 50¢ per tree rather than by the day. My expertise in pruning resulted in pruning one tree the first day, when I should have done eight in order to make a living wage. Despite my realization of the inadequacies of the nondegree program, I did obtain a certificate of completion, utilizing at the same time the opportunities at Davis for taking as many degree courses as I could possibly schedule. One of these was in pomology in which Chandler's book on *Fruit Growing* was used. I sensed that this man had a great deal to offer and realized that this was so when I returned to Berkeley.

Prior to my resumption of studies toward a BS degree in horticulture at Berkeley, I took an eight week summer session course in citriculture which was given at Riverside by R. W. Hodgson and staff from the Division of Subtropical Horticulture in Berkeley. The course attracted students from nearly all citrus producing regions of the world and was famous in particular for the weekly all-day field trips. Moving in a long caravan of cars and stopping in groves, packinghouses, and storage plants, the student learned about various problems not so much from the staff as from the farm advisers, extension specialists, growers, and managers. Hodgson's lectures presented a masterpiece of organization, easy for students to follow and reproduce, but with little attention to the unknown and the problematic aspects of fruit growing. This type of presentation was in striking contrast to that of Chandler, who stimulated the student to question and analyze.

Horticulture and Plant Physiology at Berkeley

The plant science curriculum of the statewide College of Agriculture specified requirements in English, mathematics, physical sciences, biological sciences, with minimum exposure to the major. Thus, a student wishing to obtain a BS degree in horticulture was required to enroll in a few courses in his specialty covering about 10% of total semester units (12 out of 120). He could take more if he wished to since provision was made for electives. The curriculum had considerable flexibility and was subject to administrative interpretation. The assistant dean, who served as student adviser, took the view that rules can be enacted by a secretary and it was his function to make allowances for individual cases. This attitude coupled with credits for my European high school enabled me to graduate in one year after the Davis experience.

The point that I wish to stress is that the plant science and other four-year curricula in the College of Agriculture, in contrast to the nondegree program, prepared the student for various agricultural activities such as teaching, advising, appraising. As farm advisers in the numerous counties of the state and as extension specialists, the graduates of the college not only serve the growers, but they serve as a bridge between the investigator and the orchardist; often they assist in setting up field experiments to test out new findings. With the decrease in rural population, few of the graduates returned to the farm, but those who did with the BS degree were prepared to follow new developments. Years later when some of these people returned as alumni, they complained that the faculty should have insisted on their taking more science and humanities; they were never concerned about insufficient courses in agriculture. Some, if they had to do it again, said they would have majored either in social sciences or in humanities.

In the postgraduate plant program leading to the PhD degree in the College of Agriculture, no specialization in any of the crops was available. The degree had to be in plant physiology, administered by an interdivisional committee on an individual basis even though certain requirements pertained to everybody, as, for example, reading knowledge of two foreign languages, calculus, physical chemistry, biochemistry, and advanced plant physiology. There was a great deal of freedom in the choice of a topic for research, but one could expect interest and helpful suggestions from any member of the teaching and research staff. The doors of some of the very busy professors were open to students not only for professional inquiries but also for a chat on politics, economics, literature, etc.

The atmosphere in Berkeley was conducive to graduate studies, for free exchange of ideas, and for a great deal of latitude in the choice of the dissertation topic. The doctoral candidate was not required to tailor his thesis research to the activities of a particular laboratory as long as significant physiological questions were raised and a reasonable experimental approach selected. Students associated with crop departments could easily formulate a problem that fitted well in the "interface" of agriculture and plant physiology. My own doctoral research was of this kind. The selection of a study of water relations in citrus was motivated partially by my affiliation with the Division of Subtropical Horticulture in which I held the appointment of research assistant. My work was sponsored by this division as well as the Division of Plant Nutrition. The control chambers of Davis and Hoagland were essential for an investigation of the saturation vapor deficit as a factor in the rate of transpiration of rooted citruc cuttings. Fick's law of evaporation was found to be applicable within a narrow range of temperatures, while outside that range significant changes took place as a consequence of physiological effects. Subsequently, when I transferred to UCLA, I continued these studies for a few years, stressing in particular the relationship between the absorbing system and the transpiring surface. An interesting and unexpected by-product of this work was the observation of periodicity in the rate of transpiration of rooted lemon cuttings under constant environmental conditions. The water loss from plants grown on 4-hour light periods alternating with 4 hours of darkness depended on prior light history. The light period which coincided with previous day or artificial light caused a greater rate of transpiration than an equal light period which corresponded with previous night or darkness. In other words, the plants remembered for several days when there was supposed to be day and night. This problem was not pursued further because of my transfer to a new field of research dealing with fruit physiology.

POSTHARVEST PHYSIOLOGY—MODEL FOR RESEARCH AT INTERFACE

The transfer from studies of transpiration to respiration and fruit physiology took place some three to four years after I came to UCLA and was working on a temporary basis during the height of the depression of the 1930s. The opportunity for a regular academic position opened up when I was offered and agreed to take over a project initiated by the California Fruit Growers Association (Sunkist) through a $2000 donation. This was probably one of the first, if not the first, extramural grant received by UCLA. The citrus growers were interested in certain physiological disorders which caused serious losses in oranges and in lemons subjected to low temperatures. The regents accepted the fund without strings attached, but it was understood that the research would concentrate on postharvest problems.

A Fortunate Break

Lacking experience and having only scanty knowledge of the literature, I followed a lead from work with apples and bananas which showed that ripe fruit produced a gas that accelerated the ripening of unripe fruit. Accordingly, a simple experiment was designed. Air was passed from jar A with yellow lemons to jar B with green lemons. In the control, air was passed from jar C (green) to jar D (green). Each of the jars contained 50 lemons. Measurements of CO_2 evolution were made on the comparable jars B and D. For weeks no significant differences were recorded and the experiment was about to be terminated. Then an unexpected result was observed as the respiration rate rose in jar D, but not in the expected jar B. The possibility that mold on fruit had developed in jar D, thus contributing to the increased rate of respiration, proved to be negative. Instead we found one lemon partially covered with mold in jar C only. Since no respiration determinations were made on jar C, the suspicion arose that the fungus was producing a potent emanation which affected the rate of CO_2 evolution of the sound fruit. After extensive studies with pure cultures, it was established that the common green mold *Penicillium digitatum* and not some of the other storage fungi, not even the closely related blue mold *Penicillium italicum,* produced an emanation which caused a rise in CO_2 production, destruction of chlorophyll, and abscission of stem tissue. The potency of the fungal gaseous product was demonstrated by passing air from a single infected fruit over 500 green lemons and observing a respiratory rise in the entire sample.

The actual identification of the gaseous emanation as ethylene took several years. This was possible only after studies of the nutritional requirements of the fungus and after the development of a manometric method for the determination of low concentrations of ethylene. It was more than two decades afterwards when S. F. Yang traced ethylene biosynthesis by *P. digitatum* to glutamic acid involving the citric acid cycle. The mechanism of ethylene formation in the fungus is distinctly different than in fruits in which methionine was shown to be the ethylene precursor.

Going Out on a Limb with Ethylene

As the manometric method became operational, a survey was undertaken of 14 species of fruit of different climatic zones with respect to the relationship between ethylene evolution and CO_2 production. As a result of this study "the hypothesis was advanced that native ethylene is a product of the ripening process rather than a causal agent" (from Biale, Young & Olmstead, *Plant Physiology*, 1954). We decided to make this statement even though we realized our methodological limitations, which did not allow for collection of information on the relationship between external ethylene evolution and the internal concentrations in fruit tissue. I am pleased that this daring statement was made because it served as a stimulus for a great deal of work during the ensuing decade. Stanley Burg at first, and others later, challenged our hypothesis on the basis of results obtained by the newly introduced gas chromatographic procedure which was much more sensitive than the manometric method. Ethylene was proposed as the ripening hormone because concentrations higher than threshold were detected prior to the climacteric rise in respiration. The fact that physiologically active amounts were present in some fruits without inducing ripening was countered by the contention that the effectiveness of ethylene depends on the sentitivity of the tissue to it. In present-day thinking the resistance of the tissue might be ascribed to auxin, suggesting the need to follow changes in auxin along with ethylene prior to the respiratory rise. Recent precise studies by Roy Young and associates on avocado and cherimoya indicate that the rise in O_2 uptake either precedes or follows closely the increase in ethylene. Reservations about ethylene as the sole triggering agent emanated also from the work with grapes by Coombe and associates. Burg supplied evidence for the role of ethylene as ripening hormone by suppressing banana ripening under hypobaric conditions; contradictory results were reported on tomato by Bruinsma and associates. Obviously, the field is still in a state of flux though the onus of proof is on those who question the role of ethylene. The complications resulting from interaction with ABA and other growth-regulating substances were discussed in a previous section of this paper.

Unfinished Research

Much more can be written about the problems not completed and about studies that went out on a tangent than on the published reports of work done. I shall limit myself here to a few examples to indicate the spectrum of interests of those who have been associated with the laboratory and possibly to stimulate interest in pursuing some of the unresolved questions.

By working simultaneously with avocados and citrus fruits we were exposed continuously to the differences between the species. To obtain an orange fit for consumption one waits until it ripens on the tree, while the avocado, at least those grown in California, does not ripen on the tree. If a Fuerte avocado is picked in December and kept at 20°C, it will be in proper edible condition in 8–15 days. The same fruit may be left on the tree until April or May in unripe condition. The number of days for ripening of the late-harvested fruit are reduced, but the pattern of ripening is the same as that of the early pick. Thus far, we have no inkling of what this inhibitor of ripening present in attached avocados is, despite many attempts to pinpoint its nature.

The differences between avocados and citrus in postharvest respiratory behavior prompted us to differentiate between climacteric and nonclimacteric classes of fruits. Can the difference be explained simply by differential rates of ethylene production, or should we look for metabolic patterns that might be different? In the avocado, apple, and banana a great deal has been learned about protein and nucleic acid metabolism and about energetics, while there is only scanty work along these lines with fruits classified as nonclimacteric.

When fruits of either class are harvested and placed under controlled conditions, one may predict certain responses to temperature and to the gaseous composition of the atmosphere which do not differ too significantly between species. An important exception was discovered when citrus fruit were subjected to different levels of CO_2. The respiration rate in terms of oxygen uptake was stimulated rather than suppressed as the CO_2 level was increased, and more so in air than at lower oxygen levels. In following up this problem with labeled CO_2, it was established that radioactivity was incorporated rapidly into malate, citrate aspartate, suggesting oxaloacetate as common precursor. We left the problem at this point and did not establish whether increased CO_2 tension raises the rate of respiration by increasing the content of Krebs cycle acids.

An attractive feature of postharvest physiology is the opportunity and desirability of working at various levels of complexity. In attempting to understand the events in the detached fruit, we looked into reactions taking place in tissue slices and in subcellular fractions with concomitant studies of responses of the whole fruit. Investigating metabolism at several levels of organization also raised a number of perplexing questions up to now unresolved. I want to list one which has to do with the response to cyanide. We observed years ago that the oxidation rate of avocado tissue slices is not only insensitive to concentrations of cyanide inhibitory to the cytochrome oxidase, but is, in fact, highly stimulated by the inhibitor. On the other hand, mitochondrial oxidations are highly sensitive. HCN applied to the intact fruit was shown by T. Solomos to bring about a climacteric rise in respiration and to stimulate ethylene production. These discrepancies are amenable to experimentation in terms of studying the relative roles of the cytochrome system versus the alternate pathway of oxidation. It is gratifying to me to see that George Laties and his associates are following up these problems.

FRUIT RIPENING AND PLANT SENESCENCE

As more knowledge is acquired on the metabolism of the detached fruit, the question arises whether ripening is typically a senescence phenomenon or a prelude to it. Plant senescence has been viewed as a phase in the development of an organism or an organ in which irreversible events lead to cellular deterioration culminating in death. The essence of the stated question is to weigh the various processes taking place during ripening in terms of catabolic or anabolic reactions. A comparison of ripening with foliar senescence might be enlightening inasmuch as extensive post-maturation studies were conducted on leaves and on fruits.

In comparing these two organs, certain striking differences and certain similarities are evident. In the leaf both total protein content as well as incorporation of labeled amino acids decline with yellowing, while in fruits there is enhanced protein synthesis at the preclimacteric minimum as well as during the respiratory rise. In the avocado, incorporation of ^{14}C valine and leucine proceeded actively until close to the peak of the climacteric. Puromycin inhibited protein synthesis but not the respiratory rise, thus suggesting an independence of the two processes. A conclusion can also be reached that no ADP generated by protein synthesis is required to initiate the rise. As far as specific proteins are concerned, the indications are that hydrolytic enzymes are formed in leaves during yellowing and in fruits during ripening. There is perhaps a more striking rate of formation of cell wall degradative enzymes such as cellulase, pectinmethylesterase and polygalacturonase in fruits than in leaves. We know more about synthesis of proteolytic enzymes in the latter than in the former. The observations on increased activity of certain oxidative and peroxidative enzymes with the onset of the climacteric are indicative of the operation of the machinery for transcription and translation during senescence.

The differences between fruit ripening and leaf senescence extend also to changes in nucleic acids. In most cases reported for fruits there was little upward or downward trend in the content of total RNA or of the various components of RNA. In foliar senescence, on the other hand, total RNA declined and nucleic acid metabolism was suppressed compared with activities in mature green leaves. During fruit ripening incorporation of radioactive inorganic phosphate into nucleic acids was progressing at an active rate. In the avocado, ^{32}P was incorporated actively into the regular and into the heavy ribosomal fractions during the preclimacteric stage as well as during the period which corresponded to the first half or two-thirds of the rise. The rate of incorporation fell off drastically when the respiration of the fruit was close to the peak. On the other hand, labeling in the soluble RNA fractions progressed more actively in the fruit close to the fully ripe stage than in the unripe. It is not known whether the soluble RNA fraction represents transfer RNA or RNA degraded from ribosomes. In some fruits it was found that uridine was incorporated into nucleic acids and into ribosomal RNA in particular. Of special interest are the findings that ethylene enhanced the uridine incorporation and that inhibitors of RNA synthesis inhibited ripening. It appears, therefore, that from the standpoint of nucleic acid metabolism there is a wide divergence between leaf senescence and fruit ripening.

The differences recorded thus far might be correlated with differences in function and structure of the two organs. In leaves the photosynthetic activity declines with age along with yellowing and loss of insoluble nitrogen. The respiration proceeds at a constant rate until the stage of advanced senescence when, in a few species, a slight rise in oxygen uptake was recorded. At the ultrastructural level it can be observed during leaf senescence that endoplasmic reticulum and ribosomes deteriorate first, followed by disorganization of chloroplast structure. It appears that chloroplasts are more vulnerable than mitochondria. In green fruits prior to yellowing, or in those fruits which retain chlorophyll, no significant function can be ascribed to the chloroplasts. In avocados no Hill reaction could be demonstrated with isolated chloroplasts. On the other hand, mitochondria retain intact structure at least until the climacteric peak. Their oxidation activities are more pronounced during the rise and at the peak than during the preclimacteric stage. The oxidation rates of succinate may not be significantly higher in mitochondria from avocados in the process of ripening than unripe avocados, but they are certainly higher in the case of malate, α-ketoglutarate and pyruvate. Another important difference between mitochondria from preclimacteric and climacteric fruit is the dependence of the oxidation of the former and not the latter on the addition of thiaminepyrophosphate to the reaction medium. The hypothesis was advanced that α-keto acids limit the respiration rate of preclimacteric fruit. Support for this idea may be secured from studies on apples in which malic enzyme activity rises with ripening.

In drawing comparisons between fruit ripening and leaf senescence it was taken for granted that in fruits exhibiting the climacteric pattern the beginning of the ripening process coincides with the onset of the respiratory rise. This is assumed to be the case by fruit physiologists generally. If so, one must come to the conclusion that the events occurring during ripening prior to the climacteric peak are in many respects different from those in foliar senescence. The temptation is therefore to suggest that the major part of the rise reflects a signal to senescence rather than senescence itself. Ripening is not a form of senescence, but a prelude to it. According to this view, the logical conclusion to reach is that in ripening we find an interplay of synthetic and degradative processes.

FROM SUBTROPICAL HORTICULTURE TO BIOLOGY

Research at the "interface" of agriculture and plant physiology demands constant interest in additional disciplines such as genetics, biochemistry, cell physiology, and cell ultrastructure. Consequently, one is prepared for teaching in a variety of subjects. After the early years of teaching fruit physiology and respiration I had the opportunity of participating in cooperative courses in plant physiology. The program was initiated by Sam Wildman when he came to UCLA, and was joined later by Anton Lang, George Laties, and Roy Sachs. It included an advanced undergraduate course in which the students had the opportunity of working in the laboratories of the staff members. Of special interest to graduate students, postdoctoral fellows, and plant physiologists in several departments was a three year seminar-lecture course that covered the advances in the major fields of plant physiology. This course served also as a forum for discussions by visiting scholars. A large percentage of students participating in these courses came to UCLA from distant countries because of interest in citriculture and other subtropical fruits. The program toward the PhD degree broadened their training and interests. A good number of the doctoral recipients went into fields other than horticulture and made notable contributions in plant physiology and biochemistry.

As the College of Agriculture started to be phased out from the UCLA campus because of the low undergraduate enrollment, the number of graduate students from abroad also decreased. The orientation in the graduate program shifted from inter- to intralaboratory. At that stage I redirected my teaching interest toward an introductory course in cell and molecular biology. For the past decade I have been enjoying the contacts with younger and less sophisticated students. I feel strongly that the more senior members of departments should teach the elementary courses. I have been trying to convince my colleagues, without too much success, that it is highly rewarding to direct and stimulate students early in their career.

ACADEMIC FREEDOM

An item in a recent issue of *Newsweek* brought back to me the problem of academic freedom which has come up from time to time. The report was entitled "To Shrink a Scientist" and dealt with the dismissal of a biophysicist in the USSR. This man was not a dissident, but neither was he a comformist. He preferred not to attend prescribed political meetings and did not choose to include the name of the chief as co-author on a paper. Our academic system certainly has more safeguards against arbitrary decisions by administrators. I recall that at least on two occasions I did not hesitate to oppose deans on matters of considerable importance. I knew that the tenure system gave me a great measure of protection. We have had our share of bitter struggles for academic freedom. We know, of course, of sufficient instances of suppression of unpopular ideas and we realize the need to be on guard. We remember only too well the stormy period of 1949–50 when the regents demanded of the faculty a special loyalty oath. A number of professors, mostly from the Berkeley campus, resigned rather than take the oath. Eventually the oath was rescinded and the nonsigners were reinstated.

The hysteria of those days touched the lives of many people in Academia. I, too, had my own encounter with the FBI. In 1958 I was invited by the government of Israel to assist in the establishment of a laboratory for fruit physiology at the Volcani Agricultural Research Institute in Rehovot. Since the assignment was sponsored by an agency of the United Nations (FAO), FBI clearance was required before appointment could be made. After a long period of uncertainty I was presented with a bill of particulars. The FBI had a full list of my activities no matter how trivial. A serious charge was that on a certain date in 1947 my name appeared among others on telegrams to President Truman and to the Speaker of the House urging the abolition of the House Committee on Un-American Activities. They wanted to know the circumstances that induced me to take this step. They also inquired about the nature and extent of my association with members of the faculty who lectured before the People's Education Center.

I promptly replied that I trusted their information about the date and content of the messages, though I myself didn't keep a record of such protest telegrams. The reason that I gave my signature was that I felt the activities of that House Committee were undemocratic and un-American. I told the FBI that having immigrated from a country in which there was no freedom I was particularly sensitive to the witch hunt of the Congressional Committee. As to my friends on the faculty, I replied that I saw these individuals almost daily and I was proud of my association with them.

I considered them fine members of the faculty and good citizens. The clearance promptly arrived. Mine was an insignificant case but it is indicative of the times. It reminds me that other members of the academic community had more serious encounters with the authorities without any justification and that we must be constantly on guard.

NO BETTER LIFE

The occasional inconveniences caused by extra- and intramural politics do not subtract from the great attractions of the academic way of living; any other life style can hardly compete with it. While serving on various committees of the academic senate I heard a great deal of complaining about the low salaries compared to the incomes of other professionals. Only too often do we forget that we recieve a good living wage to do what we enjoy doing. Not too many people can say that. Here you have the privilege of determining your own research program and of teaching in your own style. You have the opportunity for professional associations with colleagues throughout the world and of traveling to meetings held in countries far and near. In some places, such as California, you have other advantages which cannot be measured in money. The lofty mountains are close enough for back-packing trips in summertime and for skiing expeditions in winter. When you finally retire after a lifetime of service you are supported by a good pension, you get an office or you share an office, and, if you can justify it, you frequently can count also on laboratory space. You can continue doing what you did before or you can take advantage of the numerous offerings by the university and start as a student all over again. For the privileges extended to me I am deeply grateful to the University of California and to the people of California.

ACKNOWLEDGMENTS

My appreciation to graduate students, postdoctoral fellows, and associates who contributed materially toward this chapter. In chronological order of their association with the laboratory—PhD recipients: H. K. Pratt, H. W. Siegelman, J. M. Tager, M. Avron, C. T. Chow, R. J. Romani, S. Ben-Yehoshua, S. H. Lips, C. Carmeli, D. L. Ketring, and H. A. Schwertner. Postdoctoral fellows: M. Lieberman, S. Uota, E. K. Akamine, W. O. Griesel, J. P. Nauriyal, R. Kaur, J. T. Wiskich, P. K. Macnicol, G. G. Dull, H. A. Kordan, M. Gibson, G. E. Hobson, C. Lance, A. E. Richmond, J. E. Baker, and A. D. Deshmukh. My thanks to G. G. Laties and D. Appleman for their ever-ready assistance to the students. A very special role in our program was fulfilled by R. E. Young, whose contributions were indispensable.

I wish to express gratitude for arrangements to do research or to lecture during sabbaticals to: H. A. Krebs, A. A. Benson, D. Koller, and B. Jacoby. My appreciation also to F. Lattar and M. Schiffmann-Nadel and their associates for the opportunity of working with them at the Volcani Research Institute.

Special thanks to Marjorie Macdonald for superb work on the manuscript.

Ann. Rev. Plant Physiol. 1978. 29:25–46
Copyright © 1978 by Annual Reviews Inc. All rights reserved

HEAT EFFECTS
ON PROTEIN BIOSYNTHESIS

❖7643

Victor A. Bernstam[1]

Department of Cell Cultures, Institute of Cytology, USSR Academy of Sciences,
Leningrad, USSR

CONTENTS

INTRODUCTION

Effects of temperature are being most intensively studied in ecology-oriented research (2, 103, 137). The instrumental potential of temperature treatments has long
been recognized and widely employed. At the same time, the analysis of temperature
effects on various stages of protein biosynthesis has been only sporadically performed by various researchers and the information available is rather fragmentary.
Nonetheless, some insight into the regulation of protein biosynthesis in cells exposed
to an adverse temperature environment may be obtained. The present review, by no
means comprehensive, only briefly summarizes available evidence on the effects of

[1]Present address: Cellular Chemistry Laboratory, School of Public Health, University of
Michigan, Ann Arbor, Michigan 48104

25

0066-4294/78/0601-0025$01.00

supraoptimal temperatures on DNA, RNA, and protein synthesis. Particular emphasis will be placed on the relevance of temperature studies on protein biosynthesis to the general problem of regulation of cell activity involving cellular membrane structures beginning at the cell surface. The latter have proved to be effective also in transducing nonspecific external stimuli into a rather specific intracellular response such as a change in the rate of translation. The role of the cell surface in regulation of cellular activity is being investigated most frequently by employing various specific agents such as lectins, antibodies, hormones, etc (44). The author's intention is to complement the important findings reported in such studies with observations on the effects of nonspecific agents, in particular supraoptimal temperature.

HEAT EFFECTS ON DNA SYNTHESIS

Studies of the effects of supraoptimal temperatures on replication indicate that once a round of DNA replication has begun, the process displays a rather high resistance to heating. Thus, in the course of repeated 30 min heat shocks (at 6°C above the optimum temperature for growth), which synchronize the division of the protozoan *Tetrahymena pyriformis* cells, the DNA synthesis is not blocked by heating (6, 29). Similarly, exposure of the myxomycete *Physarum polycephalum* in the S period does not interrupt the already commenced replication, but delays the subsequent mitosis and the immediately following period of DNA synthesis. The highest sensitivity of replication to heating as well as to inhibitors of protein synthesis (37) is observed 2 hr prior to metaphase (25). Again, the incorporation of ^{3}H-thymidine into replicating DNA was not inhibited by exposure of *Bacillus subtilis* cells to 10–12°C above the optimum growth temperature (10). Unfortunately, no detailed studies of the effects of elevated temperatures on individual steps of replication have been reported. At the same time, exposure of cells to supraoptimal temperatures, as is the case with amino acid starvation and inhibition of protein synthesis by inhibitors, has been shown to diminish the rate of DNA synthesis gradually so that the chromosomes, which are in the process of replication, terminate ongoing rounds of replication, whereas new cycles are not begun (88).

Interestingly, cell cycle-dependent variations in the heat sensitivity of replication in eukaryotic cells correlate with cyclic variations in the sensitivity of the cells to ionizing irradiation. In both instances, the highest resistance is observed in the S and early G_2 periods (40, 166). In this context, an interesting synergism has been observed in the effects of γ irradiation and heating in *E. coli* cells (52°C for 15 min). The radiosensitivity of DNA was 2.7 times as high in the heated cells (26).

Repair of the thermal injury of replication also has not been studied in detail. Observations have been reported, however, that single- and double-strand breaks in DNA produced by pulse exposures of cells to elevated temperatures can be repaired (55, 178). The rate of repair depends on the stage of the cell cycle at which the cells were heated (53), as well as on the physiological condition of the cells (56, 57) during repair.

HEAT EFFECTS ON RNA SYNTHESIS

In bacterial cells, the effect of supraoptimal temperatures on transcription has been studied in the psychrophiles *Micrococcus cryophilus* (109, 110), *Vibrio marinus* (124), and the mesophile *E. coli* (131). The incorporation of labeled uridine in *M. cryophilus* cells at supraoptimal temperatures proved to be significantly more thermoresistant than the amino acid incorporation. Moreover, an analysis of RNA species synthesized at elevated temperatures failed to detect any difference in the pattern of transcription compared to that at normal temperature.

In contrast to the early and drastic reduction in the accumulation of protein and DNA attributable to an increase in the incubation temperature of *V. marinus* by 10°C above optimum for growth, the accumulation of RNA continued for considerably longer periods of time (124). Similarly, prolonged exposure of *P. polycephalum* plasmodium to a temperature 6°C above the optimum for growth inhibited the accumulation of DNA and protein without notably affecting RNA accumulation for 72 hr (12). When analyzing the resistance of RNA and protein syntheses by the incorporation of labeled precursors in *E. coli* cells, Patterson & Gillespie (130, 131) found the former was more thermostable than protein synthesis. Moreover, acrylamide gel electrophoresis failed to detect any changes in the RNA species transcribed at elevated temperatures. Again, RNA synthesis exhibits a much higher thermostability than DNA and protein syntheses in *T. pyriformis*, judging from precursor incorporation experiments performed on intact cells and isolated nuclei (29, 30). That was also the case for the psychrophilic yeast *Candida gelida* (160) and for *P. polycephalum* (13, 14).

Electron microscopy (EM) has long been used to demonstrate alterations in the nuclear structure correlated with biochemically detected abnormalities in RNA synthesis in Chinese hamster kidney (BHK) and HeLa cells in culture (158). A selective destruction of nucleoli—the site of ribosomal RNA synthesis—could be observed following only 15 min exposure of BHK cells to 42°C. Similarly, the intranucleolar portion of chromatin was seen to undergo destruction followed by disintegration of the granular ribonucleoprotein structures in ascites tumor cells as a result of heating the cells to 43–44.5°C for 30 min (157). These morphological alterations have been shown to be accompanied by a drastic reduction in the synthesis of the nucleolar RNA as revealed by gradient fractionation of RNA isolated from heated cells (39°, 41°, 43°C, 30 min). These investigations were apparently the first combined EM and biochemical studies on the selective thermolability of the nucleolar functions and RNA processing. Essentially similar findings were reported in HeLa cells exposed to 42°C for 12 hr (174). An analysis of RNA isolated from heated cells revealed that the synthesis of rRNA precursors continued at an elevated temperature, whereas RNA processing proved to be thermolabile. The metabolism of mRNAs was assumed to be impaired by heating to a lesser extent than that of other RNA classes as evidenced by fractionation experiments. The disappearance of the granular component in nucleoli as a result of heating has been observed in the embryo cells of the amphibian *Pleurodeles waltilia* (43), in the Jerusalem artichoke tuber cells (62), and in *P. polycephalum* plasmodium (106). The comparatively higher thermostability of RNA synthesis over that of protein and DNA syntheses has also been reported for intact cells and isolated nuclei of a mutant BHK cell line thermosensitive with respect to DNA synthesis (84).

The biological significance of the higher thermostability of transcription as compared to that of protein synthesis has been explicitly shown by Penman and co-workers (54, 115, 162) in HeLa cells incubated at 42°C. At this temperature the transcription of specific RNA classes promoting the association of ribosomes with mRNA could be observed. These findings are consistent with the cited observations of selective inhibition by heat of the transcription of rRNA and continuation of the synthesis of other RNAs.

One of the possible ways in which the specificity of transcription may be affected by supraoptimal temperatures becomes apparent from the experiments of Shields & Tata (154). These workers demonstrated the essentially different sensitivity of RNA polymerases A and B isolated from rat liver cell nuclei to 10 min heating at 40°, 45°, and 50°C. RNA polymerase A was 90% inactivated by 5 min exposure to 45°C, whereas the activity of polymerase B was only 20% decreased. A similar difference could be observed in heating isolated nuclei, although the same degree of inactivation could be obtained at a slightly higher temperature (48°C). Again, similar findings were reported for the enzymes isolated from the yeast, where polymerase A was less thermostable than the respective enzyme from rat liver, whereas the yeast polymerase B was more thermoresistant than its counterpart from rat liver.

This differential heat sensitivity of RNA polymerases is directly relevant to the reported changes in the pattern of transcription at supraoptimal temperatures since polymerases of the A type (Mg-stimulated, α-amanitine resistant) are associated with nucleolar structures, while those of the B type are associated with the extranucleolar portions of chromatin (e.g. 31). In this context, the selective impairment of rRNA synthesis in nucleoli of heated ascites tumor cells (44.5°C for 30 min) may be readily understood (5, 157). Thus the selective switch-off of transcription of some genes and continuation of transcription of other genes in cells exposed to supraoptimal temperature may be accounted for, among other reasons, by the differing thermostability of various RNA polymerases.

Aside from observations of negative regulation of transcription in heated cells, the induction of new species of RNA, i.e. positive regulation, attributable to the action of elevated temperatures has been unequivocally shown to occur. As already mentioned, new RNA species are transcribed in HeLa cells incubated at 42°C. Inhibition of protein synthesis by cycloheximide was used to demonstrate that this response of transcription in heated cells might in fact result from inhibition of protein synthesis by heating (115). Specific changes in the pattern of transcription have been established by in situ hybridization in *Drosophila* salivary gland cells and in cultured cells at 37°C (162). Exposure to elevated temperature inhibited the transcription of some RNA species while at the same time inducing the synthesis of others. Particularly notable changes could be detected in low-molecular weight RNAs in heated *D. melanogaster* cells (142). Some of the observed changes in the population of transcribed RNAs could be attributed to impaired RNA processing in heat-shocked cells. More straightforward evidence showing that the synthesis of new RNA classes did occur in cultured *D. melanogaster* cells was obtained by autoradiography and hybridization in situ (22). In addition to establishing the transcription of new RNA species, it was noted that the synthesis of various RNA populations specifically transcribed in heat-shocked cells may not be strictly coordinated and various RNA species may be synthesized independently of one another. These elaborate and informative investigations unfortunately gave no answer as to what extent the changes observed in the transcription pattern had been accounted for by the action of elevated temperature itself and to what extent that was essentially a response to impaired translation in heat-shocked cells.

Investigations where effects of supraoptimal temperature on individual steps in transcription were studied directly are extremely few in number. Nevertheless, some relevant observations are available. Thus, unbound RNA polymerase has been shown to display a significantly lower thermostability than the enzyme bound to DNA. The bound enzyme also acquired an elevated resistance to various chemical agents, i.e. became nonspecifically stabilized (86). Likewise, the heat stability of polymerase A from rat liver increased upon binding to DNA and initiation of transcription (154). Visualization by EM of the RNA polymerase activity in *E. coli* cells revealed a reduction in the density of polymerase molecules per unit DNA length when the growth rate was lowered by changing the incubation temperature (65). This decrease was largely attributed to a reduction in the rate of initiation of transcription. Corroborative evidence comes from observations that rigorous temperature requirements are imposed on efficient formation of the RNA polymerase-DNA complex (73, 180). Below 17°C the initiating complex derived from *E. coli* dissociates rapidly. Stable binding of the enzyme to DNA occurs at physiological temperatures. Again, no observations have been made in these studies on the initiation of transcription at elevated temperature.

An evaluation of the RNA-synthesizing ability of intact cells and of isolated nuclei incubated at supraoptimal temperatures indicates that once commenced the process of transcription displays a comparatively high thermostability (29, 30, 130, 131). In contrast, the initiation of transcription was consistently found to be extremely thermosensitive. Termination of transcription appears to be rather thermoresistant in the systems studied. The posttranscriptional processing of RNA may be affected, however, by supraoptimal temperatures as found in HeLa, BHK, ascites tumor and *D. melanogaster* cells (100, 142, 157, 174, 176). Changes in the nuclear envelope permeability may also interfere with normal RNA processing at elevated temperature (48).

In addition to impaired processing, exposure of cells to elevated temperature has been repeatedly shown to enhance RNA degradation. Ribosomal RNA was predominantly degraded in heated *Aerobacter aerogenes* (164) and *E. coli* (143) cells. A complete degradation of 16S RNA and a partial breakdown of 23S RNA were observed in *Salmonella typhimurium* cells heated for 30 min to 48°C (168). Following this treatment the 30S ribosomal subunits were found to be completely degraded, whereas the sedimentation constant of the 50S subunits was reduced to 47S, reflecting a partial degradation of the larger subunit. A similar selective breakdown of 16S

RNA in heat-shocked cells was detected in *Staphylococcus aureus* MF-1 (141). In eukaryotic rabbit reticulocytes the situation was essentially similar (138).

In various cells, enhanced degradation of RNA at elevated temperatures was accompanied by a stimulation of RNA synthesis as found in *T. pyriformis* (30) and *P. polycephalum* (14, 15). On the other hand, in *E. coli* cells an enhanced degradation of mRNA could be detected (159), while no increase in either mRNA or rRNA breakdown was found in heated HeLa cells (54).

To sum up the evidence on effects of supraoptimal temperatures on RNA metabolism, it may be concluded that on the whole the process of transcription displays a relatively high thermostability. Combined with different thermostabilities of various RNA polymerases, this characteristic may account for the specific changes occurring in the pattern of transcription, including the induction of new RNA species in cells exposed to elevated temperatures. The comparatively higher thermostability of transcription compared with that of translation constitutes one of the mechanisms responsible for survival of cells exposed to temperature extremes. This property of transcription is apparently of fundamental importance for the control of protein synthesis in thermal environment. So far very little is understood about the control of transcription at elevated temperatures, but the most thermosensitive step in transcription is obviously the initiation. In some cases, the RNA processing and breakdown appear to be markedly affected at supraoptimal temperatures.

HEAT EFFECTS ON PROTEIN SYNTHESIS

The already apparent lower thermostability of translation as compared to that of RNA synthesis has been extensively documented for various types of cells. Impairment of protein synthesis is one of the earliest events among metabolic disturbances in heated *Micrococcus cryophilus* (109), *Vibrio marinus* (124), HeLa cells (115), and *P. polycephalum* (14, 16). In practically all cases, the inhibition of translation by supraoptimal temperatures has been shown to be accompanied with a reduction in the size and number of polysomes: in HeLa cells (115), mouse fibroblasts (150), rabbit reticulocytes (163), *P. polycephalum* plasmodium (24, 148), *T. pyriformis* (29), *E. coli* (130), *S. aureus* (141), etc.

Thermostability of Ribosomes

The reported degradation of rRNA in heated cells is obviously related to thermal injury of ribosomal subunits. Incubation of *S. aureus* for 15 min at 55°C results in an almost complete (85–100%) destruction of the 30S subunits and only slight damage of the 50S subunits (141). Likewise, a selective damage of the 30S subunits was observed in heated *S. typhimurium* (168). Reconstruction experiments combining the 30S or 50S subunits from heated cells revealed that the small subunit was selectively injured (87). Not only the rRNA, but the proteins of the subunits were affected by heating.

In addition to the demonstrated lower thermostability of the small subunit, it has been shown that the more thermostable large subunit can also impart elevated thermostability to the small one. This phenomenon has been shown in reconstruction experiments employing ribosomal subunits derived from *E. coli* and *Bacillus stearothermophilus* (4, 50). The influence of the large subunit extends beyond the observed elevation of the heat stability of the small subunit: it can also influence the functional properties of the small subunit. Thus the large subunit isolated from rabbit reticulocytes was found to inhibit the formation of the initiating complex by the 40S subunit with natural initiating codons, and this inhibitory activity could be eliminated by heating the 60S subunit to above 50°C (85). The AUG-dependent initiation was only possible with the 40S subunit rather than with 80S ribosomes, whereas poly U-dependent initiation could be observed with 80S ribosomes. The difference in the heat stability of the subunits was considerable: the activity of the small subunit was drastically reduced by heating to above 50°C, whereas that of the large subunit was increased twofold after exposure to 60° for 20 min.

The loss of the functional activity of heated ribosomal subunits was not necessarily associated with damage to rRNAs; changes in the protein moiety could be responsible (177). Thus heated ribosomes from mammalian brain tissue lost their ability to bind in vitro with mRNA and aminoacyl-tRNA. Again the small subunit proved to be the more thermolabile (61). A contradictory observation indicating the higher thermostability of the 40S subunit over that of the 60S one has been made in rat liver (140).

Complex conformational changes of ribosomal subunits produced by heating have been studied in detail (34). Comparisons of these changes for subunits isolated from pro- and eukaryotes revealed the already amply documented correlation between the thermostability of ribosomes and the temperature of the organism's life, which has been repeatedly described for individual proteins and complex enzyme systems alike (2).

Thermostability of Individual Translational Stages

The above observations are already suggestive of an extreme lability of the initiation of translation in heated cells. In some cases, the high thermolability of aminoacyl-tRNA synthetases was held responsible for this lability. Thus incubation of the psychrophile *Micrococcus cryophilus* at 30°C impaired the activation and binding of amino acids to tRNA. Aminoacyl-tRNA synthetases specific for histidine, glutamic acid, and proline were found to display particularly high thermolability (109–111). Structural analysis of purified synthetases in conjunction with observations of rapid repair of protein synthesis upon transfer to normal temperature was interpreted as corroborating the conclusion that changes in the rate of dissociation and association of subunits of the labile synthetases might explain the injuring action of supraoptimal temperatures on translation.

In a like manner, the heat lability of protein synthesis in the yeast *Candida gelida* was accounted for, at least in part, by thermolability of seven aminoacyl-tRNA synthetases as well as of some enzymes concerned in polymerization of the polypeptides being synthesized at elevated temperatures (125). In *Saccharomyces cerevisae* cells, the lysyl-tRNA synthetase was found to be thermolabile (18). Consequently, thermolability of aminoacyl-tRNA synthetases may be one of the possible sites of application of the inhibitory action of supraoptimal temperatures on translation.

What specific reactions in the formation of the initiating complex are particularly thermolabile is not known in detail for all of the systems studied. The heat lability of the initiating factor IF-2 has been implicated in thermal sensitivity of translation in *E. coli,* and the stability of this factor was found to increase upon addition of GTP and the formation of a stable complex comprising polyphenylalanyl-tRNA, GTP, and IF-2 (99). In contrast, other workers failed to detect the reported stabilizing action of GTP on IF-2 (121).

Changes in the tertiary structure of tRNA have also been considered among the reasons accounting for the thermolability of initiation of translation (7). An analysis of the stability of the mRNA-ribosome-tRNA complex reconstructed in vitro revealed that each of the components, including the state of tRNA molecules, contributed to the stability. Conformational changes of tRNA molecules beyond the anti-codon region have been found to affect the stability of the complex at elevated temperatures (119). The temperature-dependent loss of the acceptor activity of *E. coli* tRNA has been related to changes in the secondary or tertiary structure of tRNA rather than to the denaturation of respective synthetases (83). At the same time, slight alterations of the secondary structure of tRNA (ca 5–10%) produced by supraoptimal temperatures may not interfere with aminoacylation (179). Nonetheless, in a reconstituted system composed of tRNA from *E. coli* and a synthetase from the thermophile *Thermus aquaticus,* the optimum temperature for aminoacylation was found to correlate with the heat lability of tRNA from *E. coli* rather than with the thermophilic synthetase.

Elegant investigations of the regulation of protein synthesis at elevated temperatures have been performed by McCormick & Penman (115) in HeLa cells. The association of ribosomes with mRNA was found to be impaired by heating. In mouse fibroblast L cells, the inhibition of translation at an elevated temperature (42°C) is accompanied by the release of mRNA from disassembled polysomes (150). The formerly translated mRNA was retained in the cytoplasm as free RNP or in a complex of mRNP-monoribosome. The thermolabile step in initiation proved to be the association of the mRNP-monoribosome complex with ribosomes and the resulting formation of functionally active polysome complexes.

Again, a reduction in the rate of initiation of translation of hemoglobin mRNA in rabbit reticulocytes has been found to be responsible for the inhibition of polypeptide synthesis at 41–45°C (163). No accumulation of polysomes could be observed as the incubation temperature was elevated, i.e. the release of synthesized polypeptides—the termination step—appeared to be normal. By analyzing the time period required for incorporation of labeled tyrosine into specific sites of the hemoglobin chain being synthesized at 45°C, the possible inhibition of elongation could also be ruled out.

From a study of the regulation of the synthesis of globin by hemin, other workers reported on the temperature-dependent appearance of an inhibitor of initiation of translation in reticulocytes (59, 60). Unfortunately, no evidence on the action of temperatures above normal has been obtained in these studies.

In light of the abundantly documented association of functionally active polysomes with membrane structures in various types of cells [for detailed reviews see

(70, 71, 118, 156)], the reports on the effects of temperature on the functioning of polysome-membrane complexes acquire particular significance for understanding the in vivo effects of supraoptimal temperatures. Actually, phase changes in membranes attributable to lipid rearrangements at elevated temperatures have been shown to influence the activity of ribosomes associated with membranes (170). Studies of this sort are regrettably few in number and do not warrant any conclusive extrapolations to be made to the situation actually found in the cell. Another study concerned with the involvement of membranes in the control of initiation of translation was performed by Craig (35, 36). By comparing the activation energies for the in vivo and in vitro processes in pro- and eukaryotic cells, this worker deduced that temperature effects on protein synthesis are not mediated via membranes. On the other hand, the whole wealth of indirect evidence to be discussed below points to the putative involvement of membranes in regulation of protein synthesis in cells exposed to an adverse temperature environment.

Repair of Protein Synthesis

If evidence on repair of thermal injury of cells is rather fragmentary (3, 11, 17), the information on repair of the thermal injury of protein biosynthesis is still more scarce. References were made above to studies on repair of single- and double-strand breaks produced in DNA by heating. The author is unaware of any investigations of repair of thermal injury of transcription which might allow meaningful conclusions to be drawn. On the other hand, some observations have been made concerning the repair of translation impaired by exposure of cells to supraoptimal temperatures. As with the demonstrated ability of cells to repair thermal injury of some cellular functions such as protoplasmic streaming, even during incubation at elevated temperatures (17), translation inhibited by heating has been shown to recover in cells during heating. In the latter case, the synthesis of new RNA species promoting the association of mRNA and ribosomes was responsible for the recovery (54, 115). The accumulation of this RNA factor in HeLa cells was proportional to the length of exposure of the cells to 42°C. Inhibitor analysis revealed that the cells responded to the thermally induced suppression of protein synthesis rather than to the heating itself. Similar mechanisms are probably operating in other organisms such as *P. polycephalum* plasmodium, where repair of thermal injury has been found to occur either directly or indirectly through the differentiation of the plasmodium into sclerotium (17). This transformation could be seen as a result of the direct action of certain doses of heating and could also be observed during heating. Considering the triggering factor in this thermally induced differentiation to be the suppression of translation, it might be expected that preliminary inhibition of translation by an inhibitor would have promoted the subsequent heat-induced transformation. In fact, a 3 hr preincubation of the plasmodium in the presence of cycloheximide, as well as transfer to the starvation medium, considerably accelerated the transformation —the process dependent on the synthesis of new RNAs and proteins. Thus it cannot be excluded that repair of thermal injury of protein synthesis in *P. polycephalum,* much like that in HeLa cells, occurs with the aid of new RNA species promoting thermally impaired initiation of translation. RNA may be involved in this repair in view of the higher thermostability of RNA synthesis compared to that of protein synthesis (14, 15).

Comparatively more information is available on the resumption of thermally inhibited translation upon return of cells to normal temperature of growth. Thus repair of translation in *P. polycephalum* plasmodia after moderate heating (38°C for 10 min) recovers almost instantaneously (15, 24) and before repair of RNA synthesis has occurred. Consistent with these observations is the normalization of the heat-induced alteration in nucleolar structure which can be seen later than the recovery of translation (106). Inhibition of protein synthesis during repair of thermal injury of *P. polycephalum* interfered with the recovery of RNA synthesis in a way apparently related to mitotic delay mechanisms (V. A. Bernstam, unpublished). It remains unclear, however, whether recovery of protein synthesis is required for the repair of nucleolar structures.

The rapid recovery of translation after moderate heating of *P. polycephalum* is in accord with instantaneous recovery of translation on termination of heating HeLa cells (54), reticulocytes (21, 163), on warming up precooled *E. coli* cells (38), on rehydration of maize seedling cells (75), and on termination of exposure of bacterial cells to hydrostatic pressure (93). However diverse all these influences are, a common mechanism may be assumed to be responsible for the effects on translation and its recovery. In view of the reported association of translation with membranes, and before discussing some relevant findings testifying to the involvement of membranes in the temperature dependent regulation of protein synthesis, it would be appropriate to consider observations indicating that it is the initiation of translation that is the most sensitive to the action of diverse external influences.

HIGH SENSITIVITY OF TRANSLATION
TO ENVIRONMENTAL STRESS

The initiation step of translation is inhibited by factors other than supraoptimal temperatures. At 0° the rate of protein synthesis in *E. coli* cells goes down to a halt. An almost immediate resumption of translation takes place when the cells are returned to normal growth temperatures (37°C). The impaired association of free ribosomes with mRNA was found responsible for the inhibition of translation by low temperatures (38). Existence of a cold-induced blockage of the initiation step of translation in *E. coli* cells was later confirmed by Friedman et al (49). Indications of the general nature of this phenomenon have also been obtained in observations of inhibition of initiation of translation by lowering the temperature of incubation of eukaryotic (Chinese hamster ovary) cells (128). Likewise, in mouse L cells, the inhibition of protein synthesis at temperatures below 25°C occurs at the initiation step, whereas above this temperature impairment of elongation or other steps in translation may be occurring (35, 36). A review of effects of cold on cells is available (81). The involvement of membranes in the injury produced by low temperatures has been repeatedly considered (68, 108).

The striking selective sensitivity of the initiation step of translation can be traced also in effects of high hydrostatic pressure (HHP) (8, 66, 133). It is noteworthy that the barotolerance of protein synthesis has been shown to depend on the resistance of the small ribosomal subunit to HHP (134, 161). A disturbance in the HHP-induced inhibition of translation occurs at the stage of association of aminoacyl-tRNA with the ribosome-mRNA complex (151, 152). In considering the striking similarity in the action of temperature and HHP on protein synthesis in light of the association of translation with cellular membranes, the effect of HHP on the initiation of translation in cells may be largely related to modification of membranes by HHP (see 92, 93). Effects of HHP on membranes have been investigated in detail (52).

Interestingly, the effect of dehydration on protein synthesis is also similar to that of supraoptimal temperatures in that at early stages of dehydration protein synthesis is injured well before impairment of RNA synthesis. Thus degradation of polysomes has been reported in cells of dehydrated maize and bean seedlings (72, 75, 126, 127, 146, 165), and wheat (33) and cotton (112) leaves. An in-depth analysis of voluminous literature on effects of dehydration has been presented by Hsiao (76) and Lange et al (95).

The above evidence on effects of temperature and other injuring agents on protein synthesis, considered in the perspective of the newer structural observations of membranes in cells, strongly suggests that the control of protein synthesis in cells exposed to adverse environment may also be mediated through cell membranes. Furthermore, the abundant, although mostly indirect, evidence to be briefly outlined below indicates that the chain of control events constituting the response of cells to adverse environment, including supraoptimal temperatures, apparently originates at the cell periphery.

INVOLVEMENT OF MEMBRANES IN REGULATION OF TRANSLATION DURING ENVIRONMENTAL STRESS

From the observations discussed above it follows that translation, and most often the initiation step of translation, may be regarded as the most sensitive to external influences such as supraoptimal temperatures, HHP, low temperatures, or dehydration. Ultrastructural investigation of cells exposed to heat (39) and dehydration (75) revealed alterations in polysome distribution on endoplasmic reticulum membranes. Detailed biochemical studies of the effects of various external treatments of cells ranging from temperature to phenethylalcohol offered strong evidence in favor of the view that alterations of cellular membranes were responsible for impaired translation (23, 49, 70, 71, 145, 170). Relevant background information will not be discussed here, and the interested reader is referred to extensive descriptive and analytical reviews (71, 118, 156).

In the author's opinion, one additional point deserves consideration. It has been shown that polysomes are associated with the endoplasmic reticulum membranes via the large subunit (94, 104, 122) and the binding of mRNA to the membranes (47, 94, 120). On the other hand, the small subunits have been shown to be involved in detecting the initiating sites on mRNA and producing the initiating complexes (82). Furthermore, it is the small subunit that proved to be the more labile with respect to various environmental stresses (4, 85, 87, 134, 141, 161), and, importantly, the small subunit is the rate-limiting factor in controlling translation under various physiological conditions (113). These observations together with the known profound effects of changes of the physical state of membranes on the initiation of translation (23, 170) make a strong case that some early steps in the initiation of translation are likely to take place in the range of the immediate influence of the membranes concerned and occur either in close proximity to or on membrane structures.

It is conceivable that environmental effects extending to membrane alterations, however minute they may be, can distort those vectorial restrictions which are responsible for providing an efficient and specific interaction of all the components participating in the realization of initial stages of translation. Thus membrane influence on the rate and probable specificity of translation may constitute an extremely sensitive system reacting to diverse stimuli. An elaborate hypothesis for translational regulation of genetic expression visualizing polysome-membrane interactions as crucial in controlling protein synthesis has been developed by Shires et al (156) in their Membron model. In the author's opinion, an important development of these ideas comes from analysis of the effects of various external stimuli, including supraoptimal temperatures, on protein synthesis. Such analysis indicates that the control of translation also commences at the cell surface when cells are exposed to nonspecific external influences.

Effects on the Cell Surface Affecting Translation

An analytical summary of earlier findings concerning effects of colicins and other nonpenetrating agents on initiation of translation, supporting the ideas of membrane involvement in protein synthesis, has been given by Hendler (70, 71). The observations most frequently considered in this respect have been made with rather specific agents. In addition, there are several lines of evidence which point to the existence of intimate reciprocal relationships between translation and the cell surface topography. The impairment of the cell surface membrane function has been shown to be among the earliest manifestations of the cell injury (12, 16). It is significant in this context that inhibition of initiation of translation is also one of the earliest events in cell injury produced by diverse agents. There is no straightforward evidence exposing the immediate cause-effect relationships between changes in the surface membrane function produced by nonspecific external agents and inhibition of translation; however, some pertinent observations are available. With the two-phase polymer system capable of detecting rather delicate changes in cell surface characteristics in various physiological states (1, 132), changes in HeLa cell surface characteristics could be detected as a result of mild heating (39–43°C for 15 min) (H. V. Andreyeva and V. A. Bernstam, unpublished). These changes were more pronounced in log phase cells than in stationary phase cells, a finding in agreement with the known lower thermostability of protein synthesis in vigorously growing young cells (58, 89). More direct treatments may be cited which, acting at the cell surface, affect protein synthesis. Proteolytic attack results in a dramatic but reversible inhibition (90, 101, 171) or stimulation (20) of translation. Likewise, inhibition of protein synthesis has been observed when ascites tumor cells are treated with dextrane sulfate (116), HeLa cells with DEAE-dextrane (144), reticulocytes with valinomycin and dicyclohexyl-18-crown-6 (74), and lymphocytes with ouabain (139). All of these findings pointed to a relationship existing between the surface membrane (Na, K)-ATPase and protein synthesis. Effects of temperature on surface morphology (153) and (Na, K)-ATPase function (77) have been described. The non-specificity of temperature effects on the cell surface in suppressing protein synthesis (117) has been demonstrated by the reversal of temperature-induced alterations of the cell surface by polyunsaturated fatty acids (46) and adjustment of the osmotic milieu (19).

The relation of protein synthesis to the state of cell surface also emerges from comparison of normal and malignant cells known to differ substantially in the both characteristics (114, 129, 159, 169, 173). A notably lower cholesterol content of transformed cells (97, 155) is matched with the markedly lower thermoresistance of translation (41, 64, 67, 107, 123, 167, and references therein). This finding agrees well with the reported thermally induced phase transitions of membranes which inhibit translation (170). Phase transitions in fluidized membranes have repeatedly been shown to occur at lower temperatures (e.g. 77), and in view of the amply documented higher fluidity of membranes of transformed cells (28, 79, 80), the lower thermoresistance of protein synthesis characteristic of malignant cells may be readily understood by implicating membranes as efficient regulators of protein synthesis.

An elegant EM study of the surface membrane morphology in a Chinese hamster temperature-sensitive mutant strongly suggests the existence of cause-effect relationships between translation and surface morphology. Thus supplementation of the growth medium with excess leucine, which allowed growth to proceed at nonpermissive temperatures, eliminated the otherwise observed alterations of surface morphology in the mutant cells (63).

Conversely, abundant information on effects of various surface acting, nonpenetrating agents, including mitogens, indicates the existence of a complementing relationship, namely, alterations of cell surface topography influence protein synthesis. The involvment of surface-modulating structures in regulation of cellular activity has been elaborated by Edelman et al (44). Consonant with their ideas, the author has independently suggested on the basis of cytophysiological observations that cell membranes may act as efficient systems transducing nonspecific external stimuli into a relatively specific cellular response such as a change in the rate of protein synthesis (11, 17). The evidence obtained thus far concerning control of protein synthesis in cells exposed to diverse external influences is only suggestive, albeit strongly, of the involvement of membranes, including surface membranes.

Putative Structural Mechanisms of Translational Response to Environmental Stress

One of the so far inexplicable puzzles of cellular response to diverse effects produced at the cell surface is the striking directedness in mediation of external stimuli. A naturally appealing assumption would be that structures capable of transmitting signals link the site of application of the signal and the target. A likely candidate for such structures inside cells may be visualized in the omnipresent network of tubulin structures demonstrated by Porter (135). According to the proposed scheme, microtubules extend from the surface to various intracellular structures including ER with polysomes. Such a structural linkage of the sites of protein synthesis with the cell surface structures has been reported by numerous workers for various cells (42, 91, 102, 147, 149). In view of the mentioned higher fluidity of membranes and differences in surface topography of transformed and normal cells, with a higher randomness of surface structures in the former correlated with the higher thermal lability of protein synthesis in malignant cells, it is of interest to note that malignant cells feature lower amounts of microtubules and an essentially different pattern of their intracellular distribution (98, 173). Evidence supporting the view that changes in tubulin structures may be involved in mediation of temperature effects in cells comes from studies showing that the degree of polymerization of tubulin in vitro (96) as well as the pattern of intracellular distribution of microtubules (9, 69, 96, 175) are both affected by various physiological influences, including temperature. Moreover, a direct relationship has been demonstrated between changes in the cell surface topography and the organization of microfilaments in the course of malignization of cells (28, 172, 173). Obviously, further studies are required to relate the cited observations to diverse intracellular responses.

When analyzing the relationship of altered microtubular distribution to the characteristics of transformed cells, Brinkley et al (27) relate these to the regulation of the distribution of cell surface receptors, thereby affecting cell surface-dependent functions such as cell contact phenomena, etc. On the other hand, these workers refer to the disappearance of cytoplasmic microtubular complex during mitosis as the most consistent finding. This finding may certainly have bearing on the selective sensitivity of mitotic delay to heat shock and to inhibitors of protein synthesis also showing cyclic variations over the mitotic cycle. Similar variations as a function of the cell cycle have also been reported in the efficiency of translation and the characteristics of the cell surface (e.g. 45, 78, 136).

Not touching on the immense literature on the involvement of cyclic nucleotides in mediation of signals in cells, since only putative structural mechanisms are briefly considered here, it may be appropriate to refer to the view that calcium ions are regarded as likely candidates mediating signals from the cell surface to intracellular structures (105). This is pertinent to the above considered mechanism since calcium ions have been shown to be released from cellular membranes under various conditions and to act as regulators of assembly-disassembly of cytoplasmic microtubules (51). Significantly, brief trypsinization or exposure of cells to drugs with local anesthetic activity cause a dramatic loss of the cytoplasmic microtubular complex correlated with changes in the intracellular calcium concentrations. As already mentioned, translation is inhibited by trypsinization of the cell surface (90, 171).

CONCLUDING REMARKS

Our understanding of the effects of supraoptimal temperature on protein biosynthesis, much like that of other environmental stresses, is far from complete. Various researchers at different times have approached this problem by studying diverse organisms and employing more or less sophisticated techniques. In only a few of the studies reported the elucidation of the temperature effects as such has been approached directly, and frequently relevant information has been obtained only as a byproduct of research aimed at solving other problems. In this rather schematic review, the author has only attempted to bring the so far fragmentary evidence on heat effects on protein biosynthesis into the perspective of the available information on the general behavior of the cell responding to adverse environment. An important realization is in the now progressively recognized fact that every manifestation of biochemically definable cell activity cannot be coherently integrated into the continually expanding knowledge of diverse regulatory mechanisms without at least a putative topological assignment of the process concerned within the cell. The reasoning briefly outlined in this paper and based on the information gained sometimes in unrelated fields of research has been aimed at emphasizing the role of topological alterations in the surface and internal cell membranes in determining the ability of the cell to react to the environment. The so far rather distant and often speculative correlates of various specific and widely nonspecific actions on cells strongly suggest there are basic general regularities governing cellular response at the level of protein synthesis. It may be assumed that changes in surface topography extending beyond genetically determined allowable variations are propagated via membrane and tubulin structures inside the cell to the sites of protein synthesis. Membrane alterations showing a cooperative response to signal (32) are supposed to cause the micromilieu for the translational process to undergo reversible modification in response to external nonspecific and specific stimuli thereby influencing protein synthesis. Thus the high sensitivity of translation—the process relatively distal to transcription and replication—may be advantageous in triggering appropriately regulated responses of the cell. In analyzing the available information, it now becomes apparent that aside from the genetic code there probably operate other code systems in the cell, some of which comprise the whole membrane network. Discriminate use of temperature effects may certainly be helpful in cracking one of the cell codes—the surface code.

Literature Cited

1. Albertsson, P.-Å. 1971. *Partition of Cell Particles and Macromolecules.* Stockholm: Almqvist & Wiksell
2. Alexandrov, V. Ya. 1977. *Cells, Macromolecules and Temperature.* Transl. V. A. Bernstam from Russian. Berlin, Heidelberg, New York: Springer-Verlag
3. Alexandrov, V. Ya. 1978. Manuscript in preparation
4. Altenburg, L. C., Saunders, G. F. 1971. Properties of hybrid ribosomes formed from the subunits of mesophilic and thermophilic bacteria. *J. Mol. Biol.* 55:487–502

5. Amalric, F., Simard, R., Zalta, J. P. 1969. Effet de la temperature supraoptimale sur les ribonucleoproteines et le ARN nucleolaire. II. Etude biochimique. *Exp. Cell Res.* 55:370–77
6. Andresen, H. A., Brunk, C. F., Zeuthen, E. 1970. Studies on the DNA replication in heat synchronized *Tetrahymena pyriformis. C. R. Trav. Lab. Carlsberg* 38:123–31
7. Arca, M., Frontali, L., Sapora, O., Tecce, G. 1967. Lack of specificity of isoleucyl-tRNA synthetase: evidence for anomalous charging of tRNA. *Biochim. Biophys. Acta* 145:284–91

8. Arnold, L. M., Albright, L. J. 1971. Hydrostatic pressure effects on translation stages of protein synthesis in a cell-free system from *E.coli. Biochim. Biophys. Acta* 238:347–54

9. Bajer, A. S., Lambert, A. M. 1976. Reversible arrest of chromosome movement and microtubule (MT) rearrangements at low temperature. *J. Cell Biol.* 70:128 (Abstr.)

10. Bazil, G. W., Retief, Y. 1969. Temperature sensitive DNA synthesis in a mutant of *Bacillus subtilis. J. Gen. Microbiol.* 56:87–97

11. Bernstam, V. A. 1973. *A study of thermal injury of the myxomycete Physarum polycephalum.* Biol. Sci. dissertation. USSR Acad. Sci., Komarov Bot. Inst., Leningrad. 163 pp.

12. Bernstam, V. A. 1973. Temperature effects on *Physarum polycephalum* plasmodia. *Myxomycete Conf., 4th Miami, Florida,* p. 27 (Abstr.)

13. Bernstam, V. A. 1973. See Ref. 12, p. 28

14. Bernstam, V. A. 1974. Effects of supraoptimal temperatures on the myxomycete *Physarum polycephalum.* II. Effects on the rate of protein and ribonucleic acid synthesis. *Arch. Mikrobiol.* 95:347–56

15. Bernstam, V. A. 1974. Effects of heating on the incorporation of RNA and protein synthesis precursors *in vivo* in the plasmodium of *Physarum polycephalum. Tsitologiya* 16:160–66 (In Russian)

16. Bernstam, V. A., Arndt, S. 1973. Effects of supraoptimal temperatures on the myxomycete *Physarum polycephalum.* I. Protoplasmic streaming, respiration and leakage of protoplasmic substances. *Arch. Mikrobiol.* 92:251–61

17. Bernstam, V. A., Arndt, S. 1974. Effects of supraoptimal temperatures on the myxomycete *Physarum polycephalum.* III. Effects of starvation and cycloheximide on repair of thermal injury in plasmodia. *Arch. Mikrobiol.* 95:357–63

18. Berry, S. A., Grunberg-Manago, M. 1970. Yeast lysyl-tRNA synthetase. Complex formation and heat protection by substrates. *Biochim. Biophys. Acta* 217:83–94

19. Bilsky, A. Z., Armstrong, J. B. 1973. Osmotic reversal of temperature sensitivity in *Escherichia coli. J. Bacteriol.* 113:76–81

20. Blumberg, P. M., Robbins, P. W. 1975. Effect of proteases on activation of resting chick embryo fibroblasts and on cell surface proteins. *Cell* 6:137–47

21. Bonanou-Tzedaki, S. A., Arnstein, H. R. V. 1976. Subcellular localization of a lesion in protein synthesis in rabbit reticulocytes incubated at elevated temperatures. *Eur. J. Biochem.* 61:397–407

22. Bonner, J. J., Pardue, M. L. 1976. The effect of heat shock on RNA synthesis in *Drosophila* tissues. *Cell* 8:43–50

23. Bont, W. S., Geels, J., Huizinga, A., Mekkelholt, K., Emmelot, P. 1972. The influence of the physical state of microsomal membranes from rat liver on translational processes of polyribosomes. *Biochim. Biophys. Acta* 262:514–24

24. Brewer, E. N. 1972. Polysome profiles, amino acid incorporation *in vitro* and polysome reaggregation following disaggregation by heat shock through the mitotic cycle in *Physarum polycephalum. Biochim. Biophys. Acta* 277:639–45

25. Brewer, E. N., Rusch, H. P. 1968. Effect of elevated temperature shocks on mitosis and on the initiation of DNA replication in *Physarum polycephalum. Exp. Cell Res.* 49:79–86

26. Bridges, B. A., Ashwood-Smith, M. J., Munson, R. J. 1969. Correlation of bacterial sensitivities to ionizing radiation and mild heating. *J. Gen. Microbiol.* 58:115–24

27. Brinkley, B. R., Fuller, G. M., Highfield, D. P. 1976. Tubulin antibodies as probes for microtubules in dividing and nondividing mammalian cells. In *Cell Motility, A, Motility, Muscle and Nonmuscle cells,* ed. R. Goldman, T. Pollard, J. Rosenbaum. *Cold Spring Harbor Conf. Cell Proliferation,* 3:435–56

28. Brocklehurst, J. R., Graham, J. M., McLaughlin, A. 1976. Biochemical studies on cell membranes of normal and transformed cells. *J. Cell Biol.* 70:350A

29. Byfield, J. E., Lee, Y. C. 1970. The effect of synchronizing temperature shifts on the synthesis and translation of replication supporting messengers in *Tetrahymena pyriformis. Exp. Cell Res.* 61:42–50

30. Byfield, J. E., Lee, Y. C. 1970. Do synchronizing temperature shifts inhibit RNA synthesis in *Tetrahymena pyriformis? J. Protozool.* 17(3):445–53

31. Chambon, P., Gissinger, F., Kedinger, C., Mandel, J. L., Meihlac, M., Nuret, P. 1972. Structural and functional properties of three mammalian nuclear DNA-dependent RNA polymerases. In *Gene Transcription in Reproductive Tis-*

sue, ed. E. Diczfalusy, pp. 222–46. Stockholm: Karolinska Inst. 453 pp.

32. Changeux, J. P., Thiéry, J. 1968. On the excitability and cooperativity of biological membranes. In *Regulatory Functions of Biological Membranes.* ed. J. Järnefelt, pp. 116–38. Amsterdam, London, New York: Elsevier. 311 pp.

33. Chen, D., Sarid, S., Katchalski, E. 1968. The role of water stress in the inactivation of messenger RNA of germinating wheat embryos. *Proc. Natl. Acad. Sci. USA* 61:1378–83

34. Cox, R. A., Pratt, H., Huvos, P., Higginson, B., Hirst, W. 1973. A study of the thermal stability of ribosomes and biologically active subribosomal particles. *Biochem. J.* 134:775–93

35. Craig, N. 1975. Effect of reduced temperatures on protein synthesis in mouse L cells. *Cell* 4:329–35

36. Craig, N. 1976. Regulation of protein synthesis by temperature in mammalian cells: non-involvement of the plasma membrane. *J. Cell Biol.* 70:4(Abstr.)

37. Cummins, J. E., Rusch, H. P. 1966. Limited DNA synthesis in the absence of protein synthesis in *Physarum polycephalum. J. Cell Biol.* 31:577–83

38. Das, H. K., Goldstein, A. 1968. Limited capacity for protein synthesis at zero degree centigrade in *Escherichia coli. J. Mol. Biol.* 31:209–26

39. David, H., Uerlings, I. 1968. Strukturververänderungen von Lebermitochondrien nach Kurzfristiger Erwärmung bis 50°C *in vitro* und *in vivo. Acta Biol. Med. Ger.* 20:65–70

40. Dewey, W. C., Furman, S. C., Miller, H. H. 1970. Comparison of lethality and chromosomal damage induced by x-rays in synchronized Chinese hamster cells *in vitro. Radiat. Res.* 43:561–81

41. Dickson, J. A., Suzangar, M. 1974. *In vitro-in vivo* studies on susceptibility of the solid Yoshida sarcoma to drugs and hyperthermia (42°C). *Cancer Res.* 34:1263–74

42. Dollevoet, P. L. 1976. Microfilament attachment to the intracellular organelles in neural crest derived melanocytes of the fowl. *J. Cell Biol.* 70:203 (Abstr.)

43. Duprat, A. M. 1969. Effets de temperatures supranormales sur le nucleole de cellules embryonnaires d'urodeles en culture *in vitro. Exp. Cell Res.* 57: 37–42

44. Edelman, G. M., Wang, J. L., Yahara, I. 1976. Surface-modulating assemblies in mammalian cells. See Ref. 28, pp. 305–21

45. Engelhardt, D. L., Sarnoski, J. 1975. Variations in the cell-free translating apparatus of cultured animal cells as a function of time during cell growth. *J. Cell Physiol.* 86:15–29

46. Erwin, J. A. 1970. The reversal of temperature-induced cell-surface deformation in *Tetrahymena* by polyunsaturated fatty acids. *Biochim. Biophys. Acta* 202:21–34

47. Faiferman, I., Pogo, A. O., Schwartz, J., Kaighn, M. E. 1973. Isolation and characterization of membrane bound polysomes from ascites tumor cells. *Biochim. Biophys. Acta* 312:492–501

48. Feldherr, C. M. 1973. The effect of temperature on nuclear permeability, *Experientia* 29:546–47

49. Friedman, H., Lu, P., Rich, A. 1971. Temperature control of initiation of protein synthesis in *Escherichia coli. J. Mol. Biol.* 61:105–21

50. Friedman, S. M. 1971. Heat stabilities of ribosomal subunits and reassociated ribosomes from *Bacillus stearothermophilus. J. Bacteriol.* 108:589–91

51. Fuller, G. M., Artus, C. S., Ellison, J. J. 1976. Calcium as a regulator of cytoplasmic microtubule assembly and disassembly. *J. Cell. Biol.* 70:68a (Abstr.)

52. Gause, E. M., Mendez, V. M., Rowlands, J. R. 1974. A spin label study of the effects of hydrostatic pressure and temperature on cellular lipids. *Spectrosc. Lett.* 7:477–90

53. Gerweck, L. E., Gillette, E. L., Dewey, W. C. 1975. Effect of heat and radiation on synchronous Chinese hamster cells: killing and repair. *Radiat. Res.* 64: 611–23

54. Goldstein, E. S., Penman, S. 1973. Regulation of protein synthesis in mammalian cells. V. Further studies on the effect of actinomycin D on translation control in HeLa cells. *J. Mol. Biol.* 80:243–54

55. Gomez, R. F., Sinskey, A. J. 1973. Deoxyribonucleic acid breaks in heated *Salmonella typhimurium* LT-2 after exposure to nutritionally complex media. *J. Bacteriol.* 115:522–28

56. Gomez, R. F., Sinskey, A. J. 1975. Effect of aeration on minimal recovery of heated *Salmonella typhimurium. J. Bacteriol.* 122: 106–9

57. Gomez, R. F., Sinskey, A. J., Davies, R., Labuza, T. P. 1973. Minimal medium recovery of heated *Salmonella typhimurium* LT-2. *J. Gen. Microbiol.* 74:267–74

58. Gorban, I. S. 1962. On the relation of growth and thermostability of plant cells. *Tsitologiya* 4:182–92 (In Russian)
59. Gross, M. 1974. Control of globin synthesis by hemin. An intermediate form of the translational repressor in rabbit reticulocyte lysates. *Biochim. Biophys. Acta* 366:319–32
60. Gross, M., ...binovitz, M. 1973. Control of globin synthesis by hemin. Effect of temperature on globin synthesis by the reticulocyte cell-free system and the activity of translational repressors formed in the absence of hemin. *Biochim. Biophys. Acta* 299:472–79
61. Grove, B. K., Johnson, T. C., Gilbert, B. E. 1974. Thermostability of mammalian brain ribosomes and the effects of nucleoside triphosphates on their heat sensitivity. *Biochem. J.* 137:291–98
62. Guern, N., Genevès, L. 1975. Modifications ultrastructurales provoquèes sur des tissus isoles de Topinambour (*Helianthus tuberosus* L., Composees) par une culture prolongée à une temperature élevée (38°C). *C. R. Acad. Sci. Ser. D* 281:1698–1700
63. Haars, L., Hampel, A. 1975. Cell cycle surface alterations of the mammalian cell culture mutant *ts* H1. *J. Cell Biol.* 67:151(Abstr.)
64. Hahn, G. M. 1974. Metabolic aspects of the role of hyperthermia in mammalian cell inactivation and their possible relevance to cancer treatment. *Cancer Res.* 34:3117–23
65. Hamkalo, B. A., Miller, O. L. 1972. Cited by Miller, O. L., Bakken, A. H. See Ref. 31, pp. 155–77
66. Hardon, M. J., Albright, L. J. 1974. Hydrostatic pressure effects on several stages of protein synthesis in *Escherichia coli*. *Can. J. Microbiol.* 20:359–65
67. Harris, J. W. 1976. Effects of tumor-like assay conditions, ionizing radiation and hyperthermia on immune lysis of tumor cells by cytotoxic T-lymphocytes. *Cancer Res.* 36:2733–39
68. Heber, U., Tyankova, L., Santarius, K. A. 1973. Effects of freezing on biological membranes *in vivo* and *in vitro*. *Biochim. Biophys. Acta* 291:23–37
69. Hemperly, J. J., McClain, D., Yahara, I., Edelman, G. M. 1976. Immunofluorescence studies on polymerization and depolymerization of microtubules in 3t3 cells. *J. Cell Biol.* 70:334 (Abstr.)
70. Hendler, R. W. 1968. *Protein Biosynthesis and Membrane Biochemistry*. New York:Wiley. 344 pp.
71. Hendler, R. W. 1974. Protein synthesis by membrane-bound polyribosomes. In *Biomembranes*, ed. L. A. Manson, 5:147–212. New York, London: Plenum. 284 pp.
72. Henkel, P. A., Satarova, N. A., Tvorus, E. K. 1967. Effect of drought on protein synthesis and ribosomes in plants. *Fiziol. Rast.* 14:898–907 (In Russian)
73. Herzberg, M., Breitbart, H., Atlan, H. 1974. Interaction between membrane functions and protein synthesis in reticulocytes. Effects of valinomycin and dicyclohexyl-18-crown-6. *Eur. J. Biochem.* 45:161–70
74. Hinkle, D. C., Chamberlain, M. J. 1972. Studies of the binding of *Escherichia coli* RNA polymerase to DNA. I. The role of sigma subunit in site selection. *J. Mol. Biol.* 70:157–85
75. Hsiao, T. C. 1970. Rapid changes in levels of polyribosomes in *Zea mays* in response to water stress. *Plant Physiol.* 46:281–85
76. Hsiao, T. C. 1973. Plant responses to water stress. *Ann. Rev. Plant Physiol.* 24:519–70
77. Hsung, J.-C., Huang, L., Hoy, D. J., Haug, A. 1974. Lipid and temperature dependence of membrane-bound ATPase activity of *Acholeplasma laidlawii*. *Can. J. Biochem.* 52:974–80
78. Hynes, R. O., Bye, J. M. 1974. Density and cell cycle dependence of cell surface proteins in hamster fibroblasts. *Cell* 3:113–20
79. Inbar, M., Ben-Bassat, H. 1976. Fluidity difference in the surface membrane lipid core of human lymphoblastoid and lymphoma cell lines. *Int. J. Cancer* 18:293–97
80. Inbar, M., Shinitzky, M. 1974. Cholesterol as a bioregulator in the development and inhibition of leukemia. *Proc. Natl. Acad. Sci. USA* 71:4229–31
81. Inniss, W. E. 1975. Interaction of temperature and psychrophilic microorganisms. *Ann. Rev. Microbiol.* 29:445–65
82. Jay, G., Kaempfer, R. 1975. Initiation of protein synthesis. Binding of messenger RNA. *J. Biol. Chem.* 250:5742–48
83. Johnson, L., Söll, D. 1971. Temperature dependence of the aminoacylation of tRNA by *Bacillus stearothermophilus* aminoacyl-tRNA synthetases. *Biopolymers* 10:2209–21
84. Kane, A., Basilico, C., Baserga, R. 1976. Transcriptional activity and chromatin structural changes in a temperature-sensitive mutant of BHK cells

blocked in early G1. *Exp. Cell Res.* 99:165–73
85. Kazemie, M. 1974. Influence of heating on the formation of ribosome couples and 80S initiation complex from the 40S and 60S ribosomal subunits from rabbit reticulocytes. *Mol. Gen. Genet.* 128: 171–82
86. Khesin, R. B., Astaurova, O. B., Shemyakin, M. F., Kamzolova, S. G., Manyakov, V. F. 1967. Changes in RNA polymerase properties with association with DNA and initiation of RNA synthesis. *Molek. Biol.* 1:736–53 (In Russian)
87. Kikuchi, A., Monier, R. 1971. Heat inactivation of *Escherichia coli* ribosomal subunits. *Biochimie* 53:755–61
88. Klein, A., Bonhoeffer, F. 1972. DNA replication. *Ann. Rev. Biochem.* 41: 301–32
89. Klyachko, N. L., Kulaeva, O. N. 1969. Thermostability of protein synthesis in leaves of different age. *Dokl. Akad. Nauk SSSR* 188:230–32
90. Koch, G. 1974. Reversible inhibition of protein synthesis in HeLa cells by exposure to proteolytic enzymes. *Biochem. Biophys. Res. Commun.* 61:817–24
91. Kochhar, O. S. 1976. *In vitro* association between microtubules and plasma membranes. *J. Cell Biol.* 70:143 (Abstr.)
92. Landau, J. V. 1966. Protein and nucleic acid synthesis in *Escherichia coli:* a hydrostatic pressure study. *Science* 153: 1273–74
93. Landau, J. V. 1970. Hydrostatic pressure effects on the biosynthesis of macromolecules. In *High Pressure Effects on Cellular Processes*, ed. A. M. Zimmerman, pp. 45–70. New York: Academic
94. Landé, M. A., Adesnik, M., Sumida, M., Tashiro, Y., Sabatini, D. D. 1975. Direct association of messenger RNA with microsomal membranes in human diploid fibroblasts. *J. Cell Biol.* 65: 513–28
95. Lange, O. L., Kappen, L., Schulze, E.-D., eds. 1976. *Water and plant life. Problems and Modern Approaches.* Berlin, Heidelberg, New York: Springer-Verlag. 521 pp.
96. Langford, G. M., Satelle, D. B., Langley, K. H., Dufresne, W. J. 1976. *In vitro* polymerization of tubulin studied by laser light scattering. *J. Cell. Biol.* 70:243 (Abstr.)
97. Lavietes, B. B., Potter, J. E. R., Coleman, P. S. 1976. Stimulation of lym-

phoma cell growth by cholesterol enrichment. *J. Cell Biol.* 70:266 (Abstr.)
98. Lee, M. M. L., Tannenbaum, S., Tannenbaum, M. 1976. Ultrastructural characteristics of normal, preneoplastic and neoplastic human transitional epithelium. *J. Cell. Biol.* 70:375 (Abstr.)
99. Lelong, J. C., Grunberg-Manago, M., Dondon, J., Gros, D., Gros, F. 1970. Interaction between guanosine derivatives and factors involved in the initiation of protein synthesis. *Nature* 226: 505–10
100. Lengyel, J. A., Pardue, M. L. 1975. Analysis of hnRNA made during heat shock in *Drosophila melanogaster* cultured cells. *J. Cell Biol.* 67:240 (Abstr.)
101. Letter, B. R., Chen, L. B., Buchanan, J. M. 1976. Effects of protease treatment on growth, morphology, adhesion and cell surface proteins of secondary embryo fibroblasts. *Cell* 7:407–12
102. Levine, R. F. 1976. Microtubule-ribosome complexes induced by vincristine, colchicine and podophyllotoxin. *J. Cell Biol.* 70:210 (Abstr.)
103. Levitt, J. 1972. *Responses of Plants to Environmental Stresses.* New York, London: Academic
104. Lewis, J. A., Sabatini, D. D. 1976. A large ribosomal protein involved in the binding of ribosomes to endoplasmic reticulum membranes. *J. Cell Biol.* 70:153 (Abstr.)
105. Loewenstein, W. R. 1976. Permeable junctions. *Cold Spring Harbor Symp. Quant. Biol.* 40:49–63
106. Lomagin, A. G. 1978. Repair of functional and ultrastructural alterations after thermal injury of *Physarum polycephalum. Planta.* In press
107. Love, R., Soriano, R. Z., Walsh, R. J. 1970. Effect of hyperthermia on normal and neoplastic cells *in vitro. Cancer Res.* 30:1525–33
108. Lyons, J. M. 1973. Chilling injury in plants. *Ann. Rev. Plant Physiol.* 24:445–66
109. Malcolm, N. L. 1968. Synthesis of protein and ribonucleic acid in a psychrophile at normal and restrictive growth temperatures. *J. Bacteriol.* 95:1388–99
110. Malcolm, N. L. 1968. Temperature-induced lesion in aminoacid-transfer RNA attachment in a psychrophile. *Biochim. Biophys. Acta* 156:493–503
111. Malcolm, N. L. 1969. Subunit structure and function of *Micrococcus cryophilus* glutamyl transfer RNA synthetase. *Biochim. Biophys. Acta* 190:347–57

112. Marin, B., Vierira de Silva, J. B. 1971. Mise en evidence de l'action de la carence hydrique sur la taneur en polysomes des feuilles adultes de cotonnier. *C. R. Acad. Sci. Ser. D* 273: 1714–17

113. Martin, S. E., Iandolo, J. J. 1975. Translational control of protein synthesis in *Staphylococcus aureus. J. Bacteriol.* 122: 1136–43

114. Maser, M. D. 1976. Differences in cell surface morphology between malignant and benign human breast lesions are a function of specimen preparation. *J. Cell Biol.* 70:224 (Abstr.)

115. McCormick, W., Penman, S. 1969. Regulation of protein synthesis in HeLa cells: translation at elevated temperatures. *J. Mol. Biol.* 39:315–33

116. McCoy, G. D., Racker, E. 1976. Protein synthesis in dextran-sulfate treated ascites tumor cells. *Cancer Res.* 36:3346–49

117. McGroarty, E. J., Koffler, H., Smith, R. W. 1973. Regulation of flagellar morphogenesis by temperature: involvement of the bacterial cell surface in the synthesis of flagellin and the flagellum. *J. Bacteriol.* 113:295–303

118. McIntosh, P. R., O'Toole, K. 1976. The interaction of ribosomes and membranes in animal cells. *Biochim. Biophys. Acta* 457:171–212

119. McLaughlin, C. S., Dondon, J., Grunberg-Manago, M., Michelson, A. M., Saunders, G. 1968. Stability of the messenger RNA–transfer RNA-ribosome complex. *J. Mol. Biol.* 32:521–42

120. Mechler, B., Vassalli, P. 1975. Membrane-bound ribosomes of myeloma cells. III. The role of the messenger RNA and the nascent polypeptide chain in the binding of ribosomes to membranes. *J. Cell Biol.* 67:25–37

121. Miller, M. J., Wahba, A. J. 1973. Chain initiation factor 2. Purification and properties of two species from *Escherichia coli* MRE 600. *J. Biol. Chem.* 248:1084–90

122. Mok, W., Freienstein, C., Sabatini, D., Kreibich, G. 1976. Specificity and control of binding of ribosomes to endoplasmic reticulum membranes. *J. Cell Biol.* 70:393 (Abstr.)

123. Mondovi, B., Strom, R., Rotilio, G., Agro, A. F., Cavaliere, R., Fanelli, A. R. 1969. The biochemical mechanism of selective heat sensitivity of cancer cells. 2. Studies on nucleic acids and protein synthesis. *Eur. J. Biochem.* 5:137–46

124. Morita, R. Y., Albright, L. J. 1968. Moderate temperature effects on protein, ribonucleic acid and deoxyribonucleic acid synthesis by *Vibrio marinus:* an obligately psychrophilic marine bacterium. *Z. Allg. Mikrobiol.* 8:269–73

125. Nash, C. H., Grant, D. W., Sinclair, N. A. 1969. Thermostability of protein synthesis in a cell free system from the obligately psychrophilic yeast *Candida gelida. Can. J. Microbiol.* 15:339–43

126. Nir, I., Klein, S., Poljakoff-Mayber, A. 1969. Effects of moisture stress on submicroscopic structure of maize roots. *Aust. J. Biol. Sci.* 22:17–33

127. Nir, I., Klein, S., Poljakoff-Mayber, A. 1970. Changes in fine structure of root cells from maize seedlings exposed to water stress. *Aust. J. Biol. Sci.* 23: 489–91

128. Oleinick, N. L. 1976. The control of protein synthesis at suboptimal temperatures. *J. Cell Biol.* 70:93 (Abstr.)

129. Pardee, A. B. 1975. The cell surface and fibroblast proliferation: some current research trends. *Biochim. Biophys. Acta* 417:153–72

130. Patterson, D., Gillespie, D. 1971. Stringent response of RNA synthesis in *Escherichia coli* produced by a temperature shift up. *Biochem. Biophys. Res. Commun.* 45:476–82

131. Patterson, D., Gillespie, D. 1972. The effect of elevated temperature on protein synthesis in *Escherichia coli. J. Bacteriol.* 112:1177–83

132. Pinaev, G., Hoorn, B., Albertsson, P. Å. 1976. Counter-current distribution of HeLa and mouse mast cells in different stages of the life cycle. *Exp. Cell Res.* 98:127–35

133. Pope, D. H., Berger, L. R. 1973. Inhibition of metabolism by hydrostatic pressure: what limits microbial growth? *Arch. Mikrobiol.* 93:367–70

134. Pope, D. H., Smith, W. P., Swartz, R. W., Landau, J. V. 1975. Role of bacterial ribosomes in barotolerance. *J. Bacteriol.* 121:664–69

135. Porter, K. R. 1976. Introduction: motility in cells. See Ref. 28, pp. 1–28

136. Porter, K. R., Prescott, D., Frye, J. 1973. Changes in surface morphology of Chinese hamster ovary cells during the cell cycle. *J. Cell. Biol.* 57:815–36

137. Precht, H., Christophersen, J., Hensel, H., Larcher, W. 1973. *Temperature and Life.* Berlin, Heidelberg, New York: Springer-Verlag. 779 pp.

138. Prehn, S., Rosental, S., Rapoport, S. M. 1972. The temperature dependent enzymatic breakdown of rRNA of

reticulocytes. *Eur. J. Biochem.* 24: 456–60

139. Quastel, M. R., Kaplan, J. G. 1970. Lymphocyte stimulation: the effect of ouabain on nucleic acid and protein synthesis. *Exp. Cell Res.* 67:407–20

140. Rebound, A. M., Arpin, M., Reboud, J. P. 1972. Ribosomal subunits from rat liver. 1. Isolation and properties of active 40S and 60S subunits. *Eur. J. Biochem.* 26:347–53

141. Rosenthal, L. J., Iandolo, J. J. 1970. Thermally induced intracellular alteration of ribosomal ribonucleic acid. *J. Bacteriol.* 103:833–35

142. Rubin, G. M., Hogness, D. S. 1975. Effect of heat shock on the synthesis of low molecular weight RNAs in *Drosophila*: accumulation of a novel form of 5S RNA. *Cell* 6:207–13

143. Russell, A. D., Harries, D. 1968. Damage to *Escherichia coli* on exposure to moist heat. *Appl. Microbiol.* 16: 1394–99

144. Saborio, J. L., Wiegers, K. J., Koch, G. 1975. Effect of DEAE-dextran on protein synthesis in HeLa cells. *Arch. Virol.* 49:81–87

145. Sarma, D. S. R., Reid, I. M., Verney, E., Sidransky, H. 1972. Studies on the nature of attachment of ribosomes to membranes in liver. I. Influence of ethionine, sparsomycin, CCl4 and puromycin on membrane-bound polyribosomal disaggregation and on detachment of membrane-bound ribosomes from membranes. *Lab. Invest.* 27:39–47

146. Satarova, N. A., Tvorus, E. K. 1971. Changes in the functional activity of ribosomes isolated from kidney bean and horse bean seedlings after desiccation. *Fiziol. Rast.* 18:523–38

147. Schatten, G., Thoman, M., Gerhart, J. 1976. The nuclear envelope as observed with the scanning electron microscope. *J. Cell Biol.* 70:41 (Abstr.)

148. Schiebel, W., Chayka, T. G., DeVries, A., Rusch, H. P. 1969. Decrease of protein synthesis and breakdown of polyribosomes by elevated temperatures in *Physarum polycephalum*. *Biochem. Biophys. Res. Commun.* 35:338–45

149. Schlessinger, J., Axelrod, D., Koppel, D. E., Elson, E. L., Webb, W. W. 1976. The lateral transport of surface proteins and a lipid probe on the plasma membrane by a cultured myoblast. *J. Cell Biol.* 70:137 (Abstr.)

150. Schochetman, G., Perry, R. P. 1972. Characterization of the messenger RNA released from L cell polyribosomes as a result of a temperature shock. *J. Mol. Biol.* 63:577–90

151. Schwarz, J. R., Landau, J. V. 1972. Hydrostatic pressure effects on *E. coli:* site of inhibition of protein synthesis. *J. Bacteriol.* 109:945–48

152. Schwarz, J. R., Landau, J. V. 1972. Inhibition of cell-free protein synthesis by hydrostatic pressure. *J. Bacteriol.* 112: 1222–27

153. Shelton, E., Orenstein, J. M. 1976. Effect of temperature and antimetabolites on surface architecture of murine lymphocytes, mast cells and macrophages. *J. Cell Biol.* 70:152 (Abstr.)

154. Shields, D., Tata, J. R. 1973. Differential thermal sensitivity of eukaryotic DNA dependent RNA polymerases. *FEBS Lett.* 31: 209–13

155. Shinitzky, M., Inbar, M. 1974. Difference in microviscosity induced by different cholesterol levels in the surface membrane lipid layer of normal lymphocytes and malignant lymphoma cells. *J. Mol. Biol.* 85:603–15

156. Shires, T. K., Pitot, H. C., Kauffman, S. A. 1974. The Membron: a functional hypothesis for the translational regulation of genetic expression. See Ref. 71, pp. 81–146

157. Simard, R., Amalric, F., Zalta, J. P. 1969. Effet de la temperature supraoptimale sur les ribonucleoproteines et le RNA nucleolaire. I. Etude ultrastructurale. *Exp. Cell. Res.* 55:359–69

158. Simard, R., Bernhard, W. 1967. A heat sensitive cellular function localized in the nucleolus. *J. Cell. Biol.* 34:61–76

159. Simon, M., Apirion, D. 1972. Increased inactivation of messengers in *Escherichia coli* ts mutant. *Nature New Biol.* 239: 79–81

160. Sinclair, N. A., Grant, D. W. 1967. Thermal destruction of enzyme activity and enzyme formation in *Candida gelida. Bacteriol. Proc.* 67:34 (Abstr.)

161. Smith, W., Pope, D., Landau, J. V. 1975. Role of bacterial ribosome subunits in barotolerance. *J. Bacteriol.* 124:582–84

162. Spradling, A., Penman, S., Pardue, M. L. 1975. Analysis of *Drosophila* mRNA by *in situ* hybridization: sequences transcribed in normal and heat shocked cultured cells. *Cell* 4:395–404

163. Sprechman, L. M., Ingram, V. 1972. Hemoglobin synthesis at elevated temperatures. *J. Biol. Chem.* 247:5004–10

164. Strange, R. E., Shon, M. 1964. Effects of thermal stress on viability and ribonucleic acid of *Aerobacter aerogenes*

in aqueous suspension. *J. Gen. Microbiol.* 34:99–114

165. Sturani, E., Cocucci, S., Marre, E. 1966. On a possible relationship between mRNA synthesis and hydration in the endosperm of germinating castor bean seeds. *G. Bot. Ital.* 73:43–44

166. Terasima, T., Tolmach, L. J. 1963. Variations in several responses of HeLa cells to X-irradiation during the division cycle. *Biophys. J.* 3:11–33

167. Thrall, D. E., Gillette, E. L., Dewey, W. C. 1975. Effect of heat and ionizing radiation on normal and neoplastic tissue of the C3H mouse. *Radiat. Res.* 63:363–67

168. Tomlins, R. I., Ordal, Z. J. 1971. Precursor ribosomal ribonucleic acid and ribosome accumulation in vivo during the recovery of *Salmonella typhimurium* from thermal injury. *J. Bacteriol.* 107:134–42

169. Tooze, J., ed. 1973. In *The Molecular Biology of Tumour Viruses,* pp. 173–268. Cold Spring Harbor Lab.

170. Towers, N. R., Raison, J. K., Kellerman, G. M., Linnane, A. W. 1972. Effects of temperature-induced phase changes in membranes on protein synthesis by bound ribosomes. *Biochim. Biophys. Acta* 287:301–11

171. Ulrich, F. 1976. Effects of trypsin on protein synthesis in macrophages. *Exp. Cell Res.* 101:267–77

172. Vollet, J. J., Butel, J. S. 1976. Temperature-dependent surface changes in cells transformed by group A mutants of simian virus 40. *J. Cell Biol.* 70:51 (Abstr.)

173. Wang, E., Goldberg, A. R. 1976. Changes in surface topography and microfilament organization upon transformation of chick embryo fibroblasts with Rous sarcoma virus. *J. Cell Biol.* 70:122 (Abstr.)

174. Warocquier, R., Scherrer, K. 1969. RNA metabolism in mammalian cells at elevated temperature. *Eur. J. Biochem.* 10:362–70

175. Weisenberg, R. C., Deery, W. 1976. Tubulin-nucleotide reactions during polymerization and depolymerization. *J. Cell Biol.* 70:225 (Abstr.)

176. Winicov, I. 1975. The role of 5S RNA in temperature-sensitive ribosomal RNA maturation. *Biochim. Biophys. Acta* 402:62–68

177. Wireman, J. W., Sypherd, P. S. 1975. Temperature dependence for physical and functional reconstitution of 30S ribosomes of *E.coli. Biochem. Biophys. Res. Commun.* 66:570–77

178. Woodcock, E., Grigg, G. W. 1972. Repair of thermally induced DNA breakage in *Escherichia coli. Nature New Biol.* 237:76–79

179. Zeikus, J. G., Brock, T. D. 1971. Protein synthesis at high temperatures: aminoacylation of tRNA. *Biochim. Biophys. Acta* 228: 736–45

180. Zillig, W., Zechel, K., Rabussay, D., Schachner, M., Sethi, V. S., Palm, P., Heil, A., Seifert, W. 1970. On the role of different subunits of DNA dependent RNA polymerase from *E.coli* in the transcription process. *Cold Spring Harbor Symp. Quant. Biol.* 35:47–58

Ann. Rev. Plant Physiol. 1978. 29:47–66

DELAYED FLUORESCENCE IN PHOTOSYNTHESIS

♦7644

J. Amesz and H. J. van Gorkom

Department of Biophysics, Huygens Laboratory of the State University,
2300 RA Leiden, The Netherlands

CONTENTS

1. INTRODUCTION

Delayed fluorescence of chlorophyll was discovered accidentally by Strehler & Arnold (97) in an attempt to use the firefly luminescence method to measure ATP production by algae. Delayed fluorescence was also observed with leaves (97) and chloroplasts (96) of higher plants and with photosynthetic bacteria (6).

The early experiments of Arnold, Strehler, and co-workers had already given various indications that the phenomenon of delayed light emission is related to the process of photosynthesis. The action spectrum (6, 97) and light saturation (96, 98) were similar to that of photosynthetic reactions, and the emission spectrum of the green alga *Chlorella pyrenoidosa* was found to resemble that of chlorophyll fluorescence in the same species (4). Strehler & Arnold (97) advanced the hypothesis that delayed fluorescence of photosynthetic material is a chemiluminescence process

47

caused by the reversal of photosynthetic reactions [ultimately involving the reversal of the primary photochemical reaction (7)]. The "recombination" hypothesis[1] has been widely accepted, and evidence related to this concept will be discussed in later sections of this review. Nevertheless, it should be mentioned here that other theories have also been advanced to explain delayed light emission. These include electron-hole recombination (1–3, 15) and triplet-triplet annihilation (91, 94). For a discussion we refer to (71) and (77).

More than a quarter of a century has passed since the discovery of delayed chlorophyll fluorescence, and it has become increasingly apparent that the study of this phenomenon is an important tool for obtaining information about the mechanism of photosynthesis. During recent years some reviews have appeared on the subject. Much of the material that appeared before 1971 has been covered by Kraan (68) and by Crofts, Wraight & Fleischman (23); a very recent review is that by Malkin (76). Detailed reviews, mainly dealing with green plant material, were given by Lavorel (71) and Malkin (77).

2. PIGMENTS AND PIGMENT SYSTEMS

Several lines of evidence indicate that, in oxygen-evolving organisms, delayed fluorescence mainly originates from PS II. As with fluorescence, the intensity of delayed light is stimulated by excitation of PS II and depressed by light mainly absorbed by PS I (14, 50). Mutants of algae lacking PS II activity showed only a very weak luminescence, whereas delayed light emission was not impaired in a mutant lacking PS I (8). Relatively strong delayed light emission was observed with subchloroplast particles enriched in PS II, but less light was emitted by a PS I particle fraction (60, 74, 112). Recent studies with PS I particles indicate that PS I emits delayed fluorescence as well (91). However, the intensity is lower than that of PS II, and therefore PS I emission probably did not significantly complicate the earlier studies on luminescence.

Emission spectra of delayed fluorescence were found to be similar to those of prompt fluorescence (4, 6, 8, 20, 21, 115). With algae, the most precise spectra were obtained by Azzi (8). The spectra of the green algae *Chlorella* and *Scenedesmus* were almost indistinguishable from those of prompt (chlorophyll *a*) fluorescence in these organisms, with maxima at 685 nm. The same was observed with *Rhodopseudomonas viridis* (20). Within the error of measurement, the emission spectra of prompt and delayed fluorescence were identical in this bacterium, both spectra representing the emission spectrum of bacteriochlorophyll *b*, the only chlorophyll pigment present in this species.

[1]For practical purposes, the primary electron donor and so-called "primary" acceptor of bacterial photosynthesis will be denoted by P and X, respectively. (Depending on the species, P may be either bacteriochlorophyll *a* or bacteriochlorophyll *b*). For Photosystem II (PS II) of oxygen-evolving organisms, the symbols P680 and Q will be used; P700 denotes the primary electron donor; P430 is an electron acceptor of Photosystem I (PS I) (probably an iron-sulfur protein). P680 and P700 are probably both chlorophyll *a*.

These measurements show that the light is emitted by the lowest excited singlet state of chlorophyll *a* or bacteriochlorophyll, and that it indeed represents a delayed fluorescence emission, rather than a phosphorescence from a long-lived excited (triplet) state, which would be emitted at longer wavelengths. The emission spectra also suggest that at least the bulk of the light is emitted by light-harvesting, rather than by reaction center chlorophyll or bacteriochlorophyll. The evidence is clearest for *Rps. viridis,* where both delayed and prompt fluorescence are emitted in a band at 1040 nm. This emission band very likely arises from the light-harvesting bacteriochlorophyll absorbing at 1020 nm, since the reaction center bacteriochlorophyll (the primary electron donor P) absorbs at a wavelength about 35 nm shorter. In PS I at low temperature, delayed fluorescence occurs at 740 nm (91), while prompt fluorescence emission occurs at shorter wavelength (695 nm) as well. At room temperature the emission maxima of prompt and delayed fluorescence of PS I are at 695 and 710 nm, respectively.

With blue-green and red algae, the emission spectra of prompt fluorescence contain a significant contribution of phycocyanins, but delayed fluorescence showed at most only a minor contribution of these pigments (8). Similar observations were made with the green photosynthetic bacterium *"Chloropseudomonas ethylica"* (*Chlorobium limicola*). In this species, the emission spectrum of prompt fluorescence comes in large part from chlorobium chlorophyll, emitting at 770 nm, whereas delayed light emission is predominantly from bacteriochlorophyll *a,* and shows a maximum at 820 nm (21). In fact, the latter spectrum closely matched the emission spectrum of the increase of fluorescence intensity that is observed upon continued strong illumination, and which is caused by a closure of the reaction center traps (34). A similar situation exists for *Rps. sphaeroides.* The emission spectrum of prompt fluorescence in this bacterium shows, in addition to emission by the long-wavelength bacteriochlorophyll *a* (B870), a small contribution of a bacteriochlorophyll *a* at shorter wavelength (B850). The latter component is absent, or at least significantly smaller, in delayed fluorescence, and the same applies to the emission spectrum of the light-induced increase in prompt fluorescence (115). A bacterial mutant that lacks functional reaction centers showed no delayed light emission (22).

The above observations are in line with the recombination hypothesis mentioned in the introduction. According to this hypothesis, excited reaction center pigment is the first product of the reversal of the primary charge separation. Excitation of the reaction center chlorophyll normally leads to photochemistry again, and the excited reaction center (bacterio)chlorophyll may have an extremely short lifetime. The probability of energy transfer back to the antenna chlorophyll is therefore very small. Nevertheless, it probably exceeds that of fluorescence emision by the reaction center chlorophyll considerably. Therefore, it is likely that delayed fluorescence is observed only when back transfer of the excitation to antenna pigments has taken place. It may be further concluded that photosystems which contain antenna pigments (like phycocyanins), absorbing at significantly shorter wavelengths than the chlorophylls close to the reaction center, emit delayed fluorescence from these chlorophylls only. Unfavorable overlap (33) of emission and absorption bands provides an explanation of this phenomenon.

3.   THE RECOMBINATION HYPOTHESIS

3.1   The Primary Charge Pair

As mentioned in the introduction, it is widely accepted that delayed fluorescence results from a back reaction of the primary photoproducts of photosynthesis. Fluorescence emission can in fact be induced chemically in the dark, by oxidizing the primary electron donor and reducing the primary electron acceptor (40, 43). In bacterial chromatophores the emission induced by a reductant was proportional to the concentration of the oxidized electron donor P^+ prior to addition (43).

Carithers & Parson (20) have demonstrated that delayed fluorescence induced by short flashes in membrane fragments from *Rps. viridis* requires the presence both of P^+ and of the reduced acceptor X^-. When secondary electron transport was inhibited, the intensity of delayed fluorescence decayed after a flash with the same kinetics as the charge recombination $P^+ X^- \rightarrow P X$. Similar arguments come from the delayed fluorescence accompanying charge recombination of $P700^+$ $P430^-$ in subchloroplast fragments enriched in PS I (91).

In spinach chloroplasts at pH 4.0, the primary charge pair in PS II, $P680^+ Q^-$, disappears after a flash mainly by charge recombination, and although in this case a direct comparison has not been made, delayed fluorescence at pH 4.0 seemed to decay with similar kinetics (106). In preilluminated chloroplasts the intensity of delayed fluorescence can be greatly enhanced by reducing the primary acceptor with dithionite (109, 111), and can be suppressed completely by reduction of oxidants produced by PS II with artificial electron donors like hydroxylamine, if the primary acceptor is kept in the reduced state (13). These and similar arguments add up to a convincing body of evidence for the recombination hypothesis.

The intensity of delayed fluorescence thus is a measure of the concentration of the primary charge pair, which is difficult to determine otherwise. It is often technically difficult to determine the concentrations of both the oxidized primary donor and the reduced primary acceptor by direct methods, especially in PS II, where delayed fluorescence is relatively easy to measure. Moreover, knowledge of the concentrations of oxidized primary donors and reduced primary acceptors alone is not always sufficient for determining the primary charge pair concentration. This is possible if either the donors or the acceptors are all oxidized or all reduced, or if the charges occur in pairs only, which is the case after their production by the photochemical reaction when secondary electron transport has not (yet) occurred. Nevertheless, the quantitative interpretation of delayed fluorescence measurements is in general very complicated, because other factors are involved which are difficult to determine, as discussed below.

3.2   Rate Constant, Exciton Yield, and Emission Yield

The recombination hypothesis predicts that the intensity of delayed fluorescence should be proportional not only to the concentration of the primary charge pair ($P680^+ Q^-$ in PS II and $P^+ X^-$ in bacteria), but also to the rate constant of the luminescent charge recombination, to the probability that this reaction results in electronic excitation of chlorophyll and, finally, to the fluorescence yield of those chlorophylls which become excited via charge recombination.

The total number of quanta emitted as delayed fluorescence is several orders of magnitude smaller than the number of charge recombinations taking place. Moreover, in *Rps. viridis*, this delayed fluorescence yield exhibits a strong dependence on temperature and on pH, while neither the overall rate of the charge recombination nor the prompt fluorescence yield is similarly affected (20). To explain these phenomena it may be assumed that the probability of producing excited chlorophyll during recombination (the "exciton yield") is low and temperature- and pH-dependent. Alternatively, two different recombination reactions may occur in parallel, one of which produces delayed fluorescence and proceeds at a small rate compared to the other, nonluminescent charge recombination. In this case variations of the rate of the luminescent back reaction rather than a variable exciton yield may be involved and in fact the exciton yield may be unity, as suggested by recent results discussed below.

It seems unlikely that the fluorescence yield of the chlorophylls reexcited by back reaction plays an important role in the variations of delayed fluorescence intensity, even though the prompt fluorescence yield in chloroplasts is seen to vary by a factor of five.

Pronounced variations of prompt fluorescence may occur without corresponding changes of delayed fluorescence. Prompt fluorescence is strongly quenched by carotenoid triplets (27, 37), but delayed fluorescence is not affected (102). This result suggests that prompt and delayed fluorescence may not originate in the same population of chlorophyll molecules. On the other hand, in certain conditions prompt and delayed fluorescence are equally affected by magnesium ions (10, 110). Presumably the fluorescence emitted when the reaction centers are in the quenching state P680 Q, the so-called F_0 level, originates at least in part from excitations lost in the antenna chlorophylls during the random walk toward the reaction centers (18, 34). Excitations produced by charge recombination always start out from the reaction center, which then is left in the quenching state P680 Q, and therefore transfer of excitation energy to P680 may be significantly faster than if excitations are produced at random in the antenna.

Thus delayed fluorescence may originate largely from chlorophyll molecules in the vicinity of the reaction center, and the fluorescence yield of this population of chlorophyll molecules probably is lower than the conventionally measured yield, which is an average of all chlorophylls. If excitations produced by charge recombination do not leave the close vicinity of the reaction center, it also seems unlikely that quenching by neighboring reaction centers will affect them, unless energy transfer from one center to another is more probable than from a center back to the bulk pigments. These considerations suggest that the fluorescence yield factor which governs delayed fluorescence is very low and little affected by the variable fluorescence yield of the bulk chlorophylls. The emission yield is low because of photochemical quenching, which regenerates the charge pair P680$^+$ Q$^-$. This quenching decreases the net rate of charge recombination and does not decrease the number of quanta emitted per net charge recombination. Thus, contrary to what is normally done, it should be disregarded if one wants to estimate the contribution of the luminescent recombination reaction to the overall decay rate of P680$^+$ Q$^-$ from the intensity or total amount of delayed fluorescence emitted. The fluorescence yield to be assumed for the purpose of such estimates is not necessarily identical to the maximum overall fluorescence yield measured when all reaction centers are in the nonquenching state P680 Q$^-$ because the populations of emitting chlorophyll molecules are not identical in both cases.

Quantum yields in the order of 10^{-4} photons emitted per net charge recombination have been reported for delayed fluorescence (77). These may be minimal estimates (71), but even a value of 10^{-3} together with a fluorescence yield of more than 10^{-2} would still mean that less than 10% of the charge recombination proceeds via the luminescent back reaction. Carithers & Parson (20) calculated a value of 0.2% in membrane fragments from *Rps. viridis*. It is therefore not surprising that large variations of delayed fluorescence may occur without concomitant changes of the overall recombination rate. The most obvious example is the temperature dependence of delayed fluorescence. As discussed in section 4.3, the intensity of delayed fluorescence is strongly temperature-dependent, while the decay rate, probably determined by the overall recombination rate of the primary charge pair, depends very little on temperature. Carithers & Parson (20) showed that both delayed fluorescence intensity and the recombination rate are pH-dependent, both decreasing toward lower pH values, while the activation energy of luminescence was not much affected, and the prompt fluorescence yield increased toward lower pH values.

3.3   Delayed Fluorescence from "Closed" Reaction Centers

In photosynthetic bacteria the "primary" charge separation has been shown to proceed via an intermediate state involving reduced bacteriopheophytin: P* I X → P$^+$ I$^-$ X → P$^+$ I X$^-$(32). P$^+$ I$^-$ can still be formed in the light after chemical reduction of X and charge recombination of P$^+$ I$^-$ then occurs. At low temperature this charge recombination results in the formation of a bacteriochlorophyll triplet state with a quantum yield close to 1. Correspondingly, the reaction centers still act as efficient fluorescence quenchers when X is reduced, At room temperature, however, fluorescence appears to be higher in the state P I X$^-$ than in P I X and less triplets are formed. As there seems to be no obvious reason why X$^-$ should prevent photochemistry in such a temperature-dependent way, it has been suggested that the increased fluorescence at room temperature is actually delayed fluorescence resulting from an efficient return of singlet excitations to the bulk chlorophyll by charge recombination of P$^+$ I$^-$ X$^-$ → P* I X$^-$ (92; N. G. Holmes, in preparation).

A somewhat similar behavior was postulated for PS I (91) because after accumulation of the primary acceptor in the reduced state, illumination was found to induce a chlorophyll triplet state. The hypothesis that this triplet is formed by charge recombination in the reaction center remains to be confirmed by more direct evidence. Nevertheless, it is interesting to note that the triplet did give rise to delayed fluorescence at room temperature by thermal activation to the excited singlet level.

In PS II a delayed fluorescence with a half-life of about 0.6 μsec has been detected which seems to originate from reaction centers illuminated in the state P680 Q$^-$ (102, 103). To maintain the recombination hypothesis, an alternative primary electron acceptor W was postulated and the luminescence was ascribed to charge recombination of P680$^+$ W$^-$. W might be an intermediate electron carrier between P680 and Q, analogous to I in bacteria. The amplitude of the emission was found to saturate at about the same flash energy as normal PS II photochemistry (102, 103). This result is somewhat surprising since the increased fluorescence yield in the presence of Q^- (36) implies a lowered trapping efficiency. Obviously the apparent increase of prompt fluorescence cannot be ascribed to the 0.6 μsec luminescence itself, because its lifetime is much shorter. It seems possible, however, that the precursor state of the 0.6 μsec emission is actually formed with low quantum efficiency and that the emission intensity saturates only as a result of quenching by carotenoid triplets, since the excitation energy in this case is probably not restricted to the population of chlorophylls involved in "normal" delayed fluorescence. Thus it may reach a constant level at flash energies well below those needed to saturate the production of carotenoid triplets and the formation of the luminescence precursor. Half-saturation of the 0.6 μsec luminescence intensity should occur at 50% quenching by carotenoid triplets. On the basis of the calculations of den Haan (27), one may estimate that this concentration of carotenoid triplets may be reached at a flash energy comparable to that needed for half-saturation of normal PS II photochemistry.

The 0.6 μsec luminescence depends on the presence of the secondary electron donor Z, which normally reduces $P680^+$ within a microsecond. It is suppressed completely after inactivation of Z by hydroxylamine, or in spinach chloroplasts by incubation at pH 4.0 (102). These observations suggest that the luminescence originates from Z^+ P680 W^- rather than from $P680^+$ W^- directly. By analogy to the hypothesis proposed for bacteria, one may speculate that a direct recombination reaction of $P680^+$ and W^- causes the apparent increase of prompt fluorescence in the presence of Q^-. The implication then is that this recombination takes less than a nanosecond. The reduction of $P680^+$ by Z apparently is much slower, but should be faster than 0.6 μsec.

Finally, it must be mentioned that the 0.6 μsec luminescence appears to originate in part of the reaction centers only. Inactivation of Z by hydroxylamine proceeds with biphasic kinetics, and the suppression of luminescence is correlated with the fast phase, which accounts for about 20% of the reaction centers. The suggestion made by van Best (102) that only these centers cause the flash number dependence of the submicrosecond fluorescence rise described by Delosme (24) may explain the observation that the luminescence is strongly suppressed in the higher S states. It seems possible that in the centers where Z is less easily inactivated the recombination of Z^+ P680 W^- is more rapid than could be detected with the apparatus used.

4. SECONDARY ELECTRON TRANSPORT IN PHOTOSYSTEM II

Unlike PS I, where delayed fluorescence is difficult to measure, and bacterial photosystems, where electron transport is more easily studied by measuring absorbance changes, PS II has been studied extensively by measuring its relatively intense delayed fluorescence emission. The various electron transfer steps involved in photosynthetic oxygen evolution are still largely unknown. A few aspects of delayed fluorescence which are particularly relevant to this matter will be discussed in some detail in the present section. Other aspects are mentioned only briefly and have been dealt with more extensively by Lavorel (71) and Malkin (77).

4.1   S states

Measurements of oxygen evolution in flashes have shown that the oxidation of water results from the successive photochemical transfer of four electrons by one reaction center of PS II (64–66). The results were explained by the following scheme (66):

$$S_0 \xrightarrow{h\nu} S_1 \xrightarrow{h\nu} S_2 \xrightarrow{h\nu} S_3 \xrightarrow{h\nu} S_4$$

Each successive step represents the light-driven transfer of an electron from P680 to Q, followed by several secondary electron transfer reactions. In S_3 three positive charges have accumulated; in a subsequent flash S_4 is formed, which reacts in about a millisecond with water, giving O_2 and S_0.

The intensity of delayed fluorescence emitted by intact cells of *Chlorella* and *Scenedesmus,* like oxygen evolution, shows a fourfold periodicity with flash number (12, 35, 65, 102, 116). When delayed light is measured in the time range of 20 μsec to about 5 msec, the maximum intensity occurs after the third and the seventh or eighth flash (35, 102, 116), which seems to indicate that luminescence is stimulated in state S_4. The amount of stimulation, estimated by comparison with the emission intensity after the first flash, varied between three- and tenfold, depending on the time of measurement and perhaps also the species used. A stimulation of about two- to fivefold was observed after the second flash, indicating a considerable stimulation in S_3 also. When the luminescence was measured at longer times than about 5 msec, the maximum stimulation was observed after the second flash (12, 65), apparently because S_4 is converted rapidly to S_0 by reaction with water. In the presence of a low concentration of hydroxylamine, which delayed the maximum in the evolution of oxygen by two flashes by a reaction with an oxidized product of PS II (19), delayed fluorescence was similarly delayed (12).

With spinach chloroplasts a similar dependence on flash number as for intact algae, with a maximum after the third flash, was observed in the microsecond region (116). A maximum after the third flash was also observed in delayed fluorescence emitted in the time region around 40 msec if the sample was transferred to –35 °C before the last flash (108, 109), indicating that S_4 (or a similar condition with four positive charges) is stabilized considerably at –35 °C (see also 62). The same was observed if the last flash of a series was given at pH 10.0, rather than at about neutral pH (108, 109). However, at room temperature and normal pH, the 40 msec-delayed fluorescence of chloroplasts depends very little on flash number, for reasons that are not clearly understood (65, 109). Delayed fluorescence stimulated by treatments such as the addition of salt solutions shows a maximum after the second flash (see section 4.4).

As will be discussed in section 4.2, the dependence of delayed fluorescence on flash number can, at least in the submillisecond region, be explained by a dependence on the S state of the concentration of $P680^+$ after a flash. However, a direct effect of the accumulated charge on the intensity of delayed fluorescence cannot be excluded.

One might ask if delayed fluorescence is also emitted by reaction centers in state S_1. This question cannot be answered directly, because in dark-adapted algae or chloroplasts most reaction centers are in state S_1 already and would convert to

S_2 by a flash. Etienne & Lavorel (40) measured the emission of dark-adapted *Chlorella pyrenoidosa* upon the addition of DCMU, which partly reduces Q by causing reversed electron transport from the secondary acceptor (109). A weak light emission was observed, which may have arisen from reaction centers in state S_1, but the possibility that the emission came from reaction centers in higher S states that had not fully relaxed in darkness cannot be ruled out.

We already mentioned that isolated spinach chloroplasts near pH 7.0 do not show a clear flash number dependence of delayed fluorescence emitted in the time region of 20–40 msec. One might speculate that in these conditions most of the delayed fluorescence is emitted by reaction centers in which some secondary electron transfer reaction is inhibited so that the higher S states are not produced. However, this explanation does not apply to experiments of Velthuys (109) where DCMU was added some seconds before the last flash of a series. In these experiments reoxidation of Q^- other than by a back reaction with an oxidized product of PS II is inhibited (13). Velthuys observed that the intensity of light emission in the time region of about 100 msec to several seconds was somewhat larger after the second than after the first flash, and approximately the same after the second and third flash. This was an unexpected result, since after three flashes S_4 should reconvert rapidly to S_0 and therefore only a weak luminescence would be expected in the msec time range. A similar result was obtained by Etienne (39) with *Chlorella*. Velthuys concluded that a positive charge, able to react with Q^- (presumably via P680), is present in state S_0 also. For further discussion of this point we refer to the original publication (109). An alternative explanation was recently proposed by Lavorel (72), who postulated an exchange of the charge-accumulating enzymes between different PS II reaction centers in order to account for apparent anomalies in the oxygen yields obtained during a flash series.

Measurements of delayed fluorescence, in addition to those of oxygen evolution, are thus an important tool to obtain information about S states and about the mechanism of the oxidation of water. A clear example is also given by studies on the effect of NH_3 on delayed fluorescence. At low concentration NH_4Cl is an uncoupler of photosynthetic phosphorylation, but at high concentration it has been reported to inhibit the Hill reaction of chloroplasts, presumably by inhibiting oxygen evolution (26). Zankel (116) observed that the luminescence, measured 0.5 msec after each of a series of flashes, did not show the normal oscillation with flash number, but increased with the number of flashes given if NH_4Cl was added before illumination. Velthuys (107, 109) observed that the effect was even more pronounced if the emission was measured at about 40 msec after illumination. Delayed fluorescence showed a ten- to fifteenfold stimulation after the third and following flashes at a saturating concentration of NH_4Cl. The pH dependence indicated that NH_3 rather than NH_4^+ is the agent that stimulates delayed fluorescence and inhibits oxygen evolution. By varying the dark time between flashes and by adding NH_4Cl after the first or subsequent flashes instead of before illumination, Velthuys (109) obtained evidence that the stimulation of delayed fluorescence is due to a binding of NH_3 to the water-oxidizing enzyme. One molecule is bound in state S_2, a second one in state S_3, presumably in competition with water. When two molecules of

NH$_3$ are bound, delayed fluorescence is stimulated, apparently because water oxidation is inhibited and the system is unable to store more than three positive charges on the oxidizing side of PS II. These data may suggest that NH$_3$ and water compete for the same binding sites on the oxidizing enzyme.

4.2 Decay Kinetics

The most rapid decay component in delayed fluorescence from PS II discovered as yet is the 0.6 μsec phase discussed in section 3.3. With the same apparatus, subsequent phases with half-times about 15 μsec and 150 μsec were observed in *Chlorella* (35, 102). Earlier reports by Zankel (116) and Lavorel (70) indicated half-times of 5 to 10 μsec, about 35 and about 200 μsec. The properties of the 35 μsec component seem to correspond to those of the 15 μsec component of van Best and Duysens (35, 102); the measurement of the 5 to 10 μsec decay time in the earlier measurements may not have been very reliable because of technical limitations. Remarkably, a delay or even an increase accompanying the 3 μsec decay of carotenoid triplets, which strongly quench prompt fluorescence, has never been observed (102).

Since the reoxidation of Q$^-$ has an initial half-time of about 0.5 msec (95, 117) and its inhibition by DCMU suppresses the 200 μsec component of delayed fluorescence rather than preventing its decay (116), it seems likely that the rapid decay phases in delayed fluorescence reflect the reduction of P680$^+$. Rapid reactions of P680$^+$, which is an efficient fluorescence quencher (27, 28, 86, 106), have been studied by means of fluorescence and absorbance measurements. Most of the P680$^+$ reduction takes place with as yet unresolved kinetics in less than a microsecond (27, 28, 49), but additional phases with half-times of 35 and 200 μsec have been detected in spinach chloroplasts by absorbance measurements (30, 48). The amplitudes of these decay components of P680$^+$ oscillate with a period of four in a flash series (49), just like the corresponding luminescence decay components discussed in section 4.1. In agreement with this result, the amplitude of the fast fluorescence rise upon flash illumination suggests that the fraction of reaction centers in which P680$^+$ is reduced within a microsecond is in fact significantly lower in higher than in lower S states (24). This suggests that the stimulation of delayed fluorescence by high S states is caused by an inhibition of the submicrosecond reduction of P680$^+$ in a varying number of reaction centers, rather than by a direct effect of the accumulated charge on the luminescent back reaction.

The slow phase in P680$^+$ reduction may be caused by the absence of the secondary donor, resulting in charge recombination with Q$^-$, or the presence of the secondary donor in its oxidized form (105), in which case P680$^+$ reduction should follow the kinetics of the subsequent step in electron transport. A slow phase in the flash-induced increase in prompt fluorescence (35, 63, 117) correlates with the 15–35 μsec decay of delayed fluorescence, suggesting that this component reflects the reduction of some P680$^+$ by a compound other than Q$^-$, which remains in the nonquenching, reduced state. The electron donor might very well be the component which in its oxidized state causes the electron spin resonance signal known as signal IIvf (16), which has a rise time of 20 μsec (17).

Van Best and Duysens (35, 102) assumed, partly on the basis of experiments with hydroxylamine, that the 15 μsec luminescence reflects an electron donation that does not lead to formation of a higher S state. They explained the dependence of luminescence on flash number by the hypothesis of Delrieu (25), that most reaction centers in S_2 (and not in other S states) would be inactive in advancing the S state. However, this hypothesis does not explain the luminescence intensities measured with spinach chloroplasts and *Scenedesmus* at somewhat longer times after a flash (116), which showed a much more pronounced emission intensity after the third flash than *Chlorella* (35, 102). Moreover, it predicts only a maximum after the third flash if the photochemical efficiency in S_2 is quite low; the pattern of oxygen evolution (26, 65) shows that this is not the case for spinach chloroplasts.

The 150–200 μsec component observed in delayed fluorescence and $P680^+$ absorbance has not been found in prompt fluorescence. It seems likely that this component reflects a back reaction of $P680^+$ with Q^- in reaction centers which do not have a functional secondary electron donor. A 100 to 200 μsec recombination time for $P680^+$ Q^- was observed after inactivation of the secondary electron donor by subjecting chloroplasts to low pH (pH 4.0) (56, 106), and a pronounced 120 μsec luminescence is also observed after inactivation of oxygen evolution by detergent or Tris-treatment (55). The rereduction of the component responsible for signal IIvf takes 0.1 to 1 msec depending on the S states (9). No corresponding S-state dependence of the decay rate of delayed fluorescence in this time region has been reported. On the other hand, the intensity is strongly dependent on S state, and the slowest decay of signal IIvf is therefore much more likely to reflect significantly in delayed fluorescence kinetics than the more rapid reduction observed at lower S states.

Kinetic analysis of delayed fluorescence emitted at times longer than a millisecond after the flash becomes very complicated as is well verified by abundant data in the literature. Delayed fluorescence in this time range presumably is correlated with the deactivation of S_2 and S_3, the reduction level of the plastoquinone pool, and the decay of the pH gradient and membrane potential formed during reduction of the pool and the oxidation of water, and hence with photophosphorylation. For a detailed discussion we refer to the reviews of Lavorel and Malkin (71, 77).

4.3 Temperature Dependence

EMISSION AT LOW TEMPERATURES   Upon lowering the temperature, many secondary reactions of photosynthesis become inhibited, but even at a few degrees Kelvin the primary photoreactions of both PS I and PS II have been shown to occur. Delayed fluorescence in the millisecond range, at least in spinach chloroplasts, shows a maximum at –30 to –40°C (61, 101, 108, 109). In this temperature range oxygen evolution is largely inhibited and other electron transfer reactions are slowed down, so that the luminescence back reaction becomes more predominant. Optical and electron spin resonance studies have shown that upon further lowering the temperature secondary electron transport becomes even less able to compete with the back reaction between $P680^+$ and Q^-. The half-time of the back reaction is a few milliseconds, independent of temperature (75, 80, 113), whereas the oxidation of secondary electron donors by $P680^+$ appears to be several times slower. Therefore, at temperatures below about $-100°C$, the first flash given produces a charge separation which is largely reversible; a series of flashes or continuous illumination gives a stabilization with Q in the reduced and a secondary donor in the oxidized state, which condition decays only slowly in the dark (113).

In most experiments, continuous or repetitive illumination was used to excite delayed fluorescence at low temperature (2, 31, 61, 87). Upon illumination with red light, no or only low intensities of delayed fluorescence were observed below about $-100°C$ (2, 31, 61), which is not surprising in view of the charge stabilization that occurs under these conditions. The latter effect also explains why a preillumination at low temperature decreases the yield of delayed fluorescence (61). At -68 and $-122°C$ most of the delayed fluorescence was emitted as about a 350 μsec component upon illumination with repetitive flashes (61).

In 1957, Tollin & Calvin (100) already reported that luminescence, measured at longer times than 0.1 sec, could only be observed at $-180°C$ if blue light was used for excitation. In agreement with this result, Drissler and co-workers (31) recently reported that a much higher intensity of delayed light emission occurs with blue than with red illumination of *Chlorella,* especially near liquid helium temperature. The relation of this phenomenon to photosynthesis is not clear. It is possible that this luminescence is actually prompt fluorescence of chlorophyll excited by delayed light emission from a blue absorbing pigment. The same effect may have been observed by Ruby (87). Apart from the uncertainty induced by the "blue light effect," the most clear-cut information on low temperature delayed fluorescence comes from the early work of Tollin and co-workers (101). They measured the intensity and decay characteristics between 1.5 msec and 10 sec of luminescence from *Chlorella* and spinach chloroplasts induced by single flashes of blue light at various temperatures down to $-170°C$. Long-lived components of delayed fluorescence were found to disappear upon cooling, and at sufficiently low temperature the luminescence showed only two components, of 1–2 and of about 30 msec, respectively. The first of these might correspond to the back reaction between $P680^+$ and Q^-. The emission spectrum was roughly the same as that of prompt chlorophyll fluorescence.

"THERMOLUMINESCENCE" Arnold & Sherwood (5) were the first to observe that light-generated precursors of delayed fluorescence can be stabilized at low temperature. Subsequent heating in the dark results in delayed fluorescence emission, which in this case is generally referred to as thermoluminescence. Illumination may take place before, during, or after lowering the temperature, resulting in different precursor states being revealed in the emission profile observed upon heating. The so-called glow curve, emission intensity plotted versus temperature, shows several bands peaking at characteristic temperatures. Some of these bands are clearly related to photosynthetic activity and normal delayed fluorescence. In PS II-containing material, most of the emission occurs either in a band at about $-10°C$, designated A by Arnold & Azzi (2), or in the so-called B band, which consists of two components, B_1 and B_2, peaking at $+25$ and $+40°C$ (57, 73, 88). The relative heights of the A and B bands seem to be complementary and depend strongly on the temperature during illumination. Illumination at $-10°C$ results in a high A band and low B bands, while the reverse is observed after illumination at $-55°C$ (57). The A and B bands appear simultaneously with the capacity to evolve oxygen during the greening process (59) and during reactivation of manganese-deficient algae (58).

It seems quite likely that the A and B bands result from a recombination of charges produced by PS II and stabilized by the low temperature on different components of the electron transport chain. Apparently, positive charges stored in the oxygen-evolving apparatus are involved. The negative charges may come directly from the reduced primary acceptor Q^- in the case of the A band, since reoxidation of Q^- by the secondary acceptor upon heating occurs in the same temperature range as the emission of the A band (29). The emission of the two B bands may involve reversed electron flow from the secondary acceptor (R^-) and the plastoquinone pool (PQH_2). This cannot be the only difference between the A and B bands, however, since it does not explain the different effects of excitation at -10 and $-55°C$. Moreover, the presence of DCMU does not cause just an increase of the A band at the expense of emission at higher temperatures, but rather the B bands seem to be replaced by a new band at $+10°C$, at least in spinach leaves (57). Apparently conflicting evidence has been reported concerning the effects of DCMU in other material (2, 3, 93).

It seems possible that the A band arises from reaction centers which had accumulated three positive charges (S_3) and that the B bands require S_2 only. Remarkably, there is little evidence concerning the number of photochemical turnovers in PS II required to generate these thermoluminescence bands. Just recently, experiments of this type were reported by Inoue & Shibata (59a). Arnold & Azzi (2) have mentioned that in *Chlorella* the excitation of the A and B bands requires two short flashes at $-30°C$, spaced by several minutes, but otherwise no data on flash excitation seem to be available. Reoxidation of Q^- by secondary acceptors is possible down to $-50°C$ (62). The data of Ichikawa et al (57) show that the B bands can be excited at this temperature and below.

In addition to the A and B bands, which occur at fixed temperatures independent of the temperature at which excitation took place, Ichikawa et al (57) observed a minor emission band at 10 to 30° above the excitation temperature. This band, designated Z_v, could be measured from -150 to $-40°C$; at higher temperatures it was presumably drowned in the much stronger A and B bands. Like the A and B bands, the Z_v band was absent in etiolated leaves and in PS I subchloroplast particles. It was observed, however, after greening of wheat leaves under intermittent illumination, which allows development of PS II but not the capacity to oxidize water. The Z_v band also differed from the A and B bands in its resistance to heat treatment. Pretreatment for 5 min at $45°C$ abolished the A and B bands, while the Z_v band disappeared only at $55°C$. Thus the Z_v band appears to be dependent on active PS II reaction centers, but unlike the A and B bands, it does not require a functional oxygen-evolving enzyme. It was found to be abolished by DCMU, but this can hardly be related to the well-known inhibition of electron flow from the primary to secondary acceptors in PS II, since the Z_v component was observed at temperatures where such electron flow is blocked anyway. The origin of the Z_v band and its temperature dependence remains unclear. A minor thermoluminescence band at about 50°C has also been reported (57, 88). Its relation to photosynthetic activity is doubtful since it occurs in etiolated leaves, PS I particles, and PS II particles in the presence of an artificial electron donor.

In *Rps. viridis* a thermoluminescence band around 20°C is observed, which seems to originate from a charge recombination of the oxidized reaction center chlorophyll with electrons trapped at secondary electron acceptors (44).

Glow curves also show other types of emission which are not related to the subject of the present review. An oxygen-dependent emission has been reported both for green plants (3) and for bacteria (44). After illumination at –196°C, chlorophyll *a*, both in vivo and in vitro, shows an emission at 740 nm upon heating to –160°C (88). This may be caused by fluorescence of aggregated chlorophyll resulting from triplet-triplet annihilation (91). In *Rps. sphaeroides* thermoluminescence bands at –160 and –130°C have been found to originate from magnesium protoporphyrin IX, an intermediate in bacteriochlorophyll biosynthesis (51).

4.4 Stimulation of Delayed Fluorescence

The intensity of delayed fluorescence emission can be stimulated by various treatments. Stimulation by the addition of reductants or oxidants has been mentioned already (section 3.1); in these cases the effect can be explained in a straightforward way by an increase in the concentration of the oxidized primary electron donor or reduced acceptor. If both an oxidant and a reductant are applied, illumination may not be necessary at all to produce delayed fluorescence.

In addition to this, a number of treatments have been found to enhance the intensity of delayed light emission when applied after a preillumination. These stimulations have generally been studied in such a way that the suspension of photosynthetic material (usually chloroplasts) was first illuminated by continuous light or one or more saturating light flashes, and subsequently mixed with a liquid or a solution containing the desired reagent. Therefore, the stimulation occurs at least many milliseconds and often much longer after the preillumination, i.e. at a time when at least one of the components of the primary charge pair has almost completely disappeared. Thus an increase of the rates of "reversed" electron transport should be considered in explaining the stimulation effects (82, 89), but other mechanisms, like an enhanced exciton yield or rate of the recombination reaction that produces delayed fluorescence, as may be suggested by the experiments of Nishizaki (85), cannot be ruled out either.

Mayne & Clayton (83) discovered the so-called acid-base induced stimulation. Chloroplasts, when illuminated at neutral pH and subsequently mixed with a weak acid such as succinic acid, showed a strong, temporary stimulation of delayed fluorescence when the pH was suddenly brought to a higher value. This effect has been studied in more detail by Kraan and co-workers (68, 69). Inhibition by uncouplers indicates that the stimulation is caused by a temporary difference in pH across the thylakoid membrane, the pH being low on the inside and high on the outside of the thylakoid.

Stimulation of delayed fluorescence was also observed upon salt addition to (preilluminated) chloroplasts or bacterial chromatophores (11, 45, 68, 69, 84). With KCl, the stimulation was several times higher in the presence of valinomycin (11, 68), which enhances the permeability of membranes for K^+ ions. This result indicates that the stimulation is a consequence of the generation of an electrical potential which is negative on the outside with respect to the inside of the thylakoid or chromatophore. Both the salt and acid-base stimulated delayed fluorescence showed a pronounced S state dependence (54).

The acid-base induced stimulation was explained by Kraan et al (68, 69) by the assumption of a protonation and deprotonation reaction of the primary electron donor and acceptor of PS II. However, this hypothesis cannot be maintained in view of more recent evidence (e.g. 47, 52, 104). It seems more likely that the acid-base effect should be explained by the formation of negative charge on membrane proteins in the region of high pH and positive charge in the region of low pH, and that the stimulation may thus have a mechanism similar to that of salt addition. In addition, a stimulation of reversed electron flow from the plastoquinone pool to Q appears to be involved (114), and, if the starting pH is not too low, may be the most important mechanism (89). These results, as well as the partial inhibition by uncouplers (68, 81), indicate that delayed fluorescence may also be stimulated to a varying degree by the membrane potential and pH gradient generated by photosynthetic electron transport (41). This also explains why delayed fluorescence and electrochromic pigment changes often show a related behavior (42, 46, 67, 98).

Some other treatments have also been found to stimulate delayed fluorescence. A stimulation by the addition of organic solvents was tentatively explained by an increase of the dielectric constant in the membrane (53). As discussed by Malkin (77), a stimulation observed upon a sudden increase in temperature (78, 79) may be used to calculate the activation energy of luminescence emission. In addition, recent reports (90, 99) suggest that changes of pH and membrane potential may also be involved in this phenomenon. The most effective treatment is the application of an external electrical field to a suspension of chloroplasts, which may result in a more than a hundredfold stimulation of delayed fluorescence (2, 38). This method has the unique advantage that it allows the observation of rapid kinetics induced by the stimulation.

Literature Cited

1. Arnold, W. 1965. An electron-hole picture of photosynthesis. *J. Phys. Chem.* 69:788–91
2. Arnold, W., Azzi, J. 1971. The mechanisms of delayed light production and a new effect of electric fields on chloroplasts. *Photochem. Photobiol.* 14:233–40
3. Arnold, W., Azzi, J. R. 1968. Chlorophyll energy levels and electron flow in photosynthesis. *Proc. Natl. Acad. Sci. USA* 61:29–35
4. Arnold, W., Davidson, J. B. 1954. The identity of the fluorescent and delayed light emission spectra in *Chlorella. J. Gen. Physiol.* 37:677–84
5. Arnold, W., Sherwood, H. K. 1957. Are chloroplasts semiconductors? *Proc. Natl. Acad. Sci. USA* 43:105–14
6. Arnold, W., Thompson, J. 1956. Delayed light production by blue-green algae, red algae and purple bacteria. *J. Gen. Physiol.* 39:311–18
7. Arthur, W. E., Strehler, B. L. 1957. Studies on the primary process in

photosynthesis. I. Photosynthetic luminescence: multiple reactants. *Arch. Biochem. Biophys.* 70:507–26

8. Azzi, J. R. 1966. The delayed light and fluorescence emission spectra for green, blue-green, red algae, and nonphotosynthetic mutants. *Oak Ridge Natl. Lab. Rep. ORNL-TM-1534.* 31 pp.

9. Babcock, G. T., Blankenship, R. E., Sauer, K. 1976. Reaction kinetics for positive charge accumulation on the water side of chloroplast photosystem II. *FEBS Lett.* 61:286–89

10. Barber, J. 1977. *Effect of cations on prompt and delayed chlorophyll fluorescence.* Presented at Int. Symp. Membr. Bioenerg., Spetsai, Greece

11. Barber, J., Kraan, G. P. B. 1970. Salt-induced light emission from chloroplasts. *Biochim. Biophys. Acta* 197:49–59

12. Barbieri, G., Delosme, R., Joliot, P. 1970. Comparison entre l'émission d'oxygène et l'émission de luminescence à la suite d'une série d'éclairs saturants. *Photochem. Photobiol.* 12:197–206

13. Bennoun, P. 1970. Réoxidation du quencher "Q" en présence de 3-(3,4-dichlorophenyl)-1,1-dimethylurée. *Biochim. Biophys. Acta* 216:357–63

14. Bertsch, W. F. 1962. Two photoreactions in photosynthesis: evidence from the delayed light emission of *Chlorella. Proc. Natl. Acad. Sci. USA* 48:2000–4

15. Bertsch, W. F., West, J., Hill, R. 1971. Delayed light studies on photosynthetic energy conversion. III. Effect of 3-(3,4-dichlorophenyl)-1,1-dimethyl urea on the millisecond emission from chloroplasts performing photoreduction of ferricyanide. *Photochem. Photobiol.* 14:241–50

16. Blankenship, R. E., Babcock, G. T., Warden, J. T., Sauer, K. 1975. Observation of a new epr transient in chloroplasts, that may reflect the electron donor to photosystem II at room temperature. *FEBS Lett.* 51:287–93

17. Blankenship, R. E., McGuire, A., Sauer, K. 1977. Rise time of epr signal II$_{vf}$ in chloroplast photosystem II. *Biochim. Biophys. Acta* 459:617–19

18. Borisov, A. Yu., Godik, V. I. 1973. Excitation energy transfer in photosynthesis. *Biochim. Biophys. Acta* 301:227–48

19. Bouges-Bocquet, B. 1971. Action de faibles concentrations d'hydroxylamine sur l'émission d'oxygène des alges *Chlorella* et des chloroplastes d'épinards. *Biochim. Biophys. Acta* 234:103–12

20. Carithers, R. P., Parson, W. W. 1975. Delayed fluorescence from *Rhodopseudomonas viridis* following single flashes. *Biochim. Biophys. Acta* 387:194–211

21. Clayton, R. K. 1965. Characteristics of fluorescence and delayed light emission from green photosynthetic bacteria and algae. *J. Gen. Physiol.* 48:633–46

22. Clayton, R. K., Bertsch, W. F. 1965. Absence of delayed light emission in the millesecond time range from a mutant of *Rhodopseudomonas spheroides* which lacks functional reaction centers. *Biochem. Biophys. Res. Commun.* 18:415–19

23. Crofts, A. R., Wraight, C. A., Fleischman, D. E. 1971. Energy conservation in the photochemical reactions of photosynthesis and its relation to delayed fluorescence. *FEBS Lett.* 15:89–100

24. Delosme, R. 1971. Variations du rendement de fluorescence de la chlorophylle in vivo sous l'action d'éclairs de forte intensité. *C.R. Acad. Sci. Ser. D* 272:2828–31

25. Delrieu, M. J. 1974. Simple explanation of the misses in the cooperation of charges in photosynthetic oxygen evolution. *Photochem. Photobiol.* 20:441–54

26. Delrieu, M. J. 1976. Inhibition by ammonium chloride of the oxygen yield of photosynthesis. *Biochim. Biophys. Acta* 440:176–88

27. Den Haan, G. A. 1977. *Chlorophyll-a fluorescence as a monitor for rapid reactions in system II of photosynthesis.* PhD thesis. Univ. Leiden, The Netherlands. 123 pp.

28. Den Haan, G. A., Duysens, L. N. M., Egberts, D. J. N. 1974. Fluorescence yield kinetics in the microsecond-range in *Chlorella pyrenoidosa* and spinach chloroplasts in the presence of hydroxylamine. *Biochim. Biophys. Acta* 368:409–21

29. Desai, T. S., Sane, P. V., Tatake, V. G. 1975. Thermoluminescence studies on spinach leaves and *Euglena. Photochem. Photobiol.* 21:345–50

30. Döring, G., Renger, G., Vater, J., Witt, H. T. 1969. Properties of the photoactive chlorophyll-a II in photosynthesis. *Z. Naturforsch.* 24b:1139–43

31. Drissler, F., Hägele, W., Schmid, D., Wolf, H. C. 1977. Delayed emission from green algae "*Chlorella pyrenoidosa*" at various temperatures. *Z. Naturforsch.* 32a:88–95

32. Dutton, P. L. 1976. Pheophytins and the photosynthetic reaction center. *Photochem. Photobiol.* 24:655–57
33. Duysens, L. N. M. 1952. *Transfer of excitation energy in photosynthesis.* PhD thesis. Univ. Utrecht, The Netherlands. 96 pp.
34. Duysens, L. N. M. 1967. Primary photosynthetic reactions in relation to transfer of energy. *Brookhaven Symp. Biol.* 19:71–79
35. Duysens, L. N. M., Den Haan, G. A., Van Best, J. A. 1975. Rapid reactions of photosystem 2 as studied by the kinetics of the fluorescence and luminescence of chlorophyll *a* in *Chlorella pyrenoidosa.* In *Int. Congr. Photosynth., 3rd, Rehovot,* ed. M. Avron, pp. 1–12. Amsterdam: Elsevier. 2194 pp.
36. Duysens, L. N. M., Sweers, H. E. 1963. Mechanism of two photochemical reactions in algae as studied by means of fluorescence. In *Studies on Microalgae and Photosynthetic Bacteria,* special issue of *Plant Cell Physiol.,* pp. 353–72. Tokyo: Univ. Tokyo Press, 636 pp.
37. Duysens, L. N. M., Van der Schatte Olivier, T. E., Den Haan, G. A. 1972. Light-induced quenching of the yield of chlorophyll a_2 fluorescence, with microsecond backreaction stimulated by oxygen. *Int. Congr. Photobiol., 5th, Bochum,* abstract 277
38. Ellenson, J. L., Sauer, K. 1976. The electrophotoluminescence of chloroplasts. *Photochem. Photobiol.* 23: 113–23
39. Etienne, A.-L. 1974. New results on the properties of photosystem II centers blocked by 3-(3,4-dichlorophenyl)-1,1-dimethylurea in their different photoactive states. *Biochim. Biophys. Acta* 333:320–30
40. Etienne, A.-L., Lavorel, J. 1975. Triggered luminescence in dark adapted *Chlorella* cells and chloroplasts. *FEBS Lett.* 57:276–79
41. Evans, E. H., Crofts, A. R. 1973. The relationship between delayed fluorescence and the H^+ gradient in chloroplasts. *Biochim. Biophys. Acta* 292: 130–39
42. Evans, E. H., Crofts, A. R. 1974. The relationship between delayed fluorescence and the carotenoid shift in chromatophores from *Rhodopseudomonas capsulata. Biochim. Biophys. Acta* 333:44–51
43. Fleischman, D. E. 1969. Chemiluminescence in photosynthetic bacteria. In *Progress in Photosynthesis Research,* ed.

H. Metzner, pp. 952–55. Tübingen: Laupp. 1807 pp.
44. Fleischman, D. E. 1971. Glow curves from photosynthetic bacteria. *Photochem. Photobiol.* 14:65–70
45. Fleischman, D. E. 1971. Luminescence in photosynthetic bacteria. *Photochem. Photobiol.* 14:277–86
46. Fleischman, D. E., Clayton, R. K. 1968. The effect of phosphorylation uncouplers and electron transport inhibitors upon spectral shifts and delayed light emission of photosynthetic bacteria. *Photochem. Photobiol.* 8:287–91
47. Fowler, C. F., Kok, B. 1974. Proton evolution associated with the photooxidation of water in photosynthesis. *Biochim. Biophys. Acta* 357:299–307
48. Gläser, M., Wolff, C., Buchwald, H. E., Witt, H. T. 1974. On the photoactive chlorophyll reaction in system II of photosynthesis. Detection of a fast and large component. *FEBS Lett.* 42:81–85
49. Gläser, M., Wolff, C., Renger, G. 1976. Indirect evidence for a very fast recovery kinetics of chlorophyll-a_{II} in spinach chloroplasts. *Z. Naturforsch.* 31c: 712–21
50. Goedheer, J. C. 1962. Afterglow of chlorophyll in vivo and photosynthesis. *Biochim. Biophys. Acta* 64:294–308
51. Govindjee, Desai, T. S., Tatake, V. G., Sane, P. V. 1977. A new glow peak in *Rhodopseudomonas sphaeroides. Photochem. Photobiol.* 25:119–22
52. Haehnel, W. 1976. The reduction kinetics of chlorophyll a_1 as an indicator for proton uptake between the light reactions in chloroplasts. *Biochim. Biophys. Acta* 440:506–21
53. Hardt, H., Malkin, S. 1972. Luminescence of isolated chloroplasts induced by organic solvents. *Biochim. Biophys. Acta* 267:588–94
54. Hardt, H., Malkin, S. 1973. Oscillations of the triggered luminescence of isolated chloroplasts preilluminated by short flashes. *Photochem. Photobiol.* 17: 433–40
55. Haveman, J., Lavorel, J. 1975. Identification of the 120 μs phase in the decay of delayed fluorescence in spinach chloroplasts and subchloroplast particles as the intrinsic back reaction. *Biochim. Biophys. Acta* 408:269–83
56. Haveman, J., Mathis, P. 1976. Flash-induced absorption changes of the primary donor of photosystem II at 820 nm inhibited by low pH or Tris-treatment. *Biochim. Biophys. Acta* 440: 346–55

57. Ichikawa, T., Inoue, Y., Shibata, K. 1975. Characteristics of thermoluminescence bands of intact leaves and isolated chloroplasts in relation to the water-splitting activity in photosynthesis. *Biochim. Biophys. Acta* 408:228–39
58. Inoue, Y. 1976. Manganese catalyst as a possible cation carrier in thermoluminescence from green plants. *FEBS Lett.* 72:279–82
59. Inoue, Y., Furuta, S., Oku, T., Shibata, K. 1976. Light dependent development of thermoluminescence, delayed emission and fluorescence variation in dark-grown spruce leaves. *Biochim. Biophys. Acta* 449:357–67
59a. Inoue, Y., Shibata, K. 1977. *Thermoluminescence bands of chloroplasts characterized by flash excitation.* Presented at Int. Congr. Photosynth., 4th, Reading, England
60. Itoh, S., Murata, N. 1973. Correlation between delayed light emission and fluorescence of chlorophyll *a* in system II particles derived from spinach chloroplasts. *Photochem. Photobiol.* 18:209–18
61. Itoh, S., Murata, N. 1974. Temperature dependence of delayed light emission in spinach chloroplasts. *Biochim. Biophys. Acta* 333:525–34
62. Joliot, A. 1974. Effect of low temperature (-30 to -60°C) on the reoxidation of the photosystem II primary electron acceptor in the presence and absence of 3-(3,4-dichlorophenyl)-1,1-dimethylurea. *Biochim. Biophys. Acta* 357:439–48
63. Joliot, A. 1977. Flash induced fluorescence kinetics in chloroplasts in the 20 μs – 100 s time range in the presence of 3-(3,4-dichlorophenyl)-1,1-dimethylurea. *Biochim. Biophys. Acta* 460:142–51
64. Joliot, P., Barbieri, G., Chabaud, R. 1969. Un nouveau modèle des centres photochimiques du système II. *Photochem. Photobiol.* 10:309–29
65. Joliot, P., Joliot, A., Bouges, B., Barbieri, G. 1971. Studies of system II photocenters by comparative measurements of luminescence, fluorescence and oxygen emission. *Photochem. Photobiol.* 14:287–305
66. Kok, B., Forbush, B., McGloin, M. 1970. Cooperation of charges in photosynthetic O_2 evolution, a linear four step mechanism. *Photochem. Photobiol.* 11:457–75
67. Kononenko, A. A., Venediktov, P. S., Chemeris, Yu. K., Adamova, N. P., Rubin, A. B. 1974. Relation between electron transport-linked process and delayed luminescence in photosynthesizing purple bacteria. *Photosynthetica* 8:176–83
68. Kraan, G. P. B. 1971. *Stimulation of delayed fluorescence of chlorophyll a.* PhD thesis. Univ. Leiden, The Netherlands. 108 pp.
69. Kraan, G. P. B., Amesz, J., Velthuys, B. R., Steemers, R. G. 1970. Studies on the mechanisms of delayed and stimulated delayed fluorescence of chloroplasts. *Biochim. Biophys. Acta* 223:129–45
70. Lavorel, J. 1973. Kinetics of luminescence in the 10^{-6} – 10^{-4} s range in *Chlorella. Biochim. Biophys. Acta* 325:213–29
71. Lavorel, J. 1975. Luminescence. In *Bioenergetics of Photosynthesis,* ed. Govindjee, pp. 223–317. New York: Academic. 698 pp.
72. Lavorel, J. 1976. An alternative to Kok's model for the oxygen evolving system in photosynthesis. *FEBS Lett.* 66:164–67
73. Lurie, S., Bertsch, W. F. 1974. Thermoluminescence studies on photosynthetic energy conversion. 1. Evidence for three types of energy storage by photoreaction II of higher plants. *Biochim. Biophys. Acta* 357:420–28
74. Lurie, S., Cohen, W., Bertsch, W. F. 1971. Delayed light studies on photosynthetic energy conversion. V. Millisecond emission from digitonin subchloroplast fractions. *Int. Congr. Photosynth., 2nd, Stresa,* pp. 197–205
75. Malkin, R., Bearden, A. J. 1975. Laser-flash-activated electron paramagnetic resonance studies of primary photochemical reactions in chloroplasts. *Biochim. Biophys. Acta* 396:250–59
76. Malkin, S. 1977. Delayed luminescence. In *Photosynthesis I, Encyclopedia of Plant Physiology,* New Ser., ed. A. Trebst, M. Avron, 5:473–91. Berlin, Heidelberg, New York: Springer. 730 pp.
77. Malkin, S. 1977. Delayed luminescence. In *Primary Processes of Photosynthesis,* ed. J. Barber, pp. 349–431. Amsterdam: Elsevier/North-Holland. 516 pp.
78. Malkin, S., Hardt, H. 1973. Kinetic characterization of T-jump thermoluminescence in isolated chloroplasts. *Biochim. Biophys. Acta* 305:292–301
79. Mar, T., Govindjee, 1971. Thermoluminescence in spinach chloroplasts and *Chlorella. Biochim. Biophys. Acta* 226:200–3

80. Mathis, P., Vermeglio, A. 1974. Direct evidence for a back-reaction in photosystem II of spinach chloroplasts following flash excitation at low temperature. *Biochim. Biophys. Acta* 368: 130–34

81. Mayne, B. C. 1967. The effect of inhibitors and uncouplers of photosynthetic phosphorylation on the delayed light emission of chloroplasts. *Photochem. Photobiol.* 6:189–97

82. Mayne, B. C. 1968. The light-requirement of acid-base transition induced luminescence of chloroplasts. *Photochem. Photobiol.* 8:107–13

83. Mayne, B. C., Clayton, R. K. 1966. Luminescence of chlorophyll in spinach chloroplasts induced by acid-base transition. *Proc. Natl. Acad. Sci. USA* 55:494–97

84. Miles, C. D., Jagendorf, A. T. 1969. Ionic and pH transitions triggering chloroplast post-illumination luminescence. *Arch. Biochem. Biophys.* 129: 711–19

85. Nishizaki, Y. 1976. Relation between slow delayed light emission and acid-base triggered luminescence in chloroplasts. *Biochim. Biophys. Acta* 449: 368–75

86. Okayama, S., Butler, W. L. 1972. The influence of cytochrome b_{559} on the fluorescence yield of chloroplasts at low temperature. *Biochim. Biophys. Acta* 267:523–29

87. Ruby, R. H. 1974. Delayed fluorescence from *Chlorella:* 1. Low temperature observations. *Biochim. Biophys. Acta* 368:1–8

88. Sane, P. V., Tatake, V. G., Desai, T. S. 1974. Detection of the triplet states of chlorophylls in vivo. *FEBS Lett.* 45:290–94

89. Shahak, Y., Siderer, Y., Avron, M. 1977. *Acid-base induced reversed electron flow in chloroplasts.* Presented at Int. Symp. Membr. Bioenerg., Spetsai, Greece

90. Shimizu, M., Nishimura, M. 1977. Formation of electrical field accompanying temperature jump in isolated spinach chloroplasts. *Biochim. Biophys. Acta* 459:412–17

91. Shuvalov, V. A. 1976. The study of primary photoprocesses in photosystem 1 of chloroplasts. *Biochim. Biophys. Acta* 430:113–21

92. Shuvalov, V. A., Klimov, V. V. 1976. The primary photoreactions in the complex cytochrome-P890-P760 (Bacteriopheophytin 760) of *Chromatium minutissimum* at low redox potentials. *Biochim. Biophys. Acta* 440:587–99

93. Shuvalov, V. A., Litvin, F. F. 1969. Mechanism of prolonged after luminescence of plant leaves and energy storage in the photosynthetic reaction centers. *Molek. Biol.* 3:59–73

94. Stacy, W. T., Mar, T., Swenberg, C. E., Govindjee. 1971. An analysis of the triplet exciton model for the delayed light in *Chlorella. Photochem. Photobiol.* 14:197–219

95. Stiehl, H. H., Witt, H. T. 1968. Die kurzzeitigen ultravioletten Differenzspektren bei der Photosynthese. *Z. Naturforsch.* 23b:220–24

96. Strehler, B. L. 1951. The luminescence of isolated chloroplasts. *Arch. Biochem. Biophys.* 34:239–48

97. Strehler, B. L., Arnold, W. 1951. Light production by green plants. *J. Gen. Physiol.* 34:809–20

98. Strehler, B. L., Lynch, V. 1957. Studies on the primary processes in photosynthesis. II. Some relationships between light-induced absorption changes and chemiluminescence during photosynthesis. *Arch. Biochem. Biophys.* 70: 527–46

99. Takahama, U., Shimizu, M., Nishimura, M. 1976. Temperature–jump-induced release of hydrogen ions from chloroplasts and its relaxation characteristics in the presence of ionophores. *Biochim. Biophys. Acta* 440:261–65

100. Tollin, G., Calvin, M. 1957. The luminescence of chlorophyll-containing plant material. *Proc. Natl. Acad. Sci. USA* 43:895–908

101. Tollin, G., Fujimori, E., Calvin, M. 1958. Delayed light emission in green plant materials: temperature-dependence and quantum yield. *Proc. Natl. Acad. Sci. USA* 44:1035–47

102. Van Best, J. A. 1977. *Studies on primary reactions of system 2 of photosynthesis by means of luminescence and fluorescence.* PhD thesis. Univ. Leiden, The Netherlands. 151 pp.

103. Van Best, J. A., Duysens, L. N. M. 1977. A one microsecond component of chlorophyll luminescence suggesting a primary acceptor of system II of photosynthesis different from Q. *Biochim. Biophys. Acta* 459:187–206

104. Van Gorkom, H. J. 1976. *Primary reactants in system 2 of photosynthesis. Spectroscopy in subchloroplast fragments.* PhD thesis. Univ. Leiden, The Netherlands. 112 pp.

105. Van Gorkom, H. J., Donze, M. 1973. Charge accumulation in the reaction center of photosystem 2. *Photochem. Photobiol.* 17:333–42

106. Van Gorkom, H. J., Pulles, M. P. J., Haveman, J., Den Haan, G. A. 1976. Primary reactions of photosystem II at low pH. Prompt and delayed fluorescence. *Biochim. Biophys. Acta* 423: 217–26

107. Velthuys, B. R. 1975 A. Binding of the inhibitor NH_3 to the oxygen evolving apparatus of spinach chloroplasts. *Biochim. Biophys. Acta* 376:162–68

108. Velthuys, B. R. 1975 B. Flash number dependent luminescence of isolated spinach chloroplasts at different pH's, low temperature and in the presence of NH_4Cl. See Ref. 35, pp. 93–100

109. Velthuys, B. R. 1976. *Charge accumulation and recombination in system 2 of photosynthesis.* PhD thesis. Univ. Leiden, The Netherlands. 108 pp.

110. Velthuys, B. R., Amesz, J. 1972. The relation between delayed luminescence and the redox level of the electron acceptors of photosystem 2. See Ref. 37, abstract 273

111. Velthuys, B. R., Amesz, J. 1973. The effect of dithionite on fluorescence and luminescence of chloroplasts. *Biochim. Biophys. Acta* 325:126–37

112. Vernon, L. P., Klein, S., White, F. G., Shaw, E. R., Mayne, B. C. 1971. Properties of a small photosystem II particle obtained from spinach chloroplasts. See Ref. 74, pp. 801–12

113. Visser, J. W. M. 1975. *Photosynthetic reactions at low temperatures.* PhD thesis. Univ. Leiden, The Netherlands. 116 pp.

114. Wraight, C. A., Kraan, G. P. B., Gerrits, N. M. 1971. Investigations on pH dependent and energy-linked delayed light emission. See Ref. 74, pp. 951–61

115. Zankel, K. L. 1969. Transfer of energy from reaction center to light harvesting chlorophyll in a photosynthetic bacterium. *Photochem. Photobiol.* 10: 259–66

116. Zankel, K. L. 1971. Rapid delayed luminescence from chloroplasts: kinetic analysis of components; the relationship to O_2 evolution. *Biochim. Biophys. Acta* 245:373–85

117. Zankel, K. L. 1973. Rapid fluorescence changes observed in chloroplasts; their relationship to the O_2 evolving system. *Biochim. Biophys. Acta* 325:138–48

Ann. Rev. Plant Physiol. 1978. 29:67–93

NATURE OF OBLIGATE PHOTOAUTOTROPHY

♦7645

C. R. Benedict

Department of Plant Sciences, Texas A&M University, College Station, Texas 77843

CONTENTS

INTRODUCTION

The purpose of this review is to examine carbon metabolism in obligate photoautotrophs—organisms which fix CO_2 as the prime carbon source in the light and use a reduced inorganic chemical as the source of electrons (37, 68). Obligate photoautotrophy occurs in photosynthetic bacteria, algae, and higher plants. In photosyn-

67

0066-4294/78/0601-0067$01.00

thetic bacteria obligate photoautotrophy occurs only in the Chlorobacteriaceae and here as obligate photolithoautotrophy—the growth of organisms on CO_2 as the prime carbon source in the light using reduced sulfur compounds as electron donors. The Thiorhodaceae, the purple sulfur bacteria, are facultative photoautotrophs capable of growing photolithoautotrophically or photoorganotrophically. Photoorganotrophs obtain all of the energy for growth from light, but their photosynthesis uses the oxidation of organic compounds. The Athiorhodaceae, the nonsulfur purple bacteria, are capable of photolithoautotrophic, photoorganotrophic, and dark chemoheterotrophic growth. The Thiorhodaceae and Athiorhodaceae are facultative photoautotrophs as well as photomixotrophs—organisms where both autotrophic and heterotrophic pathways function. The blue-green algae, like higher plants, obtain energy for growth and carbon assimilation from light using H_2O as the sole H donor. The algae span the range from photoautotrophic and photomixotrophic growth to light and dark heterotrophic growth. Higher plants span the range from photoautotrophy to dark heterotrophy in organ or tissue culture. To understand why obligate photoautotrophs are uniquely restricted to utilizing only CO_2 as a source of carbon, the carbon metabolism of obligate photoautotrophs will be compared to the carbon metabolism of facultative autotrophs grown autotrophically, mixotrophically, and heterotrophically. In this manner an assessment can be made of the basis of obligate photoautotrophy.

Recently it has become fashionable to recognize classes of autotrophic organisms on the basis of biochemical pathways. Whittenbury & Kelly (136) have updated the autotroph concept to include all microorganisms utilizing C_1 compounds. Three autotrophic categories exist: The "ribulose bisphosphate pathway" group which includes organisms now considered to be autotrophs; the "ribulose monophosphate pathway" group which includes methane or methanol utilizers; and, the "serine pathway" group which consists of C_1 as well as methane and methanol utilizers. Thus photoautotrophic or chemoautotrophic organisms should be able to obtain the bulk of their biosynthetic carbon from CO_2 or C_1 compounds by one of the above pathways. In this review, the ribulose bisphosphate pathway will be examined in obligate photoautotrophic organisms along with an examination of other proposed autocatalytic CO_2 cycles or unique pathways of CO_2 utilization which are not included in the three groups of autotrophic organisms. The three autotrophic categories are meant to apply only to microorganisms and not to include higher plants. Higher plants exposed to the environment are by nature obligate photoautotrophs which possess a ribulose bisphosphate pathway for the net assimilation of carbon. This classification would tend to minimize the importance of β-carboxylation, anatomy, and symplastic transport in serving up CO_2 to the autocatalytic Calvin cycle in the bundle sheath cells of C_4 plants. Thus the importance of β-carboxylation to obligate photoautotrophy will be examined throughout this review as well as the assessment of the C_4 photosynthetic pathway to the photoautotrophic growth of organisms other than terrestrial plants.

The topic of photoautotrophy was included in van Niels' review in the *Annual Review of Plant Physiology* in 1962 (129), and material published since that time will be included in this present review. The recent review articles by Jackson & Volk

(65), Hatch & Slack (56), Tolbert (125), Black (15), Zelitch (141), and Kelly et al (70) on photosynthetic carbon metabolism and photorespiration in higher plants will not be covered in this review.

PHOTOSYNTHETIC BACTERIA

Isotope analyses and enzyme profile studies have indicated the presence of the Calvin cycle in *Chromatium vinosum* (47, 113), *Chromatium okenii* (97), *Rhodospirillum rubrum* (3), and *Rhodopseudomonas palustris* (45) if they are grown on CO_2 as the sole carbon source. The presence of the Calvin cycle in *Chlorobium thiosulfatophilum* is not a settled issue (14, 20, 24, 43, 108, 109, 112, 123, 123a). The Calvin cycle is a major path of autotrophic CO_2 fixation in species of *Hydrogenomonas* (80), *Thiobacillus thiooxidans* (120), *Micrococcus dentrificans* (72), *Nitrobacter winogradskyi* (71), and *Thiobacillus ferroxidans* (36). It has been concluded that the Calvin cycle operates in all autotrophic species for the net assimilation of CO_2 because of the presence of the Calvin cycle in photosynthetic bacteria, nonphotosynthetic bacteria (79), and in the following plants: *Phormidium, Synechococcus,* and *Nostoc* (blue-green algae); *Chlorella, Scenedesmus, Haematococcus, Spirogyra,* and *Chlorococcum* (green algae); *Nitella, Vaucheria* (a yellow-green alga); *Fontinalis* and *Funazia* (mosses); *Conocephalum* (a liverwort); *Ceratopteris* and *Polystichum* (ferns); yew juniper, squash, soybean, *Kalanchoe,* tomato, ivy, avocado, and barley (84). The above group of microorganisms and higher plants might be included in Whittenbury & Kelly's group of autotrophic microorganisms which contain the ribulose-1,5-bisphosphate cycle (136). The purpose of this section is to examine obligate photolithoautotrophy, facultative photoautotrophy, photoorganotrophy, and photomixotrophy in the photosynthetic bacteria for a more complete understanding of autotrophy in these organisms. Fuller (45) has recently reviewed the photosynthetic carbon metabolism in green and purple bacteria.

Thiorhodaceae

FACULTATIVE PHOTOAUTOTROPHY   Genera of Chromatiaceae are facultative photoautotrophs capable of photolithoautotrophic and photoorganotrophic growth. Fuller et al (47) have shown the presence of the Calvin cycle in photolithoautotrophic cultures of *C. vinosum* and the presence of a modified glyoxylate cycle in acetate-grown cultures. Malate dehydrogenase (46) and α-ketoglutarate dehydrogenase (45) are missing in *C. vinosum.* Malate dehydrogenase is derepressed in *C. okennii* grown on acetate (97), and this species has a normal glyoxylate cycle. In photoautotrophic cells of *C. vinosum* there is an active β-carboxylation of PEP (47). In resting cells $^{14}CO_2$ is rapidly incorporated into PGA and aspartate. The synthesis of aspartate occurs by a double carboxylation as follows:

$$RuBP \xrightarrow{\quad CO_2 \quad} PGA \longrightarrow PEP \xrightarrow{\quad CO_2 \quad} OAA \longrightarrow aspartate.$$

The synthesis of C_4 acids is absolutely dependent on substrates furnished by the Calvin cycle (44). In short-term exposures of *Chromatium* cells to $^{14}CO_2$, 28% of the label is found in PGA and 44% in aspartate (47). β-Carboxylation in *Chromatium* is relatively more important than in *Chlorella pyrenoidosa*, where Bassham & Kirk (7) have calculated 3% of the total CO_2 fixed is by β-carboxylation. Ferredoxin-dependent reductive carboxylation of acetyl CoA but not succinyl CoA is found in *C. vinosum* (21) and may also be important in the synthesis of C_4 acids. The $\delta^{13}C$ value of metabolic intermediates of photoautotrophically grown *C. vinosum* can be accounted for by carbon assimilation by the Calvin cycle and double carboxylation reactions (137). The comparative $\delta^{13}C$ values of aspartate and glucose give no indication of a decarboxylation of C_4 acids and a subsequent refixation of the CO_2 by the Calvin cycle for carbohydrate synthesis.

The lack of a complete TCA cycle does not render *Chromatium* an obligate photoautotroph. Under autotrophic growth conditions the TCA intermediates can be synthesized from Calvin cycle intermediates by β-carboxylation of PEP and generation of acetyl CoA from pyruvate. The modified TCA cycle and the β-carboxylation of PEP will account for the synthesis of C_4 acids, porphyrin precursors, and glutamate. Under autotrophic conditions the modified TCA cycle is used for biosynthetic purposes. Thiosulfate is the electron donor for the photoreduction of CO_2, and ATP is furnished by photophosphorylation. There is no need for the dissimilation of substrates by the TCA cycle. The modified TCA cycle and gluconeogenesis will account for the photoorganotrophic growth of *Chromatium* on C_4 acids, and the modified glyoxylate cycle and gluconeogenesis will account for the growth of *Chromatium* on acetate (47). Established pathways of carbon metabolism will account for the physiological range of the Thiorhodaceae from complete photolithoautotrophy to complete photoorganotrophy. The glyoxylate cycle is induced in *Chromatium* cells grown on acetate as the sole carbon source (47). The increased synthesis of enzymes accounts for the growth on C_2 compounds. The induction of enzymes by organic compounds for the utilization of these compounds for heterotrophic growth is not typical of obligate autotrophs (68), but may be a general property of facultative autotrophs.

Athiorhodaceae

FACULTATIVE PHOTOAUTOTROPHY AND PHOTOORGANOTROPHY   Anderson & Fuller (3) have shown that *Rhodospirillum rubrum* grown photolithoautotrophically on CO_2 and H_2 has a Calvin cycle. In these cultures $^{14}CO_2$ is rapidly incorporated into PGA followed by phosphate esters. The incorporation of radioactivity into TCA intermediates is low and the anaerobic TCA cycle may not operate in photoautotrophic cells. In these cells the incorporation of CO_2 into alanine and glutamic acid was low. Buchanan et al (22) discovered ferredoxin-dependent pyruvate and α-ketoglutarate synthetases in *R. rubrum*, but the above labeling pattern seems to rule out the operation of the reductive carboxylic acid cycle in photoautotrophic cultures of this photosynthetic bacterium. Sirevag et al (110) have shown that the $\delta^{13}C$ value for *R. rubrum* grown on CO_2 and H_2 is $-20.5‰$. This value indicates that RuBP carboxylase is the major CO_2-fixing enzyme in photoautotrophic cells.

R. rubrum will grow anaerobically or aerobically on C_4 dicarboxylic acids. In these photoorganotrophic or chemoheterotrophic cells, polysaccharides are synthesized by gluconeogenesis (117). Anderson & Fuller (5) have shown that the Calvin cycle is repressed in malate-grown cells. Gest et al (48) have shown the presence of an anaerobic TCA cycle in heterotrophic cells. Rinne et al (106) have shown that the anaerobic TCA cycle is important for the synthesis of glutamic acid from CO_2 or acetate, in the light, in cells grown on malate.

PHOTOMIXOTROPHY   Anderson & Fuller (4) have shown that short-term exposure of resting cells of *R. rubrum*, grown photomixotrophically on acetate and CO_2, to $^{14}CO_2$ primarily labels aspartic, fumaric, citric, glutamic, and malic acids and alanine and PGA. Hoare (57) has shown that in acetate and CO_2-grown cells, CO_2 is necessary for the incorporation of acetate into soluble compounds other than β-OH butyrate. In these cells, $^{14}CO_2$ is incorporated into phosphate esters but in the presence of acetate, $^{14}CO_2$ is incorporated less into phosphate esters and more into glutamic and malic acids. Anderson & Fuller (5) have shown RuBP carboxylase activity is less in acetate and CO_2 cultures compared to CO_2 and H_2 cultures. The distribution of isotopes in glutamic acid in cells grown photomixotrophically on acetate and CO_2 is:

```
b   c   m   m   c
C－C－C－C－C
1   2   3   4   5
```

when b = bicarbonate, c = carboxyl group of acetate, and m = methyl group of acetate (57). This isotopic distribution indicates a "novel" mechanism for the biosynthesis of glutamate which cannot be accounted for in mixotrophically grown *R. rubrum* by the operation of the TCA cycle or the operation of the reductive carboxylic acid cycle. The isotopic distribution in glutamic acid synthesized from ^{14}C-acetate and $^{14}CO_2$ by the reductive carboxylic acid cycle is as follows:

$$
\begin{array}{l}
\underset{\text{C–C Pyruvate}}{\overset{\text{m   c}}{}} \xrightarrow[\text{synthase}]{\overset{b}{CO_2}} \underset{\text{C–C–C}}{\overset{\text{m   c   b}}{}} \xrightarrow[\text{carboxylase}]{\overset{b}{CO_2}} \underset{\text{PEP}}{\overset{\text{b   m   c   b}}{}} \underset{\text{C–C–C–C}}{} \xrightarrow[\text{synthase}]{\overset{b}{CO_2}} \underset{\text{α-KG}}{} \underset{\substack{\text{C–C–C–C–C.}\\ \text{5   4   3   2   1}}}{\overset{\text{b   m   c   b   b}}{}}
\end{array}
$$

The reaction scheme that Hoare (57) and Elsden (42) envisage for glutamate synthesis involves the carboxylation of acetate to form pyruvate followed by a condensation of pyruvate with glycine to form glutamic acid. Rinne et al (106) have pointed out that isotopic distribution in glutamic acid is consistent with the operation of the citramalate pathway for glutamate synthesis as originally proposed by Losada et al (78). The labeling pattern of glutamic acid synthesized by the citramalate pathway is:

$$
\underset{\text{C–C Pyruvate}}{\overset{\text{m   c}}{}} \xrightarrow[\text{synthase}]{\overset{b}{CO_2}} \underset{\text{C–C–C}}{\overset{\text{m   c   b}}{}} \xrightarrow[\text{Citramalate synthase}]{\overset{\text{m   c}}{C–C}} \underset{\substack{\text{C–C–C}\\ \text{m   C}\\ \text{c   C}}}{\overset{\text{m   c   b}}{}} \xrightarrow[\substack{\text{dehydrogenation}\\ \text{and}\\ \text{transamination}}]{\text{isomerization}} \underset{\substack{\text{C–C–C–C–C}\\ \text{5   4   3   2   1}}}{\overset{\text{c   m   m   c   b}}{}}
$$

However, pyruvate synthase and citramalate synthase are the only reactions in this pathway found in *Chromatium* (78) and *R. rubrum* (106). It is probable that glutamate is synthesized by the anaerobic TCA cycle in *R. rubrum* and the incomplete TCA cycle in *Chromatium*. Pyruvate synthase and PEP carboxylase could function in the purple bacteria to form C_4-dicarboxylic acids from acetate and CO_2 (45).

Chlorobacteriaceae

OBLIGATE PHOTOLITHOAUTOTROPHY Species of *Chlorobium* are obligate photolithoautotrophs and dependent on strict anaerobic conditions for growth. Sadler & Stanier (107) showed that although *Chlorobium limicola* is a strict photoautotroph, it is able to use acetate in promoting increases in cell yield and chlorophyll formation. Calley et al (26) have shown that *Chloropseudomonas ethylicum* lacks α-ketoglutarate dehydrogenase and therefore lacks a complete TCA cycle. The photoassimilation of acetate requires CO_2 and a source of reducing power. Hoare & Gibson (58) studied the distribution of ^{14}C-acetate and $^{14}CO_2$ into the carbons of glutamic acid in proteins of *Chlorobium thiosulfatophilum*. The isotope distribution in glutamic acid in *Chlorobium* resembled but was not entirely similar to that of acetate and CO_2 into glutamic acid in *R. rubrum*. Kelly (69) has shown that numerous amino acids, formate, and glucose can be photoassimilated by *Chlorobium*. The distribution of label from these radioactive compounds into cell constituents indicate pathways of intermediary metabolism in *Chlorobium* similar to those in many organisms. Numerous amino acids inhibited growth, probably due to feedback inhibition of primary enzymes in the biosynthesis of these amino acids. The unique feature of this green bacterium resides in its anaerobic photolithoautotrophy and not in the feedback inhibition phenomenon or its intermediary metabolism. *Chlorobium* probably shows photomixotrophic carbon nutrition in its natural environment.

Smillie et al (113) have shown the presence of the Calvin cycle enzymes in photoautotrophic cultures of *C. thiosulfalophilum*. RuBP carboxylase activity was low in these extracts compared to the activities of other enzymes of the Calvin cycle. There is a continuing controversy on the presence of this CO_2-fixing enzyme in the green sulfur bacteria. Buchanan et al (23) reported that *C. thiosulfatophilum* "Tassajara" lacks RuBP carboxylase. Sirevåg (108) could not detect RuBP carboxylase or phosphoribulokinase in cell-free extracts of *C. thiosulfatophilum*. Tabita et al (123) isolated a relatively unstable RuBP carboxylase from *C. thiosulfatophilum* "Tassajara." Buchanan & Sirevåg (24) found no evidence for RuBP carboxylase or ribulose-5P kinase in *C. thiosulfatophilum*. Calley et al (26) could not detect RuBP carboxylase in *C. ethylicum*.

Buchanan (20) found ferredoxin-dependent pyruvate synthase and α-ketoglutarate synthase in extracts of *Chlorobium*. Evans et al (43) proposed a new ferrodoxin-dependent carbon reduction cycle in *C. thiosulfatophilum*. Specifically, the new enzymes in this reductive carboxylic cycle are: ferrodoxin-dependent pyruvate and α-ketoglutarate synthases, fumarate reductase and citrate lyase. Other enzymes in this cycle are: aceto-CoA synthetase, PEP synthetase, PEP carboxylase, malate dehydrogenase, succinyl CoA synthetase, isocitrate dehydrogenase, and aconitate hydratase. The lowest enzyme activity was citrate lyase, which was 0.1 the rate of CO_2 fixation in resting cells (100). This cycle would account for the autocatalytic generation of CO_2 acceptors and thus provide carbon for the net synthesis of amino acids, lipids, and porphyrins. Sirevåg & Ormerod (112) showed acetate (a product of the cycle) could be directly incorporated into carbohydrates independently of the Calvin cycle. In later work, Sirevåg (109) showed ^{14}C-acetate labels carbons 1, 2 and 5,6, but not carbons 3,4 of glucose. Therefore, it is not possible to totally exclude the Calvin cycle in the synthesis of carbohydrate in *Chlorobium*.

Buchanan et al (23), Sirevåg & Ormerod (111, 112), and Sirevåg (108) present isotope labeling patterns which support the operation of the reductive carboxylic acid cycle. Buchanan (23) showed PGA to be a principle product after 5 sec of fixation in 0.8 mM bicarbonate. The molarity of the bicarbonate might effect the first products of fixation, and the authors state that labeled PGA might result from the metabolism of acetate synthesized by the reductive carboxylic acid cycle. Sirevåg (108) studied the path of carbon in *C. thiosulfatophilum*. Kinetic analysis in 8 mM bicarbonate supported the operation of the reductive carboxylic acid cycle. Beuscher & Gottschalk (14) were unable to detect citrate lyase in *C. thiosulfatophilum* and concluded the complete reductive carboxylic acid cycle does not occur. The distribution of acetate and CO_2 carbons in glutamic acid in *Chlorobium* (58) could not be the result of the operation of the reductive carboxylic acid cycle. Sirevåg et al (110) have reported the $\delta^{13}C$ values of photoautotrophic cells of *Chromatium, R. rubrum,* and *Chlorobium*. The $\delta^{13}C$ values of *Chromatium* and *R. rubrum* agree with the earlier $\delta^{13}C$ values for *Chromatium* which result from the operation of the Calvin cycle (137). The $\delta^{13}C$ value of the *Chlorobium* cells shows CO_2 fixation does not occur by RuBP carboxylase. The authors state that this work does not definitely show CO_2 being assimilated by the reductive carboxylic acid cycle but point out that CO_2 is assimilated in the photolithoautotrophic green sulfur bacteria by a route other than RuBP carboxylase. Recently Takabe & Akazawa (123a) have found negligibly small amounts of RuBP carboxylase in *C. thiosulfatophilum*. The first product of photosynthetic CO_2 fixation was glutamic acid, and radioactive PGA was entirely missing on the chromatograms. Cyanide did not exhibit CO_2 fixation, and although O_2 inhibited CO_2 fixation, no glycolate was detected in an O_2-containing environment. These workers conclude that the Calvin cycle is absent in the obligate photolithoautotrophic growth of *Chlorobium*. The sensitivity of photosynthetic CO_2 fixation to O_2 may be at pyruvate synthase and α-ketoglutarate synthase, both pivotal steps in the reductive carboxylic acid cycle.

ALGAE

Twenty years ago it was fashionable to consider that obligate photoautotrophy in algae resulted from a lack of penetration of organic compounds into the cells. However, Sadler & Stanier (107) and Hoare & Moore (60), by the use of ^{14}C tracers, have shown that organic acids penetrate photosynthetic green sulfur bacteria and blue-green algae, and they discounted permeability as a factor in obligate photoautotrophy. Lewin (76, 77) studied photoautotrophy in *Chlamydomonas* and diatoms. Organic acids are respired by these algae but these compounds will not support growth in the dark. She suggested a lack of coupling between electron transfer and oxidative phosphorylation as a reason the algae were dependent on light for growth. This work has provided an incentive for investigations on the biochemistry of obligate photoautotrophy. Stanier & Cohen-Bazire (116) have discussed recent experiments on the metabolism and photoautotrophy of the cyanobacteria.

Obligate Photoautotrophy in Blue-Green Algae

Most blue-green algae are obligate photoautotrophs. In 1955, Kratz & Myers (73) nutritionally described *Anabaena variablis, Anacystis nidulans,* and *Nostoc muscorum* as strict photoautotrophs. Pelroy & Bassham (93) firmly established that CO_2 fixation in blue-green algae could be accounted for by the reductive pentose phosphate cycle. Ihlenfeldt & Gibson (63) confirmed this work and showed CO_2 incorporation into aspartate was low in *A. nidulans.* The Hatch and Slack pathway is thus not operable in this organism. Hoare et al (59) have shown that four obligate photoautotrophic blue-green algae assimilate acetate. This assimilation is light dependent and greatly reduced in the absence of CO_2. ^{14}C-Acetate is primarily incorporated into glutamate, arginine, proline, and leucine, and partial degradation of these amino acids shows that they are synthesized from acetate by conventional pathways. Smith et al (114) have shown that pyruvate, acetate, and glutamate are incorporated into restricted groups of amino acids in blue-green algae. This incorporation pattern suggests a block in the TCA cycle, and enzyme analyses showed an absence of α-ketoglutarate dehydrogenase, NADH oxidase, and low levels of succinate and malate dehydrogenase. Succinate and acetate could be used to synthesize the essential carbon compounds, but a lack of NADH oxidase shows the cells are incapable of coupling ATP synthesis with the respiration of organic acids. This is a basic obstacle to heterotrophic growth. In the blue-green algae, NADPH and ATP could be generated from noncyclic and cyclic photophosphorylations, and a complete TCA cycle is unnecessary as long as C_4 acids are present for porphyrin synthesis and C_4 and C_2 acids are available for glutamate synthesis. Peters & Aleem (95) have demonstrated NADH oxidase in many obligate autotrophs. Peters et al (96) were unable to detect α-ketoglutarate dehydrogenase in *Thiobaccillus denitrificans*, and the results show an absence of a complete TCA cycle in most autotrophic organisms. In *Thiobaccillus A-2,* a facultative autotroph, α-ketoglutarate dehydrogenase is repressed under autotrophic growth. Apparently the TCA cycle loses its energetic function under autotrophic conditions and is only necessary for biosynthesis, for which α-ketoglutarate dehydrogenase is not essential. Leach & Carr (74) have shown that growth and respiration do not increase when organic substrates are supplied to obligate photoautotrophic blue-green algae. The low respiration which does occur is inhibited by CN^-, azide, and CO, suggesting that the electron transport chain is similar to aerobic bacteria. This work showed that oxidative phosphorylation is coupled to the oxidation of reduced pyridine nucleotides in extracts and whole cells, but it is low because of limiting rates of respiration. Pelroy et al (94) have shown that oxidative phosphorylation accounts for the dark aerobic synthesis of ATP in blue-green algae.

Pearce & Carr (90) have shown that extracts of *A. nidulans* and *A. variabilis* contain low levels of isocitric lyase and malate synthetase. ^{14}C-Acetate metabolism in *A. nidulans* gave no indication of a glyoxylate cycle and indicated acetate was not incorporated beyond glutamic acid in the TCA cycle (59). Pearce et al (92) describe the incomplete TCA cycle in *A. variabilis* showing the lack of α-ketoglutarate dehydrogenase and succinyl-CoA synthetase. There was no alteration in the level of TCA enzymes when acetate was added to the media, although it is well known that acetate markedly influences the level of TCA enzymes in the facultative autotroph *Hydrogenomonas*. They conclude that failure of acetate to increase the growth rate, even though it is assimilated, could be due in part to the lack of gene derepression. This lack of transcriptional control could be a characteristic feature of obligate autotrophs. Cheung & Gibbs (29) showed that the oxidative pentose phosphate pathway is a major pathway in *Tolypothrix tenuis* for carbohydrate breakdown. Pearce & Carr (91) showed that glucose contributed up to 46% of the dry weight of *A. variabilis* and the oxidative pentose phosphate cycle is the major route of glucose respiration. There was no evidence that glucose increased the level of glycolytic or oxidative pentose phosphate pathway enzymes. Thus, blue-green algae considered to be obligate photoautotrophs can assimilate glucose and acetate even though CO_2 is still the major carbon source. Failure of an increased level of enzymes in response to added glucose or acetate could prevent the use of these compounds at a rate sufficient to support heterotrophic growth (68).

Pelroy et al (94) proposed a unitary concept for carbon and energy metabolism of blue-green algae. In the light, CO_2 fixation is through the reductive pentose phosphate cycle. The glycogen synthesized in the light is metabolized through the oxidative pentose phosphate cycle in the dark and accounts for the endogenous respiration. Doolittle & Singer (40) have isolated a mutant of *A. nidulans* which is deficient in 6-phosphogluconate dehydrogenase. The mutant behaves like the wild type in the light, but rapidly loses viability in the dark. This work shows that the oxidative pentose phosphate pathway plays a major role in the endogenous respiration of this photosynthetic organism. Pulich & Van Baalen (98) have presented studies suggesting a direct correlation between the presence of glucose dehydrogenase and the capability of blue-green algae for heterotrophic growth. Pulich et al (99) have purified and characterized glucose dehydrogenase from a heterotrophically grown blue-green algae.

Obligate Photoautotrophy in Green Algae

Neilson et al (82) have demonstrated the biochemical basis for obligate photoautotrophy in a mutant of *Chlamydomonas, Chlamydomonas dysosmos,* and a unicellular flagellate, green alga. Wild-type cells which are normally photosynthetic are capable of heterotrophic growth on acetate in the dark. In these heterotrophic cells, acetate is metabolized by the TCA cycle for energy production and by the glyoxylate cycle for biosynthesis. Isocitric lyase is formed only under conditions of acetate assimilation when photosynthesis is blocked by DCMU or darkness. A mutant induced by ultraviolet light lacked the ability of growing heterotrophically and formed only negligible amounts of isocitric lyase. In the mutant, the glyoxylate cycle is impaired and these cells will grow only on an inorganic medium in the light. An analogous situation occurs in *Chlorella pyreniodosa* (121, 122), which can assimilate acetate in the dark, dependent on the induction of the glyoxylate cycle. Growth in the light is not dependent on the presence of the glyoxylate cycle. Goulding & Merrett (50) and Merrett (81) have studied the photoassimilation of acetate by *Pyrobotrys* (*Chlamydomonas*) *Stellata*. In this organism, the glyoxylate cycle is essential for growth on acetate in the light, but it will not grow on acetate in the dark. There is an incomplete TCA cycle due to the absence of a α-ketoglutarate dehydrogenase and succinate thiokinase. The lack of these enzymes leads to a deficient synthesis of ATP, and the organisms require light for photophosphorylation.

β-Carboxylation in Algae

Raven (101, 102) has discussed the importance of dark CO_2 fixation or β-carboxylation to the photoautotrophic growth of algae. PEP and pyruvate are synthesized from Calvin cycle intermediates, and the carboxylation of these C_3 acids is important in autotrophic as well as heterotrophic growth. Bassham & Kirk (7) estimate that 3% of the total CO_2 fixed by *C. pyrenoidosa* is by β-carboxylation. A part of this β-carboxylation is attributable to a nonphotosynthetic stimulatory action of blue light (130). Walker (131) has discussed the importance of oxaloacetate production by β-carboxylation for the synthesis of the aspartate family of amino acids and of pyrimidines and in supplying one of the substrates for citrate synthetase for TCA cycle intermediates.

Under certain growth conditions, β-carboxylation has been observed to be a primary CO_2 fixation site in algae. Abelson & Hoering (1) have shown that the $\delta^{13}C$ value of *C. pyrenoidosa* is −25.8‰ if the alga is grown on 5% CO_2 and 95% air. In poorly aerated cultures grown on the same gas mixture, the $\delta^{13}C$ value is −11.3‰. The $\delta^{13}C$ value indicates the operation of the Calvin cycle in well-aerated cultures. Under poor growth conditions in poorly aerated systems, the $\delta^{13}C$ value indicates that the major CO_2 fixation is β-carboxylation. Ogasawara & Miyachi (85) have shown that at low light intensities, which do not allow net photosynthesis in *Chlorella*, C_4-dicarboxylic acids and citrulline are primary products of CO_2 fixation. Graham & Whittingham (52) have studied the path of carbon in photosynthesis in *Chlorella* under different CO_2 levels. The transfer of the cells from a high CO_2 to a low CO_2 concentration involves an adaptation period during which the rate of CO_2 fixation is low and the primary product of CO_2 fixation is malate. Reed & Graham (104) have shown that carbonic anhydrase is synthesized during this lag period followed by a normal operation of the Calvin cycle. There is no evidence in the experiments that malate is decarboxylated to CO_2 which is refixed by the Calvin cycle as found in C_4 photosynthesis. Döhler (38) has studied the photosynthetic carbon metabolism of *Anacystis* and *Chlorella* during the transition period of dark to light. *Chlorella* has a normal Calvin cycle at 10, 25, and 25°C. In autospore mother cells of *Chlorella*, $^{14}CO_2$ was mainly incorporated into aspartate. In N_2, $^{14}CO_2$ was incorporated into aspartate in *Chlorella* and *Anacystis*. In *Anacystis* at 30°C under 3.0% CO_2, label from ^{14}C-aspartate was distributed into PGA, glutamate alanine, hexose phosphates, and threonine. The C_4 pathway of photosynthesis seems operable during the induction period.

Patil & Joshi (89) and Karekar & Joshi (67) have studied the importance of β-carboxylation in the photosynthesis of green algae. About 24% of the CO_2 fixed in the light was found in amino acids after 30 sec. Aspartate was the major initial product of CO_2 fixation. The original work of Calvin et al (27) with *Scenedesmus* showed that 80% of the CO_2 fixed was initially found in PGA and sugar phosphates and only 4.5% in amino acids. Glover et al (49) have shown that the diatom *Phaeodactylum tricornutum* incorporated 50% of the CO_2 fixed into amino acids and amides in short-term photosynthesis. Beardall et al (9) have further studied the path of carbon in the diatoms *P. tricornutum* and *Skeletonema costatum*. In heavy cell suspensions, 70% of the CO_2 fixed in 2 sec was located in amino acids and TCA cycle intermediates. Malate and aspartate accounted for 36% of the total radioactivity, whereas only 10% was found in PGA and sugar phosphates. $^{14}CO_2$ fixation for 60 sec increased the formation of radioactive PGA and sugar phosphate while decreasing the proportion of ^{14}C in amino acids and TCA intermediates. Photosynthesis in these cells was only inhibited by O_2 levels higher than 21% (8). The activity of PEP carboxylase was usually higher than RuBP carboxylase. The authors propose the functioning of a C_4-dicarboxylic acid pathway in these diatoms involving a primary β-carboxylation to give C_4 acids which are decarboxylated and the CO_2 refixed by the Calvin cycle for carbohydrate synthesis. A problem in these β-carboxylation studies is to distinguish between CO_2 fixation in C_4 acids (C_4 metabolism) and CO_2 fixation into C_4 acids and subsequent decarboxylation, followed by refixation of the CO_2 by the Calvin cycle (C_4 photosynthetic pathway). This has been discussed by Kelly et al (70). The work of Degens et al (33) and Wong (138) may offer an explanation of the pronounced degree of β-carboxylation in the diatoms (9). The $\Delta^{13}C$ values ($\Delta^{13}C = \delta^{13}C$ of the cells $- \delta^{13}C$ of CO_2) of *S. costatum* is $-20.9\%o$ (138) and of *Cyclotella nana* is $-18.7\%o$ (33). These values indicate the operation of the Calvin cycle in these organisms. The $\Delta^{13}C$ value of *C. nana* in 5%, CO_2 is $-18.7\%o$, and in air is $-10.7\%o$. The latter value is indicative of CO_2 fixation to C_4 acids. Degens et al (33) explain this phenomenon as caused by heavy cell suspensions and limited CO_2 supply in these cultures. The heavy cell suspensions deplete the dissolved CO_2 supply and this pool is replaced with a ^{13}C-enriched HCO_3^- pool. The HCO_3^- pool is at equilibrium with the dissolved CO_2 and has a higher ^{13}C content. The utilization of the enriched ^{13}C HCO_3^- by β-carboxylation results in a $-10.7\%o$ $\Delta^{13}C$ value. The use of heavy suspensions of *P. tricornutum* and *S. costatum* by Beardall et al (9) could have resulted in the depletion of the dissolved CO_2 and a marked utilization of HCO_3^- by β-carboxylation.

SUBMERGED MARINE ANGIOSPERMS

Obligate Photoautotrophy

Higher plants are obligate photoautotrophs unless cells from these plants are grown heterotrophically in tissue culture. Higher plants can be divided into two groups based on the presence of a particular type of photosynthetic carbon metabolism. C_3 plants possess a Calvin cycle and C_4 plants possess a Hatch and Slack pathway. An outstanding characteristic of obligate photoautotrophy in C_4 plants is the primary β-carboxylation reaction for CO_2 fixation. Hatch (53, 54) has shown that fixation of CO_2 by PEP carboxylase in the mesophyll cells followed by transport and decarboxylation of C_4 acids in the bundle sheath cells enables a compartment of CO_2 to exist in these cells which is not in equilibrium with atmospheric CO_2. Autocatalytic assimilation of CO_2 occurs in the bundle sheath cells where CO_2 concentration is 50 times in excess of the concentration in the mesophyll cells. Bowes et al (18) have suggested that the high concentration of CO_2 in the bundle sheath cells depresses RuBP oxygenase activity and photorespiration and contributes to the high rate of CO_2 fixation in C_4 plants. Raven (103) has shown that the properties of the RuBP carboxylase—oxygenase enzyme together with the O_2 production in the bundle sheath chloroplasts, the CO_2 pump, and the resistances of O_2 and CO_2 diffusion—can be used to explain glycolate synthesis and the extent of CO_2 recycling in C_4 plants. The $\delta^{13}C$ values of submerged marine angiosperms are similar to C_4 plants and indicate a primary β-carboxylation reaction during CO_2 fixation. Since $\delta^{13}C$ values have been used to indicate the type of photosynthetic carbon metabolism in plants, this section assesses these values and photosynthetic characteristics of marine angiosperms.

Photosynthetic Characteristics

An important photosynthetic characteristic of marine angiosperms is their high productivity. Thayer et al (124) report values from the annual production of *Thalassia* and *Zoostera* of 200–3000g C/m^2, rice at 497 g C/m^2 and hay fields at 420 g C/m^2. Craig (31) reported a $\delta^{13}C$ value of $-12.5\%o$ for *Thalassia* over 25 years ago. Parker (88) reported $\delta^{13}C$ values of $-9.1\%o$, $-9.5\%o$, and $-9.7\%o$ for *Thalassia testudinum, Diplanthera wrightii,* and *Ruppia maritima,* respectively. Smith & Epstein (115) reported $\delta^{13}C$ values of $-5.6\%o$, $-9.3\%o$, $-10.0\%o$ for *Cymodocea manatorum, T. testudinum, Zoostera marina,* and *D. wrightii.* Whelan (132) noted a $\delta^{13}C$ value of $-12.6\%o$ for *T. testudinum* and $\delta^{13}C$ values of $-14.3\%o$, $-10.3\%o$, $-16.3\%o$, and $-16.4\%o$ for the organic acids, amino acids, sugars, and lipids of *Ruppia.* Doohan & Newcomb (39) reported $\delta^{13}C$ values of $-12.4\%o$, $-6.9\%o$, and $-8.9\%o$ for *C. serrulata, T. hemprichii,* and *C. rotundata.* Black & Bender (16) reported a $\delta^{13}C$ value of $-7.4\%o$ for *Halophila ovata,* and Benedict & Scott (12) reported a $\delta^{13}C$ value of $-9.04\%o$ for *T. testudinum.*

Jagels (66) examined the ultrastructure of *T. testudinum* and showed that the epidermal cells contain the majority of chloroplasts. The mesophyll cells surround air lacunae and the vascular bundles. In mature cells, there are no plasmadesmata connecting epidermal and mesophyll cells. Chloroplasts of the epidermal cells contain no starch. Photosynthesis seems to be concentrated in the epidermal cells, and the mesophyll cells contain only small chloroplasts confined to the parietal cytoplasm. Doohan & Newcomb (39) showed the cells of the epidermal layer to be extremely thick walled. The ratio of the chloroplasts to microbodies in the epidermal cells is 4.5 : 1 which is typical of C_3 plants. These workers showed that there are no bundle sheath cells surrounding the vascular tissue. Benedict & Scott (12) noted that the vascular tissue occurs between fiber cells and is surrounded by mesophyll cells. The epidermal cells are similar to C_3 type chloroplasts and packed with grana. The grana system in the mesophyll chloroplasts is not as developed as the grana in the epidermal chloroplasts. These authors noted striations in the walls of *Thalassia* epidermal cells similar to those reported by Albersheim (2). Thus, submerged marine angiosperms have $\delta^{13}C$ values similar to terrestrial C_4 plants, yet the abundance of chloroplasts in the epidermal cells and lack of bundle sheath cells differ from C_4 plants. Downton et al (41) noted a stimulation of photosynthesis by O_2 concentrations below that of air-saturated sea H_2O in *C. rotundata*. Black et al (17) observed about a 15% reduction of photysynthesis in air in *H. ovata* which indicates the presence of photorespiration in this marine angiosperm. Burris et al (25) noted about a 40% increase in radioactivity from $^{14}CO_2$ fixation incorporated into glycine, serine, and alanine in 100% O_2 over helium or air in *H. ovata*. An increase in O_2 increases the flow of carbon through the glycollate pathway, thus increasing photorespiration. Graham & Smillie (51) showed high levels of carbonate dehydratase in *T. testudinum* which may correlate with C_3 type photosynthesis and high rates of photorespiration. Hough (61) has shown that photorespiration in the light in *C. rotundata* and *H. ovata* is enhanced by high O_2 concentrations. The light : dark respiration ratios of less than one in aquatic angiosperms is interpreted as representing extensive internal refixation of respired CO_2 in the light. Refixation of CO_2 in submerged marine angiosperms may be greater than in terrestrial plants because the diffusive resistance of H_2O to CO_2 is so high.

Interpretation of $\delta^{13}C$ Values

Craig (32) and Park & Epstein (86) have shown that a fractionation of stable carbon isotopes of CO_2 occurs during photosynthesis. Tregunna et al (126), Smith & Epstein (115), Bender (10), and Troughton (127) have shown a direct correlation between the $\delta^{13}C$ values and the type of photosynthetic carbon metabolism. Plants with C_4 characteristics have $\delta^{13}C$ values of -6 to $-19\%o$, whereas plants with C_3 characteristics have $\delta^{13}C$ values of -24 to $-34\%o$. Park & Epstein (86) showed an enzymatic fractionation of stable carbon isotopes of CO_2 of $-8.2\%o$ for RuBP carboxylase and suggested this enzyme might be responsible for the fractionation of isotopes of CO_2 during photosynthesis. Whelan et al (133) have measured the $\delta^{13}C$ content of several metabolic intermediates in C_3 and C_4 plants. The isotope data suggest that CO_2 fixation through RuBP carboxylase or PEP carboxylase is primarily responsible for carbon isotope fractionation in C_3 and C_4 plants. The carbon isotope fractionation by RuBP carboxylase has been reported to be $-18.3\%o$ (134), $-28.3\%o$ (30), and $-24.8\%o$ (139) for an average fractionation value of $-23.8\%o$. The equations for calculating the fractionation of stable carbon isotopes of CO_2 by RuBP carboxylase are as follows:

$$5/6\delta^{13}C\ RuBP + 1/6\delta^{13}C\ HCO_3^-\ fixed = \delta^{13}C\ PGA \tag{1.}$$

$$\Delta = enzyme\ fractionation = \delta^{13}C\ HCO_3^-\ fixed - \delta^{13}C\ HCO_3^-\ source \tag{2.}$$

$$\Delta_{CO_2} = \Delta_{HCO_3^-} - equilibrium\ fractionation\ factor\ (35, 135) \tag{3.}$$

$$\Delta_{CO_2} = -23.8\%o$$

A model for the fractionation of stable carbon isotopes by C_3 plants is shown in Figure 1. The $\delta^{13}C$ value of the dissolved CO_2 in the cytoplasm is the same as the $\delta^{13}C$ value for atmospheric CO_2. There is no fractionation accompanying CO_2 dissolving in the cytoplasm. The enzymatic fractionation of cytoplasmic CO_2 by RuBP carboxylase is $-23.8\%o$. This gives a predicted value of $-30.8\%o$ for PGA and other sugar components in C_3 plants. This predicted value is within the range of $\delta^{13}C$ values of C_3 plants.

The carbon isotope fractionation by PEP carboxylase has been reported to be $-2.7\%o$ (134) and $-2.03\%o$ (105) for an average fractionation value of $-2.37\%o$. The equations for calculating the fractionation of stable carbon isotopes of HCO_3^- by PEP carboxylase are as follows:

$$3/4\delta^{13}C\ PEP + 1/4\delta^{13}C\ HCO_3^-\ fixed = \delta^{13}C\ malate \tag{4.}$$

$$\Delta = enzyme\ fractionation = \delta^{13}C\ HCO_3^-\ fixed - \delta^{13}C\ HCO_3^-\ source \tag{2.}$$

$$\Delta_{HCO_3^-} = -2.37\%o$$

A model for the fractionation of stable carbon isotopes by C_4 plants is shown in Figure 2. The range of $\delta^{13}C$ values for C_4 plants is -6 to $-19\%o$ (115). The $\delta^{13}C$ value for malate isolated from C_4 plants is $-9.0\%o$. A fractionation of $-2\%o$ has occurred between atmospheric CO_2 and the fixed carbon compounds in the leaves. Possible mechanisms which cause the carbon isotope fractionation associated with photosynthesis in C_4 plants include: (a) fractionation associated with the absorption

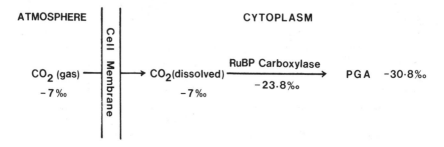

Figure 1   A model for the fractionation of stable carbon isotopes of atmospheric CO_2 during photosynthesis in C_3 plants.

of CO_2 into the mesophyll cells, (b) equilibrium fractionation associated with atmospheric CO_2 and dissolved HCO_3^-, and (c) fractionation associated with PEP carboxylase.

Atmospheric CO_2 has a general $\delta^{13}C$ value of $-7\%o$. A fractionation of -2 to $-7\%o$ is associated with dissolving CO_2 in a solution of hydroxide or cell sap (6, 32, 86, 87). This isotope effect between atmospheric CO_2 and dissolved HCO_3^- in $Ba(OH)_2$, NaOH, and leaf cytoplasm has been measured by Baertschi (6), Craig (32), and Park & Epstein (86, 87). The $\delta^{13}C$ value for dissolved CO_2 in leaf cytoplasm is -9 to $-14\%o$ (86). In dissolving CO_2 into leaf cytoplasm, it is possible that an exchange between dissolved HCO_3^- and atmospheric CO_2 can occur, resulting in an enrichment in ^{13}C in the dissolved HCO_3^-. Deuser & Degens (35) and Wendt (135) have established a $\delta^{13}C$ value of approximately $0\%o$ for dissolved HCO_3^- in equilibrium with atmospheric CO_2. The $\delta^{13}C$ value of dissolved HCO_3^- in leaf cytoplasm can therefore range from 0 to $14\%o$ depending on how rapidly CO_2 is fixed into malate. In steady-state photosynthetic CO_2 fixation in C_4 plants (with little equilibration of HCO_3^- and atmospheric CO_2), the $\delta^{13}C$ value of dissolved HCO_3^- is probably close to -9 to $-14\%o$, which is the measured value according to Park & Epstein (86). In Figure 2, there is a -2 to $-7\%o$ fractionation associated with the absorption of atmospheric CO_2 and conversion to HCO_3^- in the cell cytoplasm. The dissolved HCO_3^- would have a $\delta^{13}C$ value between -9 to $14\%o$. A $\Delta_{HCO_3^-}$ of $-2.37\%o$ by PEP carboxylase would give malate with a $\delta^{13}C$ value of -11 to $-16\%o$. These values are within the range of $\delta^{13}C$ values of C_4 plants.

$\delta^{13}C$ Values have been used to indicate the type of photosynthetic carbon metabolism in other photoautotrophic organisms. In succulents, the $\delta^{13}C$ values vary from

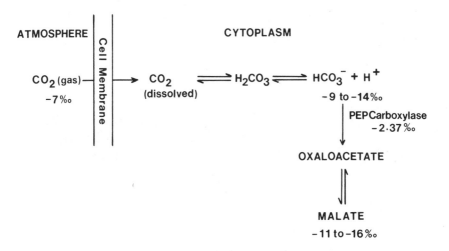

Figure 2   A model for the fractionation of stable carbon isotopes of atmospheric CO_2 during photosynthesis in C_4 plants.

−10 to −33‰. Bender et al (11) have suggested that the $^{13}C/^{12}C$ ratios of CAM are indicative of CO_2 fixation by RuBP or PEP carboxylase. Lerman et al (75) have shown the wide range of $\delta^{13}C$ values to be the result of the contribution of C_3 and C_4 pathways in CAM plants. Wong et al (137) have investigated isotope fractionation in anaerobic photosynthetic bacteria during CO_2 assimilation. The $\delta^{13}C$ values of *Chromatium* resulted from the operation of the reductive pentose phosphate cycle.

The high $\delta^{13}C$ values of marine angiosperms have been studied by Benedict & Scott (12). The $\delta^{13}C$ values of these plant cells are primarily determined by the $\delta^{13}C$ values of the dissolved CO_2 or HCO_3^- incorporated into the aquatic material and the amount of fractionation of the stable carbon isotopes at the initial CO_2 fixation site. In Redfish Bay, Texas, where *T. testudinum, D. wrightii, R. maritima,* and *C. manatorum* are collected (12, 88, 115), the pH of the H_2O is 8.2 and 96% of the total carbon is HCO_3^- ion. The $\delta^{13}C$ value of the bay H_2O is −6.7‰, but may fluctuate between −2.7‰ and −6.7‰ during the day because of respiration of aquatic organisms (88). Applying an equilibrium correction factor of −6.8‰ due to isotope fractionation between CO_2 and HCO_3^- at equilibrium at 30°C (35), the $\delta^{13}C$ value of the dissolved CO_2 during the day would be between −9.5‰ and −13.5‰. If all of the photosynthetic CO_2 fixation by *T. testudinum* was catalyzed by RuBP carboxylase, this would result in an enzyme fractionation of stable carbon isotopes of CO_2 (Δ_{CO_2}) of −18.3‰ (134), −28.3‰ (30), and −24.8‰ (139), an average of −23.8‰. The $\delta^{13}C$ value of *T. testudinum* would be determined by the following:

$$\delta^{13}C\ CO_2\ \text{dissolved} + \Delta_{CO_2}\ \text{RuBP carboxylase} = \delta^{13}C\ \text{of leaves} \qquad 5.$$

substituting

$$-9.5\ \text{to}\ -13.5‰ + (-23.8‰) = -33\ \text{to}\ -37.3‰ \qquad 6.$$

The determined $\delta^{13}C$ value of *T. testudinum* is 9.04‰ and differs appreciably from the predicted $\delta^{13}C$ value of −33 to −37.‰ if CO_2 fixation was similar to C_3 plants through RuBP carboxylase.

If photosynthetic CO_2 fixation in *T. testudinum* is similar to C_4 plants and catalyzed by PEP carboxylase, this would result in an enzyme fractionation of stable carbon isotopes of HCO_3^- ($\Delta_{HCO_3^-}$) of −2.03 to 2.7‰ (105). The $\delta^{13}C$ value of *T. testudinum* would be determined by the following:

$$\delta^{13}C\ \text{bay}\ HCO_3^- + \Delta_{HCO_3^-}\ \text{PEP carboxylase} = \delta^{13}C\ \text{of leaves} \qquad 7.$$

substituting

$$-2.7\ \text{to}\ -6.7‰ + (-2.37‰) = -5.07\ \text{to}\ -9.07‰ \qquad 8.$$

This predicted range of $\delta^{13}C$ values agrees with the determined $\delta^{13}C$ values for *T. testudinum* and other submerged marine angiosperms (12, 88, 115). Table 1 shows the $\delta^{13}C$ values for leaves, metabolic fractions, metabolic intermediates, and lipids of *T. testudinum,* sorghum, a C_4 plant, and cotton, a C_3 plant. The $\delta^{13}C$ values of the organic acid, amino acid, and sugar fractions of the marine angiosperms are −11.2‰, −13.1‰, and −10.1‰, respectively. The $\delta^{13}C$ values of malic acid and glucose in *T. testudinum* are −11.1‰ and −11.5‰. The $\delta^{13}C$ values of the metabolic intermediates of *T. testudinum* are similar to the $\delta^{13}C$ values of these intermediates in C_4 plants. In sorghum, the $\delta^{13}C$ values of organic acid, amino acid, and sugar fractions are −12.3‰, −12.7‰, and −9.9‰, respectively. In cotton, the $\delta^{13}C$ values of these fractions are −24.8‰, −33.1‰, and −24.6‰, respectively. The $\delta^{13}C$ values of malic acid and glucose in leaves of sorghum and cotton are −8.9‰, −9.9‰, and −21.0‰, −24.6‰ respectively.

The pathway of synthesis of sugars from CO_2 in terrestrial C_4 plants is through malic acid by the Hatch and Slack pathway. The fact that the $\delta^{13}C$ values of malic acid and glucose in sorghum are similar reflects the synthesis of glucose from the β-COOH group of malic acid by the C_4-dicarboxylic acid pathway. There is no fractionation of the stable carbon isotopes of CO_2 derived from the malic acid because all of the CO_2 is fixed by RuBP carboxylase (133). This fixation in the bundle sheath cells is similar to CO_2 fixation in a closed system. In such a system there is no fractionation of the $^{12}CO_2$ or $^{13}CO_2$ because all of the CO_2 is consumed in the carboxylation reaction (13). If glucose was synthesized from atmospheric CO_2 exclusively by the Calvin cycle, in sorghum leaves the $\delta^{13}C$ value of glucose would be about −25.0‰, as found in C_3 plants. The fact that the $\delta^{13}C$ values of malic acid and glucose in *T. testudinum* are similar to each other and similar to the $\delta^{13}C$ value of these compounds in sorghum attests to either the presence of the photosynthetic C_4-dicarboxylic acid pathway in the marine angiosperm or the fixation of the entire cellular pool of HCO_3^- (or CO_2) in a closed system. In either case, no fractionation of the stable carbon isotopes of HCO_3^- or CO_2 would occur and the $\delta^{13}C$ value of the cells would resemble the $\delta^{13}C$ value of the bay HCO_3^- ion.

Table 1   The $\delta^{13}C$ values of some plant constituents of cotton (C_3 plants), sorghum (C_4 plants), and *Thalassia testudinum*[a]

Plant constituent	$\delta^{13}C°/_{oo}$ vs PDB		
	Sorghum	Cotton	*T. testudinum*
Whole leaf	−10.9	−27.0	−9.04
Lipids	−16.1	−32.3	—
Carotenoids	−14.9	−29.2	—
Proteins	−10.2	−27.9	—
Amino acids	−12.7	−33.1	−13.1
Organic acids	−12.3	−24.8	−11.2
Sugars	−9.9	−26.4	−10.1
Malic acid	−8.9	−21.0	−11.1
Glucose	−9.9	−24.6	−11.5
Fructose	—	—	−11.1

[a] See (12, 133).

Raven (101) has discussed the ability of plants to use HCO_3^- ions for photosynthesis. This utilization does not occur in *Bryophyta* or terrestrial *Tracheophyta*, but it is widespread among the algae and is common in secondarily aquatic plants. The evidence (101) shows PGA to be the initial product of HCO_3^- utilization in *Scenedesmus*. The process involves active uptake of the HCO_3^- into the cells, followed by a dehydration to produce dissolved CO_2 for RuBP carboxylase. The preferential use of HCO_3^- at high pH is probably due to the low rate of diffusion of CO_2 in H_2O. The pH in marine bays is 8.2 and the concentration of HCO_3^- is about 2 mM. This provides a large pool for HCO_3^- utilization in submerged angiosperms. HCO_3^- utilization by these plants might be due to the large pool of available HCO_3^- and to the fact that CO_2 diffuses five times slower than HCO_3^- ions in aqueous environment. If HCO_3^- utilization in *T. testudinum* follows the reaction scheme of Raven's (101), the $\delta^{13}C$ values of the angiosperm would be determined by the $\delta^{13}C$ value of the cytoplasmic HCO_3^-, the $\delta^{13}C$ value of the dissolved CO_2, and the Δ_{CO_2} value of RuBP carboxylase as follows: $\delta^{13}C$ bay HCO_3^- (−2.7 to −6.7‰) $\xrightarrow[\text{uptake}]{\text{active}}$ $\delta^{13}C$ cytoplasmic HCO_3^- (−2.7 to −6.7‰) $\rightleftharpoons$ $\delta^{13}C$ CO_2 dissolved (−9.5 to −13.5‰) plus Δ_{CO_2} RuBP carboxylase (−23.8‰) which equals $\delta^{13}C$ value of leaf (−33.3 to −37.3‰). This calculated range of $\delta^{13}C$ values does not agree with the $\delta^{13}C$ value of −9.04‰ for *T. testudinum*. If CO_2 dissolved in sea H_2O diffuses into the angiosperm cells, the $\delta^{13}C$ value of *T. testudinum* would be determined as follows: $\delta^{13}C$ bay HCO_3^- (−2.7 to −6.7‰) $\rightleftharpoons$ $\delta^{13}C$ CO_2 dissolved (−9.5 to −13.5‰ → $\delta^{13}C$ CO_2 dissolved in cytoplasm (−9.5 to −13.5‰) plus Δ_{CO_2} RuBP carboxylase (−23.8‰) which again equals −33.3 to −37.3‰ for the $\delta^{13}C$ values for the leaf.

A model for the fractionation of stable carbon isotopes of marine HCO_3^- during photosynthesis by submerged marine angiosperms is given in Figure 3. This model incorporates the features of HCO_3^- utilization by aquatic plants (101) and the fea-

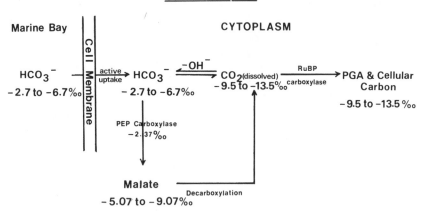

Figure 3   A model for the fractionation of stable carbon isotopes of marine HCO_3^- during photosynthesis in submerged marine angiosperms.

tures of the photosynthetic carbon metabolism by aquatic plants (12). The $\delta^{13}C$ value of marine bay HCO_3^- is -2.7 to $-6.7\%o$. An active uptake mechanism accounts for HCO_3^- entry into plant cells (101). The $\delta^{13}C$ value of the cytoplasmic HCO_3^- is projected to be -1.7 to $-6.7\%o$. The cytoplasmic HCO_3^- is not in equilibrium with bay HCO_3^- because of active uptake mechanism, and the "CO_2" utilization in the plant cells may be viewed as utilization in a closed system (13). The fixation of the cytoplasmic HCO_3^- ion by PEP carboxylase would give malate with a $\delta^{13}C$ value of -5.07 to $-9.07\%o$. This might provide a store for inorganic carbon. The decarboxylation of the C_4 acid, followed by a complete fixation of the dissolved CO_2 by RuBP carboxylase and the Calvin cycle, would give glucose and cellular carbon with a $\delta^{13}C$ value of -5.07 to $-9.07\%o$. Alternatively, the cytoplasmic HCO_3^- may be dehydrated by carbonic anhydrase to dissolved CO_2. A $-6.8\%o$ fractionation factor is associated with this step at 30°C (35) and would give a $\delta^{13}C$ value for the CO_2 of -9.5 to $-13.5\%o$. The epidermal cells may be a closed system with no equilibration of internal CO_2, produced from dehydration of HCO_3^- or decarboxylation of malate, with external CO_2 because of the large diffusion resistance of CO_2 in the cytoplasm. This may be analogous to the high diffusion resistance of CO_2 resulting in compartmentalization of CO_2 in the bundle sheath cells of C_4 plants, which leads to CO_2 fixation in a closed system (103). If epidermal cells are a closed system and all of the internal CO_2 is fixed by RuBP carboxylase, no fractionation of the carbon isotopes of CO_2 would occur with this fixation and the $\delta^{13}C$ value of PGA and cellular carbon would be -9.5 to $-13.5\%o$. The actual photosynthetic CO_2 fixing system in these angiosperms may involve a balance of these two mechanisms based on the relative activities of RuBP carboxylase and PEP carboxylase. These mechanisms would give a range of $\delta^{13}C$ values of the cells similar to the range of $\delta^{13}C$ values reported for the submerged marine angiosperms (12, 88, 115).

This type of CO_2 metabolism in the marine angiosperms, together with the features of epidermal photosynthesis, refixation of photorespired CO_2, mesophyll cells surrounding air lacunae and vascular tissue, no bundle sheath cells, and a high photosynthetic productivity, may place the submerged angiosperms in a group distinct from terrestrial C_3, C_4, and CAM plants.

SUBMERGED FRESHWATER ANGIOSPERMS

Photosynthetic Characteristics

Photosynthesis of submerged freshwater angiosperms has not been studied as extensively as photosynthesis in terrestrial plants, but the data indicates that both C_3 and C_4 photosynthetic characteristics are present in this group of aquatic plants. The photosynthetic rates of *Elodea occidentalis, Hydrilla verticillata,* and *Vallisneria denseserrulata* are between 2.1 and 3.6 mg $CO_2/dm^2 \cdot hr$ (64), and the photosynthetic rates of *H. verticillata, Ceratophyllum demersum,* and *Myriophyllum spicatum* are between 3.3 and 4.9 μmoles CO_2/mg chl·hr (128). These rates are only 1% as high as the photosynthetic rates of 500–650 μmoles CO_2/mg chl·hr for tobacco and maize (141). Zieman (142) has shown that the measurement of photosynthetic rates of aquatic plants by gas exchange methods may be underestimated because of the storage of CO_2 and O_2 in the air lacunae of the leaves. Internal gas production and storage in air lacunae was shown to swell the leaf blades of aquatic plants 200–250% during the day. Photosynthesis was saturated between 600–700 $\mu E/m^2$ sec for *H. verticillata, C. demersum* and, *M. spicatum* (128). Photosynthesis in *Egeria densa* and *Lagarsiphon major* was saturated at 1000 fc, whereas photosynthesis in *Elodea canadensis* did not reach light saturation at 3000 fc (19).

Brown et al (19) determined a CO_2 compensation point of near zero for *E. canadensis,* and Stanley & Naylor (118) determined a near zero value for the CO_2 compensation point of *M. spicatum.* Van et al (128) determined CO_2 compensation points for *H. verticillata, M. spicatum, C. demersum, Glycine max,* and *Zea mays* of 17, 9, 11, 5, and 0 respectively in 1% O_2, and 44, 19, 41, 44, and 0 respectively in 21% O_2. The CO_2 compensation points of the aquatic plants in 1% O_2 are higher than the CO_2 compensation of *G. max.* This may indicate that dark respiration continues in the light in these plants. The high CO_2 compensation points in aquatic plants in 21% O_2 indicate active photorespiration. Glycollate oxidase in these aquatic plants is two to three times the activity in corn leaves and one-third the oxidase activity in spinach leaves. Hough & Wetzel (62) have directly measured photorespiration in the leaves of *Naja flexis.* Release of CO_2 in the light is definitely stimulated by O_2. However, the rate of CO_2 release in the light in 1% O_2 is less than CO_2 released in the dark at this O_2 concentration. The rate of photorespiration in 21% O_2 is about the same as dark respiration. Photorespiration in aquatic angiosperms is limited by comparison with terrestrial C_3 plants because of extensive refixation of photorespired CO_2, which may be related to the slow rate of diffusion of CO_2 from the leaves and limited due to the low oxygen concentration in the H_2O surrounding the leaves.

Steemann Nielsen (119) noted that *Elodea* uses free CO_2 and HCO_3^- ions for photosynthesis, whereas *Fontinalis antipyretica* assimilates only free CO_2. The ability of *M. spicatum* to use HCO_3^- ions is dependent on the total CO_2 concentration. At 0.5 mM total CO_2 concentration, HCO_3^- utilization at pH 8.3 was one-fifth the utilization of free CO_2 at pH 4.6. At 15 mM total CO_2 concentration, HCO_3^- utilization at pH 8.3 was equal to the utilization of free CO_2 at pH 4.6. Carr (28) observed that HCO_3^- ion is practically useless to *C. demersum.* Van et al (128) have reinvestigated the active species of "CO_2" used in photosynthesis in aquatic plants. At saturating free CO_2 levels (0.5 mM) at pH 4 and 8, there was no indication of HCO_3^- use. At subsaturating levels of CO_2, the photosynthetic rates were higher at pH 8 than pH 4 and may indicate the use of HCO_3^- ions in addition to the utilization of free CO_2.

Carbon Metabolism

Stanley & Naylor (118) examined the carbon metabolism of *M. spicatum.* Exposure of the plants to $^{14}CO_2$ for less than 30 sec labeled primarily PGA and hexose phosphates and indicates C_3 type photosynthetic carbon metabolism. In addition, this plant has a low CO_2 compensation point and a high temperature optimum for photosynthesis, which are characteristics of C_4 plants. The low CO_2 compensation point means that plants without the β-carboxylation pathway can assimilate CO_2

at a low concentration. Brown et al (19) noted that C_4 acids were never more than 30% of the total in short-term $^{14}CO_2$ studies. DeGroote & Kennedy (34) studied $^{14}CO_2$ fixation in *E. canadensis.* Exposure of the cells to $^{14}CO_2$ for 2 sec resulted in 45% of label in C_4 acids, 15% in PGA, and 12% in sugars. Up to 45 sec exposure of the leaves to $^{14}CO_2$ gave a labeling pattern in PGA similar to C_3 plants. In pulse-chase experiments, the turnover of label in C_4 acids was slow. This is compared to C_4 plants accumulating 90% of the label in short-term exposures to $^{14}CO_2$ and relatively rapid turnover of the label in the C_4 acids (55). *M. spicatum* showed a relatively low ratio of RuBP carboxylase activity to PEP carboxylase activity. The authors conclude that the presence of both C_3 and C_4 carboxylating systems in *M. spicatum* may mean that under certain circumstances this aquatic plant can use both enzymes to synthesize C_4 acids and C_3 products. The synthesis of C_4 acids may serve as a reservoir of CO_2 which could be available to RuBP carboxylase by decarboxylation.

Anatomy and $\delta^{13}C$ Values

Newton et al (83) have examined the leaf structure and δ^{13}C values of *H. verticillata.* The leaves are two cells thick, with abundant air lacunae, and 4–5 cells thick around the central vascular tissue. The epidermal cells are specialized for protection and photosynthesis. The epidermal cells have a thick outer wall and contain numerous large chloroplasts and mitochondria. The chloroplasts contain a single large starch grain and stacks of grana. The thin-walled mesophyll cells contain an occasional chloroplast. There are no chlorenchymatous bundle sheath cells around the vascular bundles. The δ^{13}C values of *H. verticillata* are: leaves −25.5‰, carotenoids −24.0‰, malate −17.4‰, and glucose −16.6‰. The δ^{13}C value of the lake H_2O was 10.6‰. The pH of the H_2O was 7.5 and thus contained about 85% HCO_3^- ion and 15% free CO_2. On this basis the δ^{13}C value of the HCO_3^- is about −10.6‰, and the value of the free CO_2 is about −17.4‰. There is a −68‰ difference between lake HCO_3^- and malate. Once CO_2 or HCO_3^- enters the leaves there is little fractionation of stable carbon isotopes by RuBP or PEP carboxylase. The amount of fractionation of stable carbon isotopes of inorganic carbon by *H. verticillata* is very similar to C_4 plants.

CONCLUSION

Obligate photoautotrophy is found in photosynthetic bacteria, algae, and higher plants. Data in the literature support the presence of both the Calvin and the reductive carboxylic acid cycles in *Chlorobium thiosulfatophilum,* but the carbon metabolism in this green sulfur bacteria is disputed. The study of the fractionation of stable carbon isotopes during photosynthetic CO_2 assimilation may clarify this picture. α-Ketoglutarate dehydrogenase is missing in the blue-green algae, and the TCA cycle in these obligate photoautotrophs is used for the biosynthesis of porphyrin precursors and glutamate. The basis of obligate photoautotrophy in the Chlorobacteriaceae and cyanobacteria may be due to the lack of induction of enzymes necessary to increase growth on heterotrophic substances, and therefore there is a complete dependency on autocatalytic cycles for CO_2 assimilation. The Calvin cycle is operable in facultative photoautotrophs of the Thiorhodaceae and Athiorhodaceae. In *Chromatium* the glyoxylate cycle is induced by acetate. The induction of enzymes for heterotrophic growth is a major reason *Chromatium* is not an obligate photoautotroph. The anaerobic TCA cycle is present in *R. rubrum*, but α-ketoglutarate dehydrogenase is missing in photoautotrophic *Chromatium*. In the latter case the TCA cycle is used mainly for biosynthetic purposes. When *R. rubrum* is grown photomixotrophically, a "novel" mechanism for glutamate synthesis may be operable, although less is known of carbon metabolism in photomixatrophic cultures compared to photoautotrophic or photoheterotrophic cultures. Interest in β-carboxylation reactions has been revived with the discovery of the photoautotrophic C_4-carbon pathway in higher plants. β-Carboxylation may be prominent in algae under certain conditions, but whether this is C_4 metabolism or C_4 photosynthesis is not clear. The fractionation of stable carbon isotopes in marine angiosperms is similar to C_4 plants. $\delta^{13}C$ Analysis of these aquatic plants indicates the presence of CO_2 fixation in a closed system. These non-Kranz plants have photosynthesis localized in epidermal and mesophyll cells, and they may be in a photosynthetic group separate from C_3, C_4, and CAM plants.

ACKNOWLEDGMENTS

I am indebted to Drs. R. C. Fuller and R. Y. Stanier for making their unpublished reviews available to me and to many others who sent me unpublished or recent research articles. This work was supported by a research grant (A-482) from the Robert A. Welch Research Foundation.

Literature Cited

1. Abelson, P. H., Hoering, T. C. 1961. Carbon isotope fractionation in formation of amino acids by photosynthetic organisms. *Proc. Natl. Acad. Sci. USA* 47:623–32
2. Albersheim, P. 1975. The walls of growing plant cells. *Sci. Am.* 232:80–95
3. Anderson, L., Fuller, R. C. 1967. Photosynthesis in *Rhodospirillum rubrum* I. Autotrophic carbon dioxide fixation. *Plant Physiol.* 42:487–90
4. Anderson, L., Fuller, R. C. 1967. Photosynthesis in *Rhodospirullum rubrum* II. Photoheterotrophic carbon dioxide fixation. *Plant Physiol.* 42:491–96
5. Anderson, L., Fuller, R. C. 1967. Photosynthesis in *Rhodospirillum rubrum* III. Metabolic control of reductive pentose phosphate and tricarboxylic acid cycle enzymes. *Plant Physiol.* 42:497–502
6. Baertschi, P. 1953. Die Fractionierung der natürlichen Kohlenstoffisotopen im Kohlendioxydstoffwechsel grüner Pflanzen. *Helv. Chim. Acta* 36:773–81
7. Bassham, J. A., Kirk, M. 1960. Dynamics of the synthesis of carbon compounds. I. Carboxylation reactions. *Biochim. Biophys. Acta* 43:447–64
8. Beardall, J., Morris, I. 1975. Effects of environmental factors on photosynthesis patterns in *Phaeodactylum tricornutum (Bacillario-phyceae)* II. Effect of oxygen. *J. Phycol.* 11:430–34
9. Beardall, J., Mukerji, D., Glover, H. E., Morris, I. 1976. The path of carbon in photosynthesis by marine phytoplankton. *J. Phycol.* 12:409–17
10. Bender, M. M. 1971. Variation in the $^{13}C/^{12}C$ ratios of plants in relation to the pathway of photosynthetic carbon dioxide fixation. *Phytochemistry* 10:1239–44
11. Bender, M. M., Rouhani, I., Vines, H. M., Black, C. C. Jr. 1973. $^{13}C/^{12}C$ ratio changes in crassulacean acid metabolism plants. *Plant Physiol.* 52:427–30
12. Benedict, C. R., Scott, J. R. 1976. Photosynthetic carbon metabolism of a

marine grass. *Plant Physiol.* 57:876–80
13. Berry, J. A., Troughton, J. H. 1974. Carbon isotope fractionation by C_3 and C_4 plants in "closed" and "open" atmospheres. *Carnegie Inst. Wash. Yearb.,* pp. 785–90
14. Beuscher, N., Gottschalk, G. 1972. Lack of citrate lyase—the key enzyme of the reductive carboxylic acid cycle—in *Chlorobium thiosulfatophilum* and *Rhodospirillum rubrum. Z. Naturforsch.* 27:967–73
15. Black, C. C. Jr. 1973. Photosynthetic carbon fixation in relation to net CO_2 uptake. *Ann. Rev. Plant Physiol.* 24:253–86
16. Black, C. C. Jr., Bender, M. M. 1976. $\delta^{13}C$ value in marine organisms from the great barrier reef. *Aust. J. Plant Physiol.* 3:25–32
17. Black, C. C. Jr., Burris, J. E., Everson, R. G. 1976. Influence of oxygen concentration on photosynthesis in marine plants. *Aust. J. Plant Physiol.* 3:81–96
18. Bowes, G., Ogren, W. L., Hageman, R. H. 1971. Phosphoglycolate production catalyzed by ribulose diphosphate carboxylase. *Biochem. Biophys. Res. Commun.* 45:716–22
19. Brown, J. M. A., Dromgoole, F. I., Towsey, M. W., Browse, J. 1974. Photosynthesis and photorespiration in aquatic macrophytes. In *Mechanisms of Regulation of Plant Growth,* ed. R. L. Bieleski, A. R. Ferguson, M. M. Cresswell, pp. 243–49. Wellington: R. Soc. New Zealand. 934 pp.
20. Buchanan, B. B. 1972. Ferredoxin-linked carboxylation reactions. *Enzymes* 6:193–216
21. Buchanan, B. B., Bachofen, R., Arnon, D. I. 1964. Role of ferredoxin in the reductive assimilation of CO_2 and acetate by extracts of the photosynthetic bacterium *Chromatium. Proc. Natl. Acad. Sci. USA* 52:839–47
22. Buchanan, B. B., Evans, M. C. W., Arnon, D. I. 1967. Ferredoxin-dependent carbon assimilation in *Rhodospirillum rubrum. Arch. Mikrobiol.* 59:32–40
23. Buchanan, B. B., Schurmann, P., Shanmugam, K. T. 1972. Role of the reductive carboxylic acid cycle in a photosynthetic bacterium lacking ribulose-1,5-diphosphate carboxylase. *Biochim. Biophys. Acta* 283:136–45
24. Buchanan, B. B., Sirevåg, R. 1976. Ribulose-1,5-diphosphate carboxylase from *Chlorobium thiosulfatophilum. Arch. Microbiol.* 190:15–19

25. Burris, J. E., Holm-Hansen, O., Black, C. C. Jr. 1976. Glycine and serine production in marine plants as a measure of photorespiration. *Aust. J. Plant Physiol.* 3:87–92
26. Calley, A. G., Rigopoulos, N., Fuller, R. C. 1968. The assimilation of carbon by *Chloropseudomonas ethylicum. Biochem. J.* 106:615–22
27. Calvin, M., Bassham, J. A., Benson, A. A., Lynch, V. H., Quellet, C., Schou, L., Stepka, W., Tolbert, N. E. 1951. Carbon dioxide assimilation in plants. *Symp. Soc. Exp. Biol.* 5:284–305
28. Carr, J. L. 1968. The primary productivity of *Ceratophyllum demersum* II. Micro primary productivity, pH and the P/R ratio. *Aust. J. Mar. Freshwater Res.* 19:127–42
29. Cheung, W. Y., Gibbs, M. 1966. Dark and photometabolism of sugars by a blue-green alga: *Tolypothrix tenuis. Plant Physiol.* 41:731–37
30. Christeller, J. T., Laing, W. A., Troughton, J. H. 1976. Isotope discrimination by ribulose-1,5-diphosphate carboxylase. No effect of temperature or HCO_3^- concentration. *Plant Physiol.* 57:580–82
31. Craig, H. 1953. The geochemistry of the stable carbon isotopes. *Geochim. Cosmochim. Acta* 3:53–93
32. Craig, H. 1954. Carbon 13 in plants and the relationships between carbon 13 and carbon 14 variations in nature. *J. Geol.* 62:115–49
33. Degens, E. T., Guillard, R. R. L., Sackett, W. M., Hellebust, J. A. 1968. Metabolic fractionation of carbon isotopes in marine plankton. I. Temperature and respiration experiments. *Deep-Sea Res.* 15:1–9
34. DeGroote, D., Kennedy, R. A. 1977. Photosynthesis in *Elodea canadensis* Michx: four carbon acid synthesis. *Plant Physiol.* 59:1133–35
35. Deuser, W. G., Degens, E. T. 1967. Carbon isotope fractionation in the system $CO_2(gas)$-$CO_2(aqueous)$-HCO_3^- (aqueous). *Nature* 215:1033–35
36. Din, G. A., Suzuki, I., Lees, H. 1967. Carbon dioxide fixation and phosphoenol-pyruvate carboxylase in *Ferrobacillus ferredoxin. Can. J. Microbiol.* 13:1413–19
37. Doelle, H. W. 1975. *Bacterial Metabolism.* New York: Academic. 738 pp.
38. Döhler, G. 1974. C_4-Weg in *Anacystis* and *Chlorella* wahrend der photosynthesis-induction? *Ber. Dtsch. Bot. Ges.* 87:229–38

39. Doohan, M. E., Newcomb, E. H. 1976. Leaf ultrastructure and $\delta^{13}C$ values of three seagrasses from the great barrier reef. *Aust. J. Plant Physiol.* 3:9–23

40. Doolittle, W. F., Singer, R. A. 1974. Mutational analysis of dark endogenous metabolism in the blue-green bacterium *Anacystis nidulans. J. Bacteriol.* 119: 677–83

41. Downton, W. J. S., Bishop, D. G., Larkum, A. W. D., Osmond, C. B. 1976. Oxygen inhibition of photosynthetic oxygen evolution in marine plants. *Aust. J. Plant Physiol.* 3:73–79

42. Elsden, S. R. 1962. Assimilation of organic compounds by photosynthetic bacteria. *Fed. Proc.* 21:1047–52

43. Evans, M. C. W., Buchanan, B. B., Arnon, D. I. 1966. A new ferrodoxin-dependent carbon reduction cycle in a photosynthetic bacterium. *Proc. Natl. Acad. Sci. USA* 55:928–34

44. Fuller, R. C. 1971. The evolution of photosynthetic carbon metabolism: The role of sequences ancillary to the Calvin cycle. In *Biochemical Evolution and the Origin of Life*, ed. E. Schoffeniels, pp. 259–73. Amsterdam: North Holland. 398 pp.

45. Fuller, R. C. 1977. Photosynthetic carbon metabolism in the green and purple bacteria. In *Bacterial Photosynthesis*. In press

46. Fuller, R. C., Kornberg, H. L. 1961. A possible route for malate oxidation by *Chromatium. Biochem. J.* 79:8–9

47. Fuller, R. C., Smillie, R. M., Sisler, E. C., Kornberg, H. L. 1961. Carbon metabolism in *Chromatium. J. Biol. Chem.* 236:2140–49

48. Gest, H., Ormerod, J. G., Ormerod, K. S. 1962. Photometabolism of *Rhodospirillum rubrum:* light-dependent dissimilation of organic compounds to carbon dioxide and molecular hydrogen by an anaerobic citric acid cycle. *Arch. Biochem. Biophys.* 97:21–33

49. Glover, H., Beardall, J., Morris, I. 1975. Effects of environmental factors on photosynthesis patterns in *Phaedactylum tricorntum* (Bacillariophyceae) I. The effect of nitrogen deficiency and light intensity. *J. Phycol.* 11:424–29

50. Goulding, K. H., Merrett, M. J. 1967. The photoassimilation of acetate by *Pyrobotrys* (*Chlamydomonas*) *stellata. J. Gen. Microbiol.* 48:127–36

51. Graham, D., Smillie, R. M. 1976. Carbonate dehydratase in marine organisms of the great barrier reef. *Aust. J. Plant Physiol.* 3:113–19

52. Graham, D., Whittingham, C. P. 1968. The path of carbon during photosynthesis in *Chlorella pyrenoidosa* at high and low carbon dioxide concentrations. *Z. Pflanzenphysiol.* 58:418–27

53. Hatch, M. D. 1971. The C_4-pathway of photosynthesis. Evidence for an intermediate pool of carbon dioxide and the identity of the donor C_4-dicarboxylic acid. *Biochem. J.* 125:425–32

54. Hatch, M. D. 1976. The C_4-pathway of photosynthesis: Mechanism and function. In *CO_2 Metabolism and Plant Productivity*, ed. R. H. Burris, C. C. Black, pp. 59–81. Baltimore: Univ. Park Press. 431 pp.

55. Hatch, M. D., Slack, C. R. 1967. Photosynthesis by sugar cane leaves. A new carboxylation reaction and the pathway of sugar formation. *Biochem. J.* 101: 103–11

56. Hatch, M. D., Slack, C. R. 1970. Photosynthetic CO_2-fixation pathways. *Ann. Rev. Plant Physiol.* 21:141–62

57. Hoare, D. S. 1963. The photoassimilation of acetate by *Rhodospirillum rubrum. Biochem. J.* 87:284–302

58. Hoare, D. S., Gibson, J. 1964. Photoassimilation of acetate and the biosynthesis of amino acids by *Chlorobium thiosulphatophilum. Biochem. J.* 91: 546–59

59. Hoare, D. S., Hoare, S. L., Moore, R. B. 1967. The photoassimilation of organic compounds by autotrophic blue-green algae. *J. Gen. Microbiol.* 49:351–70

60. Hoare, D. S., Moore, R. B. 1965. Photoassimilation of organic compounds by autotrophic blue-green algae. *Biochim. Biophys. Acta* 109:622–25

61. Hough, R. A. 1976. Light and dark respiration and release of organic carbon in marine macrophytes of the Great Barrier Reef region. *Aust. J. Plant Physiol.* 3:63–68

62. Hough, R. A., Wetzel, R. G. 1972. A ^{14}C-assay for photorespiration in aquatic plants. *Plant Physiol.* 49:987–90

63. Ihlenfeldt, M. J. A., Gibson, J. 1975. CO_2 fixation and its regulation in *Anacystis nidulans* (*Synechococcus*). *Arch. Microbiol.* 102:13–21

64. Ikusima, I. 1966. Ecological studies on the productivity of aquatic plant communities II. Seasonal changes in standing crop and productivity of a natural submerged community of *Vallisneria denseserrulata. Bot. Mag.* 79:7–19

65. Jackson, W. A., Volk, R. J. 1970. Photorespiration. *Ann. Rev. Plant Physiol.* 21:385–432

66. Jagels, R. 1973. Studies of marine grass, *Thalassia testudinum* I. Ultrastructure of the osmoregulatory leaf cells. *Am. J. Bot.* 60:1003–9

67. Karekar, M. D., Joshi, G. V. 1973. Photosynthetic carbon metabolism in marine algae. *Bot. Mar.* 16:216–20

68. Kelly, D. P. 1971. Autotrophy: Concepts of lithotrophic bacteria and their organic metabolism. *Ann. Rev. Microbiol.* 25:177–210

69. Kelly, D. P. 1974. Growth and metabolism of the obligate photolithotroph *Chlorobium thiosulfatophilum* in the presence of added organic nutrients. *Arch. Microbiol.* 100:163–74

70. Kelly, G. J., Latzko, E., Gibbs, M. 1976. Regulatory aspects of photosynthetic carbon metabolism. *Ann. Rev. Plant Physiol.* 27:181–205

71. Khondohormoff, V. A. 1961. L'assimilation de l'anhydride carbonique par *Nitrobacter winogrodshy*. *Ann. Inst. Pasteur* 100:257–60

72. Kornberg, H. L., Collins, J. F., Bigley, D. 1960. The influence of growth substrates on metabolic pathways in *Micrococcus denitrificans*. *Biochim. Biophys. Acta* 39:9–24

73. Kratz, W. A., Myers, J. 1955. Nutrition and growth of several blue-green algae. *Am. J. Bot.* 42:282–87

74. Leach, C. K., Carr, N. G. 1970. Electron transport and oxidation phosphorylation in blue-green alga *Anabaena variabilis*. *J. Gen. Microbiol.* 64:55–70

75. Lerman, J. C., Deleens, E., Nato, A., Moyse, A. 1974. Variation in the carbon isotope composition of a plant with crassulacean acid metabolism. *Plant Physiol.* 53:581–84

76. Lewin, J. C. 1950. Obligate autotrophy in *Chlamydomonas moeurissii* Gerloff. *Science* 112:652–53

77. Lewin, J. C. 1954. Heterotrophy in diatoms. *J. Gen. Microbiol.* 9:305–13

78. Losada, M. A., Trebst, A. V., Ogata, S., Arnon, D. I. 1960. Equivalence of light and adenosine triphosphate in bacterial photosynthesis. *Nature* 86:753–60

79. McFadden, B. A. 1973. Autotrophic CO_2 assimilation and the evolution of ribulose diphosphate carboxylate. *Bacteriol. Rev.* 37:289–319

80. McFadden, B. A. 1959. Some products of $^{14}CO_2$ fixation by *Hydrogenomonas facilis*. *J. Bacteriol.* 77:339–43

81. Merrett, M. J. 1976. Enzyme levels in relation to obligate phototrophy in *Chlamybotrys*. *Plant Physiol.* 58:179–81

82. Neilson, A. H., Holm-Hansen, O., Lewin, R. A. 1972. An obligately autotrophic mutant of *Chlamydomonas dysosmos*: a biochemical elucidation. *J. Gen. Microbiol.* 71:141–48

83. Newton, R. J., Scott, R. J., Benedict, C. R. 1977. Leaf structure and $\delta^{13}C$ values of the aquatic *Hydrilla verticillata*. *Plant Physiol.* Suppl. 59:65 (Abstr.)

84. Norris, L., Norris, R. E., Calvin, M. 1965. A survey of the rates and products of short term photosynthesis in plants of nine phyla. *J. Exp. Bot.* 6:64–74

85. Ogasawara, N., Miyachi, S. 1970. Regulation of CO_2 fixation in *Chlorella* by light of varied wavelength and intensities. *Plant Cell Physiol.* 11:1–14

86. Park, R., Epstein, S. 1960. Carbon isotope fractionation during photosynthesis. *Geochim. Cosmochim. Acta* 21:110–26

87. Park, R., Epstein, S. 1961. Metabolic fractionation of ^{13}C and ^{12}C in plants. *Plant Physiol.* 36:133–38

88. Parker, P. L. 1964. The biogeochemistry of the stable isotopes of carbon in a marine bay. *Geochim. Cosmochim. Acta* 28:1155–64

89. Patil, B. A., Joshi, G. V. 1970. Photosynthesis studies in *Ulva Lactuca*. *Bot. Mar.* 13:111–15

90. Pearce, J., Carr, N. G. 1967. The metabolism of acetate by the blue-green algae, *Anabaena variabilis* and *Anacystis nidulans*. *J. Gen. Microbiol.* 49:301–13

91. Pearce, J., Carr, N. G. 1969. The incorporation and metabolism of glucose in *Anabaena variabilis*. *J. Gen. Microbiol.* 54:451–62

92. Pearce, J., Leach, C. K., Carr, N. G. 1969. The incomplete tricarboxylic acid cycle in the blue-green alga *Anabaena variabilis*. *J. Gen. Microbiol.* 55:371-78

93. Pelroy, R. A., Bassham, J. A. 1972. Photosynthetic and dark metabolism in unicellular blue-green algae. *Arch. Mikrobiol.* 86:25–38

94. Pelroy, R. A., Rippka, R., Stanier, R. Y. 1972. Metabolism of glucose by unicellular blue-green algae. *Arch. Mikrobiol.* 87:303–22

95. Peters, T. L., Aleem, M. I. H. 1970. Oxidation of sulfur compounds and electron transport in *Thiobacillus denitrificans*. *Arch. Mikrobiol.* 71:319–30

96. Peters, T. L., Liu, M. S., Aleem, M. I. H. 1970. The tricarboxylic acid cycle in *Thiobacillus dentrificans* and *Thiobacillus A-2*. *J. Gen. Microbiol.* 64:29–35

97. Pfennig, N., Truper, H. G. 1971. The phototrophic bacteria. In *Bergey's Manual of Determinative Bacteriology, 8th Edition,* ed. R. E. Buchanan, N. E. Gibbons, pp. 24–57. Baltimore: Williams & Wilkins. 1268 pp.

98. Pulich, W. M., Van Baalen, C. 1973. Pyridine nucleotide-dependent glucose dehydrogenase in blue-green algae. *J. Bacteriol.* 114:28–33

99. Pulich, W. M., Van Baalen, C., Gibson, J. L., Tabita, F. R. 1976. Purification and characterization of glucose dehydrogenase from a heterotrophically grown blue-green alga. *Plant Physiol.* 58:393–97

100. Quayle, J. R. 1972. The metabolism of one-carbon compounds by microorganisms. *Adv. Microbiol. Physiol.* 7:119–203

101. Raven, J. A. 1970. Exogenous inorganic carbon sources in plant photosynthesis. *Biol. Rev.* 45:167–221

102. Raven, J. A. 1974. Carbon dioxide fixation. In *Algal Physiology and Biochemistry,* ed. W. O. P. Stewart, pp. 434–55. Berkeley: Univ. California Press. 989 pp.

103. Raven, J. A. 1977. Ribulose bisphosphate carboxylase activity in terrestrial plants: Significance of O_2 and CO_2 diffusion. *Curr. Adv. Plant Sci.* 9:579–90

104. Reed, M. L., Graham, D. 1977. Carbon dioxide and the regulation of photosynthesis: Activities of photosynthetic enzymes and carbonic dehydratase *(carbonic anhydrase)* in *Chlorella* after growth and adaptation in different carbon dioxide concentrations. *Aust. J. Plant Physiol.* 4:87–98

105. Reibach, P. H., Benedict, C. R. 1977. Fractionation of stable carbon isotopes by phosphoenolpyruvate carboxylase from C_4 plants. *Plant Physiol.* 59:564–68

106. Rinne, R. W., Buckman, R. W., Benedict, C. R. 1965. Acetate and bicarbonate metabolism in photosynthetic bacteria. *Plant Physiol.* 40:1066–73

107. Sadler, W. R., Stanier, R. Y. 1960. The function of acetate in photosynthesis by green bacteria. *Proc. Natl. Acad. Sci. USA* 46:1328–34

108. Sirevåg, R. 1974. Further studies on carbon dioxide fixation in *Chlorobium. Arch. Microbiol.* 98:3–18

109. Sirevåg, R. 1975. Photoassimilation of acetate and metabolism of carbohydrate in *Chlorobium thiosulfatophilum. Arch. Microbiol.* 104:105–11

110. Sirevåg, R., Buchanan, B. B., Berry, J. A., Troughton, J. H. 1977. Mechanisms of CO_2 fixation in bacterial photosynthesis studied by the carbon isotope fractionation technique. *Arch. Microbiol.* 112:35–38

111. Sirevåg, R., Ormerod, J. G. 1970. Carbon dioxide-fixation in photosynthetic green sulphur bacteria. *Science* 169:186–88

112. Sirevåg, R., Ormerod, J. G. 1970. Carbon dioxide fixation in green sulphur bacteria. *Biochem. J.* 120:399–408

113. Smillie, R. M., Rigopoulos, N., Kelly, H. 1962. Enzymes of the reductive pentose phosphate cycle in the purple and in the green photosynthetic bacteria. *Biochim. Biophys. Acta* 56:612–14

114. Smith, A. J., London, J., Stanier, R. Y. 1967. Biochemical basis of obligate autotrophy in blue-green algae and *Thiobacilla. J. Bacteriol.* 94:972–83

115. Smith, B. N., Epstein, S. 1971. Two categories of $^{13}C/^{12}C$ ratios for higher plants. *Plant Physiol.* 47:380–84

116. Stanier, R. Y., Cohen-Bazire, G. 1977. Phototrophic prokaryotes: The cyanobacteria. *Ann. Rev. Microbiol.* 31:225–74

117. Stanier, R. Y., Doudoroff, M., Kunisawa, R., Contopoulous, R. 1959. The role of organic substrates in bacterial photosynthesis. *Proc. Natl. Acad. Sci. USA* 45:1246–60

118. Stanley, R. A., Naylor, A. W. 1972. Photosynthesis in Eurasian watermilfoil *(Myriophyllum spicatum L.) Plant Physiol.* 50:149–51

119. Steemann Nielsen, E. 1960. Uptake of CO_2 by the plant. In *Encylopedia of Plant Physiology,* ed. W. Ruland, 1:70–80. Berlin: Springer-Verlag. 1013 pp.

120. Suzuki, I., Werkman, C. H. 1958. Chemoautotrophic fixation of carbon dioxide by *Thiobacillus thiooxidans. Iowa State Coll. J. Sci.* 32:475–83

121. Syrett, P. J., Bocks, S. M., Merrett, M. J. 1964. Acetate assimilation through *Chlorella vulgaris. J. Exp. Bot.* 15:35–47

122. Syrett, P. J., Merrett, M. J., Bocks, S. M. 1963. Enzymes of the glyoxylate cycle in *Chlorella vulgaris. J. Exp. Bot.* 14:249–64

123. Tabita, F. R., McFadden, B. A., Pfennig, N. 1974. D-ribulose-1,5-bisphosphate carboxylase in *Chlorobium thiosulfatophilum* Tassajara. *Biochim. Biophys. Acta* 341:187–94

123a. Takabe, T., Akazawa, T. 1977. A comparative study on the effect of

O_2 on photosynthetic carbon metabolism in *Chlorobium thiosulfatophilum* and *Chromatium vinosum*. *Plant Cell Physiol.* 18:102–15

124. Thayer, G. W., Wolfe, D. A., Williams, R. B. 1975. The impact of man on seagrass systems. *Am. Sci.* 63:288–96

125. Tolbert, N. E. 1971. Microbodies—peroxisomes and glyoxysomes. *Ann. Rev. Plant Physiol.* 22:45–74

126. Tregunna, E. B., Smith, B. N., Berry, J. A., Downton, W. J. S. 1970. Some methods for studying the photosynthetic taxonomy of angiosperms. *Can. J. Bot.* 48:1209–14

127. Troughton, J. H. 1971. Aspects of the evolution of photosynthetic carboxylation reaction in plants. In *Photosynthesis and Respiration*, ed. M. D. Hatch, C. B. Osmond, R. O. Slatyer, pp. 124–29. New York: Wiley Interscience. 565 pp.

128. Van, T. K., Haller, W. T., Bowes, G. 1976. Comparison of the photosynthetic characteristics of three submerged aquatic plants. *Plant Physiol.* 58:761–68

129. van Niel, C. B. 1962. The present status of the comparative study of photosynthesis. *Ann. Rev. Plant Physiol.* 13:1–26

130. Voskresenskaya, N. P. 1972. Blue light and carbon metabolism. *Ann. Rev. Plant Physiol.* 23:219–34

131. Walker, D. A. 1966. Carboxylation in plants. *Endeavor* 25:21–26

132. Whelan, T. 1971. *Stable carbon isotope fractionation in photosynthetic carbon metabolism*. PhD thesis. Texas A&M Univ. College Station, Texas. 93 pp.

133. Whelan, T., Sackett, W. M., Benedict, C. R. 1970. Carbon isotope discrimination in a plant possessing the C_4 dicarboxylic acid pathway. *Biochem. Biophys. Res. Commun.* 41:1205–10

134. Whelan, T., Sackett, W. M., Benedict, C. R. 1973. Enzyme fractionation of carbon isotopes by phosphoenolpyruvate carboxylase from C_4 plants. *Plant Physiol.* 51:1051–54

135. Wendt, I. 1968. Fractionation of carbon isotopes and its temperature dependence in the system CO_2—gas—CO_2 in solution and HCO_3^- CO_2 in solution. *Earth Planet. Sci. Lett.* 4:64–68

136. Whittenbury, R., Kelly, D. P. 1977. Autotrophy: A conceptual phoenix. *Symp. Soc. Gen. Microbiol.* 26:122–49

137. Wong, W., Sackett, W. M., Benedict, C. R. 1975. Isotope fractionation in photosynthetic bacteria during carbon dioxide assimilation *Plant Physiol.* 55: 475–79

138. Wong, W. W. L. 1976. *Carbon isotope fractionation by marine phytoplankton*. PhD thesis. Texas A&M Univ., College Station, Texas. 116 pp.

139. Wong, W. W. L., Benedict, C. R., McGrath, T., Kohel, R. J. 1977. The fractionation of stable carbon isotopes by RuBP carboxylase. *Plant Physiol.* Suppl. 59:42 (Abstr.)

140. Zelitch, I. 1971. *Photosynthesis, Photorespiration and Plant Productivity*. New York: Academic. 347 pp.

141. Zelitch, I. 1975. Pathways of carbon fixation in green plants. *Ann. Rev. Biochem.* 44:123–45

142. Zieman, J. C. 1974. Methods for the study of the growth and production of turtle grass *Thalassia testudinum* König. *Acquaculture* 4:139–43

Ann. Rev. Plant Physiol. 1978. 29:95–120
Copyright © 1978 by Annual Reviews Inc. All rights reserved

δ-AMINOLEVULINIC ACID IN PLANTS: ITS BIOSYNTHESIS, REGULATION, AND ROLE IN PLASTID DEVELOPMENT[1],[2]

❖7646

Samuel I. Beale

Department of Botany, University of California, Davis, California 95616

CONTENTS

[1]This article is dedicated to the memory of Dr. Sam Granick.
[2]Abbreviations used: ALA (δ-aminolevulinic acid); DOVA (γ,δ-dioxovaleric acid).

0066-4294/78/0601-0095$01.00

INTRODUCTION

This article is concerned with the biosynthetic origins in plants of the group of compounds known as tetrapyrroles: hemes, chlorophylls, and related molecules that are central to the energy economy of virtually all living systems. The emphasis here will be on the initial biochemical steps of the plant tetrapyrrole pathway and the important role of these events in the regulation of chlorophyll synthesis and the development of photosynthetic competence. The apparent uniqueness of the initial steps of the plant pathway will be examined critically, and comparisons will be made with the pathway in bacteria and animals. Finally, the regulation of the plant tetrapyrrole pathway will be discussed from the viewpoint of mechanism. For a more general perspective on tetrapyrroles, readers are directed to recent reviews covering tetrapyrrole biosynthesis in general (29), chlorophyll biosynthesis (12), and chlorophyll synthesis in vitro (71).

UNITY IN TETRAPYRROLE BIOSYNTHESIS

The earliest biochemical evidence for the common biosynthetic origins of hemes and chlorophylls was obtained in the late 1940s by Granick (27). He examined mutant strains of the alga *Chlorella* that were deficient in chlorophyll synthesis. Some of the strains accumulated protoporphyrin IX, then known to be the immediate precursor of protoheme (Figure 1A). Other strains accumulated magnesium protoporphyrin IX and magnesium protoporphyrin IX monoester. It was concluded from these observations that heme and chlorophyll share a common biosynthetic pathway up to the stage of protoporphyrin IX where the pathway branches, iron insertion forming heme, and magnesium insertion leading to the chlorophylls.

Primary Products of the Pathway

The general outline of the tetrapyrrole pathway is illustrated in Figure 2. In addition to hemes and chlorophylls, products include the corrinoids, e.g. vitamin B_{12}, siroheme (the prosthetic group of some nitrite and sulfite reductases), and the bilins, which include the photosynthetic accessory pigments of blue-green, red, and cryptomonad algae as well as the chromophore of phytochrome. It is clear that any pathway with this many endproducts must be finely regulated in order to insure the proper distribution of products that are called for at different stages of development. The regulation of tetrapyrrole synthesis in a wide range of organisms has been recently reviewed (29).

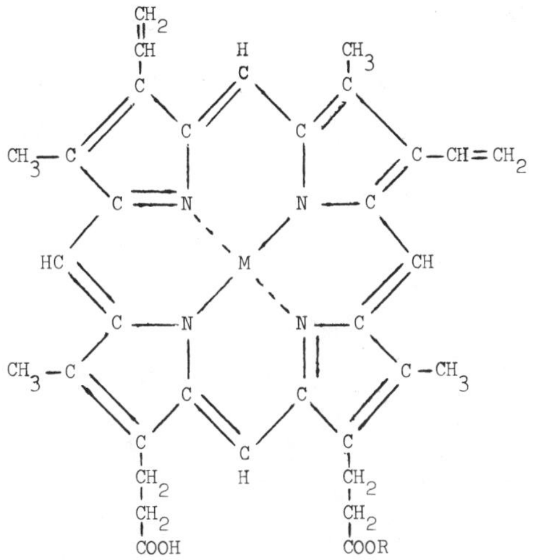

	R	M
Protoporphyrin IX	H	(2H)
Protoheme	H	Fe
Mg Protoporphyrin	H	Mg
Mg Protoporphyrin monoester	CH_3	Mg

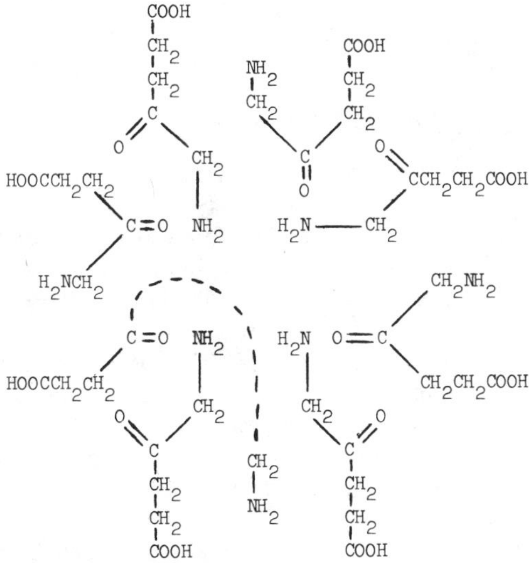

Figure 1 (A) Chemical structure of protoporphyrin IX and derivatives (B) Eight molecules of ALA shown in the positions that they occupy in protoporphyrin IX.

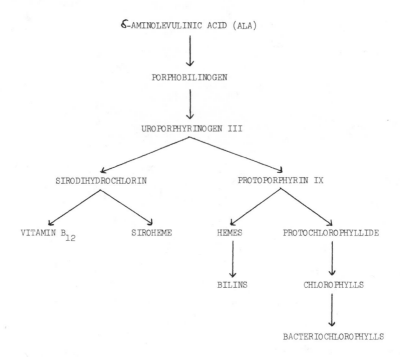

Figure 2 Outline of the branched tetrapyrrole biosynthetic pathway and major products of the pathway.

δ-*Aminolevulinic acid: the Key Precursor*

In 1953 Shemin & Russell (85) described a new compound, δ-aminolevulinic acid (ALA), which could replace glycine and "active succinate" in an in vitro heme forming system from avian erythrocytes. A condensation between glycine and "active succinate" was proposed, leading to α-amino-β-ketoadipic acid, which upon decarboxylation would yield ALA. Then in 1958, the enzymatic formation of ALA from glycine and succinyl CoA was reported in avian erythrocyte extracts (24) and in a preparation from the photosynthetic bacterium *Rhodopseudomonas spheroides* (40). Isotopic labeling studies have since shown ALA to be the source of the atoms of carbon and nitrogen in heme (85), and to be the precursor of the corrinoid nucleus of vitamin B_{12} (84), the tetrapyrrole portion of chlorophyll (14, 18, 28, 50), and the phycobilin chromophores (92). Eight molecules of ALA are required for each tetrapyrrole nucleus formed; this stoichiometry has been observed for heme (85), vitamin B_{12} (83), chlorophyll (50), and phycobilins (92). Figure 1B illustrates the position of the eight ALA molecules with respect to the tetrapyrrole product.

ALA FORMATION IN BACTERIA AND ANIMALS

Mechanism of the ALA Synthetase Reaction

The formation of ALA from succinyl CoA and glycine, catalyzed by ALA synthetase from *R. spheroides,* has been subjected to a detailed mechanistic analysis by Zaman et al (Figure 3) (104). The first step in the reaction appears to be formation of a Schiff base between the pyridoxal phosphate cofactor and glycine. Next the pro-*R* proton of glycine is lost, and succinyl CoA condenses with the resulting carbanion. Then decarboxylation of the intermediate β-keto acid occurs while it is still associated with the enzyme. Finally H^+ is added and ALA is released from the pyridoxal-enzyme complex. Note that only one of the two carbon atoms of glycine finds its way into ALA, the carboxyl carbon being lost as CO_2.

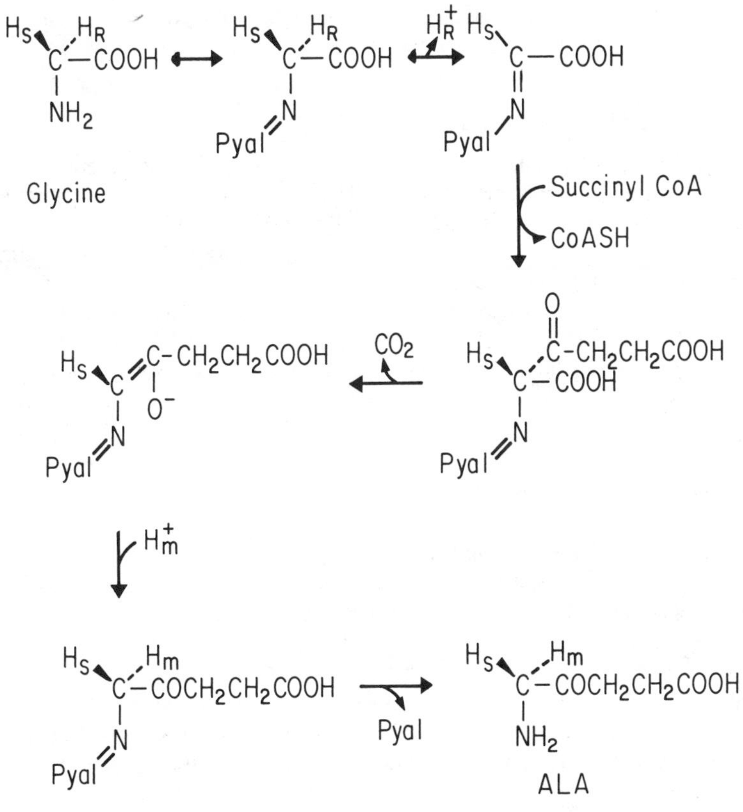

Figure 3 Mechanism of ALA formation by condensation of glycine and succinyl CoA catalyzed by ALA synthetase. Pyal: pyridoxal phosphate.

Properties of ALA Synthetase

The most highly purified preparations of ALA synthetase have been obtained from *R. spheroides* by Nandi & Shemin (59). The 1600-fold purified enzyme weighs 80,000 daltons, and it appears to be a dimer with equal sized subunits. Similarly, Whiting & Granick (101) reported that ALA synthetase purified 120-fold from chick embryo liver mitochondria has a molecular weight of 87,000 and is composed of 49,000 dalton subunits. In the absence of glycine, the pyridoxal phosphate appears to be bound in Schiff base linkage to the ϵ-amino group of a lysine residue on the enzyme (58, 101). Maximal enzymatic activity was 20.5 moles ALA-hr^{-1}-mg^{-1} protein at 37° for the chick liver enzyme (101) and 150 moles ALA-hr^{-1}-mg^{-1} protein for the *R. spheroides* enzyme (58). Affinity of the enzyme for substrates and cofactors varies with the source of enzyme and perhaps is sensitive to treatment during isolation. The K_m for glycine has been reported at 2 to 10 mM for enzyme derived from animal sources, and from 0.1 to 30 mM for *R. spheroides* ALA synthetase. K_m values for succinyl CoA range from 5 to 70 μM, and from 2 to 10 μM for pyridoxal phosphate (37, 101).

Occurrence of ALA Synthetase

ALA synthetase was originally described in extracts from photosynthetic bacteria (40) and from avian erythrocytes (24). Activity has subsequently been reported in diverse sources including bacteria, yeast, avian and mammalian liver and blood cells, and bone marrow (37). In animal cells, ALA synthetase is usually found within the mitochondria (76). This location places the enzyme near a source of the substrate succinyl CoA and also near the site of the terminal steps of heme synthesis. The physical proximity of the initial and final steps in the heme pathway may be important for feedback regulation of the pathway (see section on Regulation). In yeast cells, however, activity may be present in both the mitochondria and the cytoplasm (46).

ALA FORMATION IN PLANTS

Unlike the case for animals and bacteria, the precise mode of ALA formation in plants is not yet known. We will now examine evidence for and against the presence of ALA synthetase in plants and consider the proposed pathways.

Detection of ALA and Assays for ALA Synthetase

ALA synthetase is usually assayed by incubation of a cell extract with glycine, pyridoxal phosphate, and either succinyl CoA or a succinyl CoA generating system (succinate + CoA + ATP, or α-ketoglutarate + NAD + CoA) followed by colorimetric measurement of the accumulated ALA. After the incubation is stopped by addition of trichloroacetic acid or perchloric acid to precipitate protein, the supernatant is heated either with acetylacetone at pH 4.6 or with ethylacetoacetate at pH 6.8 (52). These treatments result in condensation with ALA, to form a pyrrole with a free α-position. The pyrrole is subsequently detected by formation of a highly colored Ehrlich salt upon exposure to p-dimethylaminobenzaldehyde in strong acid solution. Because in crude extracts there may be substances other than ALA which can give positive Ehrlich tests, it is important to characterize the ALA-pyrrole-Ehrlich salt spectrophotometrically (it has a peak at 553 nm and a shoulder at 520 nm). It is also desirable to compare the chromatographic behavior of the ALA and ALA-pyrrole with authentic materials to assure positive identification of the ALA.

Sensitive ALA synthetase assays employing radiotracers have recently been developed. These all require extensive purification to separate the ALA from radioactive substances and other contaminants (11, 35). Positive identification of ALA is difficult with these radioassays.

Unsuccessful Attempts at ALA Synthetase Detection

A number of investigators have reported negative results of attempts at ALA synthetase detection in plant extracts (5, 21, 66–68, 90). The methods employed included colorimetric (5, 21) and radiotracer (21, 66–68) assays. Gassman reported that extracts of *Chlorella* and angiosperm leaves contain substances that inhibit ALA synthetase from *R. spheroides* (21). He suggested that the presence of the inhibitors might prevent detection of ALA synthetase present in plant extracts. Inhibitors of ALA synthetase have been found in *Chlorella* by other investigators also, but the degree of inhibition was not sufficient to account for the total lack of ALA synthetase activity in the *Chlorella* extracts (Beale, unpublished).

Reports of ALA Synthetase in Plant Extracts

The term "ALA synthetase" has been used by some investigators to indicate the formation of ALA in their preparations, rather than to imply a specific enzymatic activity (79–81, 93a). The possibility of confusion exists when the name of a particular enzyme is employed in this more general sense.

Evidence supporting the formation of ALA via ALA synthetase in plants has been presented in a few reports. The evidence falls into two categories: (*a*) glycine- and succinyl CoA-dependent formation of ALA in plant extracts; (*b*) incorporation of radioactivity from ^{14}C-labeled glycine or succinate into ALA or chlorophyll by whole plants, tissues, or isolated plastids. Each category of evidence will be examined separately.

DETECTION BASED ON COLORIMETRIC ASSAY   In 1971 Wider de Xifra et al (102) reported the occurrence of ALA synthetase activity in extracts of cultured soybean callus cells. These cells, which did not form appreciable quantities of chlorophyll, had maximum ALA forming ability 11 days after transfer to new culture medium. Maximum activity of the cell extracts occurred after 40 min of storage at 4–6°, and activity could be increased by passage of the crude extract through Sephadex G-25. The ALA product was identified by thin layer chromatography. ALA forming activity was found to increase when the cells were incubated in the light and to be inhibited when exogenous ALA was supplied during incubation in the light or dark (3). These investigators did not report evidence that the reaction they observed was actually glycine and succinyl CoA dependent. Concentration dependence on substrates and cofactor was not reported, and neither rate dependence on protein concentration nor inactivity of heat-denatured protein was shown.

When potatoes are stored at low temperature in weak light, the skins become green with chlorophyll. Ramaswamy & Nair (69) have studied this process, and they reported the presence of ALA synthetase activity in extracts of the skins. Maximum activity was reached after 3 weeks of storage at 0–4° under 30–40 lux light intensity. Enzyme was extracted by grinding the peelings in cold phosphate buffer and purified by acetone precipitation. Assay of ALA was by colorimetry, but absorption spectra were not reported. ALA was identified by paper chromatography. Maximal activity required addition of pyridoxal phosphate, $MgCl_2$, ATP, and succinyl CoA synthetase, in addition to glycine and succinate. Experiments with ^{14}C-labeled glycine and succinate indicated that they are incorporated in equimolar amounts into ALA, and that both substances are required in order for either one to be incorporated. A later report from that laboratory (70) indicated that the ALA synthetase activity may be unique to greening potato tuber peels because greening leaves did not show activity, and they had a different pattern of incorporation of label from substrate (see below).

A third report claiming detection of ALA synthetase activity by colorimetry may be in error (30). The authors employed trichloroacetic acid containing $HgCl_2$ to stop the enzyme reaction and precipitate protein. Hg^{2+} has been found to prevent coupling of ALA with acetylacetone or ethylacetoacetate, and thus it prevents the generation of the pyrrole that reacts with Ehrlich reagent to form the colored species (Beale, unpublished). No data were presented in this report identifying the enzymatic reaction product as ALA.

DETECTION BASED ON RADIOISOTOPE INCORPORATION   Even before the discovery of ALA synthetase in animals and bacteria, early workers attempted to trace the biosynthetic pathway of chlorophyll by incubating intact *Chlorella* cells with various radioactive compounds. Della Rosa et al (16) found that both carbon atoms of glycine were incorporated into chlorophyll, but to a lesser extent than are the carbon atoms of acetate. Degradation of the chlorophyll molecules revealed that much of the radioactivity was incorporated into the tetrapyrrole-derived portion of the chlorophyll molecules. These results are difficult to interpret as either favoring or not favoring the ALA synthetase route of formation because of the relatively low levels of incorporation (1.5 to 6%) and the extremely long incubation periods (5 to 6 days). It is now well known that glycine decarboxylation occurs rapidly in plants, and the resulting fragments can be randomized over the entire metabolic carbon pool (103). Brzeski & Rücker (13) also incubated *Chlorella* cells with specifically labeled ^{14}C-glycine, but with much shorter incubation times of 1 and 6 hr. They also obtained incorporation of both carbon atoms of glycine into chlorophyll. However, since they did not degrade the chlorophyll molecules, there is no certainty that the ^{14}C was located in the tetrapyrrole-derived portion of the chlorophyll. Similarly, Roberts & Perkins (74, 75) found that both carbon atoms of glycine were incorporated into chlorophyll in greening wheat leaves. Although degradation of the chlorophyll molecules was carried out as far as dephytylization, demethylation of the phorbide was not performed, thus allowing the possibility that all or most of the labeled carbon resided in the nontetrapyrrole-derived methyl carbon atom. In these experiments, acetate was able to label the chlorophyll about as well as glycine.

Other workers have concluded that ALA synthetase is present, based on the ability of ^{14}C-succinate or ^{14}C-glycine to label chlorophyll or ALA, either in whole tissues (32a, 49, 100) or in chloroplast preparations (55, 91), but important control experiments were not reported. In particular: (a) glycine or succinate must be shown to donate carbon more readily than more general metabolic intermediates such as acetate; (b) the label must be specifically incorporated, i.e. C_2 of glycine must be incorporated primarily into C_5 of ALA or into the tetrapyrrole portion of chlorophyll, and C_1 of glycine should be only poorly incorporated compared to C_2; (c) in whole tissue experiments, permeability barriers to substrates must be shown not to be responsible for differential ability of the various compounds to donate label; (d) the products must be unequivocally demonstrated to be radiochemically pure.

Alternative Pathways for ALA Formation

From the above discussion it is evident that the existence of ALA synthetase in plants has not been demonstrated beyond reasonable doubt. Its presence has been most strongly suggested in two unusual systems—callus culture of soybeans and potato peels—neither of which may have any relevance to greening leaf tissue that performs the bulk of tetrapyrrole synthesis in plants.

Because of the general inability to find ALA synthetase in plants, especially in greening tissues which would logically be expected to form large amounts of ALA, some workers have considered other possible routes to ALA.

One commonly considered ALA precursor is γ,δ-dioxovaleric acid (DOVA) (Figure 4), which would be transformed to ALA by transamination. DOVA was first postulated by Shemin & Russell (85) to be a product of ALA catabolism in a "succinate-glycine" cycle that would effectively transfer the C_2 of glycine to the ureido group of purines. Also, oxidation of DOVA at the aldehyde group would yield α-ketoglutarate (85). Although the "succinate-glycine" cycle has not yet been shown to be of physiological significance, a transaminase activity capable of inter-converting ALA and DOVA has been detected, first in rat tissues (42, 45) and then in bacteria (2), the photosynthetic bacterium R. spheroides (25, 60, 93), and in Chlorella (22, 23) and bean leaves (22). The presence of DOVA was not reported in any of these systems, suggesting that possibly the observed activity was due to an enzyme that normally serves to catalyze other transaminations. Alternatively, the DOVA transaminase could serve to degrade ALA to DOVA, which might then be rapidly oxidized to α-ketoglutarate in vivo. Although formation of ALA via DOVA transamination has not been considered important in organisms that have ALA synthetase, this route or a closely related one has been proposed to operate in plants where the presence of ALA synthetase is still in doubt (22).

Recent results indicate the operation of an alternative route of ALA formation in plants, utilizing the intact carbon skeleton of glutamate or α-ketoglutarate and not involving ALA synthetase. These results will be examined next.

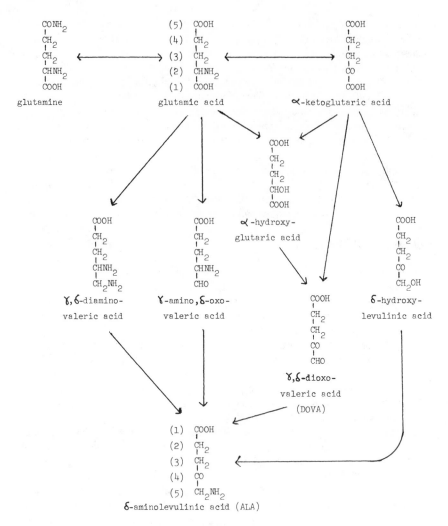

Figure 4 Hypothetical pathways for ALA formation from the intact carbon skeleton of glutamic acid. Numbers in parentheses indicate the conventional numbering of the carbon atoms of glutamic acid and ALA.

LEVULINIC ACID, A TOOL FOR THE STUDY OF ALA FORMATION In their studies on the mechanism of action of ALA dehydrase, Nandi & Shemin (57) employed levulinic acid as a competitive inhibitor of the enzyme. Later it was found that levulinic acid can act in vivo in organisms that are actively synthesizing tetrapyrroles (4, 5). The inhibitor causes a partial block in tetrapyrrole synthesis and an intracellular accumulation of ALA. Often some of the ALA is excreted from or leaks out of the cells. Experiments with ^{14}C-labeled levulinic acid indicate that ALA was formed from cellular precursors and not by amination of the added levulinic acid (5, 79). Preliminary studies (4) constituted the first direct demonstration that ALA is indeed formed in plants. Conditions were found where levulinic acid seems not to interfere with cellular functions other than to partially inhibit tetrapyrrole formation. Under these conditions, the accumulated ALA was stoichiometrically related to the deficit in chlorophyll formed (4), indicating that the accumulated ALA was intended for chlorophyll synthesis. Levulinic acid-induced ALA accumulation was first reported in *Chlorella* (4, 5) and soon thereafter in *Euglena* (73), maize (31, 43), bean leaves (8, 31, 43), cucumber cotyledons (8), barley leaves (8), *Cyanidium caldarium* (38), *Scenedesmus* (63), mustard seedlings (51), and root cultures of carrot (65) and peanut (93a). The technique has also been used with bacterial (33), blue-green algal (40a), and animal (9) ALA-forming cells. The use of levulinic acid, in addition to providing evidence that plants produce ALA and that this ALA is a precursor of chlorophyll, also allowed the study of this rate-limiting step of the pathway (see section on Regulation). Moreover, the early steps of the pathway could now be probed more directly than previously, because ALA is smaller, simpler, and closer biochemically to the process of its formation than is chlorophyll.

FORMATION OF ^{14}C-ALA FROM VARIOUS COMPOUNDS BY INTACT GREENING TISSUES   Excised cucumber cotyledons were allowed to become green in a bathing solution containing levulinic acid plus a ^{14}C-labeled compound. After 4 hr of incubation in the light, the cotyledons were homogenized and the accumulated ALA was extracted, purified by column chromatography, chemical reaction, and solvent extraction, and its radioactivity was measured by liquid scintillation counting (7). It was found that both glycine and succinate were relatively poor contributors of carbon to ALA. Moreover, both carbon atoms of glycine contributed equally, and neither was as efficiently incorporated as the more metabolically general compound acetate (7). On the other hand, the five-carbon compounds glutamate, glutamine, and α-ketoglutarate, were relatively good donors of carbon to ALA. Surprisingly, C_1 of glutamate was as effective as the internal carbon atoms in labeling ALA (see Figure 4 for carbon numbering conventions). Reference to Figure 3 indicates that these results are incompatible with the ALA synthetase route of ALA formation: (*a*) in the ALA synthetase reaction, C_1 of glycine is lost as CO_2, and only C_2 is incorporated; (*b*) if glutamate were serving as an indirect source of carbon, via α-ketoglutarate and succinyl CoA, C_1 of glutamate would be lost as CO_2 at the α-ketoglutarate dehydrogenase step, and only carbon atoms 2 through 5 would enter ALA; (*c*) in the ALA synthetase route, the direct precursors, glycine and succinate, should be more efficient donors of carbon than the metabolically more distant acetate or glutamate.

Results similar to the above were found with bean and barley leaves (9). Avian blood, a tissue known to contain ALA synthetase, had a ^{14}C incorporation pattern very different from the plants, and this pattern was compatible with the ALA synthetase route (9). The plant ALA labeling results could not be explained by gross permeability differences to the tested compounds, because they all entered the tissues and were respired at comparable rates (9). Similar results were also obtained with maize leaves (54) and one alga, the unicellular rhodophyte *Cyanidium caldarium* (38). Results with the green alga *Chlorella fusca* (67) suggest that in this alga the ALA synthetase pathway might be operating. Glycine and succinate were better donors of carbon to ALA than were glutamate and α-ketoglutarate. Moreover, C_2 of glycine was incorporated more readily than C_1, again suggesting the presence of ALA synthetase activity. Unfortunately, the permeability of the cells to the various ^{14}C compounds was not measured, either directly or indirectly by measurement of their ability to form CO_2 by respiration. Moreover, the long incubation time of 6 hr in an organism that is developing the capacity for photosynthetic carbon fixation might result in indirect incorporation of ^{14}C that has entered the general metabolic pools. Nevertheless, this report suggests that some greening plants, under some conditions, may contain ALA synthetase activity.

Hendry & Stobart (32a) have reported the interesting observation that etiolated barley leaves incorporated ^{14}C-glycine into the small amount of ALA that accumulated in the presence of levulinic acid. However, after 4 hr of preillumination, ^{14}C-glycine was not incorporated into the larger amounts of ALA that were produced during the stage of rapid greening. These results can be interpreted as suggesting the operation of two ALA forming pathways: one utilizing glycine and not being involved in the synthesis of chlorophyll, and the other, not utilizing glycine, that produces the pool of ALA which is used for chlorophyll (and perhaps heme) synthesis in the developing plastids. In this study, the positions of ^{14}C within the glycine and ALA molecules were not reported. Studies of the specificity of label transfer from glycine to ALA could resolve the question of whether the route was direct or indirect.

SPECIFICITY OF ^{14}C INCORPORATION INTO ALA BY INTACT GREENING PLANT TISSUES   The specific pattern of incorporation—which carbon atom of the substrate becomes which carbon atom of the product—can reveal information about the pathway of incorporation and the directness of the pathway. For example, C_2 of glycine becomes C_5 of ALA in the ALA synthetase reaction (85) (Figure 3). Any C_2 of glycine that appears elsewhere in ALA, and any C_1 of glycine that enters ALA at all, is due to indirect incorporation.

Greening barley leaves were incubated with levulinic acid plus ^{14}C-glutamate labeled either in C_1 or in C_3 and C_4. The accumulated ALA was degraded by periodate cleavage (86), and the C_5 fragment was separated from the C_1–C_4 fragment. The results indicated that C_1 of glutamate was incorporated predominantly into C_5 of ALA, while C_3 and C_4 of glutamate labeled only the C_1-C_4 fragment of ALA (6, 10). These results are clearly incompatible with the ALA synthetase route, wherein C_1 of glutamate should not appear in ALA at all, while C_3 and C_4 should be incorporated only indirectly, via α-ketoglutarate and succinyl CoA.

The specific pattern of incorporation of glutamate into ALA was subsequently reported in greening maize leaves (54) and in *C. caldarium* (38). In *C. caldarium*, α-ketoglutarate was found to have a specificity of label donation to ALA similar to that of glutamate: C_1 of α-ketoglutarate contributed label mainly to C_5 of ALA, whereas C_5 of α-ketoglutarate labeled the C_1-C_4 fragment of ALA. C_2 of glycine was found to label both fragments of ALA to a very small extent (38). In both maize (54) and *C. caldarium* (38), α-ketoglutarate incorporation was not as specific as glutamate incorporation, indicating randomization and suggesting that either the route of incorporation into ALA is not as direct from α-ketoglutarate as from glutamate, or that α-ketoglutarate more readily enters a general metabolic stream.

Two reports have appeared which suggest that the above pattern of incorporation is not universal in plants. Ramaswamy & Nair (70) found that greening leaves of gram (*Phaseolus radiatus*) have a label incorporation pattern similar to barley, maize and *C. caldarium*—low but equal incorporation of either carbon atom of glycine, low incorporation of succinate, and a relatively high level of incorporation of all of the carbon atoms of glutamate. On the other hand, the pattern of label incorporation was very different in the case of greening potato peels. These authors had previously reported the detection of ALA synthetase activity in greening potato peels (69), and the pattern of label incorporation in that tissue is consistent with the ALA synthetase pathway: glutamate was a poorer donor of label to ALA than was either glycine or succinate. Only C_2 of glycine was incorporated, and this carbon was found predominantly in C_5 of ALA, while carbon atoms of glutamate appeared only in the C_1-C_4 fragment of ALA.

It appears that the greening potato peel provides the strongest case at present for the operation of ALA synthetase in plant tissue. The unusual nature of that system, however, prevents generalization to other plant systems. The evidence on specific label incorporation into ALA by leaf tissues that are in the process of developing photosynthetic competence indicates the operation of a biosynthetic route that does not involve ALA synthetase, and in which glutamate or α-ketoglutarate are rather direct ALA precursors.

SPECIFICITY OF ^{14}C INCORPORATION INTO PORPHYRINS AND CHLORO-PHYLL BY INTACT GREENING PLANT TISSUES In the earlier discussion on radioisotope incorporation into chlorophyll, it was concluded that interpretation of results is difficult because not all of the chlorophyll molecule is tetrapyrrole-derived. Some workers failed to make the distinction between label incorporation into whole chlorophyll and into its tetrapyrrole moiety. Recently, other workers have studied ^{14}C incorporation into chlorophyll and porphyrins. Their results are consistent with the operation of alternative pathways to ALA, and thus support the conclusions reached from the results with ^{14}C incorporation into ALA in greening leaf tissues and *C. caldarium*.

Castelfranco & Jones (14) reported that in greening barley leaves, glutamate was more effective than glycine in donating ^{14}C to both protoheme and pheophorbide (derived from chlorophyll by removal of phytol and Mg). Low levels of incorporation of both carbon atoms of glycine were observed. Glutamate containing ^{14}C, either in C_1 or uniformly distributed, labeled protoheme equally well, while [[14]C_1]-glutamate was somewhat more effective than uniformly labeled glutamate in labeling the pheophorbide. It was also noted that glycine and glutamate were taken up equally well into the tissues, and that the intracellular pools of glutamate and glycine were 670 and 140 nmoles-g^{-1} fresh weight respectively, indicating that simple dilution of exogenous substrate by endogenous pools could not account for their results.

Wellburn (99) incubated greening oat leaves with citric acid specifically labeled in C_1 and C_5. After 24 hr, the newly formed chlorophyll was isolated and chemically degraded into hematinic imide and methylethylmaleimide by chromic acid oxidation. The degradation products were purified and their radioactivity was determined. If ALA arose via ALA synthetase, only C_1 would be labeled from the 1,5-[^{14}C]-citric acid, whereas ALA formation from the citric acid via glutamate or α-ketoglutarate directly would result in ^{14}C in both C_1 and C_5 of ALA. Tracing the route through chlorophyll and then to the degradation products, it can be shown that if only C_1 of ALA is labeled, then only the hematinic imide fragment of chlorophyll would have label, whereas if both C_1 and C_5 of ALA are labeled, then the ratio of label in hematinic imide to the methylethylmaleimide would be 2:1. The actual ratio found was 1.4:1 to 1.2:1 in duplicate experiments. While generally supporting the direct formation of ALA from a 5-carbon precursor, the above results could also be obtained by randomization of the label from citric acid during the long incubation period of 24 hr, with resulting indirect incorporation of label into ALA.

Although the results with whole tissues are consistent with ALA formation from the intact carbon skeleton of glutamate, they do not provide conclusive evidence for the reasons indicated in each case.

IN VITRO FORMATION OF ALA AND PORPHYRINS   Two laboratories have reported the formation of ^{14}C-labeled ALA by isolated chloroplasts. Gough & Kannangara (26) incubated chloroplasts from immature spinach leaves with ^{14}C-α-ketoglutarate and measured ^{14}C incorporation into ALA which accumulated in the presence of levulinic acid. α-Ketoglutarate with ^{14}C either in C_1 only or uniformly distributed was equally able to contribute label to ALA. Activity was confined to chloroplasts, was absent in mitochondria and microbodies, and was stimulated by light. Chloroplasts from mature leaves were inactive. Activity was not affected by physiological concentrations of heme or protoporphyrin IX. The authors did not report on the location of the ^{14}C within the ALA molecule, nor whether glycine or succinate could also contribute ^{14}C to ALA in their system.

Weinstein & Castelfranco (98) have reported the incorporation of ^{14}C-glutamate into ALA by chloroplasts isolated from greening cucumber cotyledons. Activity was stimulated by ATP. No specificity of incorporation was stated. These authors also reported (15a, 97) that glutamate is incorporated into protoporphyrin IX by intact chloroplasts. Both ATP and molecular oxygen were required for this activity.

While these experiments with isolated plastics are consistent with the pathway of ALA formation from α-ketoglutarate or glutamate, not involving ALA synthetase, the results are still too preliminary to be more than suggestive.

At the beginning of this section on alternative pathways for ALA formation, the DOVA transaminase reaction was described. This reaction has been proposed as a step in the conversion of glutamate or α-ketoglutarate to ALA (6, 10), and such a pathway would be consistent with the measured specificity of incorporation of ^{14}C from these precursors to ALA in greening plant leaf tissues and *C. caldarium*. There are, however, other possible routes from glutamate or α-ketoglutarate to ALA that don't involve DOVA (6, 10). All of the hypothetical pathways illustrated in Figure 4 result in the same specificity of incorporation of the intact carbon skeleton of glutamate into ALA. The elucidation of the precise route of ALA synthesis will require the demonstration of enzymes catalyzing each step in the path and the correlation of their activities with rates of chlorophyll synthesis in developing plant tissues.

ALA transaminase activity in greening leaf tissue has been the subject of only one brief report by Gassman et al (22). A more thorough study of this enzyme in *Chlorella* was reported by the same investigators (23). A third report claiming detection of ALA transaminase in maize leaves (48) is subject to the limitation that DOVA was neither chemically synthesized nor chemically characterized, its identity being based on a single low electrophoretic mobility that was not corrected for solvent flow (neutral spot migration). DOVA transaminase activity in *Chlorella* (23) was measured by incubating enzyme extract with chemically synthesized DOVA and amino donor, and measuring the ALA product by standard colorimetric procedures (52). A large number of α-amino acids could serve as the amino donor, glutamate, alanine, and phenylalanine having the highest activity. K_m values for DOVA and alanine were 3.0 mM and 30 mM, respectively. DOVA transaminase activity was equal in greening and nongreening cells of a mutant *Chlorella* strain that requires light for chlorophyll formation. Results similar to those reported for *Chlorella* have been found in greening etiolated barley leaves (Beale, Gough, Gold & Granick, unpublished).

Schemes for ALA synthesis via DOVA (Figure 4) require a mechanism for DOVA formation from glutamate or α-ketoglutarate. Enzymatic formation of DOVA from α-ketoglutarate plus NADH in extracts of maize leaves has been claimed in a preliminary report (48). As stated above, the DOVA was neither chemically synthesized nor identified in this report, so that further work is necessary before the identity of the product is established as DOVA. Nevertheless, the investigators did report that the presumed DOVA synthetase reaction could be coupled to a presumed DOVA transaminase reaction, yielding ALA from α-ketoglutarate.

Although the above report on conversion of α-ketoglutarate to DOVA is the only such report in the literature, observations of the reverse reaction yielding α-ketoglutarate suggest that it may occur in two steps. Jerzykowsky et al (36) found that DOVA is converted to α-hydroxyglutarate by the glyoxylase enzyme system in beef liver, while Okuyama et al (64) reported the conversion of α-hydroxyglutarate to α-ketoglutarate by enzymes from *R. spheroides*.

Another possible route from α-ketoglutarate to ALA would be through δ-hydroxylevulinic acid. Conversion of ^{14}C-hydroxylevulinic acid to ALA has been reported in sonicated rat liver mitochondria (94), while α-ketoglutarate has been reported to be converted to α-hydroxylevinulate by α-ketoglutarate:glyoxylate carboligase, an enzyme from beef heart (77). In the latter reaction, however, C_1 of α-ketoglutarate was lost as CO_2, while both C_1 and C_2 of the product are derived from glyoxylate. This reaction sequence is therefore not in accord with the measured label incorporation from α-ketoglutarate to ALA in greening leaf tissues.

In summary, elucidation of the enzymology of an alternative plant ALA synthetic route is still at a very early stage. In most cases, only one or a few reports have appeared, and often these have been brief, preliminary accounts. While these reports are generally consistent with a pathway from glutamate or α-ketoglutarate, utilizing the intact carbon skeletons of the precursors as outlined in Figure 4, much more work is needed before the actual steps can be established. One frequently encountered difficulty is that of synthesis, purification, and characterization of DOVA. Newer methods described by Kissel and Heilmeyer (32, 42) will be of considerable help in future studies of DOVA involvement in ALA synthesis.

REGULATION OF ALA FORMATION AND CHLOROPLAST DEVELOPMENT

The process of chlorophyll biosynthesis is imbedded within the scheme of development of photosynthetic competence in chloroplasts. The onset of chlorophyll synthesis in greening leaf tissue is accompanied by a complex developmental sequence within the plastids. The two processes are interdependent to a large extent. Biochemical (43) and genetic (89) blocks in the chlorophyll pathway result in altered chloroplast morphology and arrested development of internal structure, while treatments that inhibit chloroplast structural development also inhibit chlorophyll formation (40b, 43).

Pigment Formation in Greening Tissues

The chlorophyll pathway is thought to be regulated at three places: (a) at the conversion of protochlorophyllide to chlorophyllide a, which requires light in angiosperms and some algae, but not in gymnosperms and most algae; (b) at the branch point of metal insertion into protoporphyrin IX, leading to heme in the case of iron incorporation, and to chlorophylls upon magnesium insertion; (c) at ALA formation, which is the earliest known step of the tetrapyrrole pathway. Figure 5 depicts a general scheme for regulation of tetrapyrrole synthesis in greening plant tissues.

In most cases studied, ALA formation has been found to be the rate-limiting step of chlorophyll synthesis. Etiolated leaves contain all of the enzymes required for chlorophyll synthesis from ALA. They are all present in dark grown tissue, and no further enzyme synthesis is required for chlorophyll synthesis from ALA upon exposure to light (56, 79, 80). In the dark, large amounts of protochlorophyllide accumulate when leaf tissues are incubated with ALA (15, 88), and some of this protochlorophyllide is converted to chlorophyll upon subsequent exposure of the tissue to light (15, 88). Photoreduction of protochlorophyllide occurs on an enzyme (holochrome). Excess protochlorophyllide which is formed in the dark from exogenous ALA has a different absorption spectrum from holochrome-associated protochlorophyllide, and the two spectral forms of protochlorophyllide are partially interconvertible.

When etiolated leaves are first exposed to light, after the initial photoreduction of holochrome-associated protochlorophyllide there is a lag phase of a few hours duration before the onset of rapid chlorophyll synthesis. The lag phase can be eliminated by preincubation of the tissue with exogenous ALA (15, 88). In the green algae *Chlorella prototothecoides* (61) and *Golenkinia minutissima* (19), exogenous ALA allows the cells to overcome the inhibition of chlorophyll synthesis caused by darkness and glucose or acetate. In *C. caldarium,* which normally requires light for chlorophyll and phycobilin synthesis, exogenous ALA in the light or dark causes the formation of large amounts of phycocyanobilin, the chromophore of phycocyanin, and some of the pigment is excreted into the medium (92).

Euglena gracilis also has a lag phase of chlorophyll biosynthesis upon exposure of dark-grown cells to light, but in this organism added ALA does not overcome the lag (34, 73, 82), indicating a different state of plastid development in the dark

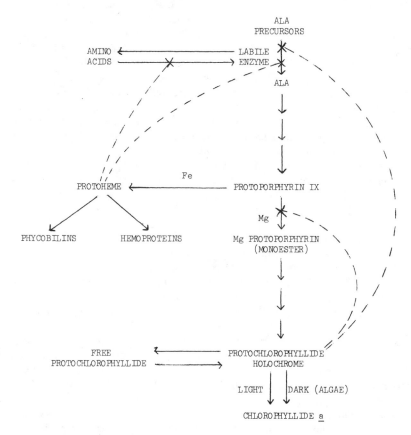

Figure 5 Regulation of chlorophyll synthesis in greening leaves. Dashed lines and crosses indicate proposed negative feedback loops.

than is the case in higher plant leaves and other algae. In some ways, the response in *Euglena* resembles that occurring in very young tissues of higher plants, where instead of etioplasts, only small, undeveloped proplastids are found (82, 89).

Although *Euglena* does not appear to contain the phytochrome system, there is evidence that plastid development is under the control of two chromophore systems: one is sensitive to both red and blue light, is present within the plastids, and is probably identical with protochlorophyllide; the other is cytoplasmic and responds to blue light alone (82). Both systems have been found to be necessary for complete development of the plastids, but the nature of their influence on chlorophyll formation has not been demonstrated directly.

ALA Formation in Greening Tissues

After it was discovered that the ALA dehydrase inhibitor levulinic acid causes intracellular accumulation of ALA, it became possible to study the regulation of ALA formation more directly than through observation of chlorophyll accumulation. Preliminary work (4) showed a stoichiometric relationship between the amount of ALA accumulated and the deficit in chlorophyll synthesis caused by administration of levulinic acid to *Chlorella vulgaris*. This stoichiometry has subsequently been observed with the algae *C. fusca* (67), *Euglena gracilis* (73), and *Cyanidium caldarium* (38), as well as in greening tissues of maize (43), cucumber (8), and mustard (51). In barley leaves, total ALA formed in the presence of levulinic acid was equal to only 70% of the deficit in chlorophyll synthesis, perhaps because of other inhibitory effects of the levulinic acid or the accumulated ALA (8). On the other hand, in bean leaves (43) and *Scenedesmus obliquus* cells (63), the accumulated ALA was greater than could be accounted for by the deficit in chlorophyll formation. These differences can be accounted for by different degrees of regulatory control over ALA formation. In organisms exhibiting exact equivalence of ALA accumulation to chlorophyll deficit, the ALA forming system may be in a "free-running" state, completely derepressed and uninhibited. There would be no further stimulation of ALA synthesis caused by interruption of negative feedback loops between chlorophyll and ALA forming steps. On the other hand, in bean leaves and *S. obliquus* cells ALA formation may be under closer regulatory control, so that when levulinic acid is added, the ALA forming system responds to lowered chlorophyll synthesis by compensatory formation of larger quantities of ALA.

In tissues that normally require light for chlorophyll synthesis, light is required for continued formation of ALA in the presence of levulinic acid. When greening tissues are returned to the dark, chlorophyll synthesis ceases immediately. If levulinic acid is present, ALA accumulation also ceases, but not immediately (20, 63). The period between the onset of darkness and the cessation of ALA formation may represent the time required for the buildup of a feedback of ALA synthesis. If the inhibitor is a tetrapyrrole, e.g. protoporphyrin IX, protoheme, or protochlorophyllide, its buildup would be slowed in the presence of levulinic acid. The accumulation of tetrapyrrolic chlorophyll precursors when chlorophyll synthesis is rapidly halted by darkness would then be the internal signal to the cells to stop ALA synthesis.

In photosynthetic bacteria, ALA synthetase is inhibited and its formation is repressed by low concentrations of heme (47). Heme also represses ALA synthetase formation in animal cells (29), and it probably inhibits the enzyme as well. There is indirect evidence that heme inhibits ALA formation in plants. Chelators of ferrous iron, such as α,α-dipyridyl, stimulate porphyrin formation in etiolated leaves (17, 28). Moreover, the stimulation of porphyrin formation caused by addition of α-α-dipyridyl to greening bean leaves is accompanied by a fall in the heme content of the leaves (21a). α,α-Dipyridyl has also been reported to stimulate the incorporation of ^{14}C-glutamate into ALA and Mg protoporphyrin IX in chloroplasts isolated from greening cucumber cotyledons (15a, 98). The chelators may function by preventing heme formation, and in the absence of heme, ALA formation escapes regulatory control and becomes derepressed. It is of interest in this regard that in rapidly greening barley leaves, considerable turnover of heme has been reported to occur (14). Although heme has been found to inhibit chlorophyll synthesis in *Chlamydomonas reinhardii* (33a), the high concentration employed [500 μM, compared to 0.1 μM effective concentration in photosynthetic bacteria (13a)] and the lack of demonstrated site of action or specificity of the inhibition renders interpretation difficult. Gough & Kannangara (26) reported that 200 μM heme did not inhibit ALA formation from ^{14}C-α-ketoglutarate in greening spinach chloroplasts. Moreover, α,α-dipyridyl may be exerting its effect at sites other than ALA formation, and through mechanisms other than prevention of heme formation. The chelator has been reported to stimulate the formation of Mg protoporphyrin IX from both ALA (15a) and protoporphyrin IX (89a) in plastids obtained from greening cucumber cotyledons.

Photosynthetic bacteria respond to high oxygen tension by immediately ceasing bacteriochlorophyll synthesis. Oxygen appears to act directly at the step of magnesium insertion and also indirectly at ALA synthetase inactivation [see (29) for a discussion of regulation of bacteriochlorophyll synthesis]. These effects of oxygen would not be expected to be observed in plants, because unlike the bacteria, plants are aerobic photosynthesizers, and light, rather than low oxygen tension, serves as the primary developmental switch for generation of photosynthetic competence. Contrary to bacteria, in plant tissues oxygen is required for both chlorophyll synthesis and ALA formation in the presence of levulinic acid (8).

It appears that the phytochrome system may be involved in the greening process in higher plants. Masoner & Kasemir (51) have reported that preillumination of etiolated mustard seedlings with red light eliminates the lag phase of greening upon subsequent light exposure. If the red light preillumination is followed by far-red preillumination, the lag phase is once again observed upon subsequent light exposure. Thus the effect of red light is photoreversible by far-red light. In maize leaves (44) preillumination with either red or far-red light causes an increase in the amount of ALA formed during subsequent white light illumination. While red light might act by phototransforming the protochlorophyllide present in the etiolated leaves, far-red light was reported not to cause the transformation, and was therefore suggested to act through another chromophore, perhaps phytochrome (44).

Site of ALA Formation during Greening

Evidence bearing on the intracellular site or sites of ALA formation is very preliminary. Available evidence is consistent with the location being within the plastids. Chloroplasts are capable of chlorophyll synthesis from exogenous ALA (72). ALA dehydrase is found in chloroplasts (78, 87). Gough & Kannangara (26) reported that chloroplasts were the only subcellular fraction capable of ^{14}C-ALA formation from ^{14}C-α-ketoglutarate. Similarly, Weinstein & Castelfranco reported that glutamate stimulated protoporphyrin IX formation in plastids isolated from cucumber cotyledons (97), and that plastids are capable of forming ^{14}C-ALA (98) and Mg protoporphyrin IX (15a) from ^{14}C-glutamate.

Multiple Pathways

It is conceivable that during plant development ALA is formed at different times, or in different plant tissues, by different pathways. Perhaps mitochondria possess ALA synthetase, which is responsible for the synthesis of mitochondrial cytochromes, and developing plastids contain another ALA forming system that produces the precursors of the chloroplast tetrapyrroles. Plant mitochondria have not yet been shown to be capable of ALA synthesis. Castelfranco & Jones (14) found that heme and chlorophyll are equally labeled in greening barley leaves regardless of whether the ^{14}C-labeled substrate was a good or poor donor of label to the products studied. Their results indicate that a single path is operating with only one intracellular pool of ALA. However, in greening leaf tissue, most of the heme synthesis would be expected to occur within the developing plastids, and any mitochondrial contribution to total heme synthesis might be masked.

The results of Hendry & Stobart (32a) suggest that in barley leaves ALA is formed by the synthetase reaction only in the dark, while greening leaves utilize another pathway. Because leaves in complete darkness presumably form little or no plastid tetrapyrroles, the observed incorporation of ^{14}C-glycine into the small amount of ALA formed in the dark might be attributable to the mitochondria.

It is more revealing perhaps to examine the evidence in nongreening tissues or in tissues that are not developing photosynthetic competence. Two of these tissues, soybean callus (3, 102) and potato peels (69, 70), provide the strongest evidence for ALA synthesis via the condensation of glycine and succinyl CoA.

In summary, although the evidence is very preliminary, it seems possible that different routes of ALA formation occur within different subcellular compartments, and each may be under separate regulatory control at different stages of development. Conclusive evidence must await the demonstration of ALA synthesizing activity in vitro and identification of the subcellular location of the enzymes.

Site of Synthesis of ALA Forming Enzymes

Although the plastid appears to be the site of ALA formation in greening plants, the enzymes responsible for ALA synthesis are thought to be synthesized in the cytoplasm. Cycloheximide is a powerful inhibitor of protein synthesis on cytoplasmic ribosomes, while chloramphenicol inhibits protein synthesis on chloroplast ribosomes (1). Chlorophyll formation in plants is sensitive to both inhibitors (5, 40b, 41) but cycloheximide inhibition is more rapid and complete (5, 40a, 41, 62). Although these results strongly suggest that an enzyme responsible for ALA formation has a short lifetime in vivo, caution is required in view of reports that cycloheximide has many side effects (53).

Ribulose bisphosphate carboxylase is a plastid enzyme composed of a large and a small subunit. Both subunits are required for activity, and the large subunit has been demonstrated to be synthesized within the plastid and therefore sensitive to inhibition by chloramphenicol (1). Schneider & Beisenherz (81) found that low concentrations of chloramphenicol completely inhibit ribulose bisphosphate carboxylase formation in tobacco callus cultures, while still allowing chlorophyll synthesis. This result indicates that all of the enzymes of the chlorophyll pathway are either stable or are not synthesized in the plastid. Taken together with evidence indicating lability of the ALA forming system, the most likely conclusion is that it is not made in the plastid.

Genetic evidence also supports cytoplasmic synthesis of enzymes of the chlorophyll pathway. A number of chlorophyll mutants are known in barley (39) and *Chlamydomonas reinhardii* (95, 96). All of the mutations, including those that are thought to affect ALA forming enzymes, are inherited in a Mendelian fashion, indicating the nucleus as the site of the genes for the enzymes and implying cytoplasmic enzyme formation (39, 95, 96).

CONCLUSION

ALA is the first known intermediate committed to the tetrapyrrole biosynthetic pathway that has chlorophyll as its major product in green plants. ALA in greening leaf tissues and in some algae is formed from the intact carbon skeleton of glutamate or α-ketoglutarate, rather than by the condensation of glycine and succinyl CoA that occurs in animals and bacteria. The plant ALA forming pathway is incompletely characterized at present. It appears to operate within the chloroplasts, although the enzymes are formed in the cytoplasm and coded on nuclear genes. Different ALA forming pathways, under separate metabolic control, may exist within different plant organelles. The regulation of ALA formation is central to the coordination of chlorophyll synthesis and the development of photosynthetic competence in plants.

ACKNOWLEDGMENTS

Supported by grant No. BMS 7502289 from the National Science Foundation. I wish to thank the members of the Department of Cellular and Comparative Biology, State University of New York, Stony Brook, for their hospitality during the preparation of this article.

116   BEALE

Literature Cited

1. Arron, G. P. 1974. The use of two-dimensional polyacrylamide gel electrophoresis in the study of ribulose bisphosphate carboxylase. In *Proceedings of the Third International Congress on Photosynthesis,* ed. M. Avron, 3:2081–88. Amsterdam: Elsevier. 2194 pp.
2. Bagdasarian, M. 1958. A new transaminase of *Corynebacterium diphtheriae. Nature* 181:1399
3. Batlle, A. M. del C., Llambias, E. B. C., Wider de Xifra, E. A., Tigier, H. A. 1975. Porphyrin biosynthesis in the soybean callus tissue system. XV. The effect of growth conditions. *Int. J. Biochem.* 6:591–606
4. Beale, S. I. 1970. The biosynthesis of δ-aminolevulinic acid in *Chlorella. Plant Physiol.* 45:504–6
5. Beale, S. I. 1971. Studies on the biosynthesis and metabolism of δ-aminolevulinic acid in *Chlorella. Plant Physiol.* 48:316–19
6. Beale, S. I. 1976. The biosynthesis of δ-aminolevulinic acid in plants. *Philos. Trans. R. Soc. London Ser. B* 273:99–108
7. Beale, S. I., Castelfranco, P. A. 1973. ¹⁴C incorporation from exogenous compounds into δ-aminolevulinic acid by greening cucumber cotyledons. *Biochem. Biophys. Res. Commun.* 52:143–49 (printer's error corrected in Vol. 53)
8. Beale, S. I., Castelfranco, P. A. 1974. The biosynthesis of δ-aminolevulinic acid in higher plants. I. Accumulation of δ-aminolevulinic acid in greening plant tissues. *Plant Physiol.* 53:291–96
9. Beale, S. I., Castelfranco, P. A. 1974. The biosynthesis of δ-aminolevulinic acid in higher plants. II. Formation of ¹⁴C-δ-aminolevulinic acid from labeled precursors in greening plant tissues. *Plant Physiol.* 53:297–303
10. Beale, S. I., Gough, S. P., Granick, S. 1975. Biosynthesis of δ-aminolevulinic acid from the intact carbon skeleton of glutamic acid in greening barley. *Proc. Natl. Acad. Sci. USA* 72:2719–23
11. Bishop, D. F., Wood, W. A. 1977. An assay for δ-aminolevulinic acid synthetase based on a specific, semiautomatic determination of picomole quantities of δ-[¹⁴C]aminolevulinate. *Anal. Biochem.* 80:466–82
12. Bogorad, L. 1976. Chlorophyll biosynthesis. In *Chemistry and Biochemistry of Plant Pigments,* ed. T. W. Goodwin,

1:64–148. New York: Academic. 870 pp. 2nd ed.
13. Brzeski, W., Rücker, W. 1960. Biosynthesis of chlorophylls *a* and *b* in *Chlorella vulgaris. Nature* 185:922–23
13a. Burnham, B. F., Lascelles, J. 1963. Control of porphyrin biosynthesis through a negative-feedback mechanism. *Biochem. J.* 87:462–72
14. Castelfranco, P. A., Jones, O. T. G. 1975. Protoheme turnover and chlorophyll synthesis in greening barley tissue. *Plant Physiol.* 55:485–90
15. Castelfranco, P. A., Rich, P. M., Beale, S. I. 1974. The abolition of the lag phase in greening cucumber cotyledons by δ-aminolevulinic acid. *Plant Physiol.* 53:615–18
15a. Castelfranco, P. A., Schwarcz, S. 1978. Mg protoporphyrin IX and δ-aminolevulinic acid synthesis from glutamate in isolated greening chloroplasts. I. Mg protoporphyrin IX synthesis. *Arch. Biochem. Biophys.* In press
16. Della Rosa, R. J., Altman, K. I., Salomon, K. 1953. The biosynthesis of chlorophyll studied with labeled glycine and acetic acid. *J. Biol. Chem.* 202:771–79
17. Duggan, J., Gassman, M. 1974. Induction of porphyrin synthesis in etiolated bean leaves by chelators of iron. *Plant Physiol.* 53:206–15
18. Duranton, J., Galmiche, J.-M., Roux, E. 1958. Metabolisme des pigments chlorophylliens chez le tabac. *C. R. Acad. Sci.* 246:992–95
19. Ellis, R., Spooner, T., Yakulis, R. 1975. Regulation of chlorophyll synthesis in the green alga *Golenkinia. Plant Physiol.* 55:791–95
20. Fluhr, R., Harel, E., Klein, S., Meller, E. 1975. Control of δ-aminolevulinic acid and chlorophyll accumulation in greening maize leaves upon light-dark transitions. *Plant Physiol.* 56:497–501
21. Gassman, M. L. 1967. *Studies on the control of chlorophyll synthesis.* PhD thesis. Univ. Chicago, Ill. 86 pp.
21a. Gassman, M., Duggan, J. 1974. Chemical induction of porphyrin synthesis in higher plants. See Ref. 1, 3:2105–13
22. Gassman, M. L., Pluscec, J., Bogorad, L. 1966. δ-Aminolevulinic acid transaminase from *Chlorella* and *Phaseolus. Plant Physiol.* 41:xiv
23. Gassman, M., Pluscec, J., Bogorad, L. 1968. δ-Aminolevulinic acid transaminase in *Chlorella vulgaris. Plant Physiol.* 43:1411–14

24. Gibson, K. D., Laver, W. G., Neuberger, A. 1958. Initial stages in the biosynthesis of porphyrins. 2. The formation of δ-aminolaevulic acid from glycine and succinyl-coenzyme A by particles from chicken erythrocytes. *Biochem. J.* 70:71–81
25. Gibson, K. D., Matthew, M., Neuberger, A., Tait, G. H. 1961. Biosynthesis of porphyrins and chlorophylls. *Nature* 192:204–8
26. Gough, S. P., Kannangara, C. G. 1976. Synthesis of δ-aminolevulinic acid by isolated plastids. *Carlsberg Res. Commun.* 41:183–90
27. Granick, S. 1950. The structural and functional relationships between heme and chlorophyll. *Harvey Lect.* 44:220–45
28. Granick, S. 1959. Magnesium porphyrins formed in barley seedlings treated with delta-aminolevulinic acid. *Plant Physiol.* 34 Suppl.:xviii
29. Granick, S., Beale, S. I. 1978. Hemes, chlorophylls, and related compounds: biosynthesis and metabolic regulation. *Adv. Enzymol.* 46. In press
30. Hampp, R., Sankhla, N., Huber, W. 1975. Effect of EMD-IT-5914 on chlorophyll synthesis in leaves of *Pennisetum typhoides* seedlings. *Physiol. Plant.* 33:53–57
31. Harel, E., Klein, S. 1972. Light dependent formation of δ-aminolevulinic acid in etiolated leaves of higher plants. *Biochem. Biophys. Res. Commun.* 49:364–70
32. Heilmeyer, L. Jr. 1965. *Uber γ-δ-Dioxovaleriansäure Synthese, Vorkommen in der Natur, biologische Bedeutung.* PhD thesis. Albert-Ludwigs Univ., Freiberg, Germany. 128 pp.
32a. Hendry, G. A. F., Stobart, A. K. 1977. Glycine metabolism and chlorophyll synthesis in barley leaves. *Phytochemistry* 16:1567–70
33. Ho, Y. K., Lascelles, J. 1971. δ-Aminolevulinic acid dehydratase of *Spirillum itersonii* and the regulation of tetrapyrrole synthesis. *Arch. Biochem. Biophys.* 144:734–40
33a. Hoober, J. K., Stegeman, W. J. 1973. Control of the synthesis of a major polypeptide of chloroplast membranes in *Chlamydomonas reinhardi. J. Cell. Biol.* 56:1–12
34. Hovenkamp-Obbema, R. 1975. Effect of added aminolaevulinic acid upon synthesis of chlorophyll in *Euglena gracilis. Z. Pflanzenphysiol.* 75:1–5
35. Irving, E. A., Elliott, W. H. 1969. A sensitive radiochemical assay for δ-aminolevulinic acid synthetase. *J. Biol. Chem.* 244: 60–67
36. Jerzykowski, T., Winter, R., Matuszewski, W. 1973. γ,δ-Dioxovalerate as a substrate for the glyoxylase enzyme system. *Biochem. J.* 135:713–19
37. Jordan, P. M., Shemin, D. 1972. δ-Aminolevulinic acid synthetase. *The Enzymes* 7:339–56
38. Jurgenson, J. E., Beale, S. I., Troxler, R. F. 1976. Biosynthesis of δ-aminolevulinic acid in the unicellular rhodophyte, *Cyanidium caldarium. Biochem. Biophys. Res. Commun.* 69:149–57
39. Kahn, A., Avivi-Bleiser, N., von Wettstein, D. 1976. Genetic regulation of chlorophyll synthesis analyzed with double mutants in barley. In *Genetics and Biogenesis of Chloroplasts and Mitochondria,* ed. Th. Bücher, N. Neupert, W. Sebald, S. Werner, pp. 119–31. New York: North Holland. 895 pp.
40. Kikuchi, G., Kumar, A., Talmage, P., Shemin, D. 1958. The enzymatic synthesis of δ-aminolevulinic acid. *J. Biol. Chem.* 233:1214–19
40a. Kipe-Nolt, J. A., Stevens, S. E., Jr. 1977. δ-Aminolevulinic acid production by the blue-green alga *Argmenellum quadruplicatum* strain PR-6. *Plant Physiol.* 59 Suppl:91
40b. Kirk, J. T. O. 1974. The relation of chlorophyll synthesis to protein synthesis in the growing thylakoid membrane. *Port. Acta Biol.* 14:127–52
41. Kirk, J. T. O., Allen, R. L. 1965. Dependence of chloroplast pigment synthesis on protein synthesis: effect of actidione. *Biochem. Biophys. Res. Commun.* 6:523–30
42. Kissel, H. J., Heilmeyer, L. Jr. 1969. Nachweis und bestimmung von γ,δ-dioxovaleriansäure reversibele umwandlung von γ,δ-dioxovaleriansäure und δ-aminolävulinsäure in ratten. *Biochim. Biophys. Acta* 177:78–87
43. Klein, S., Harel, E., Neeman, E., Katz, E., Meller, E. 1975. Accumulation of δ-aminolevulinic acid and its relation to chlorophyll synthesis and development of plastid structure in greening leaves. *Plant Physiol.* 56:486–96
44. Klein, S., Katz, E., Neeman, E. 1977. Induction of δ-aminolevulinic acid formation in etiolated maize leaves controlled by two light reactions. *Plant Physiol.* 60:335–38

45. Kowalski, E., Dancewicz, A., Szot, Z. 1957. Aminolaevulinic acid transaminase activity in tissue. *Bull. Acad. Pol. Sci. Cl.2*, 5:223–26

46. Labbe-Bois, R., Volland, C. 1977. Changes in the activities of the protoheme-synthesizing system during the growth of yeast under different conditions. *Arch. Biochem. Biophys.* 179: 565–77

47. Lascelles, J., Hatch, T. P. 1969. Bacteriochlorophyll and heme synthesis in *Rhodopseudomonas spheroides:* Possible role of heme in regulation of the branched biosynthetic pathway. *J. Bacteriol.* 98:712–20

48. Lohr, J. B., Friedmann, H. C. 1976. New pathway for δ-aminolevulinic acid biosynthesis: formation from α-ketoglutaric acid by two partially purified plant enzymes. *Biochem. Biophys. Res. Commun.* 69:908–13

49. Machold, O., Stephan, U. W. 1969. The function of iron in porphyrin and chlorophyll biosynthesis. *Phytochemistry* 8:2189–92

50. Manetas, Y., Akoyunoglu, G. 1975. The stoichiometric relationship between δ-aminolevulinic acid and protochlorophyllide. *Plant Sci. Lett.* 5:375–78

51. Masoner, M., Kasemir, H. 1975. Control of chlorophyll synthesis by phytochrome. I. The effect of phytochrome on the formation of 5-aminolevulinate in mustard seedlings. *Planta* 126: 111–17

52. Mauzerall, D., Granick, S. 1956. The occurrence and determination of δ-aminolevulinic acid and porphobilinogen in urine. *J. Biol. Chem.* 219:435–46

53. McMahon, D. 1975. Cycloheximide is not a specific inhibitor of protein synthesis *in vivo. Plant Physiol.* 55:815–21

54. Meller, E., Belkin, S., Harel, E. 1975. The biosynthesis of δ-aminolevulinic acid in maize leaves. *Phytochemistry* 14:2399–2402

55. Miller, J. W., Teng, D. 1967. The purification and kinetics of aminolevulinic acid synthetase from higher plants. *Int. Congr. Biochem., 7th, Tokyo*, p. 1059

56. Nadler, K., Granick, S. 1970. Controls on chlorophyll synthesis in barley. *Plant Physiol.* 46:240–46

57. Nandi, D. L., Shemin, D. 1968. δ-Aminolevulinic acid dehydratase of *Rhodopseudomonas spheroides.* III. Mechanism of porphobilinogen synthesis. *J. Biol. Chem.* 243:1236–42

58. Nandi, D. L., Shemin, D. 1976. Quaternary structure and mechanism of action of δ-aminolevulinic acid synthetase. *Fed. Proc.* 35:1522

59. Nandi, D. L., Shemin, D. 1977. Quaternary structure of δ-aminolevulinic acid synthetase from *Rhodopseudomonas spheroides. J. Biol. Chem.* 252:2278–80

60. Neuberger, A., Turner, J. M. 1963. γ,δ-Dioxovalerate aminotransferase activity in *Rhodopseudomonas spheroides. Biochim. Biophys. Acta* 67:342–45

61. Ochiai, S., Hase, E. 1970. Studies on chlorophyll formation in *Chlorella prototothecoides.* 1. Enhancing effects of light and added δ-aminolevulinic acid, and suppressive effect of glucose on chlorophyll formation. *Plant Cell Physiol.* 11:663–73

62. Oh-hama, T., Hase, E. 1975. Syntheses of δ-aminolevulinic acid and chlorophyll during chloroplast formation in *Chlorella prototothecoides. Plant Cell Physiol.* 16:297–303

63. Oh-hama, T., Senger, H. 1975. The development of structure and function in chloroplasts of greening mutants of *Scenedesmus.* III. Biosynthesis of δ-aminolevulinic acid. *Plant Cell Physiol.* 16: 395–405

64. Okuyama, M., Tsuiki, S., Kikuchi, G. 1965. α-Ketoglutarate-dependent oxidation of glyoxylic acid catalyzed by enzymes from *Rhodopseudomonas spheroides. Biochim. Biophys. Acta* 110: 66–80

65. Pamplin, E. J., Chapman, J. M. 1975. Sucrose suppression of chlorophyll synthesis in tissue culture: Changes in the activity of the enzymes of the chlorophyll biosynthetic pathway. *J. Exp. Bot.* 26:212–20

66. Porra, R. J., Grimme, L. H. 1973. The regulation of chlorophyll formation in *Chlorella fusca* and a new assay for chlorophylls *a* and *b. Enzyme* 16: 115–23

67. Porra, R. J., Grimme, L. H. 1974. Chlorophyll synthesis and intracellular fluctuations of 5-aminolaevulinate formation during the regreening of nitrogendeficient *Chlorella fusca. Arch. Biochem. Biophys.* 164:312–21

68. Porra, R. J., Irving, E. A. 1970. Tetrapyrrole biosynthesis in plant and yeast organelles. *Biochem. J.* 116:42P

69. Ramaswamy, N. K., Nair, P. M. 1973. δ-Aminolevulinic acid synthetase from cold-stored potatoes. *Biochim. Biophys. Acta* 293:269–77

70. Ramaswamy, N. K., Nair, P. M. 1976. Pathway for the biosynthesis of delta-aminolevulinic acid in greening potatoes. *Indian J. Biochem. Biophys.* 13: 394–97

71. Rebeiz, C. A., Castelfranco, P. A. 1973. Protochlorophyll and chlorophyll biosynthesis in cell-free systems from higher plants. *Ann. Rev. Plant Physiol.* 24:129–72

72. Rebeiz, C. A., Mattheis, J. R., Smith, B. B., Rebeiz, C. C., Dayton, D. F. 1975. Chlorophyll biogenesis. Biosynthesis and accumulation of protochlorophyll by isolated etioplasts and developing chloroplasts. *Arch. Biochem. Biophys.* 171:549–67

73. Richard, F., Nigon, V. 1973. La synthése de l'acide aminolevulinique et de la chlorophylle lors de l'éclairement d' *Euglena gracilis* étiolées. *Biochim. Biophys. Acta* 313:130–49

74. Roberts, D. W. A., Perkins, H. J. 1962. Chlorophyll biosynthesis and turnover in wheat leaves. *Biochim. Biophys. Acta* 58:499–506

75. Roberts, D. W. A., Perkins, H. J. 1966. The incorporation of the two carbons of acetate and glycine into the phorbide and phytol moieties of chlorophylls *a* and *b*. *Biochim. Biophys. Acta* 127: 42–46

76. Sano, S., Granick, S. 1961. Mitochondrial coproporphyrinogen oxidase and protoporphyrin formation. *J. Biol. Chem.* 236:1173–80

77. Schlossberg, M. A., Richert, D. A., Bloom, R. J., Westerfield, W. W. 1968. Isolation and identification of 5-hydroxy-4-ketovaleric acid as a product of α-ketoglutarate:glyoxylate carboligase. *Biochemistry* 7:333–37

78. Schneider, H. A. W. 1970. Anreicherung und Eigenschaften von δ-Aminolävulinat-dehydratase aus Spinat (*Spinacea oleracea*). *Z. Pflanzenphysiol.* 62:328–42

79. Schneider, H. A. W. 1973. Regulation der chlorophyllbiosynthese. Licht- und entwicklungsbedingte Aktivitätsänderungen von vier aufeinander folgenden Enzymen der Porphyrin- und Chlorophyllbiosynthesekette. *Z. Naturforsch.* 28C:45–58

80. Schneider, H. A. W. 1976. Enzymic capacities for chlorophyll biosynthesis. Activation and *de novo* synthesis of enzymes. *Z. Naturforsch.* 31C:55–63

81. Schneider, H. A. W., Beisenherz, W. W. 1974. Determination of the sites of synthesis of chlorophyll synthesizing enzymes in cell cultures of *Nicotiana tabacum*. *Biochem. Res. Commun.* 60: 468–73

82. Schwartzbach, S. D., Schiff, J. A., Klein, S. 1976. Biosynthetic events required for lag elimination in chlorophyll synthesis in *Euglena*. *Planta* 131:1–9

83. Scott, A. I., Townsend, C. A., Okada, K., Kajiwara, M., Whitman, P. J., Cushley, R. J. 1972. Biosynthesis of corrinoids. Concerning the origin of the methyl groups in vitamin B_{12}. *J. Am. Chem. Soc.* 94:8267–69

84. Shemin, D., Bray, R. C. 1964. The biosynthesis of the corrin structure of vitamin B_{12}. *Ann. NY Acad. Sci.* 112:615–21

85. Shemin, D., Russell, C. S. 1953. δ-Aminolevulinic acid, its role in the biosynthesis of porphyrins and purines. *J. Am. Chem. Soc.* 75:4873–74

86. Shemin, D., Russell, C. S., Abramsky, T. 1955. The succinate-glycine cycle. 1. The mechanism of pyrrole synthesis. *J. Biol. Chem.* 215:613–26

87. Shibata, H., Ochiai, H. 1976. Studies on δ-aminolevulinic acid dehydratase in radish cotyledons during chloroplast development. *Plant Cell Physiol.* 17: 281–88

88. Sisler, E. C., Klein, W. H. 1963. The effect of age and various chemicals on the lag phase of chlorophyll synthesis in dark grown bean seedlings. *Physiol. Plant.* 16:315–22

89. Smillie, R. M., Nielsen, N. C., Henningsen, K. W., von Wettstein, D. 1974. Ontogeny and environmental regulation of photochemical activity in chloroplast membranes. See Ref. 1, 3: 1841–60

89a. Smith, B. B., Rebeiz, C. A. 1977. Chloroplast biogenesis: detection of Mg-protoporphyrin chelatase *in vitro*. *Arch. Biochem. Biophys.* 180:178–85

90. Tait, G. H. 1968. General aspects of haem synthesis. In *Porphyrins and Related Compounds*, ed. T. W. Goodwin, pp. 19–34. New York: Academic. 174 pp.

91. Teng, D. M. 1967. *The biosynthesis of aminolevulinic acid in relation to iron and enzyme*. PhD thesis. Utah State Univ., Logan, Utah. 77 pp.

92. Troxler, R. F., Lester, R. 1967. Biosynthesis of phycocyanobilin. *Biochemistry* 6:3840–46

93. Turner, J. M., Neuberger, A. 1970. L-Alanine:4,5-dioxovalerate aminotransferase (*Rhodopseudomonas spher-*

oides). *Methods Enzymol.* 17A:188–92

93a. Van Huystee, R. B. 1977. Porphyrin and peroxidase synthesis in cultured peanut cells. *Can. J. Bot.* 55:1340–44

94. Wang, F. K., Koch, J., Stokstad, E. L. R. 1970. Metabolism of 5-hydroxy-4-keto-valeric acid in the rat. *Biochem. Biophys. Res. Commun.* 40:576–82

95. Wang, W., Boynton, J. E., Gillham, N. W. 1977. Genetic control of chlorophyll biosynthesis: Effect of increased δ-aminolevulinic acid synthesis on the phenotype of the Y-1 mutant of *Chlamydomonas. Mol. Gen. Genet.* 152:7–12

96. Wang, W., Boynton, J. E., Gillham, N. W., Gough, S. 1975. Genetic control of chlorophyll biosynthesis in *Chlamydomonas:* Analysis of a mutant affecting synthesis of δ-aminolevulinic acid. *Cell* 6:75–84

97. Weinstein, J. D., Castelfranco, P. A. 1977. Protoporphyrin IX biosynthesis from glutamate in isolated greening chloroplasts. *Arch. Biochem. Biophys.* 178:671–73

98. Weinstein, J. D., Castelfranco, P. A. 1978. Mg protoporphyrin IX and δ-aminolevulinic acid synthesis from glutamate in isolated greening chloroplasts. II. δ-Aminolevulinic acid synthesis. *Arch. Biochem. Biophys.* In press

99. Wellburn, A. R. 1975. δ-Aminolaevulinic acid formation in greening *Avena laminae. Phytochemistry* 14:699–701

100. Wellburn, F. A. M., Wellburn, A. R. 1971. Chlorophyll synthesis by isolated intact etioplasts. *Biochem. Biophys. Res. Commun.* 45:747–50

101. Whiting, M. J., Granick, S. 1976. δ-Aminolevulinic acid synthase from chick embryo liver mitochondria. I. Purification and some properties. *J. Biol. Chem.* 251:1340–46

102. Wider de Xifra, E. A., Batlle, A. M. del C., Tigier, H. A. 1971. δ-Aminolaevulinate synthetase in extracts of cultured soybean cells *Biochim. Biophys. Acta* 235:511–17

103. Woo, K. C., Osmond, C. B. 1976. Glycine decarboxylation in mitochondria isolated from spinach leaves. *Aust. J. Plant Physiol.* 3:771–85

104. Zaman, Z., Jordan, P. M., Akhtar, M. 1973. Mechanism and stereochemistry of the 5-aminolaevulinate synthetase reaction. *Biochem. J.* 135:257–63

Ann. Rev. Plant Physiol. 1978. 29:121–48
Copyright © 1978 by Annual Reviews Inc. All rights reserved

PHYSICS OF TURGOR- AND OSMOREGULATION

❖7647

U. Zimmermann

Institute of Biophysical Chemistry, Nuclear Research Center, Jülich, FRG

CONTENTS

INTRODUCTION

Supplies of salt and water and the maintenance of turgor pressure are important prerequisites for the growth and survival of plant cells. In the course of evolution plant cells have developed efficient mechanisms in order to tolerate large changes in the salinity of the environment without detriment to their metabolic functions. The ability to adjust their internal osmotic pressure and thus turgor pressure in response to salt and water stress has been observed in many plant cells. It is seen impressively in algae living in tidal or estuarine zones which have large and rapid fluctuations in salinity. Cells in higher plant tissues have also developed fascinating osmoregulatory mechanisms in order to withstand salt stress and drought and to maintain constant turgor pressure since turgor pressure has to exceed a certain level for growth to proceed. In the past decade research into turgor- (and osmo-) regulation has revealed that the basic mechanisms underlying the adjustment of internal osmotic pressure in response to osmotic stress or growth demand may be comparable and under direct control of turgor pressure, both in higher plants and algal cells, despite their anatomical, ultrastructural, and physiological differences.

0066-4294/78/0601-0121$01.00

In this review the author will attempt, in a highly personal analysis of the available data, to elaborate on some interesting physical aspects of the fundamental processes employed in turgor regulation and turgor pressure sensing. Without doubt, any attempt to relate the bewildering array of phenomenological observations to a few fundamental processes may lead to a dangerous oversimplification of the complex force-flow relationships in cells and organs of higher plants. The author is well aware of this problem and of difficulties arising from inadequate techniques and from an over-emphasis on algal cells. On the other hand, an approach of this kind seems necessary to produce order out of a wide diversity of phenomena. It also reveals the gaps in our knowledge and thus provides a guideline for new technical developments and future experiments.

The limitations of this review prohibit a rigorous mathematical treatment of turgor regulation and the closely related field of water transport. On the other hand, omitting the mathematical side certainly makes it easier for biologists who may be unfamiliar with this subject matter to gain an insight into a field which the author believes to be of general interest to scientists working on plants.

A more rigorous mathematical treatment of aspects of water and salt transport from a biological point of view may be found in the reviews by Dainty (25, 27) and in the recent review by Zimmermann & Steudle (142). In the latter, a detailed survey of passive and active water transport across planar, folded, and composite membranes in isolated cells and tissue cell systems is presented on the basis of the thermodynamics of irreversible processes. The terminology introduced and discussed critically in that review will be used here.

METHODS FOR MEASURING AND MANIPULATING TURGOR PRESSURE

For a long time progress in the area of turgor- (and osmo-) regulation was hampered by the great experimental difficulties involved in measuring and manipulating turgor pressure directly, particularly in very small cells of higher plants. Turgor pressure has been estimated in turgid cells by means of osmotic measurements, i.e. turgor pressure was determined either from measurements of the internal and external osmolarity (freezing-point depression measurements) (65) or calculated from the osmotic pressure of the external medium required to induce "incipient" plasmolysis (100). The sources of error associated with these procedures are well known and have been discussed extensively (48, 142).

Initially the introduction of the pressure bomb technique (13, 53, 93, 116) and the vapor pressure equilibration technique (10, 11) seemed to be an important step in the right direction. These methods supplied average values both for turgor pressure and the related parameters in plant tissues (e.g. values for the elastic modulus of the cell walls; see below), but were unable to provide a satisfactory solution to the problems. The main reason for this is that on the one hand turgor pressure values of single cells are required for an understanding of the complicated water relations of higher plants (27, 142), while on the other hand so many assumptions have to be made for the calculation of bulk turgor pressure values and the values of turgor-pressure–related parameters that the validity of these estimations is considered doubtful (14). In addition, a number of terms, such as the matric potential and water potential, have not been correctly defined or used with thermodynamic exactitude. The negative values for turgor pressure derived theoretically from such experimental data render these methods even more doubtful (see 115). For a general criticism of these points the reader is advised to consult the reviews by Weatherley (118) and Zimmermann & Steudle (142). The limitations of these techniques have stimulated several laboratories in the last decade to develop methods for the direct measurement and manipulation of turgor pressure in isolated cells. Meanwhile the techniques are so advanced that the author feels justified in discussing them at the beginning of this review before considering the osmoregulatory responses of the cell, turgor-triggered processes, and turgor-sensing mechanisms.

The first direct pressure measurements in plant cells were performed by Green and co-workers (41, 42, 44), who inserted a microcapillary which was sealed at one end and filled with air into the internode of the giant algal cell *Nitella axillaris*. The air was compressed by the turgor pressure and the changes in turgor pressure were calculated (after calibration) from optical measurements of the changes in the dimensions of the air bubble (Boyle-Mariotte's law). Although this technique is of ingenious simplicity, its broader application is limited by cell size, since there is a considerable transfer of cell sap into the capillary and the resistance of the tip becomes rate-limiting when the diameter of the capillary tip is too small. As a result, the kinetics of turgor pressure changes in small cells are falsified (see below). Other sources of interference which impair accurate measurements of turgor pressure relaxation processes arise from the solubility of the gas in the water phase at various pressures and from changes in the elastic behavior of the whole cell system due the presence of the air bubble which can lead to dramatic changes in the kinetics of turgor regulation (127). The latter point is also relevant to a consideration of another method recently suggested by Zimmermann [quoted in (56)] for turgor pressure measurements following results obtained with gas vesicles in some plant cells (117a). The technique is based on the introduction of a gas bubble directly into the cell interior. This is easily achieved by means of capillaries with very narrow tips or electrode processes. The measuring principle is the same as in the method of Green and co-workers. Experiments on *Valonia utricularis* have shown that this method works in essence, but that great effort is required in order to arrive at an efficient device for pressure measurements in small plant cells. The method suffers from the same inadequacies as the technique of Green and co-workers, but offers the advantage of allowing the use of very small tip diameters so that gas bubbles can be introduced into several cells of a tissue for the measurement of pressure profiles. The main difficulty to be overcome is that this technique in its simplest form is not sufficiently sensitive to measure pressure changes of the desired order of magnitude (0.1 to 1.0 bar) with any accuracy because of the small volume of the gas bubble which must not exceed 10% of the cell volume. The pressure in the gas bubble is inversely proportional to the third power of the radius, so that the changes in diameter to be measured under the light microscope are very small in the physiological pressure range (0.1 μm).

Gutknecht and co-workers (46, 48, 49) introduced a quite different approach to the measurement and manipulation of turgor pressure in giant algal cells. A cell is perfused by means of two microcapillaries connected to a pressurized perfusion system which consists of two sealed plexiglass reservoirs pressurized by a common gas supply. The height of the inflow and outflow reservoirs is adjusted so as to maintain a gravity-driven flow. This method permits direct manipulation of turgor pressure inside the cell in small pressure ranges (up to 2 bar in *Valonia ventricosa*). The major limitation of this technique is that only giant algal cells with diameters of more than 4 mm can be used.

Several authors have attempted to manipulate turgor pressure in intact cells by applying external forces and concurrently measuring the cell response (in terms of volume changes, water flow, action potentials) (1, 34, 73, 111). The most interesting technique in this context is the one recently introduced by Ferrier & Dainty (34). In this method the external force is applied by means of a displacement transducer resting on a group of cells (8 to 30) in a single tissue layer (e.g. onion). The cells are deformed as a result of compression and the time course of displacement is measured. This technique does not permit the measurement of absolute values of turgor pressure or pressure changes inside the cell. On the other hand, some conclusions can be drawn from the kinetics of displacement as to the nature of turgor-related parameters such as the hydraulic conductivity of the cell membrane and the elastic properties of the cell wall [for criticism of this method, see (56, 142)].

Tazawa (111) and Barry (1) have independently developed a setup for measuring turgor pressure externally in an intact cell. Turgor pressure was estimated by measuring the deflection of a thin wedge resting transversely across the cell. The magnitude of the deflection is directly related to the radius and turgor pressure of the cell. This method is limited in its application to cylindrical giant algal cells and subject to various sources of error, especially to temperature fluctuations. It has been used by Barry (1) for the determination of very small turgor pressure changes (2×10^{-2} bar) in *Chara corallina* which occur during an action potential.

In contrast to all the methods discussed here, the pressure probe technique introduced by Zimmermann and co-workers (56, 103, 135) is universally applicable to cells of any size and allows the measurement of a number of cell variables, i.e. measurement of very small turgor pressure changes (0.03 bar), direct manipulation of cell turgor pressure, measurement of very small changes in volume of walled cells, and the determination of the elastic properties of the cell wall. The new version of the pressure probe (56) can be used on cells with a diameter of larger than 20 μm and thus for the first time provides direct access to the parameters of a single tissue cell. The pressure probe works on a compensation principle. A microelectrode filled with oil is introduced into the cell and the pressure inside the cell is transmitted through the oil to a plexiglass chamber also filled with oil. A pressure transducer which transforms the pressure into a proportional voltage is mounted in the chamber. The boundary between the cell sap and the oil in the tip of the capillary is adjusted by a metal plunger introduced into the chamber. The volume available to the oil in the chamber and, in turn, the position of the boundary, is changed by displacing the metal plunger by means of a micrometer screw. Pressure pulses can also be injected into the cell in this way and the cell volume change calculated concurrently from the dimensions of the metal plunger and its displacement. This technique thus allows the evaluation of the elastic properties of the cell wall (140) which require the measurement of small pressure changes and the corresponding volume changes for their calculation (see below). The simple version of the pressure probe can be applied to cells with diameters of more than 200 μm (101). In order to use it on smaller tissue cells, the volume of the measuring apparatus and its compressibility must be in the right relation to cell size and compressibility (i.e. elasticity).

This crucial point was completely overlooked by Meidner & Edwards (80; see also 32), who used essentially the same measuring principle as Zimmermann & Steudle (135) for determining turgor pressure in stomatal guard cells. Meidner & Edwards were successful in applying pressure to the guard cells in order to make them open or close, but not in recording the actual pressure inside the cell because of the compressibility of their measuring device and its unfavorable dimensions in relation to cell size. Interference effects arising from both compression and temperature fluctuations can be ignored if the effective volume of the apparatus is drastically reduced. This was achieved by Hüsken et al (56) by fixing the oil/cell sap boundary at a certain point of the capillary, thus reducing the effective volume to the volume of the sap in the very tip of the microcapillary. When shifts occur, the boundary is adjusted very rapidly (in less than 1 sec) by means of an electronic feedback mechanism based on the resistance changes of a silver wire (in reference to an external electrode) introduced into the tip of the microcapillary. By analogy with the older version of the pressure probe, pressure is applied to the cell interior by shifting the boundary by a defined amount with the metal plunger. The corresponding change in cell volume is calculated from the shift of the boundary observed under the microscope. The application of the pressure probe to plant cells is limited by the tip diameter. When the tip falls short of a certain diameter ($<$ 1 μm) the tip resistance becomes the rate-limiting step (see above), and the occurrence of capillary forces and shock waves can no longer be neglected. The pressure probe has so far been successfully used for the measurement of turgor pressure profiles and the elastic modulus of the cell wall in cells of the pepper fruit (*Capsicum annuum*) (56, 142) and in root cells of maize (*Zea mays*) (Zimmermann and co-workers, unpublished data).

THE BIPHASIC OSMOTIC REGULATORY RESPONSE

The extensive literature published to date on osmoregulation in fungi, algal cells, and higher plants has been reviewed by Cram (24), Hellebust (51), and Kauss (61, 62), with particular reference to the physiological and biochemical aspects of osmoregulation. A summary of the state of research on animals is provided by Gilles (39). The interested reader should consult these papers in order to gain an impression of the diversity of the regulatory responses in cell systems exposed to salt and water stress. Only a few topics can be covered in this review and these have been selected for their relevance to both physiological and ecological aspects of the physical regulatory responses of plant cells to osmotic stress.

Wall-less Cells

Empirically, the physical response of a cell to changes in the salinity of the environment can be divided into two processes. Single cells without walls (4, 59) or with very elastic walls (40) or organic scales (68, 72) shrink and swell very rapidly (within seconds) and markedly if they are exposed to hypertonic or hypotonic solutions. In the subsequent second phase, which is generally characterized by a substantially longer time constant (minutes and hours), a reverse volume regulation is observed which may lead to a close readjustment to the original volume. Red blood cells of various species (e.g. 74, 113) and the wall-less flagellate *Ochromonas malhamensis* (59, 61) are typical examples for the regulation of volume over a wide range of external osmotic pressures to a constant value independent of osmolarity. The first instantaneous volume change observed immediately after the onset of osmoregulation can be shown experimentally to be almost exclusively due to water flow into or out of the cell depending on the direction of the applied osmotic stress. In other words, during this phase of shrinking or swelling the intracellular concentration of osmotically active particles is changed, but not the absolute number of particles (ideal osmometer) (58). Solute transport across the membrane or metabolically induced changes in the total number of particles in the cell interior play a minor role during this phase because the hydraulic conductivity (water permeability) of the cell membrane is, as a rule, several orders of magnitude larger than both the membrane permeability to solutes and the metabolic turnover rate of osmotically active solutes in the cell interior. The half-time for water exchange and, in turn, for the volume changes of the cell is thus determined by the geometry of the cell, the elastic properties, and the hydraulic conductivity of the cell membrane. In cells which behave like ideal osmometers, volume regulation is terminated after the completion of water exchange. Osmotic equilibrium is established; that is, the small osmotic pressure difference between the cell interior and the external medium is counterbalanced by an equal but opposite hydrostatic pressure difference (turgor pressure). In hypotonic conditions excess turgor pressure and tension in the membrane are set up in the cell, whereas in hypertonic conditions low pressure is developed [which does not, however, represent a negative pressure; only the sign of the pressure gradient is negative with reference to the external pressure of 1 bar]. Although the turgor pressures which can be created in wall-less cells are relatively small [$2-3 \times 10^{-4}$ bar in red blood cells (90)], they have to be taken into account for theoretical reasons. In conditions of hypertonic stress, on the other hand, the cell is faced with the problem of water loss which is known to have detrimental effects on metabolism and growth (e.g. 29, 30, 55). Therefore, in order to withstand large fluctuations in the external osmolarity, cells have to be equipped with an adaptive mechanism which allows them to decrease or increase the total number of osmotically active particles in the cell interior.

The number of particles is regulated in the second phase of osmoregulation, in which the cell volume is shifted back to its original value by means of metabolic turnover and controlled loss or uptake of osmotically active particles. These processes are accompanied by water transport. Since the half-times of the two regulatory phases generally differ markedly, cells of various species can be shown to behave like ideal osmometers during the initial rapid phase of water exchange. The Boyle-Van't Hoff law is obeyed in *Platymonas subcordiformis* (70), *Dunaliella parva* (6), and *O. malhamensis* (60) over a wide range of osmotic pressures. Deviations which may occur for a number of reasons (52, 70) are only found under conditions of extreme hypotonic or hypertonic stress. If the maximum volume established after the completion of water transport is plotted against the inverse of the external osmotic pressure, a straight line is obtained. The intercept of this straight line with the ordinate corresponds to the nonosmotic volume, i.e. the volume of the cell which is not involved in internal osmoregulation, and this can be correlated with various cell structures such as organelles, starch grains, cell walls, and with hydration water etc. The nonosmotic volume of the fresh-water alga *O. malhamensis* and the halophilic alga *D. parva* occupies 40 to 50% (60) and 60 to 80% (89), respectively, of the total cell volume. In *P. subcordiformis* (70) the absolute value of the nonosmotic volume is constant over a large range of salinities (0.1 to 0.6 M NaCl), whereas the total cell volume decreases. Thus the relative proportion of the nonosmotic volume is shifted from 45% at low salinity to 80% at high salinity.

The biphasic kinetics of volume regulation is not always expressed as clearly as implied by this generalized discussion of experiments on certain species. For example, differences in the regulation of volume in response to hypertonic and hypotonic stress have even been reported in one and the same species. *D. parva* regulates its volume back to the original level 90 min after exposure to hypotonic stress (a transfer from 1.5 M to 0.7 M NaCl) (89). On the other hand, this algal species responds to hyperosmotic stress by rapid shrinking and the new cell volume is maintained almost constant over a period of 70 min and more without any significant tendency to revert to its original volume (89). Nevertheless, the content of osmotically active particles inside the cell is regulated by metabolic turnover after the completion of water transport (6). Kirst (70, 71) has reported similar findings for *P. subcordiformis* which has a theca consisting of organic scales embedded in a matrix. In this particular species the cell volume returns only partially to the volume of the control even in conditions of hypoosmotic stress, indicating that close readjustment of the cell volume in response to salinity changes is not always of physiological and ecological relevance. The disparity in these results may reflect either differences in the intrinsic membrane properties under hypo- and hypertonic stress [e.g. elastic properties of the cell membrane, polarity of water flow (89); see also (104) and (112); comparable salt and water permeabilities, etc] and/or inadequacies in the methods of determination. The most common method for volume determination in isolated cells is the estimation of the sedimentation volume of a pellet obtained by centrifugation, taking into account the extracellular space. Although this method yields relatively accurate values for average cell volume, it is too time-consuming for the determination of the rapid kinetics of water transport. Similar arguments apply to volume determinations by measuring the cell dimensions under the light microscope, especially if only a small number of cells is measured (52). Thus in many cases it is extremely difficult to achieve a correct temporal correlation of the measured values with the kinetics of volume regulation so that an interpretation of the present data from a physical point of view is very difficult or even impossible. The use of a Coulter counter, an electronic device for counting and measuring cells, seems to be the most promising method for future work in this field. The measurements are based on a resistance change which occurs when cells pass through an electric field set up in the orifice of the Coulter counter. The resistance change is proportional to the size of the particle (in low field ranges, see below). This method is described in more detail elsewhere (127, 131).

Some sources of error must be taken into account when using the conventional, commercially available Coulter counter system such as the one used for measurements of volume regulation in *D. parva* (89). Artifacts arise from the inhomogeneity of the electrical field and the orientation of nonspherical particles in the orifice (resulting in a skewed size distribution of the cell population) and from electrical field effects which can influence membrane permeability above a certain electric field level (dielectric breakdown, see below). Physically impeccable measurements can only be achieved with the hydrodynamically focusing Coulter counter (131, 133, 136). In this system the cells are forced to pass through the inhomogeneous field in the orifice in the same place, i.e. in the center, by means of hydrodynamic focusing. The modified version of this Coulter counter system (Pilwat et al, in preparation), which incorporates two hydrodynamically focusing orifices in parallel, allows volume changes of single isolated cells to be determined in a matter of μsec, so that considerable progress in this area can be expected in the very near future.

Walled Cells

In contrast to cells lacking walls, walled cells are capable of producing substantial internal osmotic pressures in excess and, in turn, turgor pressures which may be of the order of 20 bar or more (137), without cell rupture. The rigidity of the cell wall thus demands that turgor pressure is the dominating macroscopic parameter to be regulated during the opposite biphasic response of the cell to salt and water stress. The transport processes involved in turgor regulation are identical to those observed in the volume regulation of wall-less cells. Turgor pressure has been found to be maintained within narrow limits over wide ranges of external osmolarity in the marine algal cells of *Chaetomorpha linum* (10 bar) (66, 67), *Valonia utricularis* (1.5 bar, depending on cell size) (138), *V. macrophysa* (1.5 bar) (50), *Halicystis parvula* (0.5 bar) bar) (40) and *Codium decorticatum* (2.3 bar) (8, 67). The kinetics of the turgor regulation have been followed experimentally with the pressure probe technique in *V. utricularis* (127, 138) and found to be biphasic.[1] In general, the relative volume changes are small in contrast. They are only of the order of 0.1 to 10% per bar, i.e. the absolute volume changes are of the order of between 0.1 to 0.6 μl/bar and 5×10^{-4} to 5×10^{-1} nl/bar (for giant algal cells and tissue cells, respectively). Such small volume changes in isolated cells cannot be measured with sufficient accuracy with the sedimentation procedure and electronic volume determination methods. In addition, the anisotropic structure of the cell wall renders a determination of volume changes in isolated cells and tissue cells from the appropriate dimen-

[1]In contrast, the freshwater alga *Nitella* seems to favor a regulatory mechanism based on the maintenance of constant internal concentration rather than constant turgor pressure (82).

sional changes observed under light microscope extremely difficult. On the other hand, it is possible to measure these small volume changes with the pressure probe technique. Experimental determination of the volume changes and the theoretical calculations based on the kinetics of turgor pressure changes have shown (25, 103, 138) that cells of *Valonia, Chara,* and *Nitella* spp. behave like ideal osmometers during the first, rapid regulatory phase. In walled cells turgor pressure changes are linked to volume changes by the elastic properties of the cell wall, described by the so-called volumetric elastic modulus, ϵ : ϵ determines the slope of the pressure-volume curve of a plant cell and is defined by the following equation (86):

$$\Delta p = \epsilon \, \frac{\Delta V}{V}. \qquad \qquad 1.$$

ϵ is defined in the absence of external forces and describes the behavior of isolated cells, but not of cells embedded in a tissue [however, see (34)]. If, as a first approximation, the equation for the definition of ϵ is to be applied to tissue cells, interactions with neighboring cells and the effect of their elastic properties have to be incorporated. This means that ϵ values of single tissue cells are not necessarily comparable to those of isolated cells. By definition the parameter ϵ comprises the elastic properties of both the cell wall and the plasmalemma coupled to the cell wall. In general, the magnitude of ϵ in walled cells is determined exclusively by the elastic properties of the cell wall as demonstrated by measurements of this parameter in intact cells and isolated cell walls of Characeae (140). In walled cells with a very low ϵ value (less than 1 bar), e.g. *H. parvula* (40), the contribution of the elastic properties of the cell membrane to the overall value may be considerable. In the extreme case, that is in cells without walls, ϵ is completely determined by the elasticity of the membrane (see above). Equation 1 states that both turgor regulation in walled cells and volume regulation in wall-less cells are identical macroscopic phenomena from a physical point of view. The transition between these two "types" of regulation is fluent and dependent on the absolute value of ϵ. For geometrically simple cells such as the internodes of *Nitella* and *Chara* spp. it can be shown theoretically (see 142) that ϵ is a function of the Young's moduli, the Poisson ratios for longitudinal and transverse strain, the thickness of the cell wall, and the radius of the cell. In general, ϵ is a very complex function of cell shape (curvature) and dimensions.

The ϵ measurements in cells of various species, using the pressure probe techniques which for the first time allow a direct experimental evaluation of this parameter, provide a satisfactory insight into the complex relationships between the elastic modulus and other cell parameters. The ϵ values for the cell walls of fully turgid marine and freshwater giant algal cells are of the order of several hundred bars, whereas the corresponding values for single cells of higher plant tissues are lower by one or more orders of magnitude. The elastic modulus is a function of both turgor pressure and cell volume. The value of ϵ increases with increasing turgor pressure and cell volume (56, 104, 107, 138–140, 143). In the low pressure ranges ϵ is a linear function of pressure in a first approximation, whereas at higher pressures ϵ seems to approach a constant value. The volume dependence of ϵ is more pronounced at higher turgor pressures. For *V. utricularis* (143) ϵ ranges from 30 to 600 bar (pressure range 0.2 to 5 bar and volume range from 10 μl to 200 μl); for *Chara fragilis* (140) from 240 to 480 bar ($P=0$ to 8 bar); for *Chara intermedia* (140) from 130 to 530 bar ($P=0$ to 8 bar); for *Nitella flexilis* (140) from 50 to 300 bar ($P=0$ to 8 bar); for *N. obtusa* (142) from 80 to 550 bar ($P=0.2$ to 8 bar, 30 μl to 220 μl); for bladder cells of *Mesembryanthemum crystallinum* (107) from 5 to 110 bar ($P=0$ to 4 bar, 0.3 μl) and for *C. annuum* (56) from 8 to 25 bar ($P\sim2.5$ bar, 2.5 nl to 10 nl). The pressure dependence of ϵ is confirmed by measurements of average ϵ values in bulk tissues of various plants, using the vapor pressure technique and the pressure bomb technique (14, 53). The volume dependence of ϵ, on the other hand, could not be detected with these methods. This is hardly surprising as these techniques yield average values of tissues with locally quite different anisotropic extensibilities. In addition, these measurements are subject to several sources of error (see above) and have been recently criticized by several authors (118, 142). At first sight the volume dependence of ϵ seems surprising because for cylindrical cells theory predicts that ϵ is an inverse function of the radius. This relationship between ϵ and the radius is indeed verified when cylindrical cells of *N. flexilis* (140) and *Nitellopsis obtusa* (142), of differing radii but equal lengths, are compared. On the other hand, comparison of cells of different lengths (volume) at constant radius still reveals a marked increase in the value of ϵ with increasing volume (142). Since variations in the thickness of the cell wall alone cannot explain the increase in ϵ with increasing volume (140), the volume dependence must be due to other factors. Zimmermann & Steudle (140) discussed the volume effect in *Characean* cells in terms of two cell wall regions of different elastic extensibilities. These authors claimed that the cylindrical part of the internode had a higher ϵ value than the node region which was thought to have a very small ϵ value and thus a much higher elastic extensibility. This assumption seems to be supported by observations with the light microscope. Since the contribution of the elasticity of the cell wall in the node regions to the overall ϵ value of the cell should be larger in smaller cells, the volume dependence of ϵ is easily explained. An alternative explanation is a volume dependence arising from a stress-hardening effect since the tension T in the cell is proportional to the radius. Steudle et al (107) believe that this explanation probably holds for the bladder cells of *M. crystallinum* and the tissue cells of *C. annuum* (56).

The volume and pressure dependence of ϵ in plant cells has an important bearing on two important apparently contradictory aspects of the regulation of turgor pressure and of water relations: that is, the rate (half-time) of the response of the cell to osmotic stress and the regulation of the internal water content. It is evident from the preceding discussion that the half-time of the rapid phase of turgor regulation is controlled not only by the geometry of the cell and the hydraulic conductivity of the cell membrane, but also by the elastic properties of the cell wall. For exponential water exchange which as a rule occurs in isolated cells and cells in a tissue [demonstrated by the pressure probe technique (e.g. 103, 127)] the half-time of turgor regulation or water exchange τ for a single cell is given by the following equation:

$$\tau = \frac{\ln 2 \times V}{A \times Lp \, (\epsilon + \Pi_i)}. \qquad 2.$$

The derivation of this equation is based on the concept of water transport across a membrane barrier in terms of the thermodynamics of irreversible processes (25, 103, 138).

If the geometry of the cell (i.e. the ratio of the volume V to the area A) is excluded from our considerations, an examination of Equation 2 reveals that the half-time is inversely proportional to the hydraulic conductivity Lp and the elastic modulus ϵ since the latter is the dominating term in the brackets of the denominator. The internal osmotic pressure Π_i is usually smaller than the value of ϵ both in giant algal cells and tissue cells of higher plants. The lower the values of Lp and ϵ, the longer the half-time of water exchange. Long half-times thus imply that the cell is physically protected against short-term water and salt stress. Some authors (26, 107) have thus postulated that the values of both Lp and ϵ should be much smaller in cells of a tissue than in algal cells living in an aqueous environment. In spite of the direct methods of measurement now available, the Lp values of higher plant cells are still not known with any certainty so that the trend of the Lp values of giant algal cells and tissue cells implied by the postulate cannot be confirmed (27, 142). The reason for this is our lack of knowledge concerning the contribution of the individual pathways to water transport in a tissue. As a result, accurate calculations of Lp from pressure measurements are impossible. The ϵ values of giant algal cells and tissue cells of higher plants, on the other hand, seem to support this hypothesis whereby the volume dependence of ϵ is of physiological importance. The increase in ϵ can be so considerable that the increase in the value of the half-time with increasing geometric dimensions can be compensated or even overcompensated. Steudle et al (107) demonstrated in the bladder cells of $M.$ $crystallinum$ that the half-time was identical for different cell sizes.

While low ϵ values thus provide the cells with a high resistance to short-term fluctuations in the salinity of the environment, high ϵ values may in contrast also be of physiological and ecological advantage. A high ϵ value ensures (Equation 1) that the relative change in the water content of a cell in a tissue and, in turn, in the concentration in response to osmotic stress, is much smaller than in a cell with a low ϵ value. This may be of great ecological relevance, particularly to plants living in arid zones of the earth. A decision as to the function of ϵ of the various species in water relations cannot be made with any certainty at the present time. The role of ϵ in water relations can only be elucidated when it is known whether changes in the internal concentration or changes in turgor pressure (no matter how small these may be, such as in wall-less cells) are the signals which trigger the biochemical and biophysical regulatory processes during the second phase of osmoregulation.

THE NATURE OF OSMOTIC AGENTS

In marine algal cells of $Valonia$ spp., $Ch.$ $linum,$ $Codium$ $decorticatum,$ and $H.$ $parvula,$ the number of osmotically active molecules is preferentially regulated by changing K^+ and Cl^- (e.g. 48, 67), the main cation and anion in the vacuole [with the exception of $H.$ $parvula$ (40), where Na^+ is very high and K^+ is very low as in some higher plants]. The contribution of other ions (Na^+, Ca^{2+}, SO_4^{2-}, Mg^{2+}) to the readjustment of turgor pressure to its original value is negligible. The magnitude of the ion fluxes in these species seems to be under the direct control of turgor. Because of the special relevance of turgor-triggered processes, this subject matter will be discussed in more detail in the following chapter.

In a wide range of walled and wall-less cells and in organs of higher plants, the internal osmotic pressure and, in turn, the turgor pressure or cell volume is regulated and restored by synthesis and degradation of osmotically active organic molecules. The accumulation of organic molecules in response to increasing osmotic pressure is not unique to plant cells. The concentration of these compounds is also known to be positively correlated with the external osmotic pressure in fungi, some bacteria, and invertebrates and vertebrates (39, 51). It is of particular interest that a rather narrow range of compounds, principally polyols and dipolar nitrogen derivates, are employed in osmoregulation, thus providing a striking example of convergent evolution in the fundamental regulatory processes in response to environmental stress. The osmotic balance is preferentially readjusted by glycerol in *Dunaliella* spp. (4–6, 9), by isofloridosid in *O. malhamensis* (59, 60) and *Porphyra perforata* (61), by cyclohexane-tetrol in *Monochrysis lutheri* (23), by mannitol in *P. subcordiformis* (68, 71) and *P. suecica* (52), by sucrose in *Chlorella pyrenoidosa* (54), by proline in *Chara salina* (51, 69) and in a number of halophytes (55, 109, 114), and by (glycine-) betaine in Chenopodiaceae, Amaranthaceae, and Gramineae (109, 110, 124, 125) to name but a few examples [a more detailed survey is given by Hellebust (51)].

The apparent difference between inorganic ion regulation in giant algal cells and the regulation of organic molecules in microscopic, isolated cells and tissue cells is only superficial and probably attributable to the curious fact that the regulation of the vacuolar contents has been examined chiefly from the biophysical aspect of osmoregulation in giant algal cells (where the vacuole is directly accessible to puncture with a micropipette), whereas in microscopic cells the biochemical aspects have been of more interest to many investigators. These days more and more authors tend to believe that both types of regulation are present in every osmoregulating plant system, but that their respective macroscopically dominating contribution to the osmotic relations of the whole cell depends on the relative dimensions of the vacuole with respect to the cytoplasmic compartment. This view is supported by the recent findings of Kauss et al (63) that for the osmotic balance in *O. malhamensis* the isofloridosid production accounts for about 70% of the observed volume restoration whereas 10% is due to amino acids and 10 to 20% to K^+ uptake. In *P. subcordiformis* (68, 69, 71), where mannitol synthesis only contributes to about 50% of the osmotic pressure balance, and in *Dunaliella* spp. (9), where more than half of the external osmotic pressure is compensated by glycerol, inorganic ions are also known to participate. Kirst (personal communication) showed with C-14 fixation experiments that in cells of *V. utricularis* exposed to salinity stress in the environment the carbohydrate pattern in the cytoplasm which occupies less than 5% of the whole cell volume is changed markedly. Although the carbohydrates are still unidentified, the results indicate that the osmotic pressure in the cytoplasm of marine giant algal cells is regulated not only by inorganic ions but also by organic compounds.

Metabolic reactions and enzyme activities are very sensitive to high concentrations of salt (37, 124), whereas it is now firmly established that certain organic compounds do not act as inhibitors, even at very high concentrations. The term "compatible solute" was introduced by Borowitzka & Brown (9) for organic compounds employed in osmoregulation. It is difficult to estimate whether the internal concentration of organic molecules is sufficiently high to maintain the osmotic balance of the cytoplasm, since the precise cellular localization of these compounds is not always known with certainty. Wyn Jones and co-workers (124) have shown in three halophytic plants that the level of glycine betaine is high enough for the compound to act as the major cytoplasmic osmoticum if betaine is largely but not exclusively localized in the cytoplasm. The partial exclusion of betaine from the vacuole seems to be supported by analogous investigations on isolated vacuoles from the red beet storage tissue, using the technique of Leigh & Branton (76). Wyn Jones and co-workers (124) have thus advanced the hypothesis (with special reference to betaine regulation) that the cytoplasmic inorganic ion concentration remains fairly constant (not exceeding ca 400 mOsmol) while the osmotic adaptation of the cytoplasm in response to environmental stress is achieved by the accumulation of nontoxic organic molecules. Similar concepts for cytoplasmic osmoregulation have been proposed by several other workers for algae (51), yeast (12), higher plants (84, 108, 114), and invertebrates and vertebrates (39). From the biochemical point of view, the massive accumulation of dipolar nitrogen derivates in many species under conditions of osmotic stress appears to make substantial demands on the nitrogen economy of the plant, an aspect which warrants further intensive investigation.

It is interesting to note that the initiation of the regulation of both the inorganic ion content in the vacuole of giant algal cells (see below) and the regulation of the organic compounds in *O. malhamensis* is very rapid. This suggests a very fast recognition time of changes in turgor pressure (and volume), a point of considerable relevance to concepts of turgor-sensing mechanisms which the author will return to later. In *O. malhamensis* (59) isofloridosid synthesis is activated within 3 min of the onset of hypertonic osmoregulation and is not prevented by inhibitors of protein synthesis. The same is true for K^+ uptake, although this process is complete after 20 min, whereas the completion of isofloridosid production requires ca. 90 min. Similar results were reported for *P. subcordiformis* (68, 71). These results suggest that osmotic stress does not evoke de novo synthesis of enzymes, but activates preexisting enzymes. Although a number of enzymatic steps in the biochemical pathways of both isofloridosid and glycerol synthesis in *O. malhamensis* and *D. parva,* respectively, are known (61, 64, 77, 88), no pressure-dependent enzymes have so far been isolated, indicating strongly that the membrane integrity and its pressure (and volume) dependence is the key process in osmoregulation.

TURGOR-DEPENDENT PROCESSES

Our knowledge of turgor-triggered processes is still very limited and will probably remain so for some years to come, at least until more extensive pressure measurements in tissue cells are obtained with the pressure probe technique. Nevertheless, there is sufficient experimental evidence for a direct control of membrane transport and the electrical properties of the cell membrane by turgor pressure, although the majority of data available has been confined to algal cells. There is ample indirect evidence that turgor-controlled processes play an important role in the regulatory functions of higher plants [e.g. movement of stomata and leaves (78, 91)]. Because of the indirect techniques used for the calculation of turgor pressure, the results are still too indecisive to be discussed here in more detail. On the other hand, they do highlight the relevance of the findings in giant algal cells to higher plants. The first evidence that turgor pressure can directly interfere with membrane transport was provided by Gutknecht (46). He demonstrated in perfused cells of *V. ventricosa* that the K^+ influx decreased significantly, whereas in contrast the K^+ efflux increased only slightly when the pressure inside the cell was raised from 0 to 1 bar by means of a pressurized perfusion system. Zimmermann & Steudle (106, 127, 141) extended the pressure range considerably by using the pressure probe technique and showed that the K^+ influx decreases steadily up to a pressure level of 2 bar in cells of *V. utricularis*. Above this pressure level the K^+ influx becomes almost independent of pressure. The K^+ efflux, on the other hand, showed a remarkable and progressive increase over the entire pressure range (up to 5 and 6 bar which is where larger cells usually burst). In addition, measurements on cells of various sizes revealed that the K^+ efflux increased significantly with increasing volume (by a factor of 3 with an increase in the volume from 40 to 200 μl).[2] The pressure dependence of the efflux was more pronounced in larger cells. An equivalent volume dependence of the K^+ influx would not be detected within the limits of accuracy of this method. A similar pressure and volume dependence was also observed for the Cl^- fluxes in *V. utricularis* (Steudle & Lelkes, unpublished data). Recent measurements by Bisson & Gutknecht (8) in *Codium decorticatum* and by Graves & Gutknecht (40) in *H. parvula* suggest that in these species the Cl^- flux is the key process which is stimulated by pressure in the low pressure ranges and inhibited by high turgor pressure.

The pressure and volume dependence of the K^+ and Cl^- fluxes in *V. utricularis* were confirmed by independent measurements of the pressure and volume dependence of the electrical membrane resistance (105, 138). The membrane resistance initially increases with increasing steady-state pressure to a maximum at a certain volume-dependent pressure level after which it decreases again when the pressure is raised even further. This result is to be expected if the membrane conductivity is determined largely by the K^+ and Cl^- fluxes. For small cell volumes the pressure corresponding to the maximum membrane resistance assumes very high values (5 to 6 bar) whereas in large cells the maximum membrane resistance is already achieved at pressures of 1 to 2 bar (141, 143). In smaller cells the absolute changes in membrane resistance up to the maximum value are much more pronounced (an increase by a factor of 2–3 in comparison to low pressure ranges) than in larger cells (only about 50%). The maximum membrane resistance corresponds to the condition of osmotic equilibrium in the cell, i.e. the pressure-dependent influx and the oppo-

---

[2]A volume dependence of fluxes of this type in higher plants would cast serious doubt on the compartment analysis of the fluxes in plant tissues (117).

sitely directly pressure- and volume-dependent efflux are equal. Thus, not only the net water flow disappears, but also the net ion flows. The steady-state turgor pressure should, therefore, be larger in small cells, a hypothesis which has been supported experimentally by taking average values of a large number of cells.

A very interesting finding is that indoleacetic acid (IAA) and 2,4-dichlorophen-oxyacetic acid (2,4 D), but not 3,5 D (which does not normally exhibit an auxin effect), at very low concentrations change the dependence of the maximum membrane resistance on pressure (127, 141–143).

The hormonal effects can be shown experimentally to be attributable to a reduced effect of turgor pressure on the K^+ (and probably also the Cl^-) fluxes although the characteristic pressure dependence of the fluxes is retained (141). These results shed light on the close similarities of the interactions of hormones and pressure with ion fluxes and suggest a common mechanism as might be expected on the basis of some experiments on higher plants (e.g. 57, 95). The importance of these findings to extension growth processes becomes particularly apparent if the volume dependence of the elastic modulus in *Valonia* cells is taken into account as suggested by Zimmermann & Steudle (106, 141, 143). If the volume dependence of the K^+ and Cl^- efflux and, in turn, of the electrical membrane resistance does indeed reflect the increase in the elastic modulus with increasing volume, the extent of salt uptake and extrusion is under direct control of the elastic properties of the cell wall in *Valonia* cells. Assuming that the data reflect a general behavior pattern, then plant cells would be equipped with a fascinating and simple mechanism for the regulation of extension growth. Extension growth which requires turgor pressure to exceed a certain threshold value (15, 16, 41, 43) is enhanced in small cells with small ϵ values and terminated when the cell volume reaches a certain size. At this stage the ϵ value becomes too high and the pressure too low for salt uptake to continue. Hormones, on the other hand, mask the influence of the elastic modulus on the fluxes and on turgor and, in turn, initiate salt uptake and growth (141). The termination of growth by this mechanism is also determined by the fact that the relative change in volume in response to pressure changes decreases with increasing pressure (Equation 1). Turgor pressure should thus have a dual function in growth processes. During the initiation of growth, turgor pressure is required to stretch the walls and to facilitate the breaking of chemical bonds, whereas during expansion it controls the uptake of solutes necessary to drive the growth processes.

The effect of turgor pressure on the K^+ fluxes of *V. utricularis* and *V. ventricosa* seems to occur instantaneously or at least very rapidly, although for experimental reasons a visible influence is only detectable after about 15–30 min (46, 106). Thus biochemical reactions between the primary step in turgor sensing and the output signal (alterations in the membrane transport properties) as postulated by Kauss (62) can probably be ruled out. This conclusion is supported by the recent finding of Zimmermann & Beckers (128), who showed that the resting membrane potential of *Ch. corallina* (about −160 mV) is instantaneously depolarized (in less than 1 sec) when pressure pulses are injected into the internode with the pressure probe (1 to 3 mV/bar depending on the pressure range). The depolarization of the membrane potential occurs in response to both increases and decreases in pressure. In only a few exceptional cases an initial, small hyperpolarization was observed in response to a pressure increase in the cell.

These results strictly prohibit an interpretation of the pressure-induced depolarization of the membrane potential solely in terms of electrokinetic phenomena (2, 3, 33, 79). If the pressure-induced potential changes in *Chara corallina* were due to a streaming potential, one would expect a hyperpolarizing response because of the net negative sign of the fixed charges in the membrane when the pressure inside the cell was increased and an outwardly directed water flow is created as a result. Conversely, one would expect a depolarizing response to occur only when the pressure is decreased, as has been shown to be the case with artificial membranes (123). The results under consideration show that in addition to the possible contribution of the streaming potential, other electromechanical effects must be involved in the depolarization of the membrane which are independent of the direction of the applied pressure. At the same time these findings cast doubt on the calculation of the values for the electro-osmotic coupling coefficient which is based on the reverse phenomenon of electro-osmosis (2, 33). Apparently one must take into account not only the transport number effects (3) (the creation of an osmotic water flow in addition to the electrokinetic water flow by local osmosis, i.e. by depletion and enhancement of the concentration in the interphase membrane/bulk solution), but also the electromechanical changes in the membrane activity, the nature of which has not been completely elucidated (but see below). The depolarization of the membrane potential can reach a threshold value where action potentials are generated. In terms of shape and duration these action potentials resemble those initiated by an electrical stimulus (36). Both these parameters change significantly when the cells are exposed to pressure stress for a longer time. Under these conditions the response of the cell to pressure shows more resemblance to the electrical transients frequently observed in cells and tissues of higher plants (36). In higher plants, well-defined propagated action potentials have only been shown to occur in sensitive plants such as *Mimosa, Dionea,* and *Drosera* (31, 36, 78, 87, 121, 122), i.e. in plants in which action potentials are generated by external mechanical stimuli and associated with subsequent movement. In the light of the results on *Chara corallina,* Zimmermann & Beckers have put forward the hypothesis that the transformation of a pressure signal into an action potential or an electrical transient may play an important role in the regulatory functions of a higher plant. This would provide the plant with a very efficient mechanism for responding to external osmotic stress in more distant organs since pressure signals themselves cannot be propagated over great distances (101, 127, 140), whereas there is efficient electrical coupling between cells in a tissue (98, 99).

There are several reports in the literature stating that the hydraulic conductivity in giant algal cells is directly affected by pressure in the low turgor pressure ranges (104, 138–140). Some authors (e.g. 85, 101), on the other hand, have not detected any such effect of pressure on the water permeability. In *Valonia* cells the increase in Lp as the plasmolytic point is approached can be explained in terms of a coupling between the active, pressure-dependent K^+ influx and water flow, which leads to an apparently higher thermodynamic value of the hydraulic conductivity (106, 141).

The calculation of Lp is based on Equation 2, which was derived on the assumption that only water flow occurs during the initial phase of osmoregulation. Similar pressure-dependent coupling effects may occur in *Characean* cells where an increase in Lp was observed at turgor pressures below 2 bar. The fact that Palta & Stadelmann (85) did not detect any changes in the value of Lp in onion epidermal cells under various conditions of osmotic stress only indicates that there is no coupling between water flow and active solute flow in these cells or that both the coupling coefficient and the magnitude of the flows are unaffected by pressure over the entire pressure range. For a more rigorous discussion of this point the reader should consult the review by Zimmermann & Steudle (142) and Zimmermann (127).

TURGOR-SENSING MECHANISMS

The evidence that turgor pressure can directly interfere with solute flow and the electrical properties of the cell membrane has led to an intensive discussion of the possible mechanisms involved in turgor pressure sensing during the past 2 years. We are still far from understanding the individual steps taken in the transformation of a pressure signal of the order of 1 bar into changes of the electrical properties of membrane transport. On the other hand, the author feels that there is sufficiently promising experimental evidence at least to allow speculation about some of the basic principles involved. It is beyond the scope of this review to give a detailed analysis of all the present concepts of turgor-sensing mechanisms, especially as these concepts do not fulfill the strict conditions for the formulation of a model (47, 48). The aim in this review is to point out to biologists some of the relevant literature which should be considered in the interpretation of turgor-sensing processes within the membrane. It is obvious that chemical reactions cannot be involved in the primary step of turgor-sensing, because the pressures required to reverse the direction of a chemical reaction in condensed phases are much too high (75) to play a role in the processes discussed in the foregoing chapter, which are influenced by pressure differences of less than 1 bar. We are thus driven to the conclusion that the basic steps of the turgor-sensing mechanisms must be of mechanical or electromechanical nature. On the basis of this conclusion Zimmermann and colleagues (18, 22, 127, 130, 133) conceived the so-called electromechanical model which at present represents the only quantitative formulation of the basic step in turgor-sensing.

In view of the misinterpretation of some important points of the model by Gutknecht et al (48) and Kauss (62), who criticized these concepts in their reviews, the author feels it necessary to make some fundamental remarks prior to the discussion of the electromechanical model. The crucial concept underlying the electromechanical model is that mechanical forces (created by either pressure gradients or absolute pressure) can act on the mechanics of membranes in two different ways: first, by direct compression of the membrane or parts thereof, perpendicular to the membrane plane, or second, by stretching the cell membrane only in the presence of pressure gradients. In cells with walls, stretching of the cell membrane in response to pressure gradients is controlled by the elastic properties of the cell wall to which the membrane is coupled (at least as far as the plasmalemma is concerned). It should be noted that in a comparable way to direct compression, stretching of the membrane also produces a change in membrane thickness if the membrane density (volume) remains constant (18, 129). This latter assumption seems to be correct (35, 119). The electromechanical model postulates that the pressure-induced changes in the geometric dimensions of the membrane or certain membrane areas which may be preferentially involved in turgor sensing are transformed into changes of the intrinsic electrical field distribution within the membrane and vice versa. Owing to the similarities between walled and wall-less cells with respect to the biochemical and biophysical processes during osmoregulation (see above), this model proposes the same primary transformational step in the regulatory response of both systems and thus fulfills an important criterion for the mechanism of the pressure transducer within the membrane.

In order to determine whether pressure signals are transduced preferentially by compression or alternatively by stretching or even partly by means of both these mechanisms, the elastic coefficients of the cell membrane, including the Poisson ratios, must be known. In walled cells the elastic coefficients of the cell wall must also be known. These data are almost completely lacking (18), owing to the complex anisotropic structure of the cell membrane (and cell wall). A quantitative treatment of the elastic properties of the cell membrane is thus rendered impossible.

In a first quantitative approach, Zimmermann and co-workers treated the membrane or parts thereof as a capacitor consisting of a homogeneous dielectric of perfect elastic properties between its plates. Electrical fields are created by an external membrane potential. Electrical fields within the membrane due to fixed charges and electrogenic pumps are excluded in the model since their profiles are not sufficiently well known to allow a quantitative evaluation of their influence on the entire electrical field in a membrane. The system is in equilibrium if the electrical compressive force (arising from the membrane potential difference) and the mechanical force (arising both from turgor pressure and absolute pressure) are counterbalanced by the elastic restoring forces within the membrane. Taking into account the macroscopic laws for the electrical compressive force and the elastic restoring forces (Hooke's law), the theory reveals that an equilibrium state between these three forces which determine the thickness (and area) of the membrane can only be sustained at low membrane potentials. If the membrane potential V_m is increased very rapidly to very high values (about 0.5 to 2 V), an instability is created in the membrane which leads to its electrical (dielectric) breakdown.[3] Electrical breakdown of the cell membrane has been demonstrated in giant algal cells (19, 21) and

[3]The phenomenon of "dielectric breakdown" should not be confused with the so-called "punch-through" phenomenon. Punch-through is observed at much lower membrane potential differences when current pulses of msec and sec in duration are injected into the cell (17). Dielectric breakdown, on the other hand, is observed when the membrane is taken to very high potentials in a matter of μsec. These two phenomena are based on quite different mechanisms (20, 133). Unfortunately, some authors (83) use the term dielectric breakdown for the punch-through phenomenon.

in microscopic cells with or without cell walls (127, 131, 134, 136). Breakdown is a reversible phenomenon which can be repeated several times in a given cell with identical results. In microscopic cells electrical breakdown can be demonstrated by subjecting a cell suspension in a discharge chamber to externally applied electrical field pulses of microseconds in duration and increasing field strength and by simultaneously measuring the release of intracellular solutes which increases markedly when the membrane potential is taken to a critical level (92, 127, 132). The measurement of the size distribution of a cell population at increasing electrical field strength in the orifice of a hydrodynamically focusing Coulter counter system represents a more accurate method with higher reproducibility and sensitivity (131, 133). The breakdown voltage can be calculated very accurately from the electronic underestimation of the size distribution which is observed beyond a critical external field strength in the orifice. The apparent underestimation of the size and, in turn, of the volume can be unequivocally attributed to the breakdown of the normally electrically insulating membrane which causes current to pass partly through the cell interior, so that the cell volume appears to be smaller than it is in reality. In giant algal cells, on the other hand, the breakdown voltage can be determined directly by using intra- and extracellular electrodes for injecting current pulses of very short duration and simultaneously recording the corresponding membrane potential difference set up across the membrane [for further details of these electrical breakdown techniques, see (131)].

Providing that the breakdown phenomenon is interpreted in terms of an electromechanical instability, the knowledge of the breakdown voltage provides for the first time direct access to the absolute value of the elastic compressive modulus Y_m, transverse to the membrane plane. Theory yields the following equation for the breakdown voltage V_c if electrical compression of the membrane alone at zero pressure P is considered (133):

$$V_c\ (P = 0) = \frac{0.369 \times Y_m}{\epsilon' \times \epsilon'_0} \times \delta_0 \qquad\qquad 3.$$

where ϵ' = dielectric constant, ϵ'_0 = dielectric constant of the vacuum, and δ_0 = the thickness of the membrane for $P=0$ and $V_m=0$.

On the basis of the concepts of the electromechanical compression of the membrane, the breakdown voltage should decrease with increasing pressure, i.e. both pressure gradients and absolute pressure, since the potential required for electrically compressing the membrane to a critical thickness where breakdown occurs should decrease if the membrane is first compressed mechanically. The quantitative relationship between breakdown voltage and pressure for a spherical cell is represented by the following equation (18, 129):

$$V_c = V_c\ (P = 0)\ \exp\ (-P/\gamma) \qquad\qquad 4.$$

where γ is defined as following:

$$\frac{1}{\gamma} = \frac{1}{Y_m} + \frac{2}{3\epsilon}. \qquad\qquad 5.$$

γ, the so-called effective elastic modulus incorporates both direct compression of the membrane $(1/Y_m)$ and indirect changes in the membrane thickness (and area) under the influence of membrane stretching in response to pressure gradients $(2/3\epsilon)$.

Equations 3 and 4 indicate that the elastic compressive modulus of the cell membrane Y_m can be calculated either from the electrical breakdown process itself at $P=0$ or from the pressure dependence of the dielectric breakdown voltage in such algal cells where P and ϵ can be measured directly. The other required parameters in Equation 3, i.e. the dielectric constant ϵ' and the thickness of the membrane area δ_0, in the unstressed state can be estimated in independent experiments or with the aid of certain assumptions (127).

For the membranes of algal cells, some animal cells and some species of bacteria the values of Y_m are of the order of 1 to 8×10^6 Nm^{-2} (18). In cells of V. utricularis (129) where it was possible to verify the pressure dependence of the breakdown voltage predicted by Equation 3, the value of Y_m estimated from the pressure dependence of the breakdown voltage agrees well with the value calculated from the breakdown process itself at $P=0$. This result supports the assumptions underlying the theory of the electromechanical model (18).

If we consider turgor sensing by means of a direct compression of the cell membrane alone, i.e. if either $\epsilon \gg Y_m$ or no pressure gradients are allowed in the system, the changes in membrane thickness, which are expected to occur on the basis of these Y_m values at pressure changes of 1 bar, are of the order of 0.2–0.4 nm (22).

In molecular dimensions rapid changes in the thickness of this order of magnitude represent dramatic alterations in the dynamic structure of the cell membrane. In reality, the change in the geometry of the membrane can be considerably larger, if we include the volumetric elastic modulus of the cell wall in our considerations, that is, if we permit pressure gradients, i.e. turgor pressure changes, which can lead to a stretching of the cell membrane. If $\epsilon \ll Y_m$, ϵ is the dominating parameter. The turgor pressure will be sensed by stretching of the membrane area and, in turn, by the indirect changes in the membrane thickness. On the other hand, if $\epsilon \gg Y_m$, turgor pressure will be sensed exclusively by the direct compression of the membrane perpendicular to the plane of the membrane. It is possible to predict which of these two parameters will be dominating from measurements with absolute pressure in a pressure chamber. Hastings & Gutknecht (49) and Bisson & Gutknecht (8) showed that increasing the pressure in the system to 2–3 bar has no effect on the K$^+$ and Cl$^-$ fluxes in V. ventricosa and Codium decorticatum, respectively, which, on the other hand, are very sensitive to pressure gradients. Although the absolute pressure range is too small to allow definite conclusion to be drawn, these findings at least indicate that in these species turgor will be sensed by stretching of the cell membrane, i.e. that ϵ is the dominating parameter. It is not possible to draw the conclusion on the basis of these results that the electromechanical model is not applicable, as Gutknecht et al (48) did, probably due to a misinterpretation of the theoretical concepts on which the electromechanical model is based. On the contrary, investigations of transport processes in the presence of high absolute pressure (several hundred atmospheres) show that the assertions of the electromechanical model are in principle correct in spite of its simplicity. Equation 4 predicts that a critical absolute pressure value should exist where the resting membrane potential is sufficiently high to induce (mechanical) breakdown of the cell membrane (127). Using appropriate values for the resting membrane potential for cells of various species, it can be estimated that this effect should become apparent above 300 bar for red blood cells and *Chlorella pyrenoidosa*. At a critical pressure level of about 600 bar, Pequeux et al (unpublished data) and Murphy & Libby (81) did indeed find a significant and reversible change in the K^+ efflux from both human red blood cells and cells of *Chlorella pyrenoidosa* and in the transport rate of radioactive phosphate anions in rabbit erythrocytes, respectively. In view of the numerous experimental difficulties which may result in substantially higher values for the postulated absolute critical pressure level (127), the agreement between the theoretical and experimental values can be regarded as satisfactory. Thus the absence of any evidence for absolute pressure effects on fluxes in *Valonia* and *Codium* in the low pressure range does not necessarily invalidate the electromechanical model but reinforces the need to investigate the processes in their dependence on pressure gradients and absolute pressure in greater detail.

It is not difficult to link changes in membrane thickness by compression or stretching of the membrane area to mechanisms of osmoregulation. Evidence recently presented by Berezin et al (7) has shown that distortion of pores by externally applied pressure in gels containing trapped trypsin and chymotrypsinogen leads to a dramatic increase in the conversion of chymotrysinogen into chymotrypsin. Demel et al (28) found that phospholipases which cannot hydrolyze phospholipids in the intact erythrocyte membrane will hydrolyze phospholipid monolayers, but only at surface tensions below 31 dyn/cm. On the other hand, phospholipases which can hydrolyze phospholipids in intact erythrocytes will also hydrolyze phospholipid monolayers at tensions above 31 dyn/cm. These results show that the penetration of an enzyme depends on the surface tension which itself is a function of turgor pressure. Similarly, it is very likely that mechanical and electrical changes in the environment of transport modules embedded in a membrane such as those envisaged in the fluid mosaic model (97) would alter the dynamics of the active transport system. In this way the rate of pumping of ions, and hence the osmotic pressure in the cell interior, could be directly controlled by turgor pressure. The pressure-induced action potentials in *Chara corallina* (128) can readily be explained as a direct effect of pressure on the electrogenic pump and passive ion transport pathways, which should always lead to a depolarization when the optimal conditions are disturbed, that is, in response to both an increase and decrease in pressure. External mechanical stimulation of action potentials (and plant movement) probably operates in the same way.

The fact that both electrical fields and turgor pressure create conditions of stress which result in a compression of the membrane inevitably leads to the important conclusion that osmoregulation is dependent on the membrane potential. The latter is controlled by the concentration of certain ions. Thus control of turgor pressure during osmoregulation should also depend on the contribution of such ions which do not necessarily contribute to the osmolarity of the external medium. Such effects were found in *Ch. linum* (102, 137) where low concentrations of potassium could reverse the direction of osmoregulation induced by a large decrease in the external osmolarity. Mummert & Gradmann (80a) postulated on the basis of simultaneous flux and potential measurements in *Acetabularia* that action potentials which occur spontaneously in this species have a significant function for the K^+ balance and, in turn, for turgor pressure regulation. Such an effect is expected in the light of the predictions of the electromechanical model.

The electromechanical mechanism suggested in the model of Zimmermann and co-workers is certainly not the only means by which mechanical forces can be transformed into electrical quantities. Electromechanical transduction with charged polyelectrolyte structures (cell membranes and cell walls) is conceivable (45) and undoubtedly a process which has to be taken into consideration in more sophisticated models.

Piezoelectricity is another electromechanical phenomenon which may participate in turgor pressure sensing. Piezoelectric behavior is known to exist in some inorganic crystals which display a permanent dipole moment. Pressure or tension in certain directions induce positive or negative charges on certain crystal surfaces. Piezoelectricity is not restricted to crystalline structures, but has also been shown to exist in many noncrystalline, anisotropic biological materials (38). In this context the theoretical concepts and experimental findings of R. L. Zimmerman (126) may be relevant to the mechanisms involved in turgor sensing. This author recently showed that piezoelectric behavior can be induced in amorphous isotropic materials such as gelatin, nylon, and teflon if dipole moments are induced by application of a constant external electrical field. R. L. Zimmerman showed that, due to the piezoelectric behavior of the material, current is induced in conditions of mechanical stress which is of the same order of magnitude as physiological currents. These currents could lead to a shift of the ion fluxes and thus be regarded as regulatory parameters for the changes of transport processes generated by turgor pressure.

CONCLUSIONS

The biphasic regulatory response to environmental osmotic stress is very similar in both wall-less and walled cells. The parameter regulated on a macroscopic scale is the volume in wall-less cells and the turgor pressure in walled cells. The transition between these two types of regulation is continuous and determined by the magnitude of the volumetric elastic modulus of the cell wall which is a very complex parameter dependent on both turgor pressure and cell volume. The available data suggest that the elastic modulus plays a key role in turgor pressure regulation and extension growth processes. Due to new technical developments in recent years, both turgor pressure and the elastic modulus of the cell wall have become directly accessible and measurable in single tissue cells. On the other hand, techniques for the measurement of volume kinetics in isolated wall-less cells leave much to be desired, although progress in this field may be expected in the near future if the current electrical methods for volume determination are improved to allow high speed measurements.

In giant algal cells there is convincing experimental evidence for the direct interference of turgor pressure with membrane transport and the electrical properties of the membrane. Data on tissue cells in higher plants are still lacking.

It is possible to develop a number of possible mechanisms of turgor pressure sensing which are based on the electromechanical properties of the membrane material. Development in this field is hampered by the difficulties involved in designing sufficiently sophisticated techniques for the evaluation of the mechanical properties of the anisotropic membrane (and cell wall) on the one hand, and for the experimental elucidation of the profiles of the electrical field within the membrane on the other hand.

The author feels that it would be worthwhile to put more effort into the investigation of the electromechanical properties, since the knowledge of these parameters would not only extend our knowledge of the turgor-sensing mechanisms, but probably also make a substantial contribution to the understanding of geotropic and electrotropic effects on tip growth, in which the electromechanical effects most certainly play a dominant role (94, 96, 120).

ACKNOWLEDGMENTS

Part of this work was supported by a grant from the Deutsche Forschungsgemeinschaft, Sonderforschungsbereich 160.

I am greatly indebted to numerous colleagues for access to manuscripts prior to publication. For critically reading and discussing the manuscript I am grateful to Drs. F. Beckers, Chr. Holzapfel, G. Kirst, E. Steudle, and G. Wyn Jones.

Literature Cited

1. Barry, P. H. 1970. Volume flows and pressure changes during an action potential in cells of *Chara australis. J. Membr. Biol.* 3:313–34
2. Barry, P. H., Hope, A. B. 1969. Electroosmosis in *Chara* and *Nitella* cells. *Biochim. Biophys. Acta* 193:124–28
3. Barry, P. H., Hope, A. B. 1969. Electroosmosis in membranes: Effects of unstirred layers and transport numbers. *Biophys. J.* 9:729–57
4. Ben-Amotz, A. 1974. Osmoregulation mechanism in the halophilic alga *Dunaliella parva*. In *Membrane Transport in Plants*, ed. U. Zimmermann, J. Dainty, pp. 95–100. Berlin-Heidelberg-New York: Springer
5. Ben-Amotz, A. 1975. Adaptation of the unicellular alga *Dunaliella parva* to a saline environment. *J. Phycol.* 11:50–54
6. Ben-Amotz, A., Avron, M. 1973. The role of glycerol in the osmotic regulation of the halophilic alga *Dunaliella parva. Plant Physiol.* 51:875–78
7. Berezin, I. V., Klibanov, A. M., Martinek, K. 1974. The mechano-chemistry

of immobilized enzymes. How to steer a chemical process at the molecular level by a mechanical device. *Biochim. Biophys. Acta* 364:193–99
8. Bisson, M. A., Gutknecht, J. 1975. Osmotic regulation in the marine alga *Codium decorticatum. J. Membr. Biol.* 24:183–200
9. Borowitzka, L. J., Brown, A. D. 1974. The salt relations of marine and halophilic species of the unicellular green alga *Dunaliella. Arch. Microbiol.* 96: 37–52
10. Boyer, J. S. 1966. Isopiestic technique: Measurement of accurate leaf water potentials. *Science* 154:1459–60
11. Boyer, J. S., Knipling, E. B. 1965. Isopiestic technique for measuring leaf water potentials with a thermocouple psychrometer. *Proc. Natl. Acad. Sci. USA* 54:1044–51
12. Brown, A. D., Simpson, J. R. 1972. Water relations of sugar tolerant yeasts: The role of intracellular polyols. *J. Gen. Microbiol.* 72:589–91

13. Cheung, Y. N. S., Tyree, M. T., Dainty, J. 1975. Water relations parameters on single leaves obtained in a pressure bomb and some ecological interpretations. *Can. J. Bot.* 53:1342–46
14. Cheung, Y. N. S., Tyree, M. T., Dainty, J. 1976. Some possible sources of error in determining bulk elastic moduli and other parameters from pressure-volume curves of shoots and leaves. *Can. J. Bot.* 54:758–65
15. Cleland, R. 1971. Cell wall extension. *Ann. Rev. Plant Physiol.* 22:197–222
16. Cleland, R. 1977. The control of cell enlargement. In *Integration of Activity in the Higher Plant,* ed. D. Jennings, pp. 101–15. Proc. 31st Symp. Soc. Exp. Biol. Cambridge Univ. Press
17. Coster, H. G. L. 1965. A quantitative analysis of the voltage current relationships of fixed charge membranes and the associated property of "punchthrough." *Biophys. J.* 5:669–86
18. Coster, H. G. L., Steudle, E., Zimmermann, U. 1976. Turgor pressure sensing mechanism. *Plant Physiol.* 58:636–43
19. Coster, H. G. L., Zimmermann, U. 1975. Direct demonstration of dielectric breakdown in the membranes of *Valonia utricularis.* *Z. Naturforsch.* 30c: 77–79
20. Coster, H. G. L., Zimmermann, U. 1975. Dielectric breakdown in the membranes of *Valonia utricularis.* The role of energy dissipation. *Biochim. Biophys. Acta* 382:410–18
21. Coster, H. G. L., Zimmermann, U. 1975. The mechanism of electrical breakdown in the membranes of *Valonia utricularis.* *J. Membr. Biol.* 22: 73–90
22. Coster, H. G. L., Zimmermann, U. 1976. Transduction of turgor pressure by cell membrane compression. *Z. Naturforsch.* 31c:461–63
23. Craigie, J. S. 1969. Some salinity-induced changes in growth, pigments, and cyclohexanetetrol content of *Monochrysis lutheri.* *J. Fish. Res. Board Can.* 26:2959–67
24. Cram, W. J. 1976. Negative feedback regulation of transport in cells. The maintenance of turgor, volume and nutrient supply. In *Encyclopedia of Plant Physiology,* New Ser., ed. U. Lüttge, M. G. Pitman, 2(A):284–316. Berlin-Heidelberg-New York: Springer
25. Dainty, J. 1963. Water relations of plant cells. *Adv. Bot. Res.* 1:279–326
26. Dainty, J. 1972. Plant cell water relations: The elasticity of the cell wall.

Proc. R. Soc. Edinburgh, Sect. A 70: 89–93
27. Dainty, J. 1976. Water relation in plant cells. See Ref. 24, pp. 12–35
28. Demel, R. A., Geurts van Kessel, W. S. M., Zwaal, R. F. A., Roelofsen, B., van Deenen, L. L. M. 1975. Relation between various phospholipase actions on human red cell membranes and the interfacial phospholipid pressure in monolayers. *Biochim. Biophys. Acta* 406:97–107
29. Dhindsa, R. S., Bewley, J. D. 1976. Water stress and protein synthesis. IV. Responses of a drought-tolerant plant. *J. Exp. Bot.* 27:513–23
30. Dhindsa, R. S., Cleland, R. E. 1975. Water stress and protein synthesis. *Plant Physiol.* 55:778–81, 782–85
31. Di Palma, J. R., Mohl, R., Best, W. Jr. 1961. Action potential and contraction of *Dionaea muscipula* (Venus flytrap). *Science* 133:878–79
32. Edwards, M., Meidner, H., Sheriff, D. W. 1976. Direct measurements of turgor pressure potentials of guard cells. *J. Exp. Bot.* 27:163–71
33. Fensom, D. S., Dainty, J. 1963. Electroosmosis in *Nitella.* *Can. J. Bot.* 41: 685–91
34. Ferrier, J. M., Dainty, J. 1977. A new method for measurement of hydraulic conductivity and elastic coefficients in higher plant cells using an external force. *Can. J. Bot.* 55:858–66
35. Fettiplace, R., Andrews, D. M., Haydon, D. A. 1971. The thickness, composition and structure of some lipid bilayers and natural membranes. *J. Membr. Biol.* 5:277–96
36. Findlay, G. P., Hope, A. B. 1976. Electrical properties of plant cells: Methods and findings. See Ref. 24, pp. 53–92
37. Flowers, T. J., Troke, P. F., Yeo, A. R. 1977. The mechanism of salt tolerance in halophytes. *Ann. Rev. Plant Physiol.* 28:89–121
38. Fukada, E. 1974. Piezoelectric properties of biological macromolecules. *Adv. Biophys.* 6:121–55
39. Gilles, R. 1975. Mechanisms of ion and osmoregulation. In *Marine Ecology,* ed. O. Kinne, 2(1):259–347. London-New York: Wiley-Interscience
40. Graves, J. S., Gutknecht, J. 1976. Ion transport studies and determination of the cell wall elastic modulus in the marine alga *Halicystis parvula.* *J. Gen. Physiol.* 67:579–97
41. Green, P. B. 1963. On mechanisms of elongation. In *Cytodifferentiation and*

Macromolecular Synthesis, ed. M. Locke, pp. 203–34. New York: Academic
42. Green, P. B. 1968. Growth physics in *Nitella:* a method for continuous in vivo analysis of extensibility based on a micro-manometer technique for turgor pressure. *Plant Physiol.* 43:1169–84
43. Green, P. B., Erickson, R. O., Buggy, J. 1971. Metabolic and physical control of cell elongation rate. *Plant Physiol.* 47:423–30
44. Green, P. B., Stanton, F. W. 1967. Turgor pressure: direct manometric measurement in single cells of *Nitella. Science* 155:1675–76
45. Grodzinsky, A. J., Melcher, J. R. 1976. Electromechanical transduction with charged polyelectrolyte membranes. *IEEE BioMed.* 23:421–33
46. Gutknecht, J. 1968. Salt transport in *Valonia:* inhibition of potassium uptake by small hydrostatic pressures. *Science* 160:68–70
47. Gutknecht, J., Bisson, M. A. 1977. Ion transport and osmotic regulation in giant algal cells. In *Water Relations in Membrane Transport in Animals and Plants,* ed. A. M. Jungreis, T. Hodges, A. M. Kleinzeller, S. G. Schulz. New York: Academic. In press
48. Gutknecht, J., Hastings, D. F., Bisson, M. A. 1977. Ion transport and turgor pressure regulation in giant algal cells. In *Transport Across Biological Membranes,* Vol. 3, ed. G. Giebisch, D. C. Tosteson, H. H. Ussing. Berlin-Heidelberg-New York: Springer. In press
49. Hastings, D. F., Gutknecht, J. 1974. Turgor pressure regulation: Modulation of active potassium transport by hydrostatic pressure gradients. See Ref. 4, pp. 79–83
50. Hastings, D. F., Gutknecht, J. 1976. Ionic relations and the regulation of turgor pressure in the marine alga *Valonia macrophysa. J. Membr. Biol.* 28:263–75
51. Hellebust, J. A. 1976. Osmoregulation. *Ann. Rev. Plant Physiol.* 27:485–505
52. Hellebust, J. A. 1976. Effect of salinity on photosynthesis and mannitol synthesis in the green flagellate *Platymonas suecia. Can. J. Bot.* 54:1735–41
53. Hellkvist, J., Richards, G. P., Jarvis, P. G. 1974. Vertical gradients of water potential and tissue water relations in *Sitka spruce* trees measured with the pressure chamber. *J. Appl. Ecol.* 11:637–67
54. Hiller, R. G., Greenway, H. 1968. Effects of low water potentials on some

aspects of carbohydrate metabolism in *Clorella pyrenoidosa. Planta* 78:49–59
55. Hsiao, T. C. 1973. Plant responses to water stress. *Ann. Rev. Plant Physiol.* 24:519–70
56. Hüsken, D., Steudle, E., Zimmermann, U. 1978. Pressure probe technique for measuring water relations of cells in higher plants. *Plant Physiol.* In press
57. Jenkinson, I. S., Scott, B. I. H. 1960. Bioelectric oscillations of bean roots: Further evidence for a feedback oscillator. *Aust. J. Biol. Sci.* 14:231–43
58. Katchalsky, A., Curran, P. F. 1965. *Nonequilibrium Thermodynamics in Biophysics.* Cambridge, Mass: Harvard Univ. Press
59. Kauss, H. 1967. Isofloridosid und die Osmoregulation bei *Ochromonas malhamensis. Z. Pflanzenphysiol.* 56: 453–65
60. Kauss, H. 1974. Osmoregulation in *Ochromonas.* See Ref. 4, pp. 90–94
61. Kauss, H. 1977. Biochemistry of osmotic regulation. *Int. Rev. Biochem. Plant Biochem. II,* ed. D. H. Northcote, 13:119–40
62. Kauss, H. 1978. Osmotic regulation in algae. *Progr. Phytochem.* In press
63. Kauss, H., Lüttge, U., Kirchbaum, R. M. 1975. Änderung im Kalium und Isofloridosidgehalt während der Osmoregulation bei *Ochromonas malhamensis. Z. Pflanzenphysiol.* 76:109–13
64. Kauss, H., Schobert, B. 1971. First demonstration of UDP-gal: *sn*-glycero-3-phosphoric acid 1-a-glactosyl-transferase and its possible role in osmoregulation. *FEBS Lett.* 19:131–35
65. Kesseler, H. 1959. Mikrokryoskopische Untersuchungen zur Turgorregulation von *Chaetomorpha linum. Kiel. Meeresforsch.* 15:51–73
66. Kesseler, H. 1964. Die Bedeutung einiger anorganischer Komponenten des Seewassers für die Turgorregulation von *Chaetomorpha linum. Helgol. Wiss. Meeresunters.* 10:73–90
67. Kesseler, H. 1965. Turgor, osmotisches Potential und ionale Zusammensetzung des Zellsaftes einiger Meeresalgen verschiedener Verbreitungsgebiete. *Bot. Gothob.* 3:103–11
68. Kirst, G. O. 1975. Beziehungen zwischen Mannitkonzentration und osmotischer Belastung bei der Brackwasseralge *Platymonas subcordiformis* HAZEN. *Z. Pflanzenphysiol.* 76: 316–25
69. Kirst, G. O. 1977. Ion composition of unicellular marine and freshwater algae

with special reference to *Platymonas subcordiformis* cultivated in media with different osmotic strengths. *Oecologia* 28:177–89

70. Kirst, G. O. 1977. The cell volume of the unicellular alga *Platymonas subcordiformis* HAZEN: Effect of the salinity of the culture media and of osmotic stresses. *Z. Pflanzenphysiol.* 81:386–94

71. Kirst, G. O. 1977. Coordination of ionic relations and mannitol concentrations in the euryhaline unicellular alga, *Platymonas subcordiformis* HAZEN after osmotic shocks. *Planta* 135:69–75

72. Kirst, G. O., Keller, H. J. 1976. Der Einfluss unterschiedlicher NaCl-Konzentrationen auf die Atmung der einzelligen Alge *Platymonas subcordiformis* HAZEN. *Bot. Mar.* 19:241–44

73. Kishimoto, U. 1968. Response of *Chara* internodes to mechanical stimulation. *Ann. Rep. Biol. Works, Fac. Sci., Osaka Univ.* 16:61–66

74. Kregenow, F. M. 1971. The response of duck erythrocytes to nonhemolytic hypotonic media. I. Evidence for a volume controlling mechanism and II. Further evidence for a volume-controlling mechanism. *J. Gen. Physiol.* 58: 372–95, 396–412

75. Lauffer, M. A. 1975. Entropy-driven processes in biology. In *Molecular Biology, Biochemistry and Biophysics,* ed. A. Kleinzeller, G. F. Springer, H. G. Wittmann. Berlin-Heidelberg-New York: Springer

76. Leigh, R. A., Branton, D. 1976. Isolation of vacuoles from root storage tissue of *Beta vulgaris* L. *Plant Physiol.* 58:656–62

77. Lerner, H. R., Avron, M. 1977. Dihydroxyacetone kinase activity in *Dunaliella parva. Plant Physiol.* 59:15–17

78. MacRobbie, E. A. C. 1977. Functions of ion transport in plant cells and tissues. *Int. Rev. Biochem. Plant Biochem. II,* ed. D. H. Northcote, 13:211–47

79. MacRobbie, E. A. C., Fensom, D. S. 1969. Measurements of electro-osmosis in *Nitella translucens. J. Exp. Bot.* 20:466–84

80. Meidner, H., Edwards, M. 1975. Direct measurements of turgor pressure potentials of guard cells. *J. Exp. Bot.* 26: 319–30

80a. Mummert, H., Gradmann, D. 1976. Voltage dependent potassium fluxes and the significance of action potentials in *Acetabularia. Biochim. Biophys. Acta* 443:443–50

81. Murphy, R. B., Libby, W. F. 1976. Inhibition of erythrocyte phosphate transport by high pressures. *Proc. Natl. Acad. Sci. USA* 73:2767–69

82. Nakagawa, S., Kataoka, H., Tazawa, M. 1974. Osmotic and ionic regulation in *Nitella. Plant Cell Physiol.* 15:457–68

83. Ohkawa, T., Kishimoto, U. 1977. Breakdown phenomena in the *Chara* membrane. *Plant Cell Physiol.* 18:67–80

84. Osmond, C. B. 1976. Ion absorption and carbon metabolism in cells of higher plants. See Ref. 24, pp. 347–72

85. Palta, J. P., Stadelmann, E. J. 1977. Effect of turgor pressure on water permeability of *Allium cepa* epidermis cell membranes. *J. Membr. Biol.* 33: 231–47

86. Philip, J. R. 1958. The osmotic cell, solute diffusibility, and the plant water economy. *Plant Physiol.* 33:264–71

87. Pickard, B. G. 1973. Action potentials in higher plants. *Bot. Rev.* 39:172–201

88. Quader, H., Kauss, H. 1975. Die Rolle einiger Zwischenstoffe des Glaktosylglyzerinstoffwechsels bei der Osmoregulation in *Ochromonas malhamensis. Planta* 124:61–66

89. Rabinowitch, S., Grover, N. B., Ginzburg, B. Z. 1975. Cation effects on volume and water permeability in the halophilic algae *Dunaliella parva. J. Membr. Biol.* 22:211–30

90. Rand, R. P., Burton, A. C. 1964. Mechanical properties of the red cell membrane. *Biophys. J.* 4:115–35

91. Raschke, K. 1975. Stomatal action. *Ann. Rev. Plant Physiol.* 26:309–40

92. Riemann, F., Zimmermann, U., Pilwat, G. 1975. Release and uptake of haemoglobin and ions in red blood cells induced by dielectric breakdown. *Biochim. Biophys. Acta* 394:449–62

93. Scholander, P. F., Hammel, H. T., Hemmingsen, E. A., Bradstreet, E. D. 1964. Hydrostatic pressure and osmotic potential in leaves of mangroves and some other plants. *Proc. Natl. Acad. Sci. USA* 52:119–25

94. Schröter, K., Läuchli, A., Sievers, A. 1975. Mikroanalytische Identifikation von Bariumsulfat-Kristallen in den Statolithen der Rhizoide von *Chara fragilis,* Desv. *Planta* 122:213–25

95. Scott, T. K. 1972. Auxins and roots. *Ann. Rev. Plant Physiol.* 23:235–58

96. Sievers, A., Schröter, K. 1971. Versuche einer Kausalanalyse der geotropischen Reaktionskette im *Chara*-Rhizoid. *Planta* 96:339–53

97. Singer, S. J., Nicolson, G. L. 1972. The fluid mosaic model of the structure of cell membranes. *Science* 175:720–31
98. Spanswick, R. M. 1972. Electrical coupling between cells of higher plants: A direct demonstration of intercellular communication. *Planta* 102:215–27
99. Spanswick, R. M., Costerton, J. W. F. 1967. Plasmodesmata in *Nitella translucens:* Structure and electrical resistance. *J. Cell Sci.* 2:451–64
100. Stadelmann, E. 1966. Evaluation of turgidity, plasmolysis and deplasmolysis of plant cells. In *Methods in Cell Physiology,* ed. D. M. Prescott, pp. 143–216. London, New York: Academic
101. Steudle, E., Lüttge, U., Zimmermann, U. 1975. Hydraulic conductivity of the bladder cell of the halophyte *Mesembryanthemum crystallinum. Planta* 126:229–46
102. Steudle, E., Zimmermann, U. 1971. Zellturgor und selektiver Ionentransport bei *Chaetomorpha linum. Z. Naturforsch.* 26b:1276–82
103. Steudle, E., Zimmermann, U. 1971. Hydraulic conductivity of *Valonia utricularis. Z. Naturforsch.* 26b:1302–11
104. Steudle, E., Zimmermann, U. 1974. Determination of the hydraulic conductivity and of reflection coefficients in *Nitella flexilis* by means of direct cell turgor pressure measurements. *Biochim. Biophys. Acta* 332:399–412
105. Steudle, E., Zimmermann, U. 1974. Turgor pressure regulation in algal cells: pressure-dependence of electrical parameters of the membrane in large pressure ranges. See Ref. 4, pp. 72–78
106. Steudle, E., Zimmermann, U., Lelkes, P. I. 1977. Volume and pressure effects on the potassium fluxes of *Valonia utricularis.* In *Transmembrane Ionic Exchange in Plants,* ed. M. Thellier, pp. 123–37. Paris: CNRS
107. Steudle, E., Zimmermann, U., Lüttge, U. 1977. Effect of turgor pressure and cell size on the wall elasticity of plant cells. *Plant Physiol.* 59:285–89
108. Stewart, G. R., Lee, J. A. 1974. The role of proline accumulation in halophytes. *Planta* 120:279–89
109. Storey, R., Ahmad, N., Wyn Jones, R. G. 1977. Taxonomic and ecological aspects of the distribution of glycine betaine and related compounds in plants. *Oecologia* 27:319–32
110. Storey, R., Wyn Jones, R. G. 1977. Quaternary ammonium compounds in plants in relation to salt resistance. *Phytochemistry.* In press
111. Tazawa, M. 1957. Neue Methode zur Messung des osmotischen Wertes einer Zelle. *Protoplasma* 48:342–59
112. Tazawa, M., Kamiya, N. 1966. Water permeability of a *Characean* internodal cell with special reference to its polarity. *Aust. J. Biol. Sci.* 19:399–419
113. Tosteson, D. C. 1964. Regulation of cell volume by sodium and potassium transport. In *The Cellular Functions of Membrane Transport,* ed. J. F. Hoffmann, pp. 3–22. Englewood Cliffs, NJ: Prentice-Hall
114. Treichel, S. 1975. Der Einfluss von NaCl auf die Prolinkonzentration verschiedener Halophyten. *Z. Pflanzenphysiol.* 76:56–68
115. Tyree, M. T. 1976. Negative turgor pressure in plant cells: fact or fallacy? *Can. J. Bot.* 54:2738–46
116. Tyree, M. T., Hammel, H. T. 1972. The measurement of turgor pressure and the water relations of plants by the pressure bomb technique. *J. Exp. Bot.* 23:267–82
117. Walker, N. A., Pitman, M. G. 1976. Measurement of fluxes across membranes. See Ref. 24, pp. 93–126
117a. Walsby, A. E. 1975. Gas vesicles. *Ann. Rev. Plant Physiol.* 26:427–39
118. Weatherley, P. E. 1970. Some aspects of water relations. *Adv. Bot. Res.* 3:171–206
119. White, S. K. 1974. Comments on electrical breakdown of bimolecular lipid membranes as an electro-mechanical instability. *Biophys. J.* 14:155–58
120. Wilkens, M. B. 1971. Gravity and light: Sensing guidance systems in primary roots and shoots. See Ref. 16, pp. 275–335
121. Williams, St. E., Pickard, B. G. 1972. Properties of action potentials in *Drosera* tentacles. *Planta* 103:222–40
122. Williams, St. E., Spanswick, R. M. 1976. Propagation of the neuroid action potential of the carnivorous plant *Drosera. J. Comp. Physiol.* 108:211–23
123. Woermann, D. 1974. Transport processes across membranes with narrow pores. See Ref. 4, pp. 16–27
124. Wyn Jones, R. G., Storey, R., Leigh, R. A., Ahmad, N., Pollard, A. 1977. A hypothesis on cytoplasmic osmoregulation. In *Regulation of Cell Membrane Activity in Plants,* ed. E. Marrè, O. Ciferri, pp. 121–36. Amsterdam: Elsevier/North Holland
125. Wyn Jones, R. G., Storey, R., Pollard, A. 1977. Ionic and osmotic regulation in plants particularly halophytes. See Ref. 106. In press

126. Zimmermann, R. L. 1976. Induced piezoelectricity in isotropic biomaterial. *J. Biophys.* 16:1341–48

127. Zimmermann, U. 1977. Cell turgor regulation and pressure mediated transport processes. See Ref. 16, pp. 117–54

128. Zimmermann, U., Beckers, F. 1978. Generation of action potentials in *Chara corallina* by turgor pressure. *Planta* 138:173–79

129. Zimmermann, U., Beckers, F., Coster, H. G. L. 1977. The effect of pressure on the electrical breakdown in the membranes of *Valonia utricularis*. *Biochim. Biophys. Acta* 464:399–416

130. Zimmermann, U., Beckers, F., Steudle, E. 1977. Turgor sensing in plant cells by the electromechanical properties of the membrane. See Ref. 106, pp. 155–65

131. Zimmermann, U., Pilwat, G., Beckers, F., Riemann, F. 1976. Effects of external electrical fields on cell membranes. *Bioelectrochem. Bioenerg.* 3:58–83

132. Zimmermann, U., Pilwat, G., Holzapfel, Ch., Rosenheck, K. 1976. Electrical haemolysis of human and bovine red blood cells. *J. Membr. Biol.* 30:135–52

133. Zimmermann, U., Pilwat, G., Riemann, F. 1974. Dielectric breakdown of cell membranes. *Biophys. J.* 14:881–99

134. Zimmermann, U., Pilwat, G., Riemann, F. 1974. Dielectric breakdown in cell membranes. See Ref. 4, pp. 146–53

135. Zimmermann, U., Räde, H., Steudle, E. 1969. Kontinuierliche Druckmessung in Pflanzenzellen. *Naturwissenschaften* 56:634

136. Zimmermann, U., Schulz, J., Pilwat, G. 1973. Transcellular ion flow in *E. coli* B and electrical sizing of bacteria. *Biophys. J.* 13:1005–13

137. Zimmermann, U., Steudle, E. 1971. Effects of potassium concentration and osmotic pressure of sea water on the cell turgor pressure of *Chaetomorpha linum. Mar. Biol.* 11:132–37

138. Zimmermann, U., Steudle, E. 1974. The pressure dependence of the hydraulic conductivity, the membrane resistance and membrane potential during turgor pressure regulation in *Valonia utricularis. J. Membr. Biol.* 16:331–52

139. Zimmermann, U., Steudle, E. 1974. Hydraulic conductivity and volumetric elastic modulus in giant algal cells: Pressure and volume dependence. See Ref. 4, pp. 64–71

140. Zimmermann, U., Steudle, E. 1975. The hydraulic conductivity and volumetric elastic modulus of cells and isolated cell walls of *Nitella* and *Chara* spp: Pressure and volume effects. *Aust. J. Plant Physiol.* 2:1–12

141. Zimmermann, U., Steudle, E. 1977. Action of indole acetic acid on membrane structure and transport. See Ref. 124, pp. 231–42

142. Zimmermann, U., Steudle, E. 1978. Physical aspects of water relations of plant cells. *Adv. Bot. Res.* In press

143. Zimmermann, U., Steudle, E., Lelkes, P. I. 1976. Turgor pressure regulation in *Valonia utricularis:* effect of cell wall elasticity and auxin. *Plant Physiol.* 58:608–13

Ann. Rev. Plant Physiol. 1978. 29:149–92
Copyright © 1978 by Annual Reviews Inc. All rights reserved

THE METABOLISM OF THE GIBBERELLINS[1]

❖7648

Peter Hedden
Department of Biology, University of California, Los Angeles, California 90024

Jake MacMillan
Department of Organic Chemistry, University of Bristol, Bristol, England

Bernard O. Phinney
Department of Biology, University of California, Los Angeles, California 90024

CONTENTS

[1]Abbreviations: ATP, adenosine-5'-triphosphate; CPP, copalylpyrophosphate; DMAPP, dimethylallylpyrophosphate; FPP, farnesylpyrophosphate; GA(s), gibberellin(s); GA_x, gibberellin A_x; GC-MS, combined gas-liquid chromatography-mass spectrometry; GC-RC, combined gas-liquid chromatography-radio counting; GGPP, geranylgeranylpyrophosphate; GPP, geranylpyrophosphate; GLC, gas-liquid chromatography; IPP, isopentenylpyrophosphate; MVA, mevalonic acid; MVL, mevalonic lactone; NADPH, reduced nicotinamide adenine dinucleotide phosphate; TLC, thin-layer chromatography.

149

0066-4294/78/0601-0149$01.00

INTRODUCTION

The gibberellins (GAs) are generally recognized as regulators of the growth and development of higher plants. Before the factors which control the levels of these hormones can be understood, a detailed knowledge of the metabolic pathways by which GAs are synthesized and deactivated is clearly required.

Since the metabolism of the GAs was last reviewed in this series by Lang (103) in 1970, the subject has expanded at an impressive rate, and a large volume of publications, including a number of reviews, have appeared. Graebe & Ropers (77) have written an excellent and comprehensive review of the GAs which includes a critical discussion of GA metabolism; other reviews on GA metabolism are by MacMillan (111, 113, 114), Hanson (79), MacMillan & Pryce (115), West (164), Barendse (7), Bearder & Sponsel (19) and Railton (131).

Although this review concentrates upon the progress which has been made from 1970 to 1977, earlier studies are included where appropriate in order to present a coherent assessment of present knowledge. The structures of the presently known 52 GAs are shown in Figure 1. Both the trivial names GA_1–GA_{52} (116) and the systematic names, *ent*-gibberellane and *ent*-kaurane (140), are used. The terms C_{20}- and C_{19}-GAs denote GAs which have respectively retained and lost carbon-20 (see Figure 2, which also shows the numbering of the ring system).

The plant physiologist's prime interest in GA metabolism is centered on the intact higher plant. Nevertheless, studies with the fungus *Gibberella fujikuroi* (which produces GAs as secondary metabolites) have provided basic information and an invaluable model for work with higher plants. The biosynthetic steps for the fungal GAs are now almost completely known and are described in detail in this review. In addition, we include a discussion on the metabolism by the fungus of structural analogs of fungal GAs and their precursors. These latter studies also provide useful models for GA biosynthesis in higher plants, particularly in the case of the *G.*

fujikuroi mutant B1-41a, which can mimic higher plants by biosynthesizing higher plant GAs from the appropriate precursors. While our knowledge of GA biosynthesis in higher plants is more fragmentary, notable progress has been made during the period under review, particularly with cell-free systems.

From the diversity of the naturally occurring GAs it is clear that no single biosynthetic pathway exists in fungi and higher plants. Nevertheless, some general features are beginning to emerge. Present knowledge indicates that the steps to GA_{12}-aldehyde, the first intermediate with the *ent*-gibberellane skeleton, are common to the fungus and higher plants. Thereafter the pathways diverge. The common pathway from MVA to GA_{12}-aldehyde is therefore discussed under one heading, and the diverging pathways from GA_{12}-aldehyde are discussed separately for the fungus, for cell-free systems from higher plants, and for cellular systems from higher plants. Also included is a short section on the regulation of GA levels. Since one of the major problems in a critical assessment of the literature on GA metabolism is the identification of products, we begin with a brief discussion of this subject.

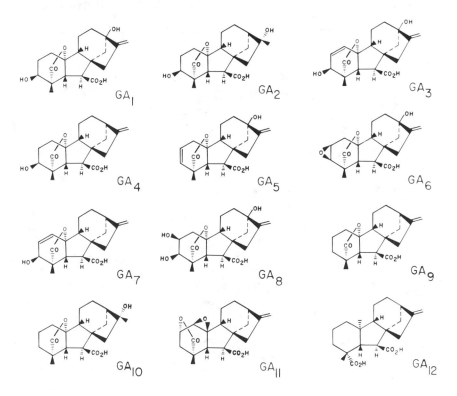

Figure 1 Structures of the gibberellins.

GA13   GA14   GA15   GA16   GA17   GA18   GA19   GA20   GA21   GA22   GA23   GA24   GA25   GA26   GA27   GA28   GA29   GA30   GA31   GA32   GA33

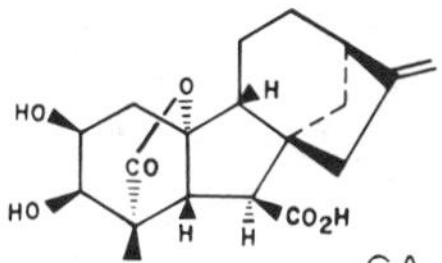

GA$_{34}$

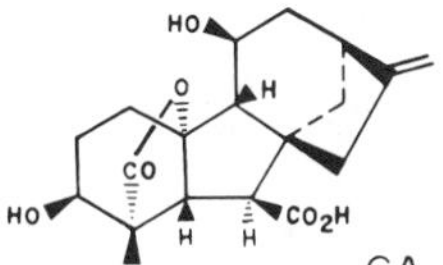

GA$_{35}$

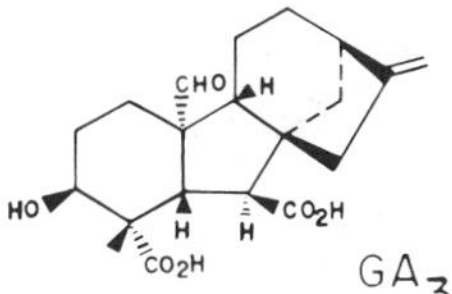

GA$_{36}$

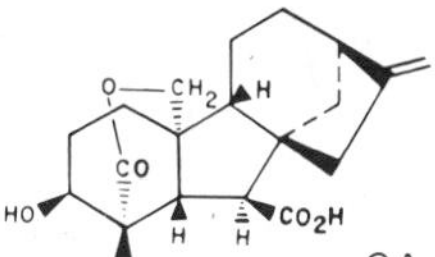

GA$_{37}$

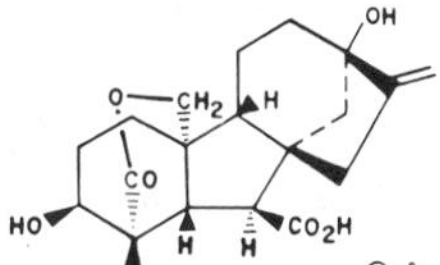

GA$_{38}$

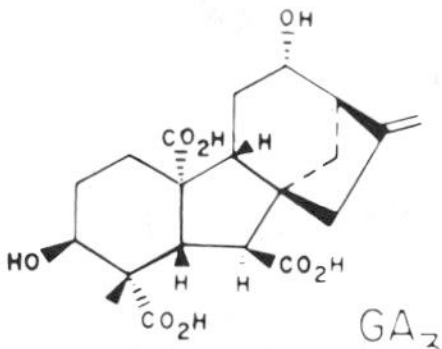

GA$_{39}$

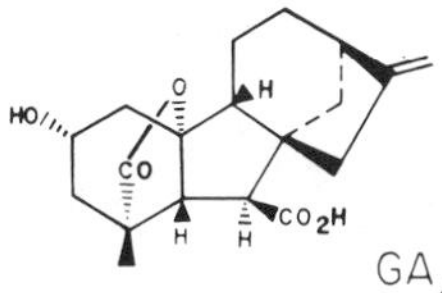

GA$_{40}$

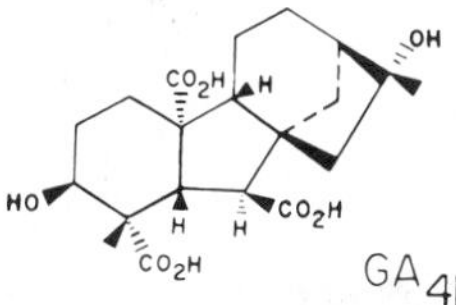

GA$_{41}$

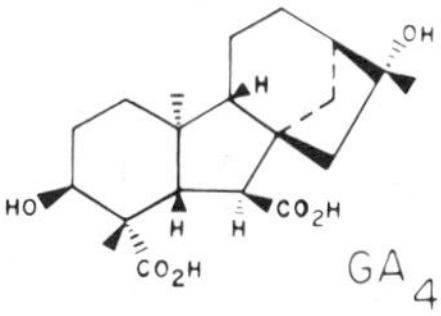

GA$_{42}$

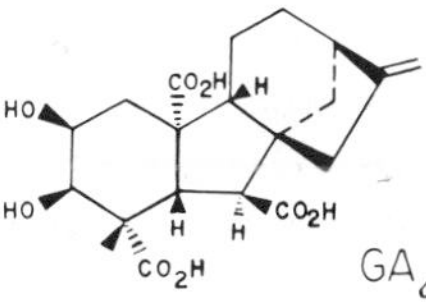

GA$_{43}$

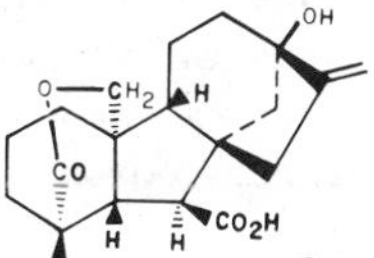

GA$_{44}$

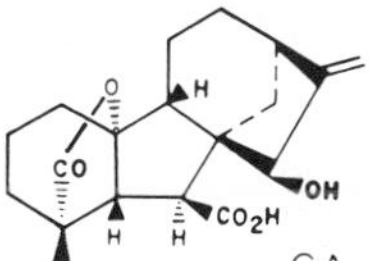

GA$_{45}$

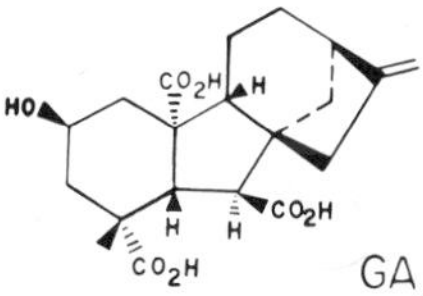

GA$_{46}$

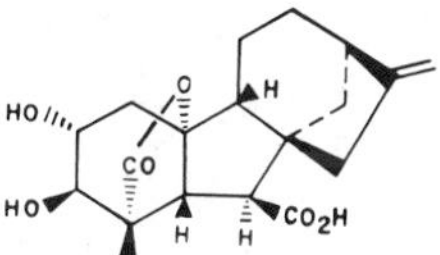

GA$_{47}$

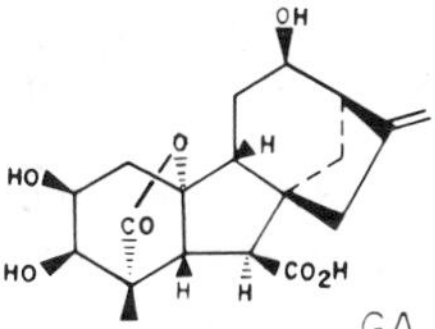

GA$_{48}$

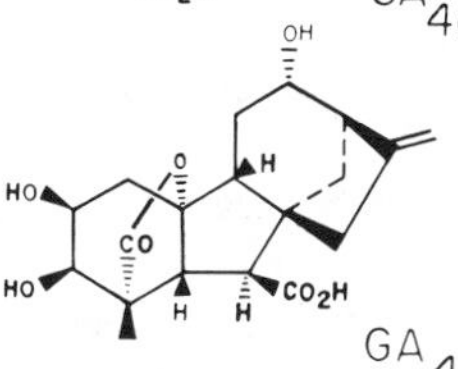

GA$_{49}$

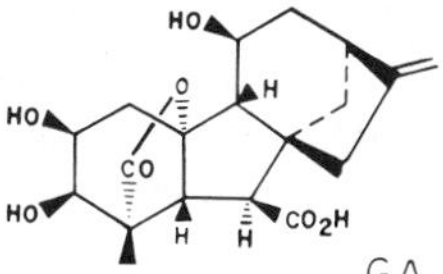

GA$_{50}$

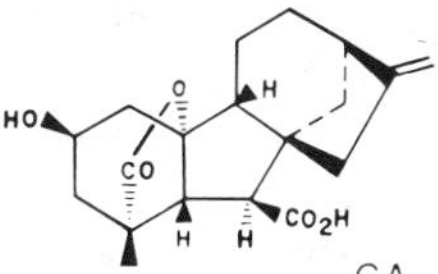

GA$_{51}$

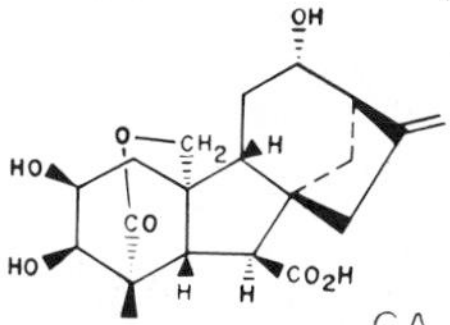

GA$_{52}$

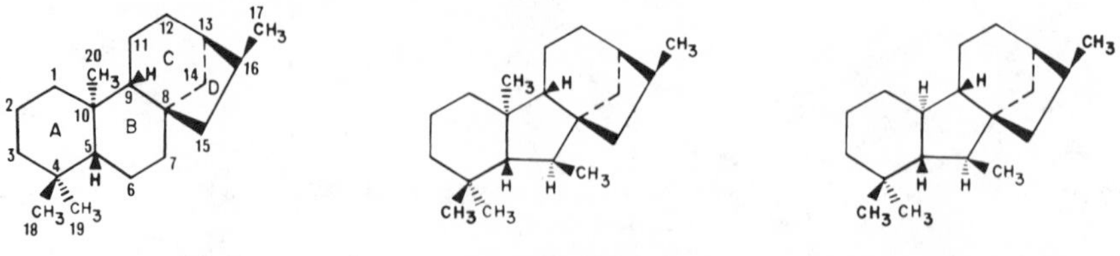

Figure 2   Structural skeletons of ent-kaurane and ent-gibberellanes.

IDENTIFICATION OF METABOLITES

Most studies on GA metabolism have used radiolabeled substrates. Where reasonable amounts of these metabolites are formed from a radiolabeled precursor, the metabolites have been isolated, identified by their physical properties, and their radiochemical purity established by a combination of crystallization to constant specific radioactivity, radio-TLC, and GC-RC. When the products from a radiolabeled precursor are formed in amounts insufficient for isolation and crystallization, and when the suspected metabolite is available, the radioactive metabolite has been diluted with the unlabeled metabolite and prepared to radiochemical purity as described above. Many examples of these conventional techniques have been published during the period under review (e.g. 18, 82). However, three novel approaches have been used.

The first relates to metabolism in fungal cultures where GA biosynthesis is blocked either genetically or chemically. In these cultures unlabeled substrates can be used and their metabolites identified by GC-MS (e.g. 15).

The second technique makes use of [14C], both as a radioactive and a heavy isotope. In enzyme preparations which can be dialyzed to remove or reduce the levels of endogenous intermediates, dilution of the radiolabel in labeled substrates is eliminated or minimized. Under these circumstances the [14C]-content of GAs and their precursors, biosynthesized from commercially available [2-14C]MVA, is sufficiently high to be detected by MS. The radioactivity of the [14C]-label can be used to follow the isolation of the metabolites, and the [14C]-content can be measured by GC-MS, allowing the simultaneous identification and determination of specific radioactivity of submicrogram quantities of metabolites (24). This method has been applied to the identification of metabolites from [2-14C]MVA in enzyme systems from seeds of Cucurbita maxima (73) and Pisum sativum (J. E. Graebe et al, unpublished information).

The third technique employs deuterium-labeled substrates. It is possible to prepare these substrates highly labeled, and the deuterium isotope can be detected and quantified by GC-MS. Thus deuterium-labeled compounds can be used as internal standards for the determination of the levels of native GAs. They can also be used in metabolic studies, doubly labeled with tritium. The radioactive isotope is used to follow the isolation of the metabolites and to quantify the process. The stable isotope permits the distinction between labeled substrate and labeled metabolite from the native GAs (154) and a comparison of the rates of metabolism of the added and natural GAs.

The foregoing discussion has begged the question of the minimal criteria for the positive identification of metabolites. Mass spectrometry (64) is the most sensitive method for identification although other spectroscopic properties are also definitive (e.g. IR and NMR). Chromatographic properties can only provide tentative identification which becomes more probable the greater the number of chromatographic systems used. In this review it has not been possible to apply strict criteria of identification to most of the metabolic studies with intact plants. However, in order to present a reasonably critical assessment of this topic, we have not considered publications in which identification of metabolites was based on TLC data only.

PATHWAY TO GA_{12}-ALDEHYDE

The complete pathway from MVA to GA_{12}-aldehyde is shown in Figure 3. Since Lang's review (103), which briefly discussed the broad outlines of this part of the pathway, detailed information has been obtained from fungal and higher plant cell-free systems.

MVA to ent-Kaurene

The pathway from MVA to ent-kaurene was first demonstrated by Graebe et al (71) in a cell-free preparation from the endosperm-nucellus of immature seeds of *Marah macrocarpus* (formerly *Echinocystis macrocarpa*). Subsequently it was also observed in cell-free systems from seeds or young pods of *Pisum sativum* (3, 33, 67), young seedlings of *Ricinus communis* (137), *P. sativum* (35), *Lycopersicum esculentum* (165) and *Zea mays* (90), immature seeds from *R. communis* (138), endosperm from *Cucurbita maxima* (68, 69), and mycelia of *Gibberella fujikuroi* (55, 144). The highest rates of conversion were obtained in the *Marah* and *Cucurbita* systems where ent-kaurene appeared to be the major product. In most other systems ent-kaurene production is low, and for cell-free systems from shoot tissues, the squalene (sterol) and phytoene (carotenoid) pathways greatly predominate (e.g. 67, 90).

The enzymes responsible for ent-kaurene formation are soluble and therefore remain in the high speed supernatant of a tissue homogenate. The first steps in the sequence, the activation of MVA to the pyrophosphate by MVA kinases, require ATP and Mg^{2+} or Mn^{2+} (92). GGPP, the precursor of all diterpenes, was first established as an intermediate in ent-kaurene biosynthesis in the *Marah* system by Oster & West (126). Its formation from IPP and DMAPP requires three steps which appear to be catalyzed by a single enzyme (125). Thus GGPP synthetase from the fruit of *Cucurbita pepo* will catalyze the condensation of IPP with DMAPP, GPP, or FPP to give GGPP as the sole product. It requires Mn^{2+} for highest activity and is distinct from FPP synthetase, which has a preference for Mg^{2+} (149).

The cyclization of GGPP to ent-kaurene has been shown to proceed in two steps (144). In the first step GGPP is converted, probably by a proton-initiated cycliza-

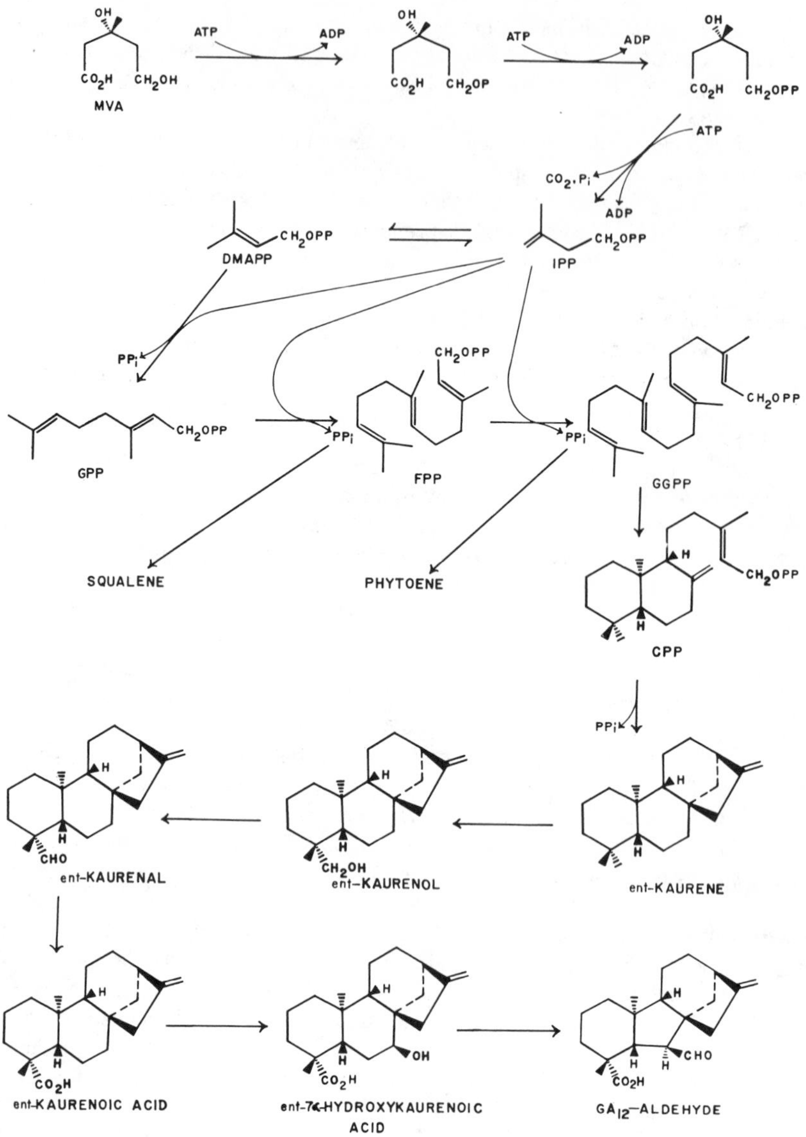

Figure 3 The biosynthetic pathway from MVA to GA_{12}-aldehyde including branch-points to other major plant terpenes. The steps before *ent*-kaurene are catalyzed by soluble enzymes and those between *ent*-kaurene and GA_{12}-aldehyde by membrane-bound mixed-function oxygenases.

tion, to a bicyclic intermediate [ent-trans-labda-8(16),13-dien-15-yl pyrophosphate, or CPP]. Dawson, Jefferies & Knox (41) have reported on the stereochemistry of cyclization of GGPP to ent-kaurene. They showed that ent-[3β-³H]kaurene was converted into GA₃ by G. fujikuroi without loss of [³H]. Thus 3β-hydroxylation occurs with retention of configuration. It had earlier been shown that the 4-pro-R hydrogen of MVA is lost in the conversion of ent-kaurene to GA₃ (85). Therefore, the 4-pro-R hydrogen of MVA appears at the 3β-position in ent-kaurene and the 3α-hydrogen is derived from the medium on cyclization of GGPP. Cyclization of GGPP may proceed by an antiplanar addition to the terminal double bond from a chair-chair conformation (41) (see Figure 4). A carbonium ion mechanism has been suggested for the further cyclization of CPP to ent-kaurene (142, 162; Figure 4). The involvement of a pimaradiene (22, 162) (i.e. a de-protonated form of the first intermediate between CPP and ent-kaurene, Figure 4) is discounted by the incorporation, into ent-kaurene, of four 4-pro-R-mevalonoid hydrogen atoms and eight 2-mevalonoid hydrogen atoms (85) and of ten deuterium atoms from [methyl-²H₃] MVA (55).

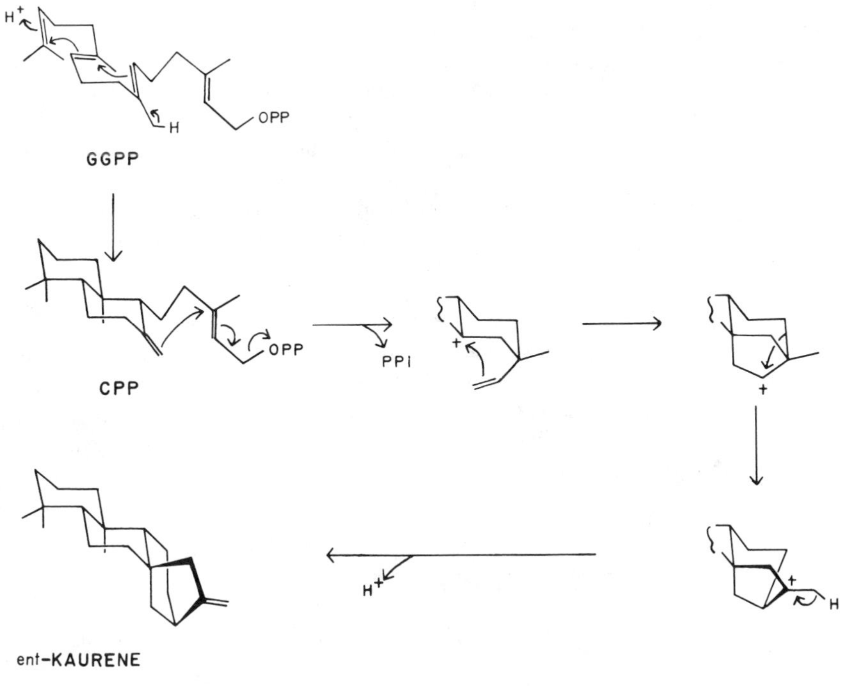

ent-KAURENE

Figure 4   The cyclization of GGPP to ent-kaurene. In this proposed mechanism, rings A and B are formed by a proton-initiated cyclization to give CPP. Ring C is then formed as the pyrophosphate is lost, followed by rearrangement of the resulting carbonium ion and loss of H⁺ from carbon-17 to produce ent-kaurene.

In most systems which have been examined, CPP is converted into *ent*-kaurene only; however, a cell-free preparation has been described (137) from *Ricinus* seedlings which converts GGPP into five diterpenes, (+)-stachene, (+)-sandarocopimaradiene, trachylobane, *ent*-kaurene, and casbene. The first four products are formed via CPP, while casbene is produced directly from GGPP. It was possible to resolve partially the enzyme activities on DEAE-cellulose (138). This multiplicity of products was found only in the cell-free system from *Ricinus* seedlings; cell-free systems from the immature seeds produced *ent*-kaurene only. The production of each diterpene reached a maximum 2 to 3 days after seed germination. Cell-free systems from *Z. mays* coleoptiles have been found to synthesize high levels of the *ent*-kaurene isomer, *ent*-kaur-15-ene (isokaurene) (Structure 1 in Figure 5) and only during the late stages of growth (P. Hedden, R. Heupel, B. Phinney & E. Wurtele, unpublished information). With the exception of casbene, which is a phytoalexin (151), the biological significance of these nonkaurenoid diterpenes is not known.

Fall & West (58) purified *ent*-kaurene synthetase 170-fold from *G. fujikuroi* mycelia and reported a molecular weight of 4.4 to 4.9 $\times 10^5$. It was not possible to resolve the two activities (GGPP $\rightarrow$ CPP, referred to as the A activity, and CPP $\rightarrow$ *ent*-kaurene, referred to as the B activity). However, their different pH optima (7.5 and 6.9 respectively) and differing susceptibilities to inhibition by plant growth retardants suggested that the activities are on different sites of the enzyme or enzyme complex. Both activities were stimulated by divalent metal ions, with Mg^{2+} being the most active. Ni^{2+} at low concentrations (0.1–1.0mM) supported activity A only. The partial purification of *ent*-kaurene synthetase from *Marah* endosperm has also been described (59). Instability of both activities prevented purification to a level comparable to that obtained with the fungal enzyme. Again it was not possible to separate the A and B activities. The molecular weight was estimated as less than 45,000, and the pH optima of the two activities (pH 7.3 and 6.9 respectively) were similar to those of the fungal enzyme.

Certain plant growth inhibitors block the cyclization of GGPP to *ent*-kaurene (42). Some of these inhibitors, such as AMO-1618 and phosphon D, strongly inhibit the A activity but not the B activity of *ent*-kaurene synthetase, while others such as Q-64 and SKF 3301A block both activities (58, 59). Recently a new plant growth retardant (*2* in Figure 5) has been described (86) which appears to be more effective than AMO-1618 with a similar site of action (91).

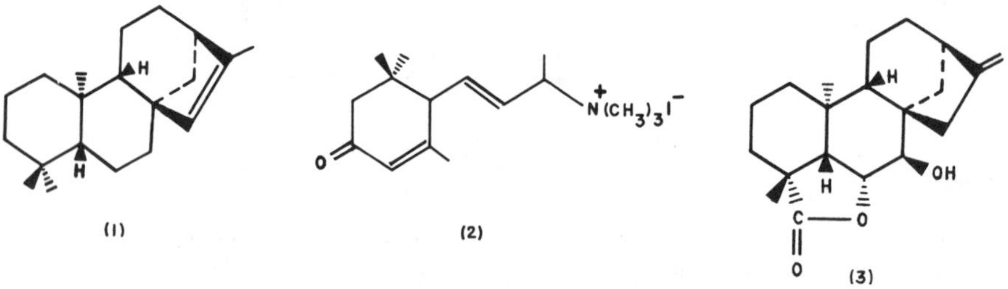

Figure 5 Structures of compounds discussed in the text.

ent-Kaurene to GA$_{12}$-aldehyde

ent-Kaurene is converted in a sequence of oxidative steps to GA$_{12}$-aldehyde, the earliest known intermediate containing the *ent*-gibberellane skeleton (Figure 3).

ENT-KAURENE TO *ENT*-7α-HYDROXYKAURENOIC ACID

The pathway   Graebe et al (71) isolated *ent*-[^{14}C]kaurenol from incubations of [2-^{14}C]MVA with the low-speed supernatant from the *Marah* cell-free system. Subsequently *ent*-[^{14}C]kaurenal and *ent*-[^{14}C]kaurenoic acid were also identified from similar incubations (43). The biosynthetic sequence of these *ent*-kaurenoids, *ent*-kaurene → *ent*-kaurenol → *ent*-kaurenal → *ent*-kaurenoic acid, was established by refeeding each intermediate followed by isolation of the products. Later, Lew & West (105) demonstrated the further hydroxylation of *ent*-kaurenoic acid to *ent*-7 α-hydroxykaurenoic acid in the *Marah* cell-free system.

The sequence of oxidations from *ent*-kaurene to *ent*-7α-hydroxykaurenoic acid has been demonstrated conclusively for the *Cucurbita* system by Graebe et al (69, 73). Coolbaugh & Moore (34) have identified *ent*-[^{14}C]kaurenol as a product from feeds of [2-^{14}C]MVA to cell-free systems of *Pisum* cotyledons. It was not possible to obtain metabolism of added *ent*-[^{14}C]kaurene with this system, although there was some evidence that *ent*-kaurene, biosynthesized in situ, was further metabolized. All the steps from *ent*-kaurene to *ent*-7α-hydroxykaurenoic acid have now been demonstrated in crude homogenates of immature *Pisum* seeds (J. E. Graebe and H.-J. Ropers, unpublished information). Murphy & Briggs (121) established the biosynthetic sequence from *ent*-kaurenol to *ent*-7α-hydroxykaurenoic acid in cell-free systems from embryos and young leaves of *Hordeum distichon*. The conversion of *ent*-[17-^{14}C]kaurenoic acid to *ent*-7 α-hydroxy-[^{14}C]kaurenoic acid has also been shown for a microsomal fraction prepared from the mycelia of *G. fujikuroi* (164).

Properties of the enzymes   Using the *Marah* cell-free system, it was first shown that the enzymes involved in the conversion of *ent*-kaurene to *ent*-kaurenoic acid are localized in the microsomal pellet (105,000 X *g* pellet) (43). These enzymes required O$_2$ and a reduced pyridine nucleotide (preferably NADPH) for activity, suggesting that they are mixed-function oxygenases. It was further shown that cytochrome P$_{450}$ was involved in the oxidation of *ent*-kaurene to *ent*-kaurenol and *ent*-kaurenal to *ent*-kaurenoic acid (122). The hydroxylation of *ent*-kaurenoic acid to *ent*-7α-hydroxykaurenoic acid was found to have characteristics similar to the oxidative steps from *ent*-kaurene to *ent*-kaurenoic acid and may also be the result of mixed-function oxygenase activity (105). Thus all the steps between *ent*-kaurene and *ent*-7α-hydroxykaurenoic acid are probably catalyzed by mixed function oxygenases. The properties of the *Marah* microsomal system for the oxidation of *ent*-kaurene to *ent*-7α-hydroxykaurenoic acid have now been examined in some detail (87, 88), and the authors have concluded that the electron transfer system in the mixed-function oxygenases in *Marah* microsomes is similar to that found in liver.

Some characteristics of the cell-free system from immature *Pisum* seeds for the oxidation of *ent*-kaurenoids have also been reported (34). Cytochrome P_{450} was shown to be present in the microsome fraction using CO difference spectra. Moore, Barlow & Coolbaugh (119) have discussed evidence that *ent*-[^{14}C]kaurene, added exogenously or generated in situ, is associated with a high molecular weight protein ($> 15 \times 10^6$) in the high-speed supernatant from the *Pisum* cotyledon system. This "*ent*-kaurene carrier protein" would be analogous to the sterol-carrier protein found in rat liver homogenates (143). However, Graebe & Ropers (77) have pointed out that the *ent*-[^{14}C]kaurene could be binding to microsomes which have been incompletely sedimented.

The growth retardant ancymidol (EL-531) inhibits shoot and root elongation (104), an effect reversed by GA treatment. In cell-free preparations of *Marah* endosperm, this retardant was shown to block the oxidation of *ent*-kaurene (30), *ent*-kaurenol, and *ent*-kaurenal, but not *ent*-kaurenoic acid (31). The authors have suggested (31) that ancymidol interacts directly with cytochrome P_{450} in the oxygenase catalyzing the steps from *ent*-kaurene to *ent*-kaurenoic acid.

ENT-7α-HYDROXYKAURENOIC ACID TO GA_{12}-ALDEHYDE   The first cell-free biosynthesis of GA_{12}-aldehyde was achieved by Graebe, Bowen & MacMillan (70) from [2-^{14}C]MVA using the *Cucurbita* endosperm system. Later the *Cucurbita* and *Marah* systems were found to convert *ent*-7α-hydroxy-[^{14}C]kaurenoic acid into radiolabeled *ent*-6α, 7α-dihydroxykaurenoic acid (see Figure 6), GA_{12}-aldehyde, and GA_{12} (72, 73, 164). In the *Cucurbita* system GA_{12}-aldehyde was further metabolized to GA_{12} and *ent*-6α, 7α-dihydroxykaurenoic acid was coverted to a number

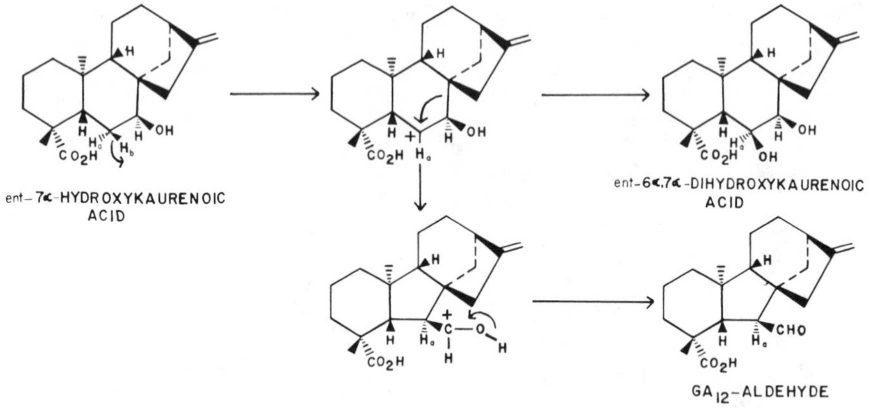

Figure 6   A formalized mechanism for the conversion of *ent*-7α-hydroxykaurenoic acid to GA_{12}-aldehyde and *ent*-6α,7α-dihydroxykaurenoic acid. Abstraction of the *ent*-6α hydrogen results in the formation of a high energy intermediate (possibly a carbonium ion) which is oxygenated to the dihydroxykaurenoic acid or undergoes contraction of the B ring to GA_{12}-aldehyde.

of metabolites, but not to GAs (72). Thus, *ent*-7α-hydroxykaurenoic acid lies on a branch point in the pathway, undergoing either *ent*-6α-hydroxylation to *ent*-6α,7 α-dihydroxykaurenoic acid or ring B contraction to give GA_{12}-aldehyde. In the fungus there appears to be a third branch which leads to the kaurenolides. Microsomes from *G. fujikuroi* mycelia have been shown to convert *ent*-[17-¹⁴C]kaurenoic acid into radiolabeled 7β-hydroxykaurenolide (*3* in Figure 5) as well as into GA_{12}-aldehyde, GA_{12}, GA_{14}, and *ent*-6α,7α-dihydroxykaurenoic acid (164). 7β-Hydroxy-kaurenolide is probably formed by *ent*-6β-hydroxylation of *ent*-7α-hydroxy-kaurenoic acid (82). The enzymes which catalyze these steps are membrane bound (72, 164) and are probably mixed-function oxygenases. The conversion of *ent*-7α-hydroxy-[¹⁴C]kaurenoic acid to [¹⁴C]GA_{12}-aldehyde has also been demonstrated in cell-free preparations from immature *Pisum* seeds (J. E. Graebe and H.-J. Ropers, unpublished information).

In summary, the steps from MVA to GA_{12}-aldehyde are the same for the three higher plant species *M. macrocarpus, C. maxima,* and *P. sativum,* and for the fungus *G. fujikuroi.*

Mechanism of ring contraction GA_{12}-aldehyde is formed from *ent*-7α-hydroxy-kaurenoic acid by the contraction of ring B from a 6 to a 5 carbon ring with carbon-7 being extruded (see Figure 6). No intermediates between the two compounds have been found and the conversion appears to be direct. Evans, Hanson & White (57) proposed that ring contraction might be initiated by the abstraction of the *ent*-6α hydrogen. This was based on the results from stereospecifically labeled [³H]MVA added to cultures of *G. fujikuroi,* in which they found that the *ent*-6α hydrogen atom was lost in the conversion of *ent*-7α-hydroxykaurenoic acid to GAs. In contrast, the *ent*-6β hydrogen atom was retained at carbon-6 in the *ent*-gibberellane skeleton. However, Hanson & Hawker (80) subsequently fed [1-³H₂]GPP to the fungus and found that both hydrogen atoms from carbon-6 of the kaurenoid skeleton were retained in GA_{12}-aldehyde. Although this finding was based on only a 0.005% incorporation of label into GA_{12}-aldehyde, the authors suggested a second mechanism in which a hydride shift from C-6 to C-7 occurs as the 7,8-bond migrates to carbon-6. In this case the original *ent*-6α hydrogen would be lost on oxidation of the 7-aldehyde to a carboxylic acid.

Using the *Cucurbita* cell-free system, Graebe, Hedden & MacMillan (76) obtained data which indicate that the first mechanism (57) may be the correct one. In this system GA_{12}-aldehyde and *ent*-6α,7α-dihydroxykaurenoic acid are formed from *ent*-7α-hydroxykaurenoic acid in almost equal amounts and at the same rates (72). The Lineweaver-Burk and Hill plots of their rates of formation are linear, and the slope of the Hill plot is nearly 1.0, indicating first order kinetics. Both reactions have the same pH and temperature optima and cofactor requirements, so that the evidence points to the two products being formed from the same high-energy intermediate, the rate of formation of which determines the rate of the overall conversion. When *ent*-7α-hydroxy-[¹⁴C,6-³H₂]kaurenoic acid was fed to the *Cucurbita* system, each of the radiolabeled products, GA_{12}-aldehyde and *ent*-6α,7α-dihydroxy-kaurenoic acid, had half the ³H/¹⁴C ratio of the substrate (76). This corresponds to the loss of one [³H] atom from carbon-6, which is in direct contrast to the results of Hanson, Hawker & White (82). Graebe et al (unpublished data) have subsequently found that the *ent*-6α hydrogen atom is lost in the formation of both GA_{12}-aldehyde and *ent*-6α,7α-dihydroxykaurenoic acid. They prepared *ent*-7α-hydroxy-[6α-²H,17-³H₂]kaurenoic acid containing 62 atoms % [²H]. It was converted by the *C. maxima* system to GA_{12}-aldehyde, GA_{12}, and to the dihydroxykaurenoic acid which contained, respectively, zero, zero, and 4 atoms % [²H]. The formation of products with the same specific radioactivity as the substrate confirms that the products came from the substrate. Thus the rate-limiting step in ring contraction appears to be the removal of a hydrogen from the *ent*-6α position. The resulting high-energy intermediate, e.g. a carbonium ion (see Figure 6), could be either oxygenated to the dihydroxy compound or undergo rearrangement to give GA_{12}-aldehyde.

Intact Higher Plants

Direct evidence for all of the steps in the pathway from MVA to GA_{12}-aldehyde is still incomplete for intact higher plants. However, *ent*-kaurene, *ent*-kaurenol, *ent*-kaurenal, and *ent*-kaurenoic acid are naturally occurring in a number of higher plants and the pathway, *ent*-kaurenol → *ent*-kaurenal → *ent*-kaurenoic acid → *ent*-7α-hydroxykaurenoic acid has been demonstrated in germinating grains of *Hordeum distichon* (121).

In addition, Hanson & White (83) have identified *ent*-[¹⁴C]kaurene from feeds of [2-¹⁴C]MVA to leaves of *Stevia rebaudiana*. This latter example was one of a series of studies (21, 83, 141) which demonstrated the biosynthetic origin of steviol (*ent*-13-hydroxykaurenoic acid; see Figure 10), found naturally as the glycoside in the composite *S. rebaudiana*. While GA_{20} has been identified in *S. rebaudiana* (2), there is no evidence yet for the suggestion (100, 103) that steviol acts as a precursor of 13-hydroxylated GAs. It is more likely that steviol may be a terminal branch product from *ent*-kaurenoic acid and thus unrelated to the GA-biosynthetic pathway. Similarly there is no evidence that *ent*-15α-hydroxykaurenoic acid (*8* in Figure 11), naturally occurring as the acetate (xylopic acid) in the fruit of *Xylopia aethiopica* (52), is a precursor of the 15β-hydroxy GAs such as GA_{32} and GA_{45}.

While there is some evidence from other feeding studies (e.g. 159) for the MVA to GA_{12}-aldehyde pathway, the metabolites were identified by TLC only.

PATHWAYS FROM GA_{12}-ALDEHYDE

The Fungus—Gibberella fujikuroi

Figure 7 shows the biosynthetic pathways from GA_{12}-aldehyde which are now established for *G. fujikuroi*. These pathways are based upon results from several studies using both GA-producing strains ACC 917, GF-1a, and REC-193A and mutants R-9 and B1-41a. Mutant R-9 is blocked for 13-hydroxylation and so produces neither GA_1 nor GA_3 (14, 152). B1-41a is blocked between *ent*-kaurenal and *ent*-kaurenoic acid (see Figure 3), with a leakage of less than 3% for the conversion of [2-¹⁴C]MVL into [¹⁴C]GA_3 (17). Comprehensive studies with the mutant B1-41a are used as a framework to establish the pathways and as a basis for the discussion of complementary and supplementary studies using other strains. For clarity the results are not presented chronologically.

3-HYDROXYLATION PATHWAY   Bearder, MacMillan & Phinney (15) studied the metabolism of unlabeled substrates using resuspension cultures of mycelia of the mutant B1-41a at pH 3.5 and pH 7.0. The substrates had either been shown to act as precursors of fungal GAs by tracer studies or possessed the structures of possible intermediates between *ent*-kaurenoic acid and fungal GAs.

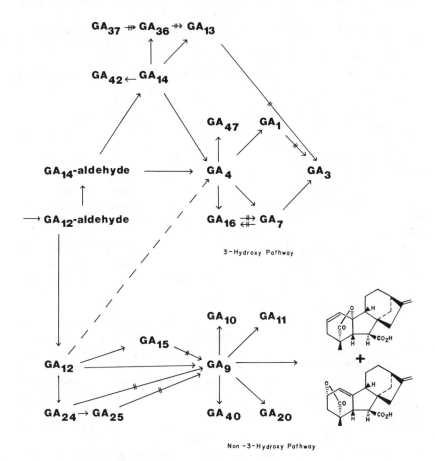

Figure 7 GA-biosynthetic pathways beyond GA_{12}-aldehyde established for cultures of the fungus *Gibberella fujikuroi*. Two major pathways are shown, both originating from GA_{12}-aldehyde. One pathway (3-hydroxylation pathway) involves the 3β-hydroxylation of GA_{12}-aldehyde to GA_{14}-aldehyde. The other pathway (non-3-hydroxylation pathway) has no 3β-hydroxylation step.

The results of the feeding experiments with the mutant B1-41a at pH 3.5 for 20 hr incubation are discussed with reference to Figure 7. It is convenient to work back from GA_3, which is the major gibberellin in GA-producing strains of the fungus and which was found not to be metabolized under the conditions of culture that were used (15). Gibberellin A_7 was converted (71%) into GA_3, and GA_4 was almost completely metabolized to give mainly GA_3 (79%) with traces (2%) of GA_1, GA_{16}, and GA_7. When re-fed, GA_1 and GA_{16} were not metabolized and are therefore probably end products. Thus GA_{16} is neither produced from, nor a precursor of, GA_7. These results agree with earlier studies by Pitel, Vining & Arsenault (130), who found that [^{14}C]GA_1 was not converted into [^{14}C]GA_3 by the GA-producing strain ACC 917 when grown on a synthetic medium. They did, however, obtain a low conversion (0.6%) of [$1,2-^3H_2$]GA_1 into [^3H]GA_3 by the same strain, grown on a nonsynthetic medium that was favorable to GA_1 production. The low or nonconversion of GA_1 into GA_3 has also been observed (14) in the mutant R-9 in which 13-hydroxylation is blocked. Recently McInnes et al (118) have detected small amounts of [^{14}C]GA_{47} from incubations of [^{14}C]GA_4 with strain ACC 917. The results of Evans et al (57) from stereospecific labeling of GAs with 2(R)-, 2(S)- and 5(R)-[^3H] MVA show that the dehydrogenation step from GA_4 to GA_7 is a *cis*-process with loss of the 1α and 2α hydrogens.

Returning to the feeding studies with mutant B1-41a, GA_{14} was only 50% metabolized in 20 hr, yielding GA_3 (32%), and traces of GA_1, GA_4, GA_7, GA_{13}, GA_{16}, GA_{36}, and GA_{42} (15). Gibberellins A_{13}, A_{36}, and A_{37} were not metabolized even after 5 days incubation. Gibberellin A_{14}-aldehyde was rapidly metabolized to GA_{14}; after 20 hr the product distribution was almost identical with that of the 20 hr feed of GA_{14}. However, there is some doubt whether GA_{14} lies on the direct pathway from GA_{14}-aldehyde to GA_4. This question was first raised from studies (89) in which GA_{14} was metabolized less efficiently than GA_{14}-aldehyde by nonreplacement cultures of the mutant B1-41a grown on a 10% ICI medium. On the other hand, GA_{14} accumulated in 20 hr feeds of *ent*-kaurenoic acid, *ent*-7α-hydroxykaurenoic acid, GA_{12}-aldehyde, and GA_{14}-aldehyde to resuspension cultures of mutant B1-41a (15). This accumulation, even more marked at pH 7.0 (15), is only temporary at pH 3.5 and does not occur to the same extent in the GA-producing parent, GF-1a. Thus the build-up of GA_{14} in the mutant B1-41a may simply indicate that the conversion of GA_{14} to GA_4 is the rate-limiting step in the mutant but not in GA-producing strains. To complicate matters, it has recently been reported (56) that GA_{14} was substantially unchanged after 24 hr incubation with 3-day-old cultures of strain ACC 917. This result contrasts with the earlier finding (38) that [^{14}C]GA_{14} was incorporated (4.7%) into [^{14}C]GA_3 by the same strain, ACC 917. Thus GA_{14} may not be on the direct pathway.

The intermediates *ent*-7α-hydroxykaurenoic acid, GA_{12}-aldehyde, and GA_{14}-aldehyde were not detected from a feed of *ent*-kaurenoic acid to the mutant B1-41a, even under conditions where GA_{14} accumulates (15). Cross, Norton & Stewart (38) first suggested that GA_{12}-aldehyde rather than GA_{12} was the intermediate in the pathway to 3-hydroxy GAs. This conclusion was supported by the finding that [$6-^3H$]GA_{12}-aldehyde was rapidly metabolized to [^3H]GA_{14} by the slow GA-producing strain REC-193A and under conditions in which GA_{12} was not metabolized (13). Direct proof that GA_{14}-aldehyde was an intermediate was provided by Hedden, MacMillan & Phinney (89) in a feed of $[6\text{-}^3H]GA_{12}$-aldehyde to the mutant B1-41a. By isotope dilution they recovered GA_{14}-aldehyde containing 0.5% of the radioactivity under conditions in which the substrate was almost completely metabolized to $[^3H]GA_{14}$.

Gibberellin A_{12}-aldehyde, like GA_{14}-aldehyde, does not accumulate in the fungus. However, its intermediacy has been demonstrated by Hanson, Hawker & White (82), who recovered GA_{12}-aldehyde with 0.1% of the radioactivity from a feed of radiolabeled ent-7α-hydroxykaurenoic acid to cultures of strain ACC 917. Previously it had been shown (38) that $[17\text{-}^{14}C]GA_{12}$-aldehyde was converted in high yield (15.4%) into $[17\text{-}^{14}C]GA_3$ by strain ACC 917. More recently, Evans & Hanson (56) and Bearder, MacMillan & Phinney (15) investigated in more detail the metabolism of GA_{12}-aldehyde into 3-hydroxylated and non-3-hydroxylated GAs. Both studies clearly showed that GA_{12}-aldehyde is metabolized to both 3-hydroxylated and non-3-hydroxylated GAs and is therefore a point of divergence to these two series. However, Evans & Hanson (56) noted that GA_{12}-aldehyde was unstable under their conditions of culture, undergoing autoxidation to, inter alia, GA_{12}, and they concluded that substantial amounts of the non-3-hydroxylated GAs, formed from GA_{12}-aldehyde, were a consequence of this autoxidation to GA_{12}. Thus they observed a higher proportion of non-3-hydroxylated GAs from a 3-hr feed of $[17\text{-}^{14}C]GA_{12}$-aldehyde to strain ACC 917 than from a 5-day feed of $[2\text{-}^{14}C]MVA$ under the same conditions.

Autoxidation of GA_{12}-aldehyde was not observed in 20-hr feeds to resuspension cultures of the mutant B1-41a (15). Moreover, a comparison of the products from feeds of GA_{12}-aldehyde at pH 3.5 and at pH 7.0 gave no significant difference in the ratio of 3-hydroxylated and non-3-hydroxylated GAs, although autoxidation of the substrate might be expected to be greater at the higher pH value. The main difference was a greater accumulation of GA_{14} at the higher pH.

NON-3-HYDROXYLATION PATHWAY   Evidence has been presented indicating that GA_{12}-aldehyde is a point of divergence to the 3-hydroxylated and non-3-hydroxylated GAs and that GA_{12} is not on the main pathway to the 3-hydroxylated GAs. GA_{12} was shown to be formed from GA_{12}-aldehyde by the mutant B1-41a at pH 3.5 and 7.0 (15). In strain ACC 917, $[17\text{-}^{14}C]GA_{12}$ was metabolized within 6 hr to radiolabeled GA_9 (23%), GA_{15} (9%), GA_{24} (25%) and GA_{25} (18%), and the product distribution was similar after 24 hr except for the level of incorporation into GA_{25} (10%) (56).

Bearder, MacMillan & Phinney (15) obtained similar results in 20-hr incubations of GA_{12} using the mutant B1-41a at pH 3.5 and 7.0, except that small amounts of the 3-hydroxylated GAs—GA_3, GA_{13}, and GA_{14}—were also formed. In these mutant studies (15) GA_{15}, GA_{24}, and GA_{25} did not act as precursors of GA_9. Gibberellins A_{15} and A_{25} were not metabolized, and GA_{24} was converted to GA_{25}.

Further metabolism of GA_9 is slow. Evans & Hanson (56) recovered 89% of GA_9 unchanged after 144 hr incubation in cultures of strain ACC 917. Earlier it was found (36, 37) that $[17\text{-}^{14}C]GA_9$ was metabolized by strain ACC 917 to give low yields of $[^{14}C]GA_{10}$ and the $[^{14}C]$-labeled 1,10-dehydro-19,2-lactone shown in Figure 7. Bearder et al (11) have also examined the metabolism of GA_9 by resuspension cultures of the mutant B1-41a at two pH values. Seventy percent of the GA_9 was unmetabolized and low yields of GA_{10} (2%) and GA_{20} (7%) were detected after 20 hr at pH 3.5. Only 25% of the added GA_9 was recovered after 7 days at pH 4.8, and the main metabolites, formed in low yield, were GA_{20} and GA_{40}. Traces of several other metabolites were also detected, including GA_{11} and two dehydroderivatives, one of which was the 1,10-dehydro-19,2-lactone previously reported (37), and the other was possibly 1,2-dehydro GA_9 (see Figure 7). It has been suggested (4) that GA_{11} is biosynthesized from GA_9 via these 1,2- and 1,10-dehydro compounds, but this postulate has not been directly tested. From the observed conversion (11) of GA_9 to GA_{20} by the mutant B1-41a it was predicted that GA_{20} would be found as a natural metabolite of GA-producing strains. This prediction has been verified recently by the detection of GA_{20} in cultures of strain ACC 917 (118). Thus all the GAs shown in the biosynthetic pathways in Figure 7 are normal metabolites of GA-producing strains of *G. fujikuroi*.

Higher Plants: Cell-free Systems

Cell-free systems from higher plants are beginning to yield information on the GA-biosynthetic pathway beyond GA_{12}-aldehyde and on the nature of the enzymes which catalyze steps in these pathways. Most progress has been made with cell-free systems from *Cucurbita maxima* endosperm, but information is also beginning to emerge using cell-free preparations from immature seeds of *Pisum sativum*. In addition, a cell-free extract from *Phaseolus vulgaris* seedlings has been used to study an enzyme which catalyzes a late step in the pathway.

CUCURBITA MAXIMA   Graebe, Bowen & MacMillan (70) originally described the conversion of $[2\text{-}^{14}C]MVA$ into $[^{14}C]GA_{12}$-aldehyde and $[^{14}C]GA_{12}$, using a low-speed supernatant fraction from the *C. maxima* endosperm in which $MnCl_2$ was included to maximize the yield of diterpenoids. However, in these early studies they obtained no conversion to GAs beyond GA_{12}. Subsequently, when $MnCl_2$ was omitted from the incubation mixture, $[^{14}C]GA_{12}$-aldehyde and $[^{14}C]GA_{12}$ were found to be metabolized to a number of $[^{14}C]$-labeled C_{20}-GAs which were identified by GC-MS (73). Nonlabeled GAs were then used to establish the biosynthetic relationship of the GAs identified from the radiolabeled feeds. Each GA was fed and the products identified by GC-MS (72, 74, 75). Nonlabeled GAs could be used because the rates of conversion were very high and the cell-free system contained no native GAs except the end product, GA_{43}. What emerged were a number of parallel pathways forming a metabolic grid (Figure 8). The presence of these pathways, which represent a series of similar reactions on different substrates, suggests that the enzymes catalyzing parallel steps in the pathways are nonspecific. However, certain substrates were converted more readily than others and a favored pathway, at least in vitro, was proposed by Graebe & Hedden (72) and is indicated in Figure 8 by the continuous arrows. In this favored pathway, GA_{12} is oxidized at carbon-20 to the aldehyde (GA_{24}) followed by 3β-hydroxylation to give GA_{36}. Further oxidation at carbon-20 to the carboxylic acid yields GA_{13} which is then 2β-hydroxylated to GA_{43}, the final product. The identification of GA_{43} as a natural product in the endosperm of *C. maxima* (20) is circumstantial evidence that the in vitro pathway observed in the cell-free system may also be operating in vivo. GA_{15} was formed from feeds of both GA_{12}-aldehyde and GA_{12}. However, GA_{15} is not on the pathway to GA_{43} since it was metabolized to only one gibberellin, GA_{37}. In short duration incubations of GA_{12} with the cell-free system, high levels of GA_{15} and low levels of GA_{43} were observed. Longer incubations resulted in reduced levels of GA_{15} and increased levels of GA_{43}. Therefore, GA_{15} was behaving as if it were an intermediate in the pathway to GA_{43}. These seemingly contradictory results may indicate that GA_{15} is an artifact formed from the true intermediate upon extraction. Thus the changes in observed levels of GA_{15} may reflect changes in levels of the true intermediate which is metabolized to GA_{43}. This intermediate may well be the open lactone form of GA_{15}. The closed lactone function in GA_{15} would block further oxidation of carbon-20 and therefore prevent the conversion of GA_{15} to GA_{43}.

The alternate pathways in Figure 8 are probably the result of the high levels of substrates used in the incubations. For example, GA_{12}-aldehyde was metabolized to GA_{43} in high yield when added at concentrations of 0.1 $\mu g/100$ μl, but in low yield when fed at concentrations of 3.6 $\mu g/100$ μl. In the latter case the major metabolite was GA_{14}-aldehyde. Although GA_{14}-aldehyde was converted to GA_{43}, it was never detected as a metabolite in low-level feeds of GA_{12}-aldehyde and is probably not on the main pathway to GA_{43}. Finally, GA_{25}, a minor product from GA_{24}, was inefficiently metabolized to GA_{13} and is probably not on the main pathway to GA_{43}.

The conversion of GA_{12}-aldehyde into GA_{43} is catalyzed by the 200,000 X g supernatant fraction (72). Thus the enzymes responsible for these conversions are distinct from the membrane-bound microsomal oxidases responsible for GA_{12}-aldehyde formation from *ent*-kaurene. Interestingly, the oxidation of GA_{12}-aldehyde to GA_{12} is catalyzed by both the soluble and microsomal fractions. The soluble enzymes are inhibited by Mn^{2+}, which explains why no conversion beyond GA_{12} could be obtained in the presence of $MnCl_2$. Dialysis of the cell-free system against EDTA inhibited activity beyond GA_{12} and this inhibition was reversed by the addition of

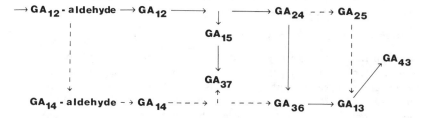

Figure 8   Biosynthetic pathways from GA_{12}-aldehyde to GA_{43} established for a cell-free system from *Cucurbita maxima* endosperm. These enzymes are water soluble and require Fe^{2+} for activity. The favored pathway is indicated by the continuous arrows.

Fe^{2+}. Fe^{2+} also overcame the inhibition due to Mn^{2+}. The soluble enzymes appear to contain Fe^{2+} in a very loosely bound form, in which case Mn^{2+} could bind reversibly to the Fe^{2+} binding site to produce an inactive enzyme.

The *Cucurbita* system has also been found to convert $[^{14}C]GA_{12}$-aldehyde to $[^{14}C]GA_4$ in small yield, which was the first demonstration of the in vitro biosynthesis of a C_{19}-GA (74). The identity of the immediate precursor of GA_4 in this system is still unknown. The cell-free preparations converted relatively large amounts of GA_9 to GA_4 (72), so that GA_9 could be the first C_{19}-GA in the pathway leading to GA_4. However, GA_9 has not been detected as a natural product in the endosperm nor is it a product from feeds of GA_{12}-aldehyde or any other substrate.

PISUM SATIVUM   The conversion of $[^{14}C]GA_{12}$-aldehyde to radiolabeled GA_{12}, 13-hydroxy GA_{12}, and GA_{44} has been demonstrated in the low-speed supernatant from a homogenate of immature *Pisum* seeds (J. E. Graebe and H.-J. Ropers, unpublished information). This is a second example of the complete cell-free biosynthesis of a C_{20}-GA from MVA since all the steps preceding GA_{12}-aldehyde have been demonstrated in this system, and GA_{44} is native (60) to *Pisum* seeds.

PHASEOLUS VULGARIS   A soluble hydroxylase has been isolated from cotyledons of germinating *P. vulgaris* cv Kentucky Wonder (127, 128). This enzyme catalyzed the 2β-hydroxylation of $[1,2-^3H_2]GA_1$ to $[^3H]GA_8$, a reaction exactly analogous to the conversion of GA_{13} to GA_{43} by the *C. maxima* system. The activity was inhibited by EDTA and could be restored by the addition of Fe^{2+} or Fe^{3+}. Fe^{3+} was less effective than Fe^{2+} and required the presence of ascorbate or NADPH which presumably acted by reducing Fe^{3+} to Fe^{2+}. A similar result was obtained with the *C. maxima* system where NADPH was required for maximum activity, presumably by keeping Fe^{2+} reduced (72). The *P. vulgaris* enzyme was inhibited by a 100% N_2 atmosphere, demonstrating the need for O_2 (128). Very high levels of CO were also inhibitory, but the inhibition was not light reversible so that cytochrome P_{450} does not seem to be involved.

It is interesting to note that the nature of the enzymes in the GA pathway changes with the nature of the substrates. Between *ent*-kaurene and GA_{12}-aldehyde the intermediates are nonpolar and the enzymes are membrane-bound. After GA_{12}-aldehyde the water solubility of the intermediates increases and, at least for the *C. maxima* system, the enzymes are water soluble.

Higher Plants: Cellular Systems

The apparent low substrate specificity of enzymes concerned with steps in the GA-biosynthetic pathway present special problems when one is interpreting the results of feeding studies with intact plants. Unless the added GA is known to be native and to be present at the time of the feed, the observed metabolism may bear no more relation to the natural process than does the metabolism of GA analogs by fungal cultures. It has been suggested that the following criteria (62) be met in order to establish that a metabolic step $GA_x \rightarrow GA_y$ is a natural process: (*a*) GA_x and GA_y are native; (*b*) labeled GA_x is fed at a time when GA_x is known to be present and probably when the level is maximal; (c) the amount of labeled GA_x fed is similar to the natural level; and (d) the formation of labeled GA_y coincides with the time at which native GA_y is present. While it may not be possible for practical reasons to meet all these criteria, experiments should always be designed with these points in mind. It is also important to verify that the added substrate is equivalent to the natural substrate, a point which can be established using a deuterium label (V. M. Sponsel, unpublished results).

PISUM SATIVUM   The seven GAs identified from the developing seeds of *P. sativum* cv. Progress No. 9 are: GA_{17}, GA_{38}, and GA_{44} (C_{20}-GAs), and GA_9, GA_{20}, GA_{29}, and GA_{51} (C_{19}-GAs) (60, 61, 154). Gibberellin A_{20} has also been identified from immature seeds of the *Alaska* cultivar (51) and pods of dwarf *P. sativum* (101). Also GA_{20} and GA_{29} have been identified from germinating seeds and seedlings of *P. sativum,* cv. Progress No. 9 (P. Kirkwood and V. M. Sponsel, unpublished information). The structures of these GAs suggest an early 13-hydroxylating pathway. Thus the C_{20} members, GA_{17} and GA_{44}, and the C_{19}-GAs, GA_{20} and GA_{29}, are 13-hydroxylated without being hydroxylated at the carbon-3 position. (While the C_{20}-GA, GA_{38}, is both 3β- and 13-hydroxylated, it is present in trace amounts only.)

There are several reports in the literature on the metabolism of radiolabeled GAs in *P. sativum*. Railton, Durley & Pharis (133) fed [^{3}H]GA_9 to dark grown seedlings of *P. sativum* cv Meteor and identified the metabolites [^{3}H]GA_{10} (possibly an artifact), [^{3}H]GA_{20}, and 12α-hydroxy [^{3}H]GA_9 with radiochemical yields ranging from 0.14 to 5.0% of the original feed. In another study Railton et al (134) fed [^{3}H]GA_{20} to imbibed seeds and to dark grown Meteor seedlings and identified [^{3}H]GA_{29} as a main metabolite. These two studies indicate that *Pisum* seedlings contain the capacity for 12α-hydroxylation ($GA_9 \rightarrow$ 12α-hydroxy GA_9), 13-hydroxylation ($GA_9 \rightarrow GA_{20}$), and 2β-hydroxylation ($GA_{20} \rightarrow GA_{29}$). Railton, Durley & Pharis (133) have inferred that the sequence $GA_9 \rightarrow GA_{20} \rightarrow GA_{29}$ may be a natural process in *Pisum* seedlings. Durley, Railton & Pharis (48) fed [^{3}H]GA_5 to dark-grown Meteor seedlings and identified [^{3}H]GA_3 as the major metabolite. Since neither the substrate nor the metabolite are known to be native in this system, the biological significance of their results is uncertain. In another study Durley, Railton & Pharis (49) also fed [^{3}H]GA_{14} to similar material and identified the following [^{3}H] metabolites after 20 and 40 hr incubations: GA_{18}, GA_{38}, GA_{23}, GA_1, GA_8, and GA_{28}. On the basis of their structural relationships and the apparent change in relative amounts with time, they proposed the metabolic sequence: $GA_{14} \rightarrow GA_{18} \rightarrow GA_{38} \rightarrow GA_{23} \rightarrow GA_1 \rightarrow GA_8$, with GA_{28} as a branch product from GA_{23}, and they suggested that the sequence may be common to leguminous plants. Since neither GA_{14} nor the metabolites from the feed have been identified as native in *Pisum* seedlings, the reader should be reminded of the steviol pitfall where the unnatural steviol was fed to the fungus *G. fujikuroi* and a series of unnatural 13-hydroxylated GA metabolites identified. Durley, Railton & Pharis may be observing a similar enzyme nonspecificity in which GA_{14} is acting as an analog of GA_{12} in the natural sequence $GA_{12} \rightarrow$ 13-hydroxy $GA_{12} \rightarrow GA_{44} \rightarrow$

$GA_{19} \rightarrow GA_{20} \rightarrow GA_{29}$. A number of the members of this latter sequence are naturally occurring in *P. sativum,* and there is direct evidence for some of these steps from metabolic studies with developing seeds of this species.

A detailed study of the native GAs in developing seeds of *Pisum* has been reported in a series of papers by Sponsel (née Frydman) and MacMillan (60–62, 154). They first identified the native GAs present in the developing seeds of the cultivar, Progress No. 9. Then, as a preliminary to metabolic studies, they measured the levels of four of these GAs by GC-selected ion current monitoring through 11 stages of seed development. They found that GA_{20} and GA_{29} predominated and GA_9 and GA_{17} were present at much lower levels. The amounts of each of these GAs increased from zero to a maximum and then returned to zero or to low values. The maximal level of each GA varied with the age of the seeds. The order was GA_9, $GA_{17}=GA_{20}$, GA_{29},, suggesting to the authors the metabolic sequence $GA_9 \rightarrow GA_{20} \rightarrow GA_{29}$. These data formed the basis for the choice of labeled substrates used, the amounts added, and the timing of each feed in subsequent experiments. In all experiments, $[^3H]GA_{20}$ and $[^3H]GA_{29}$ were added at physiological levels, i.e. close to the native levels for these GAs. $[^3H]$Gibberellin A_9 was added at levels 10–50 times that of the native GA_9 in order to identify the metabolites. Incubations were conducted mainly with seeds cultured in a nutrient medium (in vitro), with the main results being confirmed from seeds developing with pods attached to the intact plant (in vivo). When $[^3H]GA_9$ was added to seeds at an intermediate stage of development in which native GA_9 *is* present, it was metabolized to tritiated GA_{51}, 12α-hydroxy GA_9 (tentative), and a conjugate of 12α-hydroxy GA_9 (tentative). Since GA_9 and GA_{51} are present in this system at the developmental stage when $[^3H]GA_9$ was fed and $[^3H]GA_{51}$ was formed, the 2β-hydroxylation step $GA_9 \rightarrow GA_{51}$ is probably a natural process. The other two metabolites from the $[^3H]GA_9$ feed have not been identified as native GAs in *Pisum* and may be artifacts due to the high levels of substrate used. In these studies $[^3H]GA_9$ was *not* converted to $[^3H]GA_{20}$. In contrast $[^3H]GA_9$ *was* converted to $[^3H]GA_{20}$ when added to seeds at an earlier stage of development, when native GA_9 and GA_{20} are absent. The authors concluded that GA_9 is *not* a natural precursor of GA_{20}, the $[^3H]GA_{20}$ being the product of a nonspecific 13-hydroxylating enzyme present at this early stage of seed development. Thus GA_9 and GA_{20} may be synthesized by parallel pathways from an early C_{20} precursor, perhaps GA_{12}-aldehyde. The pathway to GA_{20} would originate from the 13-hydroxylation of this precursor.

$[^3H]$Gibberellin A_{20} was fed to seeds at several later stages of development in which native GA_{20} was present. $[^3H]$Gibberellin A_{29} was obtained with a 50–90% radiochemical yield. The highest yields were found when the feeding of the substrate *and* isolation of the metabolite coincided in time with the maximal levels of the native GA_{20} and GA_{29} respectively. Therefore the 2β-hydroxylation of GA_{20} to GA_{29} was considered by the authors to be a natural process in this system. Conjugates of both $[^3H]GA_{20}$ and $[^3H]GA_{29}$ were also formed from these $[^3H]GA_{20}$ feeds, but in low yield. These metabolites may represent unnatural processes since no native GA-conjugates have been identified from *Pisum.*

No metabolism was observed when [^{3}H]GA$_{29}$ was fed to seeds at a late stage of development in which native GA$_{29}$ is at a high level. Experiments were also run in which [^{3}H]GA$_{20}$ was added to young seeds and these seeds allowed to grow until the amount of native GA$_{29}$ had reached a maximum and then decreased to a low level. Surprisingly, the level of the [^{3}H]GA$_{29}$ metabolite remained high. This paradox has not been resolved.

PHASEOLUS COCCINEUS AND P. VULGARIS   The diversity and number of naturally occurring GAs in *Phaseolus* make this genus potentially useful for the study of GA metabolism in higher plants. Both *P. coccineus* cv Prizewinner and *P. vulgaris* cvs Kentucky Wonder and Master have been used in metabolic studies, and information is beginning to accumulate on the biosynthetic relationship of the C$_{19}$-GAs, especially from *P. vulgaris*.

Gibberellin A$_1$, GA$_3$–GA$_6$, GA$_8$, GA$_{17}$, GA$_{20}$, GA$_{29}$, GA$_{37}$, GA$_{38}$, and GA$_{44}$ have been identified in developing or mature seeds of *P. vulgaris* (45, 93, 95, 96, 163, 166) and GA$_1$, GA$_3$–GA$_6$, GA$_8$, GA$_{17}$, GA$_{19}$, and GA$_{20}$ in developing seeds, mature seeds, and/or seedlings of *P. coccineus* (23, 39, 45). In addition, GA$_{28}$ has been found in immature seeds of *P. coccineus* as a water-soluble conjugate (63). Mature seeds of both species contain relatively large amounts of GA-glucosyl ethers and esters. The glucosyl ether of GA$_8$ has been identified in immature and mature seeds of *P. vulgaris* (93, 96) and immature pods of *P. coccineus* (147) and the glucosyl esters of GA$_1$, GA$_4$, GA$_{37}$, and GA$_{38}$ in mature seeds of *P. vulgaris* (95, 96). Gibberellin A$_8$, GA$_{17}$, GA$_{20}$, and GA$_{28}$ have also been identified from immature seeds of *P. coccineus* (63) as unspecified conjugates.

The variety of structures of these GAs suggests that at least two pathways are operating. One pathway, in which 3β-hydroxylation occurs early and before 13-hydroxylation, would result in the formation of GA$_{37}$ and GA$_4$. A second pathway, in which 13-hydroxylation occurs early and before 3β-hydroxylation, would produce GA$_{17}$, GA$_{19}$, GA$_{44}$, GA$_5$, GA$_6$, GA$_{20}$, and GA$_{29}$. The formation of GAs which are both 3β- and 13-hydroxylated (GA$_{28}$, GA$_{38}$, GA$_1$, GA$_3$, and GA$_8$) could be indicative of the convergence of the two pathways.

Reeve et al (136) have reported the 2β-hydroxylation of [^{3}H]GA$_1$ to [^{3}H]GA$_8$ in 6-day-old seedlings of *P. coccineus*. This same conversion was shown earlier for imbibed seeds of *P. vulgaris* by Nadeau & Rappaport (123). They incubated the seeds for 30 hr in the presence of [^{3}H]GA$_1$ and identified traces of [^{3}H]GA$_8$ with [^{3}H]GA$_8$-O(2)-β-D-glucoside as the major product. Asakawa et al (5) have identified the glucosyl ether of [^{3}H]GA$_3$ from feeds of [^{3}H]GA$_3$ to young seedlings of *P. vulgaris*. The labeled GA$_3$ was added as a spray to the seedlings and the plants harvested and extracted 2 weeks later.

The most complete evidence for several related steps in the GA pathway for *Phaseolus* comes from a series of papers by Hiraga et al (93, 95, 96) and Yamane et al (166, 167). In these studies they identified the naturally occurring GAs and GA-conjugates in developing and mature seeds of *P. vulgaris*. They also fed tritiated C$_{19}$-GAs (GA$_1$, GA$_4$, GA$_5$, GA$_8$, and GA$_{20}$) to developing seeds and identified the metabolites after various lengths of incubation time.

The results are summarized in Figure 9. Thick arrows represent conversions observed in all incubations. Thin arrows denote conversions not found in the 3-day incubations with "early immature seeds" but observed in all other feeds. Since GA_4 is already 3β-hydroxylated without being 13-hydroxylated, it must originate from an early 3-hydroxylating pathway. Also GA_{20} must originate from an early 13-hydroxylating pathway since it lacks a 3β-hydroxyl group and is 13-hydroxylated. Thus GA_4 and GA_{20} are presumably formed by different pathways which in turn must come from a common precursor (e.g. GA_9 or GA_{12}-aldehyde). These hypothetical pathways are shown as dotted lines in Figure 9. GA_4 was metabolized to GA_1 and GA_8; also GA_1 was converted to GA_8. These results indicate the sequence $GA_4 \rightarrow GA_1 \rightarrow GA_8$. Under the same conditions GA_{20} was metabolized to GA_1, GA_8, and GA_{29}, suggesting the sequences $GA_{20} \rightarrow GA_1 \rightarrow GA_8$ and $GA_{20} \rightarrow GA_{29}$. Thus the 3-hydroxylation of GA_{20} and the 13-hydroxylation of GA_4 results in a convergence of the two pathways at GA_1.

The metabolism of GA_5 to GA_8 could occur via the 2,3 epoxide, GA_6, which is also naturally occurring in both species of *Phaseolus*. GA_6 would then be hydrated to GA_8. However, GA_6 was not detected as a metabolite from feeds of GA_5 to *P.*

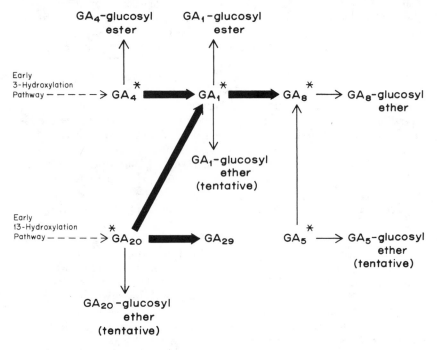

Figure 9   GA-metabolic pathways for *Phaseolus vulgaris* based on feeds of radiolabeled GAs to immature seeds (166, 167). * refer to the GAs that were fed. Thick arrows represent conversions observed in all incubations. Thin arrows denote conversions not observed in 3-day incubations with early immature seeds.

vulgaris. Gibberellin A_5 could originate from either GA_1 by dehydration or GA_{20} by dehydrogenation, but again these conversions were not observed.

Apparently glucosylating enzymes do not appear in the seeds until later stages of growth, since no GA-conjugates were found as natural products in early immature seeds (10 days after anthesis), nor were they produced in these very young seeds injected with [^{3}H]-labeled GAs and extracted 3 days later. In contrast, both GA-glucosyl ethers and esters were observed from all other incubations.

PICEA, PINUS, AND PSEUDOTSUGA   Gibberellin A_3, GA_4, and GA_7 have been identified as natural products in extracts from the pollen of *Pinus attenuata* (98). The β-D-glucosyl ester of GA_9 has been characterized from needles of *Picea sitchensis* (108), together with the tentatively identified Δ^{15}-isomer of GA_9 (isoGA_9) (109). Two zones of GA-like activity (a relatively polar "fraction A" and a less polar "fraction B") were obtained after TLC of purified extracts from buds and needles of *P. sitchensis.* The relative activities from these zones were correlated with seasonal variations in the growth of buds and needles (107). During rapid growth, fraction B was the major component; during dormancy fraction A predominated. Lorenzi, Horgan & Heald (107) have suggested that there may be a biochemical interconversion between these two forms. However, the subsequent tentative identification of the Δ^{15}-isomer of GA_9 as the main component of fraction B (109) and the identification of GA_9-glucosyl ester as the main component of fraction A (108) precludes direct interconversion. Possibly GA_9 is synthesized during rapid growth and isomerized to isoGA_9. Then, at the onset of dormancy, newly synthesized GA_9 is rapidly converted to the GA_9-glucosyl ester. Lorenzi et al (108) have suggested that the GA_9-glucosyl ester may have a storage role in *P. sitchensis.* This suggestion was based on the apparent high levels of this ester in mature needles contrasted to low levels in buds and developing needles. It is analogous to the situation in *Phaseolus vulgaris* seeds where high levels of GA-glucosyl esters build up during seed maturation (95, 166, 167); these esters are readily hydrolyzed to free GAs by higher plant glucosidases in young seedlings of many plants (106, 146). However, there is no direct evidence that GA-glucosyl esters serve to control the level of biologically active GAs in growing tissue. Wample, Durley & Pharis (160) injected [1,2-^{3}H]GA_4 into the bark of 2-year-old seedlings of *Pseudotsuga menziesii* and processed the needles and stem of the new whorls 1, 3, and 6 days later. They identified [^{3}H]GA_2 and [^{3}H]GA_{34} with radiochemical yields up to 5%. While GA_2 could be an artifact of isolation, the quantities obtained led the authors to suggest that in *P. menziesii* the hydration reaction $GA_4 \rightarrow GA_2$ occurs enzymatically, as does the 2β-hydroxylation reaction $GA_4 \rightarrow GA_{34}$. Both conversions were highest at bud set and bud break and lowest during elongation.

In another study Kamienska, Durley & Pharis (99) fed [1,2-^{3}H$_2$]GA_4 to germinating pollen of *Pinus attenuata.* More than 75% of the substrate was absorbed by the pollen of which up to 3.22% was metabolized to [^{3}H]GA_{34} and 0.43% to [^{3}H]GA_1. Their data demonstrate the 2β-hydroxylation reaction $GA_4 \rightarrow GA_{34}$, and the 13-hydroxylation reaction $GA_4 \rightarrow GA_1$. It is interesting that no evidence was obtained for the formation of [^{3}H]GA_7 or [^{3}H]GA_3 from [^{3}H]GA_4, even though

GA_3, GA_4 and GA_7 are natural products in *P. attenuata*. They point out the possibility that GA_3 and GA_7 might not have been detected because the tritium could have been lost in the formation of the 1,2-double bond.

OTHER PLANTS   There are isolated examples of feeds of radiolabeled GAs to a number of other higher plant species, using either intact plants, tissue sections, or callus cultures. In each case a single metabolic step has been demonstrated, but with one exception neither the substrate nor the metabolites from the feeds have been identified as natural products in the plant. Therefore, the results from the experiments are useful only to demonstrate that a particular plant can carry out a particular reaction, not that the observed conversion is a native process. Thus 13-hydroxylation has been observed in seedlings of *Oryza sativa* cv Tan-ginbozu (46) and in germinating seeds of *Lactuca sativa* cv Grand Rapids (44), and 3β-hydroxylation in callus tissue of *Nicotiana tabacum* cv Wisconsin-38 (102). 2β-hydroxylation has been demonstrated in normal and *dwarf-5 Zea mays* seedlings and leaf sections (40), aleurone tissue and embryoless half-seeds of *Hordeum vulgare* cv Himalaya (124, 158), seedlings of *Oryza sativa* cv Tan-ginbozu (46, 132) and callus tissue from *Nicotiana tabacum* cv Wisconsin-38 and *Olea europa* cv Manzanillo (135).

Durley, Pharis & Zeevaart (47) have shown that [^{3}H]GA_{20} was metabolized by mature leaves of *Bryophyllum diagramontianum* to tritiated GA_{29}, 3-*epi*-GA_1, and C/D rearranged GA_{20} (probably an artifact). Since both GA_{20} (65) and GA_{29} (J.A.D. Zeevaart, personal communication) have been identified as natural products from *B. diagramontianum*, this 2β-hydroxylation step, $GA_{20} \rightarrow GA_{29}$, probably occurs naturally.

Mechanism for the Conversion of C_{20}-GAs to C_{19}-GAs

The mechanism of loss of carbon-20 is a major unsolved problem in the biosynthesis of the GAs. The level of oxidation of carbon-20 at which this occurs is still not known. The known facts are: First, GA_{37}, GA_{36}, and GA_{13} do not act as precursors of GA_4 when fed to either wild-type strains of *G. fujikuroi* or the mutant B1-41a; nor do GA_{15}, GA_{24}, and GA_{25} act as precursors of GA_9. Second, in enzyme preparations from *Cucurbita maxima* endosperm which catalyze the formation of GA_4 from GA_{12}-aldehyde, there is no information on the intermediates involved. Third, Hanson & White (85) have shown by [^{3}H]-labeling experiments in fungal cultures that none of the hydrogen atoms at carbons-1, -5 and -9 are involved in the loss of carbon-20. Thus the mechanism for this loss in the GAs is different from that in which the corresponding carbon (carbon-19) is lost in the biosynthesis of estrone (4) and carbon-32 is lost in cholesterol biosynthesis (1). Fourth, Bearder et al (16) have recently shown that both oxygen atoms in the lactone bridge of C_{19}-GAs are derived from the 19-oic acid of their C_{20}-precursors. This finding limits the number of possible mechanisms for the loss of carbon-20. It indicates that the substrates GA_{12} and GA_{12}-alcohol and the subsequent intermediates are not covalently bound through the 19-oic acid to the enzyme(s) which catalyze the formation of the C_{19}-GAs. It also shows that the δ-lactone GA_{15} is not an intermediate. Furthermore the

C_{20} to C_{19} conversion must involve an intermediate with an electrophilic center at carbon-10 which is attacked by the 19-oic acid. This group may, in fact, participate in the loss of carbon-20 since the methyl ester of GA_{12}-alcohol is not converted by the mutant B1-41a into metabolites which have lost carbon-20. Whatever the mechanism, a 10α-alcohol is excluded, since lactone formation from this alcohol would involve loss of an oxygen atom from the 19-oic acid. A biological type of Baeyer-Villiger reaction (85) would similarly appear to be excluded. The interesting mechanism proposed by McCorkindale (117) would also seem unlikely since formation of the proposed intermediate 19-per acid would, by chemical analogy, involve loss of an oxygen atom from the 19-oic acid.

The fact remains, however, that no C_{20}-GA intermediates on the pathway to C_{19}-GAs have been identified having carbon-20 at a higher oxidation level than the methyl group. Direct loss of the 20-methyl group seems most improbable. The putative intermediates of higher oxidation level at carbon-20 which have been examined are either dibasic acids (GA_{36}, GA_{24}) or tribasic acids (GA_{13}, GA_{25}). The failure to demonstrate their conversion into C_{19}-GAs in fungal cultures may be due to poor transport across the cell membranes. This may explain the absence of conversion of GA_{36} to GA_{13} in cultures of the mutant B1-41a under conditions in which the less polar GA_{24} was metabolized to GA_{25} (15). The observation by Hanson & Hawker (81) that [17-^{14}C]GA_{13}-anhydride was incorporated to a small extent (0.015%) into [^{14}C]GA_3 by cultures of strain ACC 917 might possibly be accounted for by the greater penetration of the anhydride compared to the parent tribasic acid GA_{13}. Thus GA_{13} may yet prove to be the immediate precursor of GA_4 in the fungus.

It has been suggested (10, 56), but not tested directly, that the 7-aldehydes of GA_{36} and GA_{13}, rather than the carboxylic acids, are the actual intermediates between GA_{14}-aldehyde and GA_4. This suggestion calls into question the direct intermediacy of GA_{14} in the fungal pathway to 3-hydroxylated GAs.

METABOLISM OF ANALOGS OF GAs AND THEIR PRECURSORS BY THE FUNGUS

During the period under review many studies have been reported on the metabolism of structural analogs of recognized intermediates in GA biosynthesis. These studies, which have been confined almost entirely to microbiological transformations, are of interest for two reasons. First, they provide information on enzyme-substrate specificity, and second, they provide methods of preparing natural GAs which are otherwise difficult to acquire and unnatural GA-analogs which have potential biological interest. Investigations which use the GA-producing strains of *G. fujikuroi* are of direct relevance to GA biosynthesis and will be discussed in some detail.

In retrospect, the first example of the metabolism of an analog of a GA intermediate was described by Ruddat, Heftmann & Lang in 1965 (141). [^{14}C]Steviol, the 13-hydroxylated analog of *ent*-kaurenoic acid, was shown to be metabolized by cultures of the GA-producing strain LM-45-399 to a [^{14}C]GA-like compound with properties similar to the then unknown GA_{20}. Later Hanson & White (84) added unlabeled steviol to a GA-producing strain of *G. fujikuroi* and isolated 7β, 13-dihydroxykaurenolide (Figure 10) from the neutral metabolites. Whether or not the latter compound was a metabolite of the added steviol is now uncertain, since Serebryakov et al (147) have shown it to be a normal metabolite of *G. fujikuroi.*

Ring D Analogs of ent-Kaurenoic Acid

Bearder et al (18) reexamined the metabolism of steviol in resuspension cultures of the mutant Bl-41a and established the conversions shown in Figure 10. From re-feeding experiments they concluded that the metabolism of steviol by *G. fujikuroi* paralleled that of the normal pathway from *ent*-kaurenoic acid. There are two points

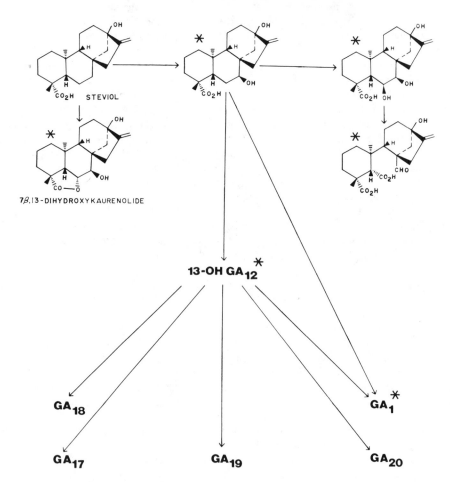

Figure 10 The metabolism of steviol in resuspension cultures of the *Gibberella fujikuroi* mutant Bl-41a. * indicate the major metabolites.

of special note. First, GA_{18} was not metabolized when re-fed, recalling the possibility raised earlier that GA_{14} was not on the direct pathway to the C_{19}-GAs. Second, the accumulation of GA_1 and the absence of GA_3 confirmed that GA_1 is not on the main pathway to GA_3. The metabolism of steviol-13-acetate (4 in Figure 11) was also examined (12). In this case GA_{20}-acetate was the main C_{19}-GA metabolite in contrast to the steviol feeds where GA_1 was the main C_{19}-GA. Thus acetylation of the 13-hydroxy group in steviol suppressed 3β-hydroxylation almost completely. This suppression by a slight structural modification of the molecule at a position distant from the site of hydroxylation is of intrinsic enzymological interest and is also of practical utility as a preparative route to GA_{20} (12).

Perhaps the most remarkable example of substrate nonspecificity is the metabolism (12) of isosteviol (7 in Figure 11) which is obtained by acid-catalyzed ring C/D rearrangement of steviol, Isosteviol was metabolized by cultures of the mutant B1-41a to, inter alia, the ring C/D rearranged products of 13-hydroxy GA_{12}, GA_{24}, GA_{25}, and GA_{20}. As in the case of steviol acetate, no 3β-hydroxylation occurred.

The metabolism of several 15-oxygenated analogs of *ent*-kaurenoic acid has also been examined using the mutant B1-41a. For example, *ent*-15α-hydroxy-kaurenoic acid (8 in Figure 11), which occurs as the acetate in the fruit of *Xylopia aethiopica* (52), was rapidly metabolized to many products which were tentatively identified by GC-MS as the 15β-hydroxy derivatives of GA_1, GA_3, GA_4, GA_7, GA_9, GA_{12}, GA_{13}, GA_{14}, and GA_{15} (J. R. Bearder and K. Kybird, personal communication). The 15β-hydroxy GA_9 was subsequently identified as a new GA (GA_{45}) in the seeds of *Pyrus communis* (9). In contrast, the following compounds were hydroxylated by the mutant B1-41a but were not converted into GAs: the *ent*-15α-acetoxykaurenoic acid (xylopic acid) (9 in Figure 11), *ent*-15-oxokaurenoic acid (10 in Figure 11), and *ent*-15β-hydroxykaurenoic acid (11 in Figure 11).

Miscellaneous Analogs of ent-Kaurenoic Acid

The acetate of *ent*-7α-hydroxykaurenoic acid (5 in Figure 11) and the methyl esters of *ent*-kaurenoic acid, *ent*-7α-hydroxykaurenoic acid, and steviol were either not metabolized or partially hydroxylated by the mutant B1-41a (112). None of these substrates was converted into GAs, indicating that a free *ent*-7α-hydroxyl group and a free carboxyl group are necessary for ring B contraction. *ent*-7-Oxokaurenoic acid (6 in Figure 11) was completely metabolized to the nor-ring B triacid (12 in Figure 11) by the mutant B1-41a (15).

Ring A Analogs of ent-Kaurenoids

Lunnon et al (110) have investigated the effect of 2- and 3-hydroxylation on the metabolism of *ent*-kaurenoic acid and *ent*-kaurenol. The hydroxy-acids were fed to cultures of the mutant B1-41a, and the hydroxy-kaurenols to cultures of the GA-producing strain GF-1a, inhibited by the quaternary ammonium compound (2 in Figure 5). The metabolites were identified by GC-MS. The results reveal the following points: (a) 2- and 3-hydroxylation does not prevent oxidation to the corresponding *ent*-kaurenoic acids; (b) 3β-hydroxylation can occur at the normal

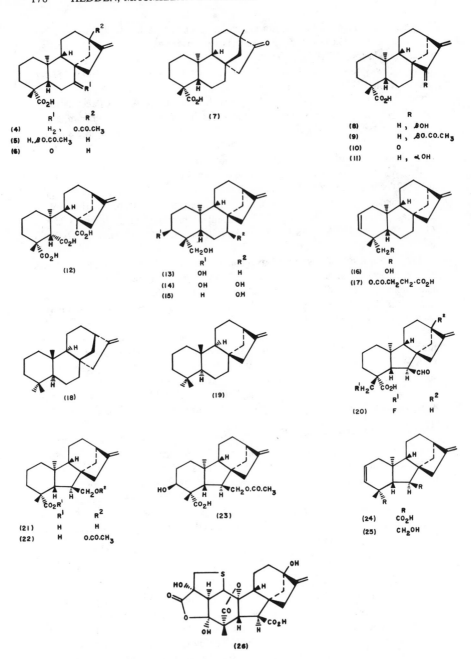

stage (i.e. after ring B contraction) in the presence of 2α- and 2β-hydroxyl substituents; (c) 2- and 3-hydroxyl groups do not prevent ring contraction; (d) a 2β-hydroxyl in a C_{20}-GA appears to prevent conversion to a C_{19}-GA; and (e) a 2α-hydroxyl may be dehydrated subsequent to ring B contraction to give the 1,2-double bond of GA_3.

In contrast, neither *ent*-3α-hydroxy-[17-^{14}C]kaurenol (*13* in Figure 11) nor *ent*-3 α,7α-dihydroxy-[17-^{14}C]kaurenol (*14* in Figure 11) was metabolized to [^{14}C]GA$_3$ by resuspension cultures of strain ACC 917 at pH 7.0 (97). However, under the same conditions (97) *ent*-[17-^{14}C]kauren-7α,19-diol (*15* in Figure 11) was converted into [^{14}C]GAs (2%). *ent*-[17-^{14}C]Kaura-2,16-dien-19-ol (*16* in Figure 11) and its 19-hemisuccinate (*17* in Figure 11) were metabolized by strain ACC 917 into several GA-analogs containing either a 2,3-double bond or a 2,3-epoxide (6).

Hedden et al (91) fed several analogs of *ent*-kaurene to cultures of strain GF-1a inhibited by the quaternary ammonium compound (*2* in Figure 5) and found that kaur-16-ene (*18* in Figure 11) (the enantiomer of *ent*-kaur-16-ene), 13β-kaur-16-ene (*19* in Figure 11) (phyllocladene), and *ent*-kaur-15-ene (*1* in Figure 5) were not metabolized to GAs. Thus the enzymes do not accept the gross stereochemical changes represented by kaur-16-ene and 13β-kaur-16-ene, nor the relatively small change represented by *ent*-kaur-15-ene.

Analogs of the C_{20}-GAs

Bateson & Cross (8) found that 18-fluoro GA_{12}-aldehyde (*20* in Figure 11) was metabolized by strain ACC 917 to give 18-fluoro GA_9 and 18-fluoro GA_3. Gibberellin A_{12}-alcohol (*21* in Figure 11) is efficiently metabolized by *G. fujikuroi;* Evans & Hanson (56) found similar ratios of 3-hydroxylated and non-3-hydroxylated GAs from feeds of [17-^{14}C]GA_{12}-alcohol and [2-^{14}C]MVL, indicating that the alcohol was metabolized via GA_{12}-aldehyde. In contrast, the mutant B1-41a metabolized GA_{12}-alcohol to only 3-hydroxylated GAs, suggesting that 3β-hydroxylation occurs before oxidation of the alcohol function (15). In agreement with this view, the acetate (*22* in Figure 11) of GA_{12}-alcohol was metabolized by the mutant B1-41a to the acetate (*23* in Figure 11) of GA_{14}-alcohol, and oxidation of carbon-20 was not observed (112). Bakker et al (6) have fed 2,3-dehydro [^{14}C]GA_{12} (*24* in Figure 11), the corresponding 2,3-epoxide, and the 2,3-dehydro analog (*25* in Figure 11) of [^{14}C]GA_{12} diol to cultures of strain ACC 917. From the results they suggested the presence of two 2,3-dehydro pathways which are analogous to the normal pathways for the fungus. Both pathways originate from 2,3-dehydro GA_{12}-aldehyde; one, equivalent to the natural non-3-hydroxylation pathway, leads to 2,3-dehydro GA_9 and the other, equivalent to the natural 3-hydroxylation pathway, leads to 13-deoxy GA_6. The authors also suggested that the β-epoxidation of the 2,3-double bond and 3β-hydroxylation in the natural pathway are catalyzed by the same enzyme system.

REGULATION OF GA LEVELS

Although there is now a great deal of information on the details of the biosynthetic pathway, virtually nothing is known about the control of GA levels. However, a number of reactions in the pathway are possible candidates for regulation by meta-bolic control, including cyclization of GGPP to *ent*-kaurene, the deactivation of GAs by 2β-hydroxylation and glucosylation. In addition, the recent discovery that GA biosynthesis may occur in plastids has led to a series of investigations on the role of compartmentalization in the regulation of GA levels, and this has in turn led to information on phytochrome mediated control of these levels. While other factors, e.g. light, temperature, and other hormones, are known to affect GA levels, their effects on GA metabolism are ill-defined and they are not discussed in this review.

Metabolic Control

BRANCH-POINTS   An early branch-point in the GA-biosynthetic pathway is at GGPP, and the enzyme controlling its cyclization to *ent*-kaurene has received the most attention as a possible site of regulation.

In higher plants, GGPP is a common intermediate for a number of vital biosyn-thetic pathways (e.g. phytol and carotenoids) of which the GA pathway is usually a very minor one. The cyclization of GGPP to *ent*-kaurene is the first committed step in GA biosynthesis (150), and the rate of cyclization may be a measure of the rate of GA biosynthesis. Coolbaugh & Moore (32) have reported that cell-free *ent*-kaurene synthesis increased during the early developmental stages of seeds of *P. sativum* cv Alaska and suggested that this increase may be correlated with the amount of extractable GA-like substances from the seeds. Ecklund & Moore (50) examined the incorporation of label from [2-^{14}C]MVA into *ent*-[^{14}C]kaurene as a function of growth, using cell-free systems from young shoots of *P. sativum* cv Alaska. They found a steady increase in the rate of *ent*-kaurene synthesis during the period of increased growth rate. When the growth rate was constant, the rate of *ent*-kaurene synthesis remained essentially constant. Hedden & Phinney (90) found that a cell-free system from etiolated seedlings of *Zea mays* synthesized *ent*-kaurene at lower rates in the *dwarf-5* mutant than in the normal. This low rate of synthesis is correlated with the apparent absence of GA-like substances in the mutant (129).

Simcox, Dennis & West (150) have suggested that it may be the A activity of *ent*-kaurene synthetase which is under regulation, since there are a number of examples in which lack of *ent*-kaurene synthetase activity is associated with a lack of the A activity only. They found that although both A and B activities could be detected in a proplastid preparation from *Marah* endosperm, etioplasts from shoots of *P. sativum* cv Progress No. 9 and proplastids from *Ricinus* endosperm contained B activity with negligible A activity. Additional examples come from studies with cell-free systems by Yafin & Shechter (165), who obtained both A and B activities from germinating seeds of *Lycopersicum esculentum* and only B activity from tissue cultures of *Nicotiana tabacum* and *L. esculentum*. As interesting as these observa-tions may be, there still remains the possibility that the A component in some plants is less stable than the B component. As a result, the A activity would not always be detected under conditions used to prepare the cell-free systems.

DEACTIVATION

2β-Hydroxylation   2β-Hydroxylation of GAs is probably of widespread occurrence in higher plants. This reaction is not known to be reversible, and since it results in a marked reduction or loss of biological activity, the reaction may serve as a means of regulating the level of biologically active GAs. However, direct evidence for this regulation remains to be established. There are several examples in which applied radiolabeled GAs are 2β-hydroxylated by higher plants (e.g. 135). In the following examples the observed conversions probably represent native processes, since both substrate and product are naturally occurring: $GA_1 \rightarrow GA_8$ in *Phaseolus coccineus* (136) and *P. vulgaris* (167), $GA_{20} \rightarrow GA_{29}$ in *Pisum sativum* (62), *Bryophyllum diagramontianum* (47) and *P. vulgaris* (166), and $GA_9 \rightarrow GA_{51}$ in *P. sativum* (154). There is evidence from the development studies with *P. sativum* seeds (60, 62, 154) that the 2β-hydroxylation of GA_{20} to GA_{29} occurs only at a particular stage in the development of the seeds.

No 2β-hydroxylated GAs have been found in *G. fujikuroi*. However, the fungus does hydroxylate at the 2α position for which there are two examples, GA_{40} (2α-hydroxy GA_9) and GA_{47} (2α-hydroxy GA_4). Both of these GAs show activity in a number of bioassays (153). The contrast between the bioactivity of 2α- and 2β-hydroxylated GAs demonstrates the high specificity of 2β-hydroxylation as a deactivating process for GAs in higher plants.

GA derivatives   The most common GA derivatives are those in which the GA is bound to glucose. The conjugates are found as glucosyl ethers in which the GA is bound to the sugar through a hydroxyl group, or as glucosyl esters in which the sugar is linked to the 7-carboxyl group of the GA. In all cases the conjugates have been found to be O-β-D-glucopyranosyl ethers or esters. Since the highest concentrations of these conjugates have been obtained from mature seeds, there has been speculation on their having a storage role (106, 147). Thus the GAs present during seed development would be conjugated at maturity and these conjugates hydrolyzed to free GAs on germination. Only a few reports have appeared which correlate changes in levels of GAs and their conjugates with development. In assigning a storage role to a GA-conjugate, the implicit assumption is made that the bioactivity of the free aglycone is appreciably greater than that of its conjugate. However, most of the literature on this subject does not distinguish between already deactivated GAs (e.g. $GA_8 \rightarrow GA_8$-conjugate) and active GAs (e.g. $GA_1 \rightarrow GA_1$-conjugate).

Of the six GA-glucosyl ethers known to be naturally occurring in higher plants, four have aglycones (GA_8, GA_{26}, GA_{27}, and GA_{29}) which are 2β-hydroxylated and as a result exhibit little or no biological activity. As 2β-hydroxylation is probably an irreversible reaction, these four conjugates cannot be a storage form of active GAs even though some or all of them are present in relatively high amounts in the seeds of *Phaseolus vulgaris* (93, 96), *P. coccineus* (145, 147), and *Pharbitis nil* (170, 172, 173). The other two naturally occurring glucosyl ethers have aglycones with high biological activity and are present in relatively large amounts in seeds of *P. nil* (GA_3-0(3)-β-glucosyl ether) (170) and immature pods of *Cytisus scoparius*

(GA$_{35}$-0(11)-β-glucosyl ether) (168). GA$_3$-glucosyl ether has little or no bioactivity when assayed under sterile conditions. However, in some bioassays conducted under nonsterile conditions, the conjugate has high activity which is attributed to hydrolysis by contaminating microorganisms (146, 171). It appears, therefore, that GA$_3$-glucosyl ether is not hydrolyzed by enzymes of the seedling used for bioassay. Similarly, GA$_{35}$-glucosyl ether shows either no or low bioactivity (169). Although the glucosyl ethers seem to be stable to higher plant glycolytic enzymes, and as such are unsuitable as storage forms of GAs, there is no relevant data on hydrolysis by the plants from which they were isolated. Five glucosyl esters have been identified from higher plants, one of them from needles of the conifer *Picea sitchensis* (GA$_9$-glucosyl ester) (108) and the others from mature seeds of *Phaseolus vulgaris* (glucosyl esters of GA$_1$, GA$_4$, GA$_{37}$, and GA$_{38}$) (96). While the five esters are highly active in some bioassays, this bioactivity has been attributed to hydrolysis by the assay plants and/or microbial contamination associated with the assay (94, 108).

Hiraga et al (93, 95, 96) identified several GAs and their conjugates from large-scale extractions of *P. vulgaris* seeds and reported high levels of glucosyl esters in mature seeds and only traces in immature seeds. Yamane et al (166, 167) fed [^{3}H]GA$_1$ and [^{3}H]GA$_4$ to both immature and mature seeds of *P. vulgaris* and found a higher incorporation of label into glucosyl esters in mature than in immature seeds. When the seeds were allowed to mature and germinate, the level of the [^{3}H]GA$_1$-glucosyl ester decreased over the period of germination. Liebisch (106) reported that [^{3}H]GA$_3$-glucosyl ester was rapidly hydrolyzed when fed to germinating seeds of *P. sativum* cv Insignis. No hydrolysis was observed when the radiolabeled ester was fed to 14-day-old seedlings. He also found rapid hydrolysis of this glucosyl ester in cell-free systems prepared from 1- to 5-day-old seedlings of the same cultivar; no hydrolysis was observed in preparations from 12-day-old seedlings.

In summary, GA-glucosyl esters are formed from free GAs as the seeds mature. On germination these esters appear to be hydrolyzed to free GAs by plant glycolytic enzymes, but this capability is lost as the seedlings age. GA-glucosyl esters therefore have the necessary properties expected for storage forms of GAs, for which they are better candidates than glucosyl ethers. However, there is still no compelling evidence that glucosyl ester formation and hydrolysis regulate GA levels during seed maturation and germination.

A sulfur-containing derivative of GA$_3$, gibberethione (*26* in Figure 11), has been isolated from immature seeds of *P. nil* (174, 175). It appears to be formed biosynthetically by the oxidation of the 3β-hydroxyl group of GA$_3$, followed by addition of mercaptopyruvic acid or cysteine to the α,β-unsaturated ketone (175). It has no GA-like bioactivity and is therefore a deactivation product.

Compartmentalization

The levels of available GAs may also be controlled if their biosynthesis is compartmentalized within an organelle and the GAs released under regulation. There is now considerable evidence that plastids contain GA-like substances and are capable of carrying out at least some steps in GA biosynthesis. In addition, there have been a number of publications indicating a phytochrome mediated, red/far-red light effect on the changes in the level of extractable GA-like substances from plastids.

Goodwin & Mercer (66) were the first to suggest that chloroplasts may be a site of terpene biosynthesis. Later Stoddart (155) extracted GA-like substances from chloroplasts of *Brassica oleracea* cv Cansons' and *Hordeum vulgare* cv Himalaya. He also showed that the *Hordeum* chloroplasts incorporated radioactivity from *ent*-[^{14}C]kaurenoic acid into an unidentified GA-like substance (156). Subsequently, numerous reports have appeared on the extraction of GA-like substances from plastids. However, in only one case have these substances been characterized; Browning & Saunders (25) extracted isolated chloroplasts of *Triticum aestivum* cv Kolibri with the detergent Triton X-100 and obtained unusually high levels of GA$_4$ and GA$_9$ identified by GC-MS.

There is now convincing evidence that the early steps in GA biosynthesis can occur in plastids. Since the chloroplast membrane is impermeable to MVA (139), chloroplasts must be dependent on their own synthesis of this precursor. However, etioplast membranes have been shown to be permeable to MVA but lose this permeability upon illumination (27, 161). It was suggested that the etioplasts have access to cytoplasmic MVA but lose this property when they fix CO$_2$ and then synthesize their own MVA (161). Green, Dennis & West (78) have shown the presence of IPP isomerase and GGPP synthetase activity in proplastids from *Ricinus* endosperm. It is interesting that the proplastid membrane was permeable to IPP. Both A and B activities of *ent*-kaurene synthetase have been demonstrated from proplastids of *Marah* endosperm (150). Moore & Coolbaugh (120) have also shown the presence of *ent*-kaurene synthetase activity in a sonicated chloroplast preparation from seedlings of *P. sativum* cv Alaska.

It has not been possible to demonstrate conversion of MVA to *ent*-kaurene by plastids due to the loss of MVA kinase activity when the organelles are prepared in aqueous media. The presence of MVA-activating enzymes can, however, be demonstrated in chloroplasts isolated in nonaqueous media (26, 92). Thus it can be inferred that chloroplasts are capable of *ent*-kaurene biosynthesis from MVA. *ent*-Kaurenol, but not *ent*-kaurene, was metabolized to *ent*-7α-hydroxykaurenoic acid via *ent*-kaurenal and *ent*-kaurenoic acid by *Hordeum* chloroplasts (121). Thus the complete GA-biosynthetic pathway may be found to operate in plastids. As yet there is no information on whether or not the pathway is limited to this organelle.

In recent years phytochrome has been implicated in the control of levels of extractable GA-like substances from etioplasts of higher plants (157). There appears to be a red-light-stimulated increase in extractable GA-like substances from etioplasts which is reversible by far-red light. Phytochrome has been demonstrated to be present at very low levels in the etioplast envelope, and the envelope has been suggested as a site of action responsible for the effect (53, 54). However, at present it is still not clear whether the increases in GA-like substances are due to the control of specific steps in the GA-biosynthetic pathway (28, 29, 53), to the release of "bound" GAs from membranes (28), to increased membrane permeability (53), or to combinations of these.

CONCLUDING REMARKS

Studies on GA metabolism in *Gibberella fujikuroi* have progressed to the stage where, except for a few details, complete pathways can be delineated. Details of the pathways in *Cucurbita maxima* and *Pisum sativum* are beginning to emerge from studies with cell-free preparations. In contrast, the pathways for intact plants are largely uncharted.

The pathway from MVA to GA_{12}-aldehyde is now known to be the same for *G. fujikuroi* and for cell-free preparations of *Marah macrocarpus*, *C. maxima*, and *P. sativum* and may well be common to all plants that biosynthesize GAs. Despite the diversity of hydroxylation patterns of the GAs native to the parent organisms, there is no evidence to date for any hydroxylated intermediates prior to GA_{12}-aldehyde. From GA_{12}-aldehyde there are different pathways which depend on the order of hydroxylation. In *G. fujikuroi* 3-hydroxylation occurs immediately after GA_{12}-aldehyde formation and 13-hydroxylation is the last step. In *Cucurbita* cell-free systems 3β-hydroxylation takes place soon after GA_{12}-aldehyde formation and 13-hydroxylation does not occur. In *Pisum* cell-free systems, 13-hydroxylation appears to occur immediately after GA_{12}-aldehyde formation and 3β-hydroxylation is apparently a very minor process when observed.

Studies with cell-free preparations are also beginning to yield information on the nature of the enzymes involved in GA biosynthesis. Such information is necessary in order to understand how GA levels may be regulated by enzyme activities.

Although cell-free systems are invaluable, this experimental approach has its limitations, e.g. the loss of compartmentalization after homogenization. It is essential, therefore, that GA metabolism continue to be studied in intact higher plants. Sadly, few studies with intact plants have been reported which clearly demonstrate native metabolic processes. Detailed qualitative and quantitative analyses of the native GAs and their precursors are required in order to investigate natural metabolic steps. Unfortunately these analyses require specialized chemical expertise and instrumentation which is just becoming accessible to plant physiologists. Lack of the necessary instrumentation has, therefore, been a major bottleneck in studies to examine GA metabolism and its relationship to plant development.

The exciting new finding that GAs can be compartmentalized in plastids opens the door to future studies on GA biosynthesis in plastids and a possible role for this compartmentalization in the regulation of the levels of available GAs. An associated area of interest is the role of phytochrome in regulating GA biosynthesis in, and GA release from, plastids.

2β-Hydroxylation and glucosylation have been shown to be normal processes that are correlated with seed development, each of which results in loss of biological activity. Detailed biochemical studies of the enzymes catalyzing these and other known metabolic steps should be rewarding in the search for mechanisms of regulation of GA levels.

Finally, the progress that has been made in GA metabolism is helping to answer the question that troubles most plant physiologists: "Why so many GAs?" By defining the role of many GAs as biosynthetic dead ends, biosynthetic intermediates, or deactivated metabolites, metabolic studies are gradually refocusing attention on the primary mode of action of a few GAs which can be considered as the active hormones in a particular plant species.

ACKNOWLEDGMENTS

The preparation of this review was supported in part by grants from the N.S.F. and N.A.T.O. We wish to thank several colleagues for helpful comments on the manuscript.

Literature Cited

1. Alexander, K., Akhtar, M., Boar, R. B., McGhie, J. F., Barton, D. H. R. 1972. The removal of the C-32 atom as formic acid in chloresterol biosynthesis. *J.C.S. Chem. Commun.,* pp. 383–85
2. Alves, L. M. 1975. The gibberellins and the gibberellin-like substances of *Stevia rebaudiana* Bertoni. *Diss. Abstr. Int. B* 1976. 36:3194 (*Chem. Abstr.* 84: 118457a)
3. Anderson, J. D., Moore, T. C. 1967. Biosynthesis of (–)-kaurene in cell-free extracts of immature pea seeds. *Plant Physiol.* 42:1527–34
4. Arigoni, D., Battaglia, R., Akhtar, M., Smith, T. 1975. Stereospecificity of oxidation at C-19 in oestrogen biosynthesis. *J.C.S. Chem. Commun.,* pp. 185–86
5. Asakawa, Y., Tamari, K., Shoji, A., Kaji, J. 1974. Metabolic products of gibberellin A₃ and their interconversion in dwarf kidney bean plants. *Agric. Biol. Chem.* 38:719–25
6. Bakker, H. J., Cook, I. F., Jefferies, P. R., Knox, J. R. 1974. Gibberellin metabolites from ent-kaura-2,16-dien-19-ol and its succinate in *Gibberella fujikuroi. Tetrahedron* 30:3631–40
7. Barendse, G. W. M. 1975. Biosynthesis, metabolism, transport and distribution of gibberellins. In *Gibberellin and Plant Growth,* ed. H. N. Krishnamoorthy, pp. 65–89. New Delhi: Wiley Eastern. 355 pp.
8. Bateson, J. H., Cross, B. E. 1974. The microbiological production of analogues of mould metabolites. Part 1. Production of fluorogibberellic acid and fluorogibberellin A₉ by *Gibberella fujikuroi. J.C.S. Perkin Trans. 1,* pp. 1131–36
9. Bearder, J. R., Dennis, F. G., MacMillan, J., Martin, B. C., Phinney, B. O. 1975. A new gibberellin (A₄₅) from seed

of *Pyrus communis* L. *Tetrahedron Lett.,* pp. 669–70
10. Bearder, J. R., Frydman, V. M., Gaskin, P., Harvey, W. E., Hedden, P., MacMillan, J., Phinney, B. O., Wels, C. M. 1974. Gibberellin biosynthesis in *Gibberella fujikuroi* using the mutant B1-41a. In *Plant Growth Substances 1973,* pp. 241–51. Tokyo: Hirokawa. 1242 pp.
11. Bearder, J. R., Frydman, V. M., Gaskin, P., Hatton, I. K., Harvey, W. E., MacMillan, J., Phinney, B. O. 1976. Fungal products. Part XVII. Microbiological hydroxylation of gibberellin A₉ and its methyl esters. *J.C.S. Perkin Trans. 1,* pp. 178–83
12. Bearder, J. R., Frydman, V. M., Gaskin, P., MacMillan, J., Wels, C. M., Phinney, B. O. 1976. Fungal products. Part XVI. Conversion of isosteviol and steviol acetate into gibberellin analogues by mutant B1-41a of *Gibberella fujikuroi* and the preparation of [³H]gibberellin A₂₀. *J.C.S. Perkin Trans. 1,* pp. 173–78
13. Bearder, J. R., MacMillan, J., Phinney, B. O. 1973. 3-Hydroxylation of gibberellin A₁₂-aldehyde in *Gibberella fujikuroi* strain Rec-193A. *Phytochemistry* 12:2173–79
14. Bearder, J. R., MacMillan, J., Phinney, B. O. 1973. Conversion of gibberellin A₁ into gibberellin A₃ by the mutant R-9 of *Gibberella fujikuroi. Phytochemistry* 12:2655–59
15. Bearder, J. R., MacMillan, J., Phinney, B. O. 1975. Fungal products. Part XIV. Metabolic pathways from ent-kaurenoic acid to the fungal gibberellins in mutant B1-41a of *Gibberella fujikuroi. J.C.S. Perkin Trans. 1,* pp. 721–26

16. Bearder, J. R., MacMillan, J., Phinney, B. O. 1976. Origin of the oxygen atoms in the lactone bridge of C_{19}-gibberellins. *J.C.S. Chem. Commun.,* pp. 834–35

17. Bearder, J. R., MacMillan, J., Wels, C. M., Chaffey, M. B., Phinney, B. O. 1974. Position of the metabolic block for gibberellin biosynthesis in mutant B1-41a of *Gibberella fujikuroi. Phytochemistry* 13:911–17

18. Bearder, J. R., MacMillan, J., Wels, C. M., Phinney, B. O. 1975. The metabolism of steviol to 13-hydroxylated *ent*-gibberellanes and *ent*-kauranes. *Phytochemistry* 14:1741–48

19. Bearder, J. R., Sponsel, V. M. 1977. Selected topics in gibberellin metabolism. *Biochem. Rev.* 5:569–82

20. Beeley, L. J., Gaskin, P., MacMillan, J. 1975. Gibberellin A_{43} and other terpenes in endosperm of *Echinocystis macrocarpa. Phytochemistry* 14:779–83

21. Bennett, R. D., Lieber, E. R., Heftmann, E. 1967. Biosynthesis of steviol from (–)-kaurene. *Phytochemistry* 6:1107–10

22. Birch, A. J., Rickards, R. W., Smith, H., Harris, A., Whalley, W. B. 1959. Studies in relation to biosynthesis—XXI. Rosenonolactone and gibberellic acid. *Tetrahedron* 7:241–51

23. Bowen, D. H., Crozier, A., MacMillan, J., Reid, D. M. 1973. Characterization of gibberellins from light-grown *Phaseolus coccineus* seedlings by combined GC-MS. *Phytochemistry* 12:2935–41

24. Bowen, D. H., MacMillan, J., Graebe, J. E. 1972. Determination of specific radioactivity of [^{14}C]-compounds by mass spectrometry. *Phytochemistry* 11:2253–57

25. Browning, G., Saunders, P. F. 1977. Membrane localised gibberellins A_9 and A_4 in wheat chloroplasts. *Nature* 265:375–77

26. Buggy, M. J., Britton, G., Goodwin, T. W. 1974. Terpenoid biosynthesis by chloroplasts isolated in organic solvents. *Phytochemistry* 13:125–29

27. Cockburn, B. J., Wellburn, A. R. 1974. Changes in the envelope permeability of developing chloroplasts. *J. Exp. Bot.* 25:36–49

28. Cooke, R. J., Kendrick, R. E. 1976. Phytochrome controlled gibberellin metabolism in etioplast envelopes. *Planta* 131:303–7

29. Cooke, R. J., Saunders, P. F., Kendrick, R. E. 1975. Red light induced production of gibberellin-like substances in homogenates of etiolated wheat leaves and in suspensions of intact etioplasts. *Planta* 124:319–28

30. Coolbaugh, R. C., Hamilton, R. 1976. Inhibition of *ent*-kaurene oxidation and growth by α-cyclopropyl-α-(p-methoxyphenyl)-5-pyrimidine methyl alcohol. *Plant Physiol.* 57:245–48

31. Coolbaugh, R. C., Hirano, S. S., West, C. A. 1977. Specificity of action of ancymidol, a plant growth inhibitor. *Plant Physiol.* 59:Suppl. 77, 1–134

32. Coolbaugh, R. C., Moore, T. C. 1969. Apparent changes in rate of kaurene biosynthesis during the development of pea seeds. *Plant Physiol.* 44:1364–67

33. Coolbaugh, R. C., Moore, T. C. 1971. Localization of enzymes catalysing kaurene biosynthesis in immature pea seeds. *Phytochemistry* 10:2395–2400

34. Coolbaugh, R. C., Moore, T. C. 1971. Metabolism of kaurene in cell-free extracts of immature pea seeds. *Phytochemistry* 10:2401–12

35. Coolbaugh, R. C., Moore, T. C., Barlow, S. A., Ecklund, P. R. 1973. Biosynthesis of *ent*-kaurene in cell-free extracts of *Pisum sativum* shoot tips. *Phytochemistry* 12:1613–18

36. Cross, B. E., Galt, R. H. B., Hanson, J. R. 1964. The biosynthesis of the gibberellins. Part I (–)-kaurene as a precursor of gibberellic acid. *J. Chem. Soc.,* pp. 295–300

37. Cross, B. E., Galt, R. H. B., Norton, K. 1968. The biosynthesis of the gibberellins. II. *Tetrahedron* 24:231–37

38. Cross, B. E., Norton, K., Stewart, J. C. 1968. The biosynthesis of the gibberellins. Part III. *J. Chem. Soc. C,* pp. 1054–63

39. Crozier, A., Bowen, D. H., MacMillan, J., Reid, D. M., Most, B. H. 1971. Characterization of gibberellins from dark-grown *Phaseolus coccineus* seedlings by gas-liquid chromatography and combined gas chromatography-mass spectrometry. *Planta* 97:142–54

40. Davies, L. J., Rappaport, L. 1975. Metabolism of tritiated gibberellins in d-5 dwarf maize. *Plant Physiol.* 55:620–25

41. Dawson, R. M., Jefferies, P. R., Knox, J. R. 1975. Cyclization and hydroxylation stereochemistry in the biosynthesis of gibberellic acid. *Phytochemistry* 14:2593–97

42. Dennis, D. T., Upper, C. D., West, C. A. 1965. An enzymic site of inhibition of gibberellin biosynthesis by AMO 1618 and other plant growth retardants. *Plant Physiol.* 40:948–52

43. Dennis, D. T., West, C. A. 1967. Biosynthesis of gibberellins. III. The conversion of (–)-kaurene to (–)-kauren-19-oic acid in endosperm of *Echinocystis macrocarpa* Greene. *J. Biol. Chem.* 242:3293–3300

44. Durley, R. C., Bewley, J. D., Railton, I. D., Pharis, R. P. 1976. Effects of light, abscisic acid, and ^{6}N-benzyladenine on the metabolism of [^{3}H]gibberellin A$_4$ in seeds and seedlings of lettuce, cv. Grand Rapids. *Plant Physiol.* 57:699–703

45. Durley, R. C., MacMillan, J., Pryce, R. J. 1971. Investigation of gibberellins and other growth substances in the seed of *Phaseolus multiflorus* and of *Phaseolus vulgaris* by gas chromatography and by gas chromatography-mass spectrometry. *Phytochemistry* 10:1891–1908

46. Durley, R. C., Pharis, R. P. 1973. Interconversion of gibberellin A$_4$ to gibberellins A$_1$ and A$_{34}$ by dwarf rice, cultivar Tan-ginbozu. *Planta* 109:357–61

47. Durley, R. C., Pharis, R. P., Zeevaart, J. A. D. 1975. Metabolism of [^{3}H]gibberellin A$_{20}$ by plants of *Bryophyllum daigremontianum* under long- and short-day conditions. *Planta* 126:139–49

48. Durley, R. C., Railton, I. D., Pharis, R. P. 1973. Interconversion of gibberellin A$_5$ to gibberellin A$_3$ in seedlings of dwarf *Pisum sativum*. *Phytochemistry* 12:1609–12

49. Durley, R. C., Railton, I. D., Pharis, R. P. 1974. Conversion of gibberellin A$_{14}$ to other gibberellins in seedlings of dwarf *Pisum sativum*. *Phytochemistry* 13:547–51

50. Ecklund, P. R., Moore, T. C. 1974. Correlations of growth rate and de-etiolation with rate of *ent*-kaurene biosynthesis in pea (*Pisum sativum* L.). *Plant Physiol.* 53:5–10

51. Eeuwens, C. J., Gaskin, P., MacMillan, J. 1973. Gibberellin A$_{20}$ in seed of *Pisum sativum* L., cv. Alaska. *Planta* 115:73–76

52. Ekong, D. E. U., Ogan, A. U. 1968. Chemistry of the constituents of *Xylopia aethiopica*. The structure of xylopic acid, a new diterpene acid. *J. Chem. Soc. C*, pp. 311–12

53. Evans, A., Smith, H. 1976. Localization of phytochrome in etioplasts and its regulation *in vitro* of gibberellin levels. *Proc. Natl. Acad. Sci.* 73:138–42

54. Evans, A., Smith, H. 1976. Spectrophotometric evidence for the presence of phytochrome in the envelope membranes of barley etioplasts. *Nature* 259:323–25

55. Evans, R., Hanson, J. R. 1972. The formation of (–)-kaurene in a cell-free system from *Gibberella fujikuroi*. *J. C. S. Perkin Trans. 1*, pp. 2382–85

56. Evans, R., Hanson, J. R. 1975. Studies in terpenoid biosynthesis. Part XIII. The biosynthetic relationship of the gibberellins in *Gibberella fujikuroi*. *J.C.S. Perkin Trans. 1*, pp. 663–66

57. Evans, R., Hanson, J. R., White, A. F. 1970. Studies in terpene biosynthesis. Part VI. The stereochemistry of some stages in tetracyclic diterpene biosynthesis. *J. Chem. Soc. C*, pp. 2601–03

58. Fall, R. R., West, C. A. 1971. Purification and properties of kaurene synthetase from *Fusarium moniliforme*. *J. Biol. Chem.* 246:6913–28

59. Frost, R. G., West, C. A. 1977. Properties of kaurene synthetase from *Marah macrocarpus*. *Plant Physiol.* 59:22–29

60. Frydman, V. M., Gaskin, P., MacMillan, J. 1974. Qualitative and quantitative analyses of gibberellins throughout seed maturation in *Pisum sativum* cv. Progress No. 9. *Planta* 118:123–32

61. Frydman, V. M., MacMillan, J. 1973. Identification of gibberellins A$_{20}$ and A$_{29}$ in seed of *Pisum sativum* cv. Progress No. 9 by combined gas chromatography-mass spectrometry. *Planta* 115:11–15

62. Frydman, V. M., MacMillan, J. 1975. The metabolism of gibberellins A$_9$, A$_{20}$, and A$_{29}$ in immature seeds of *Pisum sativum* cv. Progress No. 9. *Planta* 125:181–95

63. Gaskin, P., MacMillan, J. 1975. Polyoxygenated *ent*-kaurenes and water-soluble conjugates in seed of *Phaseolus coccineus*. *Phytochemistry* 14:1575–78

64. Gaskin, P., MacMillan, J. 1977. GC and GC-MS techniques for gibberellins. In *Isolation of Plant Growth Substances*, ed. J. Hillman. Cambridge Univ. Press. In press

65. Gaskin, P., MacMillan, J., Zeevaart, J. A. D. 1973. Identification of gibberellin A$_{20}$, abscisic acid, and phaseic acid from flowering *Bryophyllum daigremontianum* by combined gas chromatography-mass spectrometry. *Planta* 111:347–52

66. Goodwin, T. W., Mercer, E. I. 1963. The regulation of sterol and carotenoid metabolism in germinating seedlings. *Symp. Biochem. Soc.* 24:37–41

67. Graebe, J. E. 1968. Biosynthesis of kaurene, squalene and phytoene from

mevalonate-2-^{14}C in a cell-free system from pea fruits. *Phytochemistry* 7: 2003–20

68. Graebe, J. E. 1969. The enzymic preparation of ^{14}C-kaurene. *Planta* 85:171–74
69. Graebe, J. E. 1972. The biosynthesis of gibberellin precursors in a cell-free system from *Cucurbita pepo* L. In *Plant Growth Substances 1970*, ed. D. J. Carr, pp. 151–57. Berlin, Heidelberg, New York: Springer-Verlag. 837 pp.
70. Graebe, J. E., Bowen, D. H., MacMillan, J. 1972. The conversion of mevalonic acid into gibberellin A_{12}-aldehyde in a cell-free system from *Cucurbita pepo*. *Planta* 102:261–71
71. Graebe, J. E., Dennis, D. T., Upper, C. D., West, C. A. 1965. Biosynthesis of gibberellins. I. The biosynthesis of (–)-kaurene, (–)-kaur-19-ol and trans-geranylgeraniol in endosperm nucellus of *Echinocystis macrocarpa* Greene. *J. Biol. Chem.* 240:1847–54
72. Graebe, J. E., Hedden, P. 1974. Biosynthesis of gibberellins in a cell-free system. In *Biochemistry and Chemistry of Plant Growth Regulators*, ed. K. Schreiber, H. R. Schütte, G. Sembdner, pp. 1–16. Halle (Saale), G.D.R.: Acad. Sci., German Democratic Republic, Inst. Plant Biochem. 432 pp.
73. Graebe, J. E., Hedden, P., Gaskin, P., MacMillan, J. 1974. Biosynthesis of gibberellins A_{12}, A_{15}, A_{24}, A_{36}, and A_{37} by a cell-free system from *Cucurbita maxima*. *Phytochemistry* 13:1433–40
74. Graebe, J. E., Hedden, P., Gaskin, P., MacMillan, J. 1974. The biosynthesis of a C_{19}-gibberellin from mevalonic acid in a cell-free system from a higher plant. *Planta* 120:307–09
75. Graebe, J. E., Hedden, P., MacMillan, J. 1974. Gibberellin biosynthesis: New intermediates in the *Cucurbita* system. See Ref. 10, pp. 260–66
76. Graebe, J. E., Hedden, P., MacMillan, J. 1975. The ring contraction step in gibberellin biosynthesis. *J. Chem. Soc. Chem. Commun.*, pp. 161–62
77. Graebe, J. E., Ropers, H.-J. 1978. The gibberellins. In *Plant Hormones and Related Compounds*, ed. P. B. Goodwin, T. J. V. Higgins. Amsterdam: ASP Biol. Med. In press
78. Green, T. R., Dennis, D. T., West, C. A. 1975. Compartmentation of isopentenyl pyrophosphate isomerase and prenyl transferase in developing castor bean endosperm. *Biochem. Biophys. Res. Commun.* 64:976–82

79. Hanson, J. R. 1971. The biosynthesis of the diterpenes. *Fortschr. Chem. Org. Naturst.* 29:395–416
80. Hanson, J. R., Hawker, J. 1971. The ring contraction stage in gibberellin biosynthesis. *J.C.S. Chem. Commun.*, 208
81. Hanson, J. R., Hawker, J. 1972. The formation of the C_{19}-gibberellins from gibberellin A_{13} anhydride. *Tetrahedron Lett.*, pp. 4299–4302
82. Hanson, J. R., Hawker, J., White, A. F. 1972. Studies in terpenoid biosynthesis. Part IX. The sequence of oxidation on ring B in kaurene-gibberellin biosynthesis. *J.C.S. Perkin Trans. 1*, pp. 1892–95
83. Hanson, J. R., White, A. F. 1968. Studies in terpenoid biosynthesis-II. The biosynthesis of steviol. *Phytochemistry* 7:595–97
84. Hanson, J. R., White, A. F. 1968. The transformation of steviol by *Gibberella fujikuroi*. *Tetrahedron* 24:6291–93
85. Hanson, J. R., White, A. F. 1969. Studies in terpenoid biosynthesis. Part IV. Biosynthesis of the kaurenolides and gibberellic acid. *J. Chem. Soc. C*, pp. 981–85
86. Haruta, H., Yagi, H., Iwata, T., Tamura, S. 1974. Synthesis and plant growth retardant activities of quaternary ammonium compounds derived from α-ionone and isophorone. *Agric. Biol. Chem.* 38:417–22
87. Hasson, E. P., West, C. A. 1976. Properties of the system for the mixed function oxidation of kaurene and kaurene derivatives in microsomes of the immature seed of *Marah macrocarpus*. Cofactor requirements. *Plant Physiol.* 58:473–78
88. Hasson, E. P., West, C. A. 1976. Properties of the system for the mixed function oxidation of kaurene and kaurene derivatives in microsomes of the immature seed of *Marah macrocarpus*. Electron transfer components. *Plant Physiol.* 58:479–84
89. Hedden, P., MacMillan, J., Phinney, B. O. 1974. Fungal products. Part XII. Gibberellin A_{14}-aldehyde, an intermediate in gibberellin biosynthesis in *Gibberella fujikuroi*. *J.C.S. Perkin Trans. 1*, pp. 587–92
90. Hedden, P., Phinney, B. O. 1976. Kaurene biosynthesis and the dwarf-5 mutant of *Zea mays*. *Plant Physiol.* 57: Suppl. 86:1–107
91. Hedden, P., Phinney, B. O., MacMillan, J., Sponsel, V. M. 1977. Metabolism of kaurenoids by *Gibberella fujikuroi* in the presence of the plant growth

retardant N,N,N-trimethyl-l-methyl-(2',6',6'-trimethylcyclohex-2'-en-1'-yl) prop-2-enylammonium iodide. *Phytochemistry* 16:1913–17

92. Hill, H. M., Rogers, L. J. 1974. Mevalonate activating enzymes and phosphatases in higher plants. *Phytochemistry* 13:763–77

93. Hiraga, K., Kawabe, S., Yokota, T., Murofushi, N., Takahashi, N. 1974. Isolation and characterization of plant growth substances in immature seeds and etiolated seedlings of *Phaseolus vulgaris. Agric. Biol. Chem.* 38:2521–27

94. Hiraga, K., Yamane, H., Takahashi, N. 1974. Biological activity of some synthetic gibberellin glucosyl esters. *Phytochemistry* 13:2371–76

95. Hiraga, K., Yokota, T., Murofushi, N., Takahashi, N. 1972. Isolation and characterization of a free gibberellin and glucosyl esters of gibberellins in mature seeds of *Phaseolus vulgaris. Agric. Biol. Chem.* 36:345–47

96. Hiraga, K., Yokota, T., Murofushi, N., Takahashi, N. 1974. Isolation and characterization of gibberellins in mature seeds of *Phaseolus vulgaris. Agric. Biol. Chem.* 38:2511–20

97. Jefferies, P. R., Knox, J. R., Ratajczak, T. 1974. Metabolic transformations of some *ent*-kaurenes in *Gibberella fujikuroi. Phytochemistry* 13:1423–31

98. Kamienska, A., Durley, R. C., Pharis, R. P. 1976. Isolation of gibberellins A_3, A_4 and A_7 from *Pinus attenuata* pollen. *Phytochemistry* 15:421–24

99. Kamienska, A., Durley, R. C., Pharis, R. P. 1976. Endogenous gibberellins of pine pollen. III. Conversion of 1,2-[^{3}H]GA$_4$ to gibberellins A_1 and A_{34} in germinating pollen of *Pinus attenuata* Lemm. *Plant Physiol.* 58:68–70

100. Katsumi, M., Phinney, B. O. 1969. The biosynthesis of gibberellins. In *Gibberellin: Chemistry, Biochemistry, Physiology,* ed. S. Tamura, pp. 195–219. Tokyo: Univ. Tokyo Press. 372 pp. (In Japanese)

101. Komada, Y., Isogai, Y., Okamoto, T. 1968. Isolation of gibberellin A_{20} from pea pods. *Sci. Pap. Coll. Gen. Educ. Univ. Tokyo* 18:221–30

102. Lance, B., Durley, R. C., Reid, D. M., Thorpe, T. A., Pharis, R. P. 1976. Metabolism of [^{3}H] gibberellin A_{20} in light-and dark-grown tobacco callus cultures. *Plant Physiol.* 58:387–92

103. Lang, A. 1970. Gibberellins: structure and metabolism. *Ann. Rev. Plant Physiol.* 21:537–70

104. Leopold, A. C. 1971. Antagonism of some gibberellin actions by a substituted pyrimidine. *Plant Physiol.* 48:537–40

105. Lew, F. T., West, C. A. 1971. (–)-Kaur-16-en-7β-ol-19-oic acid, an intermediate in gibberellin biosynthesis. *Phytochemistry* 10:2065–76

106. Liebisch, H. W. 1974. Uptake, translocation and metabolism of GA$_3$ glucosyl ester. See Ref. 72, pp. 109–13

107. Lorenzi, R., Horgan, R., Heald, J. K. 1975. Gibberellins in *Picea sitchensis* Carriere: Seasonal variation and partial characterization. *Planta* 126:75–82

108. Lorenzi, R., Horgan, R., Heald, J. K. 1976. Gibberellin A_9 glucosyl ester in needles of *Picea sitchensis. Phytochemistry* 15:789–90

109. Lorenzi, R., Saunders, P. F., Heald, J. K., Horgan, R. 1977. A novel gibberellin from needles of *Picea sitchensis. Plant Sci. Lett.* 8:179–82

110. Lunnon, M. W., MacMillan, J., Phinney, B. O. 1977. Fungal products. Part XX. Transformation of 2- and 3-hydroxylated kaurenoids by *Gibberella fujikuroi. J. C. S. Perkin Trans. 1,* pp. 2308–16

111. MacMillan, J. 1971. Diterpenes—the gibberellins. In *Aspects of Terpenoid Chemistry and Biochemistry,* ed. T. W. Goodwin, pp. 153–80. New York: Academic. 441 pp.

112. MacMillan, J. 1974. Metabolic processes related to gibberellin biosynthesis in mutants of *Gibberella fujikuroi.* See Ref. 74, pp. 33–49

113. MacMillan, J. 1974. Recent aspects of the chemistry and biosynthesis of the gibberellins. In *The Chemistry and Biochemistry of Plant Hormones,* ed. V. C. Runeckles, E. Sondheimer, D. C. Walton, pp. 1–19. New York: Academic. 178 pp.

114. MacMillan, J. 1977. Metabolic studies of the gibberellins. In *Crop Protection Agents—Their Biological Evaluation,* ed. N. R. McFarlane, pp. 273–82. London: Academic

115. MacMillan, J., Pryce, R. J. 1973. The gibberellins. In *Phytochemistry,* ed. L. P. Miller, 3:283–326. New York: Van Nostrand-Reinhold. 448 pp.

116. MacMillan, J., Takahashi, N. 1968. Proposed procedure for the allocation of trivial names to the gibberellins. *Nature* 217:170–71

117. McCorkindale, N. J. 1976. The biosynthesis of terpenes and steroids. In *The Filamentous Fungi,* ed. J. E. Smith, D.

R. Berry, 2:369–422. New York: Wiley. 520 pp.

118. McInnes, A. G., Smith, D. G., Durley, R. C., Pharis, R. P., Arsenault, G. P., MacMillan, J., Gaskin, P., Vining, L. C. 1977. Biosynthesis of gibberellins in *Gibberella fujikuroi*. Gibberellin A_{47}. *Can. J. Biochem.* 55:728–35

119. Moore, T. C., Barlow, S. A., Coolbaugh, R. C. 1972. Participation of noncatalytic 'carrier' protein in the metabolism of kaurene in cell-free extracts of pea seeds. *Phytochemistry* 11:3225–33

120. Moore, T. C., Coolbaugh, R. C. 1976. Conversion of geranylgeranyl pyrophosphate to *ent*-kaurene in enzyme extracts of sonicated chloroplasts. *Phytochemistry* 15:1241–47

121. Murphy, G. J. P., Briggs, D. E. 1975. Metabolism of *ent*-kaurenol-[17-14C], *ent*-kaurenal-[17-14C] and *ent*-kaurenoic acid-[17-14C] by germinating *Hordeum distichon* grains. *Phytochemistry* 14:429–33

122. Murphy, P. J., West, C. A. 1969. The role of mixed function oxidases in kaurene metabolism in *Echinocystis macrocarpa* Greene endosperm. *Arch. Biochem. Biophys.* 133:395–407

123. Nadeau, R., Rappaport, L. 1972. Metabolism of gibberellin A_1 in germinating bean seeds. *Phytochemistry* 11:1611–16

124. Nadeau, R., Rappaport, L., Stolp, C. F. 1972. Uptake and metabolism of ³H-gibberellin A_1 by barley aleurone layers: Response to abscisic acid. *Planta* 107:315–24

125. Ogura, K., Shinka, T., Seto, S. 1972. The purification and properties of geranyl geranyl pyrophosphate synthetase from pumpkin fruit. *J. Biochem.* 72:1101–8

126. Oster, M. O., West, C. A. 1968. Biosynthesis of trans-geranylgeranyl pyrophosphate in endosperm of *Echinocystis macrocarpa* Greene. *Arch. Biochem. Biophys.* 127:112–23

127. Patterson, R. J., Rappaport, L. 1974. The conversion of gibberellin A_1 to gibberellin A_8 by a cell-free enzyme system. *Planta* 119:183–91

128. Patterson, R., Rappaport, L., Breidenbach, R. W. 1975. Characterization of an enzyme from *Phaseolus vulgaris* seeds which hydroxylates GA_1 to GA_8. *Phytochemistry* 14:363–68

129. Phinney, B. O. 1961. Dwarfing genes in *Zea mays* and their relation to the gibberellins. In *Plant Growth Regulation*,

ed. R. M. Klein, pp. 489–501. Ames: Iowa State Univ. Press. 850 pp.

130. Pitel, D. W., Vining, L. C., Arsenault, G. P. 1971. Biosynthesis of gibberellins in *Gibberella fujikuroi*. The sequence after gibberellin A_4. *Can. J. Biochem.* 49:194–200

131. Railton, I. D. 1976. Aspects of gibberellin biosynthesis in higher plants. *S. Afr. J. Sci.* 72:371–77

132. Railton, I. D., Durley, R. C., Pharis, R. P. 1973. Interconversion of gibberellin A_1 to gibberellin A_8 in seedlings of dwarf *Oryza sativa*. *Phytochemistry* 12:2351–52

133. Railton, I. D., Durley, R. C., Pharis, R. P. 1974. Metabolism of tritiated gibberellin A_9 by shoots of dark-grown dwarf pea, cv. Meteor. *Plant Physiol.* 54:6–12

134. Railton, I. D., Murofushi, N., Durley, R. C., Pharis, R. P. 1974. Interconversion of gibberellin A_{20} to gibberellin A_{29} by etiolated seedlings and germinating seeds of dwarf *Pisum sativum*. *Phytochemistry* 13:793–96

135. Rappaport, L., Davies, L., Lavee, S., Nadeau, R., Patterson, R., Stolp, C. F. 1974. Significance of metabolism of [³H]GA₁ for plant regulation. See Ref. 10, pp. 314–24

136. Reeve, D. R., Crozier, A., Durley, R. C., Reid, D. M., Pharis, R. P. 1975. Metabolism of ³H-gibberellin A_1 and ³H-gibberellin A_4 by *Phaseolus coccineus* seedlings. *Plant Physiol.* 55:42–44

137. Robinson, D. R., West, C. A. 1970. Biosynthesis of cyclic diterpenes in extracts from seedlings of *Ricinus communis* L. I. Identification of diterpene hydrocarbons formed from mevalonate. *Biochemistry* 9:70–79

138. Robinson, D. R., West, C. A. 1970. Biosynthesis of cyclic diterpenes in extracts from seedlings of *Ricinus communis* L. II. Conversion of geranylgeranyl pyrophosphate into diterpene hydrocarbons and partial purification of the cyclization enzymes. *Biochemistry* 9:80–89

139. Rogers, L. J., Shah, S. P. J., Goodwin, T. W. 1966. Intracellular localization of mevalonate-activating enzymes in plant cells. *Biochem. J.* 99:381–88

140. Rowe, J. W., ed. 1968. *The Common and Systematic Nomenclature of Cyclic Diterpenes*. Proposal IUPAC Comm. Org. Nomencl., 3rd rev. Forest Products Lab. USDA, Madison, Wis. 57 pp.

141. Ruddat, M., Heftmann, E., Lang, A. 1965. Biosynthesis of steviol. *Arch. Biochem. Biophys.* 110:496–99

142. Ruzicka, L. 1953. The isoprene rule and the biogenesis of terpenic compounds. *Experientia* 9:357–96

143. Scallen, T. J., Schuster, M. W., Dhar, A. K. 1971. Evidence for a noncatalytic carrier protein in cholesterol biosynthesis. *J. Biol. Chem.* 246:224–30

144. Schechter, I., West, C. A. 1969. Biosynthesis of gibberellins. IV. Biosynthesis of cyclic diterpenes from *trans*-geranylgeranyl pyrophosphate. *J. Biol. Chem.* 244:3200–9

145. Schreiber, K., Weiland, J., Sembdner, G. 1970. Isolierung von gibberellin-A_8 -0(3)-β-D-glucopyranosid aus früchten von *Phaseolus coccineus. Phytochemistry* 9:189–98

146. Sembdner, G., Borgmann, E., Schneider, G., Liebisch, H. W., Miersch, O., Adams, B., Lischewski, M., Schreiber, K. 1976. Biological activity of some conjugated gibberellins. *Planta* 132:249–57

147. Sembdner, G., Weiland, J., Aurich, O., Schreiber, K. 1968. Isolation, structure and metabolism of a gibberellin glucoside. *Plant Growth Regulators.* S. C. I. Monogr. 31, pp. 71–86. London: Staples

148. Serebryakov, E. P., Simolin, A. V., Kuchenov, V. F., Rosynov, B. S. 1970. New metabolites of *Fusarium moniliforme* Sheld. *Tetrahedron* 26:5215–23

149. Shinka, T., Ogura, K., Seto, S. 1974. Farnesyl pyrophosphate and geranylgeranyl pyrophosphate synthesis during *Cucurbita pepo* germination. *Phytochemistry* 13:2103–6

150. Simcox, P. D., Dennis, D. T., West, C. A. 1975. Kaurene synthetase from plastids of developing plant tissues. *Biochem. Biophys. Res. Commun.* 66:166–72

151. Sitton, D., West, C. A. 1975. Casbene: An anti-fungal diterpene produced in cell-free extracts of *Ricinus communis* seedlings. *Phytochemistry* 14:1921–25

152. Spector, C., Phinney, B. O. 1968. Gibberellin biosynthesis: Genetic studies in *Gibberella fujikuroi. Physiol. Plant.* 21:127–36

153. Sponsel, V. M., Hoad, G. V., Beeley, L. J. 1977. The biological activities of some new gibberellins (GAs) in six plant bioassays. *Planta* 135:143–47

154. Sponsel, V. M., MacMillan, J. 1977. Further studies on the metabolism of gibberellins (GAs) A_9, A_{20}, A_{29} in immature seeds of *Pisum sativum* cv. Progress No. 9. *Planta* 135:129–36

155. Stoddart, J. L. 1968. The association of gibberellin-like activity with the chloroplast fraction of leaf homogenates. *Planta* 81:106–12

156. Stoddart, J. L. 1969. Incorporation of kaurenoic acid into gibberellins by chloroplast preparations of *Brassica oleracea. Phytochemistry* 8:831–37

157. Stoddart, J. L. 1976. Phytochrome and gibberellins. *Nature* 261:454–55

158. Stolp, C. F., Nadeau, R., Rappaport, L. 1973. Effect of abscisic acid on uptake and metabolism of [^{3}H]gibberellin A_1 and [^{3}H]pseudogibberellin A_1 by barley half-seeds. *Plant Physiol.* 52:546–48

159. Takeba, G., Takimoto, A. 1971. Metabolism of (−)-kaurene-^{3}H and (−)-kaurenol-^{3}H during the photoperiodic floral induction in *Pharbitis nil. Plant Cell Physiol.* 12:81–88

160. Wample, R. L., Durley, R. C., Pharis, R. P. 1975. Metabolism of gibberellin A_4 by vegetative shoots of Douglas fir at three stages of ontogeny. *Physiol. Plant.* 35:273–78

161. Wellburn, A. R., Hampp, R. 1976. Uptake of mevalonate and acetate during plastid development. *Biochem. J.* 158:231–33

162. Wenkert, E. 1955. Structural and biogenetic relationships in the diterpene series. *Chem. Ind. London*, pp. 282–84

163. West, C. A. 1961. The chemistry of gibberellins from flowering plants. See Ref. 129, pp. 473–82

164. West, C. A. 1973. Biosynthesis of gibberellins. In *Biosynthesis and Its Control in Plants*, ed. B. V. Milborrow, pp. 143–69. London: Academic. 364 pp.

165. Yafin, Y., Shechter, I. 1975. Comparison between biosynthesis of *ent*-kaurene in germinating tomato seeds and cell suspension cultures of tomato and tobacco. *Plant Physiol.* 56:671–75

166. Yamane, H., Murofushi, N., Osada, H., Takahashi, N. 1977. Metabolism of gibberellins in early immature bean seeds. *Phytochemistry* 16:831–35

167. Yamane, H., Murofushi, N., Takahashi, N. 1975. Metabolism of gibberellins in maturing and germinating bean seeds. *Phytochemistry* 14:1195–1200

168. Yamane, H., Yamaguchi, I., Murofushi, N., Takahashi, N. 1974. Isolation and structures of gibberellin A_{35} and its glucoside from immature seed of *Cytisus scoparius. Agric. Biol. Chem.* 38:649–55

169. Yamane, H., Yamaguchi, I., Yokota, T., Murofushi, N., Takahashi, N. 1973. Biological activities of new gibberellins A_{30}–A_{35} and A_{35} glucoside. *Phytochemistry* 12:255–61

170. Yokota, T., Murofushi, N., Takahashi, N. 1970. Structure of new gibberellin glucoside in immature seeds of *Pharbitis nil. Tetrahedron Lett.*, pp. 1489–91

171. Yokota, T., Murofushi, N., Takahashi, N., Katsumi, M. 1971. Biological activities of gibberellins and their glucosides in *Pharbitis nil. Phytochemistry* 10: 2943–49

172. Yokota, T., Takahashi, N., Murofushi, N., Tamura, S. 1969. Isolation of gibberellins A_{26} and A_{27} and their glucosides from immature seeds of *Pharbitis nil. Planta* 87:180–84

173. Yokota, T., Takahashi, N., Murofushi, N., Tamura, S. 1969. Structures of new gibberellin glucosides in immature seeds of *Pharbitis nil. Tetrahedron Lett.*, pp. 2081–84

174. Yokota, T., Yamane, H., Takahashi, N. 1976. The synthesis of gibberethiones, gibberellin-related diterpenoids. *Agric. Biol. Chem.* 40:2507–8

175. Yokota, T., Yamazaki, S., Takahashi, N., Iitaka, Y. 1974. Structure of pharbitic acid, a gibberellin-related diterpenoid. *Tetrahedron Lett.*, pp. 2957–60

Added in proof (listed in text as J. E. Graebe and H.-J. Ropers, unpublished information):

Ropers, H.-J., Graebe, J. E., Gaskin, P., MacMillan, J. 1978. Gibberellin biosynthesis in a cell-free system from immature seed from *Pisum sativum. Biochem. Biophys. Res. Commun.* In press

Ann. Rev. Plant Physiol. 1978. 29:193–213

BIOCHEMISTRY AND FUNCTION OF VACUOLES

❖7649

Philippe Matile[1]

Department of General Botany, Swiss Federal Institute of Technology, 8092 Zürich, Switzerland

CONTENTS

INTRODUCTION

Vacuoles in particular have not been reviewed previously in this series. This is certainly not due to a lack of interest by plant physiologists in these largest cell spaces. In fact, several aspects of vacuoles have been dealt with in connection with

---

[1]The author is indebted to Mrs. Dorli Furrer and Miss Sonja Türler for their help with the manuscript.

0066-4294/78/0601-0193$01.00

other topics such as cellular compartmentation of intermediary metabolites (91), fluxes and compartmentation of ions (69), phosphate pools (7), and osmoregulation (43). Vacuoles are generally believed to represent storage compartments for inorganic ions and a variety of organic compounds. However, most of the corresponding information stems from indirect approaches to vacuolar compartmentation. The analysis of tracer kinetics, the assessment of electrical potentials in giant algal cells, and other techniques have led to views and conclusions about inactive pools of compounds which are remote from the centers of metabolism, or about the fluxes of ions in and out of vacuoles. In the past few years methods which allow a direct analysis of vacuoles have been developed and used in a number of laboratories. As a consequence, the present review covers these direct approaches to the biochemistry and function of vacuoles. Work with isolated vacuoles and attempts at selective extraction of vacuolar compounds will be stressed.

Not only ions and small molecules are deposited in vacuoles but also certain macromolecules. Protein bodies represent a type of vacuole specialized in the storage and mobilization of seed proteins. As this aspect of vacuoles has recently been reviewed (2), it will not be considered here. One feature which appears to be typical for aleurone grains, the presence of certain hydrolytic enzymes, has also been noticed when other types of vacuoles were analyzed for their enzyme content. Hence, intracellular digestion, which may be associated with vacuolar hydrolases, is another important functional aspect of vacuoles which will be discussed here.

The term vacuole designates an (optically) empty space within the cytoplasm. This space is encircled by the vacuolar membrane, the tonoplast, which faces the cell sap with its inner surface and the cytoplasmic matrix with its outer surface. It is obvious that the tonoplast must play a prominent role in metabolic processes associated with vacuoles. Some of its properties have been elucidated recently and views on the interactions between the cytoplasm and the vacuolar fluid are gradually emerging (79).

It should be mentioned that the term vacuole is subsequently used in a purely descriptive sense. In the era of ultrastructural cytology the term has become somewhat vague as vacuoles turned out to be but comparatively voluminous components of an elaborate system of endomembranes. The interassociations and conversions within this system have been discussed in earlier reviews (75, 79) and shall therefore not be considered here.

ANALYSIS OF VACUOLES

Isolation

The main difficulty in preparing vacuoles is caused by the rigidity of cell walls. Large vacuoles are inevitably disrupted if drastic mechanical means are used for disintegrating cells or tissues. At best only small vacuoles may be available for isolation in homogenates prepared by grinding young tissues with sand using a pestle and mortar (20, 57, 74, 94). In order to avoid difficulties resulting from the cell wall, naked protoplasts have been used successfully for isolating large vacuoles. A variety of procedures for disrupting yeast protoplasts gently are now available (121). Mechanical homogenization (122), metabolic lysis in the presence of glucose and a chelating agent (39, 53, 54), as well as osmotic lysis of yeast protoplasts (78, 83) have been used for liberating intact vacuoles. In contrast to the techniques which allow the maintenance of isotonic conditions, osmotic lysis of yeast protoplasts has the disadvantage that the tonoplast is rendered permeable for small molecules if the vacuoles are exposed to hypotonic media (124), yet if the medium is readjusted to isotonic conditions immediately after the osmotic bursting of yeast protoplasts, micromolecules are retained in the liberated vacuoles (83). Perhaps the most elegant method for isotonic lysis of yeast protoplasts is based on the irreversible binding to the plasma membrane of the polycation DEAE dextran which causes the disrupture of protoplasts (28). This method may be useful also for preparing vacuoles from protoplasts of vascular plants (13). Instability of the plasma membrane at pH 8 in conjunction with slightly hypotonic conditions result in the liberation of intact vacuoles from protoplasts prepared from a variety of plant tissues (117). Protoplasts have the disadvantage that the properties of vacuoles may be changed upon prolonged exposure of tissues to wall-degrading enzymes. In addition, the preparation of protoplasts depends on a number of parameters and may not be possible in all cases of strain and age of culture of fungi or of plant tissues. A method to overcome these disadvantages is based on the slicing of strongly plasmolyzed beetroot storage tissue; the slicing apparatus has been so designed that organelles (including vacuoles) from cells cut open are released into an undisturbed reservoir of osmoticum (62). Similarly, but in a more primitive fashion, vacuoles have been liberated from plasmolyzed root tips by gentle chopping with a razor blade (73). In the case of highly vacuolated parenchyma cells one would expect the slicing of the plasmolyzed tissue to result in the liberation of protoplasts rather than of free vacuoles. In fact, the same technique has been used for preparing protoplasts mechanically as an alternative to the conventional enzymatic method (95). Properties of the medium, particularly a slightly alkaline pH, may cause the instability of the plasmalemma and, hence, allow the mechanical isolation of vacuoles (62).

A good source of vacuoles is the latex released upon tapping plants with articulated laticifers. It contains large numbers of small vacuoles which can easily be separated from the cytoplasm (serum) by centrifugation (32, 77, 97).

Stepwise Extraction of Solutes from Cells

A procedure for the stepwise extraction permitting an estimate of the distribution of soluble substances between cytoplasm and vacuole is based on the observation that the retentiveness of the plasmalemma is rapidly lost if yeast cells are exposed to macromolecular polycations at low ionic strength (106). In a first step of extraction, yeast cells are treated with a polycation such as cytochrome c in the presence of an osmotic stabilizer which prevents the bursting of vacuoles. Cytoplasmic pools of solutes are extracted by this treatment. In a second step the vacuoles are disrupted by hypotonic treatment of the cells with water so that the vacuolar pools are released (106, 125). This procedure appears to be very useful for the study of interactions between cytoplasm and vacuole (49, 56, 125). Its reliability depends, however, on whether or not the cells of a given population are equally sensitive to the polycation.

Excellent effects in inducing permeability of the plasmalemma in *Candida utilis* and *Saccharomyces cerevisiae* strains were recently obtained with DEAE dextran (50). Although this compound has a molecular weight of ca 5 × 10⁵ dalton and is, therefore, unlikely to penetrate the cell walls and to bind directly to the plasmalemma, it efficiently renders the cytoplasm accessible for the fluorescent dye primulin which was used for probing the effect quantitatively. As plasma membranes of higher plant cells are sensitive to macromolecular polycations (101, 110), the application of the procedure of stepwise extraction is not necessarily restricted to unicellular fungi.

VACUOLES AS STORAGE COMPARTMENTS

Constituents of Cell Saps

It is not the aim of this section to compile the information available on constituents of vacuoles. The idea is rather to illustrate the uneven distribution of substances between vacuole and cytoplasm with a number of selected examples, and to prepare the reader for the presumably more attractive section on transport across the tonoplast and mechanisms of accumulation. In this context it is necessary to make a brief statement about the assessment of intracellular concentrations of substances.

Water is certainly the most abundant among the constituents of cell saps. In fact, it is the solvent for a majority of vacuolar substances, and quantitative data about the composition of cell saps may be given in terms of concentrations calculated on the basis of vacuolar volume. However, concentrations are meaningful only if they can be compared with concentrations in the cytoplasmic matrix. It is obvious that corresponding calculations cannot be based on estimates of the cytoplasmic volume because the fraction of that volume which is occupied by free water (available as solvent) is unknown. The cytoplasm may be conceived as an integrated system of macromolecules, micromolecules, inorganic ions, and structured water (21). The actual concentration of a compound in the cytoplasm may therefore be much higher than the concentration based on cytoplasmic volume. Hence, it is not justifiable to draw conclusions about the nature of transport processes across the tonoplast (energy dependency) merely from the uneven distribution of substances between vacuoles and cytoplasm. Yet in some cases compounds are accumulated in vacuoles to such an extent that the concentration in the cell sap appears almost certainly to be higher than in the cytoplasm. In *Neurospora crassa* more than 90% of the total arginine and ornithine are contained in vesicles (60, 118), most probably in the form of tiny vacuoles which occupy only a small fraction of the cytoplasm of exponentially growing hyphae. In isotonically isolated yeast vacuoles a concentration of α-amino nitrogen as high as about 1 molar has been measured (122). As only 0.6–0.7 M sorbitol is necessary for stabilizing isolated yeast vacuoles, it may be assumed that not all of the vacuolar amino acids are present in an osmotically active form. In yeast the vacuoles occupy about 25% of the cell volume. The basic amino acids account for a large proportion of the total amino acid pool of yeast cells. These amino acids, rich in nitrogen and particularly arginine but also glutamine, are accumulated preferentially in the vacuoles (49, 122, 125). On a volume basis, the concentration of arginine in *Saccharomyces cerevisiae* grown on arginine is about 20 times higher in vacuoles as compared with the concentration in the cytoplasm. In contrast, glutamic acid, which accounts for about one third of the total amino acid pool, is largely absent from the vacuoles (122).

The differential distribution of different classes of amino acids within yeast cells strongly suggests the existence of specific transporting capacities in the tonoplast. The same conclusion must be drawn from the differential distribution of sulfonium compounds which, under certain conditions, can be induced to accumulate in cells of bakers' yeast: S-adenosylmethionine is deposited largely in vacuoles (85, 106, 113), dimethyl-3-propiothetin is accumulated predominantly in the cytoplasm, while S-methyl-L-methionine is about equally distributed (106).

Organic acids have been assessed in the small vacuoles (so-called lutoïds) and in the cytoplasm (serum) of latex from *Hevea brasiliensis* (99). On a volume basis citric acid is enriched considerably in the lutoïds (10–15% of total latex volume), whereas malic acid is evenly distributed. A recent study with protoplasts from mesophyll cells of *Bryophyllum daigremontianum* has yielded evidence that the isolated vacuoles contain practically all of the malic acid (13).

Large storage pools of sugars present in organs such as internodes of sugarcane have commonly been thought to be located in vacuoles. In the case of red beet storage tissue, a corresponding compartmentation has now been demonstrated: as much as 90% of the total sucrose of this tissue is present in the vacuoles (34).

The accumulation of phenolics in vacuoles is obvious, especially in the case of colored compounds. These glycosides are retained in vacuoles isolated from protoplasts prepared from petals (117). Betacyanin has been used as a marker substance for the isolation of vacuoles from red beet storage tissue (62). In thin sections electron dense iron complexes of tannins appear to be localized exclusively in the vacuolar space (5, 17, 25). In the case of alkaloids the situation is more complex. On the one hand, almost all of the morphine present in the latex tapped from the capsule of *Papaver somniferum* has been recovered in vesicles, presumably small vacuoles comparable with the *Hevea* lutoïds (32). On the other hand, vacuoles isolated from the latex of *Chelidonium majus* contained the four major isochinoline alkaloids of this species, but the extent of accumulation differed greatly; sanguinarine and chelerythrine were enriched in the vacuoles, berberine and dihydrocoptisine were distributed evenly between vacuoles and cytoplasm (58, 76).

Certain inorganic substances are extremely plentiful in vacuoles. An eccentric example is provided by the statoliths of the *Chara* rhizoid. These dense bodies are identical with small vacuoles containing barium-sulfate as the main constituent (108). Another remarkable example concerns the vacuolar polyphosphate of yeast (55). A careful analysis of polyphosphate distribution in yeast cells and protoplasts provided strong evidence in favor of an exclusive location of this polyanion in the vacuole (11). In *Scenedesmus* the accumulation of polyphosphate is associated with the appearance of electron dense granules in small vacuoles (112).

As to the distribution of inorganic ions in yeast cells, the results are not yet conclusive. A considerable vacuolar accumulation of Mg^{2+} and orthophosphate has been claimed (65). Quantitative microprobe analysis of thin freeze-dried sections of bakers' yeast cells yielded evidence that several univalent ions are about equally distributed between vacuoles and cytoplasm (100). In contrast, the cytoplasm appeared to contain the bulk of K^+ and Na^+ when the distribution in protoplasts was calculated on the basis of the ion content of isolated vacuoles (M. Dürr, unpublished). It is possible that these results reflect a changeable distribution of inorganic ions in yeast cells depending on the physiological conditions.

Significant differences between the ion contents in vacuoles and cytoplasm could not be detected when whole protoplasts and intact vacuoles of *Tulipa* petal cells were analyzed (66). Only in the case of *Hevea* latex has a remarkably uneven distribution of inorganic ions been reported. The lutoïds contain a large proportion of the total Mg^{2+} but comparatively small fractions of Ca^{2+}, K^+, and Cu^{2+}. On a volume basis the concentration of Mg^{2+} is about 90 times higher in the vacuoles than in the cytoplasm, whereas in the case of K^+ the concentrations are equal (99).

Hence, at least some of the data available suggest that the deposition in vacuoles of inorganic substances is associated with a remarkable specificity. This specificity is obvious in the case of vacuolar compartmentation of organic compounds. It is also obvious that the tonoplast must play a decisive role in determining the composition of the vacuolar fluid.

Properties of Tonoplasts

Data about the physicochemical properties of tonoplasts are just beginning to accumulate. A number of observations in yeast suggest that the properties of the tonoplast and those of the plasmalemma differ considerably. Differences concern, for example, the stability of protoplasts and vacuoles as a function of pH and osmolarity of the medium and the sensitivity of plasmalemma and tonoplast to polyene antibiotics and polycations.

Although the results of chemical analysis are incomplete, they provide some hints as to the chemical background of these differences. The tonoplast of bakers' yeast is comparatively poor in sterols and rich in phospholipids, with a high proportion of unsaturated fatty acids [G. F. Fuhrmann et al, unpublished, reported in (88)]. These findings may explain the resistance of this membrane to the polyene antibiotic nystatin (109), as well as the remarkable elasticity of yeast vacuoles (89). In contrast, the microvacuoles of *Hevea* latex are sensitive to hypotonic treatment (98). The tonoplast of this organelle is characterized by a most unusual lipid composition; phosphatidic acid accounts for more than 80% of the total phospholipids, and almost half of their fatty acids are saturated (31).

Isolated yeast vacuoles do not bind concanavalin A unless they have been rendered permeable for this lectin (10). Polysaccharides associated with the yeast tonoplast have also been demonstrated cytochemically (116). The yeast plasmalemma as well as the tonoplast are asymmetric with regard to binding sites for concanavalin A: the corresponding polysaccharides appear to be absent from the membrane surfaces facing the cytoplasmic matrix (10).

The presence of ribosomal RNA in *Hevea* lutoïds (70, 71) is interesting with regard to the possibility that protein synthesis is associated with vacuoles; however, the data presented do not enable the conclusive distinction between RNA associated with the cytoplasmic surface of the membrane and RNA localized inside the lutoïds. In any case, the question of whether or not ribosomes are associated with tonoplasts deserves special attention with regard to the synthesis of vacuolar enzymes. In isolated and positively contrasted yeast vacuoles, polysome-like structures appear to be present (120).

A general feature of tonoplasts appears to be the presence of certain oxidoreductases (63, 74, 78, 82) which, however, are also typical for ER membranes. ATPase activity associated with vacuolar membranes deserves particular attention as it may be involved in transport processes requiring metabolic energy. Membrane bound, Mg-dependent ATPase activity has been detected in vacuoles isolated from petal protoplasts of *Tulipa* and *Hippeastrum* (66), from *Hevea* latex (22, 23), and in yeast vacuoles (120). ATPase seems to be absent from vacuoles of red beet storage tissue (63). Since sucrose is enriched in these vacuoles it is exciting to learn that glucose specific hexokinase is tightly bound to tonoplasts; moreover, under certain conditions sucrose synthetase activity and other elements of sugar metabolism appear to be loosely attached to this membrane (34).

Due to the lack of a specific marker enzyme, it has not yet been possible to isolate tonoplasts from conventional homogenates. Only in the case of bakers' yeast vacuoles does α-mannosidase seem to be specifically located in the tonoplast (114).

Membrane Transport in Tonoplasts

Using isotonically prepared yeast vacuoles which retain their large amino acid storage pool, the group of Wiemken (9) has discovered the existence of an arginine-specific permease in the tonoplast. If vacuoles of *Saccharomyces cerevisiae* are exposed to labeled arginine and reisolated after a period of incubation, uptake at a constant rate over 7–10 min can be assessed. Although an enormous difference in arginine concentration between cell sap (100–200 mM) and medium (e.g. 100 μM) suggests the requirement for metabolic energy to pump arginine against the chemical potential, the uptake does not depend on a corresponding supplement to the medium. According to a number of criteria, the transport across the tonoplast is due to a specific permease which facilitates diffusion of arginine between the cell sap and the medium (cytoplasm) which surrounds the vacuoles. In fact, absorption of L-arginine from the medium is associated with a stoichiometric efflux as demonstrated in double labeling experiments with preloaded vacuoles. Concisely, the arginine permease has the following properties which clearly differ from the properties of arginine transport in protoplasts (P). It exhibits saturation kinetics with $K_m = 30$ μM (P: $K_m = 1.8$ μM). It is optimally active at pH 7.0–7.5 (P: in *Candida utilis* transport is practically unchanged between pH 4.5 and 8.0; M. Dürr, unpublished). The activation energy, as drawn from the temperature dependency of transport, is 39 kJ/mol (P: 51 kJ/mol for temperatures $>$ 11°C). Metabolic inhibitors such as dinitrophenol and azide are ineffective (P: strong inhibition). As shown by competition experiments, the L-arginine-permease transports L-histidine ($K_m = 270$ μM), L-lysine ($K_m = 1.3$ mM), and L-ornithine ($K_m = 3.0$ mM). However, a number of other amino acids such as L-leucine, L-phenylalanine, L-glycine, and L-glutamic acid are not transported. Structural analogues such as D-arginine or L-canavanine inhibit the transport of L-arginine competitively (9). The pattern of inhibition by a variety of structural analogues differs clearly for transport in vacuoles and protoplasts. Lastly, the analysis of arginine transport in vacuoles isolated from a number of mutants of *Saccharomyces cerevisiae* which lack the specific arginine, and/or general amino acid-permease of the plasmalemma, has shown that the properties of the vacuolar arginine-permease are unchanged in these mutants; this permease is therefore genetically independent from the permeases that catalyze the uptake of arginine from the culture medium (8).

Preliminary transport studies with vacuoles isolated from the cell wall-deficient "slimy" mutant of *Neurospora crassa* showed the existence of an arginine-specific permease corresponding to the permease of the bakers' yeast tonoplast (Th. Boller and U. Heck, unpublished results).

The susceptibility of arginine transport in isolated yeast vacuoles to proteinases has been used for demonstrating that the permease represents a proteinaceous factor of the tonoplast (29). Thermolysin causes an activation of transport by a factor of 2–3 and even more. Pronase, in turn, increased the rate of transport at low concentrations and caused its decay at higher concentrations. The decay proceeded according to a first order reaction, indicating that a single hydrolysis in the active center of the permease results in complete inactivation. In fact, if vacuoles were incubated with pronase in the presence of L-arginine, the active center thus being occupied, the inactivation was largely prevented. The comparatively smaller protecting effects of other substrates of the permease correspond with its lower affinity for L-histidine, L-lysine, and L-ornithine. The authors tentatively conclude that the action of pronase abolishes the catalytic properties of the permease while thermolysin, as also pronase at low concentrations, alters a proteinaceous factor which hampers the "mobility" (that is, controls the reaction rate) of the permease in the membrane. Vacuoles appear to be ideally suited for this sort of investigation as the cytoplasmic face of the tonoplast is not coated with polysaccharides which may prevent the access of proteinases to membrane proteins; corresponding experiments with protoplasts may be unsuccessful because the outer surface of the plasmalemma is coated with polysaccharides (10).

In a similar fashion and with similar results a specific transport system for S-adenosyl-L-methionine has been characterized in isolated vacuoles of *Saccharomyces cerevisiae* (109). The uptake of this metabolic intermediate exhibits saturation kinetics ($K_m = 68$ μM) and is competitively inhibited by S-adenosyl-L-ethionine and S-adenosyl-homocysteine. It is not sensitive to metabolic inhibitors and is resistant to the polyene antibiotic nystatin. In all of these properties the transport of S-adenosyl-L-methionine in vacuoles differs clearly from transport in the protoplasts. An important difference with respect to the arginine permease concerns the absence of S-adenosyl-L-methionine efflux which must be expected if the permease specifically facilitates diffusion across the tonoplast. However, the efflux may concern another vacuolar constituent which escapes analysis if vacuoles preloaded with labeled S-adenosyl-L-methionine are used for assessing efflux. It should be mentioned that an earlier attempt to demonstrate transport of S-adenosyl-L-methionine, arginine, lysine, and methionine in isolated vacuoles of *Candida utilis* was unsuccessful (84); it seems that the permease systems were inactivated by the osmotic lysis of the protoplast which caused a transitory stretching of the tonoplast.

It is interesting to note that vacuoles have an extremely poor capacity for transporting S-adenosyl-L-methionine if bakers' yeast cells are cultured in the absence of L-methionine, that is, under conditions which do not induce the formation of a large vacuolar pool of S-adenosyl-L-methionine (M. Dürr, unpublished). Hence, vacuolar permeases may be inducible proteins. This is also suggested by the finding that in *Saccharomyces uvarum,* glycine has access to vacuoles and is accumulated there only if the cells are first starved of nitrogen and then fed with glycine (56). Likewise, considerable differences in the arginine-transporting capacity as dependent on the culture conditions suggest that the vacuolar arginine-permease in bakers' yeast cells is subject to N-catabolite repression (8).

In the latex of *Hevea brasiliensis,* free amino acids are largely located in the cytoplasmic fraction (serum); however, basic amino acids are enriched in the vacuoles (12). Transport of arginine and lysine in these vacuoles (lutoïds) is mediated by a permease as suggested by saturation kinetics, competitive inhibition (lys/arg), and other features (35). In contrast to the corresponding permease of the yeast vacuole, the affinity for basic amino acids is very low (10^{-2} molar range) and the transport is sensitive to dinitrophenol; moreover, uptake of lysine is not associated with efflux and the rate of transport is enhanced in the presence of ATP (35). These findings suggest that the mechanisms of transport and particularly the mechanisms of accumulation of amino acids may be different in vacuoles from fungal and vascular plant cells.

As *Hevea* lutoïds contain a large pool of citrate (99), they were also used for the study of citrate transport (24). These vacuoles take up considerable proportions of exogeneously supplied citrate against a concentration gradient (e.g. 50 mM citrate in cell sap, 7.5 mM in medium). The rate of uptake is constant for at least 30 min. Saturation kinetics ($K_m = 5$ mM at pH 7.0) suggest the existence of a specific citrate permease. Efflux of citrate was not assessed. ATP enhances the rate of uptake considerably, dinitrophenol is a potent inhibitor of citrate transport.

In conclusion, there is little doubt that tonoplasts are equipped with specific permeases. The discovery of further permeases seems to be a matter of experimental know-how in isolating and handling vacuoles. The existence of such permeases is not surprising, as the distinct distribution of individual compounds between the cell sap and the cytoplasm points to a control of fluxes in and out of the vacuolar compartment. This control is obviously exercised by specific permeases of the tonoplast. However, the existence of permeases does not explain the phenomenon of accumulation of compounds in the cell sap. In particular, the action of permeases, such as the arginine permease of yeast vacuoles which catalyze diffusion, cannot account for the enrichment of arginine in vacuoles.

Accumulation

A common feature of vacuolar permeases, which emerges from studies with isolated vacuoles, appears to be the absence of a direct dependency of transport on metabolic energy. If this property reflects the situation in the living cell, the permeases cannot be responsible for the establishment of a chemical potential between the cell sap and the medium or the cytoplasm, respectively. In a few cases of vacuolar accumulation of compounds the factors responsible for the active transport into vacuoles are now being elucidated.

Although in isolated yeast vacuoles arginine is exchanged between cell sap and medium, the large vacuolar pool is retained (9, 122). This basic observation suggests that in vivo the vacuolar arginine is partially present in a nondiffusible form. Equilibrium-dialysis studies have yielded substantial evidence that arginine cations are immobilized through binding with the vacuolar polyphosphate anions (30). Thus the retentiveness of isolated vacuoles for arginine (and other basic compounds) can be interpreted in terms of a Donnan equilibrium. The yeast vacuole can therefore be conceived as an ion exchange system, as shown in the model of transport and accumulation of arginine presented in Figure 1 (8). Its principal features include the presence of a nondiffusible anion (polyphosphate) in the cell sap and a selectively permeable tonoplast. Transport mechanisms, whether experimentally demonstrated (Figures 1A and B) or merely postulated (Figures 1C and D), are based on the condition of electroneutrality. As far as a reversible accumulation of arginine is concerned, the model predicts that changes in size of the vacuolar pool must be associated either with changes of the polyphosphate complement or with the re-placement of arginine molecules by other basic compounds or inorganic cations. Experimental data on antiport processes to support this aspect of the model have been obtained (8, 9, 30). The expansion of the vacuolar arginine pool would require the synthesis of polyphosphate. In the hypothesis presented in Figure 1E an electro-genic transfer of phosphate groups from cytoplasmic ATP to vacuolar polyphos-phate acceptor molecules is postulated. This group transfer across the tonoplast would represent an electrical coupling of net influx of arginine to the formation of the vacuolar polyanion. Nothing is known about this important aspect of arginine accumulation. However, mobilization of arginine as associated with the degradation of polyphosphate has been observed in isolated yeast vacuoles after prolonged incubation. Endo- as well as exo-polyphosphatase activity is present in these or-ganelles (K. Urech, unpublished information). In the context of the model it is important to note that upon the gradual hydrolysis of the vacuolar polyphosphate, the ratio between acid-labile phosphate groups and arginine remains constant; obvi-ously efflux of arginine takes place, and the model (Figure 1D) predicts that symport of this cation and an anion, presumably orthophosphate, takes place (K. Urech, unpublished results).

In the vacuoles isolated from *Hevea* latex, citrate is transported without the addition of an energy source to the medium (24). As this transport takes place against a gradient of citrate concentration, it must require energy. The possibility that citrate is chelated by Mg ions accumulated in the vacuoles has practically been ruled out. However, the energy required for citrate accumulation appears to be supplied by the electrical potential between the cell sap (pH 5) and the medium (pH 7). Indeed, dinitrophenol greatly inhibits the uptake of citrate, probably through the abolishment of the proton gradient. Moreover, ATP added to the medium causes an increased rate of transport (24). It is feasible, therefore, that the ATPase present in the lutoïd membrane (22, 23) acts as a pump for protons which neutralize the citrate anions transported by the citrate permease. If this is so, citrate accumulation in lutoïds has the character of a symport catalyzed by two independent carriers. A proton pump has also been proposed in connection with transport of basic amino acids in *Hevea* vacuoles. This transport is also considerably enhanced in the presence of ATP (35). In this case the proton pump is a constituent of an antiport system.

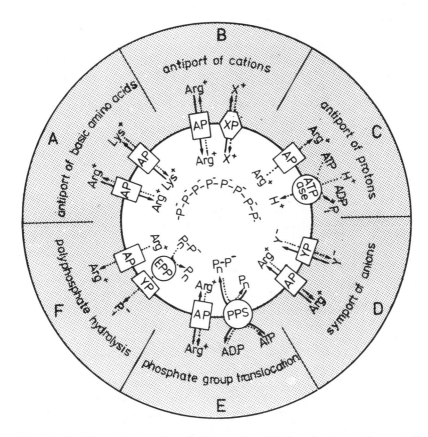

Figure 1   Possible mechanisms of accumulation and mobilization of arginine in the yeast cell vacuole. From Boller (8).

Symbols: Stippled area, Cytoplasm; Central area, Vacuolar space; AP, Arginine-permease located in tonoplast; Arg$^+$, Arginine-cation; P$^-$–P$^-$–P$^-$, Vacuolar polyphosphate; ⟶, Processes resulting in accumulation; ·····▸, Processes resulting in mobilization.

A: Antiport of basic amino acids. B: Antiport of basic amino acids and other cations. C: Antiport of arginine and protons. D: Symport of arginine and anion Y$^-$. E: Polyphosphate-synthesis through phosphate-group translocation. F: Hydrolysis of vacuolar polyphosphate.

In the light of mechanisms of vacuolar accumulation of charged molecules now being elucidated, it is interesting to consider the mechanism which may be responsible for the accumulation in vacuoles of uncharged compounds such as sugars. In sugarcane, group translocation of sucrose by the action of tonoplast-associated sucrose phosphatase has been proposed as a mechanism of sugar accumulation (33). Recent results obtained with vacuoles isolated from redbeet indeed suggest that enzymes of sucrose metabolism such as invertase and sucrose synthetase are loosely attached to the tonoplast (34). As the presence of these enzymes in preparation of tonoplasts depends on the aging of the tissue prior to the isolation of vacuoles, they may be involved in the mobilization of stored sucrose rather than in accumulation. Preliminary results obtained with vacuoles isolated from protoplasts of the pericarp of immature grapes suggest the existence of a sugar transporting system in the tonoplast; sucrose is transported at a much higher rate than glucose (18). Thus the accumulation of monosaccharides in this tissue may be brought about by a sucrose-specific permease in the tonoplast in conjunction with the vacuolar acid invertase.

Functional Aspects

A few selected examples will illustrate the functional significance of vacuolar compartmentation of certain compounds.

STORAGE POOLS OF INTERMEDIATES   The storage pool of basic amino acids localized in the yeast cell vacuole has an important advantage for the maintenance of metabolic activity under changing environmental conditions. This has been demonstrated by subjecting an exponentially growing culture of *Candida utilis* to abrupt changes in the supply of nitrogen. Surprisingly, exponential growth and concomitant protein synthesis are not interrupted if a complete medium is replaced by a medium without a source of nitrogen. It is true that the continuation of growth in the absence of exogeneous nitrogen results in the initial reduction of the small cytoplasmic pool of amino acids, yet this pool is not depleted because it is continuously refilled from the vacuolar storage pool (8, 49). Whether the mobilization of stored basic amino acids involves the hydrolysis of polyphosphate or the exchange of polyphosphate-bound amino acids with inorganic cations has not yet been investigated. It may be expected that under conditions of nitrogen deficiency the vacuolar polyphosphate is preserved, whereas nitrogen in conjunction with phosphate deficiency causes the utilization of both N- and P-reserves. It is interesting to note that yeasts behave in a species-specific fashion when they are subjected to nitrogen starvation. *Candida utilis* continues to grow at the normal growth rate and becomes stationary after about one generation when the vacuolar nitrogen reserves are exhausted. In contrast to this prodigal way of life, *Saccharomyces cerevisiae* turns immediately to a nitrogen-saving reduced growth rate and is able to remain in a growing condition for much longer (49). Needless to say, starved yeast cells immediately start to refill their vacuolar storage pools when they are supplied with appropriate nutrients.

Polyphosphate and basic amino acids of yeasts can be compared with phytic acid and reserve proteins which are stored in seeds. In both cases, but for different reasons, vacuoles (aleuron grains) are used as storage compartments. The mobilization of reserve proteins upon seed germination requires proteolysis which takes place within living cells. The spatial separation of this process from the cytoplasmic centers of metabolism appears to be meaningful. As reserve proteins of seeds make the young plant independent of exogenous nitrogen, the vacuolar storage pools of amino acids render the fungal nitrogen metabolism substantially independent of the cellular environment. The micromolecular form of nitrogen-storage has the advantage over reserve proteins of being immediately available. The significance of vacuolar compartmentation of arginine is evident when the regulation of arginine metabolism is considered: the rapid and precise regulation within the cytoplasm requires a small metabolic pool and hence the spatial separation of the large storage pool from the site of arginine metabolism (111, 119, 124, 125). Thus the vacuolar pools buffer the cytoplasm against changes in environmental conditions and, therefore, represent an important tool for maintaining homoeostasis within the cytoplasm. It is true that in this respect the plant vacuole can be conceived as a subcellular analogue of the body fluids in complex animal organisms (124).

Another example that demonstrates the importance of vacuolar compartmentation of metabolites in maintaining homoeostasis is provided by Crassulacean acid metabolism. Malic acid is the most prominent of metabolites, with a diurnally oscillating level in leaf cells of plants exercising this type of photosynthesis. With regard to the corresponding fluctuations of pH and also in consideration of the property of malate as an effector of key enzymes of malate metabolism, the spatial separation of storage and metabolic pools of malic acid appears to be crucially important. In fact, isolated vacuoles contain the bulk of malate present in protoplasts from leaf cells of *Bryophyllum daigremontianum* (13). The maintenance of homoeostasis within the cytoplasm is likely to involve the removal of excessive malate by virtue of a transport system residing in the tonoplast. A fascinating problem of regulation of membrane transport is posed by the phenomenon of circadian rhythmicity of malate accumulation and mobilization in vacuoles. A corresponding hypothesis based on changes of the permeability of the tonoplast dependent on turgor has been proposed (68). Whether or not this hypothesis will be supported by future experimental work, it is obvious that the compartmentation of malate in space and in time provides plants with Crassulacean acid metabolism a prodigious possibility of coping with severe environmental conditions.

TURGOR   In *Avena* coleoptiles, auxin-induced ion exchange reactions in the plasmalemma are associated with the accumulation (in vacuoles ?) of malate and K^+ ions (36). One aspect of these processes certainly concerns the regulation of turgor in the expanding cells. The budding process in yeast provides another example of involvement of vacuolar micromolecules in turgor production. The extrusion of buds is associated with the inflation of vacuoles (123). In *Candida utilis* grown on arginine it has been demonstrated that this inflation is due to the sudden doubling of the rates of arginine uptake from the medium and arginine catabolism, as well as to the doubling of rates of amino acid synthesis at the onset of bud formation (90). As in yeast cells amino acids account for the bulk of osmotically active constituents, this timing of their synthesis is undoubtedly significant with regard to the adjustment of turgor in the budding cell.

DETOXIFICATION   A single example will illustrate the role of vacuoles in the removal of toxic secondary products of metabolism from the cytoplasm. Two major alkaloids present in the latex of *Chelidonium majus,* sanguinarine and chelerithrine, are toxic in the sense that they abolish the semipermeability of membranes (58). In contrast, the two other major alkaloids, berberine and dihydrocoptisine, do not affect membranes. It is interesting to note that the toxic compounds have a higher affinity for the vacuolar tannins and are therefore enriched and trapped in the vacuoles (58, 76). Hence the vacuolar compartmentation of tannins appears to be a prerequisite for storing harmful alkaloids within the living laticifer.

VACUOLES AS LYSOSOMES

Vacuolar Hydrolases

The presence in vacuoles of certain hydrolases which are typical for lysosomal organelles has been demonstrated in a considerable number of plant species. This aspect of vacuolar compartmentation has recently been reviewed (75, 79). The most complete analysis of subcellular hydrolase distribution has undoubtedly been achieved in the model organism yeast. This section shall therefore be limited to the presentation of findings in this fungus and to the discussion of some recent reports on vacuolar hydrolases in other objects.

Vacuoles isolated from protoplasts of *Saccharomyces cerevisiae* contain a proteo-lytic system comprising an acid proteinase (A), a serine proteinase (B), and a serine carboxypeptidase (Y, formerly protease C). The vacuoles represent the principal compartment of this system. However, other localizations of proteases cannot yet be excluded on the basis of data available (16, 39, 64, 78). In whole extracts from yeast cells or protoplasts the assessment of proteolytic activities is complicated by the presence of several specific inhibitor proteins; the activation of the proteolytic system requires the preincubation of extracts under conditions which favor the autocatalytic degradation of inhibitor proteins by the action of proteinases A and B (103). It would be tempting to conclude that in yeast cells the proteases are present in the form of zymogens. However, it has been demonstrated that the inhibitor proteins are located outside the vacuoles, most probably in the cytoplasmic matrix (64, 72). This differential location of proteases and their specific inhibitors suggests that the proteolytic system is fully active in the living cells.

Other vacuolar hydrolases of yeast include ribonuclease (78), alkaline phospha-tase (3, 124), and α-mannosidase (114). Some hydrolases which are present in the yeast vacuole—invertase (6, 45, 81), β-glucosidase (19), aminopeptidase (78, 80), and acid phosphatase (115, 124)—are also secreted into the extracytoplasmic space.

Incidently, not all the yeast hydrolases are located in the vacuole: α-glucosidase is an enzyme of the cytoplasmic matrix (124). Tentatively it can be stated that specific and harmless hydrolases may be located in the cytoplasm, while unspecific and harmful enzymes such as phosphatases, proteinases, and nucleases are located in the "lytic compartment" of which the vacuoles are a principal intracellular component (75). Protection of the cytoplasmic constituents from an uncontrolled attack by the digestive enzymes is the suggested reason for this intracellular compartmentation.

Almost nothing is known about the site of synthesis of vacuolar enzymes. Hydrolases of the yeast cell vacuole that have been obtained in pure form turned out to be glycoproteins. This property may be important for the stability of these enzymes in, the cell sap, in terms of a possible inaccessibility of their protein moiety for proteinases. Carboxypeptidase Y contains 14% mannose (40). Its formation is inhibited by tunicamycin as is the formation of the secreted mannanprotein invertase or the vacuolar proteinase A. In the presence of tunicamycin, nonglycosilated carboxypeptidase Y is not accumulated, suggesting that synthesis of the polypeptide is linked with glycosylation (40). As mannan synthesis involves a lipid intermediate and is associated with membranes, it is tempting to assume that the synthesis of hydrolase-polypeptides and the subsequent glycosylation are integrated in the tonoplast or in components of the endomembrane system which are in communication with vacuoles. A short-lived precursor form of carboxypeptidase Y has recently been detected in a membrane preparation from bakers' yeast. Its conversion into the final form is associated with a reduction in molecular size (41). Hence, this vacuolar glycoprotein may be released from the site of its synthesis into the vacuolar compartment upon the cleavage of an extra extension of its polypeptide chain.

Apart from the isolation of vacuoles, cytochemistry has been widely used for localizing hydrolases, mainly phosphatases, in plant cells. The corresponding data are consistent with the vacuolar localization of acid unspecific phosphatase; however, the reaction product of this enzyme has also been observed within the entire endomembrane system (ER, Golgi) as well as in the cell wall space (75). Hence, vacuoles appear to be only the most voluminous components of an elaborate membrane system. A similar distribution as demonstrated cytochemically for acid phosphatase may be expected for other hydrolases. Indeed, results obtained from tissue fractionation studies reflect a complex subcellular distribution of hydrolases (26, 42, 44, 74, 86, 92, 104). It is important to note that cytochemists have observed the absence of acid phosphatase from the cytoplasmic matrix. As basic metabolism depends so much on intermediary phosphate esters, the confinement of this unspecific hydrolase to vacuoles, endomembrane system, and extracellular space convincingly illustrates the significance of lysosomal compartmentation.

Depending on the conditions of homogenization, and the tissue concerned, a variable but usually large proportion of total hydrolase activities is recovered in the soluble fraction. It is impossible to draw conclusions about the intracellular compartmentation of hydrolases from this kind of result. The enzymes concerned may be localized either in vacuoles which were disrupted upon homogenization, or in the mural space, or they may be localized in the cytoplasmic matrix as α-glucosidase in yeast cells. It is to be expected that the novel techniques for gently releasing subcellular structures, including large vacuoles, from higher plant protoplasts will be useful for elucidating the compartmentation of hydrolases. Corresponding results about the complement of hydrolases present in central vacuoles of mature plant cells are not yet conclusive. Acid phosphatase and nucleases are present in these vacuoles (13, 14), whereas glycosidases appear to be localized outside the vacuoles (14). It will be interesting to learn whether the glycosidases or the substantial fractions of phosphatase which are not recovered in the large vacuoles are localized in other components of the endomembrane system.

From *Nitella* and *Chara* cell saps have been obtained upon perfusion of cut internodes; they contain the bulk of acid phosphatase and carboxypeptidase, whereas only small proportions of oxido-reductases are extracted by this procedure (27). A corresponding result has been reported on hydrolase distribution in stratified subcells of stalks of *Acetabularia* (67). RNase has been localized, by means of immunocytochemistry, using specific fluorescing antibodies, in vacuoles of morning glory flower tissue (4).

Intracellular Digestion

THE ROLE OF COMPARTMENTATION   Although the information available on the localization of hydrolases within plant cells is far from being complete, it is sufficient to justify the consideration of compartmentation in studies on the metabolic function of hydrolase action. The necessity of complementing data from biochemical approaches with a morphological, structural frame appears convincingly from recent work on proteolytic regulation of enzyme activities in yeast. Principles which in homogenates caused the inactivation of tryptophan synthetase or the activation of chitin synthetase turned out to be identical with those of known yeast proteinases (15, 16, 37, 38, 47, 102, 107). As the proteinases in question are located in the vacuole, tryptophan synthetase, in the cytoplasmic matrix, and chitin synthetase in the plasmalemma, the discovery of proteolytic inactivation or activation of these enzymes obviously has no direct significance for the understanding of the regulation of their activity in vivo. A considerable number of similar proteolytic artifacts have been compiled, and an antiartifact methodology for preventing the proteolytic attack on native proteins upon the abolishment of compartmentation in homogenates has been proposed (96). If considered from the viewpoint of possible proteolytic artifacts, it is almost a miracle that so many enzymes have been purified in the past from autolyzed yeast under conditions which undoubtedly favor the occurrence of proteolytic inactivation!

If subcellular compartmentation of proteolytic enzymes and their potential endogeneous substrates is not considered in the first instance, one is tempted to assume that the proteolytic action bears some specificity with regard to the inactivation of distinct protein species. In fact, if cell-free extracts from yeast cells are incubated in the presence of the yeast proteinases A or B, or in the presence of carboxypeptidase Y, differential inactivations of various enzymes of the intermediary metabolism occur and suggest a selective action of proteolytic enzymes (1, 48, 59). However, this surprising selectivity of protease action is unlikely to reflect a selective degradation of enzymes in the living yeast cell. Rather does it seem that the selectivity observed is caused by the differential vulnerability of catalytic centers due to the conformation of individual enzyme proteins. Little is known about the mechanism of intracellular protein degradation. This process undoubtedly represents a major factor in the determination of cellular concentration of a protein (51, 105). Its significance is particularly obvious with regard to turnover reactions which lead to the biochemical differentiation of cells. Considering the compartmentation of unspecific hydrolases which may be responsible for the degradation of biopolymers, it must be concluded that catabolism takes place in the lytic compartment. In rat liver the products of intracellular proteolysis have in fact been localized in lysosomes (87). Corresponding experiments have not yet been performed with plant cells. Yet the similarities between the compartmentation of hydrolases in animal and plant cells suggest that protein degradation in plant cells also takes place in a lysosomal cell space. In any case, the site of protein degradation must not necessarily be identical with the site from which a species of protein disappears under certain conditions. The conclusion that the loss of carboxydismutase during senescence of detached leaves is due to proteolysis in chloroplasts (93) may not be drawn unless the corresponding localization of the protease(s) involved has been demonstrated.

AUTOPHAGIC VACUOLES The autophagic nature of vacuoles is suggested by numerous ultrastructural observations concerning the presence within vacuoles of structured cytoplasmic material. The bad preservation of such vacuolar inclusions is likely to be due to the action of digestive enzymes. Membrane processes seem to be responsible for the sequestration of cytoplasmic material in vacuoles. On the one hand the engulfment by the invaginating tonoplast results in the formation of intravacuolar vesicles containing a portion of cytoplasm. On the other hand the transfer of cytoplasm into the digestive compartment coincides with the formation of vacuoles: portions of cytoplasm are encircled by components of the endomembrane system which ultimately fuse together and form an autophagic vacuole (reviewed in 75). These observations suggest that intracellular digestion proceeds in such a fashion that the compartmentation of vacuolar hydrolases is never abolished. Yet, autophagy cannot be understood unless the morphological observations are complemented with corresponding knowledge about the biochemical events. At the moment we are dealing with a mosaic of somewhat isolated ultrastructural observations of autophagic vacuoles, assessments of turnover reactions, localizations of enzymes, and correlations between catabolic processes and hydrolase activities (see 75). What is needed is an integrated study of one organism which covers all the relevant aspects.

HYPOTHETICAL EVALUATIONS The principal problem concerns the mechanism by which a cytoplasmic macromolecule or a structure is specifically subjected to degradation. Yeast is undoubtedly one of the favorite organisms for corresponding studies. The vacuolar compartmentation of the proteolytic system and the presence in the cytoplasm of a specific inhibitor system strongly suggest that the degradation of protein takes place within the vacuoles. Furthermore, bakers' yeast is ideally suited, because biochemical differentiations which are caused by exogenous glucose are associated with the inactivation and degradation of catabolite-repressed enzymes. It is therefore not surprising that an attractive hypothesis for the selective degradation of proteins deals with yeast. It is termed "catabolite inactivation" (46) because its principal feature concerns the allosteric effects and interconversions produced in enzymes by catabolites. These structural changes convert the enzymes into inactive and vulnerable proteins which are recognized by the autophagic system. In this concept it is thought that autophagy and proteolysis in vacuoles unspecifically comprise the inactivated enzymes which are no longer integrated in metabolism. Specificity would, in turn, be provided by the interactions between enzyme molecules and effective catabolites. A similar concept attributes the specificity of degradation to the action of group-specific proteases. Such enzymes have been isolated from several animal tissues. They bring on a limited proteolysis in susceptible forms of enzymes, that is, in the absence of coenzymes, substrates, or effector molecules. This irreversible step taking place in the cytoplasm is followed by random digestion of inactivated enzymes in lysosomes (61). Corresponding group-specific proteases have so far not been detected in the plant kingdom.

These concepts may be most valuable guides for investigating the mechanism of protein degradation. It would certainly be interesting to test them with isolated vacuoles. However, the autophagic activity is likely to be dependent on the living cytoplasm. In fact, isolated lysosomes of animal cells do not take up protein (52). This is not surprising as the morphological observations suggest that autophagy is associated with pinocytosis-like membrane processes which depend on metabolism and on metabolic energy.

CONCLUDING REMARKS

In textbooks of plant physiology vacuoles are frequently referred to as the dustbins of plant cells. This statement is essentially valid, yet it can only be accepted if we consider the exemplary waste management of plant cells. Except for the secondary products of metabolism which are deposited in vacuoles but synthesized for largely unknown reasons, the production of waste is not the troublesome consequence of metabolic activity but has an important functional significance. With regard to the temporary storage of metabolites formed in excess or of inorganic substances, vacuoles are comparable to savings accounts which can supply the cytoplasm with nutrients in case of emergency. As plant cells are exposed more or less directly to the environment, the vacuolar storage compartment is essential for the maintenance of metabolism under changing external conditions. Waste may also be produced in connection with differentiation in plant cells. Vacuoles are likely to play a prominent role in its conversion into reusable material; biopolymers and structures which are eliminated upon differentiation may be digested within vacuoles as suggested by the corresponding location of typical lysosomal enzymes. In senescent tissues the catabolic aspect of differentiation is particularly obvious. Senescence proceeds within living cells as suggested by its association with the synthesis of certain proteins. Thus the spatial separation of lytic processes from the sites of macromolecular synthesis appears to be significant even in the case of a differentiation which ultimately ends with cell death.

It is not surprising that the data on vacuolar functions are comparatively abundant in the case of yeasts which have a relatively uniform system of vacuoles. When organs of vascular plants are used for preparing vacuoles, not only the polymorphy of vacuoles within single cells but also the heterogeneity of cells within the tissues must be considered. It is to be expected that the vacuoles differ biochemically and functionally from one type of cell to another and perhaps even within single cells. Isolation of vacuoles will always be associated with selection according to stability, size, and density. Thus it is necessary to consider the limits of approaches to vacuolar functions based on the isolation of vacuoles. Another limit appears when the essentially passive nature of vacuoles in metabolism is considered. Unlike mitochondria and plastids, vacuoles have no metabolism in their own right. In fact, processes in vacuoles are undoubtedly induced and controlled by the metabolic activity in the cytoplasm. By analogy with the plasmalemma, the tonoplast must be regarded as an entity of the cytoplasm. Upon the isolation of vacuoles, the cytoplasm is removed except for this membrane, the function of which is dependent on the cytoplasm. Evidently the medium for suspending vacuoles can be designed so as to allow the study of certain phenomena such as membrane transport and ion exchange between the cell sap and the surrounding medium. In the case of digestive vacuoles, isolation can only help to localize the hydrolases responsible for catabolism. The further elucidation of autophagy, however, cannot be based on isolated vacuoles exclusively. It will be necessary to use a wide spectrum of biochemical, cytochemical, and morphological methods in order to establish the function of vacuoles in intracellular digestive processes.

Literature Cited

1. Afting, E.-G., Lynen, A., Hinze, H., Holzer, H. 1976. *Z. Physiol. Chem.* 357:1771–77
2. Ashton, F. M. 1976. *Ann. Rev. Plant Physiol.* 27:95–117
3. Bauer, H., Sigarlakie, E. 1975. *J. Ultrastruct. Res.* 50:208–15
4. Baumgartner, B., Matile, Ph. 1976. *Biochem. Physiol. Pflanz.* 170:279–85
5. Baur, P. S., Walkinshaw, C. H. 1974. *Can. J. Bot.* 52:615–20
6. Beteta, P., Gascón, S. 1971. *FEBS Lett.* 13:297–300
7. Bieleski, R. L. 1973. *Ann. Rev. Plant Physiol.* 24:225–52
8. Boller, Th. P. 1977. *Die Arginin-Permease der Hefevakuole.* PhD thesis No. 5928. Swiss Fed. Inst. Technol., Zurich. 224 pp.
9. Boller, Th. P., Dürr, M., Wiemken, A. 1974. *Eur. J. Biochem.* 54:81–91
10. Boller, Th. P., Dürr, M., Wiemken, A. 1976. *Microbiology* 109:115–18
11. Boller, Th. P., Schwencke, J., Dürr, M., Wiemken, A. 1977. *J. Gen. Microbiol.* In press
12. Brzozowska, J., Hanower, P., Chezeau, R. 1974. *Experientia* 30:894–96
13. Buser, Ch., Matile, Ph. 1977. *Z. Pflanzenphysiol.* 82:462–66
14. Butcher, H. C., Wagner, G. J., Siegelman, H. W. 1977. *Plant Physiol.* 59: 1098–1103
15. Cabib, E., Ulane, R. 1973. *Biochem. Biophys. Res. Commun.* 50:186–91
16. Cabib, E., Ulane, R., Bowers, B. 1973. *J. Biol. Chem.* 248:1451–58
17. Chafe, S. C., Durzan, D. J. 1973. *Planta* 113:251–62
18. Coombe, B. G., Huber-Guyer, U., Matile, Ph. 1977. Brisbane meet., Aust. Soc. Plant Physiol.
19. Cortat, M., Matile, Ph., Wiemken, A. 1972. *Arch. Mikrobiol.* 82:189–205
20. Coulomb, Ph. 1971. *J. Microsc.* 11:299–318
21. Damadian, R. 1974. *Ann. NY Acad. Sci.* 204:211–48
22. d'Auzac, J. 1975. *Phytochemistry* 14: 671–75
23. d'Auzac, J. 1977. *Phytochemistry.* In press
24. d'Auzac, J., Lioret, C. 1974. *Physiol. Vég.* 12:617–35
25. Diers, L., Schötz, F., Meyer, B. 1973. *Cytobiologie* 7:10–19

26. Doi, E., Matoba, T., Ohtsuru, C. 1975. *Plant Cell Physiol.* 16:571–80
27. Doi, E., Ohtsuru, C., Matoba, T. 1975. *Plant Cell Physiol.* 16:581–88
28. Dürr, M., Boller, Th. P., Wiemken, A. 1975. *Arch. Microbiol.* 105:319–27
29. Dürr, M., Boller, Th. P., Wiemken, A. 1976. *Biochem. Biophys. Res. Commun.* 73:193–99
30. Dürr, M., Schwencke, J., Boller, Th. P., Wiemken, A. 1977. *Biochem. Biophys. Res. Commun.* In press
31. Dupont, J., Moreau, F., Lance, C., Jacob, J. L. 1976. *Phytochemistry* 15:1215–17
32. Fairbairn, J. W., Hakim, F., El Kheir, Y. 1974. *Phytochemistry* 13:1133–39
33. Glaszio, K. T., Gayler, K. R. 1972. *Bot. Rev.* 38:471–90
34. Goldschmidt, E. E., Branton, D. 1977. *Plant Physiol.* 59. Ann. Meet. Session 41: Organelles I. Abstr. 571, p. 104
35. Hanower, P., Brzozowska, J., Niamien Ngoran, M. 1977. *Physiol. Plant.* 39:299–304
36. Haschke, H.-P., Lüttge, U. 1975. *Plant Physiol.* 56:696–98
37. Hasilik, A. 1974. *Arch. Microbiol.* 101:295–301
38. Hasilik, A., Holzer, H. 1973. *Biochem. Biophys. Res. Commun.* 53:552–59
39. Hasilik, A., Müller, H., Holzer, H. 1974. *Eur. J. Biochem.* 48:111–17
40. Hasilik, A., Tanner, W. 1976. *Antimicrob. Agents Chemother.* 10:402–10
41. Hasilik, A., Tanner, W. 1976. *Biochem. Biophys. Res. Commun.* 72:1430–36
42. Heftmann, E. 1971. *Cytobios* 3:129–36
43. Hellebust, J. A. 1976. *Ann. Rev. Plant Physiol.* 27:485–505
44. Hirai, M., Asahi, T. 1973. *Plant Cell Physiol.* 14:1019–29
45. Holley, R. A., Kidby, D. K. 1973. *Can. J. Microbiol.* 19:113–17
46. Holzer, H. 1976. *Trends Biochem. Sci.* 1:178–81
47. Holzer, H., Katsunuma, T., Schött, E. G., Ferguson, A. R., Hasilik, A., Betz, H. 1973. *Adv. Enzyme Regul.* 11:53–60
48. Holzer, H., Saheki, T. 1976. *Tokay J. Exp. Med.* 1:115–25
49. Huber-Wälchli, V., Boller, Th. P., Wiemken, A. 1977. *J. Bacteriol.* In press
50. Huber-Wälchli, V., Wiemken, A. 1977. *Arch. Microbiol.* In press
51. Huffaker, R. C., Peterson, L. W. 1974. *Ann. Rev. Plant Physiol.* 25:363–92
52. Huisman, W., Lanting, L., Bouma, J. M. W., Gruber, M. 1974. *FEBS Lett.* 45:129–31
53. Indge, K. J. 1968. *J. Gen. Microbiol.* 51:433–40
54. Indge, K. J. 1968. *J. Gen. Microbiol.* 51:441–46
55. Indge, K. J. 1968. *J. Gen. Microbiol.* 51:447–55
56. Indge, K. J., Seaston, A., Eddy, A. A. 1977. *J. Gen. Microbiol.* 99:243–56
57. Iten, W., Matile, Ph. 1970. *J. Gen. Microbiol.* 61:301–9
58. Jans, B. 1973. *Ber. Schweiz. Bot. Ges.* 83:306–44
59. Jusic, M., Hinze, H., Holzer, H. 1976. *Hoppe-Seyler's Z. Physiol. Chem.* 357:735–40
60. Karlin, J. N., Bowman, B. J., Davis, R. H. 1976. *J. Biol. Chem.* 251:3948–55
61. Katunuma, N. 1975. *Rev. Physiol. Biochem. Pharmacol.* 72:83–104
62. Leigh, R. A., Branton, D. 1976. *Plant Physiol.* 58:656–62
63. Leigh, R. A., Branton, D. 1978. *J. Cell Biol.* In press
64. Lenney, J. F., Matile, Ph., Wiemken, A., Schellenberg, M., Meyer, J. 1974. *Biochem. Biophys. Res. Commun.* 60:1378–83
65. Lichko, L. P., Okorokov, L. A. 1976. *Proc. Acad. Sci. USSR* 227:756–58
66. Lin, W., Wagner, G. J., Siegelman, H. W., Hind, G. 1977. *Biochim. Biophys. Acta* 464:110–17
67. Lüscher, A., Matile, Ph. 1974. *Planta* 118:323–32
68. Lüttge, U., Kluge, M., Ball, E. 1975. *Plant Physiol.* 56:613–16
69. MacRobbie, E. A. C. 1971. *Ann. Rev. Plant Physiol.* 22:75–96
70. Marin, B., Trouslot, P. 1974. *Biochem. J.* 143:479–81
71. Marin, B., Trouslot, P. 1975. *Planta* 124:31–41
72. Matern, H., Betz, H., Holzer, H. 1974. *Biochem. Biophys. Res. Commun.* 60:1051–57
73. Matile, Ph. 1966. *Z. Naturforsch.* 21b:871–78
74. Matile, Ph. 1968. *Planta* 79:181–96
75. Matile, Ph. 1975. *Cell Biology Monographs,* vol. 1: *The Lytic Compartment of Plant Cells.* Wien/New York: Springer-Verlag. 183 pp.
76. Matile, Ph. 1976. *Nova Acta Leopold. Suppl.* 7:139–56. Leopoldina Symp. *Secondary Metabolism and Coevolution,* April 19–21, 1974, ed. M. Luckner, K. Mothes, L. Nover. Wartburg/Eisenach DDR: Dtsch. Akad. Naturforsch. Leopoldina Halle (Saale)
77. Matile, Ph., Jans, B., Rickenbacher, R.

1970. *Biochem. Physiol. Pflanz.* 161: 447–58
78. Matile, Ph., Wiemken, A. 1967. *Arch. Mikrobiol.* 56:148–55
79. Matile, Ph., Wiemken, A. 1976. Interaction between cytoplasm and vacuole. In *Transport in Plants III,* ed. C. R. Stocking, U. Heber, pp. 255–87. Berlin/Heidelberg/New York: Springer-Verlag. 517 pp.
80. Matile, Ph., Wiemken, A., Guyer, W. 1971. *Planta* 96:43–53
81. Meyer, J., Matile, Ph. 1975. *Arch. Microbiol.* 103:51–55
82. Moreau, F., Jacob, J. L., Dupont, J., Lance, C. 1975. *Biochim. Biophys. Acta* 396:116–24
83. Nakamura, K. D. 1973. *Prep. Biochem.* 3:553–62
84. Nakamura, K. D., Schlenk, F. 1974. *J. Bacteriol.* 118:314–16
85. Nakamura, K. D., Schlenk, F. 1974. *J. Bacteriol.* 120:482–515
86. Nakano, M., Asahi, T. 1972. *Plant Cell Physiol.* 13:101–10
87. Neely, N., Mortimore, G. E. 1974. *Biochem. Biophys. Res. Commun.* 59: 680–87
88. Niedermeyer, W. 1976. *Cytobiologie* 13: 380–93
89. Niedermeyer, W., Parish, G. R., Moor, H. 1976. *Cytobiologie* 13:364–79
90. Nurse, P., Wiemken, A. 1974. *J. Bacteriol.* 117:1108–16
91. Oaks, A., Bidwell, R. G. S. 1970. *Ann. Rev. Plant Physiol.* 21:43–66
92. Parish, R. W. 1975. *Planta* 123:15–31
93. Peterson, L. W., Huffaker, R. C. 1975. *Plant Physiol.* 55:1009–15
94. Pitt, D., Galpin, M. 1973. *Planta* 109: 233–58
95. Prat, R., Roland, J. C. 1970. *C. R. Acad. Sci.* 271:1862–65
96. Pringle, J. R. 1975. *Methods Cell Biol.* 12:149–84
97. Pujarniscle, S. 1968. *Physiol. Vég.* 6: 27–46
98. Pujarniscle, S. 1969. *Physiol. Vég.* 7: 391–403
99. Ribaillier, D., Jacob, J. L., d'Auzac, J. 1971. *Physiol. Vég.* 9:423–37
100. Roomans, G. M., Sevéus, L. A. 1976. *J. Cell Sci.* 21:119–27
101. Ruesink, A. W. 1971. *Plant Physiol.* 47:192–95
102. Saheki, T., Holzer, H. 1974. *Biochemistry* 42:621–26
103. Saheki, T., Holzer, H. 1975. *Biochim. Biophys. Acta* 384:203–14
104. Scannerini, S., Panzica-Viglietti, C., Giunta, C., Panzica, G. 1975. *G. Batteriol. Virol. Immunol.* 68:1–15
105. Schimke, R. T. 1975. In *Intracellular Protein Turnover,* ed. R. T. Schimke, N. Katunuma, pp. 173–86. New York: Academic
106. Schlenk, F., Dainko, J. L., Svihla, G. 1970. *Arch. Biochem. Biophys.* 140:28–236
107. Schött, H. E., Holzer, H. 1974. *Eur. J. Biochem.* 42:61–66
108. Schröter, K., Läuchli, A., Sievers, A. 1975. *Planta* 122:213–25
109. Schwencke, J., de Robichon-Szulmajster, H. 1976. *Eur. J. Biochem.* 65:49–60
110. Siegel, S. M., Daly, O. 1966. *Plant Physiol.* 41:1429–34
111. Subramanian, K. N., Weiss, R. L., Davis, R. H. 1973. *J. Bacteriol.* 115: 284–90
112. Sundberg, I., Nilshammar-Holmvall, M. 1975. *Z. Pflanzenphysiol.* 76:270–79
113. Svihla, G., Dainko, J. L., Schlenk, F. 1963. *J. Bacteriol.* 85:399–409
114. Van der Wilden, W., Matile, Ph., Schellenberg, M., Meyer, J., Wiemken, A. 1973. *Z. Naturforsch.* 28c:416–21
115. Van Rijn, H. J. M., Linnemans, W. A. M., Boer, P. 1975. *J. Bacteriol.* 123: 1144–49
116. Vorisek, J., Pokorny, V. 1975. *Arch. Microbiol.* 102:293–98
117. Wagner, G. J., Siegelman, H. W. 1975. *Science* 190:1298–99
118. Weiss, R. L. 1973. *J. Biol. Chem.* 248:5409–13
119. Weiss, R. L., Davis, R. H. 1977. *J. Bacteriol.* 129:866–73
120. Wiemken, A. 1969. *Eigenschaften der Hefevakuole.* PhD thesis No. 4340. Swiss Fed. Inst. Technol., Zurich. 113 pp.
121. Wiemken, A. 1975. *Methods Cell Biol.* 12:99–109
122. Wiemken, A., Dürr, M. 1974. *Arch. Microbiol.* 101:45–57
123. Wiemken, A., Matile, Ph., Moor, H. 1970. *Arch. Mikrobiol.* 70:89–103
124. Wiemken, A., Nurse, P. 1973. *Proc. 3rd Int. Symp. Yeasts,* Otaniemi, Helsinki, 2:331–47
125. Wiemken, A., Nurse, P. 1973. *Planta* 109:293–306

Ann. Rev. Plant Physiol. 1978. 29:215–37
Copyright © 1978 by Annual Reviews Inc. All rights reserved

GENETIC CONTROL ❖7650
OF PHOTOSYNTHESIS
AND IMPROVING OF CROP
PRODUCTIVITY

Yusuf S. Nasyrov

Institute of Plant Physiology and Biophysics, Tajik Academy of Sciences,
Dushanbe 734630, USSR

CONTENTS

INTRODUCTION

The chloroplast, a miniature green laboratory of a plant cell, possesses a number of surprising properties. A unique one is its capacity to convert light energy into chemical energy to accomplish the most important biological process of primary solar energy storage on the earth.

    Photophysical, photochemical, and biochemical aspects of photosynthesis have been elucidated well enough in recent reviews (46, 71, 155). However, this is the first time that hereditary properties of chloroplasts and genetic mechanisms of photosynthesis control will be discussed in the *Annual Review of Plant Physiology.*

    At present, genetic aspects of photosynthesis attract the attention of many scientists—plant physiologists and biochemists, molecular biologists and biophysicists, geneticists and plant breeders. This interest is natural because the problem is very important and complex and its solution requires a combined physiological and genetic approach. The subject involves two basic biological processes: (*a*) expression of genetic information, and (*b*) regulation of photosynthesis.

215

0066-4294/78/0601-0215$01.00

Investigation of the genetic nature of photosynthesis will enable us to understand the molecular mechanisms of self-organization and autoreproduction of chloroplasts, their inheritance and variability, the processes of plastid biogenesis, and the formation of its functional activity. On the other hand, the study of genetic determination of chloroplast structure and function will make it possible to enrich breeding search with new methods and tests and to improve photosynthetic plant productivity. Regulation of photosynthetic efficiency through inheritance is an important means of enhancing crop yield.

GENETICS OF PHOTOSYNTHESIS

The genetic material of eukaryotic organisms is localized not only in the nucleus, which is the main store of hereditary information, but it is dispersed throughout the cell in subcellular structures: mitochondria, kinetosomes, chloroplasts. The plant genotype as a complex of all cell genetic factors is subdivided into chromosomal—nuclear genome—and extrachromosomal—plasmone, comprising the cytoplasmic determinants, mitochondria and chloroplasts. Interaction of nuclear and cytoplasmic genetic systems with one another and with the environment determines both the course and the dynamics of cell differentiation, plant growth, and development.

Interaction of plant cell genetic factors has a very complex but rigid character. The nucleus as an integrating center of genetic information is responsible for the strategy of formation of constant organism-specific properties. Cytoplasmic genes and organelles determine the cell life tactics, providing its greater flexibility and adaptation to environmental conditions.

Cell organelles are closely interrelated in their development and functional activity. Their cooperative interaction provides the integration of information, energy, and substance flow in cell activity. A living cell is not a sum of autonomous or semiautonomous organelles, but a unique and highly organized dynamic system attaining new properties differing from those of single organoids due to "concert" interaction of subcellular structures.

Regulation of photosynthesis requires close cooperation of the discrete genetic systems of a plant cell. The chloroplast genome is not large enough to provide all the diverse reactions of this complex process, so a considerable part of the genetic information necessary for chloroplast development and activity is localized in the nucleus. In order to integrate photosynthetic activity in cell metabolism, it is possible that in the course of evolution chloroplasts acquired a double genetic subordination—to the nuclear genome and to their own semiautonomous one. Hereditary properties of chloroplasts were discovered long ago, whereas the study of the genetic nature of photosynthesis as a whole began only recently. We would say that genetics of photosynthesis is a new trend in plant physiological genetics. It can be defined as an interaction between the balanced plant cell genomes which control self-organization and reproduction of chloroplasts, their hereditary continuity and variability, carbon pathways, and photosynthetic potential.

History

Non-Mendelian plastid inheritance was discovered by Correns (29) in spontaneous variegated mutants of *Mirabilis jalapa*. Crossing normal and variegated forms, he showed that, independently of the pollen type, the pigmentation of progeny is determined exclusively by the egg cell. Proceeding from this fact, Correns postulated the principle of maternal or cytoplasmic inheritance which he called *Status albamaculatus*. Baur (7) made an important contribution to the understanding of the nature of cytoplasmic inheritance and attempted to give it a scientific explanation. He showed that in *Pelargonium zonale* both parents contributed to plastid inheritance. This principle was called a biparental cytoplasmic inheritance, *Status Paraalbomaculatus*. Baur was the first to assume that chloroplasts possess their own hereditary apparatus responsible for their inheritance and genetic continuity. It is plastid genome mutation that causes the appearance of variegated plants.

The intensive study of the mechanism of cytoplasmic inheritance is connected with the development of ideas and methods of molecular biology and molecular genetics. At the beginning of the 1960s a specific DNA was found in chloroplasts. Its molecule differed significantly from that of nuclear DNA in size, nucleotide content, and other physicochemical properties (43, 65, 131). At the same time, plastid ribosomes of the prokaryotic type were found which differed from the cytoplasmic ones in their sedimentation properties (89, 143).

These findings spurred the rapid development of investigations into genetics of chloroplasts and their transcription-translation system (TTS). Using gradient ultracentrifugation techniques in the presence of acridine dyes, as well as electron microscopy, autoradiography, and molecular hybridization, many advances have been made in the study of the structure and information capacity of the chloroplast, the mechanisms of its self-replication and transcription. It has been established that chloroplast DNA is associated with the lamellar system and has different configurations: linear, circular, loop-shaped, and superhelical (151, 157). Plastid genome replication has a semiconservative character (27).

Optical registration of DNA renaturation made possible determination of the chloroplast genome size in different plants. An organelle DNA ranges from 1 to 2 $\times 10^8$ daltons, which corresponds to 10^6 pairs of nucleotides. The DNA content in one chloroplast is 0.1 to 1.2×10^{-14} g, depending on plant species. These data make it possible to calculate the size of the chloroplast genome. The number of DNA copies in an individual chloroplast is 20 to 60 (73, 127, 172).

Chloroplasts contain all the components of the protein synthesizing system (PSS): ribosomes, RNA-polymerase, mRNA, tRNA, aminoacyl-tRNA synthetases, and other translation factors. Etioplasts and chloroplasts isolated from green leaves are able to synthesize nucleic acids and structural and functional proteins (33).

These data served as the basis for development of the concept of genetic and biochemical autonomy of chloroplasts (3, 139). An opinion was even expressed that chloroplasts have an independent genetic apparatus and resemble "a cell within a cell." This was an additional argument in favor of the symbiogenetic hypothesis of its origin (97). Division of chloroplasts in vitro found by Ridley & Leech (130) speaks in favor of their genetic and biochemical autonomy and confirms the possibility of obtaining self-reproducing cultures of isolated chloroplasts.

However, despite numerous attempts, nobody has yet succeeded in obtaining a self-reproducing and functionally active chloroplast culture. In experiments by Wellburn & Wellburn (163) with etioplasts isolated from oats, disorganization of outer and inner membranes was observed even after 2 hr of illumination, and after 9 hr the internal structures were completely destroyed and eliminated. Studying biogenesis of isolated maize etioplasts, Leech (87) came to the conclusion that chloroplast development is the result of collaboration of the whole cell, and "long-living" cultures of etioplasts and proplastids can be obtained by addition of a great number of cofactors and even other organelles to the suspension. Differentiation of plastids depends on interaction of both chloroplast and nuclear genome.

Indeed, possessing unique genetic information and TTS, the chloroplast is not an autonomous organelle, "a cell within a cell," because its genetic and biochemical function is semiautonomous. The size of the plastid genome is not sufficient to code for the formation of the great amount of structural and functional proteins which are necessary for proliferation of membrane systems and for carrying out diverse light and dark reactions of photosynthesis. Numerous available experimental data testify to the essential role of the nucleus in chloroplast biogenesis.

Using different physiological and chemical agents, we induced a wide spectrum of higher plant mutations blocking different stages of biosynthesis of chlorophyll, components of the photosynthetic electron transport chain (ETC), and Calvin cycle enzymes. Sixty nonallelic genes affecting biogenesis of plastid pigments were found in the model object *Arabidopsis thaliana* (L) Heynh (69, 110, 119).

Experimental mutagenesis combined with investigations using specific inhibitors of TTS enabled us to dissect the genetic regulation of synthesis of lamellar proteins, plastid enzymes, pigments, and formation of chloroplast photosystems. With these investigations as a basis, we have suggested a conception of nuclear-plastid cooperative interaction in the development of chloroplast structure and function (109, 111, 112).

Nuclear-Plastid Genetic Complementation

The presence of different genomes in a plant cell raises the question: where is the information for biosynthesis of structural and functional chloroplast-specific proteins encoded? What are the contributions of plastid and nuclear genomes to chloroplast biogenesis and to realization of diverse photosynthetic reactions?

It is clear that chloroplast DNA is of utmost importance for plastid self-organization, replication, and genetic continuity. This is well illustrated by Schiff's experiments (137) on the elimination of *Euglena gracilis* chloroplast DNA by streptomycin treatment. This antibiotic specifically blocks chloroplast DNA replication and damages the normal cycle of algal development. As a result of cell multiplication, in subsequent generations the strains formed are devoid of chloroplasts and plastid DNA. Some *Euglena* forms, such as the mutant W_3 *bul*, completely lose their greening capability and are converted from phytoflagellates to zooflagellates.

This experiment confirms that plastid DNA is essential as a master molecule for chloroplast formation and development.

Plastid genome mutations cause different kinds of hereditary abnormalities in chloroplast structure and function. Phenotypically, plastome mutants are manifested by the appearance of variegated chimeras with sectorial and periclinal localization of green tissues (74). Unlike virus mosaic, which causes the boundaries between pale and pigmented parts of a leaf to be smeared, the plastome variegation is characterized by a regular distribution of pale and green sectors or by white edging of the dull green center of a leaf. Such a picture of variegation is caused by a sorting out of normal and mutated plastids in the process of cell mitosis and tissue differentiation. "Mixed" heteroplastid cells with normal and mutated chloroplasts are found at the boundaries of green and white parts of variegated leaves (1, 50).

Plastome mutants are extremely interesting for evaluation of the amount of information and for mapping the chloroplast genome. In nature they appear spontaneously with a low frequency of 0.02–0.06%. Plastome mutations can be induced by different physicochemical mutagens (51).

Considerable progress in the investigation of genetic control of chloroplast biogenesis has been made with the model object *Chlamydomonas reinhardi.* Levine & Goodenough (88), Sager (134), and Kvitko et al (84) have induced a wide spectrum of mutations in *C. reinhardi* affecting chloroplast properties. Unlike higher plants in which the mutation blocking plastid function is lethal, in *C. reinhardi* the cells with inactive chloroplasts can be kept viable by growing the culture in heterotrophic conditions. Genetic analysis of acetate-requiring, antibiotic-resistant *C. reinhardi* mutants led Sager & Rammanis (135, 136) to the discovery of cytoplasmic gene recombination and segregation. They have concluded that in haploid vegetative cells of *C. reinhardi* the plastome is represented by a "diploid" system.

Studying the recombination frequency and cytoplasmic gene segregation in repeatedly marked *C. reinhardi* clones, Sager (134) tried to define the linkage group of genophores associated with chloroplasts. This made it possible to start cytoplasmic gene mapping. It turned out that the sequence of linkage groups in cytoplasmic genes represents a ring, which is in agreement with the circular configuration of the chloroplast DNA.

Analyzing the sequence of Mendelian genes affecting chloroplast properties in *C. reinhardi,* Levine & Goodenough (88) suggested that 8 from 16 linkage groups of genes are localized in chloroplast genophores. However, the cytological data of McVittie & Davies (100) do not support this point of view. These authors found 16 chromosomes in the metaphase and related them to 16 linkage groups of nuclear genes. According to Kvitko (83), 16 from 18 linkage groups of genes are localized in the nucleus, 2 in cellular organelles, with one of these two being inherited uniparentally. It is very probable that in meiotic division of *C. reinhardi* cells the transmission function is fulfilled not by all genophores but by single molecules (28, 120).

It should be noted that the task of mapping chloroplast genophores is very complex. Efforts will be required to elucidate quantitative localization and identification of plastogene properties and functions.

At present attempts are being made for restriction analysis and mapping of chloroplast DNA fragments. Using endonuclease-restrictase, Bedbrook & Bogorad (9) succeeded in splitting a circular DNA molecule of 85×10^6 daltons isolated from *Zea mays* chloroplasts. The analysis of DNA fragments by transcription of RNA copies showed that nearly 15% of chloroplast genome sequences were repeated. Two copies of repeats were in an inverted orientation and had 10% of nonhomologous sequence. The inverted repeats contained genes coding for 23S and 16S chloroplast rRNAs.

Tewari & Wildman (149, 150) noted that pea chloroplast DNA rapidly renatured after heat denaturation, which indicated the presence of a large number of repeated nucleotide sequences.

The high level of homologous sequences in plastid DNA chains points out that the amount of genetic information is limited. According to Smillie, Scott & Bishop (146, 147), the chloroplast genome contains about 2×10^7 nucleotide pairs. However, proceeding from the molecular weight of the chloroplast DNA ($1-2 \times 10^8$ dalton), the base content must not exceed 1×10^6 pairs. Hence it is possible to calculate the number of genes in a chloroplast genome. Admitting that about 1500 base pairs form one gene, the chloroplast genome must contain about $1.3-1.5 \times 10^3$ genes. Taking into account the existence of frequently repeating homologous chains, intercistron spacers, and regulatory genes, we can suppose that the chloroplast genome codes for about 150–300 specific proteins of 50×10^3 daltons (73, 111).

In order to determine the nature of chloroplast genetic information, the hybridization of DNA with different types of plastid and cytoplasmic RNA has been successfully used. It was shown that the plastid DNA has a high level of hybridization with rRNA and tRNA extracted from chloroplasts (142, 151). In the chloroplast genome, 30–40 cistrons were identified for each 23S and 16S rRNA. Probably each copy of the plastid DNA contains one gene for the 23S rRNA and one for the 16S rRNA. As for tRNA specific for different amino acids, they are coded for by different genophores. Cistrons of rRNA and tRNA make up about 4% of chloroplast DNA (73).

The transcription of mRNA onto chloroplast DNA was studied using ^{14}C and ^{3}H uridine (129, 141). It was shown that the formation of chloroplast mRNA is light induced. In our laboratory we have extracted a light-induced fraction of chloroplast RNA (cRNA) with 9–11S which upon incubation with ribosomes in vitro makes a "working" polysome. In the presence of the specific inhibitor rifampicin, the light-induced synthesis of all three types of RNA was repressed (4, 116).

It should be pointed out that not all the components of the PSS of chloroplasts are "products' of their own genes. Schweiger and co-workers (76, 140) transplanted the nucleus from *Acetabularia mediterranea* into an enucleated *A. cliftonii* cell, and showed that hybrid progeny was similar to donor species by the composition of chloroplast ribosomal proteins. Nuclear control of the formation of some specific chloroplast ribosomal proteins was demonstrated by Bogorad et al in *C. reinhardi* mutants (20, 102). In higher plants (hybrids of *Nicotiana*), Wildman et al (167) found that 50S subunits of chloroplast ribosomal proteins were not inherited by maternal line. On this basis the authors concluded that the information on the composition of chloroplast ribosomal proteins resides in the nuclear genome.

Chloroplast aminoacyl-tRNA-synthetases are also coded for by the nuclear genome, translated on cytoplasmic ribosomes and then compartmentalized within the chloroplasts (6, 58, 128). All these data are evidence that the formation of the PSS of chloroplasts is controlled by complementary cooperation of nuclear and plastid genes.

The two genetic systems closely interact in the processes of chloroplast biogenesis, i.e. in the formation of lamellar proteins, chlorophyll biosynthesis, photosystems, and synthesis of Calvin cycle enzymes. Electrophoretic separation of chloroplast membrane polypeptides by SDS acrylamide gel electrophoresis enabled one to identify more than 40 protein bands in thylakoids. A substantial part of these lamellar proteins is coded for by the nuclear genome, as shown in recent experiments by Bingham & Schiff (10) with light-grown *E. gracilis* wild type cells (possessing normal chloroplasts) and dark-grown cells with proplastids and the mutant W_3 *bul* devoid of detectable plastid DNA. In greening cells, five new polypeptide bands were formed in the light. The authors suggested that they were products of plastid DNA genes. Vasconcelos (159) has noted the appearance of nine labeled polypeptides of the thylakoid membranes in isolated *Euglena* chloroplasts.

Despite the fact that the number of plastid lamellar proteins is not large, they play an essential role in membrane proliferation, aggregation, and packing of the pigments in thylakoids. It is well known that chlorophyll biosynthesis is controlled mainly by the nuclear genome.

Experimental mutagenesis and induction of the so-called chlorophyll mutations is widely used in investigations of genetic control systems of chloroplast biogenesis. A wide spectrum of mutations which block different stages of synthesis of chlorophyll, yellow pigments, photosynthetic ETC components, Calvin cycle enzymes, and low-molecular weight compounds (amino acids, vitamins, etc) modifying chloroplast morphogenesis, was induced by means of physical and chemical agents (X and γ rays, protons, α particles, laser radiation, ethylmethanesulfonate, nitrosoalkylurea, and others).

Phenotypic manifestation of chlorophyll mutants depends on the mutation nature, whether this is gene or chromosome aberration. It is possible to observe forms from completely bleached up to dark green which differ also in their viability. If the mutation blocks the formation of ETC components or key enzymes of CO_2 assimilation, then the mutants are incapable of autotropic life and they are lethal. Another group of mutations affects only the pigment system of chloroplasts, so their cycle of photosynthetic reactions is not damaged. This group is used for genetic mapping of biosynthesis of chlorophyll and formation of its native forms (Figure 1).

According to Walles' classification (162), nuclear-induced plastome mutants are subdivided into three groups: (*a*) mutants of one color—white, yellow, pale green; (*b*) variegated plants of two or more colors—*alboxantha, xantha alba, alboviridis, viridoalbina, tigrina, maculata*, etc; (*c*) mutants changing the leaf color during ontogenesis from pale green to a yellow or from white to green, which is connected with photobleaching or chlorophyll stabilization.

Gustafsson (49) was the first to obtain a large collection of barley chlorophyll mutants. Later on, 240 nuclear genes from barley affecting plastid pigment biosynthesis were discribed (125).

Gottschalk (45) obtained 176 mutation types from pea with genetic blocks in chlorophyll and carotenoid biosynthesis. Using cytogenetic analysis of pea mutants of *chlorina* type, Blixt (19) identified 15 loci controlling the formation of plastid

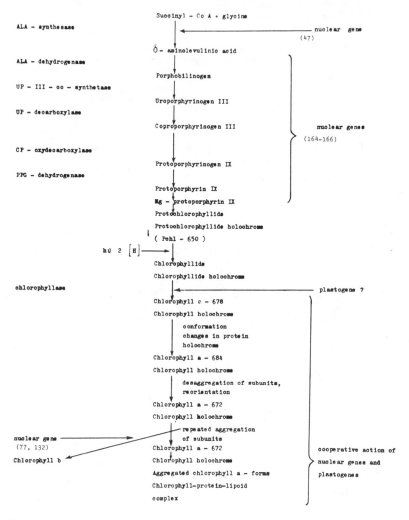

Figure 1   Scheme of genetic regulation of chlorophyll biosynthesis and the initial stages of formation of its native forms (118).

pigments. Wettstein et al (165, 166) induced 198 recessive lethal chloroplast mutations in barley. Genetic analysis revealed 86 nuclear genes controlling chloroplast
development. Five of them (*xantha*—f, g, h, l, u) were classed with structural genes
controlling the conversion of uroporphyrinogen to protochlorophyllide; 3 genes
(*tigrina* 12, "infrared" 5 and 6) were identified as regulatory ones. Among 33 *albina*
mutants, allelism was found in only two cases. Unlike structural genes, two regulatory genes exhibited a similar dominant effect in wild type and mutant alleles in
heterozygotes. Using the model plant *A. thaliana,* we have found 60 nonallelic genes
controlling chlorophyll biosynthesis and affecting chloroplast ultrastructure and
function (69, 70, 119).

An essential problem in studying the biosynthesis of chlorophyll is the elucidation
of regulatory mechanisms in the development of its native forms. Accumulation of
a definite amount of chlorophyll is not sufficient for normal functioning of photosynthetic membranes. Specific structural organization of chlorophyll into pigment-
protein complexes (PPC) responsible for primary photochemical processes of light
energy conversion in photosynthesis is required. Even at the first hours of greening
of etiolated seedlings when the total concentration of chlorophyll is far from being
normal, its aggregated forms appear which differ in their spectral properties. The
membrane lipoproteins carrying native chlorophyll forms also play an important
role in the molecular organization of pigment systems. Pigment aggregation and
packing in photosynthetic membranes are determined by lamellar proteins, synthesis of which is under the dual nuclear and plastid control (44, 118).

Complementary cooperation of nuclear-plastid genetic systems ensures the development of photosynthetically active membranes, formation of pigment-protein
photosystem (PS) assembly, and ETC components. Mutation of both nuclear and
plastid genes causes defects in PS I and PS II. Heber & Gottschalk (57) have
described a mutant of *Vicia faba* with a block in PS I. Chloroplasts of this nuclear
mutant are incapable of NADP photoreduction. Bishop (13) induced a mutation in
Scenedesmus obliquus with a block in the synthesis of cytochrome *f*-552, which
caused a suppression of cyclic photophosphorylation. A defect in PS II caused by
mutation of one nuclear gene was found by Voskresenskaya, Drozdova & Gostimskii (160) in the pea lethal mutant. Yakubova et al (173) discovered a block in the
formation of ETC components between PS I and PS II in the cotton nuclear mutant.

On the other hand, the mutation of chloroplast DNA also causes defects of
photosynthetic ETC. Investigating photochemical activity of chloroplasts from
Oenothera plastome mutants, Fork & Heber (40) and Hallier (53) found that some
mutants had defects in PS I and others in PS II. Hagemann et al (52) studied
chloroplast photochemical reactions in two plastome mutants with damaged photosynthesis. It turned out that in *Antirrhinum majus en:viridis* the mutation of chloroplast DNA caused a defect in PS II. As a result, they lost ability for the Hill reaction.
PS I in this mutant was normal; it did not differ from the wild type by the character
of light-induced ESR signals in leaves indicating the normal state of P700. On the
contrary, a damage of PS I and normal functioning of PS II were observed in the
mutants 'Mrs. Pollock' of *P. zonale.* This defect correlates with the loss of specific
proteins of PPC I.

Dissection of genetic systems controlling chloroplast biosynthesis requires a combination of methods of mutational analysis with investigations using specific inhibitors of cell organelle transcription and translation.

Site of Translation and Regulation

Studying peculiarities of chloroplast biogenesis in etiolated pea seedlings in the light, we were the first to show the asynchronous character of synthesis of plastid proteins and RNA (114, 115). The rate of protein formation in the process of plastid differentiation considerably outstripped the RNA synthesis rate. At initial stages of etioplast development the effect of chloramphenicol was not noticeable, but after 10–20 hr of illumination this agent strongly inhibited incorporation of the labeled amino acid into lamellar proteins, which was connected with the development of their own PSS. It was also shown that formation of plastid proteins is sensitive to cycloheximide (CH). From these data it was concluded that chloroplast biogenesis was carried out by cooperation of both cytoplasmic and plastid PSS.

Using specific inhibitors of translation, Hoober & Blobel (62) and Eytan & Ohad (38) have found that greening of etiolated cells from *C. reinhardi* requires protein synthesis on both chloroplast and cytoplasmic ribosomes. Cooperation of the two PSS in the formation of chloroplast enzymes has been shown in a number of papers (22, 23, 34).

Figure 2 represents a generalized scheme of genetic regulation of chloroplast biogenesis and photosynthesis. A large amount of genetic information localized in the nucleus is translated on the 80S ribosomes, and these gene products regulate and are directly involved in chloroplast biosynthesis. It has been determined that inducers of chloroplast DNA replication and plastid RNA polymerase are controlled by the nucleus and are formed in the cytoplasm (20, 117, 129, 148). Chloroplast

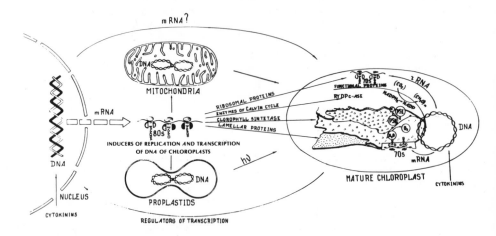

Figure 2   Genetic control of chloroplast biogenesis and photosynthesis (112).

multiplication in palisade and spongy cells is correlated with the gene dosage; increasing ploidy level causes an increase in the number of plastids per cell (24). Mitochondria considerably affect the energy supply at the initial stages of chloroplast biosynthesis (138).

The question arises whether all plastid proteins coded for by the nucleus are formed in the cytoplasm and are transferred to the organelle or whether a part of them is translated within the chloroplast with participation of nuclear mRNA. Schweiger, Apel & Kloppstech (141), Hoober & Stegelmann (64), and Parthier et al (129) admit the translation of mRNA of nuclear origin on the 70S plastid ribosomes and translation of organelle mRNA on the 80S cytoplasmic ribosomes.

Using rifampicin, Jennings & Ohad (66) obtained indirect evidence of the translation of mRNA of nuclear cytoplasmic origin within chloroplasts. By means of impulse labels ^{3}H-uracyl and ^{32}P-orthophosphate, it has been shown that the newly synthesized RNA is specifically associated with chloroplast ribosomes. Electrophoresis of RNA extracted from these ribosomes has shown that the label is incorporated neither in rRNA nor tRNA. From this it has been concluded that the labeled RNA represents an extrachloroplast template.

It should be noted that the question of transport of the nuclear mRNA into chloroplasts is still unsolved. For mitochondria, Gaitskhoki et al (41) demonstrated the transfer of nuclear mRNA into the organelle where its translation occurred. It is quite possible that some multienzymic complexes—for example, enzymes of chlorophyll biosynthesis—could be translated in the chloroplast from the templates of nuclear origin. According to Smillie et al (145) and Parthier (128), chloramphenicol strongly inhibits chlorophyll synthesis. However, the solution of this problem requires additional experimental evidence of mRNA import and tolerance of plastid PSS to alien templates. As for the transfer of cytoplasmic proteins, it can be assumed that they are synthesized on membrane-bound ribosomes and directly penetrate the organelle outer membrane. Membrane-bound polysomes can often be seen on electron micrographs of chloroplasts.

Nuclear genome replication and transcription depend, in their turn, on chloroplast gene products. Blamire, Flechthen & Sager (18) showed that inhibition of plastid protein synthesis in *Chlamydomonas* led to a decrease of labeled adenine incorporation into the chromosomal DNA. Proceeding from this, the authors made an assumption on a feedback regulation of the nuclear gene activity. Using the yellow mutant of *C. reinhardi,* Hoober & Stegelman (63) experimentally showed the stimulatory effect of photoconversion of protochlorophyll into chlorophyllide on the formation of the cytoplasmic lamellar polypeptide C. Evidence of the cytoplasmic control of the nuclear gene activity has been obtained for higher plants (171).

The expression of nuclear-plastid genes and their interaction in chloroplast biogenesis is controlled by a complex of external and internal factors (light, temperature, pH of the medium, phytohormones, phytochrome, etc).

Close cooperation of the transcription-translation system of chloroplasts, nucleus, and cytoplasm in the formation of the PPC I and II was shown on nuclear and plastome mutants (5, 42, 60) and by experiments with specific inhibitors (93, 106,

124). It was established that chloramphenicol (CAP) considerably inhibited the formation of protein components of PS I and partly reduced the synthesis of PS II proteins. As for cycloheximide, it blocks the formation of PS II proteins and slightly suppresses the synthesis of PS I proteins.

The main protein component of PPC I is 100×10^3 daltons (5) or about 70×10^3 daltons (75, 92). Apparently it is represented by two or more polypeptides which are coded for by nuclear and plastid genomes and translated mostly on the chloroplast ribosomes.

PPC 2 includes several polypeptides of $23-30 \times 10^3$ daltons. It seems that the major protein component of PS II is coded for by the nucleus and is synthesized in the cytoplasm. The minor components are coded for by plastogenes and are synthesized in chloroplasts. They apparently have a regulatory function. This is also corroborated by the data of Giller et al (44, 78) on the effect of specific inhibitors on the chlorophyll state and photochemical activity of chloroplast photosystems. It has been shown that CAP affects the formation of short-wave chlorophyll forms while CH affects the long-wave ones. Both inhibitors suppress to the same extent NADP and ferricyanide reduction.

A typical example of complementation of nuclear and cytoplasmic genes in chloroplast biogenesis is the regulation of the synthesis of ribulose-1,5-diphosphate (RuDP) carboxylase subunits in eukaryotic algae and higher plants. This key enzyme of the Calvin cycle is an oligomer protein complex totaling 56×10^4 daltons. The enzyme consists of two types of subunits: 8 large and 8 small. The large subunit is $51-58 \times 10^3$ daltons, and that of the small one is $12-18 \times 10^3$ daltons (99).

By genetic analysis of reciprocal interspecific tobacco hybrids and mutants, Wildman and associates (26, 167) showed that chloroplast DNA coded for the large subunit of the enzyme while nuclear genes controlled the formation of the small subunit. Using specific inhibitors of translation, CAP and CH, it has been established that the large subunit is synthesized on the 70S chloroplast ribosomes and the small one on the 80S cytoplasmic polyribosomes (17, 48, 133). Isolated chloroplasts incorporate labeled amino acids into the large subunit of RuDP-carboxylase (54, 159).

Using CH we have shown that the block in the synthesis of the small subunit significantly inhibits the formation of the large subunit in chloroplasts. Analogous results were obtained by Ellis (32) with another inhibitor of protein synthesis on the 80S ribosomes. From this he made an assumption on the possible role of the small subunit as a factor initiating translation of mRNA of the large subunit. However, it seems to us that the small subunit plays a regulatory role not at the translation level, but at transcription of mRNA of the large subunit. To test this assumption, we have carried out experiments adding a small subunit of the enzyme to protoplast suspensions. It has been found that addition of the small subunit to protoplasts increases ^{14}C-uridine incorporation in chloroplast RNA by 30–40% in comparison with the control. In the presence of rifampicin, the chloroplast RNA synthesis is inhibited by 60%. It has been concluded that the small subunit of RuDP-carboxylase serves as an inducer of the transcription of the large subunit mRNA (113).

PHYSIOLOGICAL AND GENETIC BASIS OF IMPROVING PHOTOSYNTHETIC PRODUCTIVITY

Analysis of advances in modern agriculture when technical progress of husbandry has reached a high level shows that an increase in the productivity of the main crops has a tendency to stabilization. Further elaboration of agricultural technology and considerable increase in mineral nutrition dosage does not cause corresponding yield enhancement. Does it mean that all the productivity potential of modern plant-growth has been exhausted and maximum yield for some crops achieved?

Basic physiological and genetic investigations of plant productivity show that the yield potential is rather high and not yet fully exploited. A rich gene pool in crop plants has not been fully utilized for the purposeful and efficient enhancement of those processes which at present limit crop productivity. Among the yield-limiting factors, we should mention first of all photosynthesis, the efficiency of which is extremely low. Efficiency of solar energy utilization for many crops does not exceed 1%. Moreover, cultivated varieties of such plants as wheat, cotton, and others have lower rates of photosynthesis than their initial wild types (35, 98, 108). However, high productivity of crops has been provided by leaf area increase, changes in the ratio of the biomass of reproductive organs to that of vegetative ones, and by other morphophysiological properties. It is quite evident that plant breeding research has not been aimed at improvement of the photosynthetic apparatus. Mass selective screening has been conducted according to the morphological properties and traits of agronomic value, with much attention being given to increasing the size of sink and storage organs—the number and size of ears, bolls, tubers, etc. Enhancement of the plant sink and storage capacity resulted in an increase of the agronomic yield as long as the photosynthetic potential permitted. At present an imbalance can be observed between the desirable number and the size of economically valuable plant organs and the possibility of providing them with the products of photosynthesis in the newly obtained promising varieties and hybrids. This imbalance between the accumulation and partition of assimilates leads to puniness and immaturity of seeds, falling of ovaries and bolls, decrease of sugar content, and other disorders. Besides, an excessive increase in the sink power can provoke, by the negative feedback mechanism, a decrease in the activity of the photosynthetic apparatus due to the withdrawal of nitrogen from leaves into other organs thereby causing their premature senescence (98).

From the above we can conclude that low photosynthetic efficiency became a "bottleneck" for productivity enhancement. Development of methods for photosynthesis regulation and the increased efficiency in utilization of solar energy up to 3–5% are the most important means of obtaining high agricultural yield. The world's experience in obtaining highly productive varieties and high yield on the basis of modern agricultural technology shows that the possibilities of crop yield enhancement by the best utilization of water, fertilizers, light energy, and other factors are related to the optimization of canopy structure and improvement of the photosynthetic apparatus on physiological and genetic bases. It is calculated that an increase of photosynthetic utilization of photosynthetically active radiation (PAR) up to 3–5% will permit the following crop yields: maize—15 tons of grain, winter wheat—10 tons of grain, seed cotton—8 tons per hectare. The relationship between photosynthesis and crop yield is very complex. In the literature there are contradictory data on the correlation between photosynthetic rate and crop yield (36, 80, 103). The absence of a direct relation between them is probably explained by the dependence of crop yield on the net assimilation value which in turn is determined not only by photosynthetic rate but also by leaf surface size, duration of vegetable period, canopy structure, dark and light respiration, translocation, and partitioning of assimilates. Figure 3 represents an integral scheme of phenotypic expression of nuclear and cytoplasmic gene action in formation of the factors of photosynthetic productivity and crop yield. It is seen from this scheme that crop yield is the result of complex diverse processes and reactions occuring at ontogenesis under the influence of external conditions.

Thus, three ways to increase the productivity follow from these conceptions: 1. optimization of the canopy structure as an optical system; 2. improvement of efficiency of the photosynthesis process itself; and 3. rational partition and usage of assimilates for formation of the agronomic yield (harvest index).

The first way, based on the morphophysiological and agroecological data, is widely used in agronomy. The theory of this problem and the principle of canopy structure optimization with favorable leaf area index (LAI) allowing improvement of radiation and aerodynamic conditions for different crops were developed in detail by Nichiporovich (122, 123) and other investigators (90, 174).

The second and the third ways to increase photosynthetic productivity concern the genetic balance of plant source and sink abilities. According to Evans (35), it is important to know when source or sink limit the crop yield. In cereals, for example, grain filling is largely dependent on photosynthesis and environmental conditions after flowering, whereas the capacity for storage is determined by conditions before flowering (105). Nalborczyk & Gej (107) showed that in different varieties of spring wheat the photosynthetic productivity during milk and wax maturity played an important role in obtaining high economic yield. A remarkable peculiarity of the intensive varieties was a coincidence of net assimilation rate (NAR) maximum with that of LAI.

The interrelation between source and sink has a pronounced feedback effect. For example, removal of the wheat ear (37) or the cotton boll (108) causes a considerable depression of photosynthesis. On the contrary, increasing sink capacity can enhance to a certain extent the rate of photosynthesis. In experiments by Thorne & Evans (152), grafting of spinach to sugar beet led to an increase in assimilating ability of the graft.

Analyzing the numerous data on the correlation between source and sink capacity, it should be noted that the one-sided approach to these processes does not give positive results. For example, CO_2 feeding usually results in considerable alteration of chloroplast ultrastructure due to an excessive storage of starch (82). At the same time, a great attractive power can lead to chloroplast "wear" and premature leaf senescence.

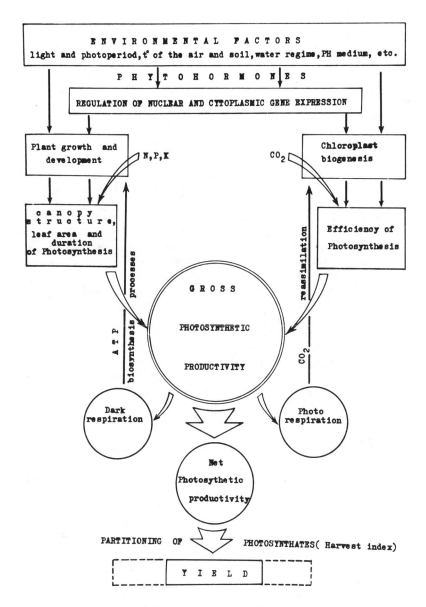

Figure 3   Scheme of phenotypic expression of plant productivity processes.

Selection of plants on a physiological and genetic basis will make it possible to get varieties and hybrids with a balanced ratio between source and sink that will provide the maximum expression of yield potential for each plant.

Analysis and Mobilization of the Germplasm

Evaluation of the diversity of photosynthetic functions and identification of the parameters of photosynthetic efficiency allow practicing breeders to manipulate the genotype for significant improvement of plant productivity. Ecological and geographical populations of plant species have a large genetic variability of chloroplast photochemical and enzymic activity which provides their different photosynthetic ability (156, 170).

The genotypic determination of chloroplast structure and function is clearly manifested in photosynthetic pathways of C_3 and C_4 plants. The plants with Kranz anatomy of the leaf (maize, sorghum, sugar cane, etc) are known to possess an additional pathway of CO_2 fixation with the participation of phosphoenolpyruvate (PEP) and the formation of C_4 dicarboxylic acids. Hatch & Slack (56) earlier proposed that the C_4 pathways are an autocatalytic cycle of CO_2 assimilation through transcarboxylation of C_4 acids. Later it became obvious that the C_4 pathway is an auxiliary channel of primary CO_2 fixation on the Calvin cycle (55, 68, 161).

In all higher plants, irrespective of the type of primary fixation, CO_2 reduction to carbohydrates occurs in the pentosephosphate cycle. However, C_4 plants have the advantage of high resistance to extreme temperature and more efficient use of water, thus adapting better to arid climates (12, 30).

Besides, C_4 plants are characterized by a CO_2 compensation point close to zero, the photosynthetic rate being independent of the concentration of oxygen since they practically do not have photorespiration (12, 94). All this, together with high light requirement, provides a very high photosynthetic capacity which is about twice as great as that of C_3 plants. The highest rate of photosynthesis (85 mg CO_2 dm^{-2} hr^{-1}) is observed in maize in natural conditions (59). Photosynthesis in C_4 plants in natural conditions is not light saturated.

The most important feature of C_4 plants is the presence in their leaves of two types of chloroplasts which differ by their ultrastructure and functions. In palisade mesophyll cells the chloroplasts have a pronounced granal structure, while in parenchyma bundle-sheath cells they are usually paucigranal (85). These chloroplasts differ greatly in their photochemical properties: PS II is active in mesophyll cells while PS I is active in bundle-sheath chloroplasts (8, 11, 79). The key enzyme of the Calvin cycle, RuDP carboxylase, is absent in mesophyll cells (67, 95). According to Hatch (55), the primary CO_2 fixation in C_4 plants occurs by PEP carboxylation which leads to the formation of oxaloacetic acid (OAA). This process proceeds in the cytoplasm since PEP-carboxylase is a purely cytoplasmic enzyme (96). In chloroplasts OAA is transformed into malate and aspartate. Further, depending on species, malate or aspartate are transported to the bundle-sheath cells where due to decarboxylation of the acids CO_2 is released and refixed in the Calvin cycle (55).

Cooperation of two types of plastids in C_4 plants leads to a concentration of CO_2 in the bundle-sheath cells where it decreases to a certain extent the limitation of photosynthesis by the diffusive CO_2 resistance and thus aids in increasing the efficiency of the process. On the other hand, all this prevents the CO_2 burst due to photorespiration. Probably the primary function of the C_4 pathway is the reassimilation of CO_2 as a result of this wasteful process (16, 71).

How can the dimorphism of chloroplasts in C_4 plants be explained from the genetic point of view? Is this a result of sorting out the genetically nonhomogeneous plastids originated from the parental pair, or are they formed under the control of the nuclear genome during cell differentiation? We believe that the second assumption is more correct. For example, maize belongs to the group with the maternal type of plastid inheritance (153); therefore it has homogeneous initial plastid material. In the process of differentiation of the cells and tissues under nuclear control, mesophyll chloroplasts are specialized for the C_4 pathway. This is probably achieved by a repression of nuclear genes for the small subunit RuDP carboxylase which, as mentioned above, plays a regulatory role in transcription of the chloroplast mRNA of the large subunit. It is quite possible that genes coding for the formation of ETC components of PS I (ferredoxin, NADP reductase, cytochrome b-563) are localized, namely on the small subunit chromosome. As a result of this gene repression, the activity in PS I of mesophyll chloroplasts is three to four times lower than that of bundle-sheath cells. Thus the nucleus controls the division of labor between the chloroplasts of mesophyll and bundle-sheath cells. However, this hypothesis requires further experimental confirmation.

The C_4 pathway is observed not only in tropical grasses, but it is also widespread among dicotyledons (31). Within one genus, C_3 and C_4 species and intermediate forms (14, 72) are encountered. Is it possible by hybridization to impart to C_3 plants the C_4 pathway? Bjorkman et al (15) successfully carried out the crossing and obtained a fertile hybrid between C_3 and C_4 *Atriplex* spp., but the efficiency of photosynthesis was lower than that of either parent in all F_1 and F_2 hybrids. These experiments are currently being continued by Nobs (126) but they have not yet led to desirable results.

The C_4 pathway is connected with the leaf Kranz anatomy, and therefore it is impossible to impart properties of cooperative photosynthesis to C_3 plants. However, we should not exclude the possibility of enhancement of the auxiliary CO_2 fixation through PEP carboxylase. As has already been mentioned, this enzyme operates in the cytoplasm and its formation is controlled by the nucleus. It has a higher affinity for HCO_3^- than for CO_2 (39); therefore it can bind the hydrated CO_2 more efficiently and transfer it to the chloroplasts, thus decreasing the limitation of photosynthesis by carboxylation resistance. The activity of PEP carboxylase in C_3 plants is 60 times lower than that in C_4 plants (144).

Since the C_4 pathway originated in the course of evolution as a result of plant adaptation to arid and hot climates, it might be assumed that the forms with high activity of PEP carboxylase can be obtained among C_3 plant mutants by genetic screening in rigid conditions. An essential part of this assumption is that the cytoplasmic system of carboxylation and CO_2 transport to the chloroplast RuDP of C_3 plants should be provided with the mechanism of acceptor regeneration, i.e. pyruvate conversion into PEP by pyruvate kinase.

Experimental mutagenesis is a powerful means of reconstructing the genome and breeding new promising forms which do not occur in nature. Nuclear mutations produce considerable shifts in the structural and biochemical organization of chloroplasts. As a result, the overwhelming majority of viable mutants have a reduced photosynthetic capacity. There are still a few mutants (1–2%) belonging to the "plus" class as measured by the increased photosynthetic efficiency. Photosynthetically positive mutants were obtained in *Chlorella* (104), pea (61), and cotton (158). In research at our institute with γ radiation, 60 cotton mutants were obtained among which there was one promising mutant *Duplex* with a compact type of branching, high frequency of double sympodial bolls, fast ripening, and high agronomic yield. Its harvest index amounts to 50%, which points to rational partition and utilization of assimilates. The economic yield of this mutant is at the rate of 1 ton per hectare of seed cotton higher than that of the initial variety *108-F.*

Physiological and biochemical studies have shown that the mutant *Duplex* is characterized by a higher photochemical and enzymic chloroplast activity during the reproductive period. In this mutant the endogenous delay of leaf senescence is observed, whereas in the initial variety, as well as in many other crops, a decrease in the specific activity of key Calvin cycle enzymes occurs on the 20th–30th day after the leaf expands, when there are no visible alterations of chloroplast ultrastructure (112, 121). Physiologic-genetic prolongation of the functionally active state of chloroplasts and prevention of premature leaf senescence are important factors in high photosynthetic productivity.

In the last few years the attention of many researchers has been attracted to the problem of photorespiration. According to the data obtained by Zelitch (175, 177) in C_3 plants (sunflower, soybean, sugar beet, etc), photosynthesis product losses upon photorespiration can reach 50% of the net assimilation. Photorespiration is considered to be a waste of organic compounds which could be used in the productive process. This is evidenced by the data on photosynthetic efficiency of C_4 plants in which photorespiration is practically absent. This circumstance can serve as one of the arguments proving that photorespiration as a process of CO_2 release in the light has no great physiological importance (91, 178).

The main source of CO_2 release in the process of photorespiration is decarboxylation of intermediates of glycolate metabolism (12, 154). The glycolate pathway is closely connected with the Calvin cycle, particularly with oxygenation of RuDP resulting in the formation of the phosphoglycolic acid (21). It is generally accepted that the key enzyme of the Calvin cycle, RuDP carboxylase, plays a bifunctional role catalyzing carboxylation and oxygenation reactions. Oxygen and CO_2 compete for the reaction substrate RuDP (86).

In the enzyme oxygenase reaction, the sulfhydryl groups take part; their total amount is 96, but the number of easily modified, "accessible" ones is 12 (2). It has been shown recently (168) that the photorespiration inhibitor glycidate irreversibly inactivates oxygenation, the carboxylase activity of the enzyme not being affected. Apparently oxygenation-specific inhibition is connected with blocking of enzyme SH groups located in its active center.

In its native state the conformation of this oligomeric protein complex and its functional activity depend on conformation and dimensions of large and small subunits. Analyzing the peptide composition of the enzyme in 60 tobacco species and 10 plants belonging to different phylogenetic groups—from blue-green algae to ginkgo—Kung (81) has found that in all species studied the large subunit contains only three polypeptides, while the number of polypeptides in the small subunit varies from 1 to 4. The latter may serve as a genetic marker in the investigations of nuclear-cytoplasmic interaction.

It may be assumed that depending on the polypeptide composition being coded for by the small subunit of the nucleus, the carboxylation or oxygenation activity of the enzyme may vary within plant species. Indeed, varieties with low photorespiration have been found within populations of C_3 species (169). By means of genetic screening, Zelitch (176, 179) has distinguished tobacco population from the variety 'Havana Seed' in which 25% of the progeny had low photorespiration. It is essential to determine what methods can be used for mass screening for the desirable forms with low photorespiration. Growing the plants in a hermetic chamber at low CO_2 concentration prior to screening them for viability is one of the simplest methods of mass genetic screening for photorespiration. However, this method has not been successful since plants in the closed chamber were not viable (25, 101). In this relation the method of photorespiration estimation by CO_2 burst measurement after illumination appears to be promising, as do investigations of dependence of NAR on O_2 concentration.

In conclusion it must be noted that estimation of photosynthetic efficiency, genetic screening of "plus" mutants, and the mobilization of species germplasm for the improvement of plant productivity should be conducted, taking into account other physiological properties such as immunity and stress resistance.

In the near future, the possibility of genome mapping and genotype manipulation by means of somatic hybridization and gene engineering will allow practicing breeders to create new, synthetic plant varieties with a desirable combination of the valuable traits, high photosynthetic efficiency and maximal expression of economic yield.

Literature Cited

1. Abdullaev, Kh. A., Usmanov, P. D., Nasyrov, Yu. S. 1972. *Dokl. Akad. Nauk Tadzh. SSR* 15:48–50
2. Akhmedov, Yu. D., Ulmasov, Kh. A., Akhmedova, L. R. 1976. In *Mater. Resp. Konf. Molodyh Uchenyh*, pp. 5–11. Dushanbe: Donish. 119 pp.
3. Aliev, K. A., Filippovich, I. I. 1971. In *Genetich Aspekty Fotosynteza*, ed. Yu. S. Nasyrov, p. 269–84. Dushanbe: Donish. 284 pp.
4. Aliev, K. A., Muzafarova, S., Radzhabov, H., Kholmatova, M., Ulug-

bekova, G., Nasyrov, Yu. S. 1975. In *Genetic Aspects of Photosynthesis*, ed. Yu. S. Nasyrov, Z. Sestak, pp. 93–103. The Hague: Dr. Junk. 392 pp.
5. Anderson, J. M., Levine, R. P. 1974. *Biochim. Biophys. Acta* 357:118–26
6. Barnett, W. E., Schwartzbach, S. D., Farrelly, J. G., Schiff, J. A., Hecker, L. I. 1976. *Arch. Microbiol.* 109:201–3
7. Baur, E. 1909. *Z. Indukt. Abstamm. Vererbungsl.* 1:330–51

8. Bazzaz, M. B., Govindjee. 1973. *Plant Physiol.* 52:257–62
9. Bedbrook, J. R., Bogorad, L. 1976. *Proc. Natl. Acad. Sci. USA* 73:4309–13
10. Bingham, S., Schiff, J. A. 1976. In *Genetics and Biogenesis of Chloroplasts and Mitochondria,* ed. Th. Bücher et al, pp. 79–86. Amsterdam: Elsevier/North Holland Biomed. Press
11. Bishop, D. G., Andersen, K. S., Smillie, R. M. 1972. *Plant Physiol.* 50:774–77
12. Bishop, D. G., Reed, M. L. 1976. *Photochem. Photobiol. Rev.* 1:1–69
13. Bishop, N. I. 1972. *Int. Congr. Photosynth. Res., 2nd, Stresa, Italy,* pp. 459–68. The Hague: Dr. Junk. 2752 pp.
14. Björkman, O., Gauhl, E., Nobs, M. A. 1970. Annual report of the director, Department of Plant Biology. *Carnegie Inst. Wash. Yearb. 1968–69,* pp. 620–33. 648 pp.
15. Björkman, O., Nobs, M. A., Pearcy, R., Boynton, J. E., Berry, J. 1971. In *Photosynthesis and Photorespiration,* ed. M. D. Hatch, C. B. Osmond, R. O. Slatyer, pp. 105–19. New York: Wiley-Interscience. 565 pp.
16. Black, C. C. 1973. *Ann. Rev. Plant Physiol.* 24:253–86
17. Blair, G. E., Ellis, R. J. 1972. *Biochem. J.* 127:42
18. Blamire, J., Flechthen, V. R., Sager, R. 1974. *Proc. Natl. Acad. Sci. USA* 71:2867–71
19. Blixt, S. 1968. *Agri Hort. Genet.* 24:87
20. Bogorad, L. 1975. See Ref. 4, pp. 51–62
21. Bowes, G., Ogren, W. L., Hageman, R. H. 1971. *Biochem. Biophys. Res. Commun.* 45:716–22
22. Bradbeer, J. W. 1971. *Int. Congr. Photosynth. Res., 2nd, Stresa, Italy* (Abstr.) 165 pp.
23. Bradbeer, J. W. 1973. In *Biosynthesis and Its Control in Plants,* ed. B. W. Milborrow. London, New York: Academic
24. Butterfass, T. 1973. *Protoplasma* 76: 167–95
25. Cannell, R. Q., Breen, W. A., Moss, D. N. 1969. *Crop Sci.* 9:840–41
26. Chan, P. H., Wildman, S. G. 1972. *Biochim. Biophys. Acta.* 277:677–80
27. Chiang, K. S. Sueoka, N. 1967. *J. Cell. Physiol.* 70(Suppl.):89–112
28. Chu-Der, O. M. Y., Chiang, K. S. 1974. *Proc. Natl. Acad. Sci. USA* 71:153–57
29. Correns, C. 1909. *Z. Indukt. Abstamm. Vererbungsl.* 1:291–329
30. Downton, W. J. S. 1971. See Ref. 15, pp. 3–17
31. Downton, W. J. S. 1975. *Photosynthetica* 9:96–105
32. Ellis, R. J. 1975. *Photochemistry* 14: 89–93
33. Ellis, R. J., Blair, G. E., Hartley, M. R. 1973. *Biochem. Soc. Symp.* 38:137–62
34. Ellis, R. J., Hartley, M. R. 1972. See Ref. 13, pp. 2677–84
35. Evans, L. T., ed. 1975. *Crop Physiology,* pp. 327–55. Cambridge Univ. Press. 374 pp.
36. Evans, L. T., Dunstone, R. L. 1970. *Aust. J. Biol. Sci.* 23:725–41
37. Evans, L. T., Wardlaw, I. F., Fisher, R. D. 1975. See Ref. 35, pp. 101–50
38. Eytan, G., Ohad, I. 1970. *J. Biol. Chem.* 245:4297–4307
39. Filmer, D. L., Cooper, T. A. 1970. *J. Theor. Biol.* 29:131–45
40. Fork, D. C., Heber, U. W. 1968. *Plant Physiol.* 43:606–12
41. Gaitskhoki, B. S., Kisilev, O. I., Puchkova, L. V. 1974. In *Genetic Functions of Cytoplasmic Organoids,* ed. S. A. Neifakh, pp. 92–107. Leningrad: Nauka. 196 pp. (In Russian)
42. Genge, S. D., Pilger, D., Hiller, R. G. 1974. *Biochim. Biophys. Acta* 347:22–30
43. Gibor, A., Izawa, M. 1963. *Proc. Natl. Acad. Sci. USA* 50:1164–69
44. Giller, Yu. E., Shcherbakova, I. Yu. 1976. *Dokl. Akad. Nauk Tadzh. SSR* 19:45–48
45. Gottschalk, W. 1964. *Die Wirking mutierter Gene auf Morphologic uns Function Pflanzliche Organe.* Jena: VEB Fisher-Verlag
46. Govindjee, Govindjee, R. 1975. In *Bioenergetics of Photosynthesis,* ed. Govindjee, pp. 2–43. New York, San Francisco, London: Academic. 698 pp.
47. Granick, S. 1967. In *Biochemistry of Chloroplasts,* ed. T. W. Goodwin, 2:373–410. London, New York: Academic. 776 pp.
48. Gray, J. C., Kekwick, R. G. O. 1974. *Eur. J. Biochem.* 44(2):491–500
49. Gustafsson, A. 1940. *Lunds Univ. Arsskr.* N.F. 36 pp.
50. Hagemann, R. 1962. *Plazmaticheskaya nasledstvennost,* ed. B. L. Astaurov. Moskva: Mir. 111 pp.
51. Hagemann, R. 1977. Unpublished data
52. Hagemann, R., Börner, Th., Herrmann, F., Knoth, R. 1974. *Ontogenez* 5: 273–83
53. Hallier, U. W. 1968. *Z. Pflanzenphysiol.* 58:289
54. Hartley, M. R., Wheeler, A., Ellis, R. J. 1975. *J. Mol. Biol.* 91:67–77
55. Hatch, M. D. 1976. *Physiol. Biochem. Cultiv. Plants (USSR)* 8:473–83

56. Hatch, M. D., Slack, C. R. 1966. *Biochem. J.* 101:103-11
57. Heber, U. W., Gottschalk, W. 1963. *Z. Naturforsch.* 136:26
58. Hecker, L. I., Egan, J., Reynolds, R. J., Nix, C. E., Schiff, J. A., Barnett, W. E. 1974. *Proc. Natl. Acad. Sci. USA* 71:1901-14
59. Heichel, G. H., Musgrave, R. B. 1969. *Crop. Sci.* 9:483-86
60. Herrmann, F. 1971. *Photosynthetica* 5:258-66
61. Highkin, H. R., Boardman, N. K., Goodchild, D. J. 1969. *Plant Physiol.* 44:1310-20
62. Hoober, J. K., Blobel, G. 1969. *J. Mol. Biol.* 41:121-38
63. Hoober, J. K., Stegeman, W. J. 1973. *J. Cell Biol.* 56:1-12
64. Hoober, J. K., Stegeman, W. J. 1975. In *Genetics and Biogenesis of Mitochondria and Chloroplasts,* ed. C. W. Birky, P. S. Perlman, T. J. Byers, pp. 225-51. Columbus: Ohio State Univ. Press. 361 pp.
65. Iwamura, T. 1962. *Biochim. Biophys. Acta* 61:472-74
66. Jennings, R. C., Ohad, I. 1972. *Arch. Biochem. Biophys.* 153:79-87
67. Kanai, R., Edwards, G. E. 1973. *Plant Physiol.* 51:1133-37
68. Karpilov, Yu. S. 1976. In *Itogi Issledovanija Mekhanizma Photosinteza,* ed. V. B. Evstigneev, pp. 58-62. Puschino. 82 pp.
69. Kasyanenko, A. G., Nasyrov, Yu. S. 1968. *Physiol. Rast.* 15:422-29
70. Kasyanenko, A. G., Nasyrov, Yu. S. 1970. *Arabidopsis Inf. Serv.* 7:31-32
71. Kelly, G. J., Latzko, E., Gibbs, M. 1976. *Ann. Rev. Plant Physiol.* 27:181-205
72. Kestler, D. P., Mayne, B. C., Ray, T. B., Goldstein, L. D., Brown, R. H., Black, C. C. 1975. *Biochem. Biophys. Res. Commun.* 66:1439-46
73. Kirk, J. T. O. 1971. *Ann. Rev. Biochem.* 40:161-96
74. Kirk, J. T. O., Tilney-Bassett, R. A. E. 1967. *The Plastids.* London, San Francisco: Freeman. 608 pp.
75. Klein, S. M., Vernon, L. P. 1974. *Photochem. Photobiol.* 19:43-49
76. Kloppstech, K., Schweiger, H. G. 1973. *Exp. Cell Res.* 80:63-68
77. Kranz, A. R. 1971. *Theor. Appl. Genet.* 41:45-51
78. Krasichkova, G. V., Lipkind, B. I., Giller, Yu. E. 1975. *Dokl. Akad. Nauk Tadzh. SSR* 18:53-56
79. Ku, S. B., Gutierrez, M., Kanai, R., Edwards, G. E. 1974. *Z. Pflanzenphysiol.* 72:320-37
80. Kumakov, V. A. 1974. In *Physiologia Rastenii v Pomoshch Selektsii,* pp. 213-25. Moskva: Nauka. 299 pp.
81. Kung, S. D. 1976. *Science* 191:429-34
82. Kursanov, A. L. 1976. *Transport Assimiliatov v Rastenii.* Moskva: Nauka. 646 pp.
83. Kvitko, K. V. 1974. *Izuchenie fiziologii kultivirovannyh vodoroslei vysokim koeffitsientom ispolzovaniya sveta.* Nauchnyi simpozium. Tezisy dokladov Leningrad:LGU
84. Kvitko, K. V., Tugarinov, V. V., Pham Thanh Ho, Chunaev, A. S., Temper, E. E., Mukhamadiev, B. T. 1975. See Ref. 4, pp. 225-36
85. Laetsch, W. M. 1974. *Ann. Rev. Plant Physiol.* 25:27-52
86. Laisk, A. H. 1977. *Kinetika photosinteza i photodyhanija C₃-rastenii.* Moskva: Nauka. 195 pp.
87. Leech, R. M. 1976. In *Perspectives in Experimental Biology,* ed. N. Sunderland, 2:145-62. Oxford, New York, Toronto, Sydney, Paris, Braunschweig: Pergamon. 523 pp.
88. Levine, R. P., Goodenough, U. W. 1970. *Ann. Rev. Genet.* 4:397-408
89. Littleton, J. W. 1962. *Exp. Cell Res.* 26:312-17
90. Loomis, R. S., Williams, W. A., Hall, A. E. 1971. *Ann. Rev. Plant Physiol.* 22:431-68
91. Lorimer, G. H., Andrews, T. J. 1973. *Nature* 243:359-60
92. Machold, O. 1974. *Biochim. Physiol. Pflanz.* 166:149-69
93. Machold, O., Aurich, O. 1972. *Biochim. Biophys. Acta* 281:103-12
94. Magomedov, I. M. 1974. *Bot. Zh.* 59:123-38
95. Magomedov, I. M. 1975. *Int. Bot. Congr., 12th, Leningrad.* (Abstr., p. 429). Leningrad: Nauka. 603 pp.
96. Magomedov, I. M., Kovaleva, L. B. 1973. *Dokl. Akad. Nauk SSSR* 209:1467-69
97. Margulis, L. 1970. *Origin of Eucaryotic Cells.* New Haven: Yale Univ. Press
98. McArthur, J. A., Hesketh, J. D., Baker, D. N. 1975. See Ref. 35, pp. 297-326
99. McFadden, B. A., Tabita, F. R. 1974. *Biosystems* 6:93-112
100. McVittie, A., Davies, D. R. 1971. *Mol. Gen. Genet.* 112:225-28
101. Menz, K. M., Moss, D. N., Cannell, R. Q., Brun, W. A. 1969. *Crop Sci.* 9:692-94

102. Mets, L., Bogorad, L. 1972. *Proc. Natl. Acad. Sci. USA* 69:3779–83
103. Moshkov, B. S. 1973. *Rol Luchistoii Energii v Vyjavlenii Potentsialnoii Prodyctivnosti Rastenii. Timirazevskie Chtenija.* Moskva: Nauka. 59 pp.
104. Mukhamadiev, B., Zalensky, O. V. 1972. *Bot. Zh.* 57:260–65
105. Murata, Y., Matsushima, S. 1975. See Ref. 35, pp. 73–100
106. Muzafarova, S. 1975. *Dokl. Akad. Nauk Tadzh. SSR* 18:63–66
107. Nalborczyk, E., Gej, B. 1975. *Pol. Ecol. Stud.* 1:71–80
108. Nasyrov, Yu. S. 1960. In *Khlopchatnik (Cotton)* 4:227–73 Tashkent: Academic. 705 pp. (In Russian)
109. Nasyrov, Yu. S. 1969. *Int. Bot. Congr. 11th.* Seattle (Abstr., p. 157). 260 pp.
110. Nasyrov, Yu. S. 1972. *Sov. Sci. Rev.* 3:294–99
111. Nasyrov, Yu. S. 1972. *Zh. Obshch. Biol.* 33:683–701
112. Nasyrov, Yu. S. 1975. *Photosynthesis and Genetics of Chloroplasts.* Moskva: Nauka. 143 pp. (In Russian)
113. Nasyrov, Yu. S. 1977. *Int. Congr. Photosynth. Res., 4th,* Reading (Abstr., pp. 268–69)
114. Nasyrov, Yu. S., Aliev, K. A. 1970. *Dokl. Akad. Nauk Tadzh. SSR* 13: 50–52
115. Nasyrov, Yu. S., Aliev, K. A. 1972. See Ref. 13, 3:2545–53
116. Nasyrov, Yu. S., Aliev, K. A. Abdullaev, Kh. A. 1974. See Ref. 41, pp. 40–44
117. Nasyrov, Yu. S., Dontsova, S. V., Makhmadbekova, L. M., Nikolaeva, M. I., Shagadaeva, L. M. 1977. In *Genetica Fotosinteza,* ed. Yu. S. Nasyrov, pp. 46–50. Dushanbe: Donish. 291 pp.
118. Nasyrov, Yu. S., Giller, Yu. E., Usmanov, P. D. 1975. See Ref. 4, pp. 133–45
119. Nasyrov, Yu. S., Kasyanenko, A. G., Abdurakhmanova, Z. N. 1971. In *Biokhimija i Biofizika Fotosinteza,* ed. F. E. Reimers, pp. 121–28. Irkutsk. 230 pp.
120. Nasyrov, Yu. S., Kvitko, K. V., Sestak, Z. 1975. See Ref. 4, pp. 369–74
121. Nekrasova, G. F., Mokronosov, A. T. 1975. See Ref. 95, p. 431
122. Nichiporovich, A. A. 1972. In *Teoreticheskie Osnovy Fotosinteticheskoi Produktivnosti,* pp. 511–27. Moskva: Nauka. 547 pp.
123. Nichiporovich, A. A. 1975. See Ref. 4, pp. 315–41
124. Nielsen, N. C. 1975. *Eur. J. Biochem.* 50:611–23
125. Nilan, R. A. 1967. *Genetika* 3:3–22
126. Nobs, M. A. 1976. Annual report of the director, Department of Plant Biology. *Carnegie Inst. Wash. Yearb. 1975–76,* pp. 421–23. 484 pp.
127. Odintsova, M. C. 1976. *Itogi Nauki Tekh. Biol. Khim.,* Vol. 10
128. Parthier, B. 1973. *FEBS Lett.* 38:70–74
129. Parthier, B., Krauspe, R., Munsche, D., Wollgiehn, R. 1975. *Chem. Biochem. Plant Proteins* 11:167–210
130. Ridley, S. M., Leech, R. M. 1970. *Nature* 227:463–65
131. Ris, H., Plaut, W. 1962. *J. Cell Biol.* 13:383–91
132. Röbbelen, G. 1959. *Z. Indukt. Abstamm. Vererbungsl.* 90:503
133. Roy, H., Patterson, R., Jagendorf, A. T. 1976. *Arch. Biochem. Biophys.* 172: 64–73
134. Sager, R. 1972. *Cytoplasmic Genes and Organelles.* New York, London: Academic. 423 pp.
135. Sager, R. 1970. In *Control of Organelle Development,* pp. 401–18. Cambridge Univ. Press. 499 pp.
136. Sager, R., Rammanis, L. 1971. In *Autonomy and Biogenesis of Mitochondria and Chloroplasts,* ed. N. K. Boardman, A. W. Linnane, R. M. Smillie, pp. 250–59. Amsterdam, London: North-Holland. 511 pp.
137. Schiff, J. A. 1971. *Stadler Genet. Symp.* 3:89–110
138. Schiff, J. A. 1975. See Ref. 4, pp. 63–91
139. Schiff, J. A., Epstein, H. T. 1966. In *Biochemistry of Chloroplasts,* Vol. 1, ed. T. W. Goodwin. London, New York: Academic. 475 pp.
140. Schweiger, H. G. 1976. *Handb. Genet.* 5:451–75
141. Schweiger, H. G., Apel, K., Kloppstech, K. 1972. *Adv. Biosci.* 8:249–62
142. Scott, N. S., Smillie, R. M. 1967. *Biochem. Biophys. Res. Commun.* 28:598–603
143. Sisakyan, N. M., Filippovich, I. I., Svetailo, E. N. 1962. *Dokl. Akad. Nauk SSSR* 147:488–89
144. Slack, C. R., Hatch, M. D. 1967. *Biochem. J.* 103:660–65
145. Smillie, R. M., Bishop, F. C., Gibbons, G. G., Graham, A. M., Grieve, A. M., Raison, J. K., Reger, B. J. 1971. See Ref. 136, pp. 422–33
146. Smillie, R. M., Scott, N. S. 1969. *Prog. Mol. Subcell. Biol.* 1:136–202
147. Smillie, R. M., Scott, N. S., Bishop, D. G. 1973. In *The Biochemistry of Gene Expression in Higher Organisms,* ed. Pollak, Lee. Sydney

148. Surzycki, S. J., Goodenough, U. W., Levine, R. P., Armstrong, J. J. 1970. See Ref. 135, pp. 13–37
149. Tewari, K. K. 1971. *Ann. Rev. Plant Physiol.* 22:141–68
150. Tewari, K. K., Wildman, S. G. 1966. *Science* 153:1269–71
151. Tewari, K. K., Wildman, S. G. 1970. See Ref. 135, pp. 147–79
152. Thorne, G. N., Evans, A. F. 1964. *Ann. Bot.* N.S. 28:499–508
153. Tilney-Bassett, R. A. E. 1975. See Ref. 64, pp. 268–308
154. Tolbert, N. E. 1971. *Ann. Rev. Plant Physiol.* 22:45–74
155. Trebst, A. 1974. *Ann. Rev. Plant Physiol.* 25:423–58
156. Treharne, K. J. 1972. In *Crop Processes in Controlled Environments,* ed. A. R. Rees, K. E. Cockshull, D. W. Hand, R. G. Hurd, pp. 285–303. London, New York: Academic. 391 pp.
157. Turishcheva, M. S. 1975. See Ref. 4, pp. 1–8
158. Usmanov, P. D., Abdullaev, Kh. A., Pinkhasov, Yu. I., Bikasiyan, G. R. 1975. *Genetika* 11:22–29
159. Vasconcelos, A. C. 1976. *Plant Physiol.* 58:719–21
160. Voskresenskaya, N. P., Drozdova, I. S., Gostimskii, S. A. 1971. In *Fotosyntes i Ispols. Solnechn. Energii,* ed. O. V. Zalensky, pp. 236–40. Leningrad: Nauka. 283 pp.
161. Walker, D. A. 1974. In *Plant Carbohydrate Biochemistry. Proc. Symp. Phytochem. Soc., 10th, Edinburgh, 1973,* ed. J. B. Pridham, pp. 7–26. London, New York: Academic
162. Walles, B. 1971. In *Structure and Function of Chloroplasts,* ed. M. Gibbs, pp. 51–88. Berlin, Heidelberg, New York: Springer-Verlag. 286 pp.

163. Wellburn, A. R., Wellburn, F. A. M. 1972. See Ref. 13, pp. 2349–65
164. Wettstein, D. Von 1967. In *Harvesting the Sun,* ed. A. San Pietro, F. A. Greer, T. J. Army, pp. 153–90. London, New York: Academic. 342 pp.
165. Wettstein, D. Von 1972. *Tesisy Vsesousn. Symp. Genet. Aspekty Fotosynteza.* Dushanbe: Donish. 119 pp.
166. Wettstein, D. Von, Henningsen, K. W., Boynton, J. E., Kannangara, C. G., Nielsen, O. F. 1971. See Ref. 136, pp. 205–23
167. Wildman, S. G., Chen, K., Gray, J. C., Kung, S. D., Kwanjuen, P., Sakano, K. 1975. See Ref. 64, pp. 309–29
168. Wildner, G. F., Henkel, J. 1976. *Biochem. Biophys. Res. Commun.* 69:268–75
169. Wilson, D. 1972. *J. Exp. Bot.* 23:517–25
170. Wilson, D., Cooper, J. P. 1969. *Heredity* 24:633–49
171. Wolf, G., Rempan, J. 1977. *Nature* 265:470–71
172. Woodcock, C. L. F., Bogorad, L. 1971. See Ref. 162, pp. 89–128
173. Yakubova, M. M., Rubin, A. B., Khramova, G. A., Matorin, O. N. 1975. See Ref. 4, pp. 263–69
174. Yoshida, S. 1972. *Ann. Rev. Plant Physiol.* 23:437–64
175. Zelitch, I. 1971. *Photosynthesis, Photorespiration and Plant Productivity.* New York, London: Academic
176. Zelitch, I. 1973. *Proc. Natl. Acad. Sci. USA* 70:579–84
177. Zelitch, I. 1973. *Plant Physiol.* 51:299–305
178. Zelitch, I. 1975. *Science* 188:626–33
179. Zelitch, I., Day, P. R. 1973. *Plant Physiol.* 52:33–37

Ann. Rev. Plant Physiol. 1978. 29:239–62

ORGANOGENESIS AT THE SHOOT APEX

❖7651

Walter Halperin

Botany Department, University of Washington, Seattle, Washington 98195

CONTENTS

INTRODUCTION

Three aspects of organ initiation at the shoot apex traditionally have been the subject of investigation. One, what determines the site of organ initiation relative to the reference points provided by preexisting organs? Two, what are the cytological and biochemical events which occur uniquely in the initiating cells so that they, and not the surrounding cells, are stimulated to produce organs? Three, are the new organs determined from the outset as a particular kind of organ or are they temporarily undetermined? A final subject of interest lies in the problem of reversibility of apical meristem function. Are shoot and root meristems interconvertible? Earlier reviews which have dealt with these questions will be cited where appropriate throughout the discussion. The emphasis here is on the vegetative apex. References to work on the structure and physiology of floral apices are included only insofar as they shed light on general problems of organogenesis at the shoot apex.

WHAT DETERMINES THE SITE OF LATERAL ORGAN INITIATION?

In rare cases, apparent lateral organs are actually the product of stem apex dichotomies in which one of the two daughter apices takes on some new function (79).

239

0066-4294/78/0601-0239$01.00

Dichotomous branching of the angiosperm apex, once thought not to occur, has been documented in several species (9, 34, 106). Another variation on organ production in the shoot apex of some species involves the utilization of a large fraction or all of the apex in the initiation of organs (113). However, most organs are produced below or to the side of the parental shoot apex and cannot be interpreted as the product of a dichotomy or of terminal differentiation of the apex.

There are two general points of view about the factors which determine the site of leaf initiation at the shoot tip. One school of investigators has emphasized the apex with its youngest leaf primordia as an independent system. Site determination in this view is not dependent on substantially older leaves or existing vascular tissue. This view is the product of surgical studies begun 50 years ago by the Snows (96) and continued since by a variety of investigators, but in particular by Wardlaw and his associates [see the reviews by Cutter (23), Steeves & Sussex (100), Wardlaw (110)]. Their essential finding has been that preexisting leaf primordia close to the apex, in addition to the shoot apex itself, determine the position of future primordia. In contrast, other investigators have proposed that sites of leaf initiation at the shoot apex are substantially influenced by stimuli emanating from relatively mature organs or vascular tissue below the apex, the classical case being the theory that leaf-initiating stimuli are propagated helically in an acropetal direction to induce organ formation in an *anneau initiale* at the apex (85). Other investigators have proposed that leaf-initiating stimuli are transmitted along acropetally developing vascular traces which enter the shoot apex and cause leaf initiation at their apical terminus. Both of these general viewpoints are supported to a considerable extent by recent papers which provide theoretical support, in the case of the independent apex, and detailed circumstantial evidence, based on anatomical and biochemical analyses, in the case of the ascending leaf trace mechanism.

The support for an independent shoot apex (apical meristem and young primordia) comes from recent studies which constitute a veritable renaissance in the field of theoretical phyllotaxis. A number of recent papers (1, 77, 104, 107) and an entire volume by Williams (114), building mostly on the foundation provided by Richards (89), have essentially succeeded in demystifying this occult science. In fact, impressive support is provided for the idea that Fibonacci phyllotaxis is an inevitable consequence of the geometry of shoot apices, given certain reasonable assumptions. Most of the models are based on the assumption that the position of leaves on the stem can be described as circles arranged on the surface of a cylinder (1, 77, 107). A line connecting the centers of successive circles takes the form of a helix. If the cylinder is sliced vertically and opened up, one obtains a strip with an x and y axis. The distance between leaves along the y axis represents internode length and along the x axis represents the divergence or angular separation between successive leaves. If the vertical and horizontal distances are assumed to be constant, a regular lattice is obtained. The vertical distances are constant in some phyllotactic systems and in others can be made so for modeling purposes by a suitable transformation.

The model described by Thornley (104) differs from the above in that the shoot apex is treated as a flattened circular disc and primordia are assumed to arise along the circumference. A fundamental difference arises between various models in that some assume the spacing of leaf primordia to be primarily generated according to field theory (89), which postulates that primordia produce an inhibitor which diffuses out and prevents further leaves from being initiated until its concentration has decayed below some threshold level, while other models assume that contact pressures between adjacent primordia are at least equally important in the mechanism of packing. In Thornley's horizontal disc model, inhibitor diffusion is one-dimensional along the circumference, a simple device aimed at predicting the angle at which successive primordia will arise. After producing a set of oppositely spaced leaves (since the minimum concentration of inhibitor would occur opposite the arbitrarily selected first site on the perimeter), if one assumes that older primordia will be weaker sources of inhibitor, the model eventually generates a steady state divergence angle which approximates the Fibonacci angle (137.5°).

The other versions of the field theory assume isotropic diffusion of the inhibitor over the surface of a cylinder—with the inhibitor originating from point sources in the apex and primordia. These models generate different kinds of touching circle patterns depending on the values assigned to certain variables.

The model of Veen and Lindenmayer is unique with regard to biological assumptions, since it incorporates parameters dealing with cellularity (107). The surface of the cylinder takes the form of two-dimensional arrays of cells arranged in rows. The inputs to any one cell are the inhibitor concentration of that cell plus its eight nearest neighbors. Leaves (cells in which the inhibitor level is held constant at some value below threshold) are put in at predetermined locations to simulate some desired initial distribution of leaves. Growth is simulated by addition of a row of new cells at the top of the array at preset time intervals, the inhibitor concentration remaining constant in such cells until a new row is added. The previous top row is then free to begin the inhibitor decay-diffusion process. The values of the crucial variables are juggled in an attempt to obtain continuous growth of the array in such a manner that the initial leaf distribution is always reproduced. Examples of such variables are: inhibitor decay constant, inhibitor diffusion constant, threshold concentration, growth rate, apex or top row concentration, number of cells per row (width), etc. This model, according to the authors, can reproduce all of the various phyllotactic patterns encountered in plants while producing "realistic values" for plastochron interval, cell dimensions, and number of cells in the apical meristem.

Adler's model (1) differs from the above in that the spacing mechanism is assumed to be contact pressure which maximizes the minimum distance between leaf primordia. As Adler points out, this model cannot explain sites of leaf initiation at a constant divergence angle, but given such a distribution can identify the conditions under which mechanical constraints produce a normal Fibonacci phyllotaxis. Adler is of the opinion that both the field theory and a pressure contact theory are necessary elements of a complete mathematical model.

The volume by Williams (114) provides three-dimensional reconstructions of the apical morphology, phyllotaxis, axial growth, and leaf growth of over ten species. His analysis also emphasizes optimal packing based on physical or mechanical constraints which impede both the initiation of primordia and their subsequent growth. Williams is of the opinion that mechanical factors operating at the apex (pressures, tensions) are not sufficiently appreciated in current theories of phyllotaxis, whereas the field theory with its emphasis on physiological zonation and chemical gradients has been overemphasized, Williams supports this opinion by stating that permanent changes in phyllotactic systems have not been achieved through the application of growth-regulating compounds, citing Schwabe's studies (93) as an example. Schwabe, however, did have considerable success in obtaining phyllotactically altered plants of *Chrysanthemum* through the use of TIBA (triiodobenzoic acid, an inhibitor of auxin transport). The main axis of a substantial number of TIBA-treated plants was converted from a spiral leaf arrangement to one which was distichous. The lateral shoots and the inflorescence which ultimately formed retained normal spiral phyllotaxy. Schwabe states, moreover, that the TIBA effect "was neither transient nor a freak condition" since the altered phyllotaxis persisted for months. Schwabe felt that these results were consistent with a field theory. The TIBA effect, however, does not enable one to distinguish between physical and chemical mechanisms of primordial spacing, since the initial effect of the growth regulator was to change the shape of the apex. The steeper and more elongate apex subsequently led to changes in the mean divergence angle as well as in the phyllotaxis index.

More recently, Maksymowych & Erickson (71) have reported the induction of a stable phyllotactic change in *Xanthium* by gibberellin treatment. The change from a 2/3 phyllotaxis in controls to a 3/5 phyllotaxis in gibberellin-treated plants was associated with a doubling in the volume of the apex. As in the case of the TIBA-altered apex of *Chrysanthemum,* the change in apical size would cause a change in the pattern of packing. It seems quite remarkable that the changes in apex size and shape induced by these experimental treatments remained stable well after the exogenous growth regulators were gone and, presumably, the normal hormonal supply to the growing points had resumed. The stability of these altered apices seems to argue against the notion that phyllotaxis depends in any way on precisely timed and spatially oriented growth-regulating substances coming from substantially older tissue, since there is no reason to expect that the movement of such substances from unaltered older tissue would be different after the experimental treatments. It seems that exogenous hormones perturb the growth of the apex so that a new shape is established, and the shape itself rather than any alteration in the physiology or structure of older tissues is self-perpetuating.

Early discussions of the possible role of precocious leaf traces in determining the sites of leaf initiation were confused by conflicting views and inadequate information on the timing and direction of differentiation of provascular tissue. Recent studies have begun to shed light on this problem, suggesting a basic plan involving one system of acropetally differentiating large traces and another system of basipetally differentiating small traces (62, 76). The hypothesis that an acropetally developing procambial trace determines the leaf initiation site has been the product of various studies in which conventional histological analysis of shoot apices has revealed the precocious arrival of procambial tissue at or near presumptive leaf initiation sites. For example, in a study of the adventitious shoot apex of *Euphorbia esula,* Ho & Raju (53) state that the elongate cells which are produced by the periclinal divisions typical of leaf initiation are in fact "identifiable as part of the procambium" and are "continuous with" preexisting procambium in the apex, or at least this is how I interpret their discussion. Although Evans & Berg (29) were unable to recognize provascular tissue in the youngest leaf primordium of *Triticum* by virtue of cell shape, they did find cells present which had enzymatic activity typical only of vascular tissue. Esau (28) discusses a number of examples in which the development of leaf traces has been shown to precede the initiation of the primordia which they will enter.

In an elegant recent study, Larson (62) analyzed the development of the primary vascular system in *Populus deltoides* seedlings at an age when the 16th leaf from the base was 2 centimeters long. This leaf is taken as a point of reference and is designated as leaf zero in his numbering system. Leaves above that point are given successively larger negative numbers and below that point successively larger positive numbers. Leaf –14 was the last recognizable leaf primordium in most of the plants observed. Larson found, however, that acropetally developing vascular traces were already present for the next 8 leaves that would arise, i.e. leaves –15 through –22. The central trace of the three which will enter each leaf arises about 7 plastochrons in advance of the leaf that it will enter and is initiated from the vascular system of a leaf which is 13 plastochrons older. The central trace for leaf –14 had, therefore, been growing for about 2½ weeks in advance of the initiation of the leaf that it would enter. The trace was detectable in toluidine blue 0-stained microtome sections about 28 μm below the apex summit at a time when leaf –14 protruded about 38 μm above the summit. Mature phloem elements, differentiating acropetally, were present in trace –14 at this time at a point 250 μm below the primordium.

The influence of the provascular strand may extend beyond the point where it can be recognized by the staining techniques used. Therefore, Larson is of the opinion that it would be difficult to isolate surgically an apex on a pith plug which did not contain incipient vascular tissue. This fact, if true, would surely necessitate a reinterpretation of earlier surgical experiments.

Larson develops an interesting hypothesis to explain the precise pathway taken by a provascular strand as it worms its way upward so as to arrive at a precisely determined site where, according to the rules of phyllotaxy, the next leaf is to be initiated. Since it is apparent that procambial strands do not cross each other, the tangential movement of an acropetally differentiating strand is closely restricted by the older strands at each side which act to align the new developing strand. Since, according to Larson, the radial movement of the ascending strand is confined to the residual meristem left behind by the apex, the pathway followed by the leaf trace is strictly defined by the tissues through which it advances. This elaborate hypothesis is strengthened by additional data on the metabolic state of leaves connected to each other along the same orthostichy. Thus the central procambial strand that will lead to leaf –22 diverges from the trace leading to primordium –9 at a time when the leaf antecedent to –9 on the same orthostichy, namely leaf +4, has expanded to one-half full size, is anatomically mature, and has approached maximum photosynthesis per unit leaf area. Leaves of that size are exporting considerable amounts of amino and organic acids upward [see references in (62)], presumably providing the stimulus for formation of the trace which will initiate primordium –22. Further evidence for the hypothesis that precocious leaf traces are the mechanism determining a particular phyllotaxy is provided, according to Larson (63), in the fact that phyllotactic transitions at the apex from 2/5 to 3/8 to 5/13 as the seedlings age are also explainable on the basis of precocious development of the additional required traces.

Larson's analysis of phyllotaxy in cottonwood is so detailed with respect to anatomical and metabolic data which favor acropetally differentiating procambial strands as the agent of leaf initiation and the mechanism which determines phyllotaxy, that it seems to pose a considerable challenge to advocates of shoot apex autonomy. Larson (63) believes it is highly unlikely that new orders of phyllotaxy arise *independently* at the apex and in the vascular system and then later join.

A major problem arises in trying to relate Larson's findings to the data provided by other methods of study. Murashige and co-workers (94, 95) have succeeded in cultivating angiosperm apical meristems that are entirely devoid of leaf primordia. Primordia form only if certain hormones are present in the medium and only after a new root apex has been regenerated. Indoleacetic acid alone is sufficient with some species and cytokinin alone is sufficient in others. These hormones apparently can be provided normally by young leaf primordia and the first expanding leaves, since apical meristems which retain these young leaves do not require hormones. These results were obtained with herbaceous angiosperms. The studies with *Populus* implied that vascular traces coming from substantially older leaves were involved in defining the leaf initiation site as well as in providing the morphogenetically active substances. While Murashige and co-workers have tentatively identified these substances as hormones, they have not attempted to pinpoint the site of hormone delivery and relate that site to positions at which leaves develop on the apex. In the case of naked cultured shoot apices which are stimulated by hormones, one wonders if the hormones move randomly into the tissue to simulate leaf production at entirely unpredictable sites, or if they move preferentially along avenues of existing prevascular tissue and stimulate leaf production at an entirely predictable site, based on preexisting phyllotaxy. Some relevant data is available from earlier studies.

Ball (4) isolated shoot apices of *Lupinus albus* by making four longitudinal cuts that left the apex without leaf primordia and sitting on a pith plug that contained no discernible vascular tissue. Those apical meristems which regenerated leaves showed a new phyllotactic system in most cases. The new systems were unrelated to the original phyllotaxis. Some showed a reversal of the original spirality. This is consistent with the finding of others that the initial establishment of left vs right-handed spirality in embryos is not inherited but established randomly (44, 90). Once established, it apparently persists because of the influence of existing primordia or existing procambial strands or both. In any case, the behavior of Ball's *Lupinus* apices seems to indicate that it is possible to isolate apices surgically so that they must reinitiate primordia according to the same random process as the embryo. The rapid establishment of a stable direction of spirality and phyllotaxis in such systems seems to indicate a mechanism of leaf site determination based on recently formed young primordia and not on the influence of acropetally ascending precocious leaf traces from much older leaves. It would certainly be interesting if Larson's superb studies were supplemented by experiments on isolated *Populus* apices, either on a pith plug or excised and cultured.

WHAT ARE THE CYTOLOGICAL CHANGES ASSOCIATED WITH INITIATION OF LATERAL ORGANS?

The universal observation seems to be that periclinal divisions in a small group of cells located in one or more subsurface layers of the shoot apex are the first signs of leaf initiation. Protrusion of the new primordium above the surrounding surface of the apex eventually occurs at a right angle to the cross-walls formed by these highly oriented divisions. The leaf initiation site is usually described as a "growth centre," defined by Wardlaw (110) as a locus of "special metabolism." It is generally assumed that growth-stimulating metabolites accumulate at the site and are responsible for an accelerated rate of cell division (2).

A review of the literature reveals, however, that there have been few quantitative studies aimed at determining whether or not leaf initiation sites are actually regions of accelerated growth. Before examining recent studies concerning this issue, it will be useful to focus on the issue of how to define "growth" at growth centers by mentioning two diametrically opposed points of view. One view holds that the initiation of new organs is the consequence of preferential enlargement of cells in the direction of future outgrowth from the parental tissue. According to this hypothesis, altered planes of cell division which are the first signs of organ initiation are a consequence not a cause of polarized growth. There is no need, according to this view, to assume an accelerated growth rate (as mitotic cycle time, mitotic index, or rate of enlargement). An opposing point of view holds that the initiation of primordia is a direct consequence of an increased rate of cell division. The many investigators who espouse the latter view generally do not specify how oriented divisions are obtained as a consequence of an increased rate of cell division, although in one case a fairly elaborate theory was proposed (97).

The hypothesis of polarized cell enlargement as the crucial early event in organ initiation has been supported by an interesting series of studies by Foard and Haber and co-workers, in which they showed that both leaves (37) and roots (38) could be initiated under conditions in which concomitant cell divisions had been inhibited. In other words, the cells in question enlarge in a manner and direction and at a site consistent with outgrowth of a new primordium, although the usual periclinal divisions are absent. The divisions which normally characterize organ initiation show preferential orientation of mitotic spindles parallel to the axis of organ outgrowth, with new walls thus forming at right angles to that axis. An essential claim, advanced by Haber (47), is that mitotic spindles are aligned parallel to the axis of greatest *relative* extension (rate of increase in length per unit length) and not the axis of greatest absolute extension (rate of increase in length). If this is invariably the case, new cell walls which mark the sites of periclinal division at leaf initiation centers may be inferred to be at right angles to the axis of greatest relative extension, although the long axis of the cell and the axis of greatest absolute growth may well lie 90° away. This is presumably true of procambial or cambial cells where divisions frequently occur so that new walls are laid down parallel to the long axis of the cell rather than parallel to the short axis, as is more commonly seen.

A search for the intracellular machinery which relates the axis of greatest relative extension to subsequent spindle orientation has turned up a possible role for microtubules. Microtubules in cylindrical cells during interphase are generally found adjacent to the plasmalemma where they are oriented at right angles to the long axis of the cell. The cellulose microfibrils in the inner (most recently synthesized) wall layers run parallel to the microtubules. Microtubules have been postulated to play a role in orienting cellulose microfibrils and, therefore, in the control of polarized cell enlargement. The evidence is not based solely on circumstantial alignment of microtubules and microfibrils, but also on experiments in which colchicine, which disrupts microtubules, also alters the direction of cell enlargement (45). Microtubules also seem to play a role in nuclear orientation and movement (12, 13, 81–84) as well as the movement of other organelles (42, 122). The machinery which relates polarized enlargement of cells to preferred spindle orientations and, therefore, new cross-wall orientations may thus be the microtubules which seem to have overlapping functions in all these cellular phenomena. However, a great deal more work on this problem will be required before these ideas move out of the realm of pure guesswork.

Another expression of the view that cell enlargement rather than cell division is the crucial cytological event associated with induction of lateral organs has been advanced by Maksymowych & Erickson, who speculate that "the site of leaf initiation is a site of heightened wall extensibility" (71). The hypothesis of Foard and Haber has also been supported indirectly by extensive studies of Lyndon on leaf initiation. On the basis of his analysis of cell division rates (65) and spindle orientations (66) in the shoot apex of *Pisum,* Lyndon concluded that the initiation of leaf primordia results from a change in the polarity of the initiating cells, not from an accelerated growth rate. Lyndon did not find marked differences in cell division rate in leaf-initiating regions at various times throughout the plastochron. In the first part of the plastochron, only anticlinal divisions occur at the leaf initiation site. Halfway through the plastochron, conditions at the I_1 site (the next leaf to be formed) are altered so that a more random distribution of mitotic spindles occurs (69). Thirty hours before a leaf primordium emerged, 20% of the cell divisions at the leaf initiation site changed from anticlinal to periclinal. The inner layers of tissue appeared to be the main site of morphogenetic activity, with the epidermis growing only in response to pressure from beneath (68).

An earlier quantitative study consistent with the data obtained with peas is the work of Jacobs & Morrow (56) on *Coleus.* They found that a diurnal rhythm of leaf initiation in *Coleus* was not accompanied by a diurnal rhythm in mitotic index. There was an increase in the absolute number of mitotic figures in association with the initiation of leaf primordia, but since the apex was at its maximum height at that time and therefore had more cells, Jacobs & Morrow were unable to find any increase in the percentage of dividing cells. Whether or not there is a change in cell division rate with the plastochronal stage seems to vary with the species (43).

The general conclusion that a higher rate of cell division is not associated with initiation of pea leaf primordia was disputed by Hussey (55), who found a higher rate in pea apices which had been excised and were initiating leaves in culture. The increased rate of cell division occurred at least 2 plastochrons before the primordium in question bulged beyond the surface of the apex. The change in rate is three- to fourfold. Hussey cited the study of Gulline & Walker (46) in which internal pressure on the epidermis of the pea apex was not demonstrable, since gaping never occurred after a cut was made. Hussey also studied leaf initiation in cultured tomato apices (54), where he found an increased percentage of periclinal divisions as well as an increased frequency of cell division at the leaf-initiating site. The existence of pressure beneath the surface causing tension on the epidermis was apparent in tomatoes where cuts made in the apex at the time of primordium initiation immediately gaped open (54). Since Hussey found an accelerated rate of cell division in association with leaf initiation in both peas and tomatoes, but gaping occurred only in the latter, it is apparent that the presence or absence of tension on the epidermis is not a very reliable indicator of what is going on underneath as far as cell division rates are concerned. One might expect tension to be a better predictor of the orientations of cell divisions since mechanical stress has been shown to influence the plane of cell division (120). Also, Lintilhac (64) has provided a theoretical analysis of how periclinal compression in epidermal cells, due to continued anticlinal divisions and cell expansion, can put internal cells under tension and ultimately create foci where one or more cells are triggered into "divergent developmental modes."

Although there is disagreement on the cellular events that actually occur in association with leaf initiation in peas, there seems to be some agreement as to the theoretical requirements for initiation and subsequent growth. In addition to his experimental data which indicated no difference in cell division rates between leaf-initiating regions and other regions, Lyndon developed a mathematical model which apparently shows that the final form of the shoot can be the same whether leaf primordia grow faster or slower than the apical dome (69). A similar conclusion was implied by Hussey, who stated that "there seems to be no simple relation between rates of cell division and enlargement and conditions of tension or pressure" (54). This conclusion was based on the observation that the upward thrust of the primordium is associated both with higher rates of cell division during the early part of the tomato plastochron and lower rates later in the plastochron. This seems to indicate, as suggested by others, that an accelerated rate of cell division at the leaf initiation site is not essential to leaf initiation or subsequent outgrowth. In this context, it has been reported in the tree fern *Dicksonia squarrosa* that the cells involved in leaf initiation are "slightly larger and less involved in division than neighboring cells" (51).

The detection of chemical differences between leaf-initiating cells and other cells is difficult. Lyndon found that DNA, RNA, and protein content per cell were constant throughout the plastochron in each region of the apex (67). Evans & Berg (30) made a semiquantitative histochemical comparison of leaf-initiating and non-primordial cells of the shoot apex of *Triticum aestivum* and found no differences in the RNA/DNA ratio or the total nuclear protein/DNA ratio. However, the autoradiographic data did suggest a higher rate of RNA synthesis and, therefore, turnover in the leaf-initiating cells. They also found higher histone/DNA ratios in the leaf-initiating cells when an acid fast-green stain was used.

A great deal of research over the years has gone into studying the early events associated with conversion of the shoot apex from a structure which produces lateral vegetative organs to one which produces lateral or terminal floral organs. Analysis of cytological changes associated with the formation of floral organs is confounded by questions concerning the transformation of the apex itself from the vegetative to the floral state prior to the appearance of floral organs. A major point of view, either expressed or implied, in most studies is that the entire vegetative apex undergoes a qualitative biochemical change during the transition to a floral apex and that the consequence of this change is the production of qualitatively different lateral organs. The biochemical changes are presumed to be the consequence of specific flowering gene transcripts. In most species there is a burst of mitotic activity shortly after the floral stimulus has arrived, with increases in protein and RNA and changes in meristem zonation and size, all events which seem compatible with substantial qualitative chemical change. However, in some species there may be little detectable change in the apex during early formation of floral organs. In recent studies new kinds of proteins have not been detectable (103) or are present as just one or two new bands in electrophoretic analyses (92). The study of Barber & Steward (6) in which they concluded that the induction of flowering in *Tulipa* led to detectable qualitative protein changes "before the floral organs had developed" has thus far proved the exception rather than the rule. A full discussion of early changes during induction was provided by Zeevart in a recent review in this series (121) and readers are referred there for details. Some aspects of organ formation during flowering are discussed also in the following section.

DETERMINATION OF LATERAL ORGAN TYPE

Two questions in particular have often been asked about the determination of lateral organ type. One, is the entire apex involved in the switch from production of one organ type to another? Two, are the lateral organs determined irreversibly from the moment of initiation, or do they pass through a stage when their fate can be shifted from one developmental pathway to another? The first question was traditionally applied to the issue of whether or not the vegetative and floral apex were homologous (39, 43); in other words, did the latter arise as a gradual transformation of the former, or were floral organs and inflorescences to be regarded as new kinds of lateral outgrowths produced by a fundamentally unchanged vegetative apex? This kind of question also provides a conceptual framework with which to view the shift from production of one kind of vegetative organ to another. In its original form the question is too vague to be amenable to experimental attack, but another way of phrasing it would be to ask whether the entire apex undergoes chemical differentiation (for example, new kinds of proteins) when a shift in organ type occurs, or whether only those cells which are destined to become part of the organ primordia are involved.

With respect to the mechanisms underlying a shift from the vegetative to floral condition, some light has been shed on the problem by experiments showing the existence of "floral gradients." Cultured tissue from the upper internodes of a plant in flower will produce adventitious buds which are floral, while tissue from lower internodes produces progressively fewer floral buds until the lowermost internodes form only vegetative buds (16, 108). One interpretation of these gradients is that every cell near the top of the plant has registered the floral stimulus, even those internodal cells which would not normally be involved in organ formation; this interpretation implies that all cells of the shoot apex are chemically differentiated in the floral condition. Cusick showed by indirect means, using *Primula,* that the cells of the developing floral apex appear to pass through qualitatively distinct and irreversible physiological states (18). However, the possibility has not been ruled out, in the case of floral gradients, that the internode cells are unaffected by flowering conditions elsewhere in the plant but regenerate buds which are subsequently induced to flower by humoral factors still present in the vascular system or elsewhere in the isolated internode. Proof of the floral differentiation of internode cells, and presumably therefore of apical cells, requires cloning of individual cells or at least adequately subculturing internodal tissue through several passages before the buds are induced so as to rule out the presence of residual factors in the tissue (50). Chailakhyan and co-workers (15) have obtained preliminary evidence that the capacity for producing flower buds does persist through several subcultures.

The fact remains that many newly induced floral apices fail to show qualitative changes in macromolecules (121), although the apices are known by other criteria to have received the floral stimulus. Either the early stages do not involve qualitative changes in proteins or they are below the level of sensitivity of our analytical methods. If the latter is true, it is possible that the conversion from the vegetative to floral condition does not involve generalized changes throughout the apex in all species, but changes which are highly localized at organ initiation sites. This situation is difficult to envision in species where the entire shoot apex undergoes substantial anatomical change after induction, the classical case being the formation of an enormously enlarged inflorescence primordium in some Compositae (86), but it may be the case for the opposite extreme of species which produce a terminal flower but show little change in apex size or zonation during formation of the first few floral organs. Some interesting ideas along this line have emerged from studies performed on species where the floral buds appear at leaf initiation sites, as in *Pinguicula* (87) and members of the Nymphaeaceae (22). In *Nymphaea* and *Nuphar,* the leaves, vegetative buds, and floral buds are all produced at leaf sites in the genetic spiral. This led Cutter (21) to postulate the existence of two sets of factors: (*a*) phyllotactic factors that determine the site of initiation, and (*b*) organogenic factors that determine organ type. While there is little data from other angiosperms to support this concept, it may apply to ferns and has the additional merit of being a useful conceptual tool in analyzing organogenesis at the shoot apex. Moseley (78) has taken the analysis of *Nuphar* further by showing that the anatomy and zonation of the floral apex, which appears as a lateral organ at a leaf site, remain identical to that of the vegetative apex until after sepals, petals, and perhaps outer stamens are initiated. He suggests, therefore, that the production of the first two or three sets of floral organs may be responsible for inducing the changes in meristem zonation that later occur during formation of the inner stamens and carpels. He further proposes that "induction first causes a change in the kind of lateral organs initiated, and that this secondarily alters the meristem late during floral development." This view is consistent with the many studies showing that floral bracts, sepals, and petals are initiated in the tunica and show histological changes during early development which are identical to those of leaves. Further data consistent with this idea are the studies of De Vos showing that the vegetative shoot apex undergoes no change in organization during the production of the diverse kinds of leaves produced by certain heterophyllous hydrophytes (see 25 and references therein), the different leaf types being more unlike morphologically, in some cases, than leaves and floral bracts or petals.

Views such as the above are a distinct minority, however. There seems to be a majority opinion that changes in meristem structure or in histochemical features precede and are causally related to dramatic changes in morphology such as heteroblasty or heterophylly or flowering. Franck (41) found substantial differences between shoot apices of *Darlingtonia* which were producing juvenile leaves and those which were producing adult leaves. He cited other similar findings, and it was his conclusion that "it is difficult to see how the structure of the shoot apex could not be significantly involved with major changes in leaf form." Cecich and co-workers (14) were of the opinion that a decrease in histone content of the spruce shoot apex (as detected by fast green staining and microspectrophotometry), followed by increases in nuclear RNA, preceded and were probably casually related to a transition by "the whole apex" from cataphyll to needle production. Stein & Fosket (101) suggested that gibberellins which seem to be involved in regulating the changes in leaf form seen in juvenile and adult plants of *Hedera helix* may do so by influencing cell division in the apical and subapical regions of the meristem. The effect of gibberellins on cell division rates, regions of cell division, and spindle orientations in the shoot apex have received considerable study [see discussion in (32, 101)]. However, even here the picture is clouded by data showing that gibberellins may act directly on lateral organs rather than through the mediation of the apex. Feldman & Cutter (31) found that gibberellins could regulate the heteroblastic leaf series in *Centaurea* independently of effects on the complexity of the apical meristem. Entire leaves, characteristic of the juvenile stage, can be produced by apices which range widely in size and complexity under the influence of applied gibberellin. In a later paper, Feldman & Cutter (32) found that typical gibberellin effects on leaf shape could be obtained with isolated cultured leaves. For a detailed discussion of early work on heteroblastic development, readers should consult the 1965 review of Allsopp (3).

A species in which the chemical control of vegetative organ type is amenable to experimental control is *Opuntia polyacantha*. In *Opuntia,* as in other cacti, the ephemeral leaves subtend highly modified axillary buds (areoles) which produce spines rather than leaves. Mauseth & Halperin (75) found that if quiescent areole meristems are excised and cultured, they initiate the production of either spines or leaves, depending on the specific hormone used to activate the meristem. Areoles grown on a medium that is complete except for hormones remain quiescent. If the areoles are placed on a medium containing an optimal level of benzylaminopurine, a cytokinin, the meristem is activated, mitotic figures appear, and leaf primordia are visible within 3 days. Leaf production is rapid, with the plastochron being 7.3 hr for the first 21 days (73). The green leafy shoots produced from each cultured areole are identical to those that normally grow out of one or two areoles near the top of intact cactus pads on the plant each spring. Gibberellic acid also activates the meristem, but there is almost no elongation of internodes, and spines instead of leaves are produced. Spine production over a 21 day period has an average plastochron of 9.4 hr. The structure of the spine-producing meristem is very similar to the quiescent meristem, in contrast to the shoot-producing meristem which becomes quite large. There seems to be no precedent for this kind of gibberellin effect, since in other experimental systems gibberellin either completely suppresses the de novo formation of shoot meristems in callus cultures (105) or only modifies the leaf shape (27, 35, 72, 91).

It is interesting to note that gibberellic acid applied to cactus areole meristems has an exactly opposite effect to that of gibberellic acid applied to *Xanthium* shoot apices. In *Xanthium,* gibberellic acid reduces the duration of the plastochron to about half that of control apices and greatly enhances the rate of internode elongation (70, 72). In cactus areoles, gibberellic acid produces a plastochron of longer duration than is obtained in leaf-producing meristems, and the internodes between the spines scarcely elongate at all. All organs are produced de novo in the cultured cactus areole, since the quiescent meristem bears no primordia, or in rare cases a single small spine primordium. In the case of gibberellin-treated areoles, the excised meristem is in effect stimulated to produce a second set of spines, an event which would not normally occur in nature. Auxins do not activate the meristem but induce root formation from nearby trace procambium. Although spines are evolutionarily derived from leaves (8), and in other systems gibberellins are known to strongly affect leaf size and shape (72), it is apparent in the case of cactus areoles that two entirely different kinds of organs are being formed. The anatomy of leaves and spines is entirely different with no overlap in cell types. Leaves have an epidermis which bears stomates, a chlorenchymous mesophyll containing mucilage cells and a single large vascular bundle (74). Spines have thick-walled, barbed epidermal cells and an inner tissue composed of fibers. No stomates or vascular tissue are present. Although the primordia are anatomically similar at the very earliest stage when they begin to protrude from the apex, they already at that time have substantially different mitotic indices (74). Mauseth hypothesizes that the primordia are never uncommitted but are determined as to organ type from the time of initiation. This interpretation and the fact that either one of two distinctly different hormones can initially activate the meristem seem to be incompatible with the notion of temporally separate phyllotactic and organogenic sets of factors as proposed by Cutter (21). Mauseth states that the site of action of the hormones is apparently on the meristem itself and not on subjacent tissue, since an explant which consists of little more than meristem reacts in typical fashion, although growth is slower.

The interconvertibility of leaves and buds at the shoot apex of ferns is the developing system in which the control of lateral organ type has been most thoroughly explored. Wardlaw (109), working with *Dryopteris dilatata,* found that if the presumptive site of the next leaf primordium which was to form (designated as I_1) was isolated from the apical meristem by a deep adaxial cut, the developing primordium grew faster than normal and a radially symmetrical solenostelic bud was formed instead of a dorsiventral leaf. Cutter extended this work by showing that existing primordia P_1–P_3 also developed as buds if they were isolated in this fashion (19, 20). Isolation was effective only if deep cuts were made in particular locations, deep enough to sever prevascular tissue and before the formation of the lenticular apical cell of the leaf. Recently there has been criticism of the designation of tissues just below the apical initials in ferns as "prevascular tissue" (24), a criticism which presumably does not affect the interpretation of experiments dealing with existing primordia which are served by distinct procambial traces, but which may muddy the water somewhat as far as I_1 is concerned.

Later experiments carried out by Steeves (98, 99) on cultured leaf primordia of *Osmunda cinnamomea* resulted in the finding that primordia as old as P_9 could produce shoots rather than leaves. In all P_1 and some P_2 primordia, the leaf apex was thought to become directly transformed into a shoot apex, whereas in P_3–P_9 the shoot apex which appeared was initiated from leaf tissue adaxially to the leaf apex which remained unchanged. These experiments are summarized in the superb review written by Cutter in 1965 (23). Other excellent reviews of research in this area may be found in the books by Steeves & Sussex (100) and Wardlaw (110). Readers are referred there for details of early work.

Steeves concluded from these experiments that the determination of a leaf as a leaf was imposed slowly over a long period of time. A different interpretation was advanced by Cutter (23), who pointed out that the apex of most P_2 primordia and all older primordia were irreversibly determined whether or not a bud arose from leaf tissue elsewhere on the primordium. The latter view was supported by the work of Haight & Kuehnert (48), who showed through careful anatomical studies that the buds produced by isolated P_2 primordia were always adventitious, the original leaf apex remaining unchanged. The considerable body of work carried out by Kuehnert and his co-workers on the physiology of developing fern leaves led them to conclude that the fate of young primordia depended primarily on "leaf-forming" substances coming from older leaves. When a P_3 primordium was removed and cultured with other leaves, the presence of intact older leaves or even homogenates of older leaves caused twice as many P_3 primordia to develop as leaves—in comparison to controls where the accompanying leaf was another P_3 (59–61). The factor(s) which influences P_3 to develop as a leaf is found largely in the three oldest primordia of that set, where a *set* refers to the leaves initiated during that growing season, four sets being present at any one time in an *Osmunda* bud.

Jordan & Kuehnert (57) were of the opinion that a physiological interface existed between sets I and II, such that leaves of set II (formed the previous year) did not contain such factors. However, if such a physiological interface existed (in contrast to a continuum) at the time of initiation of set I, one wonders how the determination of the first few leaves would be accomplished, since there are not older leaves of that set to influence them. An additional problem lies in reconciling the hypothesis of Kuehnert and co-workers with respect to the effect of older leaves on primordia determination with the results published by Hicks & Steeves (52), who also worked on *Osmunda*. Hicks & Steeves found that excised cultured *Osmunda* apices, which were devoid of visible primordia, gave rise to leaves in all cases tested. Although early investigators failed to obtain similar results with flowering plants, in the last few years success in culturing angiosperm shoot apices devoid of primordia has been obtained with a number of different species (94, 95). Under these experimental conditions, leaf initiation and determination would seem to depend on factors within the shoot apex itself, although one cannot rule out the short-term effect of factors translocated from older tissue and persisting in the isolated apex.

Hicks & Steeves found that the first evidence of primordium initiation in isolated apices was detected at 4 days when "a small nest of cells appeared as a result of localized cell division; these cells were continuous with incipient vascular tissue of the stele." If the cultured apices were incised so that the presumptive site of I_1 was isolated by a deep cut from the shoot apex, and a mica chip inserted in the cut to prevent healing, 75% of the organs which developed at I_1 were radial and developed as shoots. If no mica chip was inserted and wound healing followed, reestablishing tissue connections between the I_1 site and the apex, 80% of the organs formed at I_1 were leaves. Hicks & Steeves concluded that it is "the shoot apex of the rhizome which imposes leaf characteristics upon I_1", a conclusion which seems at odds with the work of Kuehnert and co-workers. Bierhorst (7) has recently commented on this seeming contradiction by noting briefly that there is minor circumstantial evidence for leaf-forming factors emanating from the apex in some of the species he has studied and from "some point in the opposite direction" in other species he has studied. However, it does not seem necessary to postulate different mechanisms in different species, since the two kinds of results may not be as contradictory as they seem. The evidence seems incontrovertible that the shoot apex produces leaves in the absence of preexisting primordia, although the determinative influence of factors from older leaves, persisting in the isolated apex, has not been ruled out. These factors, if they existed, would presumably be used up as new leaves formed. Since Haight & Kuehnert found leaf-forming factors only in the oldest leaves of a set, newly formed leaves on isolated apices presumably would lack factors with which to influence subsequent primordia. All these results thus seem consistent with the idea that the *initial* determination of organ type is imposed by the apex without much influence from older organs. On the other hand, it is clear that P_1 is not irreversibly determined as a leaf (in ferns) at the moment of its inception, since determination requires the continuous presence of the shoot apex during that plastochron. This is shown by the fact that the isolation of the primordium, either by removing it and culturing it, or by destroying the tissue between it and the shoot apex, allows it to grow out as another shoot apex. This pattern of behavior is reminiscent of the concept of "overtopping," a theory which proposes that megaphyllous leaves evolved from an unequal dichotomy in which the main member forces a lateral and subordinate pattern of growth on the smaller member (40). With the isolation of the lateral member from the main shoot apex, it reasserts its capacity for radial, indeterminate growth. Haight & Kuehnert (49) concluded that an *Osmunda* leaf goes through three phases. In the first phase the primordium is completely undetermined and when isolated will become transformed into a bud 100% of the time. Phase I lasts until some time shortly before the next primordium is initiated. In phase II, the leaf apex is determined irreversibly as a leaf, but adjacent tissue can produce adventitious buds. The leaves pass out of Phase II when they are P_9 primordia and in Phase III are incapable of producing buds.

The conversion of leaves to buds has in general not been successfully demonstrated in flowering plants, although radially symmetric, rather than dorsiventral, determinate organs have on occasion been obtained [see discussion in (100)]. The reverse transformation—conversion of a bud apex into a determinate leaf—has been reported on at least one occasion. According to Imaichi & Nishida (55a), if a leaf of the fern *Hypolepis punctata* is excised before it reaches a length of 10 mm, the bud at the leaf base is converted to a leaf.

INTERCONVERTIBILITY OF SHOOT AND ROOT APICAL MERISTEMS

Analysis of the factors involved in determination of apical meristems as roots or shoots is complicated by the fact that we know little about how root tips and shoot tips differ from each other biochemically. Mature apical meristems of roots and shoots differ from each other in anatomical features such as tissue zonation, which is indicative of different arrangement of initials and cell lineages, as well as in mitotic cycle dynamics, but the formative stages of the two kinds of meristems may be indistinguishable (11). The question has been asked: Can newly formed meristems exist in an undermined state, neither root nor shoot, or perhaps in an intermediate state partaking of the characteristics of both root and shoot? Direct evidence for undetermined meristems has not been obtained with seed plants, although they have been postulated on the basis of indirect evidence (10). In *Selaginella,* however, the angle meristems which form at each major dichotomous branching of the stem seem to be remarkably plastic, existing in a demonstrably undetermined state until age and position (ventral or dorsal) sets them off on a particular developmental pathway, either as a root (also called a rhizophore in older literature) or a shoot. The rhizophore, a leafless, green, cylindrical, positively geotropic organ, was so named by early students of *Selaginella* morphology who thought this organ to be neither root nor shoot, but rather an intermediate structure which ultimately produced roots at an endogenous site behind its apical meristem.

Williams discovered in 1937 (115) that if shoot pieces containing angle meristems were excised and cultured in the absence of exogenous hormone treatment, the angle meristems developed as shoots instead of rhizophores. However, if auxin paste was applied to the cut ends of the two branches formed by a dichotomy, the angle meristems behind the fork always developed normally; that is, as rhizophores. Later workers confirmed and extended the concept of auxin as the controlling factor in determining organ type in this plant, but rejected the rhizophore concept.

Webster & Steeves (112) studied the details of rootcap development, which occurs quite late in *S. martensii,* and concluded that root development on the rhizophore is not endogenous and that the young rhizophore is no more than a root without rootcap. Wochock & Sussex (117) found that rhizophores, like the unambiguous roots of other plants, showed greater auxin transport in the acropetal than basipetal direction (2:1), indicating their basically root-like physiology as well as anatomy. Webster (111) found that the developmental fate of excised angle meristems was a function not only of exogenous auxin treatment but also of the age and position of the angle meristems at the time of excision. In young segments which received no auxin treatment, the ventral angle meristem developed into a shoot first and was followed later by the development of the dorsal meristem which became a root. If the ventral angle meristem was destroyed, the dorsal angle meristem became a shoot. In older segments, both angle meristems developed simultaneously into shoots. If the distal ends of stem segments were treated with auxin, most segments developed ventral roots regardless of age. Webster postulated that the production and transport of auxin backward from the shoot apices of intact plants normally causes both angle meristems, dorsal and ventral, to develop as roots. In decapitated plants, the ventral angle meristem develops as a shoot because of its low auxin status, but becomes in turn an auxin exporter which converts the dorsal angle meristem into a root.

Wochok & Sussex (116) carried this line of investigation to its logical conclusion by studying the vascular anatomy and pattern of IAA transport in *S. wildenovii* to determine whether the patterns of auxin movement in stem and branch junctions could account for the observed determinations of meristem type in intact plants. In *S. wildenovii* the ventral angle meristem begins growth at about three branches back from the shoot tip and grows out as a root. About five to six branches back, the dorsal angle meristem grows out as a shoot. Analysis of the vascular system showed that the single vascular strand from the weaker, determinate branch (formed at each unequal dichotomous branching of the main axis) splits in two and one of its strands fuses with the upper of three vascular strands comprising the vascular system of the main indeterminate shoot axis. The second half of the strand from the determinate branch fuses with the median strand of the main axis. The third and lower strand of the main axis has no direct connection with the determinate branch. The single vascular strands coming from the angle meristems fuse with the main axis vascular system to make a solid plate of vascular tissue just ahead (nearer to the shoot apex) of the junction of the determinate axis and main axis. Wochok & Sussex speculate that a high level of auxin near the shoot tip prevents further growth of the angle meristems once they are formed. Growth recommences only after the shoot tip is far enough away so that two more dichotomies have formed. At this time the ventral angle meristem grows out. The ventral angle meristem is presumed to be the first of the two angle meristems to reach a low enough auxin level to permit its growth because it is not directly connected to the two upper strands which accept auxin from the determinate branch (which becomes a frond). The ventral angle meristem grows out as a root rather than shoot, according to this interpretation, because the auxin level is still relatively high. As the dorsal angle meristem reaches a point where it is five or six branches from the apex, it grows out as a shoot because of the relatively low auxin levels which prevail at that point. One problem with this interpretation is that it implies at least two different thresholds below which auxin is no longer inhibitory to growth. The ventral angle meristem is activated at an auxin level low enough to release it from auxin inhibition of growth, but high enough to determine the newly growing apex as a root. Why is the dorsal angle meristem not released from inhibition at a corresponding auxin level and therefore similarly determined as to organ type? Presumably one needs to invoke the presence and significance of other determining substances, perhaps cytokinins. Wochok & Sussex (116) state that their interpretation which calls for determination of roots at high auxin concentrations and of shoots at low auxin concentrations is "a situation opposite to that found in most higher plants," a statement which presumably refers to intact plants where shoots normally contain higher auxin levels than roots. In fact, other workers using tissue culture systems involving higher plants have frequently postulated that auxin levels, endogenous or exogenous, affect the determination of organs exactly as in *Selaginella* (10, 26, 102).

Although a role for endogeneous cytokinins is postulated in many organ-forming experimental systems (58, 94a), in others no role for cytokinins can be found. In their study of adventitious organ formation in cultured *Convolvulus* root segments, Bonnett & Torrey (10) interpreted their data to mean that auxin caused the initiation of large numbers of indeterminate primordia, with subsequent high auxin levels determining them as roots and low levels determining them as buds. The use of exogenous cytokinins eliminated root development, as expected, but had no effect on the number of buds which formed. The effects of auxin in this system are not fundamentally different from those proposed for the *Selaginella* system.

Further interesting studies bearing on the role of auxin in meristem determination in *Selaginella* were obtained with TIBA, an inhibitor of auxin transport. TIBA applied in a lanolin paste behind the shoot tip of intact plants caused both angle meristems at the adjacent node to simultaneously produce shoots. TIBA thus caused the ventral meristem to develop as a shoot rather than a root, and also apparently stimulated precocious outgrowth of the dorsal meristem (118). Precocious development of the dorsal angle meristem was marked if TIBA was applied to the base of the developing determinate branch as well as the subapical region of the shoot tip. These results, and other experiments using cultured dorsal angle meristems to pinpoint the exact time of determination (118), provide convincing evidence for the role of auxin in meristem growth and determination. A unique aspect of this developmental system is the apparent ability of root tips to become redetermined as shoot tips (119). Twenty percent of the root tips grown in media lacking an auxin were transformed into shoot tips. Auxin is apparently required to maintain the roots as roots. Many examples of bud formation in roots are known (88), but all these are cases where the buds are initiated de novo as lateral organs. In the case of *Selaginella,* Wochok & Sussex interpret their histological preparations to mean that the root apex was directly transformed to a shoot apex. This is an extremely interesting observation in view of the earlier studies by Cusick (17), which led to the conclusion that "the angle meristem is basically an embryonic shoot and that rhizophore formation involves a secondary change of growth pattern." This opinion was based on surgical studies which seemed to indicate that the growth centers for shoot prophylls are present even in dormant ventral angle meristems which normally give rise subsequently to rhizophores (either due to application of IAA to excised segments or due to growth regulator movement in intact plants). This interesting hypothesis by Cusick does not seem to have received a great deal of attention from later workers, but is perhaps compatible with the notion that the rhizophore concept (as opposed to the root concept) is not entirely inappropriate.

Other examples of apparent redetermination of root apices as shoot apices in ferns have turned out to be more properly interpreted as the initiation of lateral buds from recent derivatives of the root apical cell or cells (80). A possible exception in angiosperms may be the redetermination of axillary roots into shoots in *Nasturtium officinale.* According to Ballade (5), this occurs when kinetin is applied to isolated nodes bearing roots less than 0.4 mm in length. Older roots are unaffected. Unfortunately, no histological analysis was made of this interesting phenomenon.

There is an intriguing resemblance between the control by auxin of shoot-rhizophore dimorphism in *Selaginella* and the control of shoot-rhizome dimorphism in *Cordyline terminalis,* a woody monocotyledon (33, 36). In *Cordyline,* axillary buds are subjected to strong apical dominance in vertical stems, a dominance attributed to the inhibitory effects of high auxin levels. In horizontally placed stems, the single axillary buds are released, buds on the upper side growing out into leafy shoots and buds on the lower side developing into rhizomes, despite the fact that they may be initiated several meters above the ground (33). Studies of auxin transport revealed that in horizontal stems up to seven times as much auxin accumulated in the lower surface as in the upper surface (36). In girdled plants which had been decapitated and treated with tritiated IAA in lanolin, auxin levels above the girdle were ten times higher than in controls. Buds released above the girdle develop as rhizomes, whereas those released below the girdle develop as leafy shoots. The results of a variety of experiments involving removal of organs, girdling, reorienting stems with respect to gravity, and use of growth regulators were consistent with the hypothesis that an apex is determined as a positively geotropic rhizome only under relatively high auxin levels. The determination is reversible, since anything which lowers the auxin level caused a direct transformation of the rhizome apex into a negatively geotropic leafy shoot. With respect to the effect of auxin on geotropic sensitivity and the instability of the erect shoot-like vs rhizophore–rhizome-like growth habit, the resemblance between patterns of growth in *Cordyline* and *Selaginella* are strong.

CONCLUDING REMARKS

The literature dealing with mechanisms of phyllotaxis oscillates between the two extreme points of view of upstairs vs downstairs; i.e. an independent apex vs an apex dependent on substantially older tissue for phyllotactic direction. Both views are impressively supported by recent studies which, unfortunately, depend on entirely different approaches, one theoretical and the other developmental-descriptive. The development of a technique for culturing naked (leafless) angiosperm shoot apices might provide the necessary experimental system which could disprove one or the other hypothesis, but it has not yet been exploited with that end in mind. Perhaps Larson (63) will prove to have been too skeptical in ruling out simultaneous operation of both phyllotactic mechanisms (leaf-producing and vein-producing). Naked, cultured apices are able to produce leaves, *presumably* in a reproducible phyllotactic pattern which is not imposed from below by ascending leaf traces (however, the role of subtle clues from persistent prevascular tissue in such apices requires careful investigation). As the new leaves grow and expand, perhaps there is a subtle coupling of two mechanisms so that leaves are always produced at the right time and place to be served by traces developing in an acropetal direction. Surely other equally complex and exactly timed coordinating mechanisms have evolved in nature. However, one piece of evidence that may tip the argument in favor of Larson's view that ascending traces determine leaf initiation sites is the fact that changes in phyllotaxy as plants age are seen in the vascular system days or weeks in advance of such changes in the apex.

With respect to the cytological events that characterize initiation of lateral organs, it appears that the term "growth centre" (110) may be misleading. Accelerated growth may not be characteristic of organ initiation sites in all species, whereas there is universal agreement that a change in the *polarity* of growth is always characteristic of such sites. Altered polarity is seen in the change in preferred direction of mitotic spindles, a change which may in turn depend on an altered direction in such cells of the axis of greatest relative extension. Instead of thinking of organ initiation sites as regions where growth-promoting substances accumulate, it might be more fruitful in the near future to consider such areas as regions where physical parameters are altered in such a way as to shift the direction of cell enlargement. Right or wrong, an approach along these lines may well be more amenable to experimental attack than one that requires localization of incredibly minute amounts of hormones and metabolites which may not, in fact, be more characteristic of that region than other regions of the apex.

Literature Cited

1. Adler, I. 1974. A model of contact pressure in phyllotaxis. *J. Theor. Biol.* 45:1–79
2. Allsopp, A. 1964. Shoot morphogenesis. *Ann. Rev. Plant Physiol.* 15:225–54
3. Allsopp, A. 1965. Heteroblastic development in cormophytes. In *Handbuch der pflanzenphysiologie*, ed. A. Lang, pp. 1172–1221. Berlin: Springer
4. Ball, E. 1952. Morphogenesis of shoots after isolation of the shoot apex of *Lupinus albus. Am. J. Bot.* 39:167–91
5. Ballade, P. 1970. Precisions nouvelles sur la caulogenèse apical des racines axillaires du cresson. *Planta* 92:138–45
6. Barber, J. T., Steward, F. C. 1968. The proteins of *Tulipa* and their relation to morphogenesis. *Dev. Biol.* 17:326–49

7. Bierhorst, D. W. 1977. On the stem apex, leaf initiation and early leaf ontogeny in filicalean ferns. *Am. J. Bot.* 64:125–52
8. Boke, N. H. 1944. Histogenesis of the leaf and areole in *Opuntia cylindrica. Am J. Bot.* 31:229–316
9. Boke, N. H. 1976. Dichotomous branching in *Mammillaria* (Cactaceae). *Am. J. Bot.* 63:1380–84
10. Bonnett, H. T. Jr., Torrey, J. G. 1965. Chemical control of organ formation in root segments of *Convolvulus* cultured in vitro. *Plant Physiol.* 40:1228–36
11. Bonnett, H. T. Jr., Torrey, J. G. 1966. Comparative anatomy of endogeneous bud and lateral root formation in *Con-*

volvulus arvensis roots cultured in vitro. *Am. J. Bot.* 53:496–507

12. Burgess, J. 1970. Microtubules and cell division in the microspore of *Dactylorchis fuschii. Protoplasma* 69:253–64

13. Burgess, J. 1970. Interactions between microtubules and the nuclear envelope during mitosis in a fern. *Protoplasma* 71:77–89

14. Cecich, R. A., Lersten, N. R., Miksche, J. P. 1972. A cytophotometric study of nucleic acids and proteins in the shoot apex of white spruce. *Am. J. Bot.* 59:442–49

15. Chailakhyan, M. K., Aksenova, N. P., Konstantinova, T. N., Bavrina, T. V. 1975. The callus model of plant flowering. *Proc. R. Soc. London* 190:333–40

16. Chouard, P., Aghion, P. 1961. Modalités de la formation de bourgeons floraux sur des cultures de ségments de tige de tabac. *C. R. Acad. Sci.* 252:3864–66

17. Cusick, F. 1954. Experimental and analytical studies of pteridophytes. XXV. Morphogenesis in *Selaginella willdenovii* Baker. II. Angle meristems and angle-shoots. *Ann. Bot.* 18:171–81

18. Cusick, F. 1956. Studies of floral morphogenesis. I. Median bisections of flower primordia in *Primula bulleyana* Forrest. *Trans. R. Soc. Edinburgh* 63:153–66

19. Cutter, E. G. 1954. Experimental induction of buds from fern leaf primordia. *Nature* 173:440–41

20. Cutter, E. G. 1956. Experimental and analytical studies of pteridophytes. XXXIII. The experimental induction of buds from leaf primordia in *Dryopteris aristata* Druce. *Ann. Bot. N.S.* 20:143–65

21. Cutter, E. G. 1957. Studies of morphogenesis in the Nymphaeaceae. I - Introduction: Some aspects of the morphology of *Nuphar lutea* (L.) SM. and *Nymphaea alba* L. *Phytomorphology* 7:45–56

22. Cutter, E. G. 1958. Studies of morphogenesis in the Nymphaeaceae III. Surgical experiments on leaf and bud formation. *Phytomorphology* 8:74–95

23. Cutter, E. G. 1965. Recent experimental studies of the shoot apex and shoot morphogenesis. *Bot. Rev.* 31:7–113

24. De Albertis, J., Paolillo, D. J. 1972. The concept of incipient vascular in fern apices. *Am. J. Bot.* 59:78–82

25. De Vos, O. C. 1974. The anatomy of the shoot apex of *Rotala rotundifolia* (Roxb.) Koehne (Lythraceae). 1974. *Acta Bot. Neerl.* 23:7–18

26. Dore, J., Williams, W. T. 1956. Studies in the regeneration of horseradish. II. Correlation phenomena. *Ann. Bot.* 20:231–49

27. Engelke, A. L., Hamzi, H. Q., Skoog, F. 1973. Cytokinin-gibberellin regulation of shoot development and leaf form in tobacco plantlets. *Am. J. Bot.* 60:491–95

28. Esau, K. 1965. *Vascular Differentiation in Plants.* New York: Holt, Rinehart & Winston. 160 pp.

29. Evans, L. S., Berg, A. R. 1972. Qualitative histochemistry of the shoot apex of *Triticum. Can. J. Bot.* 50:241–44

30. Evans, L. S., Berg, A. R. 1972. Early histogenesis and semiquantitative histochemistry of leaf initiation in *Triticum aestivum. Am. J. Bot.* 59:973–80

31. Feldman, L. J., Cutter, E. G. 1970. Regulation of leaf form in *Centaurea solstitialis* L. I. Leaf development on whole plants in sterile culture. *Bot. Gaz.* 131:31–39

32. Feldman, L. J., Cutter, E. G. 1970. Regulation of leaf form in *Centaurea solstitialis* L. II. The developmental potentialities of excised leaf primordia in sterile culture. *Bot. Gaz.* 131:39–49

33. Fisher, J. B. 1972. Control of shoot-rhizome dimorphism in the woody monocotyledon, *Cordyline* (Agavaceae). *Am. J. Bot.* 59:1000–10

34. Fisher, J. B. 1974. Axillary and dichotomous branching in the palm *Chamaedorea. Am. J. Bot.* 61:1046–56

35. Fisher, J. B. 1976. Induction of juvenile leaf form in a palm (*Caryota mitis*) by gibberellin. *Bull. Torrey Bot. Club* 103:153–57

36. Fisher, J. B., Burg, S. P., Kang, B. G. 1974. Relationship of auxin transport to branch dimorphism in *Cordyline,* a woody monocotyledon. *Physiol. Plant.* 31:284–87

37. Foard, D. E. 1971. The initial protrusion of a leaf primordium can form without concurrent periclinal cell divisions. *Can. J. Bot.* 49:1601–3

38. Foard, D. E., Haber, A. H., Fishman, T. N. 1965. Initiation of lateral root primordia without completion of mitosis and without cytokinesis in uniseriate pericycle. *Am. J. Bot.* 52:580–90

39. Foster, A. S. 1939. Problems of structure, growth and evolution in the shoot apex of seed plants. *Bot. Rev.* 5:454–70

40. Foster, A. S., Gifford, E. M. 1974. *Com-*

parative Morphology of Vascular Plants. San Francisco: Freeman. 751 pp.

41. Franck, D. H. 1976. Comparative morphology and early leaf histogenesis of adult and juvenile leaves of *Darlingtonia californica* and their bearing on the concept of heterophylly. *Bot. Gaz.* 137:20–34

42. Freed, J. J., Lebowitz, M. M. 1970. The association of a class of saltatory movements with microtubules in cultured cells. *J. Cell. Biol.* 45:334–54

43. Gifford, E. M. Jr., Corson, G. E. Jr. 1971. The shoot apex in seed plants. *Bot. Rev.* 37:143–229

44. Gómez-Campo, C. 1970. The direction of the phyllotactic helix in axillary shoots of six plant species. *Bot. Gaz.* 131:110–15

45. Green, P. B. 1969. Cell morphogenesis. *Ann. Rev. Plant Physiol.* 20:365–94

46. Gulline, H. F., Walker, R. 1957. The regeneration of severed pea apices. *Aust. J. Bot.* 5:129–36

47. Haber, A. H. 1962. Nonessentiality of concurrent cell division for degree of polarization of leaf growth. I. Studies with radiation-induced mitotic inhibition. *Am. J. Bot.* 49:583–89

48. Haight, T. H., Kuehnert, C. C. 1969. Developmental potentialities of leaf primordia of *Osmunda cinnamomea* V. Toward greater understanding of the final morphogenetic expression of isolated set I cinnamon fern leaf primordia. *Can. J. Bot.* 47:481–88

49. Haight, T. H., Kuehnert, C. C. 1971. Developmental potentialities of leaf primordia of *Osmunda cinnamomea* VI. The expression of P_1. *Can. J. Bot.* 49:1941–45

50. Halperin, W. 1969. Morphogenesis in cell cultures. *Ann. Rev. Plant Physiol.* 20:395–418

51. Hebant-Mauri, R. 1975. Apical segmentation and leaf initiation in the tree fern *Dicksonia squarrosa. Can. J. Bot.* 53:764–72

52. Hicks, G. S., Steeves, T. A. 1969. In vitro morphogenesis in *Osmunda cinnamomea.* The role of the shoot apex in early leaf development. *Can. J. Bot.* 47:575–80

53. Ho, T. W. M., Raju, M. V. S. 1972. Developmental studies on leafy spurge (*Euphorbia esula*): Histology of the adventitious shoot apex. *Can. J. Bot.* 50:635–41

54. Hussey, G. 1971. Cell division and expansion and resultant tissue tensions in the shoot apex during the formation of

a leaf primordium in the tomato. *J. Exp. Bot.* 22:702–14

55. Hussey, G. 1972. The mode of origin of a leaf primordium in the shoot apex of the pea (*Pisum sativum*). *J. Exp. Bot.* 23:675–82

55a. Imaichi, R., Nishida, M. 1973. Studies on the extra-axillary buds of *Hypolepis punctata:* 1. External morphology and anatomy. *J. Jpn. Bot.* 48:268–80 (original in Japanese; see *Bioabstracts* 60 (8): 44281, 1975)

56. Jacobs, W. P., Morrow, I. B. 1961. A quantitative study of mitotic figures in relation to development in the apical meristem of vegetative shoots of *Coleus. Dev. Biol.* 3:569–87

57. Jordan, E. H., Kuehnert, C. C. 1976. The bud of *Osmunda cinnamomea* L. II. A physiological interface between set I and set II leaf primordia. *Bot. Gaz.* 137:52–57

58. Kefford, N. P., Caso, O. H. 1972. Organ regeneration on excised roots of *Chondrilla juncea* and its chemical regulation. *Aust. J. Biol. Sci.* 25:691–706

59. Kuehnert, C. C. 1967. Developmental potentialities of leaf primordia of *Osmunda cinnamomea* L. The influence of determined leaf primordia. *Can. J. Bot.* 45:2109–13

60. Kuehnert, C. C. 1969. Developmental potentialities of leaf primordia of *Osmunda cinnamomea* II. Further studies on the influence of determined leaf primordia on undetermined leaf primordia. *Can. J. Bot.* 47:59–63

61. Kuehnert, C. C. 1969. Developmental potentialities of leaf primordia of *Osmunda cinnamomea.* III. Studies of the expression of homogenized, determined leaf primordia on expression-potential of undetermined leaf primordia. *Can. J. Bot.* 47:65–68

62. Larson, P. R. 1975. Development and organization of the primary vascular system in *Populus deltoides* according to phyllotaxy. *Am. J. Bot.* 62:1084–99

63. Larson, P. R. 1977. Phyllotactic transitions in the vascular system of *Populus deltoides* Bartr. as determined by ^{14}C labeling. *Planta* 134:241–49

64. Lintilhac, P. M. 1974. Differentiation, organogenesis, and the tectonics of cell wall orientation. III. Theoretical considerations of cell wall mechanics. *Am. J. Bot.* 61:230–37

65. Lyndon, R. F. 1970. Rates of cell division in the shoot apical meristem of *Pisum. Ann. Bot.* 34:1–17

66. Lyndon, R. F. 1970. Planes of cell division and growth in the shoot apex of *Pisum*. *Ann. Bot.* 34:19–28
67. Lyndon, R. F. 1970. DNA, RNA and protein in the pea shoot apex in relation to leaf initiation. *J. Exp. Bot.* 21:286–91
68. Lyndon, R. F. 1971. Growth of the surface and inner parts of the pea shoot apical meristem during leaf initiation. *Ann. Bot.* 35:263–70
69. Lyndon, R. F. 1972. Leaf formation and growth at the shoot apical meristem. *Physiol. Vég.* 10:209–22
70. Maksymowych, R., Cordero, R. E., Erickson, R. O. 1976. Long-term developmental changes in *Xanthium* induced by gibberellic acid. *Am. J. Bot.* 63:1047–53
71. Maksymowych, R., Erickson, R. O. 1977. Phyllotactic change induced by gibberellic acid in *Xanthium* shoot apices. *Am. J. Bot.* 64:33–44
72. Maksymowych, R., Maksymowych, A. B. 1973. Induction of morphogenetic changes and acceleration of leaf initiation by gibberellic acid in *Xanthium pennsylvanicum*. *Am. J. Bot.* 60:901–6
73. Mauseth, J. D. 1976. Cytokinin and gibberellic acid-induced effects on the structure and metabolism of shoot apical meristems in *Opuntia polyacantha* (Cactaceae). *Am. J. Bot.* 63:1295–1301
74. Mauseth, J. D. 1977. Cytokinin and gibberellic acid-induced effects on the determination and morphogenesis of leaf primordia in *Opuntia polyacantha* (Cactaceae). *Am. J. Bot.* 64:337–46
75. Mauseth, J. D., Halperin, W. 1975. Hormonal control of organogenesis in *Opuntia polyacantha* (Cactaceae). *Am. J. Bot.* 62:869–77
76. Maze, J. 1977. The vascular system of the inflorescence axis of *Andropogon gerardii* (Gramineae) and its bearing on concepts of monocotyledon vascular tissue. *Am. J. Bot.* 64:504–15
77. Mitchison, G. J. 1977. Phyllotaxis and the Fibonacci series. *Science* 196:270–75
78. Mosely, M. F. Jr. 1971. Morphological studies of Nymphaeaceae. VI. Development of flower of *Nuphar*. *Phytomorphology* 21:253–83
79. Nolan, J. R. 1969. Bifurcation of the stem apex in *Asclepias syriaca*. *Am. J. Bot.* 56:603–09
80. Peterson, R. L. 1970. Bud development at the root apex of *Ophioglossum petiolatum*. *Phytomorphology* 20:183–90
81. Pickett-Heaps, J. D. 1969. Preprophase microtubules and stomatal differentia-

tion; some effects of centrifugation on symmetrical and asymmetrical cell division. *J. Ultrastruct. Res.* 27:24–44
82. Pickett-Heaps, J. D. 1972. Cell division in *Cosmarium botrytis*. *J. Phycol.* 8:343–60
83. Pickett-Heaps, J. D., Fowke, L. C. 1970. Mitosis, cytokinesis and cell elongation in the desmid *Closterium littorale*. *J. Phycol.* 6:189–215
84. Pickett-Heaps, J. D., Northcote, D. H. 1966. Organization of microtubules and endoplasmic reticulum during mitosis and cytokinesis in wheat meristems. *J. Cell Sci.* 1:109–20
85. Plantefol, L. 1949. A new theory of phyllotaxis. *Nature* 163:331–32
86. Popham, R. A., Chan, A. P. 1952. Origin and development of the receptacle of *Chrysanthemum morifolium*. *Am. J. Bot.* 39:329–39
87. Raju, M. V. S. 1969. Development of floral organs in the sites of leaf primordia in *Pinguicula vulgaris*. *Am. J. Bot.* 56:507–14
88. Raju, M. V. S., Coupland, R. T., Steeves, T. A. 1966. On the occurence of root buds on perennial plants in Saskatchewan. *Can. J. Bot.* 44:33–37
89. Richards, F. J. 1951. Phyllotaxis: its quantitative expression and relation to growth in the apex. *Philos. Trans. R. Soc. London* 235:509–64
90. Rijven, A. H. G. C. 1968. Randomness in the genesis of phyllotaxis. I. The initiation of the first leaf in some Trifolieae. *New Phytol.* 67:247–56
91. Robbins, W. J. 1957. Gibberellic acid and the reversal of adult *Hedera* to a juvenile state. *Am. J. Bot.* 44:743–46
92. Sawhney, S., Sawhney, N., Nanda, K. K. 1976. Gel electrophoretic studies of proteins in photo-induced and vegetative plants of *Impatiens balsamina*. *Plant Cell Physiol.* 17:751–55
93. Schwabe, W. 1971. Chemical modifications of phyllotaxis and its implications. In *Control Mechanisms of Growth and Differentiation*, ed. D. D. Davies, M. Balls, pp. 301–22. New York: Academic. 498 pp.
94. Shabde, M., Murashige, T. 1977. Hormonal requirements of excised *Dianthus caryophyllus* L. shoot apical meristem in vitro. *Am. J. Bot.* 64:443–48
94a. Skoog, F., Miller, C. O. 1957. Chemical regulation of growth and organ formation in plant tissues cultured in vitro. In *The Biological Action of Growth Substances*, ed. H. K. Porter, pp. 118–31. New York: Academic. 344 pp.

95. Smith, R. H., Murashige, T. 1970. In vitro development of isolated shoot apical meristems of angiosperms. *Am. J. Bot.* 57:562–68

96. Snow, M., Snow, R. 1931. Experiments on phyllotaxis. I. The effect of isolating a primordium. *Philos. Trans. R. Soc. London* 221:1–43

97. Stebbins, G. L. 1967. Gene action, mitotic frequency and morphogenesis in higher plants. In *Control Mechanisms in Developmental Processes*, ed. M. Locke, pp. 113–35. New York: Academic. 302 pp.

98. Steeves, T. A. 1961. A study of the developmental potentialities of excised leaf primordia in sterile culture. *Phytomorphology* 11:346–59

99. Steeves, T. A. 1962. Morphogenesis in isolated fern leaves. In *Regeneration*, 20th Growth Symp., ed. D. Rudnick, pp. 117–51. New York: Ronald

100. Steeves, T. A., Sussex, I. M. 1972. *Patterns in Plant Development*. Englewood Cliffs: Prentice-Hall. 302 pp.

101. Stein, O. L., Fosket, E. B. 1969. Comparative developmental anatomy of shoots of juvenile and adult *Hedera helix. Am. J. Bot.* 56:546–51

102. Stichel, E. 1959. Gleichzeitige induktion von sprossen und wurzeln an in vitro kultivierten gewebestücken von *Cyclamen persicum. Planta* 53:293–317

103. Stiles, J. I., Davies, P. J. 1976. Qualitative analysis by isoelectric focusing of the protein content of *Pharbitis nil* apices and cotyledons during floral induction. *Plant Cell Physiol.* 17:855–57

104. Thornley, J. H. M. 1975. Phyllotaxis I. A mechanistic model. *Ann. Bot.* 39:491–507

105. Thorpe, T. A., Meier, D. D. 1973. Effects of gibberellic acid and abscisic acid on shoot formation in tobacco callus cultures. *Physiol. Plant.* 29:121–24

106. Tomlinson, P. B., Posluszny, U. 1977. Apical dichotomy demonstrated in the angiosperm *Flagellaria. Science* 196:1111–12

107. Veen, A. H., Lindenmayer, A. 1977. Diffusion mechanism for phyllotaxis. Theoretical physico-chemical and computer study. *Plant Physiol.* 60:127–39

108. Wardell, W. L., Skoog, F. 1969. Flower formation in excised tobacco stem segments; I. Methodology and effects of plant hormones. *Plant Physiol.* 44:1402–6

109. Wardlaw, C. W. 1949. Experiments on organogenesis in ferns. *Growth* 13:93–131

110. Wardlaw, C. W. 1968. *Morphogenesis in Plants. A Contemporary Study*. London: Methuen. 451 pp.

111. Webster, T. R. 1969. An investigation of angle-meristem development in excised stem segments of *Selaginella martensii. Can. J. Bot.* 47:717–22

112. Webster, T. R., Steeves, T. A. 1967. Developmental morphology of the root of *Selaginella martensii* Spring. *Can. J. Bot.* 45:395–404

113. Wilder, G. J. 1976. Structure and development of leaves in *Carludovica palmata* (Cyclanthaceae) with reference to other Cyclanthaceae and Palmae. *Am. J. Bot.* 63:1237–56

114. Williams, R. F. 1975. *The Shoot Apex and Leaf Growth*. London: Cambridge Univ. Press. 256 pp.

115. Williams, S. 1937. Correlation phenomena and hormones in *Selaginella. Nature* 139:966

116. Wochok, Z. S., Sussex, I. M. 1973. Morphogenesis in *Selaginella*. Auxin transport in the stem. *Plant Physiol.* 51:646–50

117. Wochok, Z. S., Sussex, I. M. 1974. Morphogenesis in *Selaginella*. II. Auxin transport in the root (rhizophore). *Plant Physiol.* 53:738–41

118. Wochok, Z. S., Sussex, I. M. 1975. Morphogenesis in *Selaginella* III. Meristem determination and differentiation. *Dev. Biol.* 47:376–83

119. Wochok, Z. S., Sussex, I. M. 1976. Redetermination of cultured root tips to leafy shoots in *Selaginella willdenovii. Plant Sci. Lett.* 6:185–92

120. Yeoman, M. M., Brown, R. 1971. Effects of mechanical stress on the plane of cell division in developing callus cultures. *Ann. Bot.* 35:1101–12

121. Zeevaart, J. A. D. 1976. Physiology of flower formation. *Ann. Rev. Plant Physiol.* 27:321–48

122. Zeiger, E. 1971. Organelle distribution and cell differentiation in the formation of stomatal complexes in barley. *Can. J. Bot.* 49:1623–25

Ann. Rev. Plant Physiol. 1978. 29:263–76
Copyright © 1978 by Annual Reviews Inc. All rights reserved

BIOLOGICAL NITROGEN FIXATION

❖7652

K. T. Shanmugam, F. O'Gara,[1] K. Andersen, and R. C. Valentine

Plant Growth Laboratory, Department of Agronomy and Range Science, University of California, Davis, California 95616

CONTENTS

INTRODUCTION

Only bacteria and blue-green algae have evolved the capacity to fix nitrogen, a process governed by a set of genes called the nitrogen fixation (Nif) genes (57). The Nif genes have been defined in detail in the free-living bacterium *Klebsiella pneumoniae* (5, 12, 15, 28, 47, 53).

Free-living bacteria such as *Klebsiella* couple the NH_4^+ produced by nitrogenase to cellular biosynthesis and do not export any detectable NH_4^+ into the growth medium; nitrogenase is not produced by the organism if combined nitrogen (e.g. NH_4^+ or NO_3^-) is present in the environment. In contrast, the nitrogen fixation (Nif) genes of symbiotic bacteria such as *Rhizobium* spp. forming root nodules on leguminous plants are normally found to be "derepressed" (producing nitrogenase activity even in the presence of NH_4^+) leading to the synthesis and export of fixed nitrogen into the outside environment (cytoplasm of the host plant cell, in the case of *Rhizobium* spp.) (8, 56). Thus the derepression of the Nif genes resulting in the production of enormous quantities of fixed nitrogen from atmospheric nitrogen plays a crucial role in man's food chain on a global scale.

[1]Present address: Department of Microbiology, University College, Cork, Ireland.

0066-4294/78/0601-0263$01.00

There is now considerable evidence that genetic as well as biochemical mechanisms may function to integrate production of fixed nitrogen with utilization for cellular needs (for review see 47). The purpose of this review is to discuss current concepts of the regulation of nitrogen fixation in both free-living and symbiotic bacteria.

DEREPRESSION OF THE NIF GENES

Recent advances in the control and expression of Nif genes in *K. pneumoniae* will be discussed in this section with emphasis on nitrogenase-derepressed mutant strains which export large quantities of fixed nitrogen.

Ammonia produced by nitrogenase is assimilated by the bacterium to the level of glutamate by the enzymes glutamine synthetase and glutamate synthase (34). Biosynthesis of nitrogenase was found to be repressed by NH_4^+ or amino acids (40). It was difficult to distinguish the repressive effect of amino acids from that of NH_4^+ produced by the cell (by internal metabolism). This problem was eliminated by the use of mutant strains which produced nitrogenase even in the presence of NH_4^+ (nitrogenase-derepressed mutants) (48, 50). Studies with these strains showed that the repressive nature of NH_4^+ was connected to the cellular ability to convert the NH_4^+ to the level of glutamine and glutamate (49). In essence, these experiments show that nitrogenase was produced under conditions in which NH_4^+ was not assimilated into amino acids, and nitrogenase production was repressed whenever NH_4^+ was assimilated to the level of amino acids.

Three classes of nitrogenase-derepressed mutant strains were isolated and described in *K. pneumoniae,* starting with a mutant strain which lacked glutamate synthase activity (Asm⁻) as the parent (50; Table 1). Biochemical analysis of these

Table 1   Properties of nitrogen fixation (Nif) derepressed mutants of *K. pneumoniae*[a]

Strain	Nitrogenase (μmoles/hr per mg protein) $-NH_4^+$	Nitrogenase (μmoles/hr per mg protein) $+NH_4^+$	Glutamine synthetase (nanomoles/min per mg protein) $-NH_4^+$	Glutamine synthetase (nanomoles/min per mg protein) $+NH_4^+$	Glutamate dehydrogenase (nanomoles/min per mg protein) $-NH_4^+$	Glutamate dehydrogenase (nanomoles/min per mg protein) $+NH_4^+$	NH_4^+ excreted (μmoles/mg protein)
M5A1	4.04	0.00	878	229	<5	126	—
Asm–1	3.14	0.00	653	147	18	116	—
SK–24	2.80	2.42	684	866	<5	<5	92
SK–28	3.27	3.05	1006	1055	<5	<5	280
SK–29	2.82	2.01	739	627	<5	<5	220
SK–25	4.47	3.70	0	0	12	16	450
SK–26	3.82	2.91	0	0	17	18	—
SK–27	2.88	1.81	0	0	17	15	270
SK–55	2.53	1.92	6	0	20	20	230
SK–56	3.19	2.29	14	21	22	24	190

[a] From (1) and (50).

strains showed that one class of mutants produced glutamine synthetase activity but not glutamate dehydrogenase activity (e.g. strains SK-24, SK-28, and SK-29). The other class of mutants produced no detectable glutamine synthetase activity (*gln* A⁻). The second class was further divided into two groups: 1. strains that produce catalytically inactive glutamine synthetase protein (e.g. strains SK-27, SK-55, and SK-56); 2. strains with no detectable glutamine synthetase protein, determined immunologically (e.g. strains SK-25 and SK-26). The mutant strains of all three classes excreted large quantities of NH_4^+ from fixed N_2. Some of the strains excreted NH_4^+ for more than one week while being in a nondividing state (1).

A class of glutamine requiring mutants (isolated from an Asm+ strain of *K. pneumoniae*) was described by Streicher et al (58). These mutants, in contrast to the other *gln⁻* strains described before (for example, strain SK-27) failed to produce any detectable nitrogenase activity under conditions in which the parental strains as well as strain SK-27 produce nitrogenase activity. On further analysis these strains were found to produce nitrogenase activity under conditions in which the glutamine concentration in the medium (a necessary growth supplement) was depleted to very low levels (K. Andersen & K. T. Shanmugam, unpublished data).

It has been found recently that certain combinations of amino acids, such as glutamine and aspartate, completely repressed nitrogenase biosynthesis in strains derepressed for nitrogenase biosynthesis in the presence of NH_4^+ (49). Also, NH_4^+ in combination with high concentrations of glutamine completely repressed the biosynthesis of nitrogenase in the glutamine requiring strains. These strains assimilated NH_4^+ in the presence of high concentrations of glutamine (1 mg/ml). A strong correlation has been established between the repression of nitrogenase biosynthesis by NH_4^+ and subsequent assimilation of NH_4^+, presumably to the level of amino acids (49). The simplest interpretation of these results is that the overall mechanism of regulation of nitrogenase biosynthesis involves the conversion of NH_4^+ to the level of amino acids.

The type of control system described above for nitrogenase biosynthesis in *Klebsiella* appears to operate in other free-living N_2–fixing organisms as well. This is borne out by the fact that nitrogenase biosynthesis is derepressed in the presence of NH_4^+ in a culture medium which contains L-methionine-D,L-sulfoximine (MSX), an inhibitor of glutamine synthetase (see Table 2).

MSX, a structural analog for glutamate (see Figure 1), was first used by Gordon & Brill (20) to study the regulation of nitrogenase production in both *K. pneumoniae* and *Azotobacter vinelandii*. These workers observed that the nitrogenase was derepressed in these organisms in the presence of MSX, and the NH_4^+ produced from N_2 by *A. vinelandii* under these conditions was excreted into the medium. Similar experiments were carried out by various investigators using a variety of organisms [*Rhodospirillum rubrum* (65), *Anabaena cylindrica* (55), *Spirillum lipoferum* (38); see Table 2]. In the presence of MSX, both *R. rubrum* and *A. cylindrica* failed to assimilate NH_4^+ produced by nitrogenase and instead excreted it into the medium. In both these organisms, MSX has been shown to inhibit glutamine synthetase activity. Since glutamine synthetase is the first enzyme in the conversion of NH_4^+ to the level of glutamate and further into cellular material, it is reasonable to assume

Table 2 Relationship between levels of NH_4^+ assimilation enzymes and nitrogenase repression or derepression (by NH_4^+) in various nitrogen-fixing organisms[a]

Organism	Repression by NH_4^+	Glutamine synthetase[b]	Glutamate synthase[c]		Glutamate dehydrogenase[c]		Derepression of N_2-ase[d]	Ref.
			NADH	NADPH	NADH	NADPH		
Klebsiella pneumoniae	100%	26%	UD	53	UD	126	–	50
Klebsiella mutants	0	100%	UD	<5	UD	<5	+	50
Klebsiella pneumoniae in presence of MSX	0	ND	ND	ND	ND	ND	+	20
Azotobacter vinelandii in presence of MSX	0	ND	ND	ND	ND	ND	+	20
Spirillum lipoferum	100%	13%	<5	52	27	<5	–	38
Spirillum lipoferum in presence of MSX	0	ND	ND	ND	ND	ND	+	38
Blue-green algae in presence of MSX	0	9%	ND	ND	ND	ND	+	55
Symbiotic blue-green algae	50%	6%	ND	ND	ND	<5	+	56
Rhodospirillum rubrum in presence of MSX	0	5%	ND	ND	ND	ND	+	65
Rhizobium trifolii (free-living, aerobic) + Glutamate		100%	18	8	18	<5		35, 36
+ Leucine		64%	6	20	6	ND		51
Rhizobium trifolii mutants (free-living N_2-ase inducing)	50–70%	13%	<5	<5	<5	ND	+	37
Bacteroids–*R. japonicum*	ND	14%	55	<5	19	<5	+	13
R. leguminosarum–Vicia faba	ND	9%	<5	12	15	<5	+	13
R. leguminosarum–Pisum sativum	ND	1%	<5	<5	33	<5	+	13

[a] UD, undetected; ND, not determined. See text for other details.
[b] Enzyme activities are in the presence of NH_4^+ (calculated as % of the control value in the absence of NH_4^+).
[c] Glutamate synthase & glutamate dehydrogenase activities are nmoles/min per mg protein.
[d] Plus (+) denotes that nitrogenase is produced in the presence of NH_4^+ and minus (–) denotes that nitrogenase production is repressed by NH_4^+.

that the depression of nitrogenase production is related to the inhibition of NH_4^+ assimilation by MSX.

Based on preliminary experiments, it has been suggested that glutamine synthetase acts as a controlling element in the transcription of the Nif genes (52, 53, 58, 62). However, in view of the results discussed above, it seems important to determine the nature of other pleiotrophic effects of these regulatory mutations, such as the transport of various metabolites into the cell, the rate of assimilation of NH_4^+, etc. Additional information is therefore required before the component(s) of the cell which controls the production of nitrogenase can be identified.

ENERGY COST OF N_2 FIXATION

Experiments carried out in a number of laboratories have established that biological nitrogen fixation requires a large input of metabolic energy (for reviews see 14, 66,

67). Evidence has been presented that the supply of energy may often be a rate-limiting step in symbiotic N_2 fixation (23). Thus, indirectly, energy supply may play a crucial role in controlling N_2 fixation. Therefore, a complete picture of nitrogenase regulation will have to include the control of supplies of ATP and reductant, essential substrates for the nitrogenase reaction.

Nitrogenase Catalyzed H_2 Evolution

All nitrogenase preparations isolated so far have been found to catalyze an ATP dependent H_2 evolution, even in the presence of N_2 (14, 67). Evidence has been presented indicating that this reaction also occurs in vivo in various nitrogen fixing organisms (22, 54, 63). Schubert & Evans (45) reported that loss of energy as ATP and reducing power, in soybean and other legume root nodules, attributed to nitrogenase catalyzed H_2 evolution may be as high as 40–60% of the total energy flow through nitrogenase. Quantitative in vivo measurements are, however, complicated by the presence, in most nitrogen fixing organisms, of other hydrogenase systems which mediate evolution or uptake of H_2.

Mutant strains of *K. pneumoniae* which were blocked in the conventional hydrogen-producing system have been isolated as chlorate-resistant derivatives of the nitrogenase derepressed mutant strains SK-24 and SK-25 (1). It was determined that the only source of H_2 evolution in these chlorate-resistant mutant strains was via nitrogenase (1). Therefore, these strains provided a convenient tool for determination of nitrogenase-catalyzed H_2 evolution in vivo (1, 2). The results indicated that nitrogenase in vivo, even under optimum conditions (25°C, pH 7.3), catalyzed the production of about 1.3 moles H_2 per mole N_2 reduced. It seems probable that nitrogenase-catalyzed H_2 evolution is an important factor contributing to the high energy requirement for N_2 fixation. The data (H_2/NH_4^+ molar ratio of 0.65) sug-

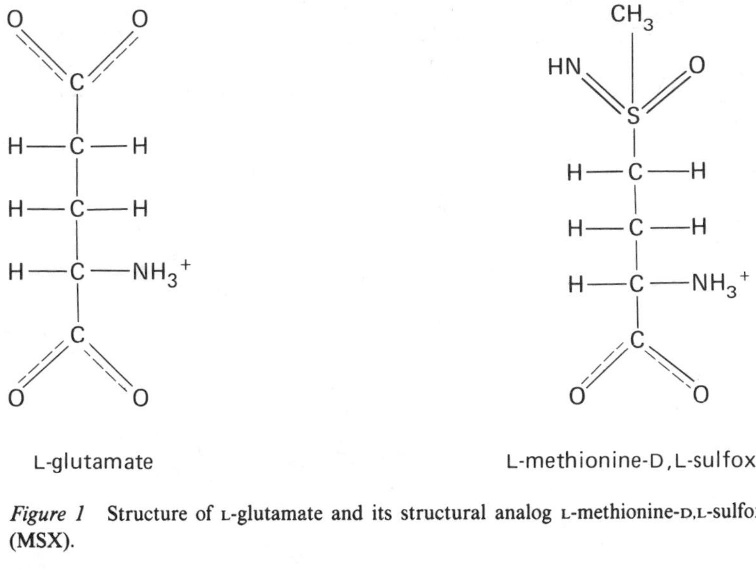

L-glutamate   L-methionine-D,L-sulfoximine

Figure 1   Structure of L-glutamate and its structural analog L-methionine-D,L-sulfoximine (MSX).

gests that almost one-third of the energy flow through nitrogenase is lost as H_2 evolved. Some of the energy lost through nitrogenase-catalyzed H_2 evolution may be recovered by recycling H_2 through uptake hydrogenase. It has been estimated that 2–3 ATP may be obtained per H_2 oxidized in hydrogen-bacteria (11).

Apparent ATP Requirement

Reduction of N_2 or other substrates by nitrogenase requires ATP in addition to a suitable reductant. Most recent in vitro studies with nitrogenase from various organisms have reported a minimal requirement of 12–15 moles ATP per mole N_2 reduced, but the values vary considerably with the experimental conditions (14, 66, 67). Estimates of the in vivo energy requirement for various organisms vary from 4–5 to 29 ATP/N_2 (Table 3). These estimates are based on comparisons of growth yields with N_2 or NH_4^+ as N source.

The low value reported for *Azotobacter chroococcum* may in part be caused by recycling of the H_2 evolved through nitrogenase (54) since H_2 can support oxidative phosphorylation in *A. chroococcum* (25). The estimated value of 4–5 ATP/N_2 also involved a rather large extrapolation to eliminate respiration loss attributed to "respiratory protection" of nitrogenase. The use of nitrogenase-derepressed mutant strains of *K. pneumoniae* allowed the products NH_4^+ and H_2 to be determined directly.

Nongrowing cells of the derepressed mutant strains consumed 7.5–8.5 glucose per N_2 fixed under optimum conditions (1). The ATP requirement for N_2 fixation may be estimated when the fermentation pathways are known. *Klebsiella pneumoniae* ferments glucose through the Embden-Meyerhof-Parnas pathway to pyruvate which yields 2 ATP per glucose. Additional ATP can be obtained through the clastic cleavage of pyruvate (21). Acetate production may be used as a measure of this additional ATP (21, 24). An apparent ATP requirement of 21–25 ATP/N_2 was obtained for five different *K. pneumoniae* mutant strains under optimum conditions (25°C, pH 7.3). These values were calculated from the total glucose consumption rates with no correction for basal levels of glucose catabolism. These calculations, therefore, also include the cells' "maintenance" energy requirement. The apparent

Table 3   In vivo ATP requirement for N_2 fixation reported for various organisms[a]

Organism	Method of estimation	ATP/N_2	Reference
Azotobacter chroococcum	By comparing growth yields on N_2 and NH_4^+	4–5	17
Clostridium pasteurianum	By comparing growth yields on N_2 and NH_4^+	20	16
Klebsiella pneumoniae	By comparing growth yields on N_2 and NH_4^+	29	24
Klebsiella pneumoniae	From NH_4^+ excretion by Nif derepressed mutant strains	14–16	1

[a] From (2).

total ATP requirement increased when the pH was lowered below 6.0 or when the temperature was increased above 25°C, and also after long incubation periods (1).

An estimate of the "maintenance" energy requirement may be obtained from the rate of glucose consumption by Nif minus mutant strains. This correction gave an apparent ATP requirement for the nitrogenase reaction of 14–16 ATP/N_2. This is considerably lower than the value of 29 ATP/N_2 estimated for growing cells of *K. pneumoniae* by comparing growth yields with N_2 of NH_4^+ as N source (Table 3).

If the observed nitrogenase-catalyzed H_2 evolution was taken into consideration (a H_2/NH_4^+ molar ratio of 0.65), then an apparent ATP/2e value of about 4 was calculated. This value is in good agreement with most recent values reported for purified nitrogenase preparations (14, 64, 66, 67).

The reduction of N_2 to NH_4^+ also requires energy in the form of low potential electrons. The observed minimal H_2/NH_4^+ ratio of 0.65 implies that at least 4.3 electron pairs were consumed per N_2 reduced. Low potential electrons and ATP are partially interconvertible energy forms in respiring organisms, and 4.3 low potential electron pairs could have given perhaps 13 ATP if used in oxidative phosphorylation (assuming an ATP/2e value of 3). This implies that the total in vivo energy cost for N_2 fixation in terms of ATP equivalents may be close to 30 ATP/N_2 for the nitrogenase reaction.

When considering the energy cost of N_2 fixation by any biological system, it is essential to take into account the cells' basal metabolic rate ("maintenance" energy requirement). In order to maintain a high level of nitrogenase activity over a longer period of time, a certain amount of protein turnover in the cell appears to be essential. Inhibition of cellular protein synthesis by chloramphenicol leads to a decay of nitrogenase activity (see 1). Taking this into consideration, the minimal energy requirement for N_2 fixation may be as high as 35–40 ATP equivalents per N_2 reduced [calculated from the total glucose consumption rate plus assumed energy content of reductant (1)].

The contribution of the "maintenance" energy requirement in the overall energy cost is probably increasing with decreasing rates of N_2 fixation. It may also vary from organism to organism. Substantial amounts of energy may be lost in aerobic N_2-fixing bacteria like *Azotobacter* in "respiratory protection" of nitrogenase (17).

In conclusion, in vivo experiments indicate that N_2 fixation requires a very large input of metabolic energy. The evolution of very sophisticated genetic control systems for nitrogen fixation may be understood in this context. Because of the high energy requirement, the organisms fixing N_2 when other N sources are available for growth would be expected to be at a disadvantage.

SYMBIOTIC NITROGEN FIXATION

Based on the discovery that certain species of *Rhizobium* are capable of producing nitrogenase in a free-living state, it is clear that the root nodule bacteria (*Rhizobium* spp.) harbor the *nif* genes (26, 30, 32, 39, 61). The levels of nitrogenase activity produced by free-living *Rhizobium* sp. have been reported to approximate that of isolated bacteroids (9, 27, 61). However, it is important to note that none of these organisms are capable of growing in the free-living state at the expense of fixed N_2 as sole N source. Using $^{15}N_2$, more than 94% of fixed N_2 was found to be exported by free-living R. japonicum (35). Similar results were reported for isolated bacteroids (8). The N_2 fixation system of free-living Rhizobium spp. presumably consists of nitrogenase (both the Fe-Mo protein and Fe protein subunits) as well as a variety of enzymes for supplying both ATP and reductant (including reduced pyridine nucleotide-ferredoxin reductase, ferredoxins, flavodoxin, and perhaps other electron coupling factors). A major shift in the pattern of synthesis of cytochromes and other components of the electron transport chain may also occur, leading to the formation of a new respiratory chain that is functional under low O_2 concentrations. Differential gene expression may account for these marked shifts in metabolism. In other words, the commitment to N_2 fixation by the free-living Rhizobium sp. not only involves the expression of the nitrogenase structural genes, but also a whole series of other supporting pathways and enzymes. It has been observed that the hydrogenase system which takes up hydrogen from the environment, as well as dissimilatory nitrate reductase, are simultaneously induced in N_2-fixing cultures of free-living Rhizobium sp. (F. O'Gara, unpublished data). As will be discussed later, these enzyme systems are capable of contributing energy to N_2 fixation. Some of these data suggest that N_2-fixing cultures of free-living rhizobia may resemble the bacteroids in the root nodule. Thus it is of considerable interest to investigate the gene products which are produced along (or only) with nitrogenase (as well as their control) in free-living Rhizobium spp.

In this section, a key set of enzymes which appear to be switched off during N_2 fixation in Rhizobium spp. are described, the NH_4^+-assimilation enzymes (glutamine synthetase and glutamate synthase), the enzymes responsible for converting the NH_4^+ derived from N_2 to the level of amino acids.

Using ^{15}N analysis, it has been found that free-living rhizobia excrete a majority of their fixed nitrogen, presumably as NH_4^+ (35). For example, as much as 94% of the $^{15}N_2$ fixed by free-living R. japonicum was recovered as NH_4^+ from the cell supernatant (Table 4). As summarized in Table 4, the ^{15}N-enrichment in the NH_4^+ fraction recovered from the cell supernatant was 65% to 80% higher for cowpea strain 32H1 and 94% higher for R. japonicum strain CB1809 than the

Table 4 Export of fixed nitrogen by free-living Rhizobium spp.[a]

| | | Atoms % ^{15}N excess[b] | | | |
Rhizobium species	Experiment	Cell nitrogen	Cell supernatant fraction	nmoles N fixed/mg protein per hr	% ^{15}N in supernatant fraction
"cowpea"	I	0.150	0.423	0.17	65
strain 32H1	II	0.040	0.202	0.09	80
R. japonicum		0.020	0.341	0.09	94

[a] From (35).
[b] Referred to control cell and supernatant fractions grown in the presence of unlabeled N_2.

enrichment detected in the NH_4^+ fraction obtained from the total cellular nitrogen. The demonstration of the relatively higher ^{15}N enrichment in the cell supernatants indicates that a major portion of the fixed nitrogen was exported by these cultures.

This corroborates well with a number of studies carried out with isolated bacteroids in which the activities of NH_4^+-assimilatory enzymes leading to biosynthesis of the glutamate-glutamine family of amino acids were found to be extremely low (13, 31, 43). Bergersen & Turner (8) reported earlier that $^{15}N_2$ was fixed and released as $^{15}NH_4^+$ using isolated bacteroids.

The mechanism of modulation of the NH_4^+ assimilation enzymes of *Rhizobium* is of considerable interest because the levels of these enzymes may in large part determine the fate of fixed N_2, permitting the bulk to flow out of the bacteroids to the plant. In other words, the partitioning of fixed N_2 between the symbiont and its host may be dictated by the activities of these enzymes (31, 35, 36, 43).

There is indirect evidence that glutamate may play a role in the regulation of the NH_4^+-assimilatory enzymes leading to export of fixed nitrogen as NH_4^+. For example, when *R. trifolii* (free-living) was presented simultaneously with both glutamate and NH_4^+, it showed a marked preference for glutamate as nitrogen source (35). The culture failed to utilize any detectable NH_4^+ as long as glutamate was present in the medium. In contrast, when glutamate in the medium was replaced by L-aspartate or L-leucine, *R. trifolii* utilized NH_4^+ for cellular growth (35, 36). Glutamate synthase activity in the cells was also found to be low when the culture medium contained L-glutamate. The presence of either aspartate or leucine in the medium (replacing glutamate) allowed the organism to induce higher levels of glutamate synthase activity. The presence or absence of glutamate synthase corresponded well with the NH_4^+ utilization pattern of the cell. NH_4^+ also repressed the levels of glutamine synthetase activity. It is possible that the block in the conversion of NH_4^+ to glutamate (due to low levels of glutamate synthase activity) is responsible for the derepression of nitrogenase, even in the presence of NH_4^+ (37).

A UNIFIED CONCEPT OF SYMBIOTIC NITROGEN FIXATION

Only three types of N_2-fixing bacteria have evolved beneficial symbiotic associations with higher plants—*Rhizobium* spp. (root nodule bacteria) of leguminous plants, *Frankia* (an unidentified, actinomycete-like soil organism) forming root nodules on *Alnus, Purshia*, etc, and heterocystous blue-green algae, the most promiscuous of the symbionts, with a variety of suitable hosts. Since the rhizobial symbiosis has been studied in greater detail, it will be the center of our attention in this section. The focus will be on the requirements for symbiotic N_2 fixation which may be shared by all forms of symbiotic N_2-fixing microorganisms (see Figure 2).

The sole purpose of the symbiont in the symbiotic N_2 fixation is the production of NH_4^+ for the host. It is of interest to note in this connection that the bacteroids in the nodule may resemble the energy-producing organelles of the plant cell, the mitochondria (60). The bacteria in the nodule (bacteroids) seem to lack a rigid cell wall and are osmotically labile (41, 59). Using a medium of high osmolarity for isolating bacteroids, Sutton observed that the percentage of viable cells (capable of colony formation) declined with nodule age. Bacteroids are known to metabolize various carbon compounds supplied by the plant cell (7). The literature is scanty regarding the major carbon compound(s) supplied by the plant cell (19). It is possible that more than one carbon compound might be made available by the plant. The presence or absence of specific permeases in the bacteroid membrane may control the transport of organic compounds into the bacteroid cytoplasm. Once inside the bacteroid, the carbon compounds are transformed and metabolized via an active TCA-cycle coupled to an energy-yielding respiratory chain capable of functioning under low O_2 concentrations (4, 6). Higher O_2 concentrations would inactivate the O_2-sensitive nitrogenase activity. Leghemoglobin is believed to function as an oxygen carrier maintaining a sufficient and constant O_2 concentration near the bacteroid membrane (3).

Two additional systems, probably membrane-bound, may play an important role in energy metabolism—the H_2 uptake system (18, 45) and energy-linked nitrate reductase (42). Since efficiency of energy metabolism is increasingly recognized as a crucial aspect of symbiotic N_2 fixation, these two systems are worth describing in some detail [see Schneider & Schlegel (44) for comparative biochemistry of H_2 uptake systems of free-living bacteria]. Most H_2-utilizing bacteria were found to induce a membrane-bound H_2 uptake system, presumably coupled to the major

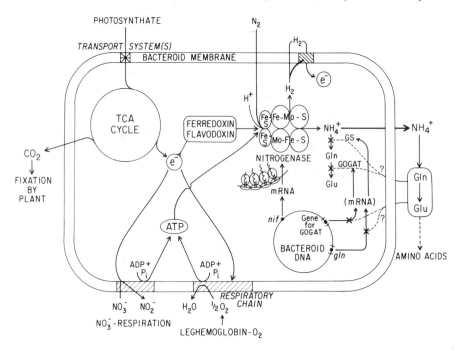

Figure 2   A model for symbiotic N_2-fixation by bacteria. See text for details. GS-glutamine synthetase; GOGAT-glutamate synthase; *nif* and *gln* are the genes for nitrogenase and glutamine synthetase respectively.

respiratory chain. Dixon (18) observed that hydrogenase activity of rhizobial bacteroids, broken by sonic disruption, was readily centrifuged down and was not detectable in the supernatant. Schubert & Evans (45) have provided evidence that the H_2 uptake system of nodules is a bacterial function since net H_2 production varied when different bacterial strains were used to inoculate the same variety of host plant.

Since nitrogenase produces certain amounts of H_2 during the reduction of N_2, the strains which are capable of utilizing H_2 as an energy source would evolve very little free H_2. On the other hand, plants inoculated with bacterial strains incapable of utilizing H_2 would evolve H_2. Based on the measurements of H_2 and C_2H_4 produced by nodules derived from a given strain of *Rhizobium* in association with the plant, Schubert and Evans developed an index called "relative energy efficiency" to measure the efficiency of energy used in the nodule (19, 45). The question of whether the H_2 uptake systems of the bacteroids contribute significantly to the "relative energy efficiency" can only be answered by the use of isogenic strains of *Rhizobium* sp. which lack the H_2 utilization reactions. Bacteroids seem to have evolved additional energy-yielding reactions. For example, it has been reported that the energy production coupled to anaerobic NO_3^- reduction can support N_2 fixation in isolated bacteroids (42). The contribution of this pathway to the whole plant remains to be determined. The plant cell in the nodule also fixes CO_2, the end product of respiration, and thus utilizes all the available material to a maximum. However, the available evidence suggests that one of the major limitations of N_2 fixation by the bacteroids is the availability of photosynthate (23). Hardy & Havelka (23) demonstrated that increasing the rate of CO_2 fixation by the plant by CO_2 enrichment (near the leaves) leads to higher rates of N_2 fixation by the nodule. The probable high energy cost of symbiotic N_2 fixation has some far-reaching implications regarding future research priorities. Work aimed at "genetic engineering" of new N_2 fixing plants must be re-evaluated to account for the energy demand of N_2 fixation. The metabolic energy cost of alternate sources of plant nitrogen, for example NO_3^- reduction to NH_4^+, must also be determined and compared with the energetics of N_2 fixation. The efficiency of photosynthetic CO_2 fixation emerges as a crucial step requiring increasing attention.

During symbiotic nitrogen fixation, the genes and operons necessary for nitrogen fixation, energy producing systems, etc are expressed. However, some bacteroid genes seem to be repressed. Nothing is known at this stage about the extent as well as identity of the various genes which are repressed under symbiotic conditions. One of the important series of reactions, the NH_4^+ assimilation pathway, seems to be either severely or completely repressed (inhibited?) (see the previous section). In isolated bacteroids, the levels of the enzymes glutamine synthetase and glutamate synthase were found to be low (Table 2). This finding provides a biochemical explanation for the export of fixed N_2 as NH_4^+ by the bacteroids. Research is now centered on the mechanism of regulation of these pathways. Plant enzymes rather than the bacteroid enzymes have been proposed to be physiologically important in the assimilation of the NH_4^+ produced by nitrogenase (43, 46). During the development of the nodule, glutamine synthetase and glutamate synthase activities increased considerably in the plant fraction but not in the bacteroid fraction of the nodule. The first step in the assimilation of NH_4^+ (see Figure 2) is proposed to be the synthesis of glutamine by the plant glutamine synthetase. The amide nitrogen of glutamine is transferred to α-ketoglutarate to produce glutamate by glutamate synthase (43, 46). The build-up of glutamate (and glutamine), known to inhibit the assimilation of NH_4^+ in free-living *Rhizobium* sp., may function to repress the NH_4^+ assimilation pathways of the bacteroid.

A summary of experiments on the mechanism of nitrogenase regulation in free-living and symbiotic organisms is presented in Table 2. Note that in all symbiotic systems, including *Rhizobium* spp., as well as blue-green algae (lichen system), both glutamine synthetase and glutamate synthase activities are found to be low. Since *Rhizobium* spp. produce higher levels of both glutamine synthetase and glutamate synthase activities under free-living conditions, the question of how the host regulates the functioning of these genes becomes an important one. Undoubtedly the regulation of the activity and biosynthesis of both the bacteroid and the plant enzymes play a crucial role in symbiotic N_2 fixation. These are studies for the future.

There is rapid progress in the genetics of *Rhizobium* with systems for gene transfer and recombination recently reported for two organisms (10, 29, 33). This provides a fresh approach to studies of the molecular biology of N_2 fixation by *Rhizobium*, including the key symbiotic genes and their regulation and function.

Literature Cited

1. Andersen, K., Shanmugam, K. T. 1977. Energetics of biological nitrogen fixation: Determination of the ratio of formation of H_2 to NH_4^+ catalyzed by nitrogenase of *Klebsiella pneumoniae* in vivo. *J. Gen. Microbiol.* 101:135–41
2. Andersen, K., Shanmugam, K. T., Valentine, R. C. 1977. Nitrogen fixation (Nif) regulatory mutants of *Klebsiella*: Determination of the energy cost of N_2 fixation in vivo. In *Genetic Engineering for Nitrogen Fixation*, ed. C. A. Hollaender et al, pp. 95–110. New York: Plenum
3. Appleby, C. A. 1974. Leghemoglobin. See Ref. 41, pp. 521–54
4. Appleby, C. A., Bergersen, F. J., Macnicol, P. K., Turner, G. L., Wittenberg, B. A., Wittenberg, J. B. 1976. Role of leghemoglobin in symbiotic N_2-fixation. In *International Symposium on Nitrogen Fixation*, ed. W. E. Newton, C. J. Nyman, pp. 274-92. Pullman: Washington State Univ. Press
5. Ausubel, F., Riedel, G., Cannon, F., Peskin, A., Margolskee, R. 1977. Cloning nitrogen fixing genes from *Klebsiella pneumoniae* in vitro and the isolation of *nif* promoter mutants affecting glutamine synthetase regulation. See Ref. 2, pp. 111–28
6. Bergersen, F. J. 1971. Biochemistry of symbiotic nitrogen fixation in legumes. *Ann. Rev. Plant Physiol.* 22:121–40
7. Bergersen, F. J. 1974. Formation and function of bacteroids. See Ref. 41, pp. 473–98
8. Bergersen, F. J., Turner, G. L. 1967. Nitrogen fixation by the bacteroid fraction of breis of soybean root nodules. *Biochim. Biophys. Acta* 141:507–15
9. Bergersen, F. J., Turner, G. L., Gibson, A. H., Dudman, W. F. 1976. Nitrogenase activity and respiration of cultures of *Rhizobium* spp. with special reference to concentration of dissolved oxygen. *Biochim. Biophys. Acta* 444:164–74
10. Beringer, J. E., Hopwood, D. A. 1976. Chromosomal recombination and mapping in *Rhizobium leguminasarium*. *Nature* 264:291–93
11. Bongers, L. 1970. Energy generation and utilization in hydrogen bacteria. *J. Bacteriol.* 104:145–51
12. Brill, W. J. 1975. Regulation and genetics of bacterial nitrogen fixation. *Ann. Rev. Microbiol.* 29:109–29
13. Brown, C. M., Dilworth, M. J. 1975. Ammonia assimilation by *Rhizobium* cultures and bacteroids. *J. Gen. Microbiol.* 86:39–48

14. Burns, R. C., Hardy, R. W. F. 1975. *Nitrogen Fixation in Bacteria and Higher Plants.* New York: Springer-Verlag

15. Cannon, F. C., Riedel, G. E., Ausubel, F. M. 1977. Recombinant plasmid that carries part of the nitrogen fixation (*nif*) gene cluster of *Klebsiella pneumoniae. Proc. Natl. Acad. Sci. USA* 74: 2963–67

16. Daesch, G., Mortenson, L. E. 1968. Sucrose catabolism *Clostridium pasteurianum* and its relation to N_2 fixation. *J. Bacteriol.* 96:346–51

17. Dalton, H., Postgate, J. R. 1969. Growth and physiology of *Azotobacter chroococcum* in continuous culture. *J. Gen. Microbiol.* 56:307–19

18. Dixon, R. O. D. 1972. Hydrogenase in legume root nodule bacteroids: Occurrence and properties. *Arch. Mikrobiol.* 85:193–201

19. Evans, H. J., Barber, L. 1977. Biological nitrogen fixation for food and fiber production. *Science* 197:332–39

20. Gordon, J. K., Brill, W. J. 1974. Derepression of nitrogenase synthesis in the presence of excess NH_4^+. *Biochem. Biophys. Res. Commun.* 59:967–71

21. Hadjipetrou, L. P., Gerrits, J. P., Teulings, F. A. G., Stouthamer, A. H. 1964. Relation between energy production and growth of *Aerobacter aerogenes. J. Gen. Microbiol.* 36:139–50

22. Hamilton, J. R., Burris, R. H., Wilson, P. W. 1964. Hydrogenase and nitrogenase in a nitrogen-fixing bacterium. *Proc. Natl. Acad. Sci. USA* 52:637–41

23. Hardy, R. W. F., Havelka, U. D. 1975. Nitrogen fixation research: A key to world food? *Science* 188:633–43

24. Hill, S. 1976. The apparent ATP requirement for nitrogen fixation in growing *Klebsiella pneumoniae. J. Gen. Microbiol.* 95:297–312

25. Hyndman, L. A., Burris, R. H., Wilson, P. W. 1953. Properties of hydrogenase from *Azotobacter vinelandii. J. Bacteriol.* 65:522–31

26. Keister, D. L. 1975. Acetylene reduction by pure cultures of *Rhizobia. J. Bacteriol.* 123:1265–68

27. Keister, D. L., Evans, W. R. 1976. Oxygen requirement for acetylene reduction by pure cultures of *Rhizobia. J. Bacteriol.* 129:149–53

28. Kennedy, C., Dixon, R. 1977. The nitrogen fixation cistrons of *Klebsiella pneumoniae.* See Ref. 2, pp. 51–66

29. Kondorosi, A., Kiss, G. B., Forrai, T., Vincze, E., Banfalvi, Z. 1977. Circular linkage map of *Rhizobium meliloti* chromosome. *Nature* 268:525–27

30. Kurz, W. G. W., LaRue, T. A. 1975. Nitrogenase activity in *Rhizobia* in absence of plant host. *Nature* 256:407–8

31. Kurz, W. G. W., Rokosh, D. A., LaRue, T. A. 1975. Enzymes of ammonia assimilation in *Rhizobium leguminosarum* bacteroids. *Can. J. Microbiol.* 21:1009–12

32. McComb, J. A., Elliott, J., Dilworth, M. J. 1975. Acetylene reduction by *Rhizobium* in pure culture. *Nature* 256:409–10

33. Meade, H. M., Signer, E. R. 1977. Genetic mapping of *Rhizobium meliloti. Proc. Natl. Acad. Sci. USA* 74:2076–78

34. Nagatani, H., Shimizu, M., Valentine, R. C. 1971. The mechanism of ammonia assimilation in nitrogen-fixing bacteria. *Arch. Microbiol.* 79:164–75

35. O'Gara, F., Shanmugam, K. T. 1976. Regulation of nitrogen fixation by *Rhizobia;* export of fixed N_2 as NH_4^+. *Biochim. Biophys. Acta* 437:313–21

36. O'Gara, F., Shanmugam, K. T. 1976. Control of symbiotic nitrogen fixation in *Rhizobia:* Regulation of NH_4^+ assimilation. *Biochim. Biophys. Acta* 451: 342–52

37. O'Gara, F., Shanmugam, K. T. 1977. Regulation of nitrogen fixation in *Rhizobium:* Isolation of mutants of *Rhizobium trifolii* which induce nitrogenase activity. *Biochim. Biophys. Acta* 500:277–90

38. Okon, Y., Albrecht, S. L., Burris, R. H. 1976. Carbon and ammonia metabolism of *Spirillum lipoferum. J. Bacteriol.* 128:592–97

39. Pagan, J. D., Child, J. J., Scowcraft, W. R., Gibson, A. H. 1975. Nitrogen fixation by *Rhizobium* cultured on a defined medium. *Nature* 256:406–7

40. Parejko, R. A., Wilson, P. W. 1970. Regulation of nitrogenase synthesis by *Klebsiella pneumoniae. Can. J. Microbiol.* 16:681–85

41. Quispel, A., ed. 1974. *The Biology of Nitrogen Fixation.* Amsterdam: North Holland

42. Riguad, J., Bergersen, F. J., Turner, G. L., Daniel, R. M. 1973. Nitrate dependent anaerobic acetylene reduction and nitrogen fixation by soybean bacteroids. *J. Gen. Microbiol.* 77:137–44

43. Robertson, J. G., Warburton, M. P., Farnden, K. J. F. 1975. Induction of glutamate synthase during nodule development in *Lupin. FEBS Lett.* 55: 33–37

44. Schneider, K., Schlegel, H. G. 1977. Localization and stability of hydrogenases from aerobic hydrogen bacteria. *Arch. Microbiol.* 112:229–38

45. Schubert, K. R., Evans, H. J. 1976. Hydrogen evolution: A major factor affecting the efficiency of nitrogen fixation in nodulated symbionts. *Proc. Natl. Acad. Sci. USA* 73:1207–11

46. Scott, D. B., Robertson, J. G., Farnden, K. J. F. 1976. Ammonia assimilation in *Lupin* nodules. *Nature* 263:703–5

47. Shanmugam, K. T. 1978. Microbial genetics and nitrogen fixation. In *Recent Advances in Biological Nitrogen Fixation,* ed. N. S. Subba Rao. New Delhi, India: Oxford Int. Book House

48. Shanmugam, K. T., Chan, I., Morandi, C. 1975. Regulation of nitrogen fixation: Nitrogenase derepressed mutants of *Klebsiella pneumoniae. Biochim. Biophys. Acta* 408:101–11

49. Shanmugam, K. T., Morandi, C. 1976. Amino acids as repressors of nitrogenase biosynthesis in *Klebsiella pneumoniae. Biochim. Biophys. Acta* 437:322–32

50. Shanmugam, K. T., Morandi, C., Valentine, R. C. 1977. Nitrogenase-derepressed mutants of *Klebsiella pneumoniae.* In *Iron-Sulfur Proteins,* 3:1–14

51. Shanmugam, K. T., O'Gara, F., Andersen, K., Morandi, C., Valentine, R. C. 1978. Genetic control of nitrogen fixation (Nif). In *Recent Developments in Nitrogen Fixation,* ed. W. E. Newton, J. R. Postgate, C. R. Barrueco, pp. 321–30

52. Shanmugam, K. T., Streicher, S. L., Morandi, C., Ausubel, F., Goldberg, R., Valentine, R. C. 1976. A model for genetic regulation of dinitrogen fixation (Nif) in *Klebsiella pneumoniae.* See Ref. 4, pp. 313–19

53. Shanmugam, K. T., Valentine, R. C. 1975. Molecular biology of nitrogen fixation. *Science* 187:919–24

54. Smith, L. A., Hill, S., Yates, M. G. 1976. Inhibition by acetylene of conventional hydrogenase in nitrogen-fixing bacteria. *Nature* 262:209–10

55. Stewart, W. D. P., Rowell, P. 1975. Effects of L-methionine-D,L-sulfoximine on the assimilation of newly fixed NH₃, acetylene reduction and heterocyst production in *Anabaena cylindrica. Biochim. Biophys. Res. Commun.* 65:846–56

56. Stewart, W. D. P., Rowell, P. 1977. Modifications of nitrogen-fixing algae in lichen symbiosis. *Nature* 265:371–72

57. Streicher, S. L., Gurney, E., Valentine, R. C. 1971. Transduction of the nitrogen-fixation genes in *Klebsiella pneumoniae. Proc. Natl. Acad. Sci. USA* 68: 1174–77

58. Streicher, S. L., Shanmugam, K. T., Ausubel, F., Morandi, C., Goldberg, R. 1974. Regulation of nitrogen fixation in *Klebsiella pneumoniae:* Evidence for a role of glutamine synthetase as a regulator of nitrogenase synthesis. *J. Bacteriol.* 120:815–21

59. Sutton, W. D., Jepsen, N. M., Shaw, B. D. 1977. Changes in the number, viability, and amino acid incorporating activity of *Rhizobium* bacteroids during *Lupin* nodule development. *Plant Physiol.* 59:741–44

60. Sutton, W. D., Robertson, J. G. 1974. Control of gene action in nitrogen-fixing bacteroids. In *Mechanism of Regulation of Plant Growth,* ed. R. L. Bieleski, H. R. Ferguson, M. M. Cresswell, pp. 23–30. Wellington: Royal Soc. N.Z. Bull. 12

61. Tjepkema, J., Evans, H. J. 1975. Nitrogen fixation by free living *Rhizobium* in a defined liquid medium. *Biochem. Biophys. Res. Commun.* 65:625–28

62. Tubb, R. S. 1974. Glutamine synthetase and ammonium regulation of nitrogenase synthesis in *Klebsiella. Nature* 251:481–85

63. Wall, J. D., Weaver, P. F., Gest, H. 1975. Genetic transfer of nitrogenase-hydrogenase activity in *Rhodopseudomonas capsulata. Nature* 258: 630–31

64. Watt, G. D., Bulen, W. A., Burns, A., Hadfield, K. L. 1975. Stoichiometry, ATP/2e values, and energy requirements for reactions catalyzed by nitrogenase from *Azotobacter vinelandii. Biochemistry* 14:4266–72

65. Weare, N. M., Shanmugam, K. T. 1976. Photoproduction of ammonium ion from N₂ in *Rhodospirillum rubrum. Arch. Microbiol.* 110:207–13

66. Winter, H. C., Burris, R. H. 1976. Nitrogenase. *Ann. Rev. Biochem.* 45: 409–26

67. Zumft, W. G., Mortenson, L. E. 1975. The nitrogen-fixing complex of bacteria. *Biochim. Biophys. Acta* 416:1–52

Ann. Rev. Plant Physiol. 1978 29:277–317

PLANT PRODUCTIVITY IN THE ARID AND SEMIARID ZONES

❖7653

R. A. Fischer and Neil C. Turner

Division of Plant Industry, CSIRO, P.O. Box 1600, Canberra City, 2601, Australia

CONTENTS

INTRODUCTION

Approximately four-tenths of the world's land surface is within the arid and semiarid zones as defined by Meigs (99). In both zones water is the major limiting factor to plant productivity. Such is the water limitation that annual net primary produc-

277

tivity (net dry matter gain above and below ground) ranges from 25 to 400 and 250 to 1000 g m^{-2} in the arid and semiarid zones, respectively (20, 46, 92, 110), much less than values of up to 3000 g m^{-2} for vegetation with abundant water (92). These zones are also important world sources of animal and crop production. Grazing of native vegetation is the main means by which man harvests plant production in the arid zone, while grazing of native vegetation and improved pastures and rainfed arable cropping dominate the land use of the semiarid zone. The magnitude of semiarid zone cropping, which has been described in detail by Arnon (4), can be assessed from a recent comprehensive survey of potential world food production (19). By assuming that the semiarid zone comprises those areas in which the calculated ratio of actual crop transpiration to potential crop transpiration (i.e. with unlimited water supply) during the growing season was between 0.2 and 0.5, this survey indicates that 32% of the world's total potential arable land, after unsuitable soils and topography have been excluded, lies in the semiarid zone. The semiarid proportion of present-day arable land is probably higher than this figure. Thus our review will emphasize the productivity of crops and pastures as well as that of natural ecosystems. Joint consideration of natural and agricultural plant communities is also desirable because of the continual interchange of concepts between people studying the two communities, and because many of our cultivated species evolved, and still have relatives in, natural ecosystems of the semiarid zone.

In this review we consider the factors determining plant productivity in arid and semiarid zone communities. While recognizing that salinity, temperature extremes, and low soil nutrient content may limit productivity in some arid and semiarid ecosystems, we will place our emphasis on the water restraint to plant productivity. Although plant responses and adaptation to water shortage have received growing attention from physiologists in recent years (9, 17, 69–71, 87, 88, 91, 146, 152, 161, 162), the relevance of some of the physiological information presented to the productivity of plant communities in the field is not evident. Our review will be concerned explicitly with the field community level of organization, and only explores at lower levels those physiological processes which appear to be of major importance for community productivity. As such it complements another review in this series, one in which light limitation of community productivity in water nonlimiting situations was emphasized (94). Furthermore, we give particular attention to genotypically determined differences in strategies for maximizing performance under water-limited conditions. Because of the broad view taken, we draw heavily upon the aforementioned reviews and upon recent reviews of research in natural ecosystems (20, 27, 41, 46–48, 110, 138). Many primary source references are to be found in these reviews.

ENVIRONMENTAL CONTEXT

The definition of arid and semiarid zones by Meigs (99) uses the Thornthwaite moisture index based on mean monthly precipitation and evaporation. Upon this moisture-based classification there can be superimposed divisions according to latitude, temperature, and season when precipitation is likely to occur. As a result, four major regions of arid and semiarid vegetation are distinguished. The names we shall use for these regions and their approximate features are as follows:

(i) *Savanna,* latitude 0° to 20°, dry winter, wet summer growing season.
(ii) *Transition,* latitude 20° to 35°, rain and growth in summer and winter, or at any time of the year.
(iii) *Mediterranean,* latitude 30° to 40°, dry summer, wet winter and spring growing season.
(iv) *Steppe,* latitude 40° to 50°, cold winter, spring, and/or summer growing season.

The approximate annual rainfall totals delineating the semiarid zone within each region are 400 to 800 mm (i and ii) and 250 to 500 mm (iii and iv) (99). The transition region, of unfortunate title, is nevertheless of considerable importance, occurring in central Argentina, central and eastern Australia, and southwest United States; the occurrence of the other regions and their plant communities is described elsewhere (e.g. 4, 171).

The pattern of water availability to plants, and the strategies adopted by plants, show unique features in each of the four regions listed. Because of the variability of rainfall between and within years, the best way of summarizing water availability is not through long-term averages, but rather through dynamic models of the soil water balance. Long runs (say 50 years) of precipitation and evaporation data are used to derive probabilistic statements about the availability of water to plants (143). For a given plant community, soil type, and root zone storage, such models calculate the change in soil water each 5 to 10 days based on precipitation, estimated runoff, and evapotranspiration as a function of evaporation, vegetation stage following the onset of growth, and soil water deficit (see Transpiration Modulation).

In the savanna and mediterranean regions, the most relevant information is not simply the mean rainfall, but the variability of the duration of the rainfall-determined growing season. For example, at Katherine, on the wetter edge of Australia's semiarid savanna region (latitude 14°S; annual rainfall 900 mm), in one-tenth of the years the growing season for crops is less than 66% of its mean value of 21 weeks (143). At drier savanna localities the variability is even greater (54, 98). In the mediterranean region, growing season duration may be less variable: at Lock in southern Australia (latitude 33°S; annual rainfall 400 mm) in one-tenth of the years, the duration of the growing season was less than 82% of the mean duration of 26 weeks (J. R. McAlpine, unpublished). Other features of the mediterranean region are that temperatures are low enough to slow growth in winter, and daily evaporation rates are generally low. However, the mediterranean growing season draws to a close when temperature, solar radiation, and evaporation are all rising rapidly, whereas in the savanna region these variables are usually steady as the wet season terminates, and the period of greatest evaporation occurs at the onset of the wet season.

A well-defined wet season does not preclude the possibility of periods of water shortage within the wet season. Estimations of their probable occurrence and duration are possible with soil water budgeting. For example, for a crop like sorghum at Katherine, a period of water shortage, with available soil water less than 75% of maximum for at least 3 consecutive weeks, can be expected once within each growing season (143). Again the mediterranean region appears less variable, for the probability of such water shortage within any growing season is less than 0.2 at Lock. However, shorter dry spells are common in both regions after the opening rains (false starts) and can have important effects on productivity via reduced or differential establishment of annual pasture species (157, 166). The probability in any year at Lock of false starts after the autumn equinox, when temperatures would favor the germination of most winter annuals, was 0.4.

The transition region has the possibility of growth and nongrowth periods at any time of the year. This calls for great flexibility of response by vegetation, and the presence of winter and summer growing species. Although lower evaporation increases the duration of growth periods for given amounts of precipitation during the winter (54), soil water budgeting suggests that semiarid transition conditions also favor flexible or opportunistic farming strategies (11).

In the steppe region, soil water models have also been developed (5, 23, 35, 131) but do not appear to have been used to summarize patterns of water availability in the above manner. Two unique features of this zone are that some precipitation occurs as snow, and that the growing season usually begins with a substantial amount of available water in the soil being controlled not by water, but by the rise in soil temperature in the spring. Furthermore, high soil water deficits and evaporation rates in the long summer days usually terminate or seriously interrupt the growing season during the summer, but some growth may occur in the autumn.

In all regions, man may increase the water available to his crops by fallowing during preceding wet periods or seasons. Usually only about 20% of precipitation is conserved, but the extra water at seeding can guarantee crop establishment at the optimum seeding date, and may increase the mean and decrease the variability of expected yields (4a). In the mediterranean and especially savanna regions, soil moisture conserved by the end of the wet season can be sufficient for a dry season crop, supplied at times entirely by this stored moisture (4a, 15). Soil moisture budgeting is well suited to predict the gains in crop productivity to be expected from fallowing (5, 11).

PLANT LIFE FORMS AND PRODUCTIVITY MODELS

The life cycle of plants in water-limited environments is usefully summarized in terms of the pulse-reserve model of ecologists (173), in which a pulse of carbon assimilation is triggered by an input of water. This results in the production of a reserve of reduced carbon to maintain the species during the rainless or drought period following the exhaustion of the water, and to facilitate its response to the next input of water sufficient to trigger assimilation.

Most classifications of life forms consider both the synchrony between the input of water and the pulse of assimilation, and the reserve form in which the plants survive. We shall exclude consideration of lower plants, such as lichens, and only refer to two main groups of higher plants which can be recognized, namely the aridopassive and the aridoactive groups (47). The aridopassive group generally carry no active photosynthetic tissue through the long dry periods which separate wet periods, while the aridoactive plants usually retain photosynthetic tissue and exhibit some, often very limited, photosynthetic activity during the dry period. Figure 1 illustrates the pattern of transpiration that might be expected for these two vegetation types in an arid mediterranean region.

Aridopassive plants tend to have an assimilation pulse closely in phase with the water input. The group includes annual plants, with seeds as their only reserve form, herbaceous perennials with storage organs such as rhizomes, bulbs, etc at or below the soil surface, and the so-called drought deciduous woody perennials. The aridoactive group comprises woody evergreen perennials, which maintain all or at least part of their green tissue during the dry season and are the true xerophytes, and succulents, which have substantial reserves of water in swollen stems and leaves and usually crassulacean acid metabolism (CAM) (see 115).

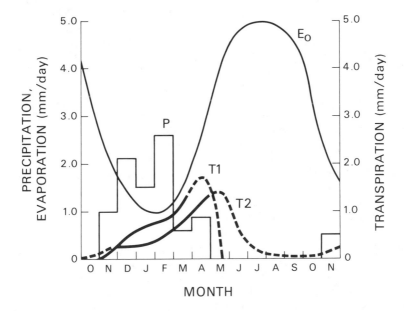

Figure 1   Probable annual distribution of daily transpiration for communities of aridopassive (*T1*) and aridoactive (*T2*) plants in a semiarid mediterranean region in the northern hemisphere, using typical values of monthly precipitation (*P*) and daily free water evaporation (*E_o*) for a given year. The areas under both transpiration curves equals 170 mm, compared to the precipitation total of 260 mm. The broken portion of each transpiration curve indicates periods when soil water limits transpiration.

Distribution of these life forms in natural ecosystems is discussed in many ecological texts (e.g. 171). It suffices here to point to some broad patterns. Annuals contribute most to productivity in the more arid parts of all regions except the steppes, although in very dry years their contribution may be zero (46, 105, 114). Herbaceous perennials, in particular the grasses, often dominate the drier portions of the semiarid zone, especially in the savanna and steppe regions (20). Many semiarid mediterranean shrubs and shrubs and trees of the savanna region adopt the drought deciduous strategy. Woody evergreens occur in most arid regions, but are strikingly dominant in the sclerophyllous vegetation of semiarid mediterranean (41, 100) and arid and semiarid transition regions (28, 123, 147). Plants exhibiting CAM tend to be found in arid areas and may be favored by low night temperatures (20, 102, 115). Domesticated grazing animals in natural ecosystems rely largely on the production of herbaceous annuals and perennials (20) and of some evergreen shrublands (147), while most sown pasture species are annual or perennial grasses or legumes. Furthermore, most crop plants are annuals or weakly perennial. In fact, at least 90% of the total crop production of semiarid regions derives from four cereals, namely: wheat (*Triticum* spp.), barley (*Hordeum* spp.), sorghum (*Sorghum* spp.) and the millets; cotton (*Gossypium* spp.), oilseeds, and leguminous pulses make up the remainder.

The terms aridoactive and aridopassive highlight life form during the survival phase, but we must emphasize that this phase contributes little directly to productivity when compared to the assimilation phase which is linked to the water input. Simple productivity models have in fact expressed annual or seasonal productivity as a function of total precipitation input (92, 150, 171). More accurate models have recognized that the water loss by the vegetation is the important component of precipitation and have related productivity to total evapotranspiration (1, 5, 61, 73, 92, 150), or for grain crops in particular, to the ratio of actual to potential evapotranspiration (11, 150). Finally, a number of productivity models have used total transpiration, rather than evapotranspiration, as the independent moisture variable (37a, 65).

The use of transpiration (T) as the central factor in explaining the influence of water limitation on productivity depends on the recognition of the inevitable association between water loss and CO_2 assimilation by terrestrial plants. This approach contrasts with models which attempt primarily to quantify water levels in plants, the amount of time when the plant is "nonstressed," and/or the rate of assimilation as a function of the stress level (e.g. 17a, 22, 98, 128). Central to the former approach is the belief that water use efficiency (WUE), meaning the ratio of assimilation to transpiration, is a reasonably predictable function of vegetation and environment. Thus dry matter production (DM) over a given period is as follows:

$$DM = T \cdot WUE \qquad\qquad 1.$$

where T is total transpiration for the period and WUE the mean water use efficiency.

For long growth periods it is important to recognize that total dry matter production is given by the sum of $T \cdot WUE$ over shorter periods (e.g. days, weeks) comprising the long period. Also, over long periods a full understanding of productivity requires consideration of how each increment of dry matter is allocated to the various growing sinks (e.g. leaves, roots, seeds, etc). Thus:

$$DM = f(T, WUE, F) \qquad\qquad 2.$$

where F refers to the allocation or partitioning of assimilate.

We shall adopt the approach represented by Equation 2 to discuss the determination of water-limited plant productivity. It is essentially that used by van Keulen (166) in a recent comprehensive effort to model the productivity of annual pastures in a semiarid mediterranean region. Its usefulness depends on the relative physiological independence of the three determinants, T, WUE, and F, a point to which we will return in the last section dealing with integration. An additional advantage of the inclusion of F in Equation 2 is that it leads logically to the concept of harvest index, which is the economic yield, for example grain yield or digestible dry matter, as a proportion of the total above ground dry matter. Harvest index is an important aspect of yield determination in crops and pastures (4a, 38, 119).

TRANSPIRATION

The maximizing on a seasonal or annual basis of the ratio of transpiration to total water supply is an important consideration for plant communities of arid and semiarid zones (110, 141), because productivity is proportional to transpiration if WUE is constant (Equation 1). The transpiration (T) of a plant community over a given time period is as follows:

$$T = P - R - E_S - \Delta S \qquad\qquad 3.$$

where P is precipitation (rainfall plus snowfall), R is the net runoff, E_s is the soil evaporation, and ΔS is the change in soil water in the root zone. The term evapotranspiration ($ET = T + E_s$) will also be used. Equation 3 ignores movement of water below the root zone (drainage or, conversely, upward flow from water tables, etc), interception of fog and mist, dew, evaporation of water intercepted by vegetation, and foliar absorption of moisture (133). Losses through drainage may be important in wetter semiarid situations, but the other components ignored are generally too small to be of any consequence for the productivity of higher plants in all but exceptional situations.

Runoff

The proportion of rainfall available for transpiration is increased by minimizing runoff and maximizing infiltration of rain into the soil. Despite low rainfall in dry regions, rainfall intensity is often sufficient to cause runoff, especially with summer rainfall. This leads to runon elsewhere and an important horizontal redistribution of water and plant productivity on a microtopographic scale, i.e. within one meter, as well as mesotopographic one. The latter effect can be seen from the greater density of vegetation along drainage lines. Microrelief, through the favoring of runoff and runon, may actually increase the overall plant productivity of annual mediterranean pastures in dry seasons by reducing soil evaporation and providing more favorable microhabitats for seedling establishment (166). Man has taken advantage of such effects by constructing small watersheds in arid regions (48) and by forming inter-row ridges treated to encourage runoff in row crops such as cotton and sorghum (56). Plants and their litter can substantially reduce runoff by increasing infiltration rates (e.g. 4a, 170), and can trap runon. One example is the natural occurrence of contour-oriented groves of mulga (*Acacia aneura*) in arid central Australia; these groves trap runon from the adjacent intergroves (147).

Another form of water redistribution of particular advantage in arid regions is stem flow in trees and large shrubs adapted to intercept precipitation and channel it down branches to the stem. For example, when rainfall events exceeded 12 mm, stem flow in *Acacia aneura* amounted to 40% of the rain falling on the canopy (142).

Soil Evaporation

Soil evaporation (E_s), representing the loss of water which could have been transpired and hence contributed to productivity, is a major component of Equation 3 in dry regions. This is because the plant cover is usually incomplete, and because a relatively large proportion of the rainfall, especially in the mediterranean zone, comes in light falls. Soil evaporation in plant communities has been reviewed elsewhere (154, 166). When the soil surface is wet, E_s depends largely upon the radiation reaching the soil surface and hence upon the plant cover or leaf area index (*LAI*). As the surface dries, the moisture content and water conductivity characteristics, and hence texture, of the uppermost soil layer control E_s (154). Thus the importance of cover is greatest when the soil surface is wet. For example, in a typical crop of wheat calculations suggest that E_s falls from 50% of ET at $LAI = 1.5$ to less than 10% at $LAI = 4$; however, since T rises with increased LAI, ET is largely independent of LAI when the soil surface is wet (36). Furthermore, at a given LAI, T was little affected by whether the soil surface was wet (E_s maximal) or very dry (E_s zero). The effect of soil texture is such that under intermittent rainfall regimes of dry regions, the cumulative loss due to E_s is least with coarse textured soil surfaces such as sands and gravels; because of their low water holding capacity, they retain less water in the surface zone subject to most evaporative losses. When rainfall is low, the favoring of productivity by this aspect of such soils has long been recognized (110, 171).

For plant communities over sufficiently long time periods, E_s can be calculated as part of a soil water budgeting procedure. For example, in a mixed grass prairie in Oklahoma (precipitation = 700 mm, heavy surface texture), the estimated E_s over one year was about one-half of ET, despite allowance for a reduction of E_s by the mulch of dead plant material common in such grasslands (131). For shrub steppe communities in the western United States, E_s estimates range from 23% of ET [*Artemisia tridentata* community, precipitation 350 mm (23)] to near 50% of ET [*Atriplex confertifolia,* precipitation 250 mm (22)]. At a mediterranean site in Israel (mean annual rainfall 250 mm, fine sandy surface texture), van Keulen (166) calculated that total E_s averaged 38% of total growing season ET over 3 years in fertilized annual pastures. The evaporative loss in each year depended very much on rainfall distribution, ranging from under 30% to over 50%. Moreover, it was predicted that seasonal productivity would increase 40% as a result of reduced E_s losses if the average seasonal rainfall was distributed in half the average number of wet days. Estimates at Akron, Colorado, suggest that E_s losses are also high for unirrigated crops, varying from 30 to 40% of total ET for winter wheat and 20 to 40% for summer sorghum (65).

Despite the importance of E_s in reducing the fraction of precipitation available for transpiration and production by plant communities, the options available to minimize this loss appear to be limited. The horizontal redistribution of water resulting in deeper water infiltration around certain plants has already been mentioned. The rapid establishment of full cover by plants should reduce E_s losses. A high density of active roots in the uppermost layer of soil, competing for water with evaporation, could be a useful mechanism and does seem to be characteristic of some cacti (108, 115, 156). However, there appear to be no measurements, as distinct from estimations, of the proportion of T to E_s losses from the uppermost soil layer. Also, in undisturbed soils, mosses and lichens often cover the soil surface in the wet season (110) and must make use of water that otherwise would have been lost by evaporation.

Change in Soil Water

Before considering the importance of the change in soil water, it is useful to point out that, based on soil water potential (ψ_{soil}) alone, the available water (i.e. that between –0.3 and –15 bars) ranges from 70 mm (sand) to 240 mm (silt loam) per meter (133). On the other hand, some prefer to define the maximum storage capacity of the root zone as the difference between the highest and lowest water contents ever measured in the whole profile under the particular community (e.g. 76, 130, 131). On favorable soils this quantity can be as high as 250 mm for sorghum and cotton (15, 130) and higher still for perennials [e.g. 325 mm for *Artemisia tridentata* (23)].

If maximizing transpiration as a fraction of rainfall is a goal for ecosystems in dry regions, then those dominated by perennials, in particular aridoactive species, should continue to transpire into the dry season until there is little soil water available (Figure 1). Change in soil water in the root zone (ΔS of Equation 3) from before until after the growing season is therefore likely to be small. An exception to this would be steppe communities, since soil water accumulates before the onset of growth in the spring.

It is also likely that the depth of the root zone of perennial communities extends to the greatest depth of the wetting front (7, 23, 35, 110). The depth of wetting in the arid and semiarid zones will depend on soil type and rainfall distribution, but most soil water measurements (22, 23, 35, 123, 149) point to minimal water movement below depths to which perennials could reasonably be expected to root (ranging from 1.5 m in heavy soils to 5 m on sandy soils). Soil water budgeting (e.g. 54, 98) suggests that if the available water storage capacity in the root zone is 100 to 150 mm, this is sufficient to prevent deep drainage losses and maximize water available for transpiration in most situations without fallow periods. Soils with physical or chemical barriers to root penetration may have a lower storage capacity than 100mm, leading to the possibility of drainage and runoff losses, reduced transpiration, and reduced productivity (e.g. 98).

What has been said with respect to root depth does not contradict the observation that there may be available soil water below the root zone in some perennial communities (e.g. 76, 131). This is likely to be water accumulated in exceptionally wet seasons, and of little importance for sustained productivity, but of some importance for the short-term productivity of deeper-rooted introduced species such as alfalfa *(Medicago sativa)* and perhaps of great importance for survival of aridoactive shrubs and trees. In mixed communities, only these last-mentioned plants, plus any perennial grass components, will root deeply; the roots of neighboring ephemerals or drought-deciduous perennials are likely to exploit a shallower portion of the profile (23, 100, 110, 122), while succulents appear to have very shallow roots [no deeper than 15 cm in the barrel cactus *Ferocactus acanthodes* (108)]. Some aridoactive species have been reported to reduce ψ_{soil} to as low as -100 bars or more (110). This requires ψ_{plant} to be even lower: the phenomenon is, however, only likely to be of importance for survival and not for productivity because the extra water obtained below a more common lower limit for aridopassive species of -20 to -40 bars is small in most soils. Salinity, which is common in arid zone soils, also complicates water extraction at very low ψ_{soil} (110).

There are aspects of ΔS over a growing season which apply more specifically to annual plant communities, in particular to crops. With the latter, substantial available soil water is often present at sowing as a result of fallowing; an important fraction, and at times all, of the crop's transpiration can be attributed to ΔS. The situation at the end of the growing season appears to vary. In many cases crops and pastures, like perennial communities, use most or all of the available water in the soil (e.g. 1, 51). In other situations, where the profile has been wet to a considerable depth, as through fallowing, not all this water may be used, and associated with this there can be differences in seasonal ΔS between crop species (e.g. 130), cultivars (e.g. 15, 72), and fertilizer levels (4a). These differences probably reflect differences in rooting depth and/or density. More extensive rooting may be associated with greater long-term crop productivity, provided the extra transpiration gained is at the expense of water which otherwise would have been lost to other plants. Annual mediterranean pasture and wheat crops can, on occasions, leave considerable available water in the root zone at maturity because of early maturity and/or rain near maturity, or low soil fertility (61, 166). In the long term, such water is probably lost to the ecosystem via soil evaporation and deep drainage. The increase in underground flow when the natural sclerophyllous vegetation of semiarid mediterranean regions is converted into annual crop and pasture is well known.

Transpiration Modulation

We have described factors influencing seasonal transpiration as a fraction of the growing season water input. This fraction, and hence total seasonal transpiration, is largely beyond the control of the vegetation, but plants have a more substantial role in modulating the use of this water throughout the season, with some important consequences for productivity. We will emphasize the strategies adopted by plants rather than the short-term mechanics of transpiration control, since the latter subject has been reviewed extensively (30, 31, 75, 133).

To discuss transpiration control it is useful to define potential transpiration (T_p), i.e. the transpiration of vegetation when the root zone water content is high and stomatal resistances are minimal, and actual transpiration (T_a), meaning transpiration when root zone water may be limiting; obviously $T_a \leqslant T_p$. This definition of T_p does not specify full plant cover as a necessary condition; plant cover is more usually incomplete in dry regions. As an index of the evaporative demand of the environment independent of vegetation type, E_o or free water evaporation is used. Also for simplicity we neglect E_s in this subsection, while recognizing that it will be contributing to the overall water use (ET) of the community.

The proportion of solar radiation intercepted by green tissue or, more loosely, the plant cover, is the major determinant of the ratio T_p/E_o; at full interception this can be close to or even greater than 1.0 Change in leaf area or cover is also the main means by which most plant communities adjust T_p/E_o on a long-term basis. The reflective properties and aerodynamic roughness of the vegetation can have small effects on T_p/E_o, as also can the minimum leaf diffusive resistances to water vapor (i.e. with wet soil and presumably high leaf water potential, ψ_{leaf}). The ratio T_a/T_p equals 1.0 in wet soil but falls below 1.0 at some point during soil drying, the major direct cause of this fall being stomatal closing and increased leaf diffusive resistance. In this context stomata close primarily in response to declining ψ_{leaf} (160), although other factors including hormones such as abscisic acid and cytokinins may also be involved (74, 124). In turn, ψ_{leaf} depends on ψ_{soil} in the root zone, resistances to liquid water flow in the rhizosphere, roots, stems, petioles, and leaves, and on the potential atmospheric demand (E_o) (30, 75). It is now recognized that the resistances to water flow in the plant can be substantial, in particular in the roots (21, 62, 107, 127), where they can exceed resistances in the soil or rhizosphere at commonly encountered root densities and all but low bulk soil water potentials in most soils ($<$ –8 to –10 bars). Plants, through control of these resistances, can influence ψ_{leaf} at any given ψ_{soil} and given water flux through the plant. This effect, combined with the sensitivity of stomata to ψ_{leaf}, provides the major way in which plants control T_a/T_p. Other changes in leaves in response to lowered ψ_{leaf}, such as increased reflectivity (e.g. 44), leaf rolling (e.g. 128), passive leaf flagging, and active leaf movement (9) will also have small effects on T_a/T_p. Considerable attention has been given by both ecologists and crop physiologists to determining the exact form of the relationship of T_a/T_p to ψ_{soil}, or more commonly to the fraction of available water left in the root zone (e.g. 76, 129, 133, 149), a question to which we shall return.

The contrasting strategies of aridoactive and aridopassive vegetation for using given total amounts of seasonal transpiration were illustrated in Figure 1. Obviously, over a whole year $T_a < T_p$ and $T_p \ll E_o$, but for productivity it is important to understand these relationships within the growing season. Turning first to the case of aridoactive shrubs and trees in the arid zone, ecologists have emphasized that the transpirational surface reaches a maximum at or soon after the end of the wet season, after which it is reduced substantially as the dry season proceeds, only to increase again with the onset of the next wet season, unless this latter increase is delayed by winter cold (37, 47, 114, 171). It may be expected that T_p/E_o follows a similar pattern. The decrease in transpirational area during the dry season comes about through the abscission and death of green tissue and the replacement of large leaves with smaller more xeromorphic leaves (23, 37, 47, 113), presumably in response to decreasing ψ_{plant} (23). At the same time T_a/T_p is likely to fall, and the net effect is that T_a in the dry season is less than the expression "aridoactive" might imply. For example, in the case of each of three shrub species in the Negev, a winter-rainfall desert, at least 90% of the annual transpiration occurred in winter and spring when the rain was received, and about 70% in the months of February, March, and April (47). Summer and autumn transpiration was clearly of little significance to productivity. The heavy investment of some arid shrub communities in new roots each growing season (e.g. 21) also suggests emphasis on extracting soil water as rapidly as T_p demands for as long as possible. Similarly, the ability of stomata of desert shrubs (e.g. 137) and of sclerophylls (e.g. 159) to remain partly open until very low values of ψ_{leaf} ($< - 50$ bars) fits this strategy.

In the semiarid zone as distinct from the arid zone, aridoactive shrubs and trees, especially the sclerophyllous vegetation of the mediterranean zone, do not generally show large seasonal leaf area changes, having a leaf area corresponding to the expectancy of precipitation (100, 148). Also, some measurements suggest that T_a/T_p of sclerophyllous vegetation is especially sensitive to soil water, falling linearly from 1.0 to zero as the fraction of root zone available water falls from 1.0 to zero (e.g. 123, 149). It has been proposed that this is a conservative strategy to avoid the possibility of complete exhaustion of soil water (148). It is not clear, however, whether this behavior is any different from that generally reported for the Californian and Chilean mediterranean sclerophyllous vegetation, where transpiration appears to proceed at high rates until by midsummer most of the soil water has been used: ψ_{leaf} falls to moderately low levels ($< - 30$ bars) before stomata close (100, 122). High minimal leaf resistances (at high ψ_{leaf}) and high cuticular resistances to water loss are other common features of sclerophyllous leaves (27, 41, 122).

Another distinctive group of aridoactive plants are the succulents for which green area also changes little if at all during long dry periods. Nevertheless, their stomata appear to close tightly when ψ_{leaf} falls below quite high values [e.g. –4 bars in barrel cactus (108)], and cuticular resistance to water loss is extremely high (156). Given this and their shallow roots, it is likely that T_a/T_p approaches zero soon after the surface soil dries and transpiration, and hence assimilation of external CO_2, is closely confined to wet periods. At the same time they respond rapidly to rain; for example, full stomatal opening was achieved within 2 days of drought-breaking rain in barrel cactus (108).

Turning to aridopassive vegetation and especially annual crops and pastures, leaf area increases rapidly with the onset of the wet season unless growth is limited by winter cold. If the water input is substantial (e.g. > 100–200 mm), complete cover is approached and T_p is close to E_o (Figure 1). However, as mentioned before, there is the possibility of water deficiency within the expected growing season, plus the probability that deficiency will terminate the growing season. During both types of stress, it appears that these plants behave so as to maximize the period during which T_a/T_p is equal to 1.0. For example, it has recently been argued that, notwithstanding the multiplicity of published relationships (e.g. 76, 133), most crops and pastures appear to show maintenance of T_a/T_p at 1.0 until the available water fraction of the root zone falls below 0.3 (129). This is achieved by having high root densities (e.g. 62, 107), rapid extension of roots into wetter deeper soil (e.g. 130), and a lowering of the ψ_{leaf} for stomatal closure (e.g. 81, 82, 161). These plants usually show sharp stomatal closing at a critical ψ_{leaf} at which leaf turgor is close to zero (160). However, with slow drying typical of field situations, extra osmotic solutes accumulate in the leaf (osmotic adjustment) so that the critical ψ_{leaf} for stomatal closing can be lower than −20 bars in, for example, cotton (82) or sorghum (81). Meaningful comparisons between genotypes must permit the full expression of osmotic adjustment; such comparisons do point to species differences in the critical ψ_{leaf} for stomatal closure (160), but only to small differences among cultivars, at least with sorghum (66).

In aridopassive plants, T_p changes during periods of water limitation are usually not considered explicitly because it is simpler to consider only changes in T_a/E_o. Nevertheless, it has been pointed out that leaf area reduction (T_p reduction) is an important adaptive response to water limitation (9, 87, 162). In early stages of ontogeny (i.e. before flowering), this arises largely because of the great sensitivity of leaf area growth to reduced leaf turgor, and hence reduced ψ_{leaf} (9, 162). As development proceeds, the stimulation of leaf senescence or leaf abscission or both by lowered ψ_{leaf} becomes the major means by which leaf area is reduced (e.g. 50, 52, 162), although recently it has been argued that lowered ψ_{leaf} stimulates leaf death rather than leaf senescence, which may in fact be suspended by water deficit (94a).

There has been considerable discussion of the strategies annual plants may adopt with respect to transpiration control in the face of soil water shortage (e.g. 63, 66). It can be suggested that the water conservative strategy (sensitive stomata resulting from a high critical ψ_{leaf}) may be better for short periods of shortage, for example within the growing season, because it lessens the reduction in ψ_{leaf} and resultant deleterious effects on leaf area or yield processes. Nevertheless, the general pattern of behavior described seems to be the opposite of a conservative strategy, namely, transpiration is maintained at the risk of complete soil water exhaustion, very low ψ_{plant}, and serious damage. This behavior may have been favored by natural selection in competitive situations (e.g. 25) and may be appropriate for crop plants in the final phase of their life cycle, since available water in the soil at maturity represents lost opportunity for photosynthesis. Nevertheless, looking at overall strategies, Passioura (117, 119) argues for breeding for more water conservative behavior in crop plants, and suggests that in wheat this may be based on selection for higher resistances in the seminal roots to water flow. With the probable future discovery of more genotypic differences in the various processes controlling transpiration, opportunities for crop breeders and physiologists to test these various hypotheses will develop eventually.

Plant Water Potential and Survival

During very dry periods, the transpiration of aridoactive plants drops to very low levels. It is probably better then to consider plant behavior in terms of survival rather than production, although the amount of tissue which survives these dry periods will of course influence recovery and production when water again becomes available. Even with succulents, which conserve tissue water and carbon very efficiently (115, 156), the level to which ψ_{leaf} falls appears to govern leaf survival. At the same time, leaves with a small change in water content per bar decrease in ψ_{leaf}, such as relatively inelastic sclerophylls (41), can tolerate very low levels of ψ_{leaf} (111). On the other hand, it is often stated that continued transpiration and assimilation, albeit at very low levels, and hence root access to some reserves of soil water, are necessary for survival of aridoactive species. Despite this, some sclerophyllous trees can survive several months of negative carbon balance during severe summer drought (e.g. 41), and it is possible that carbon reserves in these plants can substitute for continued assimilation and threatened dessication.

Consideration of survival mechanisms in plants with photosynthetic tissue is also important in the case of seedlings of pasture plants. As pointed out before, short but severe droughts are common after the first germinating rains of the wet season. A water conservative strategy to avoid low ψ_{plant} appears to be the most important means of increasing the probability of seedling survival (e.g. 157, 174).

WATER USE EFFICIENCY

The second major aspect of plant productivity that we wish to discuss is water use efficiency (*WUE*), considered here initially as the net CO_2 uptake per unit of transpiration ($mgCO_2 \ gH_2O^{-1}$), and which can be determined with gas exchange measurements of illuminated photosynthetic tissue. It is appropriate to begin the discussion at the single leaf level because the theory of CO_2 and H_2O exchange at this level is reasonably well understood (31, 32, 58, 80, 116). More importantly, both theory and measurements suggest that relative differences in *WUE* at the leaf level are reflected largely unchanged at the canopy level and in terms of dry matter gain per unit water lost, as we shall see later. It is interesting to contrast this situation in respect of *WUE* with that for photosynthetic efficiency, where the great superiority of C_4 plants at the enzyme and leaf level is steadily eroded as one proceeds to the level of canopies and crop growth rates (59).

WUE Determined by Gas Exchange

SINGLE LEAF   The important environmental and genotypic influences on *WUE* are summarized in the following equation:

$$WUE = \Delta c \cdot D_c \ (r_a + r_s \ / \ \Delta e \cdot D_e \ (r_a + r_s + r_i) \qquad\qquad 4.$$

where Δc and Δe are the leaf-to-air concentration differences for CO_2 and water vapor, respectively; D_c and D_e the diffusivities of CO_2 and water vapor, respectively; and r_a, r_s and r_i the boundary layer, stomatal, and internal resistances to diffusion, respectively. Equation 4 assumes that CO_2 and water vapor take identical paths between the leaf cell walls and bulk air, therefore ignoring the cuticular pathway of water loss.

It is sufficient for our purposes to assume that the CO_2 concentration at the chloroplast is zero. This means that the r_i term of Equation 4 includes photorespiratory effects as well as other apparent and actual internal diffusive resistances to CO_2. As a result, Δc equals the concentration of CO_2 in the atmosphere, 0.58 mg l^{-1} at 25°C. Assuming D_c/D_e is 0.6, Equation 4 simplifies to:

$$WUE = (360/\Delta e) \ [(r_a + r_s)/(r_a + r_s + r_i)] \qquad\qquad 5.$$

with *WUE* in units of mgCO$_2$ gH$_2$O^{-1} and Δe mg l^{-1}. The intercellular air spaces of the leaf are assumed to be saturated with water vapor at the leaf temperature. It should be pointed out that for reasons intrinsic in the model upon which Equation 4 is based, r_s and r_i are not entirely independent (31) and, more significantly, nor are Δe and $(r_a + r_s)$ independent. This latter complication arises because Δe depends on leaf temperature. Leaf temperature in turn depends on the leaf energy balance, one determinant of which is the influence of r_a and r_s on latent and convective heat transfer (31, 58, 80, 116). We shall return to this problem when discussing the influence of changes in r_s and r_a on *WUE*.

The highest *WUE* which might be expected under any conditions can be calculated by assuming in Equation 5 that r_i is zero (infinitely high photosynthetic affinity for CO_2). At a leaf and air temperature of 25°C and an air relative humidity of 50% (air saturation deficit of 12 mg l^{-1}) the *WUE* would be 30 mgCO$_2$ gH$_2$O^{-1}. In reality, with the exception of plants practicing CAM, *WUE* values are usually substantially lower than this.

Of the environmental factors influencing *WUE*, air saturation deficit through its influence on vapor concentration in the air, and hence Δe, has a major effect on *WUE*. From theory (Equation 5) and measurement (14, 125), *WUE* is linearly related to the reciprocal of Δe, other things remaining equal, and thus decreases as the saturation deficit increases. Air saturation deficit varies diurnally, from day to day, seasonally and regionally, depending on air temperature and absolute humidity of the air. Midday values encountered by arid and semiarid zone plants may range from 10 mg l^{-1} to as high as 60 mg l^{-1} under hot dry conditions. The major influence of air temperature on *WUE* operates via its effects on Δe; Δe is usually closely coupled to air temperature in the field (137). Thus increased air temperature reduces *WUE*, unless leaf temperature is markedly suboptimal for photosynthesis as it may be in mediterranean environments in the winter (100).

The importance of another environmental variable, incident irradiance, is seen without recourse to Equation 5. It derives from the fact that transpiration is always positive, showing a relationship which is linear or curvilinear upward with increasing irradiance, because of rising leaf temperature and falling r_s, while net photosynthesis, especially of C_3 species, shows downward curvilinearity with increased irradiance and is negative at zero irradiance. Thus there is an optimum irradiance for maximum *WUE* (14, 40, 80); this optimum is usually less than the irradiance incident upon a leaf oriented normal to the sun's rays. Thus leaf orientation at an appropriate angle to these rays, by reducing the effective incident irradiance, can increase WUE (80, 100). Leaf movements which orient the leaf parallel to the sun's rays, leaf rolling and flagging, erect leaves and needle-like leaves, all common features of dry situations especially once ψ_{leaf} begins to fall, can be considered adaptations to increase WUE. Increased reflection of incident radiation would for the same reasons tend to increase WUE. Sorghum leaves with normal wax bloom, which increases reflectivity (16), had slightly higher WUE values than bloomless leaves in a study of isogenic lines (24). Furthermore, reflectivity attributable to leaf hairs increases substantially with plant water deficit in the arid-zone species *Encelia farinosa* (44).

Passing to the influence on WUE of the leaf traits r_a, r_s, and r_i, it is obvious from what has been said that comparisons between genotypes must take place under the same ambient conditions. In addition, we shall see that genotype by environment interactions need to be considered. This complex situation is amenable to theoretical analysis (31, 80, 116). Our limited remarks will be based on analyses (80, 116) in which allowance has been made in the leaf energy balance for long wave thermal emission as well as convective and latent heat exchange.

Beginning with stomatal aperture, theory points to increased WUE as r_s increases, except when the ratio of r_i to r_a is less than a given critical value (80). This latter condition is uncommon, requiring low r_i, as in C$_4$ species, high r_a as with large leaves or low wind speeds, and high air temperature. Under conditions of water shortage when r_i is usually higher, WUE should always increase as r_s increases (80). The high minimum r_s values of many aridoactive species (27, 41) should also favor high WUE.

Calculations suggest that WUE increases as r_a is reduced, except under conditions of low radiation and high air temperature and saturation deficit (80, 116). Since r_a decreases as leaf size decreases, it has been suggested that a major factor explaining leaf size variation across all plant communities is the need to maximize WUE (116). The decrease in leaf size, and hence r_a, as aridity increases is seen to fit this hypothesis, as also would the large size of the photosynthetic organs of many CAM plants when it is considered that a large r_a maximizes WUE for dark assimilation (116). Leaf surface morphology also influences r_a; in particular pubescence can increase r_a (80). However, since increased wind speed reduces r_a, at normal wind speeds in the field r_a is small relative to r_s and r_i and unlikely to dominate the WUE of exposed leaves.

The above considerations of changes in r_s and r_a assume that r_i remains constant. However, because alterations in r_a and r_s affect leaf temperature (58), in situations where leaf temperature is markedly sub- or supraoptimal for photosynthesis, these temperature changes will influence r_i and modify predicted responses in WUE (100, 116). Change in r_i will have no direct effect on the leaf's energy balance and the result for WUE can be seen by inspection of the ratio $(r_a + r_s)/(r_a + r_s + r_i)$ to which WUE is directly proportional (Equation 5). Various workers (68, 125, 156) have used this dimensionless resistance ratio or, since r_a is usually small, the simpler $r_s/(r_s + r_i)$ (55, 144) as a useful index of genotypic effects on WUE. Notwithstanding the need for caution in the situation where r_s changes, as outlined earlier, we shall also refer to this resistance ratio. Decreased r_i increases the ratio and inevitably increases WUE. C_4 plants have high light-saturated photosynthetic rates because their r_i values are one-half or less than those of C_3 plants; their r_s values are often somewhat greater than those of C_3 plants (40, 59, 95, 125). As a consequence, the resistance ratio of C_4 plants usually ranges from 0.7 to 0.8 while that for C_3 plants ranges from 0.2 to 0.4 (125, 156), and measured WUE of the former group is two- to threefold higher under the same ambient conditions (40, 95, 125, 144). There are exceptions to this pattern, for example, jojoba (*Simmondsia chinensis*), a C_3 aridoactive shrub, showed a resistance ratio of 0.6 in one study (125). Also, since C_4 plants normally occupy warmer habitats than C_3 plants, the WUE advantage of the former under their respective field conditions may not be as great. In addition, the data of Caldwell et al (22) suggest that C_4 plants adapted to cooler regions have higher values of r_i and have lost their advantage in terms of WUE. It would be interesting to know the resistance ratios of those C_3 desert plants with exceptionally high photosynthetic rates, such as *Camissonia claviformis* (103).

Differences in WUE within the C_3 and C_4 groups have been identified in gas exchange studies with tree species (68), barley lines of different stomatal frequency (101), perennial pasture grasses (55), citrus species (85), and various crop plants (125). With the exception of the citrus study, higher WUE was associated with higher r_s rather than lower r_i, and with lower photosynthetic rates, a situation exemplified by jojoba with a WUE almost twice that of wheat, but a photosynthetic rate of only one-fifth that of wheat (125). Even so, the WUE of jojoba fell well below that of several C_4 species in the same study.

Thus far we have not considered explicitly the response of WUE to declining ψ_{leaf} and possible genotypic differences in response. As already discussed, r_s is likely to increase. Although work employing relatively rapid leaf drying suggests that r_i may be insensitive to ψ_{leaf} (69, 146), with slower field drying it is probable that r_i will also increase (77, 80). The net effect on WUE will depend on relative changes in r_s and r_i, approximately as seen in the resistance ratio. Generally gas exchange measurements show WUE is unchanged (78, 145) or increased (77) by decreased ψ_{leaf}, but there are exceptions (77, 140) and there is need for more measurements under drying rates typical of field situations.

Considerations of responses in WUE to dry situations must also include the recent demonstration of a direct effect of air saturation deficit on stomatal aperture, namely, r_s increases as saturation deficit increases even though ψ_{leaf} may not decrease (135). Such stomatal responses reduce, but do not eliminate, the decline in WUE to be expected as Δe rises (84, 136). Direct stomatal response to humidity has been demonstrated in a number of herbaceous and tree species including arid zone ones (84, 135, 139), but may not be present in all species (125, 139). Differences between species and interactions of the response with environment has been discussed recently (64). Since the response of stomata to air saturation deficit appears to show acclimation, and since many studies have used nonfield-grown material, there is need for more field data before the full ecological significance of the stomatal response to humidity is understood.

So far our discussion of WUE at the leaf level has only considered instantaneous WUE. Daily WUE (daytime CO_2 uptake/daytime transpiration) and the important question of how a plant may behave to maximize this is more complex. In the absence of adjustments in the leaf, theory points to a decline in *WUE* in the middle of the day largely because of the rise in air saturation deficit and the likely light saturation of photosynthesis. Recently Cowan & Farquhar (32) have calculated the stomatal behavior required to maximize daily *WUE*. To achieve this, especially in the case of C_3 plants but not necessarily with C_4 plants, r_s must show a midday increase and an afternoon minimum somewhat higher than the morning minimum. This is in fact the type of diurnal stomatal response often found as water becomes limited (126, 138, 163). To maximize daily *WUE*, the direct response of stomata to some external condition affecting the rate of transpiration is demanded (32); the humidity response just described fits this requirement. The response is so effective in apricot (*Prunus armeniaca*) that its daily *WUE* in the Negev changes little from the mild days of spring to the hot ones of late summer (136), and this appears also to be the case for the sclerophyllous shrub *Heteromeles arbutifolia* in mediterranean California (100).

Another example of adaptation to the diurnal changes in environmental factors affecting *WUE* is the behavior of CAM plants, reviewed separately in this volume (115). Typically CAM plants carry out gas exchange at night, when because of lower air saturation deficits and negative absorbed radiation Δe is much lower than during the day. Combined with resistance ratios similar to C_4 plants (~ 0.8) when fixing CO_2 in the dark (156), this means CAM plants can achieve high *WUE* values, for example, as high as 50 mgCO$_2$ gH$_2$O^{-1} with *Agave americana* (106). In some CAM plants, night fixation of CO_2 always predominates, while in others water stress appears to induce night fixation of CO_2, and in the absence of stress, they fix most or all of their CO_2 during the day, thereby achieving higher rates of carbon gain but at the expense of high *WUE* (106). The overall productivity of CAM plants is low, especially when fixing carbon in the CAM mode (115).

Akin to considerations of the diurnal march of *WUE* are those of its seasonal march. Where water is limited, maximum annual *WUE* will arise if greater stomatal opening and transpiration is associated with those days and/or months when the environment favors maximum *WUE*. For example, with Negev desert shrubs transpiration is concentrated in the late winter and early spring when air temperature and humidity is likely to be most favorable for *WUE* (47).

CANOPIES   Gas exchange theory has been extended to horizontally uniform plant communities such as crops and forests; resultant canopy models have been used to predict canopy *WUE* (100, 140, 169). With canopies rather than single leaves, some allowance must be made for the fact the effective r_a is greater because of additional resistances within and above the canopy (80, 144). This means that situations in which an increase in r_s does not increase *WUE* may be more common, although those when a reduction in r_a does not increase *WUE* are still likely to be rare (80). Because of the difficulties involved, direct tests of these predictions through determination of canopy gas exchange are few. Micrometerological measurements of the maize canopy have shown that *WUE* increased substantially with increased wind speed and therefore reduced r_a (93), and decreased with mild soil water stress, presumably as r_s increased (93, 140). In the study by Sinclair et al (140), the measured response of canopy WUE to the change in r_s agreed with that predicted from a single leaf model of WUE.

The above-mentioned canopy data was obtained with high LAI values and relatively humid mesic conditions. These may be of limited relevance to communities under drier conditions where smaller LAI would tend to reduce r_a relative to r_s and r_i, and horizontal advection could be greater. However, these conditions increase the likelihood that predictions and measurements based on single leaves would be faithfully reflected in differences, particularly genotypic ones, in WUE at the community level.

WUE Based on Dry Matter Accumulation

Much information on WUE is available from determinations of dry matter accumulation and transpiration of plants in containers, crops or natural communities, and sampled at intervals of one week to several months. The exact relationship between WUE in terms of $mgDM$ gH_2O^{-1} and that expressed as $mgCO_2$ gH_2O^{-1}, which we have used until now, will depend on the carbon content of dry matter: values from 0.61 to 0.68 gDM gCO_2^{-1} are common for most growing plants. Provided dry matter accumulation in roots is included, and losses due to grazing, decomposition, etc are negligible, the only other difference with respect to WUE based on daytime gas exchange arises because of respiratory losses at night and in nonphotosynthetic tissue, and possible night transpirational losses (e.g. 163). WUE based on dry matter accumulation will necessarily be lower as a result. Respiratory losses are in fact a substantial proportion of net daytime photosynthesis (94). These losses can be usefully separated into growth and maintenance components, the quantities of respiration involved being relatively fixed fractions of growth rate and of total dry matter, respectively (121). Major long-term effects of reduced ψ_{plant} on these fractions have not been reported, but the existence of a maintenance component, regardless of the level of net daytime photosynthesis, means that leaf strategies for maximum long-term WUE will be different from those giving maximum daytime WUE (80).

WUE based on dry matter accumulation often suffers from two complications. First, transpiration and soil evaporation may not be separated so that WUE is calculated using evapotranspiration. Second, roots are commonly neglected in measuring dry matter accumulation. Compared to WUE as defined here, these effects may reduce the resultant calculated WUE by as little as 20% in adequately watered annual crops, but in other situations, for example perennial species or containers from which evaporation is not prevented, the reduction could be greater than 50%. Studies where the above complications were absent or of minimal significance were for obvious reasons usually container experiments. Effects upon WUE as determined in these experiments agree with conclusions reached from gas exchange considerations and measurement, especially with regard to the major effect of air saturation deficit and the difference between C_3 and C_4 plants.

Looking at environmental effects on WUE in container studies, de Wit (37a) showed a strong inverse relationship between WUE and free water evaporation (E_o), a relationship which others pointed out probably derives largely from the effects of air saturation deficit on both WUE and E_o (14). In a careful study of six wheat cultivars planted at monthly intervals in a mediterranean environment of southern Australia, WUE was also inversely related to E_o (J. F. Warren and W. J. Lill, personal communication). This relationship combined with average monthly E_o predicts the seasonal march of WUE, which varies from as high as 8.5 mgDM gH_2O^{-1} in midwinter to only 2.5 mgDM gH_2O^{-1} in midsummer. In semiarid Israel, measured fluctuations in container-determined WUE due to seasonal changes in atmospheric conditions agreed closely with predictions from gas exchange theory (166). Further examples of the relationship between WUE and E_o are given later (see Table 1).

Downes (39), regrouping data from many early container experiments, calculated mean WUE values of 1.5 mgDM gH_2O^{-1} and 3.3 mgDM gH_2O^{-1} for C_3 and C_4 species, respectively; differences he confirmed with several common crop and pasture species. A more recent comparison of desert shrubs showed a WUE value of 1.4 mgDM gH_2O^{-1} for the C_4 species *Atriplex canescens* compared to a mean value of 0.7 mgDM gH_2O^{-1} for C_3 species, including creosote bush (*Larrea tridentata*) and mesquite (*Prosopis juliflora*) (42). In striking contrast to all these values, a CAM plant, pineapple (*Ananas comosus*), showed a gain of 20 mgDM gH_2O^{-1} (83).

Container experiments, on the other hand, suggest that there are not large differences in WUE between plants of the same life form within the C_3 and C_4 groups (e.g. 42, 166). For example, van Keulen (166) found no difference between several temperate crop species and annual pasture plants native to the semiarid zone. The above-mentioned study with six contrasting wheat cultivars (J. F. Warren and W. J. Lill, personal communication) revealed no significant differences in WUE when WUE was corrected for differences in transpiration pattern and corresponding E_o and root as well as shoot accumulation was considered.

The record of container experiments with respect to the influence of soil and presumably leaf water deficit on WUE is not so clear cut. Some experiments show relatively small changes in WUE (37a), whereas others suggest that WUE increases with increasing soil water limitation until a maximum WUE is reached, beyond which greater limitation lowers WUE (e.g. 42, 43). Earlier we pointed out that the consequences for WUE of lowered leaf water potential will depend on the relative changes in r_s and r_i and probably on the rate of drying. The effects of nutrient deficiency on WUE has also been studied in containers, but effects were generally small (2, 37a). On the other hand, increases in water-limited pasture productivity with nitrogen application (e.g. 20, 166) are indirectly suggestive of WUE increases.

The environment of container experiments may not exactly represent that of field communities, especially with respect to reproducing the canopy microclimate, and also the balance between the growth of various plant parts may change due to reduced interplant competition or reduced soil volume. While such effects may influence the absolute levels of WUE, our discussion of gas exchange would suggest that differences arising from genotypic or other treatment effects should still be valid. This is very important because, for obvious reasons, there are few field studies where measurements of WUE based on dry matter accumulation are relatively free from complications due the inclusion of soil evaporation or neglect of root dry matter. One such field study in Kansas compared summer crops of sorghum, a C_4 species, and soybean (*Glycine max*) a C_3 species: the former had a *WUE* approximately three times greater than that of the latter and a peak *WUE* of 7 mg*DM* gH_2O^{-1} (155). Very detailed investigations in the high desert of Utah determined an annual average *WUE* of 4.3 mg*DM* gH_2O^{-1} for a C_4 shrub community (*Atriplex confertifolia*) and 2.9 mg*DM* gH_2O^{-1} for an adjacent C_3 one (*Ceratoides lanata*) (22). This result did not contradict gas exchange measurements which showed little difference in *WUE* at the leaf level: the small *WUE* advantage of the *Atriplex* community was apparently due to smaller underground respiratory losses. Ludlow & Wilson (95) quote values of 3 and 1.4 mg*DM* gH_2O^{-1} for swards of a tropical C_4 grass and tropical C_3 legume, respectively. These relatively precise community values of *WUE* and others to be given later (see Table 1) fall within the range of approximate values (1 to 6 mg*DM* gH_2O^{-1}) for desert ecosystems derived simply from the slope of production-precipitation relationships (110).

Agronomists often report that improved management (e.g. fertilization, planting density, etc) and plant breeding have led to substantial gains in water use efficiency in terms of yield of economic product per unit water supplied (4, 4a, 9). However, it is unlikely that *WUE* as we have defined it (total dry matter per unit transpiration) has increased. Most of the gains reported derive from increases in transpiration as a fraction of water supply, due to greater soil extraction and greater plant cover reducing soil-evaporation, or from increases in harvest index. Even in the case of forage production, claims that efficiency doubled with nitrogen fertilization of semiarid annual pastures (166) could largely reflect savings of soil evaporation.

ASSIMILATE PARTITIONING

Discussion until now has centered around Equation 1, the production of assimilate. The partitioning of each day's assimilate will also in the longer term affect productivity (94, 102) and exert a major influence upon the yield of economic product in the case of crops. By partitioning we refer to the allocation of current assimilate, and at times mobilization of stored assimilate, to metabolic sinks in the plant.

In contrast to the situation with transpiration and water use efficiency, genotype exerts major control over partitioning. Some genotypic effects on partitioning are expressed regardless of environment in which the plant is grown, but appear to be appropriate for the environment to which the plant is adapted, for example, the plant life forms already discussed in relation to dry environments. We shall also be interested in genotypic effects on assimilate allocation which only appear when water is limiting. These two types of adaptation can be considered constitutive and facultative and are synonymous with the concepts of strategy and tactics, respectively, applied by Harper & Ogden (65a) to the allocation of energy and dry weight in plants. Tactical responses will depend on lowered ψ_{plant}, but it should be pointed out at the outset that direct effects of ψ_{plant} on phloem transport of assimilate are unlikely to be involved since such effects appear to be small (146, 172).

Selection by man has modified the allocation patterns of plants in order to achieve better performance in semiarid monoculture and greater yield of economic product, i.e. greater seed yield in the case of crops and more digestible dry matter in pastures. Natural selection in mixed plant communities has led to a great diversity of allocation patterns, but it should have favored maximum seed production and harvest index in annual plants (65a), thereby leading to some common ground with at least annual crops.

Phenology

Phenology refers to the timing of major developmental events such as germination, floral initiation, flowering, seed maturity, leaf fall, etc. These events, through the control of meristematic sinks, determine the basic temporal framework for partitioning of assimilate and represent a major mechanism by which plants adapt to water-limited environments.

ANNUALS   The phenology of annuals is such that flowering and seed filling is largely completed during the probable period of available water. Internal control mechanisms including dormancy, germination inhibitors, and sensitivity to temperature, light, and quantity of water prevent seed germination at unfavorable times and in unfavorable habitats (47, 48, 105, 110, 112). Flowering of desert ephemerals may begin soon after germination so that the whole life cycle can be completed within as little as several weeks; nevertheless, if conditions remain favorable, further vegetative growth and flowering may take place (105). While it may seem appropriate that phenology be tied to environment through direct responses to water, with the exception of the obvious need for water for germination, the important environmental stimuli for most other phenological events are temperature and, in particular, photoperiod. Sudden and/or severe early water stress has been shown to delay floral initiation (e.g. 97), but the delay was small and more commonly floral initiation has been found to be insensitive to stress (e.g. 104). Flowering is generally hastened slightly by plant water stress (162), but has also been found to be unaffected in some desert ephemerals (104); in wheat, although accelerated by mild stress, flowering was delayed by severe stress, the delay being approximately equal to the duration of severe stress (3). Photoperiodic control, on the other hand, ensures that the date of flowering is relatively independent of water supply or date of germination. This would seem appropriate since calendar date rather than germination date is the better predictor of the end of the wet season. It means that annual plants of the semiarid savanna region tend to be short-day plants and those of the mediterranean region long-day plants.

The maturation of seeds and duration of the seed filling phase is largely controlled by factors internal to the seed interacting with environmental temperature. Water stress during seed filling will usually, but not always (104), accelerate seed maturation, but to a lesser extent than the associated acceleration of leaf death (13, 104).

Looking specifically at annual plants subject to selection by man, long-term seed dormancy has largely been eliminated from crop plants, but remains important to ensure persistence in pasture plants. The opportunistic indeterminate strategy seen in many native annuals is also recognized in some crop plants, for example tropical leguminous pulses such as peanut (*Arachis hypogaea*), cowpea (*Vigna unguiculata*), and cotton (18). Natural selection in wild species and in primitive agriculture of the semiarid zone appears to have favored the indeterminate strategy in some species. Other species are determinate and flowering represents an abrupt and irreversible end to further vegetative growth. Thus for maximum yield, flowering must take place at a given time before the expected end of the supply of available water. For example, in Nigeria the flowering date of locally adapted sorghum cultivars is precisely controlled by subtle sensitivity to photoperiod in order to coincide with the average date of termination of the wet season rains at each location regardless of the sowing date (33). Such sensitivity to photoperiod is usually associated, however, with specific adaptation to small regions. On the other hand, the often spectacular increase in adaptation to drier regions (shorter wet seasons) achieved by modern plant breeders in crops such as wheat, barley, sorghum, and cotton has been closely linked to earlier flowering (63, 161) as a result of the lessening of sensitivity to photoperiod.

PERENNIALS For drought-deciduous perennials the important developmental events of leaf production at the onset of the wet season and leaf fall after its end appear to be controlled by water supply to the plant, although in the mediterranean and steppe zones, where winter temperatures are low, leaf production is often delayed until early spring (6, 37, 122). Also in some savanna species leaf production may precede the onset of rains. With evergreen perennials, leaf production appears to require a substantial pulse of assimilation and hence water (28, 114); for example, leaf production can occur at any time of the year in *Acacia harpophylla* growing in the Australian transition zone (28). Leaf fall, or the switch to a more xeromorphic leaf type in dimorphic shrubs (23, 37, 113), is probably controlled by declining ψ_{plant} (23, 89, 168).

   Seed production in perennials is not critical for survival, and flowering and seed filling often occur at times which do not appear to be the most favorable for assimilation; for example, *Artemisia tridentata,* a shrub of arid steppe regions, flowers in late summer (23, 37) and drought-deciduous perennials of the savanna zone often flower in the dry season (171). For this reason control of flowering by photoperiodism should again predominate, although in coffee (*Coffea arabica*) flowering does appear to require low ψ_{plant} followed by recovery to high ψ_{plant} (96), as would occur with the onset of rains after a dry period.

Photosynthetic Tissue

The investment of a high proportion of assimilate in new photosynthetic tissue, i.e. a high leaf area to total dry weight or leaf area to leaf weight, maximizes plant growth rate and usually community growth rate when water is not limiting (18, 94, 102). However, under water-limited conditions these ratios are usually lower and other strategies operate. There are two aspects to this: namely, the morphology of photosynthetic organs and the quantity of such organs relative to other tissues.

   A multitude of changes in the morphology of leaves and other green organs appear to be correlated with adaptation to increasing aridity and xerophytism (112). Some adaptations which may increase tolerance to low ψ_{leaf} and increase WUE have been discussed earlier. Here we will concentrate on specific leaf density (leaf weight per unit area), which generally increases with aridity. For example, the aridoactive sclerophyllous plants of the mediterranean zone have specific leaf densities of 1 to 2 gDM dm^{-2} (41), compared to values of 0.5 to 1.4 gDM dm^{-2} for aridopassive shrubs in the same zone (100), and to values of around 0.4 g.DM dm^{-2} for aridopassive herbaceous plants (60). Some aridoactive shrubs exhibit leaf dimorphism, producing denser smaller leaves during the dry season (23, 37, 113).

The increased specific leaf density in the sclerophylls results from heavy investment in such nonphotosynthetic components as fibers, vessels, cell walls, sclerenchyma, and the accumulation of silica (48). This strategy appears to favor not only survival but also photosynthetic ability at very low ψ_{leaf}; however, it is also associated with low maximal rates of photosynthesis (41, 100, 138, 165).

Amongst the herbaceous plants it is not clear whether there are differences in specific leaf density of adaptive significance. Differences do occur between crop species and cultivars and tend to be positively associated with photosynthetic rate per unit leaf area (86, 120, 158) and therefore possibly WUE. Within the $Triticum$ genus and $Brassica$ family it has been suggested that the better adaptation to more xeric environments of their more primitive members compared to the more mesophytic cultivated species is associated with smaller, denser (measured as weight of nitrogen per unit leaf area) leaves, having a greater ratio of vascular tissue to photosynthetic tissue and a greater photosynthetic rate (86, 158). Also the response of herbaceous plants to water stress, the xeromorphoses described by Stocker (151), such as the production of smaller denser leaves, could be considered adaptive.

The fact that desert annuals do not have strikingly xeromorphic leaves does not exclude the possibility of other leaf adaptations. For example, summer annuals generally have simple entire leaves and Kranz-type anatomy indicative of C_4 photosynthesis, whereas winter annuals generally have highly dissected rosette leaves that lack the Kranz anatomy (105). The rosette form may be an adaptation to increase leaf temperature and enhance growth during the winter, when the availability of soil water is greatest (105).

With regard to the overall allocation of assimilate to leaf growth, this appears to be generally lower with water limitation. Also it should be mentioned that leaf longevity, or conversely the rate of leaf abscission and death, combine with the allocation factor to determine the ratio of total quantity or area of active leaves to biomass at any point in time. Thus hastening of leaf death with decreased ψ_{plant} will lead to further downward adjustment of this ratio. The extent to which carbon and minerals such as nitrogen are translocated out of these leaves before they die is an important aspect of partitioning on which there is little information.

Roots

Perennial grasses and shrubs of dry regions generally have root/shoot ratios above 1 and higher than those of humid regions (20, 47, 112), although low temperature may also contribute to this high ratio in the steppe zone (110), and some warm desert shrubs have ratios below 1 (7, 110). Part of the root mass may represent carbon reserve rather than functional absorbing tissue. There are some situations, for example in perennial aridopassive grasses at the beginning of the growing season, when root reserves should be supplying growing leaves and hence the allocation to roots would be negative. It should also be emphasized that the root/shoot ratio at any point in time not only reflects the proportion of assimilate allocated to roots, but also the rate of death or turnover of roots relative to tops. Both components appear to favor high root/shoot ratios in arid zone perennials. With annual plants of dry regions root/shoot ratios at maturity are lower than the ratios of perennials, presumably because of accumulation of assimilate in seeds in annuals. The ratios range from 0.1 to 1.0 (26, 46, 104, 110, 153, 166) and are not clearly higher than in annuals not native to dry regions (110, 166).

It is commonly observed that the root/shoot ratio increases with lower ψ_{soil} in annuals from both mesic and arid environments (8, 43, 102, 151, 153) and in arid zone perennials (42). Soil water deficiency can double the root/shoot ratio, increasing the absolute mass of roots in some situations (10, 70). Increased air saturation deficit can also increase the root/shoot ratio (67, 151). In general, it appears that the root/shoot ratio changes so as to maintain ψ_{plant} within certain limits. Possible mechanisms for the regulation of root/shoot ratios have been discussed elsewhere (49, 70, 74). It is useful to point out here that such responses in the root/shoot ratio can be associated with deeper rooting (10) and hence greater available water in some situations, and that there may be cultivar and species differences in these responses (10, 72). Finally, while more roots may mean more water uptake by the particular plant in a competitive situation, it may not increase total water extraction by the plant community, and in crops it could be disadvantageous (117).

In grasses two types of absorbing roots are produced, the seminal roots and the nodal or adventitious roots. The latter, which require moisture in the surface layer of the soil for initial growth, may be important for establishment and growth in species where the resistance of primary seminal root to water flow is high [e.g. in *Bouteloua gracilis* (174)]. Seminal roots in wheat, on the other hand, may be responsible for a major portion of deep soil water extraction (62), and this fact forms the basis of an aforementioned hypothesis (see Transpiration Modulation) for rationing water use by wheat (117).

Reproductive Tissues

In perennials seed production each year is not critical for survival and the production of reproductive tissues is smaller as proportion of total assimilate production than in annuals (102). There are exceptions such as biennials and *Agave* species; for example, *A. deserti* flowers only once, at the end of a lifetime of 10 to 30 years, and floral and seed production depend heavily on carbon and water stored from earlier years (109). The reproductive effort of perennials in any year is very sensitive to water limitation, fluctuating widely from year to year according to the degree of water stress during the growing season (6) or even the preceding growing season. For example, the yield of unirrigated apricots was correlated, via effects on flower bud initiation, with the date at which the soil water was depleted in the previous season (164).

In most annuals, survival depends on viable seed production. It would therefore seem appropriate that annual plants should function so as to maximize the amount of assimilate going to the seed (65a). As we look at seed yield in annuals in the remainder of this section, it is useful to separate the determination of seed number from that of seed size. Also, differences in seed yield arising from the effects of water deficit on total assimilation need to be distinguished from the effects of deficits on the pattern of assimilate allocation through time. For example, the reduction in seed yield with water limitation is often in proportion to the reduction in total dry matter production (17, 132) or to the reduction in assimilation at ontogenetically important stages for dry matter accumulation in reproductive tissues. Thus, water deficit during seed filling can reduce yield without altering the pattern of assimilate allocation at any point in time.

SEED NUMBER   The production of floral primordia following floral initiation appears to be sensitive to water stress (146). However, field studies suggest that seed number and crop yield are relatively insensitive to early drought, i.e. drought until approximately halfway to flowering which corresponds to the period of production of floral primordia (53, 73, 134). The main reason for this insensitivity to early water limitation appears to be that annual plants normally produce many more reproductive primordia than can be grown to full size under the competitive conditions of most plant communities. This optimistic strategy is apparently satisfactory because the carbon investment involved in initiating primordia is minimal. Seed number is much more influenced by factors affecting the growth and survival of these primordia, and consequently the influence of water limitation upon these processes is more important.

Assimilate allocation to reproductive organs of annual plants is not substantial until flowering is approached. Because the assimilate available, especially where there is interplant competition as in crops, is insufficient to grow all potential reproductive primordia, some fail. This results in tiller mortality and the production of rudimentary spikelets and florets in, for example, wheat and barley. Water stress accelerates these processes, but from limited information in cereals, the effect probably operates via reduced assimilation because the proportion of total assimilate allocated to reproductive organs is unchanged or may in fact increase with water stress (91a; R. A. Fischer, unpublished). The effect on organ growth may not arise simply because of reduced assimilate supply since labile carbohydrate reserves often increase with water deficit (e.g. 8); direct effects of stress on the growing reproductive sink are probably also involved. The curious substantial increase in female inflorescence growth and survival in maize subsequent to water stress at the time of initiation of the terminal male inflorescence (34) illustrates the complexity of the control of this partitioning.

Although preflowering water limitations appear to be primarily reflected in reduced dry matter accumulation in reproductive tissue, additionally there are effects of water deficits on reproductive efficiency, defined here by the number of flowers, and later seeds, produced per unit of dry matter investment in the inflorescence. Water stress can interfere with microsporogenesis, pollination, and fertilization, and can induce abortion of young seeds or abscission of young fruits (9, 50, 134, 146). Such effects appear to involve direct effects of water stress on the tissues and processes involved, and would seem to fall into the category of effects on reproductive efficiency. However, few measurements of seed number per unit inflorescence weight have been made. Calculations using unpublished data of the experiments of Fischer (50) show that plant water stress for 3 days, beginning at 22 or at 2 days before ear emergence in wheat, reduced seed number in proportion to the reduction in inflorescence weight, whereas stress beginning 16 and 9 days before ear emergence, characterized by male sterility and drastic reductions in seed number, reduced both inflorescence weight and seeds per unit inflorescence weight. Seed number was relatively insensitive to plant water stress once anthesis had passed.

Comparative data on the sensitivity of reproductive efficiency in different species to water stress are unavailable, but it appears that most, if not all, species show heightened sensitivity around flowering (134). Because of the different mechanisms involved in different types of plants, comparisons between them may be of little value. Even comparisons within species are difficult because of the importance of matching both ψ_{plant} and the exact stage of inflorescence development. When ten wheat cultivars representing four related species were stressed under controlled conditions at the same stage of development just before ear emergence, effects of a given level of ψ_{plant} on seed number were not strikingly different between them (R. A. Fischer, unpublished). On the other hand, the spread of inflorescence growth over longer periods of time, as with the indeterminate habit of growth, should reduce the risk of drastic reductions in seed number with short stress periods.

The widespread existence of a critical period during which seed number is particularly sensitive to water limitation may seem, in terms of carbon efficiency, wasteful because carbon is lost when organs are shed. This adjustment of seed number, however, may be a mechanism for ensuring adequate seed size in the cases where flowering occurs toward the end of the wet season. It would seem an appropriate mechanism for those situations in which mild plant water stress at the stage when the seed number is determined provides a reliable index of more severe stress, and hence assimilate limitation, during the subsequent seed-filling phase. Man is unlikely to have selected against such mechanisms, since he also is interested in seed size.

SEED FILLING   Soon after the seeds begin to fill, they become a strong sink for current assimilate, and a large proportion, at least in determinate annual plants, of total assimilation over the whole seed-filling period goes to the seed (e.g. 13, 79). The other source of seed carbon is assimilate stored in the plant before the onset of seed filling and later transferred to the seed. This source appears to be small in adequately watered cereals (e.g. 13). Water stress during seed filling has its major effect upon current assimilation, both through reductions in assimilatory activity and assimilatory surface (9). As mentioned earlier, the duration of seed filling may also be curtailed. Water stress not only increases the proportion of current assimilate translocated to the seed (13, 79), but also may increase the contribution from assimilate stored prior to seed filling (17, 29, 118): this contribution when expressed relative to total seed yield more clearly increases with water stress (13, 57).

Differences among species in these response patterns to water deficits at seed filling have rarely been examined explicitly. Bidinger (13) compared wheat and barley crops in the presence and absence of water stress at seed filling and found no differences in the response of assimilatory surface and activity to stress which could not be explained by small differences in the date of anthesis. Also, the absolute contribution to seed yield of assimilate stored prior to anthesis as determined by repeated ^{14}C canopy labeling was unaffected by water stress or by species, but relative to seed yield the contribution rose from 12% with no water deficit to 22% when there was a deficit during seed filling. One favorable adaptation to water limitation during seed filling appears to be the presence of awns in wheat and barley. For example, in wheat under water stress, the contribution of assimilate to the grains from awns increases relative to that of other sources of assimilate (45). Hsiao et al (71) also suggest that the lack of maintenance of assimilatory activity close to the growing seed may partly explain the greater reduction of yield of maize compared to that of sorghum under water-limited conditions. In maize, dry matter accumulation in the ear comes from assimilation in the middle canopy leaves close to the cob; in sorghum it comes from upper canopy leaves; the former are physiologically older and more likely to die under stress (94a).

Harvest Index

The effects of water limitation on seed yield can be summarized usefully by the harvest index (HI) in many situations (37a, 119). Where water deficits develop early, or are mild and evenly distributed over the life of the plant, *HI* is unaffected (37a). On the other hand, if stress is concentrated around flowering or in the seed-filling stage, *HI* can be reduced substantially (52, 91a, 118, 119, 134). For example, Passioura (118, 119) showed under controlled conditions that *HI* of several wheat cultivars was linearly related to the percentage of total transpiration occurring in the postanthesis period; *HI* was maximized if this was 30% or greater. Similar results have been obtained in a study of the striking influence of soil texture on the yield of water-limited wheat (91a), and with other wheat and maize crops (1, 26).

Cultivars differ in *HI,* and increase in *HI* is the main route by which the yield of various crop species has been improved by plant breeders (38); total dry matter production and hence water use have changed little with this improvement. From studies with numerous wheat, barley, and triticale cultivars, it seems that *HI* under water-limited conditions is related to *HI* in the absence of water limitation and is in turn positively associated with yield under water limitation (R. A. Fischer, unpublished). This is probably why modern semidwarf wheats with high *HI* have usually given superior yields to supposedly drought-resistant, traditional, tall cultivars under rainfed as well as irrigated conditions (90).

INTEGRATION AND CONCLUSIONS

In this review we have discussed those factors which we believe are key determinants of plant productivity in dry regions. Table 1 illustrates these determinants in the case of four semiarid plant communities. The weather and plant variables listed are in the order that they have been introduced in the preceding discussion. Needless to say, it was very difficult to find examples in the literature where all of these variables had been measured or estimated simultaneously.

Table 1 needs little explanation except to point out that the variation in *WUE* between communities is closely related to that which would be expected from the analysis of de Wit (37a) and the container experiments of van Keulen (166). Their results indicate that the product of *WUE* and E_o was a constant of around 110 to 140 kg ha^{-1} day^{-1} for wheat and many other C_3 species (37a, 166), and 207 kg ha^{-1} day^{-1} for a C_4 species, sorghum (37a). From Table 1, $WUE \cdot E_o$ in kg ha^{-1}

Table 1 Net primary productivity and its determinants for several plant communities[a]

Site	Curlew Valley Utah	Migda Israel	Wagga Wagga New South Wales	Mandan North Dakota
Vegetation	Shrubland C. lanata	Annual pasture	Wheat cv. Heron	Maize cv. 85RM
Period	Oct. 1972 to Sept. 1974	Nov. to May 1971 to 1974	June 1962 to Nov. 1962	May to Oct. 1968 to 1970
Precipitation, P (mm)	258	315	217	228
Change in soil water, ΔS (mm)	0	39	–83	–106
Evapotranspiration, ET (mm)	258	276	300	335
Soil evaporation/ evapotranspiration, E_s/ET	0.53	0.38	0.24[c]	0.20[c]
Transpiration, T (mm)	123	186	229	268
Free water evaporation, E_o[b] (mm day^{-1})	4.8[c]	2.2	2.4	5.5
Water use efficiency, *WUE* (mg DM g H_2O^{-1})	2.9	5.2	5.1	4.2
Net primary production (g m^{-2})	358	950	1,164	1,117
Root/shoot allocation	3.2	0.38	0.13[d]	0.25[d]
Above-ground production (g m^{-2})	86	687	1,030	893
Harvest index, *HI*	—	—	0.29	0.26
Grain yield (g m^{-2})	—	—	303	241
Source	22	166	51, 52	1

[a]Calculated as annual or seasonal means.
[b]For the months of greatest transpiration within the period.
[c]Our estimates.
[d]Taken from other wheat (26) and maize (153) studies.

day^{-1} was 139 (*C. lanata*), 122 (wheat), 114 (annual mediterranean pasture), and 231 (maize). Also, variation in *WUE* from season to season in the annual pasture and maize examples of Table 1 was associated inversely with changes in E_o. Thus, despite our earlier references to many possible ways in which *WUE* may be affected by genotype and environment, in the examples of Table 1 the variation in *WUE* could be attributed largely to the two major influences identified in our discussion, namely Δe and the primary carboxylating enzyme in photosynthesis.

Grain yields are shown for the two crop situations in Table 1. It is interesting that the harvest index of the maize crop ranged from 0.12 to 0.34 across the 3 years studied, bearing a close relationship to variation in the fraction of *ET* occurring after silking. Largely as a result of this *HI* variation, yield varied fourfold, from 93 to 390 g m^{-2} (1).

The results of Table 1 suggest that primary productivity may not differ greatly between life forms in dry regions, provided allowance is made for differences in transpiration, E_o, the initial carboxylating enzymes of photosynthesis, and the root/shoot allocation ratios. Evenari et al (47) concluded that in the arid Negev desert the productivity of life forms as different as lichens and aridoactive shrubs was of the same order of magnitude. Although more data of the type shown in Table 1 is needed, and the lichen-shrub comparison has obvious limitations, it is worthwhile pursuing this point, which essentially means that, other things being equal, *WUE* on a dry matter basis is not greatly affected by life form and presumably is even more stable within life forms. The first implication of this is that maintenance respiration losses relative to net daytime photosynthesis in life forms such as aridoactive perennials with high phytomass and low relative primary productivities (primary productivity/phytomass) may not be much greater than those in other life forms. This suggestion is supported by some estimations of above and below ground respiration as a percentage of net carbon assimilation by green parts: values for two shrub communities in Utah [20% and 36% (22)] and arid acacia and *Atriplex* shrublands in Australia [65% and 55%, respectively (147)], differ little from the range of values (20 to 50%) for crops (94) or a value of 49% estimated for a semiarid steppe grassland of *Bouteloua gracilis* (17a).

The second implication of the suggestion that life forms have similar *WUE* values is that it tends to contradict the common statement that xerophytes balance their water economy at the expense of reduced productivity (e.g. 47, 138). Insofar as this implies increased *WUE* at the expense of productivity, it is worth pointing out that in terms of Equation 1, this can only come about if *T* is lower as a result. While in the short term stomatal closing when Δe is unfavorable for high *WUE* may, for example, lead to an inverse relationship between daily *WUE* and daily *T*, there seems no reason why maximizing *WUE* should affect total seasonal or annual *T*. Also, the implied conflict between water economy and productivity seems to overlook the fact that water not transpired is water lost in terms of productivity. It could be argued that water saved may be important for survival (e.g. 148), but even this seems to disagree with the fact that aridoactive species do not exercise their greatest control over water loss (maximum r_s, reduced leaf area, etc) until there is very little water left (see Transpiration Modulation). Such behavior would seem justified because maximizing T when there is soil water available first reduces losses of water due to competition from adjacent plants and due to soil evaporation (25), and second is conducive to a high WUE insofar as favorable ambient conditions (low E_o) are likely to be associated with periods when the soil is wet.

Throughout this review we have referred to strategies and adaptations of plants which seem to favor the maximization of plant productivity in dry regions through either increasing T as a proportion of available water or increasing WUE. While it is reasonable to assume that as a result of natural selection in undisturbed ecosystems features of plant life are purposeful in the environment in which the plants are found, it is not necessarily true that maximization of productivity has always been favored (43a). For example, discussion of the preceding paragraph implied that there is conflict between maximization of productivity and maximization of survival. While recognizing that uncertainty as to the exact long-term goals of evolution exists, we suggest that maximization of carbon gain, which in a water-limited environment amounts to maximizing the efficiency with which water is acquired and "traded" for carbon, remains central to other goals, such as stress resistance or survival, which may also have to be satisfied.

Another important aspect of the adaptation question is the need to consider plant traits and functions of possible adaptive significance in the proper time and space perspective (43a). In other words, possible adaptations cannot be examined in isolation from the rest of the plant and community in which the plant exists. The cost to the plant of adaptations might seem to be the respiratory cost of building and maintaining the structure, but that which is foregone as a result of the carbon and mineral investment involved needs also to be considered, i.e. we must consider the opportunity cost as economists would term it. For example, more roots may appear to be advantageous for plants in dry regions, but this is likely to arise at the expense of leaf production. Minimization of r_i by heavy investment in photosynthetic enzymes may seem desirable to maximize WUE in C_3 species, but what is the cost to the rest of the plant of the heavy investment of nitrogen in leaves that this necessarily involves? For plants in natural ecosystems the existence of intergenotypic competition will, as already mentioned, modify many strategies. The situation is obviously extremely complex and it will remain difficult to identify convincingly the adaptive significance for productivity of many plant traits in natural ecosystems (43a), although in dry regions the efficient utilization of one environmental resource, water, clearly must take precedence, and there is progress. For example, the field behavior and distribution of CAM plants in the arid zone shows satisfying agreement with what is now known about the structure and function of these plants (115).

This brief discussion of some of the difficulties of determining strategies and adaptations in plant behavior in natural ecosystems has an important bearing upon discussion of these questions in the context of crops and, to a lesser extent, improved pastures. In crops, selection and its goal is determined by man; the general goal is the maximization of yield of economic product, which usually, but not always, coincides with maximization of primary productivity. Also, there is concern not only with the determination of present levels of yield and productivity, but with improving these levels and hence with better adaptations for water-limited environments. The difficulty mentioned before of looking at adaptations out of context and ignoring the opportunity costs remains, but is not as great with crops, because being monospecific, they are less complicated by effects of competition. Certain major constitutive adaptations are widespread in crop plants, such as the annual herbaceous life form, a high harvest index associated with strong reproductive sinks, large seed size and, for many semiarid situations, earliness associated with a reduced vegetative phase. However, the significance of many other features of crop plants, advanced in the literature as desirable adaptations for water-limited environments or useful in drought resistance, is not well established. The value of awns in wheat and barley in dry situations is probably an exception to this rule. In a way, the situation with respect to crops resembles that of natural ecosystems where life form relationships and some other statistical associations with aridity are recognized, but where within any life form and environment great diversity usually exists (27, 43a). Similarly with crops within the context of general adaptations mentioned above, there seem to be many routes to high dryland productivity. The difference in the case of crops is that it is probable that man has yet to find the best way to obtain the greatest possible productivity in semiarid environments. Also with crop plants it is feasible to test the effect of morphological and physiological traits on productivity through the use of isogenic lines and isogenic populations. However, the research effort in breeding and physiology required is substantial (e.g. 152, pp. 13, 311). Mathematical modeling, in particular dynamic whole community (crop) modeling, has been proposed as a tool in this regard (49, 94, 167), and there is little doubt that such modeling will be easier in the case of monospecific communities such as crops than in most natural ecosystems.

Our attempt here to consider plants both in crops and in natural ecosystems has further implications for the improvement of crop productivity in semiarid regions. First, it has become clear that studies dealing with aridoactive plants during long dry periods when, because of low available soil water, they are basically operating in a survival rather than production mode has little relevance to crop productivity or to the response of crop plants to water shortage within the growing season (161). Yet thinking on drought resistance in crop plants appears to be considerably influenced by the survival strategies seen to operate in the case of aridoactive plants. More benefit may be gained by comparing the crop plants to the group of plants from which most were derived; namely, the herbaceous annuals of the semiarid zone. Evolution of herbaceous annuals in semiarid plant communities may have led, on the one hand, to features which are unsuited to modern agriculture. This could arise because competitiveness is favored in the former situation, or because the environment of modern agriculture (e.g. soil fertility, water supply, temperature, or photoperiod) is different. It is possible that some less obvious of these unsuitable features are still present in modern crop cultivars and that their elimination would further increase agricultural productivity under dry conditions. Possible examples of such undesirable traits have been mentioned: (*a*) excessive rooting leading to premature exhaustion of soil moisture reserves (117, 119); (*b*) too great a sensitivity of seed number to lowered ψ_{plant}; (*c*) unnecessary photoperiodic control of flowering date.

On the other hand, it has been suggested that valuable unexploited adaptations to water limitation exist among annual plants, in particular the progenitors of today's crops, in semiarid natural ecosystems (12, 63). Such adaptations could have been lost if the selection history of the particular crop was dominated by consideration of traits not related to productivity (e.g. grain quality, convenience of harvest, etc) or by use of humid environments. Hall, Foster & Waines (63) have recently pointed to the surprising lack of research on drought resistance mechanisms in the progenitors of modern crop cultivars. The recent discovery of very high rates of C_3 photosynthesis in a herbaceous desert annual (103), along with Tsunoda's emphasis upon the importance of high photosynthetic rates for adaptation to xeric environments (86, 158), may point to one useful avenue for improving crop plants for semiarid regions.

While we have been emphasizing the difficulty of knowing the exact adaptive significance of plant traits for performance in dry environments, we do not wish to obscure the fact that the approach to water-limited plant productivity represented in Equations 1 and 2 is an important guide to this problem. Some suggestions for improving dryland crop productivity derive directly from simple considerations of the relationships. For example, the seasonal march of rainfall, evaporation, and likely *WUE* in a mediterranean climate suggest that it is very difficult to store enough water in the soil to be able to grow a satisfactory summer crop of a C_3 plant like sunflower (*Helianthus annuus*), traditionally a summer crop of higher latitudes. For increased sunflower yields in a mediterranean environment it is suggested that research needs to be directed toward cold resistance in order to permit earlier planting in the spring and, among other advantages, growth when *WUE* is more favorable, rather than toward increased drought resistance (R. W. Downes, personal communication).

Of greater general importance is the fact that the simple model of productivity adopted here provides a sound framework for more detailed modeling of community productivity in dry regions, as exemplified by the work of van Keulen (166, 167). While more environmental and plant variables have been included in van Keulen's model, the objective is still to work with as few variables as are necessary for the precision required, on the assumption that these will be the most important for water-limited productivity (167). Such variables, or key determinants as we termed them earlier, assist in the identification of areas of the ecosystem in which increases in productivity are more likely to be obtained. Moreover, they help identify areas in which more detailed physiological research is likely to be the most useful for improved understanding of productivity at the community level of organization. Authors have lamented the lack of connection between physiological research on the effects of water deficit at the cellular and tissue level and phenomena in the field, such as water influences on productivity or crop yield (71, 146). It has been suggested that bridges between these levels of organization will come from models which start with phenomena at the tissue level of organization and integrate all the observed responses and interactions until the behavior of the whole plant and ultimately the whole community is derived (71). However, the possibilities of success in the short term with this approach seem very limited (43a). It is a truism to state that the ecosystem, whether natural or agricultural, is much more than the sum of all its component parts. On the other hand, we would emphasize that there are attributes of the whole ecosystem which are much simpler than is suggested by contemplation at a lower level of organization of all of the component parts of the ecosystem. Water-limited productivity is one of these attributes.

Thus the approach used in this review has aided the identification of some areas in which better physiological information would be of great benefit to understanding and perhaps improving the plant productivity of dry regions. These include the ability of roots to compete with evaporation in the surface layers of the soil, and the causes of available water being left in the root zone at maturity under annual communities in apparently water-limited environments. Under the topic of *WUE*, the effect of slow drying and hence gradual reductions in ψ_{plant} as occur in the field, and the significance of the stomatal response to humidity are important questions. The mechanism by which lowered ψ_{plant} affects root/shoot allocation is unclear and, with regard to stress effects on seed number, the relative roles of reduced assimilate supply and of direct stress effects on reproductive organs requires elucidation. Research on all these questions is particularly lacking in the case of the annual herbaceous plants found in natural ecosystems of dry regions.

In summary, we have attempted to present a simple framework in which plant productivity in arid and semiarid zones can be discussed. The first step is quantification of the physical environment, especially with respect to the total water input and the probability of periods of available soil water. The next step is the determination of the fraction of the total water input which is transpired by vegetation. Soil evaporation represents a major loss of water to plants in dry regions so that total transpiration may only be one-half of water entering the soil (see Table 1). The product of transpiration and the efficiency with which the plants use transpiration to assimilate CO_2, the water use efficiency, gives in turn productivity. Ambient humidity and the primary photosynthetic carboxylating enzyme (C_3 vs C_4) are major factors affecting water use efficiency. In the long term, respiratory losses and allocation of assimilate need also to be considered. Allocation strategies can affect water available for transpiration, for example through root growth, and water use efficiency, for example through leaf form and structure. Plants in dry situations, in particular perennials, invest large amounts of assimilate in below-ground structures so that above-ground productivity may differ substantially from total productivity (see Table 1). Similarly, water limitation can alter considerably the harvest index in crops, meaning the fraction of assimilate allocated to yield organs, and hence modify the relationship between crop yield and total productivity.

ACKNOWLEDGMENTS

We thank Drs. J. E. Begg, D. J. Connor, I. Noy-Meir, J. B. Passioura, and Professor E.-D. Schulze for helpful comments on the manuscript and Miss Y. M. Stockman for collating the bibliography. This review was written while one of us (R.A.F.) held a Reserve Bank Senior Research Fellowship.

Literature Cited

1. Alessi, J., Power, J. F. 1976. Water use by dryland corn as affected by maturity class and plant spacing. *Agron. J.* 68:547–50
2. Anderson, C. D., Read, D. W. L. 1966. Water-use efficiency of some varieties of wheat, oats, barley and flax grown in the greenhouse. *Can. J. Plant Sci.* 46:375–78
3. Angus, J. F., Moncur, M. W. 1977. Water stress and phenology in wheat. *Aust. J. Agric. Res.* 28:177–81
4. Arnon, I. 1972. *Crop Production in Dry Regions, Vol. 1. Background and Principles.* London: Hill. 650 pp.
4a. Arnon, I. 1975. Physiological principles of dryland crop production. In *Physiological Aspects of Dryland Farming,* ed. U.S. Gupta, pp. 3–145. New Delhi: Oxford and IBH. 391 pp.
5. Baier, W. 1972. An agroclimatic probability study of the economics of fallow-seeded and continuous spring wheat in Southern Saskatchewan. *Agric. Meteorol.* 9:305–21
6. Bamberg, S. A., Vollmer, A. T., Kleinkopf, G. E., Ackerman, T. L. 1976. A comparison of seasonal primary production of Mojave desert shrubs during wet and dry years. *Am. Midl. Nat.* 95:398–405
7. Barbour, M. G. 1973. Desert dogma re-examined: root/shoot productivity and plant spacing. *Am. Midl. Nat.* 89:41–57
8. Barlow, E. W. R., Boersma, L., Young, J. L. 1976. Root temperature and soil water potential effects on growth and soluble carbohydrate concentration of corn seedlings. *Crop Sci.* 16:59–62
9. Begg, J. E., Turner, N. C. 1976. Crop water deficits. *Adv. Agron.* 28:161–217
10. Bennett, O. L., Doss, B. D. 1960. Effect of soil moisture level on root distribution of cool-season forage species. *Agron. J.* 52:204–7
11. Berndt, R. D., White, B. J. 1976. A simulation-based evaluation of three cropping systems on cracking-clay soils in a summer-rainfall environment. *Agric. Meteorol.* 16:211–29
12. Berry, J. A. 1975. Adaptation of photosynthetic processes to stress. *Science* 188:644–50
13. Bidinger, F. R. 1977. *Yield physiology under drought stress: comparative responses of wheat and barley.* PhD thesis. Cornell Univ., Ithaca, NY. 161 pp.

14. Bierhuizen, J. F., Slatyer, R. O. 1965. Effect of atmospheric concentration of water vapour and CO_2 in determining transpiration-photosynthesis relationships of cotton leaves. *Agric. Meteorol.* 2:259–70
15. Blum, A. 1974. Genotypic responses in sorghum to drought stress. I. Response to soil moisture stress. *Crop. Sci.* 14:361–64
16. Blum, A. 1975. Effect of Bm gene on epicuticular wax deposition and the spectral characteristics of sorghum leaves. *Sabrao J.* 7:45–52
17. Boyer, J. S. 1976. Photosynthesis at low water potentials. *Philos. Trans. R. Soc. London Ser. B* 273:501–12
17a. Brown, L. F., Trlica, M. J. 1977. Simulated dynamics of blue grama production. *J. Appl. Ecol.* 14:215–24
18. Bunting, A. H. 1975. Time, phenology and the yield of crops. *Weather* 30:312–25
19. Buringh, P., van Heemst, H. D. J., Staring, G. J. 1975. Computation of the absolute maximum food production of the world. *Agric. Univ., Wageningen, The Netherlands, Dep. Trop. Soil Sci., Duivendaal 10.* 59 pp.
20. Caldwell, M. M. 1975. Primary production of grazing lands. In *Photosynthesis and Productivity in Different Environments IBP3,* ed. J. P. Cooper, pp. 41–73. London: Cambridge Univ. Press. 715 pp.
21. Caldwell, M. M. 1976. Root extension and water absorption. See Ref. 91, pp. 63–85
22. Caldwell, M. M., White, R. S., Moore, R. T., Camp, L. B. 1977. Carbon balance, productivity, and water use of cold-winter desert shrub communities dominated by C_3 and C_4 species. *Oecologia* 29:275–300
23. Campbell, G. S., Harris, G. A. 1977. Water relations and water use patterns for *Artemisia tridentata* Nutt. in wet and dry years. *Ecology* 58:652–59
24. Chatterton, N. J., Hanna, W. W., Powell, J. B., Lee, D. R. 1975. Photosynthesis and transpiration of bloom and bloomless sorghum. *Can. J. Plant Sci.* 55:641–43
25. Cohen, D. 1970. The expected efficiency of water utilization in plants under different competition and selection regimes. *Isr. J. Bot.* 19:50–54

26. Connor, D. J. 1975. Growth, water relations and yield of wheat. *Aust. J. Plant Physiol.* 2:353–66

27. Connor, D. J., Doley, D. 1978. The water relations of heath-adaptation to drought. In *Ecosystems of the World, Vol. 9. Heathlands and Related Shrublands,* ed. R. L. Specht. Amsterdam: Elsevier. In press

28. Connor, D. J., Tunstall, B. R., van den Driessche, R. 1971. An analysis of photosynthetic response in a brigalow forest. *Photosynthetica* 5:218–25

29. Constable, G. A., Hearn, A. B. 1978. Agronomic and physiological responses of soybean and sorghum crops to water deficits. I. Growth, development and yield. *Aust. J. Plant Physiol.* 5. In press

30. Cowan, I. R. 1965. Transport of water in the soil-plant-atmosphere system. *J. Appl. Ecol.* 2:221–39

31. Cowan, I. R. 1977. Stomatal behaviour and environment. *Adv. Bot. Res.* 4:117–228

32. Cowan, I. R., Farquhar, G. D. 1977. Stomatal function in relation to leaf metabolism and environment. *Symp. Soc. Exp. Biol.* 31:471–505

33. Curtis, D. L. 1968. The relation between the date of heading of Nigerian sorghums and the duration of the growing season. *J. Appl. Ecol.* 5:215–26

34. Damptey, H. B., Aspinall, D. 1976. Water deficit and inflorescence development in *Zea mays* L. *Ann. Bot.* 40:23–35

35. de Jong, E. 1974. Modelling: VII. Soil water simulation models. *Can. Comm. Int. Biol. Programme, Matador Proj. Tech. Rep.* 61. 31 pp.

36. Denmead, O. T. 1973. Relative significance of soil and plant evaporation in estimating evapotranspiration. In *Plant Response to Climatic Factors. Proc. Uppsala Symp. 1970,* pp. 505–11. Paris: Unesco. 574 pp.

37. Depuit, E. J., Caldwell, M. M. 1975. Gas exchange of three cool semi-desert species in relation to temperature and water stress. *J. Ecol.* 63:835–58

37a. de Wit, C. T. 1958. Transpiration and crop yields. *Versl. Landbouwk. Onderz. (Agric. Res. Rep.)* 64(6):1–88

38. Donald, C. M., Hamblin, J. 1976. The biological yield and harvest index of cereals as agronomic and plant breeding criteria. *Adv. Agron.* 28:361–405

39. Downes, R. W. 1969. Differences in transpiration rates between tropical and temperate grasses under controlled conditions. *Planta* 88:261–73

40. Downes, R. W. 1970. Effect of light intensity and leaf temperature on photosynthesis and transpiration in wheat and sorghum. *Aust. J. Biol. Sci.* 23:775–82

41. Dunn, E. L., Shropshire, F. M., Song, L. C., Mooney, H. A. 1976. The water factor and convergent evolution in Mediterranean-type vegetation. See Ref. 91, pp. 492–505

42. Dwyer, D. D., DeGarmo, H. C. 1970. Greenhouse productivity and water-use efficiency of selected desert shrubs and grasses under four soil-moisture levels. *New Mexico State Univ. Agric. Exp. Sta. Bull. 570.* 15 pp.

43. Dwyer, D. D., Wolde-Yohannis, K. 1972. Germination, emergence, water use, and production of Russian-thistle (*Salsola kali* L.). *Agron. J.* 64:52–55

43a. Eckardt, F. E. 1975. Functioning of the biosphere at the primary production level—objectives and achievements. See Ref. 20, pp. 173–85

44. Ehleringer, J., Björkman, O., Mooney, H. A. 1976. Leaf pubescence: Effects on absorptance and photosynthesis in a desert shrub. *Science* 192:376–77

45. Evans, L. T., Bingham, J., Jackson, P., Sutherland, J. 1972. Effect of awns and drought on the supply of photosynthate and its distribution within wheat ears. *Ann. Appl. Biol.* 70:67–76

46. Evenari, M., Schulze, E. D., Kappen, L., Buschbom, U. 1976. Plant production in arid and semi-arid areas. See Ref. 91, pp. 439–51

47. Evenari, M., Schulze, E. D., Kappen, L., Buschbom, U., Lange, O. L. 1975. Adaptive mechanisms in desert plants. In *Physiological Adaptation to the Environment,* ed. F. J. Vernberg, pp. 111–29. New York:Intext Educ. Publishers

48. Evenari, M., Shanan, L., Tadmor, N. 1971. *The Negev: The Challenge of a Desert.* Cambridge, Mass:Harvard Univ. Press. 345 pp.

49. Fick, G. W., Loomis, R. S., Williams, W. A. 1975. Sugar beet. In *Crop Physiology: Some Case Histories,* ed. L. T. Evans, pp. 259–95. London:Academic. 374 pp.

50. Fischer, R. A. 1973. The effect of water stress at various stages of development on yield processes in wheat. See Ref. 36, pp. 233–41

51. Fischer, R. A., Kohn, G. D. 1966. Soil water relations and relative turgidity of leaves in the wheat crop. *Aust. J. Agric. Res.* 17:269–80

52. Fischer, R. A., Kohn, G. D. 1966. The relationship of grain yield to vegetative growth and post-flowering leaf area in the wheat crop under conditions of limited soil moisture. *Aust. J. Agric. Res.* 17:281–95

53. Fischer, R. A., Lindt, J. H., Glave, A. 1977. Irrigation of dwarf wheats in the Yaqui valley of Mexico. *Exp. Agric.* 13:353–69

54. Fitzpatrick, E. A., Slatyer, R. O., Krishnan, A. I. 1967. Incidence and duration of periods of plant growth in Central Australia as estimated from climatic data. *Agric. Meteorol.* 4:389–404

55. Frank, A. B., Barker, R. E. 1976. Rates of photosynthesis and transpiration and diffusive resistance of six grasses grown under controlled conditions. *Agron. J.* 68:487–90

56. Fuehring, H. D. 1975. Yield of dryland grain sorghum as affected by antitranspirant, nitrogen and contributing micro-watershed. *Agron. J.* 67:255–57

57. Gallagher, J. N., Biscoe, P. V., Hunter, B. 1976. Effects of drought on grain growth. *Nature* 264:541–42

58. Gates, D. M., Papian, L. E. 1971. *Atlas of Energy Budgets of Plant Leaves.* London:Academic. 278 pp.

59. Gifford, R. M. 1974. A comparison of potential photosynthesis, productivity and yield of plant species with differing photosynthetic metabolism. *Aust. J. Plant Physiol.* 1:107–17

60. Grace, J., Russell, G. 1977. The effect of wind on grasses. III. Influence of continuous drought or wind on anatomy and water relations in *Festuca grundinacea* Schreb. *J. Exp. Bot.* 28:268–78

61. Greacen, E. L., Hignett, C. T. 1976. A water balance model and supply index for wheat in South Australia. *CSIRO Div. Soils Tech. Pap. 27.* 33 pp.

62. Greacen, E. L., Ponsana, P., Barley, K. P. 1976. Resistance to water flow in the roots of cereals. See Ref. 91, pp. 86–100

63. Hall, A. E., Foster, K. W., Waines, J. G. 1978. Crop adaptation to semi-arid environments. In *Agriculture in Semi-Arid Environments,* ed. G. H. Cannell, A. E. Hall, H. Lawton. New York: Springer-Verlag. In press

64. Hall, A. E., Schulze, E. D., Lange, O. L. 1976. Current perspectives of steady-state stomatal responses to environment. See Ref. 91, pp. 169–88

65. Hanks, R. J., Gardner, H. R., Florian, R. L. 1969. Plant growth-evapotranspiration relations for several crops in the Central Great Plains. *Agron. J.* 61: 30–34

65a. Harper, J. L., Ogden, J. 1970. The reproductive strategy of higher plants. I. The concept of strategy with special reference to *Senecio vulgaris* L. *J. Ecol.* 58:681–98

66. Henzell, R. G., McCree, K. J., Van Bavel, C. H. M., Schertz, K. F. 1976. Sorghum genotype variation in stomatal sensitivity to leaf water deficit. *Crop Sci.* 16:660–62

67. Hoffman, G. J., Rawlins, S. L., Garber, M. J., Cullen, E. M. 1971. Water relations and growth of cotton as influenced by salinity and relative humidity. *Agron. J.* 63:822–26

68. Holmgren, P., Jarvis, P. G., Jarvis, M. S. 1965. Resistances to carbon dioxide and water vapour transfer in leaves of different plant species. *Physiol. Plant.* 18:557–73

69. Hsiao, T. C. 1973. Plant responses to water stress. *Ann. Rev. Plant Physiol.* 24:519–70

70. Hsiao, T. C., Acevedo, E. 1974. Plant responses to water deficits, water-use efficiency and drought resistance. *Agric. Meteorol.* 14:59–84

71. Hsiao, T. C., Fereres, E., Acevedo, E., Henderson, D. W. 1976. Water stress and dynamics of growth and yield of crop plants. See Ref. 91, pp. 281–305

72. Hurd, E. A. 1974. Phenotype and drought tolerance in wheat. *Agric. Meteorol.* 14:39–55

73. Inuyama, S., Musick, J. T., Dusek, D. A. 1976. Effect of plant water deficits at various growth stages on growth, grain yield and leaf water potential of irrigated grain sorghum. *Proc. Crop Sci. Soc. Jpn.* 45:298–307

74. Itai, C., Benzioni, A. 1976. Water stress and hormonal response. See Ref. 91, pp. 225–42

75. Jarvis, P. G. 1976. The interpretation of the variations in leaf water potential and stomatal conductance found in canopies in the field. *Philos. Trans. R. Soc. London Ser. B* 273:593–610

76. Johns, G. G., Smith, R. C. G. 1975. Accuracy of soil water budgets based on a range of relationships for the influence of soil water availability on actual water use. *Aust. J. Agric. Res.* 26:871–83

77. Johnson, D. A., Caldwell, M. M. 1975. Gas exchange of four arctic and alpine tundra plant species in relation to atmospheric and soil moisture stress. *Oecologia* 21:93–108

78. Johnson, R. R., Frey, N. M., Moss, D. N. 1974. Effect of water stress on photosynthesis and transpiration of flag leaves and spikes of barley and wheat. *Crop Sci.* 14:728–31
79. Johnson, R. R., Moss, D. N. 1976. Effect of water stress on $^{14}CO_2$ fixation and translocation in wheat during grain filling. *Crop Sci.* 16:697–701
80. Jones, H. G. 1976. Crop characteristics and the ratio between assimilation and transpiration. *J. Appl. Ecol.* 13:605–22
81. Jones, M. M., Turner, N. C. 1978. Osmotic adjustment in leaves of sorghum in response to water deficits. *Plant Physiol.* 61:122–26
82. Jordan, W. R., Ritchie, J. T. 1971. Influence of soil water stress on evaporation, root absorption, and internal water status of cotton. *Plant Physiol.* 48:783–88
83. Joshi, M. C., Boyer, J. S., Kramer, P. J. 1965. Growth, carbon dioxide exchange, transpiration, and transpiration ratio of pineapple. *Bot. Gaz.* 126:174–79
84. Khairi, M., Hall, A. E. 1976. Temperature and humidity effects on net photosynthesis and transpiration of citrus. *Physiol. Plant.* 36:29–34
85. Khairi, M., Hall, A. E. 1976. Comparative studies of net photosynthesis and transpiration of some citrus species and relatives. *Physiol. Plant.* 36:35–39
86. Khan, M. A., Tsunoda, S. 1971. Comparative leaf anatomy of cultivated wheats and wild relatives with reference to their photosynthetic rates. *Jpn. J. Breed.* 21:143–50
87. Kozlowski, T. T., ed. 1972. *Water Deficits and Plant Growth, Vol. 3. Plant Responses and Control of Water Balance.* New York, San Francisco, London: Academic. 378 pp.
88. Kozlowski, T. T., ed. 1976. *Water Deficits and Plant Growth, Vol 4. Soil Water Measurement, Plant Responses, and Breeding for Drought Resistance.* New York, San Francisco, London: Academic. 383 pp.
89. Kozlowski, T. T. 1976. Water supply and leaf shedding. See Ref. 88, pp. 191–231
90. Laing, D. R., Fischer, R. A. 1977. Adaptation of semidwarf wheat cultivars to rainfed conditions. *Euphytica* 26:129–39
91. Lange, O. L., Kappen, L., Schulze, E. D., eds. 1976. *Water and Plant Life: Problems and Modern Approaches.* Berlin, Heidelberg, New York:Springer-Verlag. 536 pp.
91a. Lehane, J. J., Staple, W. J. 1962. Effects of soil moisture tensions on growth of wheat. *Can. J. Soil Sci.* 42:180–88
92. Leith, H. 1976. The use of correlation models to predict primary productivity from precipitation or evapotranspiration. See Ref. 91, pp. 392–407
93. Lemon, E. 1963. Energy and water balance of plant communities. In *Environmental Control of Plant Growth,* ed. L. T. Evans, pp. 55–78. New York: Academic. 449 pp.
94. Loomis, R. S., Williams, W. A., Hall, A. E. 1971. Agricultural productivity. *Ann. Rev. Plant Physiol.* 22:431–68
94a. Ludlow, M. M. 1975. Effect of water stress on the decline of leaf net photosynthesis with age. In *Environmental and Biological Control of Photosynthesis,* ed. R. Marcelle, pp. 123–34. The Hague: Junk
95. Ludlow, M. M., Wilson, G. L. 1972. Photosynthesis of tropical pasture plants. IV. Basis and consequences of differences between grasses and legumes. *Aust. J. Biol. Sci.* 25:1133–45
96. Magalhaes, A. C., Angelocci, L. R. 1976. Sudden alterations in water balance associated with flower bud opening in coffee plants. *J. Hortic. Sci.* 51:419–23
97. Marc, J., Palmer, J. H. 1976. Relationship between water potential and leaf and inflorescence initiation in *Helianthus annuus. Physiol. Plant.* 36:101–4
98. McCown, R. L. 1973. An evaluation of the influence of available soil water storage capacity on growing season length and yield of tropical pastures using simple water-balance models. *Agric. Meteorol.* 11:53–63
99. Meigs, P. 1953. World distribution of arid and semi-arid homoclimates. *Arid Zone Res.* 1:203–10
100. Miller, P. C., Mooney, H. A. 1974. The origin and structure of American arid-zone ecosystems. The producers: interactions between environment, form and function. *Proc. 1st Int. Congr. Ecol., The Hague,* pp. 201–9
101. Miskin, K. E., Rasmusson, D. C., Moss, D. N. 1972. Inheritance and physiological effects of stomatal frequency in barley. *Crop Sci.* 12:780–83
102. Mooney, H. A. 1972. The carbon balance of plants. *Ann. Rev. Ecol. Syst.* 3:315–46

103. Mooney, H. A., Ehleringer, J., Berry, J. A. 1976. High photosynthetic capacity of a winter annual in Death Valley. *Science* 194:322–24

104. Mott, J. J., McComb, A. J. 1975. Effects of moisture stress on the growth and reproduction of three annual species from an arid region of Western Australia. *J. Ecol.* 63:825–34

105. Mulroy, T. W., Rundel, P. W. 1977. Annual plants: adaptations to desert environments. *Bioscience* 27:109–14

106. Neales, T. F., Patterson, A. A., Hartney, V. J. 1968. Physiological adaptation to drought in the carbon assimilation and water loss of xerophytes. *Nature* 219:469–72

107. Newman, E. I. 1974. Root and soil water relations. In *The Plant Root and Its Environment,* ed. E. W. Carson, pp. 363–440. Charlottesville:Univ. Press Virginia. 691 pp.

108. Nobel, P. S. 1977. Water relations and photosynthesis of a barrel cactus, *Ferocactus acanthodes,* in the Colorado desert. *Oecologia* 27:117–33

109. Nobel, P. S. 1977. Water relations of flowering of *Agave deserti. Bot. Gaz.* 138:1–6

110. Noy-Meir, I. 1973. Desert ecosystems: Environment and producers. *Ann. Rev. Ecol. Syst.* 4:25–51

111. Noy-Meir, I., Ginzburg, B. Z. 1969. An analysis of the water potential isotherm in plant tissue. II. Comparative studies on leaves of different types. *Aust. J. Biol. Sci.* 22:35–52

112. Oppenheimer, H. R. 1960. Adaptation to drought: xerophytism. *Arid Zone Res.* 15:105–38

113. Orshan, G. 1963. Seasonal dimorphism of desert and Mediterranean chamaephytes and its significance as a factor in their water economy. In *The Water Relations of Plants,* ed. A. J. Rutter, F. H. Whitehead, pp. 206–22. London:Blackwell. 394 pp.

114. Orshan, G., Diskin, S. 1968. Seasonal changes in productivity under desert conditions. In *Functioning of Terrestrial Ecosystems at the Primary Production Level. Proc. Copenhagen Symp.,* pp. 191–201. Paris: Unesco

115. Osmond, C. B. 1978. Crassulacean acid metabolism: a curiosity in context. *Ann. Rev. Plant Physiol.* 29:379–414

116. Parkhurst, D. F., Loucks, O. L. 1972. Optimal leaf size in relation to environment. *J. Ecol.* 60:505–37

117. Passioura, J. B. 1972. The effect of root geometry on the yield of wheat growing on stored water. *Aust. J. Agric. Res.* 23:745–52

118. Passioura, J. B. 1976. Physiology of grain yield in wheat growing on stored water. *Aust. J. Plant Physiol.* 3:559–65

119. Passioura, J. B. 1977. Grain yield, harvest index, and water use of wheat. *J. Aust. Inst. Agric. Sci.* 43. In press

120. Pearce, R. B., Carlson, G. E., Barnes, D. K., Hart, R. H., Hanson, C. H. 1969. Specific leaf weight and photosynthesis in alfalfa. *Crop Sci.* 9:423–26

121. Penning de Vries, F. W. T. 1975. Use of assimilate in higher plants. See Ref. 20, pp. 459–80

122. Poole, D. K., Miller, P. C. 1975. Water relations of selected species of chaparral and coastal sage communities. *Ecology* 56:1118–28

123. Pressland, A. J. 1976. Effect of stand density on water use of mulga (*Acacia aneura* F. Muell.) woodlands in southwestern Queensland. *Aust. J. Bot.* 24: 177–91

124. Raschke, K. 1975. Stomatal action. *Ann. Rev. Plant Physiol.* 26:309–40

125. Rawson, H. M., Begg, J. E., Woodward, R. G. 1977. The effect of atmospheric humidity on photosynthesis, transpiration and water use efficiency of leaves of several plant species. *Planta* 134:5–10

126. Rawson, H. M., Turner, N. C., Begg, J. E. 1978. Agronomic and physiological responses of soybean and sorghum crops to water deficits. IV. Photosynthesis, transpiration and water use efficiency of leaves. *Aust. J. Plant Physiol.* 5. In press

127. Reicosky, D. C., Ritchie, J. T. 1976. Relative importance of soil resistance and plant resistance in root water absorption. *Soil Sci. Soc. Am. Proc.* 40:293–97

128. Ripley, E. A., Redmann, R. E. 1976. Grassland. In *Vegetation and the Atmosphere Vol. 2. Case Studies,* ed. J. L. Monteith, pp. 349–98. London, New York, San Francisco: Academic. 439 pp.

129. Ritchie, J. T. 1973. Influence of soil water status and meteorological conditions on evaporation from a crop canopy. *Agron. J.* 65:893–97

130. Ritchie, J. T., Burnett, E., Henderson, R. C. 1972. Dryland evaporative flux in a subhumid climate. III. Soil water influence. *Agron. J.* 64:168–73

131. Ritchie, J. T., Rhoades, E. D., Richardson, C. W. 1976. Calculating evaporation from native grassland watersheds. *Trans. ASAE* 19:1098–1103

132. Robelin, N. 1967. Action et arrière-action de la sécheresse sur la croissance et la production du tournesol. *Ann. Agron.* 18:579–99

133. Rutter, A. J. 1975. The hydrological cycle in vegetation. In *Vegetation and the Atmosphere, Vol. 1. Principles,* ed. J. L. Monteith, pp. 111–54. London, New York, San Francisco: Academic. 278 pp.

134. Salter, P. J., Goode, J. E. 1967. *Crop Responses to Water at Different Stages of Growth.* Farnham Royal: Commonwealth Agric. Bur. 246 pp.

135. Schulze, E.-D., Lange, O. L., Buschbom, U., Kappen, L., Evenari, M. 1972. Stomatal responses to changes in humidity in plants growing in the desert. *Planta* 108:259–70

136. Schulze, E.-D., Lange, O. L., Evenari, M., Kappen, L., Buschbom, U. 1975. The role of air humidity and temperature in controlling stomatal resistance of *Prunus armeniaca* L. under desert conditions. III. The effect of water use efficiency. *Oecologia* 19:303–14

137. Schulze, E.-D., Lange, O. L., Kappen, L., Buschbom, U., Evenari, M. 1973. Stomatal responses to changes in temperature at increasing water stress. *Planta* 110:29–42

138. Schulze, E.-D., Lange, O. L., Kappen, L., Evenari, M., Buschbom, U. 1975. Primary production of deserts. I. Physiological basis of primary production of perennial higher plants in the Negev desert. See Ref. 20, pp. 107–19

139. Sheriff, D. W. 1977. The effect of humidity on water uptake by, and viscous flow resistance of, excised leaves of a number of species: physiological and anatomical observations. *J. Exp. Bot.* In press

140. Sinclair, T. R., Bingham, G. E., Lemon, E. R., Allen, L. H. Jr. 1975. Water use efficiency of field-grown maize during moisture stress. *Plant Physiol.* 56:245–49

141. Slatyer, R. O. 1964. Efficiency of water utilization by arid zone vegetation. *Ann. Arid Zone* 3:1–12

142. Slatyer, R. O. 1965. Measurements of precipitation interception by an arid zone plant community (*Acacia aneura* F. Muell.). In *Methodology of Plant Eco-Physiology. Proc. Montpellier Symp.,* pp. 181–92. Paris:Unesco.

143. Slatyer, R. O. 1968. The use of soil water balance relationships in agroclimatology. In *Agroclimatological Methods Proc. Reading Symp.,* pp. 73–87. Paris:Unesco. 392 pp.

144. Slatyer, R. O. 1970. Comparative photosynthesis, growth and transpiration of two species of *Atriplex. Planta* 93:175–89

145. Slatyer, R. O. 1970. Carbon dioxide and water vapour exchange in *Atriplex* leaves. In *The Biology of Atriplex,* ed. R. Jones, pp. 23–29. Canberra:CSIRO. 128 pp.

146. Slatyer, R. O. 1973. The effect of internal water status on plant growth, development and yield. See Ref. 36, pp. 177–91

147. Slatyer, R. O. 1973. Structure and function of Australian arid shrublands. *Proc. 3rd Workshop USA/Australia Rangelands Panel, Tucson, Arizona,* pp. 66–73

148. Specht, R. L. 1972. Water use by perennial evergreen plant communities in Australia and Papua New Guinea. *Aust. J. Bot.* 20:273–99

149. Specht, R. L., Jones, R. 1971. A comparison of the water use by heath vegetation at Frankston, Victoria and Dark Island Soak, South Australia. *Aust. J. Bot.* 19:311–26

150. Stanhill, G. 1973. Simplified agroclimatic procedures for assessing the effect of water supply. See Ref. 36, pp. 461–76

151. Stocker, O. 1960. Physiological and morphological changes in plants due to water deficiency. *Arid Zone Res.* 15:63–104

152. Stone, J. F., ed. 1975. *Plant Modification for More Efficient Water Use.* Amsterdam:Elsevier. 320 pp.

153. Struik, G. J., Bray, J. R. 1970. Root-shoot ratios of native forest herbs and *Zea mays* at different soil-moisture levels. *Ecology* 51:892–93

154. Tanner, C. B., Jury, W. A. 1976. Estimating evaporation and transpiration from a row crop during incomplete cover. *Agron. J.* 68:239–43

155. Teare, I. D., Kanemasu, E. T., Powers, W. L., Jacobs, H. S. 1973. Water-use efficiency and its relation to crop canopy area, stomatal regulation and root distribution. *Agron. J.* 65:207–11

156. Ting, I. P. 1976. Crassulacean acid metabolism in natural ecosystems in relation to annual CO_2 uptake patterns and water utilization. In *CO_2 Metabolism and Plant Productivity,* ed. R. H. Burris, C. C. Black, pp. 251–68. Baltimore: Univ. Park Press. 431 pp.

157. Torssell, B. W. R. 1976. Drought resistance effects on species composition of an annual pasture in a dry monsoonal climate. *J. Appl. Ecol.* 13:943–53
158. Tsunoda, S., Kanda, S., Takano, Y. 1967. Relationship between vessel development and leaf photosynthesis in wild and cultivated cruciferous plants. *Jpn. J. Breed.* 17:127–28
159. Tunstall, B. R., Connor, D. J. 1975. Internal water balance of brigalow (*Acacia harphophlla* F. Muell.) under natural conditions. *Aust. J. Plant Physiol.* 2:489–99
160. Turner, N. C. 1974. Stomatal response to light and water under field conditions. *R. Soc. NZ Bull.* 12:423–32
161. Turner, N. C. 1978. Drought resistance and adaptation to water deficits in crop plants. In *Stress Physiology in Crop Plants,* ed. H. Mussell, R. C. Staples. New York:Wiley-Interscience. In press
162. Turner, N. C., Begg, J. E. 1977. Response of pasture plants to water deficits. In *Plant Relations in Pastures,* ed. J. R. Wilson, pp. 50–66. Melbourne: CSIRO
163. Turner, N. C., Begg, J. E., Rawson, H. M., English, S. D., Hearn, A. B. 1978. Agronomic and physiological responses of soybean and sorghum crops to water deficits. III. Components of leaf water potential, leaf conductance, $^{14}CO_2$ photosynthesis, and adaptation to water deficits. *Aust. J. Plant Physiol.* 5. In press
164. Uriu, K. 1964. Effect of post-harvest soil moisture depletion on subsequent yield of apricots. *Proc. Am. Soc. Hortic. Sci.* 84:93–97
165. van den Driessche, R., Connor, D. J., Tunstall, B. R. 1971. Photosynthetic response of brigalow to irradiance, temperature and water potential. *Photosynthetica* 5:210–17
166. van Keulen, H. 1975. *Simulation of Water Use and Herbage Growth in Arid Regions.* Wageningen:Centre for Agricultural Publishing and Documentation. 176 pp.
167. van Keulen, H., de Wit, C. T., Lof, H. 1976. The use of simulation models for productivity studies in arid regions. See Ref. 91, pp. 408–20
168. Viera da Silva, J. 1976. Water stress, ultrastructure and enzymatic activity. See Ref. 91, pp. 207–24
169. Waggoner, P. E. 1969. Environmental manipulation for higher yields. In *Physiological Aspects of Crop Yield,* ed. J. D. Eastin, F. A. Haskings, C. Y. Sullivan, C. H. M. Van Bavel, pp. 343–73. Madison:Am. Soc. Agron. and Crop Sci. Soc. Am. 396 pp.
170. Walker, B. H. 1974. Ecological considerations in the management of semi-arid ecosystems in south-central Africa. See Ref. 100, pp. 124–29
171. Walter, H. 1973. *Vegetation of the Earth in Relation to Climatic and the Eco-Physiological Conditions.* Berlin:Springer-Verlag. 237 pp.
172. Wardlaw, I. F. 1968. The control and pattern of movement of carbohydrates in plants. *Bot. Rev.* 34:79–105
173. Westoby, M. 1972. *Problem-oriented modelling: a conceptual framework.* Presented at Desert Biome Inf. Meet., Tempe, Arizona. Quoted in Ref. 110
174. Wilson, A. M., Hyder, D. N., Briske, D. D. 1976. Drought resistance characteristics of Blue Grama seedlings. *Agron. J.* 68:479–84

Ann. Rev. Plant Physiol. 1978. 29:319–44
Copyright © 1978 by Annual Reviews Inc. All rights reserved

HETEROCYSTS

♦7654

Robert Haselkorn

Department of Biophysics and Theoretical Biology, University of Chicago,
Chicago, Illinois 60637

CONTENTS

INTRODUCTION AND CONCLUSIONS

Cyanobacteria, as the blue-green algae are now called, have been on Earth for over 3 billion years. They are photosynthetic prokaryotes which derive electrons for CO_2 reduction from water, evolving oxygen. During the course of evolution, these organisms have provided the major source of O_2 in the atmosphere and hence are principally responsible for changing the primeval reducing atmosphere to an oxidizing one. Their photosynthetic features are identical to those found in green plant chloroplasts, organelles whose evolutionary predecessors may well have been cyanobacteria.

Prokaryotes probably evolved photosynthetic activity as a consequence of exhaustion of organic substrates and nitrogen-fixing activity as a consequence of exhaustion of ammonia in the pre-Cambrian ocean. Since nitrogen fixation requires a strictly anaerobic environment, how can this requirement be reconciled with the photosynthetic evolution of oxygen? The answer for some filamentous cyanobacteria appears to lie in the ability to differentiate specialized thick-walled cells called heterocysts at regular intervals along the filament. Hence, the oxygen-sensitive machinery for nitrogen fixation is segregated in the heterocyst from the oxygen-evolving photosynthetic apparatus in neighboring vegetative cells.

319

0066-4294/78/0601-0319$01.00

The question of the biological role of heterocysts must be considered settled. Heterocysts function as anaerobic factories for nitrogen fixation under external aerobic conditions. How they do so is one of the subjects of this review. This role has been obscured occasionally by the question of the contribution of vegetative cells to nitrogen fixation. Vegetative cells of heterocystous cyanobacteria, as well as all the cells of many species of nonheterocystous cyanobacteria, will fix nitrogen under anaerobic (or nearly anaerobic) conditions. Their only requirements are a source of reductant, a source of ATP, and derepressed nitrogen fixation (*nif*) genes. When unprotected from O_2, however, nitrogenase and probably other *nif* gene products are inactivated and cleared from the cells by protease action. Thus, unless a cyanobacterial species has developed an alternative O_2-protective mechanism, heterocysts are essential for the aerobic fixation of nitrogen.

How do heterocysts provide an anaerobic environment for the protection of nitrogenase? Structurally they reduce the entry of gases (and everything else) by synthesizing a multilayered envelope exterior to the cell wall. They reorganize the photosynthetic apparatus to shut down the O_2-evolving activity of photosystem II (PS II) while they retain the ATP-synthetic power of photosystem I (PS I). They establish efficient pumps at the junctions with neighboring vegetative cells which assure a supply of carbon to serve as reductant for nitrogenase. There even seems to be one or more enzymatic scavenging systems to remove traces of O_2. These aspects of heterocyst differentiation are now reasonably well documented, although much remains to be learned about biochemical mechanisms, particularly of the pumps.

The greatest obstacle to understanding the regulation of gene expression during heterocyst differentiation is the absence of a convenient system of genetic analysis in cyanobacteria. Some progress has been made in replica-plating techniques and in mutagenesis, but without a conjugation system or a good generalized transducing phage proper analysis of gene regulation is very difficult. Recombinant DNA, however, offers a promising way to study such questions.

Most of our knowledge about the regulation of gene expression in prokaryotes comes from the study of *Escherichia coli*. In this case, gene expression is governed by the interaction between RNA polymerase and promoter sites on the DNA; by the probability that messenger RNA transcription will be initiated, as modified by positive (gene activator proteins) and negative (repressors) factors; and by the probability that transcription of mRNA will be completed successfully without premature termination (attenuation). Very little is known about the regulation of transcription in cyanobacteria in general and nothing is known about transcription during heterocyst differentiation in particular. The limited information available about heterocyst DNA suggests that its study may reveal mechanisms of gene regulation not yet described in *E. coli*.

During the differentiation of heterocysts many vegetative cell proteins, including the phycobiliproteins which serve as light-harvesting pigments for PS II, are degraded to amino acids. At least one of the proteases active during this differentiation is activated in response to nitrogen starvation, while another is synthesized de novo. Proteases have been implicated recently in the control of bacterial virus gene expression as well as in various regulatory phenomena in animal cells. Heterocyst development appears to provide an exceptionally good system in which to study the mechanism of specific protease activation in detail.

A final point concerns the intercellular connections between heterocysts and vegetative cells. These appear to be crucial both to development of the heterocyst and to its proper operation. Early in its development the presumptive heterocyst produces and exports a diffusible inhibitor that prevents the differentiation of neighboring cells. Several other transport problems, including the export of the products of nitrogen fixation, the import of carbon to serve as reductant, the exclusion of oxygen, and the retention of factors controlling heterocyst gene expression, must be solved by the heterocyst. All of these processes are mediated by thin cytoplasmic channels called microplasmodesmata, about which little more than their size is known.

In what follows I shall review some of the data on the structure and biochemical properties of heterocysts in order to see what has to happen when a vegetative cell differentiates. Next I shall describe the differentiation as seen microscopically and biochemically, and finally discuss models for the control of differentiation and formation of the pattern of heterocysts in the filament. This field has received a great deal of attention as evidenced by numerous reviews, with each of the major laboratories contributing one recently. Wolk has summarized his work on the biochemistry of differentiation (117), Wilcox, his on pattern formation (111), and Stewart, in his presidential address to the British Phycological Society, covered many of the topics to be presented below, emphasizing nitrogen metabolism (87). In addition, a massive review covering cellular organization, metabolism, and development of cyanobacteria by Stanier & Cohen-Bazire has just appeared (84). Somewhat older reviews are those by Fay on heterocysts (29), Stewart on nitrogen fixation (85, 86, 89) and an exhaustive one by Wolk, with 839 references (116). I trust that some of the points to be made below are sufficiently novel to justify adding yet another review to the list.

CHOICE OF EXPERIMENTAL MATERIAL

A wide variety of cyanobacterial species has been used for studies of heterocyst biology. Many, but not all, are currently maintained in axenic unialgal condition in the collection of the Pasteur Institute and at the American Type Culture Collection. We are nearly at the stage at which studies of heterocyst differentiation should be confined to a few species. The choice of species probably will be dictated eventually by the discovery of a convenient system for genetic analysis, such as a generalized transducing phage or conjugation.

Historically, *Anabaena cylindrica* Lemm has been studied most frequently. Present advantages gained by using this species include the ability to prepare highly active nitrogen-fixing heterocysts free of vegetative cells (97, 102, 123) and the existence of mutants with altered patterns of heterocyst spacing (110). *Anabaena catenula,* a related strain with large, distinct cells, has been useful for microscopy and surgical manipulation (109). Wolk has described methods for replica-plating and mutagenizing *Anabaena variabilis,* previously called *Anabaena flos-aquae* (20, 125). This strain is capable of vigorous heterotrophic growth on fructose, a potential advantage for the isolation of mutants defective in photosynthesis (120). This *Anabaena variabilis* should not be confused with another cyanobacterium by the same name (strain 7118 in the Pasteur collection) originally described by Kratz & Myers (49). The latter *A. variabilis* has been known for years as a strain incapable of fixing nitrogen and incapable of forming heterocysts. This taxonomic problem was resolved recently when it was found that Kratz & Meyers' *A. variabilis* 7118 synthesizes nitrogenase proteins and reduces acetylene perfectly well under anaerobic conditions (73). Thus it seems that strain 7118 is merely a heterocyst-less mutant isolated accidentally. In fact, heterocystous revertants of 7118 have been selected recently; they fix nitrogen aerobically (R. Rippka and R. Stanier, personal communication). One additional correction to the literature is also necessary. All of the studies by H. Fleming on the proteins synthesized during heterocyst differentiation (33–35) were reported to have used *Nostoc muscorum.* This strain is now in the Pasteur collection where it has been identified as an *Anabaena* species; in subsequent publications it is referred to as *Anabaena* 7120. It yields very active heterocysts (71) but does not grow heterotrophically (73).

Cyanophage N1 was originally isolated on *Anabaena* 7120 (2); N1 lyses many of the *Anabaena* strains in the Pasteur collection but none of the true *Nostocs* (R. Haselkorn, R. Rippka, J. Deruelles, unpublished). Another phage, whose host is an *Anabaena variabilis* strain, has been reported by Gromov to be lysogenic (38, 48). If Gromov's *Anabaena* phage is capable of transducing host genes, it will provide the long-sought system for genetic analysis. It should be tested for that activity with the existing mutant collections in the United States, Great Britain, and India.

The other large group of cyanobacteria containing intercalary heterocysts at frequent intervals are the *Nostocs.* In fact, these strains are distinguished from *Anabaena* only with some difficulty, the major differences being the size of the cells shortly after spore germination and the formation of gelatinous aggregates of filaments by *Nostoc* (84). Many *Nostocs,* perhaps all, are capable of heterotrophic growth on a variety of carbon sources. However, I am not aware of any property of heterocysts that has been studied uniquely or advantageously with *Nostoc,* with the important exception of Silvester's description of the *Nostoc* symbiont in *Gunnera* (80), discussed in a later section.

Two other subgroups of cyanobacteria contain heterocysts: the rivularian and the stigonematalean subgroups (84). The former, of which *Gleotrichia* and *Calothrix* sp. are examples, contain tapered filaments in which only one cell, at the blunt end, is a heterocyst. The latter, of which *Fischerella* is an example, contain branched filaments and bundles of filaments as a consequence of occasional cell divisions occurring parallel to the filament axis. To date none of these has been used for studies of heterocyst differentiation or biochemistry, perhaps because they grow slowly and are difficult to maintain in pure culture.

HETEROCYST STRUCTURE

Morphologically the heterocyst differs from its antecedent vegetative cell in five ways: 1. Its connections with neighboring cells are much less extensive; 2. it is surrounded by a thick coat; 3. it contains vast plugs of rather homogeneous material at both poles; 4. its arrangement of thylakoids is different; and 5. it has much less "nuclear" material, perhaps none.

The connections between heterocyst and vegetative cells demand much greater study in the future because they must be intimately related to the pumps which control the flow of carbon into and nitrogen out of the heterocyst. In transverse sections, the septum separating heterocyst from vegetative cell is less than one-third the diameter of that between vegetative cells (53, 54, 109), and thus the total cross-sectional area of the heterocyst-vegetative cell junction must be less than one-tenth that between vegetative cells. The septum is traversed by a set of perforations called microplasmodesmata which appear to connect the cytoplasms of the two cells. The channels are at least 400 Å long and less than 50 Å in diameter (54). There is a paucity of information about their ultrastructure, their precise number, their composition, and even whether they are all identical. There might, for example, exist subsets of channels specialized for unidirectional transport.

The coat or envelope surrounding the heterocyst is a remarkable structure. There seems to be agreement now that it consists of three layers all external to the vegetative cell's outer membrane (54). The first of these to appear during differentiation is called the "fibrous" layer because of its appearance in fixed, stained sections in the electron microscope (54, 109). Its composition has not been reported. The second central layer is called the "homogeneous" layer. This material contains a long polysaccharide with short side-branches. The major repeating unit is a substituted glucose-glucose-glucose-mannose, all in β-1,3 linkages in *A. cylindrica* (16, 25). Each of the monomer units in this oligosaccharide is linked at either the 2, 4, or 6 position to another monomer, or to a disaccharide, or to nothing. Thus a network of oligosaccharides surrounds the heterocyst; this homogeneous layer is complete except at the poles of the cell where it is penetrated by the septum containing the microplasmodesmata. The same is true of the innermost "laminated" layer which is the last to be added (54, 109). This layer has the most unusual chemical composition: it is composed entirely of glycolipids uniquely found in heterocysts (14, 52, 62, 105, 113, 121). The glycolipids are of four classes containing a C26 hydroxy acid or alcohol or a C28 dihydroxy acid or alcohol. Each class contains either glucose or galactose (roughly 9:1) attached at the acid or alcohol terminus (52). Purified laminated layers are crystalline; they "melt" at the same temperature as the pure glycolipids of which they are composed (113). Although such measurements have not been reported, it seems likely that the laminated layer would be impermeable to water, ions, neutral hydrophilic solutes, and possibly dissolved gases.

Terminal heterocysts contain a single polar granule, visible in the light microscope as a highly refractile round object (29). Intercalary heterocysts contain two polar granules (29). Electron micrographs of mature heterocysts show the granules as homogeneous plugs nearly filling the region of the cell adjacent to the septum (53, 54, 109). The composition of the plugs is not known with certainty, although Fogg suggested in 1951 that they contained arginine (37). More recent work indicates that they contain cyanophycin, the storage polymer multi-L-arginyl poly-L-aspartic acid (54, 55, 81). The plugs have not been purified yet. Since cyanophycin granules normally disappear during heterocyst differentiation (due to nitrogen starvation), it should be possible to isolate the plugs free of granule contamination to determine their chemical composition. It may seem odd that a storage material accumulates at what is an important transport location, in front of the septum.

Thylakoid reorganization in heterocysts has been described on the basis of electron microscope studies (54, 109). It is still not possible to correlate these changes with the loss of PS II activity and rearrangement of photochemical reaction centers described below, except to say that the phycobiliproteins, which serve as light-harvesting antennae for PS II, disappear. In general the thylakoid membranes are depleted from the central region of the cell and reappear near the poles, more highly coiled than in vegetative cells.

Finally, there is the important question of heterocyst DNA. Vegetative cells contain typical prokaryotic "nucleoid" regions which, in electron micrographs, contain fibrils (54, 109). No such fibrils are visible in heterocysts, suggesting that they may lack DNA. They have significantly reduced ultraviolet absorption, and isolated heterocysts contain much less DNA per cell than vegetative cells (37; M. Wilcox, personal communication). The precise amount is difficult to determine because vegetative cell DNA tends to stick to heterocysts and because heterocysts prepared by lysozyme digestion or by sonication will contain some proheterocysts which are early enough into the differentiation program to retain much of their DNA (51).

HETEROCYST ISOLATION

Methods for the rapid isolation of heterocysts have been introduced during the past few years. In succeeding sections the biochemical properties of heterocysts with respect to photosynthetic activities, carbon metabolism, and nitrogen metabolism, particularly nitrogen fixation, will be discussed. These properties, as anticipated, depend critically on the method used to isolate the heterocysts.

All of the methods published to date exploit the mechanical or chemical strength of the heterocyst envelope. Thus heterocysts require ten times more sonicating power, or pressure in a French press, then vegetative cells in order to be broken. Heterocysts are also resistant to lysozyme and to the combination of EDTA, glycerol, and the nonionic detergent NP-40. It is not known at which stage in development these resistances are acquired or whether the homogeneous layer suffices to confer lysozyme resistance.

The first systematic comparative study of these isolation methods remains definitive (31). All of the solely mechanical procedures damage heterocysts. Lysozyme alone is effective, without degrading the internal heterocyst structures as judged by electron microscopy (31), but has two drawbacks: (a) complete disruption of vegetative cells takes several hours, even at elevated temperature and high enzyme concentration, and (b) the heterocysts must be washed extensively to free them of adhering debris from the vegetative cells. Some of the debris (e.g. DNA) cannot be removed without detergent washing.

Recent improvements in these procedures start with a brief lysozyme or mannitol treatment followed by very mild sonication or passage through a French or Yeda press at very low pressure (12, 47, 60, 97, 102). In studies of incorporation and intercellular transport of ^{14}C or ^{13}N, speed of isolation is essential. For several such studies it was possible to treat with lysozyme first, label, and then disrupt the cells (47). This procedure permits labeling times on the order of seconds, cell separation times of the same magnitude, and analytical separation of the products in minutes. The results, presented below, are impressive.

Much of the effort in heterocyst isolation is aimed at producing cells containing active nitrogenase. Since nitrogenase is sensitive to oxygen the preparative methods are anaerobic. These procedures turn out to have an unexpected advantage. Cyanobacteria contain a number of proteases (127). One or more of these enzymes specifically degrades oxygen-inactivated nitrogenase components and other oxygen-sensitive proteins in vivo (73). The degradation of nitrogenase has also been observed in crude extracts in vitro (73). Thus it is possible that the levels of activity of a number of enzymes, determined in crude extracts from heterocysts and vegetative cells, will depend critically on the precautions taken to exclude oxygen during preparation of the extracts. One protease, which is active against vegetative cell proteins in vitro and which is induced during nitrogen starvation, requires Ca^{++} (126, 127). Fortuitously, this enzyme is inactive under the normal conditions for lysozyme digestion which include EDTA.

We have used a rapid and convenient method for heterocyst isolation suggested by M. Wilcox (personal communication). A concentrated suspension of filaments is made, successively, 10–12% in glycerol, 0.01 M in EDTA, and 0.2–1% in NP-40. Vegetative cell lysis takes several minutes and the heterocysts can be separated on CsCl (25) or ludox (71) gradients. Heterocysts prepared this way are deficient in some low molecular weight proteins present in cells prepared with lysozyme (68), but for some purposes the method could be very useful.

HETEROCYST BIOCHEMISTRY

Much of the work on heterocyst biochemistry takes as its point of departure the hypothesis that the heterocyst is specialized for nitrogen fixation (32). The known requirements for nitrogen fixation are nitrogenase, ATP, reductant, and an anaerobic environment. Each of these has, in turn, other special requirements. Expression of the *nif* genes in bacteria, for example, is subject to complex regulation (13). Historically, the bleached appearance of heterocysts drew attention to the possibility that they had modified photosynthetic apparatus. I shall discuss these changes first and then consider carbon and nitrogen metabolism. Throughout, two points must be borne in mind: (a) absence of an enzyme or other activity from heterocysts could be due to proteolysis during heterocyst isolation, and (b) persistence of a vegetative cell enzyme or other activity in a heterocyst preparation could be due to proheterocysts which still retain some vegetative cell properties although they are already lysis resistant. The latter problem will be particularly serious in unsynchronized populations.

Photosynthetic Activities

When cyanobacteria, whether unicellular or filamentous, nitrogen-fixing or not, are grown in nitrogen-deficient medium, they commence losing their characteristic phycobiliprotein pigments roughly at the time of exhaustion of medium nitrogen (4). Transfer of a heterocystous nitrogen-fixing strain to nitrogen-free medium results in loss of 50–70% of the phycocyanin from all the cells (12, 65); phycocyanin synthesis then resumes in the vegetative cells when fixed nitrogen becomes available (65). Resumption of phycocyanin synthesis in very old heterocysts has also been reported (100). Isolated heterocysts lack the absorption characteristic of phycocyanin (27, 121) as do heterocysts in intact filaments, as determined by microspectrophotometry (99). Loss of phycobiliprotein absorption is correlated with actual degradation of the protein: phycobiliprotein bands are absent from polyacrylamide gels of total heterocyst proteins (34, 35). The degradation appears to be caused by a protease whose preferred substrates are phycobiliproteins (37a, 127).

Cyanobacteria contain both green plant photosystems. Photosystem II, it will be recalled, produces a weak reductant and a strong oxidant, splitting water and generating O_2. The weak reductant combines with a weak oxidant, produced by PS I, through an electron transport chain that phosphorylates ADP. The latter process is called noncyclic photophosphorylation. When PS II is inoperative, either by destruction (as in heterocysts) or by blockage with the herbicide DCMU, the strong reductant and weak oxidant produced by PS I recombine through a (shortened) electron transport chain, again phosphorylating ADP. This process is called cyclic photophosphorylation.

The actual charge separation producing oxidant and reductant in each photosystem takes place in reaction centers. These reaction centers are composed of a special pair of chlorophylls, which can be photoxidized and which reside in discrete chlorophyll-protein complexes (102a), and primary electron acceptors. These assemblages are associated with the light-harvesting antennae which are also composed of chlorophyll-protein complexes (102a) and which function to absorb and transfer energy to the reaction centers. In cyanobacteria, the phycobilipigment-protein complexes, which can account for as much as 40% of the soluble cell protein, serve as the light-harvesting pigments exclusively for PS II. The absence of phycobilipigments suggested that heterocysts might lack PS II activity which, from a teleological point of view, would be to the heterocyst's advantage because the O_2 evolved from system II would inactivate its nitrogenase. Indeed, the absence of system II activity in heterocysts has been inferred from (a) their lack of Hill activity, (b) absence of delayed light, and (c) reduced chlorophyll *a* fluorescence yield (23).

Clearly, lack of phycobiliproteins is not sufficient to explain the absence of PS II activity in heterocysts. Cyanobacterial mutants exist in which phycobilins are completely absent yet the cells retain PS II activity (R. Alberte, personal communication), and green plant mutants exist which completely lack their analogous light-harvesting assemblages but are fully competent photosynthetically (102a). Thus it is clear that additional modification of PS II is required to eliminate oxygen evolution. In this respect it is known that the oxygen-evolving machinery is dependent on the presence of bound Mn^{++} (37b); the ratio of bound Mn^{++} to chlorophyll in heterocysts is only 10% that of vegetative filaments (96, 98). Presumably the sharply reduced content of bound Mn^{++} in heterocysts is symptomatic of a fundamental alteration of PS II in these cells.

Reorganization of the photosynthetic unit in heterocysts is indicated by measurements of the cellular content of P700, the size of the photosynthetic unit (ratio of chlorophyll a/P700), and by the number of these units per cell (3, 23). The system I reaction centers are characterized by a special photooxidizable chlorophyll called P700. The ratio of P700 to chlorophyll, the photosynthetic unit size, is 1 to 170–180 in vegetative cells and 1 to 60–90 in heterocysts (3, 23). The number of these units per cell is 50% higher in heterocysts than in vegetative cells (3). Therefore, the often observed decreased chlorophyll content of heterocysts (27, 121) is attributable to the size and number of photosynthetic units. It remains to be seen whether the increase in photosynthetic units is accomplished by new component synthesis or by modification of old ones.

The photosynthetic electron transport chain is known to contain at least one component (cyt b_{563}) not common to both cyclic and noncyclic photophosphorylation (59). The noncyclic chain includes cytochrome b_{559}, plastoquinone, cytochrome c_{554} (cyt f), and plastocyanin; all are present in heterocysts but the amounts relative to vegetative cells are not known (98). The cyclic chain uses cytochrome b_{563} (cyt b_6), which can donate either to plastoquinone or plastocyanin; cytochrome b_{563} is also present in heterocysts (98). Finally, heterocysts can carry out photophosphorylation in vitro at rates sufficient to provide the ATP requirement for nitrogen fixation (97, 98). These results are fully consistent with studies on whole cells which suggested that the ATP for nitrogen fixation could be supplied entirely by cyclic photophosphorylation in the light (11, 19, 24, 28, 61).

The last point to consider is the nature of the reductant normally produced by PS I under noncyclic conditions. In vegetative cells, one of the primary acceptors of PS I is a membrane-bound ferredoxin (26) detectable by a characteristic EPR spectrum below 30°K. Subsequent electron transfer involves a soluble ferredoxin and pyridine nucleotide, the last providing reductant for CO_2 fixation via the Calvin cycle. The two ferredoxins have been purified from *Nostoc;* the major one contains one 2Fe-2S center per molecule with $E_o' = -406$ mV (39). Heterocysts retain the EPR signal characteristic of the membrane-bound ferredoxin with g values = 2.05, 1.94, 1.92, and 1.89 (15). Some form of ferredoxin is believed to be the ultimate electron donor to nitrogenase. However, the bacterial *nif* operon includes a gene which is believed to code for an electron carrier to nitrogenase (13), and derepressed *Plectonema* synthesize an oxygen-sensitive low molecular weight protein in addition to nitrogenase (73). These observations suggest that heterocysts might contain a new electron carrier whose molecular weight is in the range of known ferredoxins.

Carbon Metabolism

The modifications of the photosynthetic apparatus of heterocysts just described are closely tied to drastic changes in carbon metabolism. In the vegetative cells, the two photosystems cooperate to produce both ATP and reductant for CO_2 fixation. We have seen that in the heterocyst PS I activity is devoted to cyclic photophosphorylation and therefore is not likely to be able to provide reductant for CO_2 fixation. Moreover, if CO_2 fixation continued in the heterocyst, the process would compete with nitrogen fixation for reductant and ATP.

Failure of heterocysts to incorporate CO_2 was first shown by autoradiography following brief exposure of whole filaments to $^{14}CO_2$ (115). Label was shown, however, to move rapidly into heterocysts from neighboring vegetative cells. The nature of the transported label is a matter for continuing study at present (47) and will be discussed below. Failure of heterocysts to incorporate CO_2 has a directly demonstrable cause: ribulose-1,5-bisphosphate (RuBP) carboxylase activity is absent from heterocysts (112). Absence of this activity, which normally adds CO_2 to RuBP to give two molecules of phosphoglycerate, is correlated with the absence of polyhedral bodies (carboxysomes) in the heterocysts of some 15 strains of cyanobacteria (88) and more recently with the total absence of carboxylase antigen in *Anabaena* heterocyst extracts (18). Therefore, without an operative Calvin cycle, the heterocyst can devote most of the ATP made by cyclic photophosphorylation to nitrogen fixation and still provide enough ATP for protein synthesis which continues throughout differentiation (34, 35).

The source of reductant for nitrogen fixation is still not certain. There is agreement that the activity of hexokinase in crude extracts is two times higher in heterocysts than in vegetative cells and that the activities of glucose-6-phosphate dehydrogenase and 6-phosphogluconate dehydrogense are at least six to eight times higher (60, 112). This sequence of enzymes, working on glucose, will produce two moles of NADPH for each glucose. The reduced pyridine nucleotide could enter a respiratory chain to produce ATP or, alternatively, could be used to reduce a ferredoxin (5). As mentioned previously, it is not known whether an old or a new or, for that matter, any ferredoxin is the electron donor to nitrogenase in cyanobacteria. Nevertheless, it is possible to demonstrate in crude extracts of *Anabaena* acetylene reduction supported by light-dependent ferredoxin reduction at rates equal to the maximum rate observed with the artificial donor dithionite (83). It is also possible to show much lower (10%) rates of acetylene reduction in vitro supported by pyruvate and ferredoxin, either with pyridine nucleotide (83) or coenzyme A (CoA) (17). In other experiments, initially with *A. variabilis* (58) but subsequently with *A. cylindrica* (8, 9), crude extracts were found to contain a significant ATP-dependent decarboxylation of pyruvate coupled to ferredoxin reduction. This reaction is either independent of (58), stimulated by (9), or dependent on (8) CoA, which illustrates the difficulty of working with oxygen-labile enzyme systems in crude extracts. The activity is said to be repressed fivefold or more by growth of the cells on NH_4^+ (8, 9), suggesting the possibility that the enzyme system is induced in heterocysts. It would be most rewarding to purify the putative pyruvate: ferredoxin oxidoreductase, even on a small scale. Once the polypeptide band(s) is (are) identified on acrylamide gels it would then be possible to determine the enzyme's regulation and distribution simply by reference to published gel patterns (34, 35).

Nitrogen Metabolism

Mature heterocysts differ from vegetative cells, with respect to nitrogen metabolism, in three important ways: they contain nitrogenase, a higher level of glutamine synthetase (GS) (when the cyanobacteria are free-living) and a lower level of glutamine-oxoglutarate amido transferase (GOGAT).

Early studies of nitrogen metabolism attempted to exploit the Calvin approach, namely, to label briefly with a nitrogen isotope, to determine the kinetics of labeling of individual compounds, and then to deduce the metabolic pathway (89). Unfortunately, ^{15}N is not suited for such studies because in the time required for sufficient incorporation to be measured (5 min) 95% of the label is transported out of the heterocysts (67, 118). ^{13}N, a radioactive isotope of nitrogen with a half-life of 10 min, is far better. In a first series of "Calvin" experiments in which ^{13}N was administered to intact filaments of A. cylindrica for periods up to 120 sec and the 80% methanol-soluble products analyzed by high voltage electrophoresis on thin layer plates, the flow of label was from N_2 to NH_3, from NH_3 to the amide of glutamine, and then to the α-NH_2 of glutamate and finally to other amino acids (122). When methionine sulfoximine (MSX), an inhibitor of glutamine synthetase, was added, only NH_3 was labeled. Azaserine, an inhibitor of GOGAT, caused label to accumulate in glutamine (122). These results are completely consistent with assimilation of NH_3 via the GS/GOGAT pathway, as had been suggested from the study of amino acid pool sizes (22, 89).

Nitrogen assimilation was also studied in isolated heterocysts. Heterocysts incorporate $[^{13}N]N_2$ into NH_3 and glutamine in 120 sec; longer labeling periods put all the label into the amide of glutamine (102). Heterocysts also incorporate $^{13}NH_3$ into glutamine; they require ATP, reductant, and glutamate for this reaction which is inhibited by MSX (102). Isolated heterocysts export the ^{13}N-labeled glutamine. Since ^{13}N does not enter glutamate in heterocysts, although it does in whole filaments (122), it seems likely that GOGAT is found only in vegetative cells. The enzyme is in fact solubilized rapidly by mild sonication, suggesting that it is located in vegetative cells (102).

The formation of glutamine from ammonia and glutamate can be followed in another way, using ^{14}C-labeled glutamate. Isolated heterocysts convert ^{14}C-glutamate to glutamine, dependent on ATP and inhibited by MSX (102). Taken together these results strongly suggest that heterocysts export glutamine to vegetative cells and import glutamate.

Once the label passes through the glutamate pool, the pattern of flow is a bit confused. When whole filaments are labeled for 30 min with $^{14}CO_2$ and then the fate of the recently incorporated ^{14}C followed after addition of N_2 or NH_3, the soluble pool shows principally a large increase in aspartate (56). Isolated heterocysts have also been shown to contain an aminotransferase activity capable of converting

2-oxoglutarate to glutamate; this activity can use glutamate, glutamine, or aspartate as the amino donor (102). Rapid interconversion of these amino acids is indicated by the following observations: the addition of NH_3 to filaments actively fixing N_2 results in the rapid accumulation in heterocysts of cyanophycin, which contains aspartate and arginine; ^{14}C-labeled glutamine is incorporated without detectable lag into cyanophycin under conditions promoting cyanophycin synthesis (R. Haselkorn, unpublished results).

At this point it will be useful to return briefly to studies on the transport of recently labeled carbon compounds from vegetative cells to heterocysts (47). Isolated heterocysts retain some [14]CO_2 incorporation activity unrelated to the Calvin cycle, about 1% of that of vegetative cells. The major products are citrate/isocitrate, glutamate, and other amino acids. Recently fixed carbon flows abundantly into heterocysts from vegetative cells; of the label transported into heterocysts, 62% is found in maltose. All sugars, and UDP-sugars, are in higher concentrations in heterocysts than in vegetative cells. The ratio of glutamate to aspartate is high in heterocysts, low in vegetative cells.

These results, together with the labeling studies using ^{13}N, lead to the model shown in Figure 1, whose details are given in the figure legend. If the heterocyst envelope is impermeable to gases, nitrogen must enter the heterocyst through the

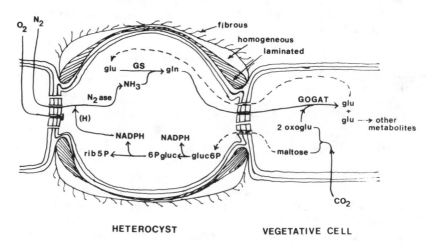

HETEROCYST   VEGETATIVE CELL

Figure 1 Model of the flow of carbon and nitrogen between heterocyst and vegetative cell in nitrogen-fixing cyanobacteria. Enzymes: N_2ASE = nitrogenase, GS = glutamine synthetase, GOGAT = glutamine-oxoglutarate amido transferase. The mechanism of maltose transport is unknown, as are the steps from maltose to glucose-6-phosphate. NADPH probably reduces a ferredoxin. An alternate pathway for ferredoxin reduction by pyruvate is not shown. The three layers of the heterocyst envelope (fibrous, homogeneous, laminated) are described in the text; they are believed to be impermeable to N_2, CO_2, and O_2. Microplasmodesmata are shown connecting the two cells but the polar bodies are omitted. The heterocyst, lacking photosystem II, neither fixes CO_2 nor produces O_2.

microplasmodesmata connecting the vegetative cells and heterocysts. Nitrogen is reduced to NH_3 by nitrogenase, using ATP produced by cyclic photophosphorylation and reductant whose ultimate source is either glucose-6-phosphate or pyruvate (not shown). The NH_3 is added to glutamate by GS in the heterocysts; the resulting glutamine is transported through the microplasmodesmata to the vegetative cells. There the amide group is transferred to 2-oxoglutarate by GOGAT, yielding two molecules of glutamate, one of which is returned to the heterocyst to be amidated again by GS.

While there is no dispute over the fact that heterocysts contain nitrogenase (32, 101, 104, 106), there has been controversy over the enzyme's distribution among other cells. Now that we understand a little more about the control of *nif* gene expression and the lability of *nif* gene products it is possible to resolve most of the historical conflicts. The original observations leading to the assignment of nitrogenase exclusively to heterocysts included 1. the ability of heterocysts to reduce silver salts in a photographic emulsion, 2. the formation in heterocysts of formazan crystals from triphenyl tetrazolium chloride, 3. the loss of nitrogenase activity when heterocysts are detached from vegetative cells, and 4. the recovery of nitrogenase activity in heterocyst pellets supplemented with ATP and dithionite (90). The opposing view, that some (or much) nitrogenase is in vegetative cells, was based on the release of active enzyme following mild sonication (124), in one case the recovery being totally independent of heterocyst breakage (82). In the latter study there seems little doubt that the enzyme was in vegetative cells because the cultures were derepressed for 7 days on 95% Argon/5% CO_2; under these conditions heterocysts do not mature and the enzyme is fully oxygen-sensitive in vivo (74). The time course of solubilization by sonication is harder to explain without the ad hoc (but not unreasonable) assumption that there are several classes of heterocysts, some of which break or leak nitrogenase more rapidly than others.

Cell-free extracts of cyanobacteria can reduce acetylene at rates usually in the range of 4–15 nmoles ethylene produced/min/mg protein (41, 42, 71, 97, 124). The reaction requires dithionite and an ATP generating system although light spares both requirements (71, 123). The activity is irreversibly inactivated by oxygen in vitro and is reported to be cold-sensitive, losing 60% of the activity in 12 hr at 0°C (41). The nitrogenase from *A. cylindrica* has been purified to homogeneity (103). Component I (MoFe protein) has a molecular weight of 250,000 and contains two each of subunits of molecular weight 67,000 and 59,000. Component II (Fe protein) is a dimer of identical subunits each of molecular weight 29,500. Acetylene reduction activities are 400 nmoles/min/mg protein for component I and 340 for component II. Component I complements in vitro with component II from *Clostridium* but no activity (1.5%) is seen with the opposite combination.

Very similar molecular weights were found for the proteins thought to be nitrogenase components in *Anabaena* 7120 (34). These proteins are synthesized exclusively in heterocysts under aerobic conditions (34), except for a brief period following transfer from nitrogen-containing to nitrogen-free medium, when they are made in all the cells of the filament (35). Under anaerobic conditions, synthesis of these same proteins is derepressed by transfer to nitrogen-free medium in nonheterocyst as well as heterocyst-forming strains (73). Admission of oxygen to such cultures results in the rapid loss of nitrogenase activity (73–75, 91) and the disappearance of the proteins from the gel pattern (73). Thus, in the absence of the specific protection from oxygen provided by the heterocyst, nitrogenase proteins are first inactivated and then cleared from the cell by protease(s). It follows that nitrogenase activity must be confined to heterocysts under aerobic conditions.

Glutamine synthetase plays a dual role in bacterial nitrogen fixation. In addition to transferring the NH_3 produced by fixation to glutamate, the structural protein of GS in its deadenylylated form appears to be a positive regulator of *nif* operon transcription (95). The *Anabaena* enzyme has been studied in crude extracts (21, 77) and purified to homogeneity (68). No evidence for adenylylation of the enzyme from NH_3-grown cells could be found (68, 77). The purified enzyme is a dodecamer with subunit molecular weight 50,000 showing the characteristic double hexameric disc appearance in the electron microscope (68). GS activity increases about twofold following transfer from NH_3-containing to nitrogen-free medium (68, 77); the activity in isolated heterocysts is twice that of vegetative cells (21, 68, 102). The most potent feedback inhibitors of the purified enzyme are glycine and alanine (68); these amino acids, as well as AMP, aspartate, and carbamoyl phosphate, are effective in crude extracts (77).

The effects of methionine sulfoximine (MSX) on cyanobacterial GS are paradoxical. MSX inhibits the purified GS of bacteria; it derepresses the *nif* operons of *Klebsiella* and *Azotobacter* in the presence of normally repressing levels of NH_3 (13). When added to *Anabaena* at levels as low as $1\,\mu M$ it results in rapid, irreversible inactivation of GS (68, 93) accompanied by derepression of nitrogenase and excretion of NH_3 into the medium (68, 93). However, purified *Anabaena* GS is not affected by levels of MSX 100-fold higher than needed to inhibit *E. coli* GS by 95% (68). It is possible, of course, that MSX is metabolized in vivo to another compound that is the active inhibitor of GS.

The sum of these results is that the cyanobacterial *nif* operon is not likely to be regulated by the adenylylation state of GS, or even by GS at all, although *gln⁻* mutants will be needed to prove the point. Glutamine itself is a good candidate for a co-repressor. Direct demonstration of that role for glutamine is difficult because it is so rapidly metabolized to cyanophycin and sequestered. In this connection it will be useful to explore other analogs of glutamine for repressing or derepressing activity. Even in *Klebsiella,* glutamine and aspartate may play a more direct role in *nif* operon regulation than is currently accepted (79).

The final enzyme in the ammonia assimilation pathway does not properly belong in this review because it is not present in heterocysts: GOGAT (102, 122). This enzyme, which performs the second step in the coupled reaction with GS, produces two molecules of glutamate from one each of glutamine and 2-oxoglutarate. The history of cyanobacterial GOGAT is interesting. It was first reported to be absent from cyanobacteria, based on a survey in which reduced pyridine nucleotide was used as the hydrogen donor (64). It was then found in *Anabaena* extracts; 6.5 nmoles NADP reduced/mg protein/min (22). Later, similar extracts were shown to have both glutaminase and GDH activity, so the claim to have demonstrated

GOGAT was withdrawn (40). Finally, GOGAT was unequivocally demonstrated by substituting ferredoxin for pyridine nucleotide as the reductant; ferredoxin drives the chloroplast GOGAT (57). Location of the enzyme in vegetative cells means that the heterocysts export glutamine (neutral) and import glutamate (acid). If GOGAT had been in the heterocysts, they would have to export glutamate (acid) and import 2-oxoglutarate (acid).

One other enzyme, whose relevance to nitrogen metabolism is unknown, has been described and purified from *Anabaena*. Alanine dehydrogenase is a hexamer of subunits of molecular weight 43,000; it is active in both heterocysts and vegetative cells (78). The total ADH activity is higher in cells grown on nitrogen-free medium (64, 78).

Finally, we close this section with a brief mention of hydrogenase activity in cyanobacteria, relevant because in one sense the activity is a manifestation of nitrogenase and in another it is concerned with protecting the enzyme and recycling waste. Hydrogenase catalyzes the reversible reaction $2H^+ + 2e^- \rightleftharpoons H_2$, while nitrogenase catalyzes the reaction in the forward direction only, requiring light and ATP. Hydrogen evolution is insensitive to DCMU or CO, but is inhibited by N_2, O_2, or acetylene (46, 66). Like nitrogenase, this hydrogenase activity is repressed by NH_3 and, to a lesser extent, NO_3^-, except in certain symbiotic associations (66). A separate enzyme, present in cyanobacteria, catalyzes the backward reaction. It can be shown to support nitrogenase activity under reductant-limiting conditions (6). This enzyme is inhibited by CO and is also repressed by NH_3; presumably it is present in heterocysts although that has not been demonstrated yet (10). The enzyme's function is thought to be recycling H_2 made as a byproduct of nitrogenase action, returning electrons to a chain transporting them to nitrogenase (10).

HETEROCYST DIFFERENTIATION

Two aspects of heterocyst differentiation have attracted attention, one recently, one since the beginning of modern studies on cyanobacteria. The latter is the control of heterocyst spacing, the former the biochemistry of development.

Heterocysts form at regularly spaced intervals along the filaments of *Anabaena* and *Nostoc*. Fogg initially observed that NH_4^+ inhibits heterocyst production and that, under derepressed conditions (nitrogen-free medium), heterocysts develop midway between existing heterocysts (36). He also noticed that low light intensity and molybdenum starvation increased heterocyst frequency. He proposed that "the formation of a heterocyst from a vegetative cell occurs when the concentration within it of a specific nitrogenous inhibitory substance, probably ammonia or a simple derivative of it, falls below a critical level" (36). Mature heterocysts were subsequently postulated to be the source of inhibitor, which diffused through the vegetative cells (114). This proposal, augmented by the assumption that the diffusible inhibitor is destroyed by vegetative cells, is in general supported by subsequent work (72, 108, 111, 114, 119).

One important modification of Fogg's proposal is that NH_3 or other *products* of nitrogen fixation are not required to establish the pattern. First, the pattern is established long before nitrogen fixation begins (51, 107). Second, the pattern is established in an atmosphere of A/CO_2, in which nitrogen fixation cannot occur (65). Finally, some mutants incapable of fixing nitrogen establish a normal pattern (20, 110).

When differentiation is initiated by transfer of cells from NH_4^+-containing to N-free medium, the heterocyst pattern is precisely anticipated by the spacing of precursor cells called proheterocysts (51, 107, 108, 111). Proheterocysts can be distinguished from heterocysts in the light microscope and in the electron microscope (51, 109). Proheterocysts are resistant to lysozyme and are the site of vigorous cell-specific protein synthesis, including nitrogenase structural proteins (35), but they cannot protect nitrogenase against O_2 inactivation and their development is reversible by NH_4^+ (33, 50). Proheterocysts have been further subdivided by developmental stages on the basis of their morphology and on the fraction of cells whose development can be reversed by detaching them from neighboring vegetative cells (109, 111). Proheterocysts, according to the Wilcox-Mitchison model, are also subject to inhibition of development. If two proheterocysts begin to differentiate within each other's "zone of inhibition," they usually compete, with the result that one regresses to become a vegetative cell. When "early" proheterocysts are detached from neighboring cells they can no longer eliminate inhibitor fast enough, and so regress (111).

Based on what is known about the path of nitrogen assimilation (see above), glutamine appears to be a reasonable candidate for the diffusible inhibitor of differentiation. Mature heterocysts and vegetative cells have several ways to destroy glutamine, as they must if the pattern generated is to be stable. Glutamine can be sequestered by incorporation into protein (probably minor) or by conversion to aspartate and/or arginine followed by incorporation into cyanophycin. The latter process, which probably builds up the polar granules, is a major pathway by which heterocysts could remove a corepressor of the *nif* operon locally.

Very little is known about the biochemical basis of the pattern. Two compounds are known to break down the inhibitory zone, that is, to increase the heterocyst frequency and to permit heterocysts to develop in pairs or higher multiples. The first of these is 7-azatryptophan, a tryptophan analog which is incorporated into proteins (63). The effect is not general for amino acid analogs because canavanine, fluorophenylalanine, ethionine, norleucine, and triazolealanine do not alter the pattern. Compounds which either increase or decrease the effectiveness of azatryptophan do so by altering transport of the analog. Only a brief exposure to azatryptophan (several hours) is needed to provoke a maximum effect, measured as the regression frequency of fragment proheterocysts, while a much longer time (12 hr) is needed for recovery (111). These results are consistent with at least two models: the analog provokes the synthesis of something which prevents regression and *that* something is turned over slowly; alternatively, the analog provokes the destruction of an inhibitor of development whose resynthesis is slow.

Rifampicin also impairs the inhibition normally exerted by proheterocysts on the differentiation of neighboring cells (119). One puzzling aspect of this observation is that the concentration of drug used is very low (0.025 μg/ml), some three orders of magnitude below that necessary to inhibit RNA synthesis measured in conventional ways (111, 119). While there is one report stating that RNA synthesis is needed for heterocyst development, based on inhibition of the process by actinomycin D (7), the molecular basis for the effect of rifampicin on the spacing pattern remains obscure.

Molybdenum starvation increases heterocyst frequency (30, 36). Presumably this is due to the fact that nitrogenase requires molybdenum and without fixed nitrogen the level of diffusible inhibitor falls. This is, of course, a long-term effect; we noted above that the products of nitrogen fixation are not needed to establish the pattern.

There is no clear relationship between the few biochemical facts known regarding events immediately following transfer of filaments to nitrogen-free medium and establishment of the pattern. Following transfer, phycocyanin and cyanophycin are degraded in all the cells (12, 51, 56, 127). Phycocyanin degradation is due to a protease activated under nitrogen-starvation conditions (127). A second protease (a soluble enzyme requiring Ca^{++}) is synthesized de novo during the first hour following transfer (126, 127). Thus it would be possible for amino acids, liberated by protease action, to provide the diffusible inhibitors needed to establish the pattern. But these amino acids are available in all the cells initially; formation of a pattern-establishing gradient requires pumps to provide gradients of the amino acids. How the pumps are made and function is a complete mystery.

Protease action early in development may account for the striking results on "commitment" to morphological differentiation of heterocysts obtained with *Anabaena cylindrica* (12). Cells were derepressed by transfer to nitrogen-free medium and, at various times afterward, were rerepressed by the addition of 1 mM NH_4^+. Proheterocysts and heterocysts were counted after 24 hr. Under the conditions used, proheterocysts were first detected at 5.5 hr and heterocysts at 14.5 hr. Commitment to morphological development as proheterocysts was observed at 2.3 hr and as heterocysts at 5 hr. Commitment defined in other ways takes longer: failure of detached proheterocysts to regress was first seen after 12 hr in *Anabaena catenula* (111); resistance of heterocyst-specific protein synthesis to rerepression by NH_4^+ required 20 hr in *Anabaena* 7120 (33). In each case commitment means the ability to express heterocyst-specific genes in the presence of (NH_4^+-derived) substances which normally repress those genes. No current data shed light on the mechanism(s) of these commitments.

Important new information on these questions should flow from studies of developmental mutants of *Anabaena*. Nitrosoguanidine mutagenesis of *A. variabilis* (IU 1444) followed by penicillin selection yielded 83 auxotrophs, of which 65 required NH_4^+ or NO_3^- for growth (20). Among the latter were at least six morphological phenotypic classes: 1. heterocyst envelopes of uneven thickness, 2. heterocyst pore regions not fully differentiated, 3. pore regions unusually large, 4. protoplast separated from cell wall and shrunken, 5. reduced heterocyst frequency, and 6. increased heterocyst frequency. In terms of the earlier discussion, classes 5 and 6 could be attributed to elevated and reduced levels, respectively, of the hypothetical diffusible inhibitor of differentiation. Classes 1–4 presumably result from specific defects in the enzyme machinery needed to make heterocyst structures. Since the selection was based on a requirement of fixed nitrogen for growth, specific *nif*⁻ mutants which can make heterocysts should be in the collection. Perhaps they are in class 6 for the same reason that molybdenum starvation increases heterocyst frequency.

In an earlier study, plates of nitrosoguanidine mutagenized *Anabaena cylindrica* were searched for mutant colonies with a microscope (110). Among the mutant classes found were: 1. multiple heterocysts, 2. terminal heterocysts only, 3. no heterocysts, and 4. normal heterocyst pattern but *nif*⁻ (this one after penicillin selection). Again, in terms of the earlier model, class 1 would correspond to a decrease in the level of self-inhibition, class 2 to an increase in self-inhibition combined with leakage of inhibitor from terminal cells, and classes 3 and 4 to defects in heterocyst-specific enzymes and the *nif* operon, respectively. Class 2 is phenotypically *nif*⁻ although other cyanobacterial species can get by with only terminal heterocysts (72).

These mutant studies help prove the necessity of heterocysts for aerobic nitrogen fixation. Each of the *nif*⁻ mutant classes was examined for revertants (20). Invariably, when nitrogen fixation was restored, a normal heterocyst phenotype was restored.

Returning to the biochemistry of differentiation, one systematic study of gene expression, as displayed in the program of protein synthesis during development, has been published (35). In these experiments *Anabaena* 7120 was labeled with $^{35}SO_4^{2-}$ during successive 9 hr intervals following transfer to nitrogen-free medium. The cells were harvested either immediately after the labeling period or after the completion of differentiation (54 hr), separated into heterocysts and vegetative cells on the basis of lysozyme sensitivity, and their proteins analyzed by acrylamide gel electrophoresis and autoradiography. For each protein resolved as a separate radioactive band on the gels, such experiments tell (*a*) when the protein is made, (*b*) which cell type it is made in, and (*c*) whether its existence is stable or fleeting in each cell type. Nitrogenase structural components, for example, are made in *both* cell types early in differentiation. Their synthesis is shut off in vegetative cells, where the proteins made early on are degraded; their synthesis in developing heterocysts is continuous. Other proteins of unknown function are synthesized early only in the proheterocysts; those proteins disappear from mature heterocysts. Other proteins are synthesized only after nitrogen fixation has begun. In general, mature heterocysts display an average rate of protein synthesis comparable to that of vegetative cells, but the number of proteins made is much smaller. In other experiments, vegetative cell proteins were labeled *prior* to transfer to nitrogen-free medium. When the proteins were examined by gel electrophoresis 20 hr after transfer, nearly half the vegetative cell protein bands were missing from the proheterocysts, including the major phycobiliproteins (126). Thus the program of development includes not only the synthesis of many new proteins but the degradation of many old ones as well.

Virtually nothing is known about gene transcription during heterocyst differentiation. In the absence of specific information we can only speculate that modification of the DNA template occurs (based on the paucity of DNA in mature heterocysts) and that some operons are regulated negatively by a repressor whose co-repressor is glutamine. Here, progress requires the synthesis of specific probes to measure transcription in vivo and to serve as templates for transcription in vitro; recombinant DNA is essential for that progress.

One final speculation concerns the nature of the signal that indicates the cell is starving for nitrogen. Following transfer to nitrogen-free medium, cyanophycin is mobilized, the phycocyanin protease is activated, and amino acid pumps are established. What triggers all of these activities? In principle, the protein synthetic machinery could monitor the size of the amino acid pool. When the pool size drops, transfer RNA accumulates in uncharged form, and the ribosomes manufacture "magic spot" nucleotides (guanosine tetra- and penta-phosphate). An increase in the level of these nucleotides could be the signal of nitrogen starvation. Unfortunately, direct measurements of magic spot nucleotides in *Anabaena cylindrica* revealed none before or after transfer to nitrogen-free medium (1).

HETEROCYSTS IN SYMBIOTIC CYANOBACTERIA

Nitrogen-fixing heterocystous cyanobacteria are found as symbionts in a small number of plant species: lichens, liverworts, the fern *Azolla,* some cycads, and the angiosperm *Gunnera.* The cyanobacteria have, in a few instances, been isolated in pure culture and identified as *Anabaena* or *Nostoc* species. Almost invariably the symbiotic organism differs from the free-living in such ways that the entire symbiont can be considered as heterocysts and the host plant as vegetative cells. That is, the symbiotic cyanobacteria fix nitrogen and export NH_3 (not glutamine) in return for photosynthate provided by the host.

The adaptation of a *Nostoc* symbiont in the angiosperm *Gunnera* has been described in considerable detail (80). Compared with the free-living *Nostoc,* the symbiont has eightfold higher heterocyst frequency; no detectable phycocyanin; and tenfold higher nitrogenase activity per unit of cyanobacterial protein. There is no CO_2 fixation even though 70% of the cells look like vegetative cells, so they must behave like heterocysts in this respect. Fructose stimulates acetylene reduction in the light and entirely supports it in the dark. More is known about sources of ATP and reductant (80); what remains to be determined is the activity of glutamine synthetase in the symbiont.

The fern *Azolla* has attracted attention because of its potential utility as a green fertilizer for rice plants. Nitrogen fixation by its symbiont *Anabaena* can satisfy all of the nitrogen requirements of the host. The pattern of development of the *Anabaena* in *Azolla* leaf cavities parallels the development of the host cells (43, 44): in young host cells at the leaf apex, the *Anabaena* cells are small, dividing, and do not fix nitrogen. As the plant cells get older (further from the apex) the heterocyst frequency increases up to 30% and active nitrogen fixation follows. The fern can be freed of *Anabaena* by antibiotic treatment (70) or by a drastic shift-up in light intensity (44). The cyanobacterial symbiont can be studied free of the fern for some hours (70) and may have been isolated in pure culture (J. Newton, personal communication). Qualification of the last point is due to the fact that the sterile fern has not yet been successfully reinfected with a cyanobacterium. Nevertheless, certain important properties of the symbiont can already be contrasted with those of free-living *Anabaena:* glutamine synthetase activity in the symbiont is miniscule; 50% of the nitrogen fixed in situ during a 4-hr incubation is excreted as NH_3; the cultured symbiont continues to excrete NH_3 continuously for hours; and it reduces acetylene continuously in air for hours in the presence of 5 mM NH_3 (70). Unlike the situation in *Gunnera,* however, the *Anabaena* retain their photosynthetic activity in the symbiotic association (69); their heterotrophic potential is still unknown.

The liverworts *Anthoceros punctatus* and *Blasia pusilla* contain *Nostoc* colonies in mucilaginous cavities on the undersurface of the gametophyte (76). The alga-free gametophyte can be infected with *Nostoc* isolated from either liverwort or from *Gunnera,* but not with four other *Nostocs* or related nitrogen-fixing cyanobacteria. The basis for successful adaptation to symbiotic existence is unknown. The symbiotic *Nostoc* has heterocyst frequencies up to 40%, very high rates of acetylene reduction, does not fix CO_2 or evolve O_2, and has no phycobiliprotein (76). Both the free-living and symbiotic *Nostoc* fix $^{15}N_2$. Fixation is higher in the light than in the dark but the cells can grow on nitrogen-free medium containing sucrose in the dark (92). Excised *Nostoc* colonies excrete newly fixed nitrogen into the medium, 98% of it as NH_3. The ability to excrete is lost after 3 days in culture (92).

Lichens containing cyanobacterial phycobionts also fix nitrogen. In a survey of 40 species of lichen, those containing a single phycobiont were found to have low frequencies of heterocysts (4%) and modest acetylene reduction activity; those with a second phycobiont (a green alga and/or a fungus) contain the cyanobacterium in a special structure permitting up to 30% heterocysts and much higher rates of acetylene reduction (45). One pair of lichens has been studied in detail. Discs punched from the lichen thallus fix $^{15}N_2$; if the discs are treated with digitonin to make the fungus surrounding the cyanobacterium permeable, most of the $^{15}N_2$ fixed is released into the medium as NH_3. As expected, the symbiotic *Nostoc* glutamine synthetase activity is very low, less than 10% of that of the free-living *Nostoc* (94).

All of these results are consistent with a model in which the host plant modifies the cyanobacterial pathway for ammonia assimilation by acting on glutamine synthetase, either at the level of synthesis or activity (87). Since the addition of methionine sulfoximine to a nitrogen-fixing culture of *Anabaena* results in the inhibition of glutamine synthetase and the excretion of NH_3 (68, 93), it has been suggested that the few plants adapted to function as symbiotic hosts have that ability because they contain compound(s) that act like methionine sulfoximine (87). The suggestion perhaps should not be taken too literally because NH_3 excretion provoked by methionine sulfoximine is only observed after acetylene reduction is substantially inhibited, presumably by the high internal buildup of NH_3 (68; J. Newton, personal communication). The idea is nevertheless provocative and will undoubtedly lead to interesting experiments.

FUTURE DIRECTIONS

Heterocyst differentiation clearly provides a prokaryotic experimental system with great potential for the elucidation of problems of wide interest in developmental biology. Some progress has been made in understanding the basis of formation and maintenance of the pattern of heterocyst spacing, and the isolation of pattern mutants gives promise of more to come. Envelope assembly can be studied profitably with the mutants already on hand. Proteases seem to play a significant role in the early stages of differentiation, so the study of their regulation, again taking advantage of developmental mutants, should be fruitful. On the other hand, understanding the structure and function of the microplasmodesmata seems more remote.

Heterocyst differentation displays commitments in the sense that processes, normally regulated by fixed nitrogen, can be set in motion in a way that is refractory to subsequent regulation. The molecular details of these commitments are unknown at present. They might involve proteolysis and/or sequential operon derepression.

Very little can be said about RNA transcription during heterocyst differentiation because specific probes for such studies are not yet available. Recombinant DNA, consisting of cloned fragments of cyanobacterial DNA containing genes expressed during differentiation, will provide powerful tools for such experiments. The cloned DNA can be used to follow the transcription program in vivo, in wild type and mutant strains, with various regulators of differentiation. It can also be used in vitro to assay for the factors that regulate the development-specific transcription.

Finally, in view of the increasing awareness of the importance of biological nitrogen fixation, the study of nitrogenase activity in heterocysts will continue with vigor. The role of glutamine synthetase in *nif* gene expression in cyanobacteria is still open, as is the path of electron flow to nitrogenase in vivo. Progress in these areas will be aided by the discovery of nonmetabolizable analogs of the postulated regulatory molecules, by studies with recombinant DNA containing the *nif* genes, and by purification of the protein components of the nitrogenase complex.

ACKNOWLEDGMENT

I should like to thank my colleagues Barbara Mazur, Jim Orr, Doug Rice, and Nancy Wood for reading and improving this review. I am also grateful to Peter Wolk and Randall Alberte for extensive comments and corrections. The mistakes that remain, however, are mine. My research on heterocyst differentiation is supported by a grant from NIH (GM 21823).

Literature Cited

1. Adams, D. G., Phillips, D. O., Nichols, J. M., Carr, N. G. 1977. The presence and absence of magic spot nucleotide modulation in cyanobacteria undergoing nutritional shiftdown. *FEBS Lett.* 81:48–52
2. Adolph, K. W., Haselkorn, R. 1971. Isolation and characterization of a virus infecting the blue-green alga *Nostoc muscorum. Virology* 46:200–8
3. Alberte, R. S., Tel-Or, E. 1977. Characteristics of the photosynthetic apparatus of heterocyst and vegetative cells of *Nostoc* and *Anabaena. Plant Physiol.* 59:129
4. Allen, M. M., Smith, A. J. 1969. Nitrogen chlorosis in blue-green algae. *Arch. Microbiol.* 69:114–20
5. Apte, S. K., Rowell, P., Stewart, W. D. P. 1977. Electron donation to ferredoxin in heterocysts of the nitrogen-fixing alga *Anabaena cylindrica. Proc. R. Soc. London Ser. B.* In press
6. Benemann, J. R., Weare, N. M. 1974. Nitrogen fixation by *A. cylindrica:* III.

Hydrogen-supported nitrogenase activity. *Arch. Microbiol.* 101:401–8

7. Bhattacharya, N. C., Wahal, C. K., Talpasayi, E. R. S. 1974. Transients in nucleic acids and proteins during heterocyst differentiation in *Anabaena ambigua. Biochem. Physiol. Pflanz.* 165:239–51

8. Bothe, H., Falkenberg, B. 1973. Demonstration and possible role of a ferredoxin-dependent pyruvate decarboxylation in the nitrogen-fixing blue-green alga *Anabaena cylindrica. Plant Sci. Lett.* 1:151–56

9. Bothe, H., Falkenberg, B., Nolteernsting, U. 1974. Properties and function of the pyruvate:ferredoxin oxidoreductase from the blue-green alga *Anabaena cylindrica. Arch. Microbiol.* 96:291–304

10. Bothe, H., Tennigkeit, J., Eisbrenner, G., Yates, M. G. 1977. The hydrogenase-nitrogenase relationship in the blue-green alga *Anabaena cylindrica. Planta* 133:237–42

11. Bottomley, P. J., Stewart, W. D. P. 1977. ATP and nitrogenase activity in nitrogen-fixing blue-green algae. *New Phytol.* In press

12. Bradley, S., Carr, N. G. 1976. Heterocyst and nitrogenase development in *Anabaena cylindrica. J. Gen. Microbiol.* 96:175–84

13. Brill, W. J. 1975. Regulation and genetics of bacterial nitrogen fixation. *Ann. Rev. Microbiol.* 29:109–29

14. Bryce, T. A., Welti, D., Walsby, A. E., Nichols, B. W. 1972. Monohexoside derivatives of long chain polyhydroxy alcohols; a novel class of glycolipid specific to heterocystous algae. *Phytochemistry* 11:295–302

15. Cammack, R., Tel-Or, E., Stewart, W. D. P. 1977. EPR spectra of photosystem I constituents in heterocyst preparations from *Anabaena cylindrica. FEBS Lett.* 70:241–44

16. Cardemil, L., Wolk, C. P. 1976. The polysaccharides from heterocyst and spore envelopes of a blue-green alga: methylation analysis and structure of the backbones. *J. Biol. Chem.* 251:2967–75

17. Codd, G. A., Rowell, P., Stewart, W. D. P. 1974. Pyruvate and nitrogenase activity in cell free extracts of the blue-green alga *Anabaena cylindrica. Biochem. Biophys. Res. Commun.* 61:424–31

18. Codd, G. A., Stewart, W. D. P. 1977. Ribulose-1,5-bisphosphate carboxylase in heterocysts and vegetative cells of *Anabaena cylindrica. FEMS Lett.* 1. In press

19. Cox, R. M., Fay, P. 1969. Special aspects of nitrogen fixation by blue-green algae. *Proc. R. Soc. London Ser. B* 172:357–66

20. Currier, T. C., Haury, J. F., Wolk, C. P. 1977. Isolation and preliminary characterization of auxotrophs of a filamentous cyanobacterium. *J. Bacteriol.* 129:1556–62

21. Dharmawardene, M. W. N., Haystead, A., Stewart, W. D. P. 1973. Glutamine synthetase of the nitrogen-fixing alga *Anabaena cylindrica. Arch. Mikrobiol.* 90:281–95

22. Dharmawardene, M. W. N., Stewart, W. D. P., Stanley, S. O. 1972. Nitrogenase activity, amino acid pool patterns and amination in blue-green algae. *Planta* 108:133–45

23. Donze, M., Haveman, J., Schiereck, P. 1972. Absence of Photosystem II in heterocysts of the blue-green alga *Anabaena. Biochim. Biophys. Acta* 256:157–61

24. Donze, M., Raat, A. J. P., van Gorkom, H. J. 1974. Supply of ATP and reductant to nitrogenase in the blue-green alga *Anabaena cylindrica. Plant Sci. Lett.* 3:35–41

25. Dunn, J. H., Wolk, C. P. 1970. Composition of the cellular envelopes of *Anabaena cylindrica. J. Bacteriol.* 103:153–58

26. Evans, M. C. W., Reeves, S. G., Telfer, A. 1973. The detection of a bound ferredoxin in the photosynthetic lamellae of blue-green algae and other oxygen-evolving photosynthetic organisms. *Biochem. Biophys. Res. Commun.* 51:593–96

27. Fay, P. 1969. Cell differentiation and pigment composition in *Anabaena cylindrica. Arch. Mikrobiol.* 67:62–70

28. Fay, P. 1970. Photostimulation of nitrogen fixation in *Anabaena cylindrica. Biochim. Biophys. Acta* 216:353–56

29. Fay, P. 1973. The heterocyst. In *The Biology of Blue-Green Algae,* ed. N. G. Carr, B. A. Whitton, pp. 238–59. Oxford: Blackwell

30. Fay, P., de Vasconcelos, L. 1974. Nitrogenase metabolism and ultrastructure in *A. cylindrica* II. Effect of molybdenum and vanadium. *Arch. Microbiol.* 99:221–30

31. Fay, P., Lang, N. J. 1971. The heterocysts of blue-green algae I. Ultrastructural integrity after isolation. *Proc. R. Soc. London Ser. B* 178:185–92

32. Fay, P., Stewart, W. D. P., Walsby, A. E., Fogg, G. E. 1968. Is the heterocyst the site of nitrogen fixation in blue-green algae? *Nature* 220:810–12

33. Fleming, H. 1974. Protein synthesis during cellular differentiation in *Nostoc muscorum*. PhD thesis. Univ. Chicago, Chicago, Ill. 184 pp.

34. Fleming, H., Haselkorn, R. 1973. Differentiation in *Nostoc muscorum:* nitrogenase is synthesized in heterocysts. *Proc. Natl. Acad. Sci. USA* 70:2727–31

35. Fleming, H., Haselkorn, R. 1974. The program of protein synthesis during heterocyst differentiation in nitrogen-fixing blue-green algae. *Cell* 3:159–70

36. Fogg, G. E. 1949. Growth and heterocyst production in *Anabaena cylindrica* Lemm II. In relation to carbon and nitrogen metabolism. *Ann. Bot.* 13:241–59

37. Fogg, G. E. 1951. Growth and heterocyst production in *Anabaena cylindrica* Lemm III. The cytology of heterocysts. *Ann. Bot.* 15:23–36

37a. Foulds, I. J., Carr, N. G. 1977. A proteolytic enzyme degrading phycocyanin in the cyanobacterium *Anabaena cylindrica*. *FEMS Microbiol. Lett.* 2:117–21

37b. Goldbeck, J. H., Lieu, S., San Pietro, A. 1977. Electron transport in chloroplasts. In *Encyclopedia of Plant Physiology*, ed. A. Trebst, M. Avron, 5:94–116

38. Gromov, B. V., Khudyakov, I. Ya., Mamkaeva, K. A. 1975. Electron microscope study of the intracellular development of cyanophage A-4(L). *Vestn. Leningr. Univ. Biol.* 3:74–76

39. Hall, D. O., Cammack, R., Rao, K. K., Evans, M. C. W., Mullinger, R. 1975. Ferredoxins, blue-green bacteria, and evolution. *Biochem. Soc. Trans.* 3:361–68

40. Haystead, A., Dharmawardene, M. W. N., Stewart, W. D. P. 1973. Ammonia assimilation in a nitrogen-fixing blue-green alga. *Plant Sci. Lett.* 1:439–45

41. Haystead, A., Robinson, R., Stewart, W. D. P. 1970. Nitrogenase activity in extracts of heterocystous and non-heterocystous blue-green algae. *Arch. Mikrobiol.* 75:235–43

42. Haystead, A., Stewart, W. D. P. 1972. Characteristics of the nitrogenase system of the blue-green alga *Anabaena cylindrica*. *Arch. Mikrobiol.* 82:325–36

43. Hill, D. J. 1975. The pattern of development of *Anabaena* in the *Azolla-Anabaena* symbiosis. *Planta* 122:179–84

44. Hill, D. J. 1977. The role of *Anabaena* in the *Azolla-Anabaena* symbiosis. *New Phytol.* 78:611–16

45. Hitch, C. J. B., Millbank, J. W. 1975. Nitrogen metabolism in lichens VII. Nitrogenase activity and heterocyst frequency in lichens with blue-green phycobionts. *New Phytol.* 75:239–44

46. Jones, L. W., Bishop, N. I. 1976. Simultaneous measurement of oxygen and hydrogen exchange from the blue-green alga *Anabaena*. *Plant Physiol.* 57:659–65

47. Juttner, F., Carr, N. G. 1976. The movement of organic molecules from vegetative cells into the heterocysts of *Anabaena cylindrica*. In *Proc. 2nd Int. Symp. Photosynth. Prokaryotes*, ed. G. A. Codd, W. D. P. Stewart, pp. 121–23. Univ. Dundee, Scotland

48. Khudyakov, I. Ya., Gromov, B. V. 1973. Temperate cyanophage A-4(L) of the blue-green alga *Anabaena variabilis*. *Mikrobiologiya* 42:904–7

49. Kratz, W. A., Myers, J. 1955. Nutrition and growth of several blue-green algae. *Am. J. Bot.* 42:282–87

50. Kulasooriya, S. A., Fay, P. 1974. On the reversibility of heterocyst differentiation. *Br. Phycol. J.* 9:97–100

51. Kulasooriya, S. A., Lang, N. J., Fay, P. 1972. The heterocysts of blue-green algae III. Differentiation and nitrogenase activity. *Proc. R. Soc. London Ser. B* 181:199–209

52. Lambein, F., Wolk, C. P. 1973. Structural studies on the glycolipids from the envelope of the heterocyst of *Anabaena cylindrica*. *Biochemistry* 12:791–98

53. Lang, N. J. 1965. Electron microscopic study of heterocyst development in *Anabaena azollae* Strasburger. *J. Phycol.* 1:127–34

54. Lang, N. J., Fay, P. 1971. The heterocysts of blue-green algae II. Details of ultrastructure. *Proc. R. Soc. London Ser. B* 178:193–203

55. Lang, N. J., Simon, R. D., Wolk, C. P. 1972. Correspondence of cyanophycin granules with structured granules in *Anabaena cylindrica*. *Arch. Microbiol.* 83:313–20

56. Lawrie, A. C., Codd, G. A., Stewart, W. D. P. 1976. The incorporation of nitrogen into recent products of photosynthesis in *Anabaena cylindrica*. *Arch. Mikrobiol.* 107:15–24

57. Lea, P. J., Miflin, B. J. 1975. Glutamine (amide): 2 oxoglutarate amino transferase in blue-green algae. *Biochem. Soc. Trans.* 3:381–84

58. Leach, C. K., Carr, N. G. 1971. Pyruvate:ferredoxin oxidoreductase and its activation by ATP in the blue-green alga *Anabaena variabilis. Biochim. Biophys. Acta* 245:165–74
59. Lee, S. S., Young, A. M., Krogmann, D. W. 1969. Site specific inactivation of the photophosphorylation reactions of *Anabaena variabilis. Biochim. Biophys. Acta* 180:130–36
60. Lex, M., Carr, N. G. 1974. The metabolism of glucose by heterocysts and vegetative cells of *Anabaena cylindrica. Arch. Mikrobiol.* 101:161–67
61. Lex, M., Stewart, W. D. P. 1973. Algal nitrogenase, reductant pools and photosystem I activity. *Biochim. Biophys. Acta* 292:436–43
62. Lorch, S. K., Wolk, C. P. 1974. Application of gas liquid chromatography to study of the envelope lipids of heterocysts. *J. Phycol.* 10:352–55
63. Mitchison, G. J., Wilcox, M. 1973. Alteration in heterocyst pattern of *Anabaena* produced by 7-azatryptophan. *Nature New Biol.* 246:229–33
64. Neilson, A., Doudoroff, M. 1973. Ammonia assimilation in blue-green algae. *Arch. Mikrobiol.* 89:15–22
65. Neilson, A., Rippka, R., Kunisawa, R. 1971. Heterocyst formation and nitrogenase synthesis in *Anabaena* sp.: a kinetic study. *Arch. Mikrobiol.* 76:139–50
66. Newton, J. W. 1976. Photoproduction of molecular hydrogen by a plant-algal symbiotic system. *Science* 191:559–61
67. Ohmori, M., Hattori, A. 1971. Nitrogen fixation and heterocysts in the blue-green alga *Anabaena cylindrica. Plant Cell Physiol.* 12:961–67
68. Orr, J., Toan, N. D., Haselkorn, R. 1978. Purification and properties of glutamine synthetase from *Anabaena* 7120. In preparation
69. Peters, G. A. 1975. Studies on the *Azolla-Anabaena azollae* symbiosis. *Proc. 1st Int. Symp. Nitrogen Fixation,* ed. W. E. Newton, C. J. Nyman, pp. 592–610. Pullman: Washington State Univ. Press
70. Peters, G. A. 1977. The *Azolla-Anabaena azollae* symbiosis. In *Genetic Engineering for Nitrogen Fixation,* ed. A. Hollaender, pp. 231–58. New York: Plenum
71. Peterson, R. B., Burris, R. H. 1976. Properties of heterocysts isolated with colloidal silica. *Arch. Mikrobiol.* 108:35–40
72. Reddy, P. M., Talpasayi, E. R. S. 1974. Heterocyst formation in blue-green

alga, *Cylindrospermum. Nature* 249:493–94
73. Rippka, R., Haselkorn, R. 1978. Anaerobic induction and aerobic destruction of nitrogenase proteins in non-heterocystous cyanobacteria. In preparation
74. Rippka, R., Stanier, R. Y. 1976. Observations on nitrogenase synthesis by cyanobacteria under strict anaerobiosis. In *Proc. 2nd Int. Symp. Photosynth. Prokaryotes,* ed. G. A. Codd, W. D. P. Stewart, pp. 138–39. Univ. Dundee, Scotland
75. Rippka, R., Waterbury, J. B. 1977. The synthesis of nitrogenase by non-heterocystous cyanobacteria. *FEMS Microbiol Lett.* 2:83–86
76. Rodgers, G. A., Stewart, W. D. P. 1977. The cyanophyte-hepatic symbiosis I. Morphology and physiology. *New Phytol.* 78:441–58
77. Rowell, P., Enticott, S., Stewart, W. D. P. 1977. Glutamine synthetase and nitrogenase activity in the blue-green alga *Anabaena cylindrica. New Phytol.* 79:41–54
78. Rowell, P., Stewart, W. D. P. 1976. Alanine dehydrogenase of the blue-green alga *Anabaena cylindrica. Arch. Mikrobiol.* 107:115–24
79. Shanmugam, K. T., Morandi, C. 1976. Amino acids as repressors of nitrogenase biosynthesis in *Klebsiella pneumoniae. Biochim. Biophys. Acta* 437:322–32
80. Silvester, W. B. 1976. Endophyte adaptation in *Gunnera-Nostoc* symbiosis. In *Symbiotic Nitrogen Fixation in Plants,* ed. P. S. Nutman, pp. 521–38. Cambridge Univ. Press
81. Simon, R. D. 1971. Cyanophycin granules from the blue-green alga *Anabaena cylindrica:* a reserve material consisting of copolymers of aspartic acid and arginine. *Proc. Natl. Acad. Sci. USA* 68:265–67
82. Smith, R. V., Evans, M. C. W. 1971. Nitrogenase activity in cell-free extracts of the blue-green alga *Anabaena cylindrica. J. Bacteriol.* 105:913–17
83. Smith, R. V., Noy, R. J., Evans, M. C. W. 1971. Physiological electron donor systems to the nitrogenase of the blue-green alga *Anabaena cylindrica. Biochim. Biophys. Acta* 253:104–9
84. Stanier, R. Y., Cohen-Bazire, G. 1977. Phototrophic prokaryotes: the cyanobacteria. *Ann. Rev. Microbiol.* 31:225–74
85. Stewart, W. D. P. 1973. Nitrogen fixa-

tion by photosynthetic microorganisms. *Ann. Rev. Microbiol.* 27:283–316

86. Stewart, W. D. P. 1973. Nitrogen fixation. See Ref. 29, pp. 260–78

87. Stewart, W. D. P. 1977. A botanical ramble among the blue-green algae. *Br. Phycol. J.* 12:89–115

88. Stewart, W. D. P., Codd, G. A. 1975. Polyhedral bodies (carboxysomes) of blue-green algae. *Br. Phycol. J.* 10: 273–78

89. Stewart, W. D. P., Haystead, A., Dharmawardene, M. W. N. 1975. Nitrogen assimilation and metabolism in blue-green algae. In *Nitrogen Fixation by Free-Living Microorganisms,* ed. W. D. P. Stewart, 129–58. Cambridge Univ. Press

90. Stewart, W. D. P., Haystead, A., Pearson, H. W. 1969. Nitrogenase activity in heterocysts of blue-green algae. *Nature* 224:226–28

91. Stewart, W. D. P., Lex, M. 1970. Nitrogenase activity in the blue-green alga *Plectonema boryanum* strain 594. *Arch. Mikrobiol.* 73:250–60

92. Stewart, W. D. P., Rodgers, G. A. 1977. The cyanophyte-hepatic symbiosis II. Nitrogen fixation and interchange of nitrogen and carbon. *New Phytol.* 78: 459–71

93. Stewart, W. D. P., Rowell, P. 1975. Effects of L-methionine-DL-sulfoximine on the assimilation of newly fixed NH₃, acetylene reduction and heterocyst production in *Anabaena cylindrica. Biochem. Biophys. Res. Commun.* 65: 846–56

94. Stewart, W. D. P., Rowell, P. 1977. Modification of nitrogen-fixing algae in lichen symbioses. *Nature* 265:371–72

95. Streicher, S. L., Shanmugan, K. T., Ausubel, F., Morandi, C., Goldberg, R. B. 1974. Regulation of nitrogen fixation in *Klebsiella pneumoniae:* evidence for a role of glutamine synthetase as a regulator of nitrogenase synthesis. *J. Bacteriol.* 120:815–21

96. Tel-Or, E., Stewart, W. D. P. 1975. Manganese and photosynthetic oxygen evolution by algae. *Nature* 258:715–16

97. Tel-Or, E., Stewart, W. D. P. 1976. Photosynthetic electron transport, ATP synthesis and nitrogenase activity in isolated heterocysts of *Anabaena cylindrica. Biochim. Biophys. Acta* 423: 189–95

98. Tel-Or, E., Stewart, W. D. P. 1977. Photosynthetic components and activities of nitrogen-fixing isolated hetero-cysts of *Anabaena cylindrica. Proc. R. Soc. London Ser. B* 198:61–86

99. Thomas, J. 1970. Absence of pigments of photosystem II of photosynthesis in heterocysts of a blue-green alga. *Nature* 258:715–16

100. Thomas, J. 1972. Relationship between age of culture and occurrence of the pigments of photosystem II of photosynthesis in heterocysts of a blue-green alga. *J. Bacteriol.* 110:92–95

101. Thomas, J., David, K. A. V. 1972. Site of nitrogenase activity in the blue-green alga *Anabaena* sp.L-31. *Nature New Biol.* 238:219–21

102. Thomas, J., Meeks, J. C., Wolk, C. P., Shaffer, P. W., Austin, S. M., Chien, W.-S. 1977. Formation of glutamine from [¹³N]ammonia, [¹³N]dinitrogen, and [¹⁴C]glutamate by heterocysts isolated from *Anabaena cylindrica. J. Bacteriol.* 129:1545–55

102a. Thornber, J. P., Alberte, R. S., Hunter, F. A., Shiozawa, J. A., Kan, K.-S. 1976. The organization of chlorophyll in the plant photosynthetic unit. *Brookhaven Symp. Biol.* 28:132–48

103. Tsai, L.-B., Mortenson, L. E. 1977. Nitrogenase of *Anabaena cylindrica:* complementation with nitrogenase components of *Clostridium pasteurianum. Abstr. Ann. Meet. Am. Soc. Microbiol.* p. 206

104. Van Gorkom, H. J., Donze, M. 1971. Localization of nitrogen fixation in *Anabaena. Nature* 234:241–42

105. Walsby, A. E., Nichols, B. W. 1969. Lipid composition of heterocysts. *Nature* 221:673–74

106. Weare, N. M., Benemann, J. R. 1973. Nitrogen fixation by *Anabaena cylindrica* I. Localizaton of nitrogen fixation in heterocysts. *Arch. Mikrobiol.* 90: 323–32

107. Wilcox, M. 1970. One dimensional pattern found in blue-green algae. *Nature* 228:686–87

108. Wilcox, M., Mitchison, G. J., Smith, R. J. 1973. Pattern formation in the blue-green alga *Anabaena* I. Basic mechanisms. *J. Cell Sci.* 12:707–23

109. Wilcox, M., Mitchison, G. J., Smith, R. J. 1973. Pattern formation in the blue-green alga *Anabaena* II. Controlled proheterocyst regression. *J. Cell Sci.* 13:637–49

110. Wilcox, M., Mitchison, G. J., Smith, R. J. 1975. Mutants of *Anabaena cylindrica* altered in heterocyst spacing. *Arch. Mikrobiol.* 130:219–23

111. Wilcox, M., Mitchison, G. J., Smith, R. J. 1975. Spatial control of differentiation in the blue-green alga *Anabaena*. *Microbiology 1975*, ed. D. Schlessinger, pp. 453–63. Am. Soc. Microbiol. Washington, DC

112. Winkenbach, F., Wolk, C. P. 1973. Activities of enzymes of the oxidative and the reductive pentose phosphate pathways in heterocysts of a blue-green alga. *Plant Physiol.* 52:480–83

113. Winkenbach, F., Wolk, C. P., Jost, M. 1972. Lipids of membranes and of the cell envelope in heterocysts of a blue-green alga. *Planta* 107:69–80

114. Wolk, C. P. 1967. Physiological basis of the pattern of vegetative growth of a blue-green alga. *Proc. Natl. Acad. Sci. USA* 57:1246–51

115. Wolk, C. P. 1968. Movement of carbon from vegetative cells to heterocysts in *Anabaena cylindrica*. *J. Bacteriol.* 96:2138–43

116. Wolk, C. P. 1973. Physiology and cytological chemistry of blue-green algae. *Bacteriol. Rev.* 37:32–101

117. Wolk, C. P. 1975. Differentiation and pattern formation in filamentous blue-green algae. In *Spores VI*, ed. P. Gerhardt, H. Sadoff, R. Costilow, pp. 85–96. Am. Soc. Microbiol., Washington, DC

118. Wolk, C. P., Austin, S. M., Bortins, J., Galonsky, A. 1974. Autoradiographic localization of ^{13}N after fixation of ^{13}N-labeled nitrogen gas by a heterocyst-forming blue-green alga. *J. Cell Biol.* 61:440–53

119. Wolk, C. P., Quine, M. P. 1975. Formation of one-dimensional patterns by stochastic processes and by filamentous blue-green algae. *Dev. Biol.* 46:370–82

120. Wolk, C. P., Shaffer, P. W. 1976. Heterotrophic micro- and macrocultures of a nitrogen-fixing cyanobacterium. *Arch. Microbiol.* 110:145–47

121. Wolk, C. P., Simon, R. D. 1969. Pigments and lipids of heterocysts. *Planta* 86:92–97

122. Wolk, C. P., Thomas, J., Shaffer, P. W., Austin, S. M., Galonsky, A. 1976. Pathway of nitrogen metabolism after fixation of ^{13}N-labeled N$_2$ by *Anabaena cylindrica*. *J. Biol. Chem.* 251:5027–34

123. Wolk, C. P., Wojciuch, E. 1971. Photoreduction of acetylene by heterocysts. *Planta* 97:126–34

124. Wolk, C. P., Wojciuch, E. 1971. Biphasic time course of solubilization of nitrogenase during cavitation of aerobically grown *Anabaena cylindrica*. *J. Phycol.* 7:339–44

125. Wolk, C. P., Wojciuch, E. 1973. Simple methods for plating single vegetative cells of, and for replica-plating, filamentous blue-green algae. *Arch. Mikrobiol.* 91:91–95

126. Wood, N. B., Haselkorn, R. 1976. Protein degradation during heterocyst development in *Anabaena*. In *Proc. 2nd Int. Symp. Photosynth. Prokaryotes*, ed. G. A. Codd, W. D. P. Stewart, pp. 125–27. Univ. Dundee, Scotland

127. Wood, N. B., Haselkorn, R. 1977. Protein degradation during heterocyst differentiation in the blue-green alga *Anabaena* 7120. *Fed. Proc.* 36:886

Ann. Rev. Plant Physiol. 1978. 29:345–78

ENERGY DISTRIBUTION IN THE PHOTOCHEMICAL APPARATUS OF PHOTOSYNTHESIS

♦7655

Warren L. Butler

Department of Biology, University of California, San Diego, La Jolla, California 92093

CONTENTS

345

0066-4294/78/0601-0345$01.00

INTRODUCTION

Studies of energy distribution in photosynthetic systems have played an important role in the evolution of our understanding of photochemical mechanisms of photosynthesis. Early in the formulation of the currently accepted Z scheme (i.e. a linear electron transport system involving two photochemical pigment systems operating in series to drive electrons from water to pyridine nucleotide) questions arose as to the partitioning of energy between the two pigment systems. The series formulation indicated that optimal operation should occur when the excitation energy was distributed equally between the two photochemical pigment systems. Since the two pigment systems appeared to have different absorption characteristics, the Z scheme predicted that the maximum yield of photosynthesis should be obtained only at specific wavelengths (e.g. near 685 nm) where the excitation energy is absorbed equally by the two pigment systems and that substantially lower yields should be obtained at other wavelengths. However, Emerson & Lewis (13) had reported earlier that the quantum yield of photosynthesis for green algae was maximal and essentially independent of wavelength from 570 to 685 nm. This "quantum yield anomaly," as the wavelength-independent quantum yield of photosynthesis came to be known, at least for a time, commanded considerable attention (at that time) since it seemed to harbor the seeds of destruction for the Z scheme. An excellent discussion of the "quantum yield anomaly" can be found in an early paper by Myers (32), as well as in a later review article (33). It was concluded that either the data of Emerson & Lewis were not sufficiently precise to reveal the wavelength variations in the quantum yield or that mechanisms existed in the chloroplast to redistribute the excitation energy equally between the two pigment systems when unequal amounts of energy were absorbed. In fact, Myers & Graham (34) first proposed the "spillover" hypothesis, in which energy could be transferred from the short wavelength pigment system (PS II) to the long wavelength pigment system (PS I) to account for the wavelength independence of the quantum yield. I will return to this question of the wavelength dependence of energy distribution later in the chapter.

The study of enhancement phenomena and chromatic transients dominated photosynthetic research in the first half of the 1960s, but these studies gradually gave way to other more physiological manifestations of energy distribution by the latter part of that decade. Murata (30) and Bonaventura & Myers (2) proposed independently that slow readjustments in the distribution of excitation energy between PS I and PS II occur as the steady-state rate of photosynthesis is approached. This slow adjustment of energy distribution, which involves gradually increasing the fraction of the absorbed energy delivered to PS I, accounts for the slow decline in the yield of fluorescence which was observed in some of the earliest measurements of fluorescence from photosynthetic cells (29). According to the terminology which has built up around this phenomenon, dark-adapted cells (or cells equilibrated in light absorbed predominately by PS I) are said to be in State 1, while cells at steady-state photosynthesis (and therefore equilibrated with light absorbed at least partially by PS II) are said to be in State 2, and the transition from the dark-adapted state to the light-adapted state is called a State 1-State 2 transition.

Studies showing marked effects of divalent cations on fluorescence and energy distribution in chloroplasts were made at the same time that State 1-State 2 phenomena were being studied in whole cells. Homann (16) found that the fluorescence of variable yield was stimulated strongly when divalent cations such as Mg^{2+} were added to otherwise depleted chloroplasts. Murata (31) observed the same phenomenon and showed from studies of photochemical activities at room temperature as well as from studies of fluorescence at low temperature that a larger fraction of the excitation energy was delivered to PS II when the chloroplasts were suspended in the presence of divalent cations. Furthermore, Murata saw a connection between the effects of divalent cations in chloroplasts and the State 1-State 2 phenomena in whole cells, and he proposed that the State 1-State 2 transition was a consequence of ion movements across the thylakoid membranes. More recently the role of cations in State 1-State 2 phenomena has been examined in studies with chloroplasts (1, 22).

The first half of the 1970s witnessed a synthesis of evidence and ideas from a number of different experimental approaches into the realization that the active transport of protons, the counter movement of cations, the activation of coupling factors and stroma enzymes by Mg^{2+}, the synthesis of ATP, and conformational changes of thylakoid membranes are all interrelated in a complex feedback system designed to optimize the overall process of photosynthesis. That such feedback controls occur in the biochemical pathways of photosynthesis is to be expected by analogy with other metabolic processes. However, we now recognize that the distribution of excitation energy in the primary photochemical apparatus is also regulated by membrane conformational changes and that these changes are integrated into the overall control system. The absorption characteristics of the photosynthetic apparatus favors PS II over PS I so that at the onset of irradiation the PS II photoreaction is overdriven. The control processes then take over and function to redistribute some of the excess energy in PS II to PS I with the possibility of fine-tuning the system to achieve an optimal rate of photosynthesis under the conditions which prevail.

The purpose of this chapter is to examine photochemical mechanisms by which energy distribution in the photosynthetic apparatus can be controlled. In order to address such questions in quantitative terms, models were developed which included specific photochemical parameters to describe energy distribution. Analytical expressions were developed within the context of these models which could be tested experimentally and which led to predictions that were testable. Initially a photochemical model was developed for PS II to account for the different patterns of quenching of fluorescence and photochemistry which are observed with different quenching agents. That model for PS II was then joined with a photochemical model for PS I to give an overall model for the entire photochemical apparatus. The model combining PS II and PS I provided quantitative assessments of the yield of energy transfer from PS II to PS I (i.e. "spillover") as well as the wavelength dependence of energy distribution between the two photochemical systems. Finally, quite recently the model was expanded to consider the light-harvesting chlorophyll *a/b* complex as a distinct pigment system which interacts with the rest of the photochemical apparatus through specific photochemical rate constants. This latter tripartite model permitted quantitative assessments of the degree of energy coupling between the chlorophyll *a/b* complex and PS II (e.g. in the presence and absence of Mg^{2+}) and established the energy coupling between these two arrays of chlorophyll as the basis of a control mechanism for energy distribution. The development of the models, the derivation of the analytical expressions which emerged from the models, and the various experimental systems in which the models were tested will be reviewed. It is hoped that this chapter will provide the diligent reader with meaningful insights into the mechanisms by which energy distribution is controlled in the primary photochemical apparatus and a fuller awareness of the kinds of information that can be extracted from fluorescence measurements.

THE BIPARTITE MODEL

The Model for PS II

The development of an adequate model of the photochemical apparatus required a fresh examination of fluorescence quenching mechanisms in PS II. Fluorescence from PS II has been generally interpreted in the context of a simple photochemical model in which fluorescence (F), photochemistry (P), and nonradiative decay (D) all compete for the excitation energy in the antenna chlorophyll of PS II by first order rate processes. Duysens & Sweers (12), following the earlier work of Kautsky, Appel & Amann (19), proposed that the primary electron acceptor of PS II quenched the chlorophyll fluorescence of PS II when the acceptor was present in its oxidized (electron accepting) form but did not quench fluorescence in the reduced state. This relationship between the redox state of the primary electron acceptor and fluorescence quenching was also consistent with the simple photochemical model in Diagram 1.

When the PS II reaction centers are all open, the yield of photochemistry is maximal, $\phi_{P_0} = k_P(k_F + k_D + k_P)^{-1}$, and the yield of fluorescence is at a minimum, $\phi_{F_0} = k_F(k_F + k_D + k_P)^{-1}$. However, when the reaction centers are closed because the primary electron acceptors are reduced, ϕ_P goes to zero and the yield of fluores-

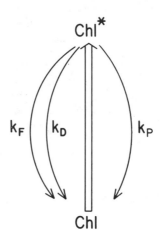

cence increases to a maximum (M), $\phi_{F_M} = k_F(k_F + k_D)^{-1}$. This increase is called variable fluorescence (F_V). Thus the simple photochemical theory predicts the general pattern of light-induced fluorescence yield changes that is observed with photosynthesis systems. However, the theory also predicts a specific relationship between the yields of photochemistry and fluorescence; namely, that:

$$\varphi_{P_0} = \frac{\varphi_{F_M} - \varphi_{F_0}}{\varphi_{F_M}} = \frac{F_V}{F_M} \qquad 1.$$

which does not always appear to be valid. In some cases, the ratio of F_V/F_M appears to be too small to account for the yield of photochemistry and in other cases, changes in the ratio of F_V/F_M do not appear to be consistent with changes in the yield of photochemistry. Such discrepancies, however, have generally been brushed aside by assuming that part of the fluorescence measured at the F_0 level was a "dead fluorescence" emanating from an inactive form of chlorophyll (11). Given this ad hoc assumption, the extent of the "dead fluorescence" could be adjusted to rationalize almost any set of fluorescence data. However, a systematic study of the quenching action of a quinone on the relative yields of photochemistry and fluorescence in chloroplasts at $-196°C$ failed to confirm the "dead fluorescence" hypothesis (20). Chloroplasts were frozen to $-196°C$ in the presence of different concentrations of the quinone, and measurements were made on the rate of photoreduction of C-550 and on the light-induced fluorescence yield changes at 692 nm. The results of this study showed that ϕ_{P_0} (measured as the initial rate of photoreduction of C-550) was decreased by the quenching action of quinone and that the decrease of ϕ_{P_0} was accompanied by a proportionate decrease in the ratio of F_V/F_M. The relationship between photochemistry and fluorescence expressed in Equation 1 was found to be valid over the entire concentration range up to 10^{-4} M, where the quinone quenched approximately 99% of the fluorescence. It was concluded that Equation 1 was valid for the quenching action of quinones and that there were no significant amounts of "dead fluorescence" in the measurements of F_0 of PS II.

However, the quenching action of other agents showed markedly different characteristics. The addition of ferricyanide to chloroplasts before freezing to $-196°C$ quenched F_V specifically with no detectable effect on F_0 (35), and even though F_V was quenched by 75%, ϕ_{P_0}, as determined by the rate of photoreduction of C-550, was unchanged. It is also known that UV radiation quenches F_V almost entirely with no effect on F_0 (28, 46) and that PS II photochemistry may still persist if artificial electron donors to PS II are supplied (46). Any acceptable photochemical model for PS II must be able to accommodate these two different types of quenching mechanisms in which some agents quench F_V and F_0 and ϕ_{P_0} in such a manner that the quenching of ϕ_{P_0} is accompanied by a proportionate decrease in the ratio of F_V/F_M while other agents quench F_V specifically with no effect on F_0 and with little or no effect on ϕ_{P_0}.

Butler & Kitajima (4) arrived at such a model (Diagram 2) by the simple expedient of considering one of the deexcitation pathways in the antenna chlorophyll of PS II to be the trapping of excitation energy by the PS II reaction centers P·A, where P is the reaction center chlorophyll and A is the primary electron acceptor.

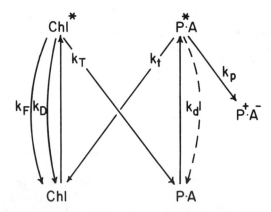

In such a model, excitation energy in the antenna chlorophyll is either emitted as fluorescence k_F, dissipated by nonradiative decay k_D, or trapped by the reaction center chlorophyll k_T. The reaction centers were assumed to be either open $P \cdot A$, or closed $P \cdot A^-$. The P^+ states of the reaction center couple were not considered because the short lifetime of P^+ precludes any appreciable accumulation of these states. Excitation energy trapped by the reaction center chlorophyll can be used for photochemistry k_p, dissipated as nonradiative decay at the reaction center chlorophyll k_d, or transferred back to the antenna chlorophyll k_t. There is no evidence for any fluorescence from the reaction center chlorophyll so none was postulated.

It is assumed that photochemistry will occur if an exciton is trapped by an open reaction center, i.e. that $k_p \gg k_t$ or k_d. If the reaction center is closed, however, the exciton can still be trapped but the energy cannot be used for photochemistry ($k_p = 0$). In that case the exciton is either transferred back to the antenna chlorophyll via k_t or dissipated by nonradiative decay via k_d. This model assumes that the act of trapping in PS II units does not involve a significant potential energy well at the reaction center chlorophyll: rather the excitation energy flows freely into and back out of the reaction center chlorophyll. The act of trapping depends on an exciton finding a reaction center with an oxidized acceptor A and the statement that $k_p \gg k_t$.

In order to set up analytical expressions for the yields of photochemistry and fluorescence from such a model, some assumptions had to be made with respect to the transfer of energy between PS II units. The expressions were derived for both a "separate package" model in which there is no energy transfer between PS II units and a "matrix" model in which all of the reaction centers are available to all of the antenna chlorophyll. Assuming the separate package model, the yield of photochemistry ϕ_P, will be equal to $\psi_T \psi_P A$ [1] where $\psi_T = k_T (k_F + k_D + k_T)^{-1}$ is the

---

[1] In the equations to follow, yield terms ϕ will be distinguished from strictly probability terms ψ. The ψ terms are constants but the ϕ terms depend on the state of the PS II reaction centers.

probability for trapping by the reaction center chlorophyll, $\psi_p = k_p(k_p + k_t + k_d)^{-1}$ is the probability for photochemistry at an open reaction center, and A is the fraction of the reaction centers which are open. It is assumed that $\psi_p \simeq 1.0$ so that at the initial state when $A = 1$:

$$\varphi_{P_0} = \psi_T \qquad\qquad 2.$$

The yield of fluorescence can be expressed as:

$$\varphi_F = \psi_F A + \psi_F(1 - A)[1 + \psi_T\psi_t + (\psi_T\psi_t)^2 + \cdots] \qquad\qquad 3.$$

where $\psi_F = k_F(k_F + k_D + k_T)^{-1}$ and $\psi_t = k_t(k_t + k_d)^{-1}$ (4). ψ_t applies only to closed reaction centers where $\psi_p = 0$. The first term in Equation 3 is the contribution to fluorescence from units with open reaction centers (A), while the second term, including the infinite series, is the fluorescence from units with closed centers (1 - A). According to the "separate package" model, an exciton in a unit with a closed reaction center remains in that unit continually cycling into and back out of the reaction center chlorophyll until it is emitted as fluorescence or dissipated by nonradiative decay. The infinite series $\Sigma_{n=0}^{\infty} (\psi_T\psi_t)^n$ in the second term of Equation 3, which describes that cycling process, converges to a simple expression $(1 - \psi_T\psi_t)^{-1}$ so that:

$$\varphi_F = \psi_F [A + \frac{1 - A}{1 - \psi_T\psi_t}] \qquad\qquad 4.$$

or written in terms of a constant and variable part:

$$\varphi_F = \psi_F [1 + \frac{\psi_T\psi_t(1 - A)}{1 - \psi_T\psi_t}] \qquad\qquad 5.$$

Since ϕ_F is ϕ_{F_0} when $A = 1$ and ϕ_{F_M} when $A = 0$ it can be shown from either Equation 4 or 5 that:

$$\frac{F_V}{F_M} = \frac{\varphi_{F_M} - \varphi_{F_0}}{\varphi_{F_M}} = \psi_T\psi_t \qquad\qquad 6.$$

If we had assumed that the "matrix" model in which an exciton trapped by a closed reaction center can return to the antenna chlorophyll and seek an open reaction center in another PS II unit, the equations would be:

$$\varphi_P = \psi_T A [\frac{1}{1 - \psi_T\psi_t(1 - A)}] \qquad\qquad 7.$$

and

$$\varphi_F = \psi_F [\frac{1}{1 - \psi_T\psi_t(1 - A)}] \qquad\qquad 8.$$

The kinetics of the transformations from the initial $A = 1$ state to the final $A = 0$ state differ substantially for the two models: ϕ_P and ϕ_F are linear functions of A in the "separate package" model but are nonlinear functions in the "matrix" model. Nevertheless the expressions are identical in either model at the initial and final states so that any conclusions which depend only on the initial and final states should be valid for any degree of energy transfer between PS II units.

This photochemical model for PS II incorporates two different fluorescence quenching mechanisms; quenching may occur in the antenna chlorophyll analogous to a k_D process or quenching may occur at the reaction center chlorophyll analogous to a k_d process. It is apparent from Equation 4 that any processes which increase k_D would quench both F_0 and F_M since ψ_F would be decreased. It is also apparent from Equations 2 and 6 that ϕ_{P_0} and F_V/F_M would be decreased to the same extent since both are proportional to ψ_T. On the other hand, processes which quench at the reaction center chlorophyll by increasing k_d would decrease ψ_t at the closed reaction centers where $\psi_t + \psi_d = 1$. It is apparent from Equation 5 that decreasing ψ_t would quench F_V but have no effect on F_0 and, so long as k_p remains large compared to k_d, ϕ_{P_0} will be unaffected. The effects of these two types of quenching processes would be the same for either the "separate package" or the "matrix" model formulations for PS II.

The Model for PS I

The development of an adequate working model of the photochemical apparatus also required more specific descriptions of the fluorescence and photochemical properties of PS I than had been recognized previously. It has been generally accepted since the work of Duysens & Sweers (12) that light-induced fluorescence yield changes reflect only the photochemical changes of PS II. That this should be the case at room temperature is not surprising since the fluorescence yield of PS I is very low at room temperature, but it is also true at low temperature where the 735 nm emission band, generally attributed to PS I, is quite prominent. One would expect that the fluorescence yield of the antenna chlorophyll in PS I should increase as the reaction center chlorophyll P700 was bleached, but that is not the case. P700 can be photooxidized specifically by irradiating the sample at $-196°C$ with far-red light ($\lambda > 720$ nm) and, so long as no changes occur in PS II, the fluorescence yield at 735 nm or at any other wavelength is unaffected. In green plants the fluorescence yield of PS I chlorophyll is completely independent of the photochemistry of PS I. Butler & Kitajima (5) suggested that the oxidized form of P700 might function as an energy trap just as effectively as the reduced form, in which case the photooxidation of P700 would not cause any fluorescence yield changes. That suggestion was supported by the earlier observation of Lozier & Butler (27) that the oxidation of P700 was characterized by an absorbance increase at 690 nm in addition to the bleaching at 700 nm; i.e. that the 690 nm band might be due to P700$^+$ and that P700$^+$ might function as an energy trap by virtue of that absorption band. Regardless of whether this explanation is valid or not, the observations with green plants are clear: there are no fluorescence yield changes associated with the photooxidation of P700. (It will be noted in a later section, however, that such changes are observed in red algae and cyanobacteria.) In green plants, all fluorescence yield changes at −196°C can be related to the primary photochemical changes of PS II.

Although it is generally accepted that the 735 nm fluorescence band which appears in the emission spectrum of chloroplasts at low temperatures is due to PS I, the relationship of this fluorescence to the photochemistry of PS I and the reasons for the strong temperature dependence of this fluorescence have not been elucidated. Satoh & Butler (35a) showed that the 735 nm fluorescence is in competition with the photochemistry of PS I since, on lowering the temperature of spinach chloroplasts from −78°C to −196°C, the rate of photooxidation of P700 decreased by a factor of about 2 while the intensity of the 735 nm emission band is increased by a factor of about 10. It was concluded previously (2a) that the 735 nm fluorescence at −196°C emanates from a small amount of a long wavelength form of chlorophyll, C-705, which acts as a trap for excitation energy in the antenna chlorophyll system of PS I. It is proposed that C-705 only forms on cooling to low temperatures and that the temperature dependence of the 735 nm fluorescence is the temperature dependence for the formation of C-705. C-705 and P700 compete to trap the excitation energy in PS I and, since there are no fluorescence yield changes associated with the photooxidation of P700, we must infer that $P700^+$ competes as effectively as P700. Energy trapping by C-705 and P700 represent irreversible processes; energy reaching C-705 cannot be used for photochemistry and energy trapped by P700 (or by $P700^+$) cannot reappear as fluorescence.

According to such a model, C-705 can be regarded as a low temperature artifact but it is, nevertheless, a very useful artifact since the fluorescence emitted from C-705 should be proportional to the exciton density in the antenna chlorophyll of PS I. The fraction of the PS I excitation energy trapped by C-705 will increase as the temperature is lowered, but at any constant low temperature, such as the boiling point of liquid nitrogen, the intensity of fluorescence of the 735 nm emission band is a relative index of the total energy reaching PS I.

The Model for the Photochemical Apparatus

The photochemical models for PS I and PS II were joined together in an attempt to formulate a model for the entire photochemical apparatus. It was recognized from the work of Wessels, Von Alphen-Van Waveren & Voorn (45) and of Thornber & Highkin (43) that higher plants contain a chlorophyll a/b complex which serves a light-harvesting, accessory pigment role but has no direct photochemical function. Based on this concept of a light-harvesting chlorophyll complex in addition to the two photochemical pigment systems, Butler & Kitajima (5, 6) proposed a tripartite model of the photochemical apparatus. PS I and PS II were presented as units each containing antenna chlorophyll, $Chla_I$ or $Chla_{II}$, and a reaction center, $P_I \cdot A_I$ or $P_{II} \cdot A_{II}$, and the light-harvesting chlorophyll a/b complex Chl LH was shown as a separate ensemble which could transfer excitation energy to either of the two photosystem units. The three emission bands which appear in fluorescence spectra of green plants at −196°C at 685, 695, and 735 nm were assigned to Chl LH, $Chla_{II}$ and $Chla_I$, respectively. The 695 and 735 nm emission bands appear only at low temperatures, so that measurements must be made at low temperature if these bands are to be used to indicate the distribution of excitation energy to PS II and PS I. It was assumed from the similarity in the dynamic characteristics of fluorescence yield changes at 685 and 695 nm at $-196°C$ that there is a fairly tight energy coupling between Chl LH and Chla$_{II}$ such that excitation energy can flow freely back and forth between these two forms of chlorophyll.

In order to combine the individual models for PS I and PS II units into a model for the entire photochemical apparatus, parameters were introduced to specify the distribution of energy between the two photosystems. The term α was used to specify the fraction of quanta absorbed by the photochemical apparatus which is delivered initially to PS I, either by direct absorption of light by the PS I units or by an initial transfer of energy from Chl LH, while β specified the fraction which is delivered initially to PS II or is dissipated in Chl LH, with the parameters being defined so that $\alpha + \beta = 1$. In addition, a rate constant for energy transfer from PS II to PS I, $k_{T(II \to I)}$, which functions in competition with the other deexcitation processes in the antenna chlorophyll of PS II units, was introduced to allow for "spillover." The rate constant diagram for such a model is shown in Diagram 3. In essence, the tight coupling between Chl LH and Chla$_{II}$ was used to reduce the tripartite model to a bipartite model consisting of two photochemical pigment systems. Chl LH was assumed to function largely as antenna chlorophyll for PS II.

Analytical expressions were written for fluorescence and photochemistry assuming either the "separate package" or the "matrix" model with respect to energy transfer between PS II units. Although we will consider primarily the "separate package" formulation, all of the conclusions we will draw would be equally valid for any degree of energy transfer between PS II units.

The equations for fluorescence can be written either as yields or intensities, but the latter may be more instructive since they incorporate the term for the quantum flux absorbed by the whole photochemical apparatus I_a. It is important to bear in mind that the absorption spectrum of the photochemical apparatus is not identical to the absorption spectrum of the sample. For instance, any pigment molecules

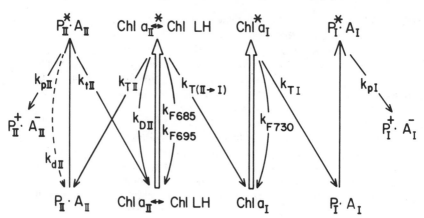

which do not transfer their excitation energy to chlorophyll are not considered to be part of the photochemical apparatus.

Equation 4 was extended to represent the intensity of fluorescence from PS II:

$$F_{II} = \beta I_a \, [A_{II} + \frac{1 - A_{II}}{1 - \psi_{TII}\psi_{tII}}] \, \psi_{FII} \qquad \qquad 9.$$

where ψ_{FII} and ψ_{TII} now include $k_{T(II \rightarrow I)}$ as one of the competing rate constants. The fluorescence from PS I will include that due to the direct excitation α, plus any excitons in the β fraction which are transferred from PS II to PS I:

$$F_I = [\alpha + \beta\varphi_{T(II \rightarrow I)}] \, I_a \psi_{FI} \qquad \qquad 10.$$

The yield of energy transfer from PS II to PS I will vary from a minimum value $\phi_{T(II \rightarrow I)(0)}$ when $A_{II} = 1$ to a maximum value $\phi_{T(II \rightarrow I)(M)}$ when $A_{II} = 0$ to the same extent that the yield of PS II fluorescence varies.

$$\varphi_{T(II \rightarrow I)} = \psi_{T(II \rightarrow I)} \, [A_{II} + \frac{1 - A_{II}}{1 - \psi_{TII}\psi_{tII}}] \qquad \qquad 11.$$

According to the model, the fluorescence of variable yield of F_I is due to energy transfer from PS II to PS I so that the fluorescence yield changes of F_I should have the same kinetics as the fluorescence yield changes of F_{II}. Murata (29a) first proposed the fluorescence of variable yield at 730 nm at $-196°C$ was due to energy transfer from PS II.

In order to subject the analytical expressions to experimental tests, it was necessary to be able to measure F_I and F_{II}, or at least wavelengths of fluorescence which were proportional to F_I and F_{II}. It was assumed that these two emissions could be measured separately by the proper choice of wavelengths; namely, that fluorescence at 692 to 695 nm at $-196°C$ was representative of F_{II} while fluorescence at 730 nm at $-196°C$ was representative of F_I. Those assumptions were based initially on low temperature emission spectra of subchloroplast particles (6), but additional criteria supporting those assumptions also developed out of the model and its application to specific experimental systems. Recently the methods introduced by Wessels, Von Alphen-Van Waveren & Voorn (45) to isolate and purify subchloroplast fractions were extended by Satoh & Butler (35b). Fractions obtained initially from a sucrose density-gradient centrifugation of digitonin-solubilized spinach chloroplasts were purified further by two steps of DEAE chromatography followed by electrofocusing on Ampholine columns in order to reduce cross-contamination between fractions to a minimum. Low temperature fluorescence emission spectra of the purified PS I, PS II and Chl LH fractions are shown in Figure 1 as F_I, F_{II}, and F_{III}, respectively. These spectra support the assumptions that the emission from PS I is negligible in the 690 nm region and that long wavelength tails of the emissions from PS II and the chlorophyll a/b complex at $-196°C$ are quite small in the 730 nm region.

It was assumed in the section on the photochemical model for PS I that the 735 nm fluorescence actually comes from the C-705 trapping centers which form in PS

I on cooling to –196°C. This assumption is not inconsistent with the use of the 735 nm fluorescence as an index of the energy reaching PS I. Even though the 735 nm fluorescence does not emanate directly from the antenna chlorophyll of PS I, the energy trapped by the C-705 molecules and, therefore, the intensity of the 735 nm fluorescence will be proportional to the exciton density in PS I. Therefore, the assumption that the 735 nm fluorescence at –196°C is representative of F_I is still valid. The 694 nm fluorescence, which shows an even steeper temperature dependence at temperatures near –196°C than the 735 nm fluorescence, may also be due to energy trapping centers which form in PS II on cooling to temperatures near –196°C. If so, the 694 nm fluorescence can still be assumed to be representative of F_{II} since it will be proportional to the exciton density in PS II. The energy emitted as the 694 nm fluorescence at –196°C appears to be a small fraction of the total excitation energy reaching PS II so that the 694 nm fluorescence does not represent a major energy drain which functions in competition with other PS II processes such as photochemistry and energy transfer to PS I.

Equations 9, 10, and 11 represent the mathematical formulation of the bipartite model. Tests and applications of that model have been made largely on the basis of the relative intensities of the F_0 and F_M levels of PS II fluorescence measured at about 692 nm at –196°C and of the F_0 and F_M levels of PS I fluorescence measured at 730 nm at –196°C. Most of the consequences and conclusions of the model follow from those four fluorescence measurements.

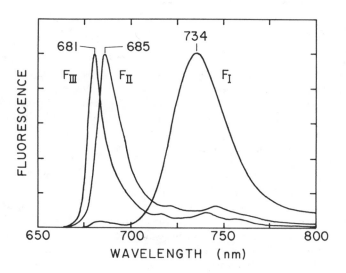

Figure 1   Emission spectra of purified PS I (F_I) and PS II (F_{II}) fractions and the light-harvesting chlorophyll a/b complex (F_{III}) measured at –196°C. Spinach chloroplasts solubilized with 1.25% digitonin were fractionated by sucrose density centrifugation. The F_I, F_{II}, and F_{III} fractions were purified further by two steps of DEAE cellulose chromatography followed by electrofocusing on Ampholine by methods described in (35b).

A word should be said about the validity of the measurements at low temperature since Harnischfeger (14) reported that the shape of the emission spectrum, the relative extent of F_V, and the calculated values of a all depend on the rate at which samples were cooled and that samples which were frozen slowly were subject to fluorescence artifacts due to membrane damage. We repeated his measurements on very thin samples frozen rapidly by direct contact with liquid nitrogen and on thicker samples frozen more slowly through the sides of the cuvette and found no such effect. The shape of the emission spectrum, the relative extent of F_V, and the calculated values of a were the same, within small limits of experimental error, for both types of sample (7).

APPLICATION OF THE BIPARTITE MODEL

Chloroplasts

EFFECT OF DIVALENT CATIONS ON ENERGY DISTRIBUTION   The model was first tested in a study of the fluorescence of chloroplasts which had been frozen to $-196°C$ in the absence and presence of 5 mM $MgCl_2$ (6). Murata (31) had concluded earlier that a greater fraction of the excitation energy was distributed to PS I when Mg^{2+} was absent. Since the equations for fluorescence included terms for the initial distribution of excitation energy as well as the rate constant for energy transfer from PS II to PS I, the measurements were analyzed in the context of the model to determine how these parameters were affected by the Mg^{2+}.

Measurements were made at $-196°C$ at the F_0 and F_V levels of fluorescence ($F_V = F_M - F_0$) at 692 and 730 nm in the absence and presence of Mg^{2+}. According to Equation 10, the fluorescence at 730 nm is due to the direct excitation of PS I via a, which is constant, plus energy transfer from PS II via $\beta\phi_{T(II\to I)}$ which varies from a minimum value when $A = 1.0$ to a maximum value when $A = 0$. Furthermore, the ratio of F_V/F_0 measured at 692 nm should be equal to the ratio of $\phi_{T(II\to I)(V)}/\phi_{T(II\to I)(0)}$. Thus, the $\beta\phi_{T(II\to I)(0)}$ component of F_0 at 730 nm can be calculated from measurements of F_V/F_0 at 692 nm and the extent of F_V at 730 nm in order to determine that part of F_0 at 730 nm which is due solely to a, $F_{I(a)}$:

$$F_{I(\alpha)} = F_{I(0)} - \frac{F_{II(0)}}{F_{II(V)}} F_{I(V)}$$

12.

That calculation from the fluorescence measured at 692 and 730 nm in the absence and presence of Mg^{2+} showed that $F_{I(a)}$ was 20% greater in the absence of Mg^{2+}, from which it was concluded that a was 20% greater in the absence of Mg^{2+}.

Information as to energy transfer from PS II to PS I should also be available since F_V at 730 nm was attributed entirely to energy transfer from PS II. In fact, the equations of the model show that the ratio of $F_{I(V)}/F_{II(V)}$ is equal to $(k_{T(II\to I)}/k_{FII})\psi_{FI}$. The measurements of chloroplasts at 692 and 730 nm indicated that that ratio was 90% greater in the absence of Mg^{2+}. It was assumed that $k_{T(II\to I)}$ would be sensitive to conformational changes which altered the physical relationship between PS I and PS II but that k_{FII} and ψ_{FI} should not be affected by such changes. These data were taken to indicate that $k_{T(II \to I)}$ was 90% greater in the absence of Mg^{2+}. Thus the model predicted that the absence of divalent cations would increase the distribution of excitation energy toward PS I, both because of an increase of a and because of an increase of $k_{T(II \to I)}$. Later (7, 21, 38) relative measurements of $F_{I(a)}$ and $k_{T(II \to I)}$ were obtained directly from X-Y plots of F_I vs F_{II} at $-196°C$ as the excitation beam caused the PS II reaction centers to close. Those measurements gave straight-line X-Y plots which could be extrapolated back to the F_I axis to give $F_{I(a)}$, while the slope of the plot $F_{I(V)}/F_{II(V)}$ was assumed to be proportional to $k_{T(II \to I)}$.

In addition to measurements of the relative changes of a and $k_{T(II \to I)}$, absolute values of a, β, and $\phi_{T(II \to I)}$ in the absence and presence of Mg^{2+} were calculated from the solution of six simultaneous equations [that solution is given in the appendix of (3)]. According to those calculations, in the presence of Mg^{2+}, a was 0.27, β was 0.73, and $\phi_{T(II \to I)}$ varied from a minimum value of 0.07 when $A = 1$ to a maximum value of 0.23 when $A = 0$. In the absence of Mg^{2+}, a was 0.32, β was 0.68, and $\phi_{T(II \to I)}$ varied from 0.12 to 0.28. It should be noted that these values which were calculated from measurements of fluorescence at 692 and 730 nm are independent of any self-absorption of fluorescence by the sample since the values of fluorescence are always used as ratios between two measurements made at the same wavelength so that any such sample artifacts will cancel out.

WAVELENGTH DEPENDENCE OF ENERGY DISTRIBUTION   The realization that the fluorescence of variable yield in the 730 to 750 nm region was due to energy transfer from PS II permitted the determination of pure excitation spectra for PS I and PS II (21). Fluorescence excitation spectra (corrected for incident quantum flux) were measured at $-196°C$ at the F_0 and F_M levels of fluorescence at 750 nm from chloroplasts, and the difference spectrum $F_{750(M)} - F_{750(0)}$ was taken to be a pure excitation spectrum for PS II. Given that excitation spectrum, a pure PS I excitation spectrum was calculated by subtracting the PS II contribution out of the excitation spectrum of $F_{750(0)}$ to give the excitation spectrum of $F_{I(a)}$. It was also shown in these measurements that the wavelength dependence of a was almost flat from 400 to 675 nm and then increased sharply toward unity as PS I became the dominant absorber. The largest variation was found in a broad band at about 515 nm where a increased approximately 15% apparently due to a carotenoid pigment which showed a preference for PS I. Those measurements were made at 750 nm on the assumption that the overlap from the PS II emission would be less at 750 nm than at 730 nm. However, later work (41) showed that PS II fluorescence in vivo actually has a small broad maximum at 750 nm and that 730 nm is the optimum wavelength to maximize the PS I emission. Thus the measurements at 750 nm would tend to decrease the variations in a because of the contamination from the emission from PS II. Later the wavelength dependence of a was calculated directly from measurements of fluorescence excitation spectra at 730 nm (39), and these data, as expected, show somewhat larger variations of a than were reported from the measurements at 750 nm. The spectrum of a determined from the measurements of 730 nm is shown in

Figure 2. The general character of α is still largely flat from 400 to 675 nm with an average value of about 0.30 with the major deviation being at 515 nm where α is 0.38. The variations in α from 540 to 675 nm are quite small consistent with the earlier results of Emerson & Lewis (13) on the wavelength dependence of the quantum yield of photosynthesis in this spectral region. Wang & Myers (44) obtained similar results on the wavelength dependence of the quantum yield of oxygen evolution from *Chlorella* cells.

The question can be raised as to why the presumed preference of chlorophyll *b* for PS II does not result in a stronger negative band at 650 nm in the spectrum of α. The answer is that the PS I also has an absorption band in the same region with a maximum at about 647 nm. This absorption band of PS I has been observed in the absorption spectra of etiolated bean leaves at early stages of greening before

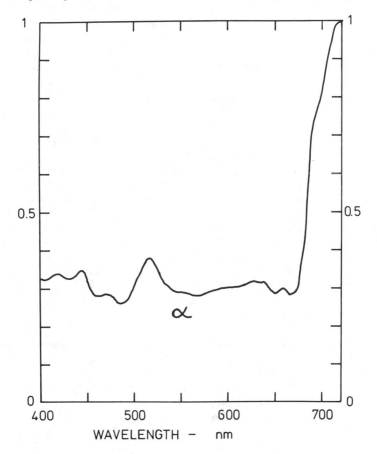

Figure 2   The wavelength dependence of α in chloroplasts determined by methods described in (39).

chlorophyll b has appeared (Baker and Butler, unpublished), in the excitation spectrum for $F_{I(\alpha)}$ of flashed bean leaves (40) which contain no chlorophyll b, and in the excitation spectrum of 730 nm fluorescence at $-196°C$ of highly purified PS I particles from spinach chloroplasts which were free of all chlorophyll b (Satoh and Butler, unpublished). Thus both PS I and PS II have absorption bands near 650 nm so that wavelengths in that region do not show a clear preference for one system or the other. It must be concluded from these results showing a flat wavelength dependence of α from 540 to 675 nm that the effective absorption spectra of PS I and PS II are very similar over this region. At wavelengths longer than 675 nm, PS I absorbance predominates and α increases toward unity. Changes of $\phi_{T(II \to I)}$ may also occur to change the distribution of energy between PS I and PS II, but these changes will not affect the wavelength dependence of α. The flat wavelength dependence of α is characteristic of mature green systems but not, as will be shown below, of leaves which lack the light-harvesting chlorophyll a/b complex or of red algae.

It should also be noted that the results of Emerson & Lewis (13) showed an appreciable decrease in the quantum yield values in the blue region of the spectrum because not all of the energy absorbed by the carotenoid pigments is used for photosynthesis. Such effects are not observed in the spectrum of α since the fluorescence measurements record only the effects of light absorbed by the active photochemical apparatus.

DIRECT DETERMINATIONS OF ENERGY TRANSFER FROM PS II TO PS I   A number of the conclusions from the bipartite model were based on the assumption that the fluorescence at 730 nm is due primarily to PS I. It was recognized that these conclusions would be jeopardized if PS II had an appreciable emission at 730 nm which would contribute directly to the fluorescence of variable yield at that wavelength. Emission spectra of purified preparations of Chl LH and of purified PS II particles at $-196°C$ supported the assumption (6) of the relative purity of the PS I emission at 730 nm, but these results did not rule out the possibility that PS II might show a low temperature fluorescence band at 730 nm in the chloroplasts which was lost during the extraction and purification. The question in essence reduced to whether F_V at 730 nm was due to energy transfer from PS II to PS I or to a direct emission from PS II. Thus direct correlates of energy transfer from PS II to PS I were sought in measurements of electron transfer activities of PS I. It was recognized that energy transfer from PS II to PS I, if it does occur, should be greater when the PS II reaction centers are closed. Thus PS I activities were examined to determine if closure of the PS II reaction centers would cause an increase in those activities. Such stimulations were found in the methylviologen mediated oxygen uptake and in the rate of photoreduction of NADP both by Tris-washed chloroplasts using ascorbate and dichlorophenolindophenol as an electron donor system to PS I at room temperature and in the rate of photooxidation of P700 in normal chloroplasts (in the presence of DCMU and hydroxylamine) at $-196°C$ (36). These results confirmed that energy transfer from PS II to PS I does occur and that at least a major part of F_V at 730 nm is due to that energy transfer.

Although the measurements of fluorescence at –196°C in the absence and presence of Mg^{2+} were very useful in that they permitted calculation of actual values of $\phi_{T(II\rightarrow I)}$ for the first time, the method for obtaining values of $\phi_{T(II\rightarrow I)}$ was not a general one since measurements had to be made on dual samples frozen to –196°C in the absence and presence of an additive. What was needed was a method which would provide values of $\phi_{T(II\rightarrow I)}$ from measurements on a single sample. Such a method was devised in order to determine $\phi_{T(II\rightarrow I)}$ in etiolated bean leaves which had been partially greened by a series of brief flashes (such leaves lack Chl LH), but the method was tested initially on spinach chloroplasts frozen to –196°C in the absence of Mg^{2+} (39). The $F_{I(M)}$ level of fluorescence measured at 730 nm at –196°C was considered to be comprised of two parts, $F_{I(\alpha)} = \alpha I_a \psi_{FI}$ and $F_{I(\beta)} = \beta \phi_{T(II\rightarrow I)(M)} I_a \psi_{FI}$. It is apparent that:

$$F_{I(\alpha)} + \frac{F_{I(\beta)}}{\varphi_{T(II\rightarrow I)(M)}} = (\alpha + \beta) I_a \psi_{FI} = I_a \psi_{FI} \qquad 13.$$

since $\alpha + \beta = 1$. $F_{I(\beta)}$ and $F_{I(\beta)}$ can be determined experimentally as excitation spectra at 730 nm. The rationale is to fit a weighted sum of the excitation spectra $F_{I(\alpha)} + KF_{I(\beta)}$ to the absorption spectrum I_a, measured on a linear photometric scale. The value of K which gives the best fit is taken to be the reciprocal of $\phi_{T(II\rightarrow I)(M)}$. This fitting procedure can be attempted only in spectral regions where I_a can be considered to be the same as the measured absorption spectrum. In practice, the first derivatives of the fluorescence excitation spectra and the absorption spectrum were used to obtain the proper fit at the absorption maximum and to achieve greater selectivity in determining the value of K. These curve fitting procedures gave a value of $\phi_{T(II\rightarrow I)(M)}$ of 0.25 ± 0.05 and, since F_M/F_0 at 694 nm was 2.5 for these chloroplasts, $\phi_{T(II\rightarrow I)(0)}$ was estimated to be 0.10. These values are in good agreement with the earlier values of 0.28 and 0.12 for chloroplasts in the absence of Mg^{2+} obtained from the fluorescence measurements made in the absence and presence of Mg^{2+}.

Each of the two independent methods for determining values for $\phi_{T(II\rightarrow I)}$ represent a considerable extrapolation of the model as initially formulated. The fact that the model supports such extrapolations in contexts which permit experimental verification lends credence to the basic validity of the model.

Flashed Bean Leaves

ENERGY TRANSFER FROM PS II TO PS I   In the initial schematic representation of the model, PS I and PS II were presented as separate units embedded in Chl LH, and the question was asked whether energy transfer from PS II to PS I would occur in the absence of Chl LH (5). That question was approached experimentally through studies with dark-grown bean leaves which had been partially greened by a series of brief flashes (38). The primary photochemical activity of these leaves, as indicated by the photoreduction of C-550 and the photooxidation of P700 at –196°C, is well developed but the leaves lack Chl LH. Measurements of fluorescence of flashed bean leaves at –196°C showed a normal extent of F_V at 730 nm, from which it was concluded that energy transfer from PS II to PS I did occur in the absence of Chl LH. Such energy transfer was also confirmed by measurements of the rate of photooxidation of P700 at –196°C in the presence of DCMU and hydroxylamine (infiltrated into the leaves prior to freezing) (38). The stimulation of the rate of photooxidation of P700 due to the closure of the PS II reaction centers was even somewhat greater in the flashed bean leaves than it was in spinach chloroplasts. Since energy transfer from PS II to PS I did not require the presence of Chl LH, the schematic representation of the model was modified to show PS I and PS II units in contact with one another with the Chl LH around the PS II units (3).

The development of the curve fitting procedure whereby a weighted sum of fluorescence excitation spectra $F_{I(\alpha)} + KF_{I(\beta)}$ was matched to the absorption spectrum I_a permitted a quantitative estimate of the yield of energy transfer from PS II to PS I to be made with the flashed bean leaves frozen to –196°C (40). The results indicated that $\phi_{T(II \to I)(M)}$ for the flashed bean leaves was 0.63. However, when the 730 nm emission was corrected for 730 nm fluorescence due to PS II (approximately 10% of the 694 nm maximum), that value was reduced to 0.50. The ratio of F_M / F_0 at 694 nm was 2.2 with these leaves so that $\phi_{T(II \to I)(0)}$ was estimated to be 0.23. Thus the yield of energy transfer from PS II to PS I in the flashed leaves was found to be about twice that of spinach chloroplasts. With further greening in continuous light, the yield of energy transfer of the flashed leaves decreases and approaches the values found in normal chloroplasts.

WAVELENGTH DEPENDENCE OF ENERGY DISTRIBUTION   The wavelength dependence of α was also determined for the flashed leaves using the same fluorescence excitation spectra that were used to determine $\phi_{T(II \to I)(M)}$ (40). According to the equations of the model:

$$\alpha = \frac{F_{I(\alpha)}}{F_{I(\alpha)} + F_{I(\beta)}/\varphi_{T(II \to I)(M)}} \qquad 14.$$

A plot of α as a function of wavelength for a flashed bean leaf (Figure 3) shows a considerable variation even in the region between 540 and 675 nm where the α of spinach chloroplasts was virtually constant. It is apparent that the absorption spectra of PS I and PS II units in flashed leaves are appreciably different from one another. An absorption band of PS I at 647 nm, which also appears as an excitation band in $F_{I(\alpha)}$ (40), gives rise to the maximum at 647 nm in the spectrum of α for the flashed leaves. At this stage, $F_{I(\alpha)}$ has a sharp maximum at 690 nm, while $F_{I(\beta)}$ is maximal at 670 nm, with the net result that α shows a pronounced minimum at 668 nm. With further greening in continuous light the chlorophyll a/b protein accumulates and presumably additional antenna chlorophyll for PS I accumulates as well. During this greening process, an excitation band at 680 nm develops and becomes dominant in $F_{I(\alpha)}$, and the appearance of chlorophyll b results in an excitation band at 650 nm in $F_{I(\beta)}$ (42). The effect of these changes is to make the effective absorption spectra of PS I and PS II, i.e. αI_a and βI_a, increasingly similar, thereby ironing out the wavelength variations in α and β.

The wavelength variation of α in the red region with flashed bean leaves permitted an additional test for energy transfer from PS II to PS I. The rate of photooxidation of P700 at $-196°C$ in the flashed bean leaves was measured at 670 nm, where α is a minimum, and at 645 nm (with equal quantum flux) where α has a maximum. If there were no energy transfer from PS II to PS I (i.e. if F_V at 730 nm were due to a direct emission from PS II), the rate of P700 oxidation should be greater at 645 nm than at 670 nm due to the direct excition of PS I. However, if energy transfer does occur and the fluorescence at 730 nm is a true reflection of PS I excitation including energy transfer, then the rate of excitation of P700 should be greater at 670 nm since the excitation of 730 nm fluorescence is greater at 670 nm. The

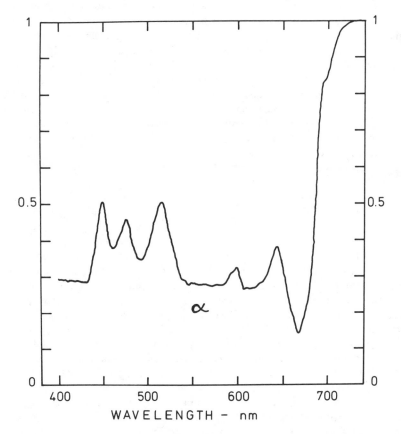

Figure 3 The wavelength dependence of α in flashed bean leaves determined by methods described in (40).

measurements showed that the rate of photooxidation of P700 was approximately twice as great at 670 nm as at 645 nm, similar to the excitation of 730 nm fluorescence (40); again confirming that spillover from PS II to PS I does occur. This particular test could not be made with spinach chloroplasts, however, because of the lack of variation of α.

EMISSION SPECTRA OF PS I, PS II, AND CHL LH   The emission spectrum of a flashed bean leaf at −196°C shows only two emission bands at 730 nm and 694 nm due to the $Chla_I$ and $Chla_{II}$. The 685 nm band attributed to fluorescence from Chl LH in mature leaves and chloroplasts is absent from the flashed leaves. It was apparent from the wavelength variation of α in the flashed leaves that excitation at 514 nm should excite a fluorescence relatively enriched in PS I emission compared to that excited at 633 nm and, indeed, the magnitude of the 730 nm emission band at −196°C was appreciably greater with the 514 nm excitation (41). Thus the difference spectrum between the 514 nm excited emission spectrum and the 633 nm excited emission spectrum, normalized at 694 nm, was taken to be a pure PS I emission spectrum. The emission spectrum of the purified PS I particles shown in Figure 1 supports the assumption that the PS I emission is negligible at 694 nm. The PS I emission spectrum was then subtracted from the measured emission spectrum to give a pure PS II emission spectrum with the criterion established from an extrapolation of a series of low-temperature emission spectra of flashed leaves of different chlorophyll content that the fluorescence of PS II at 730 nm was 12% of the peak intensity at 694 nm (41). (This estimate of the extent of the PS II emission at 730 nm agrees quite well with the low-temperature emission spectrum of the purified PS II fraction in Figure 1.)

Fluorescence emission spectra at the F_M level were also measured at −196°C in flashed leaves which had been greened for several hours in continuous light to permit the accumulation of the chlorophyll a/b protein. The difference spectrum between the 514 nm-excited emission spectrum and the 633 nm-excited emission spectrum again was used to calculate a pure PS I emission spectrum. The maximum of the PS I emission shifted from 728 nm to 735 nm during the greening, but the 694 nm maximum of the PS II emission did not change. The emission spectrum of F_I was subtracted from the measured spectrum of the leaf to give the emission spectrum due to F_{II} plus F_{LH} (see Figure 4). The emission spectrum of F_{II} obtained previously from the flashed leaf was then subtracted from the spectrum of F_{II} plus F_{LH} to give the emission spectrum of F_{LH}. The amount of F_{II} subtracted in this latter operation was determined by the criterion that $dF_{LH}/d\lambda$ should be zero at the 682 nm maximum of F_{LH} so that $dF_{II}/d\lambda$ should be equal to $d(F_{II} + F_{LH})/d\lambda$ at 682 nm. (All of these operations were carried out by a small computer on spectral data which had been measured on-line with the computer.) By this method the measured emission spectrum of a green leaf was deconvoluted into the individual emission spectra for PS I, PS II, and Chl LH shown in Figure 4. The ratios of the long wavelength to short wavelength emission bands in the spectra of the individual components in Figure 4 agree well with the ratios in the spectra of the purified components in Figure 1.

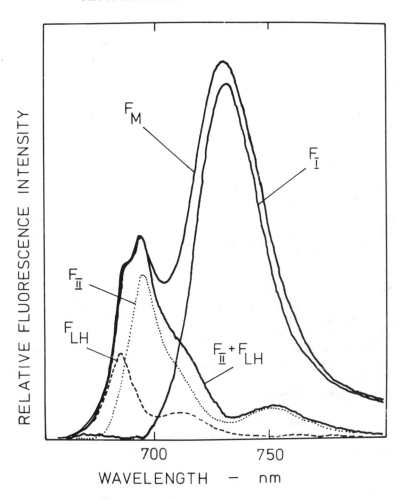

Figure 4 Emission spectrum of a green bean leaf at −196°C. The spectrum was separated into the individual emission spectra for PS I (F_I), PS II (F_{II}) and the chlorophyll a/b complex (F_{LH}) by methods described in (41).

Red Algae

WAVELENGTH DEPENDENCE OF ENERGY DISTRIBUTION   The model was also tested in an analysis of fluorescence measurements from the red alga *Porphyridium cruentum* with the assumption that the phycobilin pigments were analogous to the chlorophyll a/b complex of green plants (24). While the emission spectra from green plants at −196°C show rather little variation with different wavelengths of excitation, the emission spectra from *P. cruentum* at −196°C showed pronounced differences. Excitation with blue light absorbed predominantly by chlorophyll resulted in a single emission band at 712 nm due to PS I chlorophyll fluorescence, while the emission spectrum excited with green light absorbed predominantly by phycoerythrin showed a major band at 694 nm due to PS II chlorophyll, a shoulder at 680 nm identified as fluorescence from allophycocyanin B, a band at 712 nm due to the PS I chlorophyll, a broad weak band at 750 nm due to PS II chlorophyll (similar to the 750 nm band of PS II chlorophyll fluorescence from green plants shown in Figure 4), plus two bands at 642 and 662 nm due to phycocyanin and allophycocyanin. It was apparent from these different emission spectra from the red algae that the distribution of excitation energy between the two photosystems varied markedly for different wavelengths of exciting light.

The initial attempts to determine relative values of $F_{I(a)}$ from X-Y plots of F_I vs F_{II} for different wavelengths of excitation revealed that the X-Y plots with the red algae were not straight lines (24). It was found with both red algae and cyanobacteria that the fluorescence from PS I at $-196°C$ increased as the P700 was oxidized. If the frozen samples were preilluminated with far-red light which photooxidized P700 without affecting PS II, then an irradiation with visible light gave linear X-Y plots which could be extrapolated back to the F_I axis. The preirradiation with far-red light increased the PS I emission band at 712 nm of *P. cruentum* cells at $-196°C$ about 15%. This phenomenon can be accommodated in Equation 10 by recognizing that in *P. cruentum* ψ_{FI} increases about 15% as P700 is oxidized. However, after preirradiating the frozen samples with far-red light, ψ_{FI} is constant at its maximum value and the analysis of the effects of shorter wavelengths of excitation can proceed as with green plants.

The determination of the wavelength dependence of α for *P. cruentum* showed that α was approximately 0.95 for wavelengths at 440 and 680 nm which were absorbed predominately by chlorophyll (i.e. practically all of the light energy went to PS I) while α was approximately 0.05 in the region from 540 to 560 nm absorbed predominately by phycoerythrin (see Figure 5). These results led to specific predictions about the organization of the photochemical apparatus in these algae. The observation that 95% of the energy absorbed by chlorophyll is distributed to PS I indicates that 95% of the chlorophyll is associated with PS I. Thus the thylakoid membranes appear to have rather large PS I units and quite small PS II units, assuming the PS I and PS II units are approximately equal in number. However, since light absorbed by the phycobilisomes is directed specifically to PS II ($\beta = 0.95$ at 560 nm), the large phycobilisomes must connect directly to the small PS II units. The highly specific focusing of excitation energy from the phycobilisomes to PS II appears to be mediated through allophycocyanin B (26). The spectral properties of allophycocyanin B overlap closely with those of PS II chlorophyll in that its absorption and fluorescence maxima are at 675 and 680 nm, respectively, at $-196°C$. In fact, the energy coupling between allophycocyanin B and PS II chlorophyll is sufficiently tight that energy can be transferred from the chlorophyll back to the allophycocyanin B so that the 680 nm fluorescence of allophycocyanin B appears in the fluorescence of variable yield (24). It was estimated that there is one allophycocyanin B molecule per phycobilisome in *P. cruentum* and that the efficiency

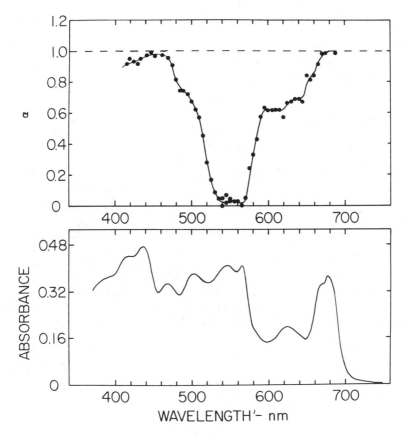

Figure 5 Lower curve: absorption spectrum of *P. cruentum* cells at –196°C. Upper curve: wavelength dependence of α determined by methods described in (24).

of energy collection by the allophycocyanin B is very high (fresh phycobilisomes showed only an emission band at 680 nm with no emission from phycocyanin or allophycocyanin at 642 and 662 nm) (26).

ENERGY TRANSFER FROM PS II TO PS I   The question arose as to how photosynthesis could function if there were such a sharp division in the distribution of energy. It has been recognized since the early experiments of Haxo & Blinks (15) that wavelengths absorbed predominantly by chlorophyll were relatively inefficient for photosynthesis while light absorbed by the phycobilin accessory pigments was used effectively. However, if the light absorbed by the phycobilisomes is funneled almost exclusively to PS II, how is photosynthesis, which presumably requires PS I activity as well, accomplished? The answer is found in the energy transfer from PS II to PS I. The yield of such energy transfer was estimated from a comparison of the relative yields of PS I fluorescence excited by 545 and 685 nm light (23). It was found that when the PS II reaction centers were all open, the yield of energy transfer from PS II to PS I was 0.50, and that as the PS II centers closed the yield increased to a maximum value of 0.91. It is apparent that even though 560 nm light does not excite PS I directly there is sufficient energy transfer from PS II to PS I to drive PS I, even when the PS II centers are all open and functional.

EXPERIMENTAL VERIFICATION   The predictions which emerged from the analysis of *P. cruentum* were tested in two ways. In the first, the action spectrum for O_2 evolution from the cells at room temperature was measured with a weak modulated beam of variable wavelength but constant intensity superimposed on a strong constant background beam, and the modulated O_2 evolution was measured with a Joliot-type O_2 electrode (24). The action spectrum of O_2 evolution produced by the weak modulated beam, shown in Figure 6, is consistent with the wavelength dependence of α in Figure 5.

In the second test the rates of photooxidation of P700 by green (560 nm) and blue (438 nm) light were measured in cells of *P. cruentum* which had been frozen to $-196°C$ in the presence of DCMU and hydroxylamine under conditions in which the PS II reaction centers were either all open (dark-adapted cells) or all closed (preilluminated cells) (25). The fraction of the energy available to PS I, $\alpha + \beta\phi_{T(II \to I)}$, should be greater when the PS II reaction centers are closed because of the greater energy transfer from PS II to PS I. For green light, where

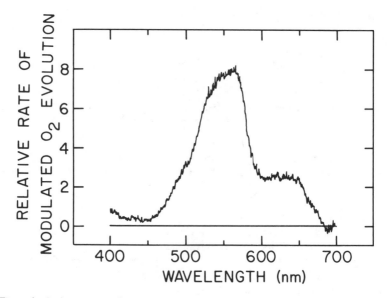

Figure 6   Action spectrum for oxygen evolution from *P. cruentum* cells at room temperature determined by methods described in (24).

$\alpha = 0.05$, $\beta = 0.95$, and $\phi_{T(II\rightarrow I)}$ varies from 0.50 to 0.91, the rate of oxidation of P700 should be 80% faster when the reaction centers are closed. With blue light, where $\alpha = 0.95$ and $\beta = 0.05$, the increase of $\phi_{T(II\rightarrow I)}$ will have much less effect and the rate should be only 2% faster when the centers are closed. In actual measurements of the initial rate of photooxidation of P700 at $-196°C$, the ratio of the rate for preilluminated cells (closed reaction centers) to that for dark-adapted cells (open reaction centers) was 1.8 ± 0.2 for the green excitation and 1.1 ± 0.23 for blue excitation, in excellent agreement with the predicted values.

THE TRIPARTITE MODEL

The Equations

The general validity of the bipartite model appears to be reasonably well established by the various experimental systems in which the model has been tested. However, it was recognized at the outset that the model was not completely rigorous because of a looseness in certain assumptions and definitions relative to the interaction of Chl LH with the rest of the photochemical apparatus. It was known, for instance, that the coupling between Chl LH and Chla$_{II}$ was not total because the ratio of F_V/F_0 was somewhat less at 680 nm than it was at 692 nm (6). Furthermore, from a theoretical point of view, if processes such as fluorescence or energy transfer to PS I occurred in Chl LH, then the energy coupling to PS II could not be 100%. These questions which focused attention on the effects of energy coupling between Chl LH and PS II led to the development of a truly tripartite model in which the interactions between Chl LH and the rest of the photochemical apparatus were included as specific photochemical rate constants (8). According to the revised nomenclature used in the photochemical rate constant diagram of the tripartite model shown in Diagram 4, k_{FIII} is the rate constant for fluorescence from Chl LH, $k_{T(32)}$ and $k_{T(31)}$ are the rate constants for energy transfer from Chl LH to Chla$_{II}$ and to Chla$_I$, respectively, and $k_{T(23)}$ and $k_{T(21)}$ are the rate constants for energy transfer from Chla$_{II}$ to Chl LH and to Chla$_I$.

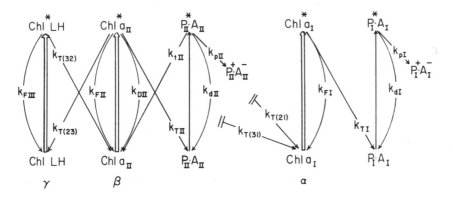

The deexcitation pathways in Chl LH and $Chla_I$ are described by constant probability terms; e.g. $\psi_{T(32)} = k_{T(32)}/\Sigma k_{III}$ where, according to Diagram 4, $\Sigma k_{III} = k_{FIII} + k_{T(32)} + k_{T(31)}$. The flux through the deexcitation pathways in $Chla_{II}$, however, depends on the state of the PS II reaction centers so that, for PS II processes, the variable ϕ terms will all be of the same form, e.g.:

$$\varphi_{T(23)} = \psi_{T(23)}(A_{II} + \frac{1-A_{II}}{1-\psi_{TII}\psi_{tII}})$$ 15.

which assumes that there is no direct transfer of energy between PS II units. The transfer of excitation energy from the closed PS II reaction centers back to $Chla_{II}$ increases the exciton density in $Chla_{II}$ by the factor indicated in the parenthesis in Equation 15. The ϕ terms all increase from minimum values, e.g. $\phi_{T(23)(0)} = \psi_{T(23)}$ when $A_{II} = 1$ to maximum values, $\phi_{T(23)(M)} = \psi_{T(23)}(1 - \psi_{TII}\psi_{tII})^{-1}$ when $A_{II} = 0$.

The rate constant diagram for the tripartite model assumes that there can be a cycling of excitation energy back and forth between Chl LH and $Chla_{II}$. The product $\psi_{T(32)}\phi_{T(23)}$ represents the fraction of the excitation energy in Chl LH which is transferred to $Chla_{II}$ and back to Chl LH or the fraction in $Chla_{II}$ which is transferred to Chl LH and back to $Chla_{II}$ in any one cycle. In setting up the equations of the model, it was shown that this cycling process appears mathematically as an infinite series which converges to a simple expression $(1 - \psi_{T(32)}\phi_{T(23)})^{-1}$ (8). It is worth noting that the energy cycling between Chl LH and $Chla_{II}$ increases as the PS II reaction centers close due to the increase of $\phi_{T(23)}$.

The equations for fluorescence and photochemistry which were derived from the tripartite model (8) are:

$$F_{III} = I_a \frac{\gamma + \beta\varphi_{T(23)}}{1 - \psi_{T(32)}\varphi_{T(23)}} \psi_{FIII}$$ 16.

$$F_{II} = I_a \frac{\beta + \gamma\psi_{T(32)}}{1 - \psi_{T(32)}\varphi_{T(23)}} \varphi_{FII}$$ 17.

$$F_I = I_a [\alpha + \frac{\gamma + \beta\varphi_{T(23)}}{1 - \psi_{T(32)}\varphi_{T(23)}} \psi_{T(31)} + \frac{\beta + \gamma\psi_{T(32)}}{1 - \psi_{T(32)}\varphi_{T(23)}} \varphi_{T(21)}] \psi_{FI}$$ 18.

$$P_{II} = I_a \frac{\beta + \gamma\psi_{T(32)}}{1 - \psi_{T(32)}\varphi_{T(23)}} \psi_{TII}A_{II}$$ 19.

$$P_I = I_a [\alpha + \frac{\gamma + \beta\varphi_{T(23)}}{1 - \psi_{T(32)}\varphi_{T(23)}} \psi_{T(31)} + \frac{\beta + \gamma\psi_{T(32)}}{1 - \psi_{T(32)}\varphi_{T(23)}} \varphi_{T(21)}] \psi_{TI}A_I$$ 20.

The functional interpretations of these equations are readily apparent. In Equation 16, for example, I_a is the quantum flux absorbed by the entire photochemical apparatus, γ is the fraction of that flux which is absorbed by Chl LH, $\beta\phi_{T(23)}$ is the fraction absorbed by Chla$_{II}$ which is transferred to Chl LH and $(1 - \psi_{T(32)}\phi_{T(23)})^{-1}$ is the factor by which the energy cycling between Chl LH and Chla$_{II}$ increases the rates of excitation in both Chl LH and Chla$_{II}$. These terms, taken together, represent the rate of excitation in Chl LH and ψ_{FIII} is the probability that an exciton in Chl LH will be emitted as fluorescence. A similar analysis of Equation 17 can be made for F_{II} except that ψ_{FII} is incorporated into ϕ_{FII} by a relationship which is equivalent to that expressed in Equation 15. In Equation 18 it is apparent that F_I has three sources of excitation, the direct excitation of Chla$_I$ via α, the transfer of excitation energy from Chl LH via $\psi_{T(31)}$, and the transfer of energy from Chla$_{II}$ via $\phi_{T(21)}$. Equations 19 and 20 for the rates of photochemistry of PS I and PS II consist of the expressions for the rates of excitation, the probabilities for trapping by the respective reaction centers, and the fraction of the reaction centers which are open.

The major innovation in the tripartite model is the recognition of energy coupling between Chl LH and Chla$_{II}$ as a specific photochemical parameter. Energy cycling between Chl LH and Chla$_{II}$ does not dissipate any energy but it may lead to a redistribution of the excitation energy. The degree of coupling will be expressed as a product of two probability terms, $\psi_{T(32)}\psi_{T(23)}$. The probability for energy transfer back and forth between Chl LH and Chla$_{II}$, $\psi_{T(32)}\phi_{T(23)}$, increases as the PS II reaction centers close, but the inherent energy coupling parameter will be specified by $\psi_{T(32)}\psi_{T(23)}$. This product appears in several analytical expressions which have been derived from the basic equations of the model.

It should be noted that even though an increase in the coupling between Chl LH and Chla$_{II}$ will lead to an increase in the rate of excitation in both beds of chlorophyll, this increased rate of excitation will not necessarily result in an increase in the fluxes through the dissipative pathways since increases of $\psi_{T(32)}$ and $\psi_{T(23)}$ must be accompanied by decreases in the probabilities for the dissipative pathways (e.g. in Chl LH, $\psi_{FIII} + \psi_{T(31)} + \psi_{T(32)} = 1.0$). For some purposes, equations based on rate constants rather than probability terms are more instructive. The equations for the fluxes through the various dissipative pathways can also be written as the product of the exciton density and the rate constant for the dissipative pathway. For example, Equation 16 can be rewritten:

$$F_{III} = I_a \frac{\gamma + \beta\varphi_{T(23)}}{1 - \psi_{T(32)}\varphi_{T(23)}} \cdot \frac{k_{FIII}}{\Sigma k_{III}}$$

and since

$$\psi_{T(32)} = k_{T(32)}/\Sigma k_{III}:$$

$$F_{III} = I_a \frac{\gamma + \beta\varphi_{T(23)}}{k_{FIII} + k_{T(31)} + k_{T(32)}[1 - \varphi_{T(23)}]} k_{FIII} \qquad \text{16a.}$$

Likewise, Equation 17 can be rewritten:

$$F_{II} = I_a \frac{\beta + \gamma \psi_{T(32)}}{1 - \psi_{T(32)} \psi_{T(23)} f(A_{II})} f(A_{II}) \frac{k_{FII}}{\Sigma k_{II}}$$

where

$$f(A_{II}) = A_{II} + \frac{1 - A_{II}}{1 - \psi_{TII}\psi_{tII}}.$$

Thus:

$$F_{II} = I_a \frac{[\beta + \gamma \psi_{T(32)}] f(A_{II})}{k_{FII} + k_{DII} + k_{T(21)} + k_{TII} + k_{T(23)} [1 - \psi_{T(32)} f(A_{II})]} k_{FII} \qquad 17a.$$

The factor which multiplies the rate constant k_{FIII} in Equation 16a represents the exciton density in Chl LH, while that which multiplies k_{FII} in equation 17a represents the exciton density in $Chla_{II}$. It is apparent in Equations 16a and 17a that the effects of $k_{T(23)}$ and $k_{T(32)}$ on the exciton densities in $Chla_{II}$ and Chl LH, respectively, are largely compensated by the reverse energy transfer process. If $k_{T(23)}$ and $k_{T(32)}$ were to both increase by the same extent while the rate constants for the dissipative pathways remained constant, the net effect of such a change on the exciton densities and on the fluxes through the dissipative pathways would be practically negligible.

Some Consequences of Energy Coupling

THE EXTENT OF F_v According to Equation 17, the fluorescence of PS II will increase as the PS II reaction centers close not only because of the increase of ϕ_{FII} but also because of the increase of $\phi_{T(23)}$ in the denominator term. In fact, if the coupling between Chl LH and $Chla_{II}$ is reasonably tight, the increase of $\phi_{T(23)}$ will contribute more to the fluorescence of variable yield than the increase of ϕ_{FII}. Equations specifying the relative extent of the variable yield of fluorescence of PS II can be derived from Equation 17:

$$\frac{F_{II(V)}}{F_{II(M)}} = \frac{\psi_{TII}\psi_{tII}}{1 - \psi_{T(32)}\psi_{T(23)}} \qquad 21.$$

or

$$\frac{F_{II(V)}}{F_{II(0)}} = \frac{\psi_{TII}\psi_{tII}}{1 - \psi_{TII}\psi_{tII} - \psi_{T(32)}\psi_{T(23)}} \qquad 22.$$

It is apparent from either Equation 21 or 22 that the relative extent of $F_{II(V)}$ will increase if either the coupling between Chl LH and $Chla_{II}$, i.e. $\psi_{T(32)}\psi_{T(23)}$, or the coupling between $Chla_{II}$ and the PS II reaction centers, i.e. $\psi_{TII}\psi_{tII}$, increases. The effect of varying degrees of coupling between Chl LH and $Chla_{II}$ on $F_{II(V)}$ was examined in flashed bean leaves after different times of greening (42). Initially

$\psi_{T(32)}\psi_{T(23)}$ is assumed to be zero since there is no chlorophyll a/b complex. At this stage the ratio of F_V/F_0 at 694 nm at $-196°C$ is generally between 1.0 and 1.2. However, if the flashed leaves are greened further in continuous light, the chlorophyll a/b complex accumulates and the ratio of F_V/F_0 increases, reaching values in excess of 3.0. While these results suggest a meaningful correlation between high values of F_V and the coupling, low ratios of $F_{II(V)}/F_{II(0)}$ do not necessarily imply a low degree of coupling between $Chla_{II}$ and Chl LH. It is true in the tripartite model, as well as the bipartite model, that agents such as UV radiation or ferricyanide at low temperature which quench excitation energy at the reaction center chlorophyll of PS II will quench F_V specifically by decreasing ψ_{tII} without affecting F_0. Thus it is possible for a photosynthetic system to show a small F_V even though the degree of coupling between Chl LH and $Chla_{II}$ is high.

ENERGY TRANSFER BETWEEN PS II UNITS   The equations of the tripartite model reveal that fluorescence and photochemistry are nonlinear functions of A_{II} due to the presence of $\phi_{T(23)}$ in the denominator terms. That nonlinearity is expressed most clearly in the expression for the normalized fluorescence increases.

$$\frac{F_t - F_0}{F_M - F_0} = \frac{1 - A_{II}}{1 + \dfrac{F_{II(V)}}{F_{II(0)}} \psi_{T(32)}\psi_{T(23)}A_{II}} \qquad\qquad 23.$$

where F_t is the fluorescence intensity at time t. Equation 23 is valid for F_I, F_{II}, or F_{III} can be derived from Equations 16, 17, or 18. Joliot and co-workers (17, 18) proposed that a nonlinearity between fluorescence and A_{II} could result from energy transfer between PS II units. Equation 23 is consistent with that interpretation. If the equations of the tripartite model had been formulated as a strictly "separate package" model with each package consisting of a PS I unit, a PS II unit with either an open or a closed reaction center, and the Chl LH associated with that particular package and with no energy transfer between the packages, Equation 23 would have been a linear function of $1 - A_{II}$ (the denominator would become unity). On the other hand, if the equations had been written assuming a "matrix" model for PS II in which all PS II reaction centers were available to all of the $Chla_{II}$, Equation 23 would have been written without the $\psi_{T(32)}\psi_{T(23)}$ term in the denominator. The model as it is formulated in Equations 16–20 is intermediate between these two extremes for energy transfer between PS II units (see 8 for a more complete discussion of these different formulations). The equations, as written, simulate a photochemical model in which energy transfer between PS II units is mediated through Chl LH. As the coupling between Chl LH and $Chla_{II}$ increases energy transfer between PS II units increases and the nonlinearity in F_t as a function of A_{II} increases. Note that as $\psi_{T(32)}\psi_{T(23)}$ increases, $F_{II(V)}/F_{II(0)}$ increases (see Equation 22) so that the nonlinearity in Equation 23 increases because of the increase of both $\psi_{T(32)}\psi_{T(23)}$ and $F_{II(V)}/F_{II(0)}$. This dependence of energy transfer between PS II units on the coupling between Chl LH and $Chla_{II}$ led to a physical representation of the photochemical apparatus as PS II units embedded in a large array of Chl LH so that

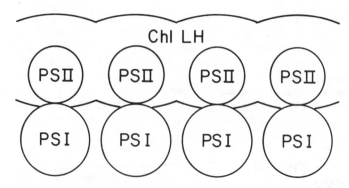

energy transfer between nearby PS II units could be mediated by Chl LH (8). The earlier results showing that energy transfer occurs from PS II to PS I in the absence of Chl LH (38) was taken to indicate that PS I and PS II units are connected together directly.

The nonlinearity in F_t as a function of A_{II} also gives rise to a small initial lag phase in the fluorescence induction curve measured in the presence of DCMU (17, 18). In essence, if an exciton can visit several PS II units in search of an open reaction center, the fluorescence rises a little more slowly at the onset of the induction curve than if the exciton is confined to a single PS II unit. The influence of coupling between Chl LH and $Chla_{II}$ on the initial lag phase in fluorescence induction was examined in flashed leaves at room temperature after infiltration with DCMU (42). [The lag phase is not observed in fluorescence induction curves at $-196°C$, presumably because of the slow rate of electron transfer to $P_{II}^+(10)$.] It was necessary to illuminate the flashed bean leaves for 5 to 10 min to activate the O_2 evolving machinery and fluorescence induction phenomena (37), but no detectable amounts of chlorophyll b were formed during the brief photoactivation period. At this stage when the chlorophyll a/b complex is still absent, the fluorescence induction curve measured in the presence of DCMU does not show the initial lag. However, that lag phase develops as the leaves are greened in continuous light and the chlorophyll a/b complex accumulates.

QUANTITATIVE DETERMINATIONS OF $\psi_{T(32)}\psi_{T(23)}$ AND OTHER PARAMETERS The tripartite model would be worthwhile if only for the qualitative insights it brings to our understanding of the significance of energy coupling between Chl LH and $Chla_{II}$. However, the model would be much more valuable and useful if it provided quantitative assessments of the coupling parameters such as the bipartite model did for $\phi_{T(II \to I)}$. Indeed, such information can be determined from experimental data within the context of the tripartite model (9).

The equations of the model predict that F_I, F_{II}, and F_{III} should all vary by the same kinetics (8) so that an X-Y plot of any pair of those emissions during fluorescence induction at $-196°C$ should give a straight line. To test that prediction, simultaneous measurements of fluorescence were made at 680, 694, and 730 nm on chloroplasts at $-196°C$ as the 633 excitation beam caused the PS II fraction centers to close and the measurements were recorded on three X-Y recorders as F_{680} vs F_{694}, F_{730} vs F_{694}, and F_{730} vs F_{680} (of course, any two of these plots determines the third). The three X-Y plots each gave a straight line which could be extrapolated back to an intercept value at the Y axis (Strasser and Butler, unpublished). Analytical expressions for the intercept values and for the slopes of F_{III} vs F_{II}, F_I vs F_{II}, and F_I vs F_{III} have been derived from the equations of the model (8).

To date, the plot F_{680} vs F_{694} has proved to be the most useful for purposes of analysis. In such a plot, the extrapolation of the straight line back to the F_{680} axis in essence extrapolates F_{II} to zero. If F_{II} is extrapolated to zero, all of the ϕ terms go to zero as well, so that it is apparent from Equation 16 that the intercept value at the F_{III} axis, $F_{III(\gamma)}$, is $\gamma I_a \psi_{FIII}$ which is the fluorescence due to the direct excitation of Chl LH (without any cycling). If that intercept value is normalized on the maximum level of F_{III} fluorescence, a pure ratio γ_N is obtained.

$$\gamma_N = \frac{F_{III(\gamma)}}{F_{III(M)}} = \frac{\gamma[1 - \psi_{T(32)}\varphi_{T(23)(M)}]}{\gamma + \beta\varphi_{T(23)(M)}} \qquad 24.$$

which can be determined readily from the data along the F_{680} axis of the X-Y plot of F_{680} vs F_{694}. It can be assumed for chloroplasts of higher plants that α, β, and γ are about 0.3, 0.2, and 0.5, respectively, and that $\phi_{T(23)(M)}$ should be about 0.90 (this latter assumption is subject to confirmation or readjustment). Given these values and the measured value of γ_N, the product of $\psi_{T(32)}\phi_{T(23)(M)}$ can be calculated from Equation 24.

$$\psi_{T(32)}\varphi_{T(23)(M)} = 1 - \frac{\gamma + \beta\varphi_{T(23)(M)}}{\gamma}\gamma_N = 1 - 1.38\,\gamma_N \qquad 24a.$$

It is assumed that $\psi_{T(32)}$ and $\phi_{T(23)(M)}$ are approximately equal with $\psi_{T(32)}$ being slightly larger. Once the value of the product has been calculated, the individual values of $\psi_{T(32)}$ and $\phi_{T(23)(M)}$ can be estimated, consistent with that assumption. If this estimated value of $\phi_{T(23)(M)}$ is appreciably different from the value assumed in order to calculate the product, the value can be revised and the product recalculated.

In order to determine the value of $\psi_{T(32)}\psi_{T(23)}$, the value of $\psi_{TII}\psi_{tII}$ is needed since according to Equation 15:

$$\psi_{T(32)}\psi_{T(23)} = \psi_{T(32)}\varphi_{T(23)(M)}(1 - \psi_{TII}\psi_{tII})$$

If this latter relationship is substituted into Equation 21:

$$\frac{F_{II(V)}}{F_{II(M)}} = \frac{\psi_{TII}\psi_{tII}}{1 - \psi_{T(32)}\varphi_{T(23)(M)}(1 - \psi_{TII}\psi_{tII})} \qquad 25.$$

or

$$\psi_{TII}\psi_{tII} = \frac{F_{II(V)}/F_{II(M)}\,[1 - \psi_{T(32)}\varphi_{T(23)(M)}]}{1 - [F_{II(V)}/F_{II(M)}]\,\psi_{T(32)}\varphi_{T(23)(M)}} \qquad 25a.$$

The ratio of $F_{II(V)}/F_{II(M)}$ can be determined from the measurements along the F_{694} axis of the X-Y plot. Thus, $\psi_{TII}\psi_{tII}$ can be calculated from the values of $F_{II(V)}/F_{II(M)}$ and $\psi_{T(32)}\phi_{T(23)(M)}$ so that $\psi_{T(32)}\psi_{T(23)}$ can be determined.

In the absence of other information, ψ_{tII} is generally assumed to be close to 1.0 (i.e. that there are no appreciable nonradiative decay losses at the reaction center chlorophyll molecules of PS II) so that the value of ψ_{TII} can be taken as the value of $\psi_{TII}\psi_{tII}$ just calculated. The overall yield of photochemistry at the initial state ($A_{II} = 1.0$) can then be calculated from Equation 19.

$$\Phi_{PII(0)} = \frac{P_{II(0)}}{I_a} = \frac{\beta + \gamma\,\psi_{T(32)}}{1 - \psi_{T(32)}\psi_{T(23)}}\,\psi_{TII} \qquad 26.$$

Thus, within the framework of the tripartite model, a single experiment of an X-Y plot of F_{680} vs F_{694} at $-196°C$ provides the information in the form of two ratios (γ_N from data along the F_{680} axis and F_V/F_M from data along the F_{694} axis) needed to calculate $\psi_{T(32)}\psi_{T(23)}$, $\psi_{TII}\psi_{tII}$ and $\Phi_{PII(0)}$.

THE EFFECTS OF Mg^{2+} In order to determine the effects that divalent cations might have on the parameters just calculated, X-Y plots of F_{680} vs F_{694} were made during the fluorescence induction period on spinach chloroplasts which had been frozen to $-196°C$ in the absence and presence of Mg^{2+} (9). In one set of data that was typical of normal "winter" chloroplasts, the presence of Mg^{2+} caused γ_N to decrease from 0.116 to 0.065 and $F_{II(V)}/F_{II(M)}$ to increase from 0.64 to 0.73. From these ratio measurements at 680 and 694 nm it was calculated from Equations 24a and 25a that the addition of Mg^{2+} caused $\psi_{T(32)}\phi_{T(23)(M)}$ to increase from 0.84 to 0.91 and $\psi_{TII}\psi_{tII}$ to decrease from 0.22 to 0.19. It was further calculated that the addition of Mg^{2+} caused $\psi_{T(32)}\psi_{T(23)}$ to increase from 0.66 to 0.74 and $\Phi_{PII(0)}$ to increase from 0.43 to 0.50. Thus the measurements of fluorescence within the context of the tripartite model predict that the primary photochemistry of PS II should increase about 15% on the addition of divalent cations.

The individual values of $\psi_{T(32)}$ and $\phi_{T(23)(M)}$ can be estimated from the value of their product given the assumption that $\psi_{T(32)}$ is the larger of the pair. Thus for chloroplasts suspended in the absence of Mg^{2+} where the product was 0.84, $\psi_{T(32)}$ and $\phi_{T(23)(M)}$ are estimated to be 0.93 and 0.90, respectively. Likewise, in the presence of Mg^{2+} where the product was 0.91, $\psi_{T(32)}$ and $\phi_{T(23)(M)}$ are estimated to be 0.97 and 0.94, respectively. Given these individual probability values, we can estimate the effect of Mg^{2+} on the individual rate constants if certain assumptions are made as to the nature of the action of Mg^{2+} on energy distribution. The simplest hypothesis is to assume that Mg^{2+} affects only the rate constants for energy transfer between the different beds of antenna chlorophyll, i.e. $k_{T(23)}$, $k_{T(21)}$, $k_{T(32)}$ and $k_{T(31)}$ (such an hypothesis follows from the presumed action of Mg^{2+} to induce membrane conformational changes). The measurements made in the absence of Mg^{2+} were consistent with the ratios between the rate constants in $Chla_{II}$, k_{FII}: $k_{TII}:k_{T(21)}:k_{T(23)}$ being $4:22:4:70$ (k_{DII} is incorporated into k_{FII} and the ratio between k_{FII} and $k_{T(21)}$ is largely arbitrary). Those values are chosen to fit the observations that $\phi_{T(23)(M)} = 0.90$, $\psi_{TII} = 0.22$ and $\psi_{T(23)} = 0.70$ in the absence of Mg^{2+}. The results obtained in the presence of Mg^{2+} are consistent with $k_{T(23)}$ increasing to a relative value of 88 and $k_{T(21)}$ decreasing to a relative value of 1.8 to give an overall ratio of $4 : 22 : 1.8 : 88$. In that case $\phi_{T(23)(M)}$ increases to 0.94, ψ_{TII} decreases to 0.19 and $\psi_{T(23)}$ increases to 0.76 in agreement with the results obtained in the presence of Mg^{2+}. The increase of $\psi_{T(32)}$ from 0.93 to 0.97 indicates that $k_{T(32)}$ increase markedly (approximately 100%) on the addition of Mg^{2+}. We assume the $k_{T(31)}$ is quite small and probably decreases even further on the addition of Mg^{2+}.

A relatively simple picture of the effects of Mg^{2+} on the photochemical apparatus emerges from these interpretations of the data in the context of the tripartite model. The binding of Mg^{2+} at Chl LH causes the Chl LH to squeeze down more tightly on the PS II units. The increased coupling between Chl LH and $Chla_{II}$ causes an increase in the ratio of F_V/F_0 and more energy transfer between PS II units. A concomitant decrease of $k_{T(21)}$ and probably $k_{T(31)}$ decreases the distribution of excitation energy to PS I. In addition, if $k_{T(32)}$ increases more than $k_{T(23)}$, excitation energy will be redirected from Chl LH to $Chla_{II}$. The net effect of adding Mg^{2+} will be to increase the excitation energy in PS II and decrease the energy in PS I.

THE TRIPARTITE MODEL VERSUS THE BIPARTITE MODEL

The bipartite model should not be abandoned because of the more rigorous tripartite model. For questions of energy distribution between PS I and PS II the bipartite model is much simpler and more tractable. For instance, the term $\phi_{T(II \rightarrow I)}$ in the bipartite model is replaced by the sum of four terms in the tripartite model which have not as yet been evaluated from experimental data. Furthermore, the high degree of coupling between Chl LH and $Chla_{II}$ found by the tripartite model confirms that the initial assumptions made for the bipartite model are reasonably valid, at least for higher plant chloroplasts. There is still much information available from the tripartite analysis which has not been put to use as yet. For instance, the data from the X-Y plots of F_I vs F_{II} or of F_I vs F_{III} have not been incorporated into the tripartite analysis. Thus the tripartite model may prove to be more powerful than has been recognized to date. However, as of now questions of energy distribution between PS I and PS II can be handled best by the bipartite model, while questions of energy coupling between Chl LH and $Chla_{II}$ can be treated with the tripartite model.

ACKNOWLEDGMENTS

This work was supported by a grant from the National Science Foundation, PCM 76-07111.

Literature Cited

1. Barber, J., Telfer, A., Nicholson, J. 1974. *Biochim. Biophys. Acta* 357: 161–65
2. Bonaventura, C., Myers, J. 1969. *Biochim. Biophys. Acta* 189:366–83
2a. Butler, W. L. 1961. *Arch. Biochem. Biophys.* 93:413–22
3. Butler, W. L. 1977. In *Encyclopedia of Plant Physiology,* ed. M. Avron, A. Trebst, pp. 149–67. Berlin: Springer-Verlag
4. Butler, W. L., Kitajima, M. 1975. *Biochim. Biophys. Acta* 376: 116–25
5. Butler, W. L., Kitajima, M. 1975. In *Proc. 3rd Int. Congr. Photosynth.,* ed. M. Avron, pp. 13–24. Amsterdam: Elsevier
6. Butler, W. L., Kitajima, M. 1975. *Biochim. Biophys. Acta* 396:72–85
7. Butler, W. L., Strasser, R. J. 1977. *Biochim. Biophys. Acta* 462:283–89
8. Butler, W. L., Strasser, R. J. 1977. *Proc. Natl. Acad. Sci. USA* 74:3382–85
9. Butler, W. L., Strasser, R. J. 1978. *Proc. 4th Int. Congr. Photosynth.,* ed. D. O. Hall, J. Coombs, T. W. Goodwin, pp. 527–36. London: Biochem. Soc.
10. Butler, W. L., Visser, J. W. M., Simons, H. L. 1973. *Biochim. Biophys. Acta* 292:140–51
11. Clayton, R. K. 1969. *Biophys. J.* 9:60–76
12. Duysens, L. N. M., Sweers, H. E. 1963. In *Studies on Microalgae and Photosynthetic Bacteria,* pp. 353–72. Univ. Tokyo Press. 636 pp.
13. Emerson, R., Lewis, C. M. 1943. *Am. J. Bot.* 30:165–78
14. Harnischfeger, G. 1976. *Biochim. Biophys. Acta* 449:593–96
15. Haxo, F. T., Blinks, L. R. 1950. *J. Gen. Physiol.* 33:389–422
16. Homann, P. H. 1969. *Plant Physiol.* 44:932–36
17. Joliot, A., Joliot, P. 1964. *C. R. Acad. Sci. Paris* 258:4617–25
18. Joliot, P., Bennoun, P., Joliot, A. 1973. *Biochim. Biophys. Acta* 305:317–28
19. Kautsky, H., Appel, W., Amann, H. 1960. *Biochem. Z.* 332:277–92
20. Kitajima, M., Butler, W. L. 1975. *Biochim. Biophys. Acta* 376:105–15
21. Kitajima, M., Butler, W. L. 1975. *Biochim. Biophys. Acta* 408:397–405
22. Kraus, G. N. 1974. *Biochim. Biophys. Acta* 333:301–13
23. Ley, A. C., Butler, W. L. 1976. *Proc. Natl. Acad. Sci. USA* 73:3957–60
24. Ley, A. C., Butler, W. L. 1977. In *Photosynthetic Organelles,* ed. S. Miyachi, S. Katoh, Y. Fujita, K. Shibata, pp. 33–46. Special issue of *Plant and Cell Physiology* (Jpn. Soc. Plant Physiol.)
25. Ley, A. C., Butler, W. L. 1977. *Biochim. Biophys. Acta* 462:290–94
26. Ley, A. C., Butler, W. L., Bryant, D. A., Glazer, A. N. 1977. *Plant Physiol.* 59:974–80
27. Lozier, R., Butler, W. L. 1974. *Biochim. Biophys. Acta* 333:465–80
28. Malkin, S., Jones, L. W. 1968. *Biochim. Biophys. Acta* 162:297–99
29. McAlister, E. D., Myers, J. 1940. *Smithson. Misc. Collect.* 99 (6):1–37
29a. Murata, N. 1968. *Biochim. Biophys. Acta* 162:106–21
30. Murata, N. 1969. *Biochim. Biophys. Acta* 172:242–51
31. Murata, N. 1969. *Biochim. Biophys. Acta* 189:171–81
32. Myers, J. 1963. In *Photosynthetic Mechanisms of Green Plants,* pp. 301–17. Natl. Acad. Sci., Nat. Res. Counc. Publ. 1145, Washington DC. 766 pp.
33. Myers, J. 1971. *Ann. Rev. Plant Physiol.* 22:289–312
34. Myers, J., Graham, J. R. 1963. *Plant Physiol.* 38:105–16
35. Okayama, S., Butler, W. L. 1972. *Biochim. Biophys. Acta* 267:523–29
35a. Satoh, K., Butler, W. L. 1978. *Biochim. Biophys. Acta.* In press
35b. Satoh, K., Butler, W. L. 1978. *Plant Physiol.* In press
36. Satoh, K., Strasser, R. J., Butler, W. L. 1976. *Biochim. Biophys. Acta* 440: 337–45
37. Strasser, R. J., Butler, W. L. 1976. *Plant Physiol.* 58:371–76
38. Strasser, R. J., Butler, W. L. 1976. *Biochim. Biophys. Acta* 449:412–19
39. Strasser, R. J., Butler, W. L. 1977. *Biochim. Biophys. Acta* 460:230–38
40. Strasser, R. J., Butler, W. L. 1977. *Biochim. Biophys. Acta* 462:295–306
41. Strasser, R. J., Butler, W. L. 1977. *Biochim. Biophys. Acta* 462:307–13
42. Strasser, R. J., Butler, W. L. 1978. *Proc. 4th Int. Congr. Photosynth.,* ed. D. O. Hall, J. Coombs, T. W. Goodwin, pp. 9–20. London: Biochem. Soc.
43. Thornber, J. P., Highkin, H. R. 1974. *Eur. J. Biochem.* 41:109–16
44. Wang, R. T., Myers, J. 1976. *Photochem. Photobiol.* 23:411–14
45. Wessels, J. S. C., Von Alphen-Van Waveren, O., Voorn, G. 1973. *Biochim. Biophys. Acta* 292:741–52
46. Yamashita, T., Butler, W. L. 1968. *Plant Physiol.* 43:2037–40

Ann. Rev. Plant Physiol. 1978. 29:379–414
Copyright © 1978 by Annual Reviews Inc. All rights reserved

CRASSULACEAN ACID METABOLISM: A CURIOSITY IN CONTEXT[1]

❖7656

C. B. Osmond

Department of Environmental Biology, Research School of Biological Sciences, Australian National University, Box 475, Canberra City, 2601, Australia

CONTENTS

[1]Abbreviations used: CAM = crassulacean acid metabolism; DHAP = dihydroxyacetone phosphate; DPGA = 1,3-diphosphoglycerate; F6P = fructose-6-phosphate; FDP = fructose-1,6-diphosphate; GAP = glyceraldehyde-3-phosphate; MDH = malate dehydrogenase; OAA = oxaloacetate; PEP = phosphoenolpyruvate; P_i = orthophosphate; 2-PGA = 2-phosphoglycerate; 3-PGA = 3-phosphoglycerate; PCR cycle = photosynthetic carbon reduction cycle; R5P = ribose-5-phosphate; RuP_2 = ribulose-1,5-bisphosphate; TCA cycle = tricarboxylic acid cycle.

0066-4154/78/0701-0379$01.00

". . . their *Taftes,* which it much importeth us more precifely to diftinguifh; . . . in *Aloes, Bitter* and *sweet;* the one in the *fifth,* the other in the *first Degree;* as upon an unprejudiced tryal may be perceived."

Grew 1682

INTRODUCTION

For at least three centuries plant biologists have been aware of the curiosity of crassulacean acid metabolism (CAM). When last reviewed in this series (131) the massive nightly increase in the malic acid content of CAM plant tissues, which presumably attracted Grew's attention (49), was the focus of physiological and biochemical interest in these plants. This emphasis was appropriate, for at that time the acid metabolism of the TCA cycle was in the forefront of biological research (15, 106). The first comprehensive survey of CO_2 exchange patterns in CAM plants using the infrared gas analyzer (113) was yet to be published, and a device for monitoring the unusual stomatal properties of these plants was in use (109). Under the circumstances it is not surprising that one of the few comments as to the environmental and ecological context of CAM stated simply "in contrast to Europe, there appears to be no close season for CAM in Bombay" (131).

Appreciation of the context of CAM has followed, rather than led, developments in the comparative physiology and biochemistry of higher plant photosynthesis and the growth of physiological ecology as a significant discipline. From relative obscurity as a property of indoor plants which reproduce by bizarre vegetative means, CAM is now in serious danger of being reviewed to an extent that is difficult to justify in terms of its significance in the biosphere (26, 53, 76, 90, 147, 151, 176). By way of apology, this review is structured so as to emphasize the significance of CAM in the broader ecological and environmental context. With this perspective, an outline of the physiological and biochemical properties which contribute to this extraordinarily flexible photosynthetic system will be developed. Many of these properties may be of little significance to the performance of CAM plants under natural conditions, but represent intriguing avenues for curiosity-orientated research in plant physiology.

DEFINITION

Crassulacean acid metabolism is a property of cells in photosynthetic leaf or stem tissues and is appropriately described in physiological rather than ecological terms.

Strictly speaking, it refers to the ability of chloroplast-containing cells to engage in significant CO_2 assimilation in the dark, leading to the synthesis of free malic acid. The acid, which is presumably stored in the cell vacuole, is decarboxylated in the subsequent light period and the CO_2 so released is refixed by photosynthesis. CAM represents one of three major classes of photosynthetic metabolism in higher plants. In common with the C_3 and C_4 pathways of photosynthesis (12, 62, 151), net CO_2 assimilation in CAM involves the primary carbon assimilating enzyme RuP_2 carboxylase-oxygenase and the integrated photosynthetic carbon reduction and photorespiratory carbon oxidation cycles (56, 62, 84). Like the C_4 pathway, CAM is a complex appendage to these cycles, based on the prior assimilation of CO_2 into C_4 dicarboxylic acids (12, 52). In CAM the prior assimilation of CO_2 into C_4 acids in the dark is separated in time from the incorporation of CO_2 into carbohydrates in the light, all of these processes taking place in a single cell. By contrast, in C_4 plants these events are spatially separated in specialized cells of limited metabolic capacities (12, 52). In quantitative terms the intermediate pool of C_4 acids in CAM plants may be as large as 200 μequiv/g fresh wt with a turnover half-time of about 10^4 sec, whereas in C_4 plants this pool is about 1 μequiv/g fresh wt and has a turnover half-time of about 10 sec (118).

The processes involved in acidification and deacidification form only part of the photosynthetic capacity of CAM plants. Depending on the prevailing environmental conditions and the species, these plants also engage in periods of CO_2 fixation in the light, and it is helpful to distinguish four phases of CO_2 assimilation in well-irrigated CAM plants, as shown in Figure 1 (117). The processes of CO_2 assimilation in all four phases are closely related and cannot be treated in isolation from each other.

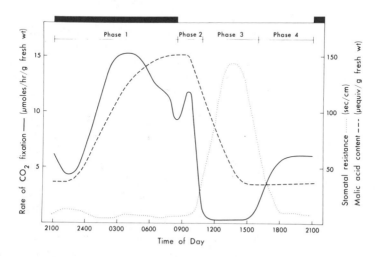

Figure 1 Relationship between rate of CO_2 fixation, malic acid content and stomatal resistance in a well-irrigated CAM plant throughout the night and day, showing the four separate phases of gas exchange distinguished in the text.

For example, the extent of CO_2 fixation and acid synthesis in the dark (phase 1) is markedly dependent on light intensity and temperature during phase 4 (60). For convenience these phases will be treated sequentially in the discussion which follows. The pattern of CO_2/H_2O exchange and of malic acid synthesis shown in generalized form in Figure 1 has now been observed in CAM plants under laboratory and field conditions. As far as possible, this review will be illustrated with examples drawn from both environments.

A capacity for CAM is usually associated with photosynthetic leaves or stems which are succulent, i.e. have a low surface/volume ratio. However, not all succulent photosynthetic plant organs are capable of CAM, and this metabolic pathway is sometimes found in plant organs which are not succulent (73, 92). Some stem succulents display CAM but produce succulent leaves which display normal C_3 photosynthesis (C. B. Osmond, unpublished; O. L. Lange and M. Zuber, unpublished). The capacity for CAM may be distinguished as obligate or constitutive in plants which are endowed with the metabolic machinery of CAM at all times, and as facultative or inducible in plants in which the metabolic machinery of CAM is synthesized in response to some environmental signal such as daylength or stress (117). In the former, the magnitude of CAM activity responds directly to external environmental conditions and to internal factors such as those associated with leaf development. Because CAM responds to a complex of external and internal factors, it is difficult to be sure that CAM is not present in a particular plant under a particular set of conditions, and difficult to categorize forms of CAM on the basis of CO_2/H_2O exchange patterns (106).

TAXONOMIC AND GEOGRAPHIC CONTEXT

The distribution of CAM among present-day higher plants suggests a polyphyletic origin of this metabolic pathway throughout the plant kingdom (45). In spite of the tremendous flexibility in the expression of CAM, recent experiments and extensive surveys have established one or more characteristics of CAM in two genera of the Filicophyta (177) and in about 110 genera (about 320 species) of the Spermatophyta (13, 146). Of the latter only one species of the Gymnospermae, *Welwitschia mirabilis*, has been shown to have a capacity for CAM (43). The pathway is well represented in the angiosperm families Agavaceae, Aizoaceae, Asclepiadaceae, Asteraceae, Bromeliaceae Cactaceae, Crassulaceae, Euphorbiaceae, Liliaceae, and Orchidaceae and has been reported in a few genera from six other families (13, 146).

The relatively sparse occurrence of CAM among present-day primitive plants is consistent with the evidence from carbon-13 isotope discrimination ratios (expressed as $\delta^{13}C$ values, relative to a standard) indicating that fossil plant carbon was almost exclusively assimilated by C_3 photosynthesis (155). Present-day CAM plants only make a significant contribution to floras in arid regions of low biomass—regions in which preservation of plant carbon in fossil form is unlikely to occur. Even if the capacity for CAM was widespread among primitive plants in more mesic environments of higher biomass, it is doubtful that the isotope ratio technique would distinguish the fact. As shown later, the CO_2 assimilated in the light by CAM plants under mesic conditions tends to be depleted in ^{13}C and similar to that of C_3 plants. The $\delta^{13}C$ value of carbon in the most ancient CAM plant so far examined (*Opuntia polycantha* approx. 40,000 yrs old) indicates it may have grown under such mesic conditions (157) and suggests that it may be impossible to detect the presence of CAM among fossil plants using this method.

Although current taxonomic and paleobotanic data give few insights into the origins and functional significance of CAM, the present-day geographical distribution is much more helpful. CAM plants are relatively more abundant the more arid the environment; they comprise 25% of the vegetative cover in Chile and Baja California where they occupy the most arid sites capable of sustaining higher plants (97).

It should be noted, however, that in some coastal deserts such as those of Atacama (Chile) and Namib (Southwest Africa), frequent heavy fogs and dew reduce evaporation and possibly serve as additional water sources (175). In tropical regions the presence and absence of CAM has been investigated among genera of the Bromeliaceae and Orchidaceae. In the Bromeliaceae, CAM is associated only with the more "recent" taxa which are found in more xeric habitats, either epiphytic or terrestrial (92, 93). Among the orchids, CAM is absent in epiphytic species so far examined and appears to be restricted to the succulent, terrestrial species (108). Overall, these observations imply that CAM is of functional significance to plants in arid habitats, an interpretation which is adequately sustained by more detailed studies of the expression and induction of CAM in response to water stress.

ENVIRONMENTAL CONTEXT

Functional significance is a phrase too often used in plant physiology and wisely regarded with suspicion by plant ecologists. Physiological characteristics which are peculiar to particular species or groups of species and are demonstrably related to the survival or performance of these plants in their habitat are few indeed. If, as the above geographical and ecological observations imply, CAM has a particular functional significance for plants in arid habitats, we might predict that in constitutive CAM plants the contribution of dark CO_2 fixation (phase 1) to total CO_2 exchange would increase in response to water stress. In the extreme, we would predict that carbon assimilation might be entirely restricted to phase 1. The fulfilment of these expectations in recent studies provides a measure of confidence in the functional significance of CAM which can be matched by few other physiological properties of higher plants.

Plant Water Relations and the Expression of CAM

Many laboratory and field studies show that dark CO_2 fixation in phase 1 makes a progressively greater contribution to total CO_2 assimilation of constitutive CAM plants during water stress. In only a few field studies, summarized in Table 1, have the parameters of soil and plant water potential been monitored, along with changes

Table 1 CO_2 and water vapor exchange patterns in CAM plants in response to soil water stress and its relation to dark acidification, transpiration ratio, and growth rate[a]

Water potential (bars) soil	−1	−5	> −50
plant	−3	−6	−15
Exchange of external CO_2/H_2O phase 1	+	+	±
phase 2	+	+	−
phase 4	+	−	−
Δ malic acid (% maximum)	100	50–80	25[b]
Transpiration ratio (g H_2O/g CO_2)	50–600	18–50	zero
Growth rate (g/m^2/day)	5–20	0.5–1.5	zero

[a] Sources: (71, 107, 112, 113, 142–145) and author's unpublished data.
[b] Cf (2, 148).

in CO_2/h_2O exchange and acid content. Table 1 shows that with decreasing soil and plant water potential the fixation of external CO_2 during phase 4 is the first component of total CO_2 assimilation to be lost, followed by successive reduction in the fixation of external CO_2 in phases 2 and 1. This sequence of change has been established during rapidly applied stress in potted leaf succulents (71, 107) and also during the slower drying cycles which occur under field conditions both with leaf succulents [*Dudleya* (5)] and stem succulents (*Opuntia,* Osmond unpublished).

It does not follow, however, that all CAM plants show all of these responses to changes in plant-soil water relations. *Opuntia bassilaris* cannot be induced to engage in CO_2 fixation during phase 4 following prolonged irrigation in the field (Z. Hanscomb and I. P. Ting, unpublished) whereas irrigation of *Agave deserti* in the laboratory abolished dark CO_2 fixation and the plant fixed CO_2 only in the light (51). In *Sedum acre* temperature interacts with soil-plant water relations to modify the patterns of CO_2 and H_2O exchange (M. Kluge, unpublished). Under extreme stress, however, many CAM plants cease altogether to exchange CO_2 and H_2O with the external environment for months at a time (112, 143, 148). Diurnal rhythms in malic acid content show that internal respiratory CO_2 continues to be cycled through the CAM pathways in these conditions. Following precipitation or irrigation, stomata open first in phase 1 (142, 145), allowing fixation of external CO_2 and increase in acid synthesis, and the normal sequence of CO_2 and H_2O exchange in phases 2–4 is usually reestablished.

Table 1 indicates that stressed CAM plants are able to maintain high tissue water potential in the face of extremely low soil water potentials. Although leaf water potentials as low as −22 bars have been measured in the leaf succulent *Kalanchoë daigremontiana* in extreme stress in the laboratory (120), leaf and stem succulents rarely show tissue water potentials below −15 bars in the field, even when soils remain dry (about −80 bars) for many months on end (143). The capacity to maintain high water potentials in environments of extremely low water potential is a function of the morphological rather than physiological properties of CAM plants. The usually shallow roots cease to function as the surface soil dries out, thus isolating the plant from the dry soil. In *Opuntia,* new functional roots, which are formed within hours of irrigation, restore plant water status and transpiration within a day (61, 145). However, it is the low stomatal frequency (151) and extraordinarily high cuticular resistance of most CAM plant surfaces (7, 111, 112) which so effectively restrict water loss in very dry environments.

In *Agave deserti* minimum leaf resistance in the dark increased from about 1.0 sec/cm to about 500 sec/cm when soil water potential declined from −1.5 bars to −3 bars in the space of a few days (111). After 5 months in soils with water potentials below −90 bars the tissue water potential of this species was −13.6 bars. Minimum leaf resistance was observed when tissue water potential was −3.8 bars. Two days after total stomatal closure in response to drying soil the potential was −6.1 bars. At this point the turgor of *Agave* leaf tissue at dawn was zero and, although some osmotic adjustment took place during the ensuing drought, the tissues remained at zero turgor. Similar results were noted with *Ferocactus* (112). Field observations with *Opuntia inermis* show a similar trend; cladode resistance changes from a minimum of 2 sec/cm in the light to a maximum of $>$ 100 sec/cm, in response to a decrease of about −3 bars in tissue water potential (C. B. Osmond, unpublished). In this sense, the stomata of CAM plants respond over much the same range of change in internal water relations as those of C_3 and C_4 crop plants (8). However, stomata are tightly closed at higher water potentials in CAM plants (−5 bars in the light, −15 bars in the dark) than in crop plants [−15 to −25 bars (8)] or in xerophytes [−30 to −60 bars (27)].

Detailed examination of stomatal responses in CAM plants is necessary. Presently available data suggest that plant water potential is the major, first order factor controlling opening in the light or dark. At high tissue water potentials the stomata respond to plant air water vapor pressure gradients (31; C. B. Osmond, unpublished) and to internal CO_2 concentration, but not to light. The complex epidermal structure of many CAM plants is a further factor which needs to be examined in relation to stomatal responses.

Although the water-containing capacity of tissues in many CAM plants is unusually high, recent studies (164) reconfirm earlier indications (162) that the matric properties of the water in storage tissues are not altered by the presence of mucilages, and neither contributes to the ability of the cells to contain more water or to retain it when exposed to drying conditions. The existence of a large water pool in the tissue simply serves as a buffer to delay the rate of change in tissue water potential after soil water becomes inaccessible, thus prolonging the period of dark assimilation of external CO_2 by as much as 40 days in *Ferocactus acanthodes* (112).

Table 1 shows that the dark assimilation of external CO_2 in phase 1 is extremely efficient in terms of water cost (cf 700 g H_2O/g CO_2 in C_3 plants). When conditions permit fixation of external CO_2 in phases 2 and 4, the additional carbon is gained at the expense of greatly increased transpiration and the water cost is comparable with that of C_3 plants. The use of transpiration ratio rather than carbon assimilation efficiency in Table 1 is appropriate because it integrates plant and environmental factors over long periods and variable conditions, and to some extent reflects performance in the field. Carbon assimilation efficiency which is "less a function of environment and more an intrinsic plant parameter" (144) is more appropriate to the short-term comparison of photosynthetic properties under controlled laboratory conditions.

Laboratory studies show that growth rates are highest under conditions which permit the maximum contribution of net CO_2 fixation in phase 4 (2). Under favorable field conditions crop growth rates in pineapple (6) approach the lower limit of C_3 crop growth rates (20–50 g/m²/day). Cultivated and wild *Opuntia* under irrigation or adequate summer rainfall grow at about 25% the rate of pineapple. (151; C. B. Osmond unpublished). Estimates for growth rate of *Ferrocactus* and *Agave* under desert rainfall conditions are only 2–8% of those measured for pineapple (111, 112). The simple correlation of maximum growth rate with greater CO_2 fixation and transpiration in phase 4 does not apply in all cases. Growth of *Echeveria pumila* was inversely correlated with transpiration ratio (95). In these and other CAM plants (37, 58), much of the CO_2 fixed in the dark is lost because stomates are not fully closed during phase 3.

Plant Water Relations and the Induction of CAM

Most convincing support for the interpretation of the functional significance of CAM in terms of water economy, and a possible indication of its origin in terrestrial plants, is provided by recent demonstrations of the induction of CAM in succulent but otherwise normal C_3 plants following water stress. Within 7–14 days following application of stress, mature leaves of plants such as *Mesembryanthemum crystallinum* show substantial dark CO_2 fixation and malic acid synthesis and stomatal closure during deacidification in the subsequent light period. This new metabolic capacity is associated with large increases in the activity of the enzymes required and seems to involve a true induction, in the sense that new enzymic proteins are synthesized. Presumably a tonoplast acid transport system is also induced. Originally thought to be a response to salinity (174), this phenomenon has now been observed in several species when subjected to salinity or when deprived of water (150, 153, 154, 169, 173). It can be induced in plants in culture solutions by simply cooling the roots or exposing the roots to anoxia (170, 171). Both treatments presumably result in reduced water uptake and water stress in the shoots. The capacity for CAM induced in these plants is lost when stress is removed (150, 159, 172). Field observations with *Mesembryanthemum nodiflorum* in Baja California (97), as with *M. crystallinum* (A. Bloom, J. H. Troughton, K. Winter, unpublished), indicate that induction of CAM makes an increasing contribution to net CO_2 assimilation late in the growing season. In none of these studies has leaf water potential been measured in parallel with the induction of CAM. Nevertheless, they may have uncovered a most significant example of enzyme induction in higher plants in response to the physical environment.

Other Environmental Responses

Many of the effects of internal and external factors on the rate of malic acid synthesis in the dark and deacidification in the light were reviewed earlier (131, 151, 175), but adequate techniques for following stomatal aperture have been developed rather recently and the role of stomata must now be reconsidered. It is obvious that stomatal movement in response to changes in plant water status, internal CO_2 concentration, ambient humidity (31), light intensity, or temperature can affect the supply of external CO_2 to the assimilating tissue. In the dark, stomatal closure reduces acid production, and in the light, stomatal closure prevents CO_2 assimilation during phase 4, thereby reducing the carbohydrate substrates available for subsequent dark fixation.

NIGHT TEMPERATURE   The long held view (131) that low night temperatures are more conducive to malic acid synthesis than high night temperatures, which was based on long-term experiments in continuous darkness (11), needs qualification. Several species show temperature optima for acidification and dark CO_2 fixation in the range 12–17° under normal day/night conditions (94, 125; E. Medina, unpublished). Field observations with *Opuntia inermis* show that when stomata are open throughout the night, acid production is insensitive to temperature over the range of 5–25° (C. B. Osmond, unpublished). In at least some instances the reduction in acid synthesis and net CO_2 exchange at high night temperatures is associated with stomatal closure (105, 112). Decreased acid synthesis at high night temperature is accompanied by reduced starch loss (67, 137) and substantial reduction in net CO_2 assimilation. Sometimes a net CO_2 efflux from the tissue is observed (2, 73, 104). In *Kalanchoë daigremontiana,* the decline in net dark CO_2 fixation between 10° and 24° was largely attributed to the increase in CO_2 evolution due to dark respiration indicated by increased O_2 uptake (24, 60).

High rates of dark respiration and endogenous CO_2 production at high night temperatures are likely to result in stomatal closure, just as the internal production of CO_2 during malic acid decarboxylation in the light causes stomata to close. The physiological implications of these observations are discussed below, but there are few indications that night temperature is a significant factor in determining distribution of CAM plant in natural habitats (94).

DAY TEMPERATURE AND LIGHT INTENSITY   The main effect of these two factors, which commonly vary together, is to modify the rate of malic acid consumption in the light. High temperatures and light intensities increase the rate of deacidification (25, 99, 135) and may therefore increase the amount of CO_2 assimilated in phase 4 (Figure 1), which in turn increases the supply of carbohydrate available for acid synthesis in the following dark period (25, 60). In many species day temperature above 25° result in CO_2 efflux throughout the day (39, 58, 78), evidently because stomatal closure is ineffective in retaining the CO_2 released from malic acid. The loss of CO_2 in this way substantially reduces the efficiency of dark CO_2 assimilation and may be an important factor in the early establishment of some CAM plants (39). The responses of deacidification in phase 3 and of external CO_2 assimilation in phase 4 to light intensity have not been examined in detail. The quantum requirements of these processes may be particularly helpful to our understanding of alternative metabolic pathways of CO_2 assimilation and dissimilation discussed below.

PHOTOPERIOD   Crassulacean acid metabolism is induced in *Kalanchoë blossfeldiana* var "Tom Thumb" by short day treatment (48, 128). In long days the young leaves of this plant are not very succulent, show no capacity for dark CO_2 fixation, and have low activities of the enzymes responsible for CAM. Following about the seventh short day, these activities begin to increase and *K. blossfeldiana* begins to resemble other constitutive CAM plants. These changes occur more slowly at low temperature and are inhibited by red light given as a night break (127). To my knowledge, the photoperiodic induction of CAM, which may be mediated by phytochrome, has not been demonstrated in other species (cf 129), and this phenomenon must therefore be considered a special case. This conclusion is all the more pertinent because some characteristics of CAM in this plant, described below, are not observed in others. Although recent studies suggest that the increased activity of CAM enzymes in this plant after short day treatments involves the production of new enzymes of different properties, and hence induction in the strict sense (23), photoperiod also controls the production of endogenous inhibitors which are quite specific for the synthetic machinery of acid metabolism (22).

Endogenous and Developmental Factors

The endogenous inhibitor believed to modulate CAM in *K. blossfeldiana* leaves following short day treatment may be similar to the widely reported but poorly documented "inhibitors" which have continually frustrated biochemical investigations of CAM. Despite present-day access to aseasonal, rigidly controlled environments, the unpredictable "close season" for CAM (131) continues to manifest itself. A more predictable feature of most leaf succulents is the increase in capacity for CAM with leaf age (131). The low capacity for acid synthesis in young leaves of *Bryophyllum fedtschenkoi* is associated with the lack of significant net CO_2 fixation and high leaf resistance in the dark (57). Older leaves show patterns of CO_2 and H_2O exchange comparable to that shown in Figure 1. This observation raises questions about the interpretation of whole plant studies. Perhaps the induction of CAM by water stress or photoperiod in some species represents an acceleration of normal developmental processes in these plants. Thus, it may be that the distinction between constitutive and facultative CAM plants made earlier is without foundation.

   In summary, investigations of the physiology of constitutive CAM plants reveal that the capacity of CAM (for acidification in phase 1 and deacidification in phase 3) persists in the most arid conditions when all exchanges of CO_2 and H_2O with the external environment have ceased. In facultative CAM plants, the induction of CAM in response to water stress prolongs net CO_2 uptake, and dark fixation in phase 1; it may also permit internal recycling of CO_2. Together with the geographical considerations above, these observations suggest that the functional significance of CAM is to maintain a fully developed photosynthetic system under conditions which in many cases can only be endured by the seed or vegetative organs of C_3 and C_4 plants. As an alternative photosynthetic system in higher plants, CAM has evidently been selected on the basis of its persistence under extremely arid conditions, rather than for its productivity under mesic conditions. CAM is essentially a survival option and, as will be developed below, is based on biochemical processes which have remarkable parallels with the highly productive C_4 plants. However, these processes are cast into an entirely different physiological framework in the two categories of higher plant photosynthesis. The additional photosynthetic capacity available to CAM plants under mesic conditions is indistinguishable from that of C_3 plants. After considering the details of these processes we shall examine recent techniques which allow us to assess the contribution of these components to the persistence and performance of CAM plants in different environments.

PHYSIOLOGICAL CONTEXT

Five key components of the cell physiology of CAM are first, the reactions involved in CO_2 assimilation, second, the reactions involved in the internal release of CO_2, third, the reactions of carbohydrate metabolism which generate substrates for dark CO_2 fixation, fourth, the reactions involved in the recovery of the 3-carbon units remaining after deacidification, and fifth, the processes involved in malic acid transport in and out of the vacuole. In this discussion, each component is examined in a phase-by-phase account of the activity and compartmentation of enzymes and processes involved. The interaction and regulation of these enzymes and process which results in the typical patterns of CO_2 and H_2O exchange shown in Figure 1 will be discussed later.

CO_2 Fixation and Malic Acid Synthesis

Previous reviews have adequately established that dark CO_2 fixation leading to malic acid synthesis in CAM plants involves the β-carboxylation of PEP by PEP carboxylase and the reduction of OAA by malate dehydrogenase (131, 147, 151, 160). The maximum rates of dark CO_2 fixation in CAM plants are rarely expressed in terms which can be related to enzyme activity, but estimates indicate it is unlikely that dark CO_2 fixation rate exceeds 30 μmoles/mg chl/hr in these plants (117, 144). The activity of the extracted enzymes involved in dark CO_2 fixation is more than adequate to sustain the rates observed (Table 2). However, the source of PEP consumed during malic acid synthesis has been one of the major preoccupations of CAM research in recent years. It was previously thought that PEP was derived from 3-PGA formed by the dark carboxylation of RuP_2, derived from the pentose phosphate pathway of carbohydrate metabolism.

The "double carboxylation hypothesis" was largely founded on the observation that malate-^{14}C extracted from CAM plants exposed to [14]CO_2 in the dark apparently contained a constant 2/3 of label in C-4 carboxyl atom and 1/3 in the C-1 carboxyl (18). A belated reexamination of this evidence showed that when the malic acid was degraded by a partially purified malic enzyme, rather than with malate adapted *Lactobacillus,* the 2/3 to 1/3 relationship was not constant and in short-term experiments > 90% of the label was found in the C-4 position (115, 140). Reexamination of the bacterial degradation method indicated that *Lactobacillus* might sometimes contain sufficient fumarase activity to randomize the label of malate-^{14}C during degradation (168). Although subsequent reports indicate that this degrada-

Table 2 Carboxylases, decarboxylases and associated enzymes in CAM plants[a, b]

Category	RuP$_2$ carboxylase	PEP carboxylase	NADP malic enzyme	NAD malic enzyme	PEP carboxykinase	Pyruvate orthophosphate dikinase	NAD MDH ($\times 10^3$)
NADP malic enzyme-type							
Crassulaceae	142	426	174	144	ND	—	11.3
Cactaceae	325	272	318	30	ND	—	12.5
Agavaceae	176	602	362	33	ND	—	11.8
3 species[c]	134	371	93	—	ND	48	8.4
PEP carboxykinase-type							
Euphorbiaceae	133	456	209	15	727	—	31.4
Liliaceae	106	865	54	20	416	—	13.9
Bromeliaceae	205	559	57	16	473	—	7.5
Asclepiadaceae	90	769	70	7	321	—	12.4
3 species[d]	123	749	58	—	283	ND	9.7

[a] Sources: (40, 42) and J. A. M. Holtum, unpublished.
[b] Activities = μmoles/mg Chl/min; ND = not detected; — = not assayed.
[c] *Kalanchoë daigremontiana, Bryophyllum pinnatum,* and *B. tubiflorum.*
[d] *Hoya carnosa, Aloe arborescens, Stapelia gigantea.*

tion artifact was unlikely to have contributed to the early observations (16), it is now clear that malic acid formed in the dark in CAM is initially labeled in the C-4 position and that subsequent randomization of this label via fumarase in the CAM plant is likely (41). This interpretation is supported by isotope dilution experiments (70). Unequivocal evidence against the "double carboxylation hypothesis" was provided by mass spectroscopy of malate extracted after 12 hr dark fixation of $^{13}CO_2$. The mass spectra indicated that only malate molecules containing a single atom of ^{13}C were present; none of the malic acid molecules could have been labeled in both C-1 and C-4 carbons (29).

Other evidence precludes the participation of RuP$_2$ carboxylase in a preliminary carboxylation reaction during dark acid synthesis. Dark CO_2 assimilation by intact leaves shows a high "affinity" for CO_2 and is insensitive to O_2 concentrations above 2%, properties consistent with CO_2 fixation by PEP carboxylase, not RuP$_2$ carboxylase (121). When CAM plants are provided with atmospheric CO_2 during the dark only, the $\delta^{13}C$ value of these plants is −10.6‰, consistent with the in vivo and in vitro discrimination properties of PEP carboxylase, not RuP$_2$ carboxylase (103, 163). These data clearly point to the direct β-carboxylation of PEP, without prior carboxylation of RuP$_2$ as the principal carboxylation reaction during dark CO_2 fixation in CAM plants. The pathways of CO_2 fixation during phase 2, the short period of light-stimulated assimilation (Figure 1), are much less clear. Labeling studies show that C-4 labeled malate is a major product of external $^{14}CO_2$ assimilation at this time (118). There is little initial stimulation of CO_2 production from dark-fixed malate on illumination (65). However, studies of O_2 exchange in the presence and absence of external CO_2 during this nonsteady state period indicate that malate decarboxylation may provide an internal CO_2 source in some circumstances (91). It is likely that this burst of CO_2 fixation may involve both PEP carboxylase and RuP$_2$ carboxylase.

In most instances the stomata are tightly closed during the consumption of malic acid in phase 3 (Figure 1), and label from malate-^{14}C formed in the dark is transferred to carbohydrates in the light with relatively little loss of $^{14}CO_2$ (77, 149). Short- and long-term exposure of excised tissues to $^{14}CO_2$ at this time reveal that the initial and final assimilation products are those expected from CO_2 assimilation by RuP_2 carboxylase and the photosynthetic carbon reduction cycle (3, 68) and that PEP carboxylase is inactive. Earlier evidence that deacidification is slowed by O_2 concentrations greater than 2% is consistent with the reassimilation of CO_2 from malate via O_2-sensitive RuP_2 carboxylase-oxygenase (100). The RuP_2 carboxylase activities of CAM plants (Table 2) are adequate to sustain the rates of CO_2 fixation implied by the rates of malic acid consumption measured in the light ($<$ 60 μmoles/mg chl/hr). Furthermore, the RuP_2 carboxylase of $K.$ $daigremontiana$ shows normal RuP_2 oxygenase activity (4).

The initial products and pulse-chase labeling during $^{14}CO_2$ fixation in phase 4 confirm that the CO_2 assimilation pathway is comparable with that in C_3 photosynthesis, based on RuP_2 carboxylase (118). The pool size of 3-PGA rises, and that of RuP_2 declines, in a light-dark transition and vice versa (66), consistent with the functioning of RuP_2 carboxylase in vivo. This interpretation has been well supported by physiological evidence that CO_2 assimilation at this time is O_2 sensitive (121), has an O_2-sensitive CO_2 compensation point of about 50 ppm (1) and an O_2-sensitive, postillumination burst (32). If CO_2 is available to the plants only during the light, the $\delta^{13}C$ value of the assimilated carbon is –25.9‰ (103). All of these observations are consistent with the in vitro properties of RuP_2 carboxylase-oxygenase and the integrated functioning of the photosynthetic carbon reduction and photorespiratory carbon oxidation cycles (84) as found in leaves of C_3 plants. These data show that leaves of CAM plants are capable of normal photorespiratory CO_2 release during phase 4, a view further substantiated by ultrastructural evidence of leaf peroxisomes (59) and by evidence for a glycine decarboxylating system in leaf mitochondria of CAM plants which is similar to that in C_3 plants (K. C. Woo, unpublished data).

It is not unusual to observe substantial $^{14}CO_2$ fixation into malic acid during photosynthesis in phase 4 (68, 70), particularly at low light intensities. Net malic acid synthesis may be observed. The malate formed in the shortest times contains substantial ^{14}C in the C-1 carbon (118). [One report to the contrary (3) was based on experiments with leaves maintained 24 hr in the light before exposure to $^{14}CO_2$ and the malate-^{14}C produced was degraded with $Lactobacillus.$] Whether a double carboxylation is involved can only be tested by analysis of the mass spectrum of malate-^{13}C formed at this time.

A small proportion of total RuP_2 carboxylase activity is retained by chloroplasts isolated from CAM plants, and these organelles then exhibit low rates of R5P-dependent CO_2 fixation (19, 83, 110). However, in-situ immunofluorescent labeling with anti-RuP_2 carboxylase confirms that this enzyme is localized in chloroplasts of $K.$ $daigremontiana$ (54). The location of PEP carboxylase is much less certain, with some activity being associated with aqueous (101) and nonaqueously prepared chloroplasts (46, 101), with mitochondria (19, 64), and with the supernatant fraction (20). In C_4 plants, PEP carboxylase appears to adhere to chloroplasts during nonaqueous isolation (52). The proportion of the enzymes in the sequence 3-PGA to malic acid which can be recovered in the mitochondrial pellet is determined by pH of the isolation medium (19, 20). Given these uncertainties, it seems best to assume that PEP carboxylase is a cytoplasmic enzyme and to explore whether there are compelling reasons for it to be distributed elsewhere. Wherever the PEP carboxylase is localized it is likely to be accompanied by NAD malate dehydrogenase, and carboxylation of PEP is likely to result in malic acid synthesis in that compartment.

Decarboxylation of Malic Acid

Until recently it was thought that the only decarboxylase of significance in the deacidification of malic acid in phase 3 was NADP malic enzyme. The activity of this enzyme (Table 2) is adequate for the rates of deacidification observed in most CAM plants, but only marginally so in the case of the Liliaceae, Bromeliaceae, Asclepiadaceae, and some other CAM plants (42). In these PEP carboxykinase is very active (Table 2) and presumably serves as the major decarboxylase (40, 42). This enzyme is not detectable in those CAM plants with high NADP malic enzyme, so it is legitimate to differentiate the NADP malic enzyme-type and PEP carboxykinase-type of CAM plants as shown in Table 2, and with the exception of the conglomerate of the Euphorbiaceae, such a classification seems to respect taxonomic boundaries. Recently, NAD malic enzyme activity has been detected in CAM plants from both of these categories (40). It is greatest in the NADP malic enzyme CAM plants, but only in the Crassulaceae are activities sufficient to support malic acid consumption fully during phase 3. In *Opuntia,* isoenzymes of NADP malic enzyme have been associated with chloroplast, mitochondrial, and the cytoplasmic fractions (102). NAD malic enzyme in *K. daigremontiana* is primarily localized in the mitochondria (40), but PEP carboxykinase activity has yet to be associated with organelles (42).

The demonstration of these alternative C_4 acid decarboxylase systems in CAM plants encourages a further comparison with C_4 plants which can also be classified on the basis of the predominant C_4 acid decarboxylase (52). However, the classification of CAM plants along these lines is much less distinct (Table 2) and thus far no separate group of NAD malic enzyme CAM plants can be distinguished. When we come to consider the regulated participation of these alternative decarboxylases in the process of malic acid decarboxylation, the functional basis of these distinctions is even more uncertain. Nevertheless, the selection of these alternative pathways during evolution is a fascinating example of the parallel (and limited) biochemical options in photosynthetic carbon metabolism.

Carbohydrate Metabolism in the Dark

Although the predicted and measured stoichiometry of carbohydrate consumption during malic acid synthesis in CAM has been discussed at length (131), two important uncertainties deserve comment. First, starch is a convenient analytical abstraction, describing a form of carbohydrate polymer which reacts with iodine. In many instances the amount of carbohydrate mobilized from starch in the dark in CAM plants is insufficient to provide for the 3-carbon units which are converted to malic acid. Recent studies emphasize that a perchloric acid soluble carbohydrate, probably a dextrin, may provide up to 40% of the carbohydrate source for malic acid synthesis (137). On a molar basis the loss of one glucose equivalent from these glucans (starch and dextrin) results in the formation of two moles of malic acid. Second, emphasis on the relationship between glucan and malic acid in CAM has diverted attention from the fact that most CAM plants are capable of growth, except under extremely arid conditions, presumably because some proportion of leaf carbohydrate reserves are translocated for use elsewhere in the plant. This aspect of carbohydrate metabolism in CAM plants has not been investigated. It is possible that soluble carbohydrates (principally sucrose) formed during phase 4 are selectively translocated from the leaves and that little glucan carbon is translocated during metabolism in the dark.

In an attempt to understand the relationship between the soluble sugars and glucans as carbohydrate sources for malic acid synthesis in the dark, leaves of B. tubiflorum were exposed to $^{14}CO_2$ for 2 hr during phase 4. The specific activity of the malic acid synthesized in the subsequent dark period was consistent with its production from the labeled glucan (137). The changes in the specific activity of the soluble sugar pool in the dark were not consistent with the flow of carbon from glucan through this pool during the synthesis of PEP for malic acid synthesis (137). These experiments suggest that the soluble sugar pool is separated from the glucan to malic acid pathway. They are consistent with evidence that glucan mobilization and malic acid synthesis decrease at high night temperatures, while the respiratory consumption of another carbon source, possibly the soluble sugars, increases (60, 67, 137). This apparent separation of pathways of carbohydrate metabolism in the dark has far-reaching implications, as discussed below, and deserves much closer attention.

The assessment of alternative pathways of hexose metabolism following glucan hydrolysis is greatly simplified if malic acid synthesis in the dark does not involve the prior dark fixation of CO_2 into RuP_2 derived from the pentose phosphate pathway, as required by the "double carboxylation" hypothesis. The mainstream of glucan breakdown in the dark is likely to be that shown in Figure 2. The mobilization of hexose units from glucan may be catalyzed either by amylase and glucokinase or by phosphorylase. In some studies amylase was inactive and glucokinase was only about 15% as active as phosphorylase (138), suggesting the latter enzyme as the main route. Subsequently, adequate activities of amylase have been found during the early stages of glucan mobilization (158), and the relative contribution of the two routes remains in doubt. Glucosephosphate isomerase was very much more active than G6P dehydrogenase (138), suggesting that most carbon flows through glycolysis. The activity of other glycolytic enzymes is adequate to sustain the carbon fluxes needed for malic acid synthesis, but phosphofructokinase activity was lower than that of other enzymes, consistent with the regulatory role discussed later.

The intracellular location of the enzymes of carbohydrate metabolism shown in Figure 2 is unclear. In C_3 plants, enzymes of glucan hydrolysis are localized in the chloroplast (35) as shown in Figure 2, but the chloroplasts of C_3 plants also contain some activity of the glycolytic enzymes converting G6P to PEP (62). If all of the glucan is metabolized to PEP in the chloroplast via amylase and glucokinase, the sequence in Figure 2 may be self-sustaining in terms of ADP, ATP, and Pi, assuming PEP is exported from the chloroplast in exchange for Pi via a Pi translocator (55, 161). A similar export of PEP from chloroplast to cytoplasm has been observed in mesophyll chloroplasts of C_4 plants (52). The NADH requirement for malic acid synthesis in the cytoplasm could be met by means of a dicarboxylate shuttle (55), preserving the self-sustaining nature of the glucan to malic acid sequence shown in Figure 2. Several experimental approaches indicate the possibility of parallel pathways of glycolysis in cells of CAM plants in the dark; one leading from glucan to PEP for malic acid synthesis, the other from soluble carbohydrates to pyruvate and TCA cycle metabolism. These may be compartmented in the chloroplast and the cytoplasm, respectively. If this were so, questions of the regulation of PEP metabolism (between PEP carboxylase and pyruvate kinase) and the location of PEP carboxylase assume added significance. The pyruvate kinase activity reported in CAM plants is disturbingly low (138) but metabolism of pyruvate by the TCA cycle is firmly established (14, 17, 63). The simple sequence of reactions shown in Figure 2 hides an unknown complexity of compartmentation and regulation, some aspects of which are discussed below.

Fate of Pyruvate and PEP during Deacidification

During phases 3 and 4 (Figure 1) the reassimilation of internal and external CO_2 via RuP_2 carboxylase and the photosynthetic carbon reduction cycle results in the

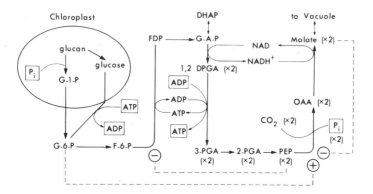

Figure 2 The principal pathway of carbohydrate metabolism from glucan to malic acid synthesis in the dark (phase 1) in CAM plants. This reaction sequence may be self-sustaining in terms of $NADH^+$ and ATP (shown linked or enclosed), but the intracellular location of most reactions is unknown. Feedback inhibition (–) and feedforward activation (+) due to some metabolites is shown.

resynthesis of soluble carbohydrates and glucans. Also, it is likely that the 3-C unit remaining after decarboxylation of malate during phase 3 is directly incorporated into carbohydrate by reversal of glycolysis. The labeling pattern in glucose formed during pyruvate-2-^{14}C metabolism in the light is consistent with this pathway, rather than complete oxidation of pyruvate by respiratory metabolism and refixation of CO_2 via RuP_2 carboxylase (50). Prodigious rates of respiration, more than 20-fold greater than those observed in the dark, would be required to support the observed rates of deacidification in *Bryophyllum calycinum* (96).

Further support for this notion of the direct recovery of the 3-C unit has been provided by the report of pyruvate orthophosphate dikinase in CAM plants (74, 136). This enzyme converts pyruvate to PEP and bypasses the irreversible pyruvate kinase of normal glycolysis. Table 2 shows that this enzyme has only been detected in CAM plants which contain high NADP and NAD malic enzyme activities. In CAM plants with high PEP carboxykinase activity the products of C_4 acid decarboxylation are CO_2 and PEP. Evidently there is no requirement for pyruvate orthophosphate dikinase, and this enzyme has not been detected in these plants. However, in *Aloe arborescens*, a PEP carboxykinase-type CAM plant, it is likely that the 3-C unit remaining after decarboxylation (PEP) is also directly converted to carbohydrate. O_2 uptake in the light is insufficient to support complete oxidation of pyruvate to CO_2 via respiratory metabolism (38). Figure 3 outlines the probable main stream of carbon metabolism via the two alternate malic acid deacidification pathways.

Compartmentation and Transport in CAM

Few plants have the capacity to store free organic acids in the vacuole, and in most instances organic acid transport to the vacuole is associated with processes of charge balance during cation uptake or nutrient anion uptake and incorporation (116, 134). A proportion of the total organic acid content of CAM leaf tissues is also involved

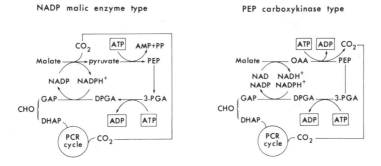

Figure 3   The principal pathways of malic acid decarboxylation in the light (phase 3) in two types of CAM plants. In both the CO_2 released is refixed during photosynthesis and the 3-C compound is incorporated into carbohydrate by reverse glycolysis which is fueled by ATP from photophosphorylation (shown enclosed). The location of these processes remains uncertain, but it is possible that they are restricted to the chloroplasts of CAM plants.

in cation balance as indicated by the response of acid content to the form of nitrogen nutrition (124). The diurnal change in free malic acid content is superimposed upon this base level of organic acid salts.

It has been tacitly assumed that the malic acid synthesized during dark CO_2 fixation is stored in the vacuole. This view is sustained by simple calculations and biochemical prejudices which suggest that if malic acid were restricted to the cytoplasm, its concentration would approach molarity at pH 3.4, a state deemed unfavorable for a working cytoplasm. Biochemical analyses of compartmentation indicated that less than 30% of the malate in *Bryophyllum* leaf slices was in equilibrium with the TCA cycle (89). Physiological analysis of the compartmentation of malic acid-^{14}C formed during $^{14}CO_2$ fixation in the dark indicates three compartments (72). However, the bathing medium used in these experiments did not contain unlabeled malate, so malic acid exchange in the strict sense was not demonstrated. The data are difficult to reconcile with other studies which show two, not three, compartments for malate following dark $^{14}CO_2$ fixation in beet tissue (122).

In CAM plants the tonoplast influx of free malic acid to the vacuole involves the unusual transport of hydrogen malate, is unusually rapid, and is evidently reversed during deacidification in the light. Present information is inadequate to distinguish whether this transport process involves active proton transport to the vacuole, analogous with the plasma membrane H^+ extrusion system (134), or active malate anion uptake, analogous with other tonoplast anion uptake systems. It is difficult to study because the rate of acid synthesis and transport rarely reaches a steady state. Studies with tissue slices are limited by transport across the plasmamembrane, and the influx of external malic acid is only about 1% of the rate of endogenous malic acid accumulation (86). Whether the isolated vacuoles, recently prepared from leaves of CAM Plants (C. Buser, Ph. Matile, unpublished), can be used to study the properties of malic acid influx at the tonoplast remains to be seen.

Malic acid efflux from the vacuole is more easily assessed, and two properties of this process may be significant in the physiology of CAM. Efflux of malic acid increases with increasing osmotic pressure difference between vacuole and bathing solution (85), and efflux also increases with malic acid content of the tissue (72, 86). Comparative studies with mannitol, a nonpenetrating solute, and glycerol, a penetrating solute, strongly suggest that malic acid efflux depends on cell turgor (U. Lüttge, E. Ball, and H. Greenway, unpublished). In experiments in which HCO_3^- is present, tissue slices of deacidified CAM plants are capable of accumulating malic acid only when the osmotic pressure of the bathing solution is adjusted to equal that of the vacuole (88). By adjusting the osmotic pressure of the bathing medium to 4.5 bars in the dark and 0.5 bars in the light a diurnal rhythm of acid accumulation and loss in the tissue slices may be simulated. The authors suggest that in vivo the synthesis and metabolically dependent transport of malic acid to the vacuole in the dark is accompanied by osmotic water flow and the generation of increased turgor pressure. By analogy with other turgor-sensitive transport systems, they infer that the properties of the tonoplast transport system may change at a critical turgor and malic acid efflux from the vacuole to the cytoplasm may increase (88). This hypothesis is difficult to test in vivo, but it should be noted that diurnal fluctuation of malic acid content, although heavily damped, continues in CAM plants which remain at zero turgor for many months during drought (111, 112, 142).

The accumulation of malic acid in the vacuole in the dark at the expense of insoluble carbohydrates in the cytoplasm also has a significant impact on cell water relations. When maintained at moderate temperatures, high humidity, and when well irrigated, *K. daigremontiana* shows lowest plant water potential just before dawn (87). The production of malic acid in the dark accounts for an increase of several bars in osmotic pressure in the vacuole. In these plants the storage of dark assimilates in the vacuole runs counter to the normal night equilibration of water potential (8). Whether the nightly accumulation of osmotic solutes in the vacuole prolongs the ability of CAM plants to absorb water at night from drying soils remains to be established.

In summary, adequate activity in vitro of the enzymes required to sustain CAM has been demonstrated for all of the major component processes. There is evidently no intercellular compartmentation of these enzyme activities, as indicated by experiments with isolated leaf cells of *Sedum telephium* (132). However, CAM plants do show differences between species in the C_4 acid decarboxylase enzymes and can be grouped into those with high activity of PEP carboxykinase and those without. Plants with high PEP carboxykinase activity appear to lack pyruvate orthophosphate dikinase which is active in members of the other group, which are distinguished by having higher NADP and NAD malic enzyme activities. The most remarkable feature of the cell physiology of CAM plants is that the activity of two CO_2-fixing enzyme systems and the balance between malic acid synthesis and consumption is effectively regulated to produce the complex diurnal patterns of CO_2 fixation and acid metabolism shown in Figure 1. Moreover, this regulation shows sufficient flexibility to accommodate the wide range of physiological responses to environmental stress shown earlier. A key feature of this regulated metabolism is the little understood process of malic acid transport between metabolic compartments and the cell vacuole.

BIOCHEMICAL CONTEXT: THE REGULATION OF CAM

There is no better demonstration of the integration and regulation of CAM metabolism than the circadian rhythms observed when CAM plants are transferred to constant day or night conditions. The most striking and widely studied of these is the circadian rhythm of CO_2 production into CO_2-free air which shows a rapidly damped oscillation for a few days after transfer to continual darkness (165, 166). This rhythm, which is measured under conditions that must introduce substantial artifacts in the functioning of CAM, represents the output of some of the regulated component processes of CAM. Any account of metabolic regulation that is used to explain the physiological performance of CAM plants through the phases shown in Figure 1 should also be compatible with these rhythms. In my view, however, it does not follow that because these rhythms appear to be circadian, there are "basic oscillators (of unknown function)" (128) which direct the overall regulation of

CAM. The principal hypotheses of regulatory systems in CAM have been reviewed recently (69, 129). The following phase-by-phase account of regulated CO_2 exchange in CAM is based, perhaps incautiously, on an incomplete knowledge of the in vitro properties of the enzymes involved and major uncertainties as to the location of enzymes in vivo.

Regulation by Changes in Enzyme Capacity

The capacity of carboxylase and decarboxylase enzymes in mature leaves of most constitutive CAM plants generally show little variation in response to environmental conditions, but some changes have been observed (33). On the other hand, induction of CAM in some plants in the Aizoaceae in response to water stress results in large increases in the capacity of PEP carboxylase and malic enzyme (171; H. Greenway, K. Winter, and U. Lüttge, unpublished). Electrophoretic evidence indicates the synthesis of a new protein with PEP carboxylase activity and this protein is lost following removal of stress (159). The kinetic properties of the new enzyme differ from those of the preexisting enzyme (171), and the higher activity at acid pH, higher affinity for PEP, and reduced sensitivity to malic acid inhibition of the induced enzyme (H. Greenway, K. Winter, and U. Lüttge, unpublished) are consistent with its participation in CAM. Similarly, the induction of CAM in *K. blossfeldiana* following exposure to short days results in the synthesis of an electrophoretically distinct protein with PEP carboxylase activity (129). These studies point to the regulation of CAM by the synthesis of new enzymic machinery.

On the other hand, there is much conflicting evidence for diurnal oscillation in the capacity of PEP carboxylase and other enzymes involved in some CAM plants. It may be that in some studies these oscillations were due to diurnal changes in the levels of metabolites or inhibitors (130), but this is unlikely in others (167). In many species there is no evidence of diurnal changes in enzyme capacity (75; H. Greenway, K. Winter, and U. Lüttge, unpublished). It is difficult to assess the regulatory implications of a diurnal change in enzyme capacity, usually about ± 30% of the mean, when the capacity of the extracted enzyme is one or more orders of magnitude greater than the rate of the process it catalyzes in vivo. Similar uncertainties apply to the metabolite regulation of many of the enzymes discussed below.

Regulation by Changes in Enzyme Activity

REGULATION OF MALIC ACID SYNTHESIS   The normal course of acid synthesis in CAM plants in the dark parallels the rate of fixation of external CO_2. The rate is slow during the initial lag in acidification, peaks during the period of most rapid acid accumulation, and declines again as the acid content of the tissue reaches a plateau (Figure 1). This very close coupling is not surprising for a system of acid synthesis which is based on an irreversible carboxylase that is subject to end product, feedback inhibition (75, 126, 160). More than this, however, the whole process of mobilization of glucan carbohydrate, its conversion to PEP, and the fixation of CO_2 into malic acid is very highly integrated during phase 1 of CAM.

Figure 2 shows that, depending on the path of glucan mobilization, the metabolic pathway can be entirely self-sustaining and independent of other cellular processes for the provision of ADP/ATP or NAD/NADH$^+$. In spite of the uncertainties of enzyme distribution, it is reasonable to discuss the regulation of this self-contained glycolytic sequence in terms of the known in vitro properties of the enzymes involved. Because we no longer suppose that the primary substrate for dark CO_2 fixation is generated via reactions of the pentose pathway, the diversion of carbon via G6P dehydrogenase can be ignored until we have a better picture of the intricacies of the pentose pathway in CAM plants. If there are parallel paths of glycolytic metabolism, utilizing the insoluble glucans and soluble carbohydrates respectively, then we may also ignore the diversion of PEP from the acid pathway to respiratory metabolism for the present.

The K_i (malate) for PEP carboxylase from CAM plants is only about five times higher than the K_m (PEP), yet it has been estimated that with the rates of dark CO_2 fixation which occur in vivo the concentration of malic acid in the cytoplasm could reach inhibitory concentrations within 10 min if the acid were not transported to the vacuole (75). Accumulation of malic acid to concentrations of 100 to 200 mM in the vacuole of CAM plant cells clearly implies transport against a concentration gradient. Whatever the mechanism of the malic acid transport system at the tonoplast, and its response to concentration or turgor in the vacuole (88), the concentration of malic acid in the cytoplasm is likely to rise as the vacuole fills. Aside from the direct inhibitory effect of malic acid on PEP carboxylase, it is probable that the cytoplasm may become more acid in the course of dark CO_2 fixation. PEP carboxylase from some CAM plants retains high activity at pH 5–6 (75), and a shift to higher activity at low pH during acid synthesis has been observed (H. Greenway, K. Winter and U. Lüttge, unpublished). The pH profile of NADP malic enzyme shows a malic acid dependent shift and broadening at high substrate concentrations (47), and whether these enzymes participate in a "pH stat" (34) in CAM plants is questionable.

Because the inhibition due to malate is partly competitive (75), one expedient to promote continued CO_2 fixation would seem to be an increase in the concentration of PEP. Alternatively, the inhibition due to malic acid could be modulated in some other way. It seems likely that both mechanisms contribute to the ability of CAM cells to continue glycolysis and malic acid synthesis in the presence of otherwise inhibitory concentrations of malic acid. In most glycolytic sequences, an increase in PEP to overcome the competitive inhibition of PEP carboxylase by malic acid would soon inhibit phosphofructokinase, which is markedly sensitive to PEP. Compared with phosphofructokinase from leaves of a C_4 plant and from pea seeds, CAM phosphofructokinase is about 100-fold less sensitive to inhibition by PEP (139), suggesting that glycolysis may continue in the presence of much higher PEP concentrations. In addition, PEP carboxylase is activated by G6P and this glycolytic intermediate is particularly effective in mitigating the inhibition of this enzyme due to malic acid (152).

These speculations as to regulated metabolism during acid synthesis have recently been tested against changes in pool sizes of glycolytic pathway intermediates in *K. daigremontiana* leaves in the dark, following transition from air to CO_2-free air and vice versa (30). Transfer from CO_2-free air to air was marked by decreases in PEP and FDP level as well as increases in G6P and F6P, consistent with the increased flow of carbon to malic acid and the likely regulatory role of phosphofructokinase. During an air to CO_2-free air transition PEP, FPD, F6P, and G6P levels increased, presumably due to a backing up in these metabolites following CO_2 deprivation. In other experiments, the cessation of malic acid synthesis at the end of the dark period was accompanied by increases in PEP and decreases in FDP pools, consistent with the interactions proposed in Figure 2.

The extent of malic acid synthesis in the dark may be further regulated by the activity of decarboxylase enzymes which might consume a portion of the acid produced according to Figure 2. Although $^{14}CO_2$ is evolved after a period of dark $^{14}CO_2$ fixation (65), it is not clear whether it originates from direct decarboxylation of malic acid or from decarboxylation of malic acid or other acids via the TCA cycle. Pulse-chase experiments in C_4 plants suggest that the decarboxylation of malic acid by NADP malic enzyme is abruptly halted by a dark period (52, 114), indicating that the enzyme is inactive in the dark. NADP malic enzyme could well be held in check in the dark by a change in the ratio of $NADP/NADPH^+$. Such control has not been examined in vitro and the significance of transhydrogenase systems, which could relieve this inhibition in vivo, has not been examined.

It has been proposed that acid synthesis in CAM plants is simply regulated by the balance of PEP carboxylase and NADP malic enzyme activity in the dark (19). This regulatory hypothesis was proposed to account for the observation that malic acid content of CAM plants is reduced at high night temperature. It was suggested that the greater thermostability of NADP malic enzyme in vitro, compared with PEP carboxylase (19), and a twofold decrease in the K_m (malate) between 17 and 39° (21), were consistent with more rapid malic acid decarboxylation than malic acid synthesis at high night temperature. If this were so, glucan mobilization would increase as acid synthesis decreased at high temperature. This prediction is not supported by evidence showing that both glucan mobilization and acid synthesis decrease at high night temperature (136). Furthermore, the temperature responses of kinetic properties described for these enzymes have not been confirmed with purified enzymes from other CAM plants (C. B. Osmond, unpublished). Although the carboxylation-decarboxylation hypothesis for the regulation of acid synthesis is presently untenable, it does draw attention to our imperfect understanding of the control of NADP malic enzyme in the dark.

REGULATION OF DEACIDIFICATION   The demonstration of alternative C_4 acid decarboxylase systems in CAM plants and uncertainties as to their compartmentation make it much more difficult to identify significant regulatory processes during deacidification. Regulation of at least four stages is likely, these being malic efflux from the vacuole, activation of the decarboxylase system, activation of the carboxylation reactions in the chloroplasts, and activation of other enzymes involved in metabolism of the 3-C unit remaining after decarboxylation.

During phase 2 there is usually a delay of up to 2 hr before any significant decrease in malic acid content occurs. During this time, C-4 labeled malate is an important product of light-stimulated CO_2 fixation (118), suggesting that the malic acid inhibition of PEP carboxylase in the dark does not persist into this phase. The relatively small malic acid pool in the cytoplasm probably is rapidly depleted on illumination. Continued deacidification might then depend on a substantial increase in malic acid efflux from the vacuole. The lengthy delay argues against a direct light stimulation of this efflux. However, illumination is likely to increase transpiration and could initiate substantial changes in leaf water relations. Small changes in cell turgor might well stimulate malic acid efflux as has been indicated by in vitro studies (88). Once malic acid efflux from the vacuole is established, PEP carboxylase would in all probability remain inhibited throughout subsequent deacidification.

NADP malic enzyme of CAM plants shows a complex of allosteric properties (47) including cooperativity due to malate at low concentrations. In vivo the activation of this enzyme by malic acid is presumably the converse of PEP carboxylase inhibition. In all probability it is fully activated at the end of the dark period but held in check in the chloroplast by low $NADP/NADPH^+$ ratio. Decarboxylation by NADP malic enzyme yields CO_2 and $NADPH^+$ and the latter must be recycled during deacidification. The recycling could be linked to the net incorporation of pyruvate via a reversal of glycolysis (Figure 3). Indeed, chloroplast glyceraldehyde phosphate dehydrogenase could regenerate NADP in the dark if pyruvate were available. Only the ATP requirement shown in Figure 3 and the dark inactivation of pyruvate orthophosphate dikinase (136) prevent the decarboxylation of malic acid by NADP malic enzyme in the dark.

In PEP carboxykinase-type CAM plants deacidification presumably proceeds via the oxidation of malic acid to OAA by a malate dehydrogenase in the cytoplasm or chloroplast. There is no evidence that the malic acid passes through aspartate and is then transaminated to OAA as occurs in C_4 plants (52). If deacidification in these CAM plants involves an NADP malate dehydrogenase in the chloroplast, it is essential that the $NADPH^+$ produced during malate oxidation be recycled. Again, it is possible that recycling could be tied to the recovery of PEP resulting from decarboxylation by reverse glycolysis (Figure 3). It is also possible that NADP malate dehydrogenase is light activated, as it is in C_3 and C_4 plants (52), and could thus control malic acid decarboxylation by this pathway in the dark. Although the formation of OAA in the cytoplasm could take place just as effectively, and the $NADH^+$ could be recycled in a reversal of cytoplasmic glycolysis, regulation of this system in the dark is not so readily envisaged.

The role of NAD malic enzyme in malic acid mobilization in CAM plants is difficult to specify. If a significant portion of malic acid is decarboxylated by this enzyme in the mitochondria of CAM tissues in the light (40), it is possible that the pyruvate and $NADH^+$ produced could be exported from the mitochondria and used during a reversal of cytoplasmic glycolysis in the cytoplasm. Alternatively, pyruvate and $NADH^+$ could be further metabolized to CO_2 and ATP within the mitochondria via the TCA cycle and electron transport pathway. In leaf mitochondria of C_4 plants pyruvate seems to escape this fate (52), possibly because the TCA cycle is unable to accommodate the high fluxes of carbon involved. Deacidification in

CAM is rather slower, but we have seen that a substantial stimulation of TCA cycle metabolism in the light is required if it is to participate in the oxidation of pyruvate in the light. It is possible that NAD malic enzyme plays a more significant role in malic acid consumption in the dark.

The activation of enzymes of the photosynthetic carbon reduction cycle on illumination is probably regulated in the way proposed for C_3 plants (56, 62). The response of deacidification to temperature and light intensity presumably reflects the capacity of the photosynthetic carbon reduction cycle to accept and reduce the CO_2 and 3-carbon units produced. It is unlikely that CO_2 levels in the tissue during deacidification would rise to the extent that they would inhibit PEP carboxylase (160). Whether the increase in O_2 tension may lower the carboxylation efficiency of RuP_2 carboxylase-oxygenase in vivo remains to be determined. In all probability, the endogenous CO_2 concentrations are sufficiently high to counteract the elevated O_2 tension.

REGULATION OF CARBOXYLASES IN PHASE 4   It is likely that PEP carboxylase is inhibited by the presence of malic acid in the cytoplasm during deacidification. This inhibition is presumably relieved when malic acid has been consumed and, if PEP is available, there is probably no restriction on CO_2 fixation via this enzyme. The major source of PEP during phase 4 is presumably 3-PGA derived from the photosynthetic carbon reduction cycle. The labeling pattern of malate-^{14}C produced during CO_2 fixation in phase 4 is consistent with synthesis via such a double carboxylation (118). Isolated cells of CAM plants can utilize either 3-PGA or 2-PGA as substrates for CO_2 fixation in the light or dark (132) and enolase, phosphoglyceromutase activities are more than adequate (139). The export of 3-PGA or DHAP from the chloroplast (55) presumably provides the 3-C units for malic acid or sucrose synthesis during phase 4 of CO_2 fixation in vivo. Further investigations of the regulation of these alternative fates of 3-PGA or DHAP are required.

REGULATION OF CARBOHYDRATE SYNTHESIS   During phase 3 the carbon of malic acid is almost quantitatively converted to carbohydrate, most of which is glucan, and the stoichiometry of this relationship has been reviewed in detail (131). During phase 4, fixation of external CO_2 results in the substantial synthesis of sucrose, but relatively little of the label from [14]CO_2 finds its way to glucan (68, 138). This apparent switch in the fate of assimilated carbon between phase 3 and 4 requires further documentation but invites speculation as to the regulatory processes involved. In other plants the production of glucan or sucrose during photosynthesis is regulated by the concentration of 3-PGA and P_i (161). Whether these metabolites have a similar role in CAM remains to be determined, but the increase in activity of PEP carboxylase in phase 4 may change the relative levels of these metabolites. Following the lowering of malic acid levels at the end of phase 3, PEP carboxylase activity presumably increases and would provide a sink for 3-PGA (converted to PEP) and a source of P_i (produced during PEP carboxylation). A decrease in the ratio 3-PGA/P_i would favor sucrose synthesis as observed, rather than glucan synthesis.

Regulation During Circadian Rhythms

Although a full account is impossible in this review, it is important to consider whether the above regulatory possibilities are consistent with the circadian rhythms of CO_2 output into CO_2-free air. The concept that these rhythms are "overt indicators" of the in vivo activity of PEP carboxylase and NADP malic enzyme (128) needs substantial qualification in the light of recent data. First, the rhythm of CO_2 output into CO_2-free air in the normal light period presumably involves NADP malic enzyme until malic acid is depleted and the subsequent release of photorespiratory CO_2. Second, there is no compelling evidence that NADP malic enzyme functions in the dark. In continuous darkness, CO_2 production during the period corresponding to the normal light period is more likely to involve NAD malic enzyme and the TCA cycle. Thus the rhythm in normal day-night cycles has an entirely different biochemical foundation to that in continuous darkness. It may be fortuitous that these lower capacity systems take the equivalent of a normal light period to deplete malic acid and release PEP carboxylase from inhibition. Once malic acid has been depleted, CO_2 fixation by PEP carboxylase could resume, providing carbohydrate reserves are available for respiration and PEP synthesis. Malic acid synthesis could presumably continue for as long as the balance of fluxes at the tonoplast ensured low malic acid concentrations in the cytoplasm. Depletion of the carbohydrate reserves presumably accounts for the damping of these rhythms after a few days of continuous darkness. Circadian rhythms of CO_2 production have been reported only in members of the Crassulaceae which have high NAD malic enzyme activities. It could be instructive to establish whether such rhythms are present in PEP carboxykinase-type CAM plants which have little NAD malic enzyme activity.

Regulation During Idling of CAM Under Stress

The above account of the physiological and biochemical regulation of CAM has been formulated on the basis of experiments with well-irrigated plants under relatively benign conditions. Under extreme stress CAM is reduced to the recycling of internal CO_2 in the dark and light, and it is well to consider whether the above regulatory possibilities are still adequate. The limited synthesis of malic acid under these conditions is commonly only a fraction of the potential level (Table 1), presumably because the internal CO_2 supply is limited. Thus malic acid synthesis is more likely to be controlled by CO_2 supply than by feedback control on PEP carboxylase under these conditions, and the regulation of PEP synthesis from glucan may also be less important (Figure 2). In the light, reassimilation of the dark fixed CO_2 evidently proceeds normally, and when malic acid is depleted the tissues of these CAM plants presumably cycle carbon through the photosynthetic carbon reduction and photorespiratory carbon oxidation cycles at the CO_2 compensation point (84).

The above discussion of potential regulatory interactions seeks to account for a wide range of physiological and biochemical behavior on a very limited understanding of the location and properties of the enzymes involved. Some significant features, such as the malic acid inhibition of PEP carboxylase, the relative insensitivity of CAM phosphofructokinase to PEP, and the light activation of pyruvate orthophosphate dikinase, are clearly established. Some fascinating questions are posed, e.g. whether the parallel glycolytic pathways exist in chloroplast and cytoplasmic compartments and how pyruvate metabolism is controlled in the dark and light. Effective methods for examination of acid fluxes into the vacuole and for the localization of enzymes continue to be major obstacles to the satisfactory resolution of regulatory problems in CAM.

CARBON ISOTOPE RATIOS AS INTEGRATORS OF CAM

Unlike the C_3 and C_4 pathway plants, CAM plants show variable $\delta^{13}C$ values which range between about $-10\%_o$ and about $-27\%_o$ (9, 79), the extremes of values found for terrestrial C_3 and C_4 plants. The $\delta^{13}C$ value in C_3 plants is determined by RuP_2 carboxylase which shows a substantial discrimination against ^{13}C during CO_2 fixation in an open system, i.e. in a system which can exchange ^{12}C and ^{13}C isotopes freely with the atmosphere at the time of carboxylation (28, 37). The $\delta^{13}C$ value of C_4 plants is determined by the very much lower discrimination against ^{13}C by PEP carboxylase, the primary CO_2 fixation step, and by the fact that the CO_2 so assimilated is further metabolized via RuP_2 carboxylase in a closed system, the relatively CO_2-tight bundle sheath cells of these plants (37, 163). Under these circumstances of restricted CO_2 exchange with the atmosphere, the discrimination characteristics of RuP_2 carboxylase cannot be expressed.

Unlike C_3 and C_4 plants, in which all carbon components except lipids show $\delta^{13}C$ values similar to the total plant carbon, substantial differences in the $\delta^{13}C$ value of some components have been reported in CAM plants. The differences between the $\delta^{13}C$ value of different classes of metabolites could thus contribute to the variation in $\delta^{13}C$ value of total plant carbon in CAM plants. More important, however, is the possibility that the $\delta^{13}C$ value of the different carbon components can be used to trace the metabolic cycles described above.

Integration of Regulated Metabolism

Deleens & Garnier-Dardart (36) have measured the $\delta^{13}C$ value (shown in parenthesis) of the major classes of metabolites in *K. daigremontiana*. These elegant studies provide a means of assessing many of the metabolic interactions discussed above. For example, they show that substrates for CO_2 fixation in phase 1, starch ($-12.5\%_o$) and phosphorylated compounds ($-11.5\%_o$) are evidently in equilibrium. At the end of phase 1, the $\delta^{13}C$ value of the malic acid formed ($-14.6\%_o$) implies the addition of CO_2 with $\delta^{13}C$ values more negative than that of the CO_2 in air ($-10.6\%_o$). Respiration of soluble carbohydrates ($-16.7\%_o$), cellulose ($-21.0\%_o$), lipids and protein (-22.3 to $-27.3\%_o$) would generate CO_2 of approximately the required $\delta^{13}C$ value. Moreover, the latter analyses imply that these compounds are largely derived from CO_2 fixation in phase 4. Except for the refixation of respiratory CO_2, there appears to be relatively little exchange of carbon between the products of carboxylation in phase 1 and the products of carboxylation in phase 4 (36, 137).

These studies support other indications, outlined above, that there may be parallel pathways of glycolysis in the dark in CAM plants: one in which glucan carbon is converted to PEP for malic acid synthesis and another in which soluble carbohydrates are converted to pyruvate and respired to CO_2. They also support the indication that malic acid carbon is converted to starch in the light and that this starch is largely isolated from the products of CO_2 fixation in phase 4, in which sucrose predominates. This fascinating approach should be applied under different environmental conditions. Earlier attempts (120) to account for differences between the $\delta^{13}C$ value of soluble and insoluble fractions in CAM plants suggest this may be rewarding. For example, in well-irrigated *K. daigremontiana* the $\delta^{13}C$ value of the soluble fraction at dawn was consistent with the addition of external CO_2 (approx. $-11‰$) to a substrate derived from the insoluble fraction (-19.5 to $-26.5‰$). Although the recycling of respiratory CO_2 may have been of little significance in these treatments, it was obviously important in water stress treatments (120), as would be expected on the basis of field experiments (142). In the stressed treatments the rate of change in $\delta^{13}C$ value of the tissue with time was slower than anticipated if the increase in dry weight was due to the addition of external CO_2 (approx. $-11‰$) only, and substantial mixing with respiratory CO_2 (approx. $-27‰$) must have occurred (120). Although the interpretation of carbon isotope analyses of metabolites in CAM plants is in its infancy, the technique offers a unique opportunity for further exploration of compartmentation and regulation of metabolism in these plants.

Integration of CO₂ Fixation in Response to Environment

In view of these intriguing but complex interactions between components differing in $\delta^{13}C$ value, it could be argued that carbon isotope discrimination analysis of total plant carbon in CAM plants shows such a high noise-to-signal ratio as to be of little value as an indicator of the carbon assimilation history of the plant. This is not so, because the bulk of total plant carbon is composed of insoluble material which is remote from concurrent metabolism. Changes in the $\delta^{13}C$ value of insoluble material and total carbon are similar (120), and the effect on $\delta^{13}C$ value, total carbon, of variations in the proportion of metabolites which differ in $\delta^{13}C$ value is slight. In the long term, however, the $\delta^{13}C$ value, total carbon, must reflect the relative contributions of the carbon fixed in the light and dark through the pathways described above.

In 1973, workers in two laboratories concluded that the $\delta^{13}C$ value of CAM plants was an indicator and integrator of CO_2 fixation in the light and dark by RuP_2 carboxylase and PEP carboxylase respectively (10, 119). This conclusion was directly validated by later studies which showed that the $\delta^{13}C$ value of *K. daigremontiana* was $-10.6‰$ when supplied with CO_2 in the dark only, $-25.9‰$ when the same CO_2 source was provided in the light only, and $-15.0‰$ when the CO_2 was available in the light and dark (103). Although variation in the $\delta^{13}C$ value of the carbon sources used in the comparative experiments on which the original interpretation was based may have been a source of error not taken into account (80), subsequent data leave little doubt as to the validity of this interpretation. Other treatments which modify the relative contribution of dark CO_2 fixation and light CO_2 fixation have been applied under strictly comparable conditions of CO_2 supply. The $\delta^{13}C$ value of *K. blossfeldiana* was 8.4‰ less negative following induction of CAM short days (82), and the $\delta^{13}C$ of *K. daigremontiana* was 6 to 9‰ more negative following water stress treatments which eliminate CO_2 fixation in the light (115, 120). When this species was grown in the same CO_2 supply but at temperatures and daylengths in which only 18% of total CO_2 fixation occurred in the light, $\delta^{13}C$ value of total plant carbon was $-18.8 \pm 0.08‰$. This value was $-22.0 \pm 1.3‰$ under conditions in which 98% of CO_2 fixation took place in the light. These relatively small changes in $\delta^{13}C$ value were evidently confounded by larger differences in the $\delta^{13}C$ value of young and old leaves observed subsequently (81, 120). Young leaves display rather more negative $\delta^{13}C$ values than old leaves, consistent with the limited dark CO_2 fixation capacity of young leaves in other CAM plants (57).

A wider appreciation of the indicator significance of $\delta^{13}C$ values in CAM plants in different environments is rapidly emerging. In the stem succulents studied under desert conditions, $\delta^{13}C$ values are uniformly in the vicinity of $-11‰$ (44, 141), indicating that these plants seldom if ever engage in net fixation of external CO_2 in the light, consistent with gas exchange studies under field conditions (143). Under more mesic conditions the stem succulent *Opuntia inermis* displays prolonged periods of significant CO_2 fixation in the light, and $\delta^{14}C$ values ranging from $-11.6‰$ to $-18.1‰$ have been recorded (115; C. B. Osmond, unpublished data). In *Welwitschia mirabilis* $\delta^{13}C$ values range from $-17.4‰$ in the most arid sites of the Namib desert to $-23.3‰$ in adjacent grassland (133). Comparisons between species of leaf succulents in the European Alps and in California suggest that the $\delta^{13}C$ value is least negative in the most arid sites and more negative in the mesic sites, as would be predicted (123, 156). A survey of $\delta^{13}C$ values indicated that European members of the genus *Sedum,* which are widely employed as CAM plants in laboratory experiments, do not engage in significant dark CO_2 fixation in relatively arid alpine habitats (123). This result was subsequently confirmed by an examination of the environmental conditions required for the expression of CAM in these plants (M. Kluge, unpublished). A survey of African leaf succulents capable of CAM shows that the $\delta^{13}C$ value of reproductive tissues is generally less negative than that of vegetative tissues (98), which may indicate that sexual reproduction takes place at a time of water stress. Such observations provide much wider insights into optional CO_2 fixation pathways of CAM plants in the ecological context. Whether it proves possible to use $\delta^{13}C$ value, total carbon, as an indicator of the growth and reproductive strategies of CAM plants under natural conditions can be determined only after much more extensive and intensive field observation.

CONCLUSIONS

During the last decade or so, access to controlled growth facilities, to the infrared gas analyzer, and to modern techniques for measuring H_2O exchange have greatly broadened our perception of the flexible photosynthetic carbon assimilation system that is CAM. In particular, research has been extended to field conditions so that the tuning of these flexible responses to particular environmental conditions has been accurately placed into context. This brief review shows, I think, how the mainstreams of crassulacean acid metabolism have been more accurately mapped and how many of the curiosities of 1960 have now given way to others. The further development of our knowledge of CAM will depend very much on finding the right plant, the "spinach chloroplast" equivalent, in which the intricacies of enzyme localization and regulation can be assessed. It is even more important perhaps to develop a satisfactory account of the malic acid transport system at the tonoplast and the relationship between acid transport and cell water relations. The paramount importance of plant and soil water relations in determining the expression and induction of CAM is obvious. More attention to these aspects is essential in future laboratory and field experiments. It is possible that most rapid progress will emerge from studies of the inducible CAM described in *Mesembryanthemum* and other species. Nehemia Grew (49) may well have given us the first word on CAM, but it is likely that he had it in mind when offering the last:

"How far, I promife not; the way is long and dark: and as travellers fometimes amongft Mountains, by gaining the top of one, are fo far from their Journeys end; that they only come to fee another lies before them: fo the way of *Nature*, is fo impervious, and, as I may fay, down Hill and up Hill, that how far forever we go, yet the furmounting of one difficulty is wont ftill to give us the profpect of another."

ACKNOWLEDGMENTS

I am grateful to P. N. Avadhani for introducing me to the problems of CAM, to many colleagues for access to papers currently in press, and to J. A. M. Holtum for furnishing unpublished data.

Literature Cited

1. Allaway, W. G., Austin, B., Slatyer, R. O. 1974. Carbon dioxide and water vapour exchange parameters of photosynthesis in a Crassulacean plant *Kalanchoë daigremontiana*. *Aust. J. Plant Physiol.* 1:399–405
2. Allaway, W. G., Osmond, C. B., Troughton, J. H. 1974. Environmental regulation of growth, photosynthetic pathway and carbon isotope discrimination ratio in plants capable of crassulacean acid metabolism. In *Mechanisms of Regulation of Plant Growth*, ed. R. L. Bieleski, A. R. Ferguson, M. M. Cresswell, pp. 195–205. Wellington: Bull. 12 R. Soc. N.Z. 934 pp.
3. Avadhani, P. N., Osmond, C. B., Tan, K. K. 1971. Crassulacean acid metabolism and the C$_4$ pathway of photosynthesis in succulent plants. See Ref. 52, pp. 288–93
4. Badger, M. R., Andrews, T. J., Osmond, C. B. 1974. Detection in C$_3$, C$_4$ and CAM plant leaves of a low-K_m (CO$_2$) form of RuDP carboxylase, having high RuDP oxygenase activity at physiological pH. *Proc. 3rd Int. Congr., Photosynth.* ed. M. Avron, 2:1421–29. Amsterdam: Elsevier. 2194 pp.
5. Bartholomew, B. 1973. Drought response in the gas exchange of *Dudleya farinosa* (Crassulaceae) grown under natural conditions. *Photosynthetica* 7:114–20
6. Bartholomew, D. P., Kadzimin, S. B. 1975. The eco-physiology of pineapple. In *Ecophysiology of Tropical Crops*, ed. P. T. Alvim, 1:1–58. Bahia: CEPLAC

7. Bartholomew, D. P., Kadzimin, S. B. 1976. Porometer cup to measure leaf resistance of pineapple. *Crop Sci.* 16:565–68

8. Begg, J. E., Turner, N. C. 1976. Crop water deficits. *Adv. Agron.* 28:161–217

9. Bender, M. M. 1968. Mass spectrometric studies of carbon-13 variations in corn and other grasses. *Radiocarbon* 10:468–72

10. Bender, M. M., Rouhani, I., Vines, H. M, Black, C. C. 1973. $^{13}C/^{12}C$ ratio changes in crassulacean acid metabolism plants. *Plant Physiol.* 52:427–30

11. Bennett-Clark, T. A. 1933. The role of organic acids in plant metabolism. *New Phytol.* 32:37–71

12. Björkman, O. 1973. Comparative studies on photosynthesis in higher plants. In *Current Topics in Photobiology, Photochemistry and Photophysiology,* ed. A. Giese, 8:1–63. New York: Academic

13. Black, C. C., Williams, S. 1976. Plants exhibiting characteristics common to crassulacean acid metabolism. See Ref. 26 pp. 407–24

14. Bradbeer, J. W. 1963. Physiological studies on acid metabolism in green plants IX. The distribution of ^{14}C in malate of darkened *Kalanchoë* leaf fragments after infiltration with labelled pyruvate. *Proc. R. Soc. London, Ser. B* 157:279–89

15. Bradbeer, J. W. 1975. A personal assessment of the state of knowledge of crassulacean acid metabolism (CAM). See Ref. 90, pp. 369–71

16. Bradbeer, J. W., Cockburn, W., Ranson, S. L. 1975. The labelling of the carboxyl carbon atoms of malate in *Kalanchoë crenata* leaves. See Ref. 90, pp. 265–72

17. Bradbeer, J. W., Ranson, S. L. 1963. Physiological studies on acid metabolism in green plants. VII. The utilization of labelled pyruvate, formate and glucose in *Kalanchoë* leaves in the dark. *Proc. R. Soc. London, Ser. B* 157: 257–89

18. Bradbeer,J. W., Ranson, S. L., Stiller, M. L. 1958. Malate synthesis in Crassulacean leaves. I. The distribution of ^{14}C in malate of leaves exposed to $^{14}CO_2$ in the dark. *Plant Physiol.* 33:66–70

19. Brandon, P. C. 1967. Temperature features of enzymes affecting crassulacean acid metabolism. *Plant Physiol.* 42: 977–84

20. Brandon, P. C. 1969. Artifacts in intracellular enzyme distribution caused by alkaline homogenates. *Plant Physiol.* 44:461–62

21. Brandon, P. C., van Boekel-Mol, T. N. 1973. Properties of purified malic enzyme in relation to crassulacean acid metabolism. *Eur. J. Biochem.* 35:62–69

22. Brulfert, J., Guerrier, D., Queiroz, O. 1973. Photoperiodism and enzyme activity : balance between inhibition and induction of the crassulacean acid metabolism. *Plant Physiol.* 51:220–22

23. Brulfert, J., Guerrier, D., Queiroz, O. 1975. Photoperiodism and enzyme rhythms. Kinetic characteristics of the photoperiodic induction of crassulacean acid metabolism. *Planta* 125:33–44

24. Brunnhöfer, H., Schaub, H., Egle, K. 1968. Der Verlauf des CO_2- und O_2- Gaswechsels bei *Bryophyllum daigremontianum* in Abhängigkeit von der Temperatur. *Z. Pflanzenphysiol.* 59: 285–92

25. Brunnhöfer, H., Schaub, H., Egle, K. 1968. Die Beziehungen zwischen den Veränderungen der Malat-und Stärkekonzentrationen und dem CO_2- und O_2- Gaswechsel bei *Bryophyllum daigremontianum.* *Z. Pflanzenphysiol.* 60: 12–18

26. Burris, R. H., Black, C. C. 1976. CO_2 *Metabolism and Plant Productivity.* Baltimore: Univ. Park Press. 431 pp.

27. Caldwell, M. M., White, R. S., Moore, R. T., Camp, L. B. 1977. Carbon balance, productivity and water use of cold winter desert shrub communities dominated by C_3 and C_4 species. *Oecologia* 29:275–300

28. Christeller, J. T., Laing, W. A., Troughton, J. H. 1976. Isotope discrimination by ribulose-1,5-diphosphate carboxylase. No effect of temperature of HCO_3^- concentration. *Plant Physiol.* 57:580–82

29. Cockburn, W., McAulay, A. 1975. The pathway of carbon dioxide formation in Crassulacean plants. *Plant Physiol.* 55: 87–89

30. Cockburn, W., McAulay, A. 1977. Changes in metabolite levels in *Kalanchoë daigremontiana* and the regulation of malic acid accumulation in crassulacean metabolism. *Plant Physiol.* 59:455–58

31. Conde, L. F., Kramer, P. J. 1975. The effect of vapour pressure deficit on diffusion resistance in *Opuntia compressa.* *Can. J. Bot.* 53:2933–26

32. Crews, C. E., Vines, H. M., Black, C. C. 1975. Post illumination burst of carbon

dioxide in crassulacean acid metabolism
plants. *Plant Physiol.* 55:652–57
33. Crews, C. E., Williams, S. L., Vines, H.
M., Black, C. C. 1976. Changes in the
metabolism and physiology of crassulacean acid metabolism plants grown
in controlled environments. See Ref. 26.
pp. 235–50
34. Davies, D. D. 1973. Control of and by
pH. *Symp. Soc. Exp. Biol.* 27:513–29
35. de Fekete, M. A. R. 1968. Die Rolle der
Phosphorylase im Stoffwechsel der
Stärke in Plastiden. *Planta* 79:208–21
36. Deleens, E., Garnier-Dardart, J. 1977.
Carbon isotope composition of biochemical fractions isolated from leaves
of *Bryophyllum daigremontianum*
Berger, a plant with crassulacean acid
metabolism: some physiological aspects
related to CO_2 dark fixation. *Planta*
135:241–48
37. Deleens, E., Lerman, J. C., Nato, A.,
Moyse, A. 1974. Carbon isotope discrimination by the carboxylating reactions in C_3, C_4 and CAM plants. *Proc.
3rd Int. Congr. Photosynth.,* ed. M. Avron, 2:1267–76. Amsterdam: Elsevier.
2194 pp.
38. Denius, H. R., Homann, P. H. 1972. The
relation between photosynthesis, respiration and crassulacean acid metabolism in leaf slices of *Aloe arborescens*
Mill. *Plant Physiol.* 49:873–80
39. Despain, D. G., Bliss, L. C., Boyer, J. S.
1970. Carbon dioxide exchange in
suguaro seedlings. *Ecology* 51:912–14
40. Dittrich, P. 1976. Nicotinamide
adeninedinucleotide-specific "malic"
enzyme in *Kalanchoë daigremontiana*
and other plants exhibiting crassulacean acid metabolism. *Plant Physiol.*
57:310–14
41. Dittrich, P. 1976. Equilibration of label
in malate during dark fixation of CO_2 in
Kalanchoë fedtschenkoi. Plant Physiol.
58:288–91
42. Dittrich, P., Campbell, W. H., Black, C.
C. 1973. Phosphoenolpyruvate carboxykinase in plants exhibiting crassulacean acid metabolism. *Plant Physiol.*
52:357–61
43. Dittrich, P., Huber, W. 1974. Carbon
dioxide metabolism in members of the
Chlamydospermae. *Proc. 3rd Int.
Congr. Photosynth.,* ed. M. Avron,
2:1573–78. Amsterdam: Elsevier.
2194 pp.
44. Eickmeier, W. G., Bender, M. M. 1976.
Carbon isotope ratios of crassulacean
acid metabolism species in relation to

climate and phytosociology. *Oecologia*
25:341–47
45. Evans, L. T. 1971. Evolutionary, adaptive and environmental aspects of the
photosynthetic pathway: assessment.
See Ref 52 pp. 130–36
46. Garnier-Dardart, J. 1965. Activities en-
zymatiques des chloroplastes isoles de
feuilles de *Bryophyllum daigremontianum* Berger: oxydation des hexoses,
formation et degradation d'acide
malique. *Physiol. Veg.* 3:215–27
47. Garnier-Dardart, J., Queiroz, O. 1974.
Malic enzyme in the leaves of *Bryophyllum daigremontianum. Phytochemistry*
13:1695–1700
48. Gregory, F. G., Spear, I., Thimann, K.
V. 1954. The interrelation between
CO_2 metabolism and photoperiodism in
Kalanchoë. Plant Physiol. 29:220–29
49. Grew, N. 1682. *An Idea of a Philofoph-
ical Hiftory of Plants.* London: Royal
Society. 24 pp. 2nd ed.
50. Haidri, S. Z. A., Burris, R. H. 1955.
Incorporation of malic acid-2-^{14}C and
pyruvic acid-2-^{14}C into starch. *Plant
Physiol.* 30: Suppl. 4
51. Hartsock, T. L., Nobel, P. S. 1976. Wa-
tering converts a CAM plant to daytime
CO_2 uptake. *Nature* 262:574–76
52. Hatch, M. D., Osmond, C. B. 1976.
Compartmentation and metabolite
transport in C_4 photosynthesis. In *Encyclopedia of Plant Physiology,* new ser.,
ed. C. R. Stocking, U. Heber, 3:144–84.
Berlin: Springer. 517 pp.
53. Hatch, M. D., Osmond, C. B., Slatyer,
R. O., eds. 1971. *Photosynthesis and
Photorespiration.* New York: Wiley-
Interscience
54. Hattersley, P. W., Watson, L., Osmond,
C. B. 1977. In situ immunofluorescent
labelling of ribulose-1.5-bisphosphate
carboxylase in leaves of C_3 and C_4
plants. *Aust. J. Plant Physiol.* 4:523–39
55. Heber, U. 1974. Metabolite exchange
between chloroplasts and cytoplasm.
Ann. Rev. Plant Physiol. 25:393–421
56. Jensen, R. G., Bahr, J. A. 1977. Ribu-
lose-1,5-bisphosphate carboxylase-oxygenase. *Ann. Rev. Plant Physiol.* 28:
379–400
57. Jones, M. B. 1975. The effect of leaf age
on leaf resistance and CO_2 exchange of
the CAM plant *Bryophyllum fedtschenkoi. Planta* 123:91–96
58. Joshi, M. C., Boyer, J. S., Kramer, P. J.
1965. Growth, carbon dioxide exchange, transpiration and transpiration
ratio of pineapple. *Bot. Gaz.* 126:
174–79

59. Kapil, R. N., Pugh, T. D., Newcomb, E. H. 1975. Microbodies and an anomalous "microcylinder" in the ultrastructure of plants with crassulacean acid metabolism. *Planta* 124:231–44
60. Kaplan, A., Gale, J., Poljakoff-Mayber, A. 1976. Resolution of net dark fixation of carbon dioxide into its respiration and gross fixation components in *Bryophyllum daigremontianum*. *J. Exp. Bot.* 27:220–30
61. Kausch, W. 1965. Beziehungen zwischen Wurzelwachstum, Transpiration und CO_2-Gaswechsel bei einigen Kakteen. *Planta* 66:229–38
62. Kelly, G. J., Latzko, E., Gibbs, M. 1976. Regulatory aspects of photosynthetic carbon metabolism. *Ann. Rev. Plant Physiol.* 27:181–205
63. Khan, A. A., Tewari, C. P., Krishnan, P. S., Sanwal, G. G. 1970. Respiratory particles from cactus phylloclades. *Phytochemistry* 9:1423–31
64. Khan, A. A., Tewari, C. P., Krishnan, P. S., Sanwal, G. G. 1970. Diurnal variation in enzymic activities in subcellular fractions of cactus phylloclades. *Phytochemistry* 9:2097–104
65. Kluge, M. 1968. Untersuchungen über den Gaswechsel von *Bryophyllum* während der Lichtperiode. I. Zum Problem der CO_2-Abgabe.*Planta* 80:255–63
66. Kluge, M. 1969. Zur Analyse des CO_2-Austausches von Bryophyllum I. Messung der Änderung des Mengenverhältnisses einiger Phosphatverbindungen im Blattgewebe während bestimmter Phasen der Licht-Dunkel-Periode. *Planta* 85:160–70
67. Kluge, M. 1969. Zur Analyse des CO_2-Austausches von *Bryophyllum* II. Hemmung des nächtlichen Stärkeabbaus in CO_2 verarmter Atmosphäre. *Planta* 86:142–50
68. Kluge, M. 1969. Veränderliche Markierungsmuster bei $^{14}CO_2$-Fütterung von *Bryophyllum tubiflorum* zu verschiedenen Zeitpunkten der Hell/Dunkelperiode I. Die $^{14}CO_2$ Fixierung unter Belichtung. *Planta* 88:113–29
69. Kluge, M. 1976. Models of CAM regulation. See Ref. 26, pp. 205–16
70. Kluge, M., Bley, L., Schmid, R. 1975. Malate synthesis in crassulacean acid metabolism (CAM) via a double carboxylation? See Ref. 90, pp. 281–88
71. Kluge, M., Fischer, K. 1967. Über Zusammenhänge zwischen dem CO_2-Austausch und der Abgabe von Wasserdampf durch *Bryophyllum daigremontianum* Berg. *Planta* 77:212–23
72. Kluge, M., Heininger, B. 1973. Untersuchungen über den Efflux von Malat aus den Vacuolen der assimilierenden Zellen von *Bryophyllum* und mögliche Einflüsse dieses Vorganges auf den CAM. *Planta* 113:333–43
73. Kluge, M., Lange, O. L., von Eichmann, M., Schmid, R. 1973. Diurnaler Säurerhythmus bei *Tillandsia usneoides* : Untersuchungen über den Weg des Kohlenstoffs sowie die Abhängigkeit des CO_2-Gaswechsels von Lichtintensität, Temperatur und Wassergehalt der Pflanze. *Planta* 112:357–72
74. Kluge, M., Osmond, C. B. 1971. Pyruvate Pi dikinase in crassulacean acid metabolism. *Naturwissenschaften* 58:414–15
75. Kluge, M., Osmond, C. B. 1972. Studies on phosphoenolpyruvate carboxylase and other enzymes of crassulacean acid metabolism of *Bryophyllum tubiflorum* and *Sedum praealtum*. *Z. Pflanzenphysiol.* 66:97–105
76. Kluge, M., Ting, I. P. 1977. *Crassulacean Acid Metabolism: Ecological Studies.* Berlin: Springer. In press
77. Kunitake, G. M., Saltman, P. 1958. Dark fixation of CO_2 by succulent leaves: conservation of the dark fixed CO_2 under diurnal conditions. *Plant Physiol.* 34:123–27
78. Lange, O. L., Schulze, E. D., Kappen, L., Evenari, M., Buschbom, U. 1975. CO_2 exchange pattern under natural conditions of *Caralluma negevensis*, a CAM plant of the Negev Desert. *Photosynthetica* 9:318–26
79. Lerman, J. C. 1972. Carbon-14 dating: origin and correction of isotope fractionation errors in terrestrial living matter. *Proc. 8th Int. Congr. Radiocarbon Dating*, ed. T. A. Rafter, T. Grant-Taylor, pp. 1116–28. Wellington: R. Soc. N. Z.
80. Lerman, J. C. 1975. How to interpret variations in the carbon isotope ratio of plants: biologic and environmental effects. See Ref. 90, pp. 323–35
81. Lerman, J. C., Deleens, E., Nato, A., Moyse, A. 1974. Variation in the carbon isotope composition of a plant with crassulacean acid metabolism. *Plant Physiol.* 53:581–84
82. Lerman, J. C., Queiroz, O. 1974. Carbon fixation and isotope discrimination by a crassulacean plant: dependence on the photoperiod. *Science* 183:1207–9
83. Levi, C., Gibbs, M. 1975. Carbon dioxide fixation in isolated *Kalanchoë* chloroplasts. *Plant Physiol.* 56:164–66

84. Lorimer, G. H., Woo, K. C., Berry, J. A., Osmond, C. B. 1978. The C_2 photorespiratory carbon oxidation cycle: pathway and function. *Photosynthesis 77. Proc. 4th Int. Congr. Photosynth. Res.*, ed. D. O. Hall, pp. 311–22. Biochem. Soc. London

85. Lüttge, U., Ball, E. 1974. Proton and malate fluxes in cells of *Bryophyllum daigremontianum* leaf slices in relation to potential osmotic pressure of the medium. *Z. Pflanzenphysiol.* 73:326–38

86. Lüttge, U., Ball, E. 1977. Concentration and pH dependence of malate efflux and influx in leaf slices of CAM plants. *Z. Pflanzenphysiol.* 83:43–54

87. Lüttge, U., Ball, E. 1977. Water relation parameters of the CAM plant *Kalanchoë daigremontiana* in relation to diurnal malate oscillations. *Oecologia* 31:85–94

88. Lüttge, U., Kluge, M., Ball, E. 1975. Effects of osmotic gradients on vacuolar malic acid storage. A basic principle in oscillatory behaviour of crassulacean acid metabolism. *Plant Physiol.* 56: 613–16

89. MacLennan, D. H., Beevers, H., Harley, J. L. 1963. Compartmentation of acids in plant tissues. *Biochem. J.* 89:316–27

90. Marcelle, R. ed. 1975. *Environmental and Biological Control of Photosynthesis.* The Hague: Junk. 408 pp.

91. Marcelle, R. 1975. Effect of photoperiod on the CO_2 and O_2 exchanges in leaves of *Bryophyllum daigremontianum* (Berger). See Ref. 90, pp. 349–56

92. McWilliams, E. L. 1970. Comparative rates of dark CO_2 uptake and acidification in the Bromeliaceae, Orchidaceae and Euphorbiaceae. *Bot. Gaz.* 131: 285–90

93. Medina, E. 1974. Dark CO_2 fixation, habitat preference and evolution within the Bromeliaceae. *Evolution* 28:677–86

94. Medina, E., Delgado, M. 1976. Photosynthesis and night CO_2 fixation in *Echeveria columbiana* v. Poellritz. *Photosynthetica* 10:155–63

95. Meinzer, F. C., Rundel, P. W. 1973. Crassulacean acid metabolism and water use efficiency in *Echeveria pumila. Photosynthetica* 7:358–64

96. Milburn, T. R., Pearson, D. J., Ndegwe, N. A. 1968. Crassulacean acid metabolism under natural tropical conditions. *New Phytol.* 67:883–97

97. Mooney, H. A., Troughton, J. H., Berry, J. A. 1974. Arid climates and photosynthetic systems. *Carnegie Inst. Wash. Yearb.* 73:793–805

98. Mooney, H. A., Troughton, J. H., Berry, J. A. 1977. Carbon isotope ratio measurements of succulent plants in Southern Africa. *Oecologia* 30:295–306

99. Moradshahi, A., Vines, H. M., Black, C. C. 1977. CO_2 exchange and acidity levels in detached pineapple, *Ananas comosus* (L.), Merr., leaves during the day at various temperatures O_2 and CO_2 concentrations. *Plant Physiol.* 59:274–78

100. Moyse, A. 1955. La métabolisme des acides organiques chez le *Bryophyllum* (Crassulacée) II. Les variations de l'acidité et la photosynthèse, en fonction de la tension d'oxygène. *Physiol. Plant.* 8:478–92

101. Mukerji, S. K., Ting, I. P. 1968. Intercellular localization of CO_2 metabolism enzymes in cactus phylloclades. *Phytochemistry* 7:903–11

102. Mukerji, S. K., Ting, I. P. 1968. Malate dehydrogenese (decarboxylating) (NADP) isoenzymes of *Opuntia* stem tissue. *Biochim. Biophys. Acta* 167: 239–49

103. Nalborczyk, E., Lacroix, L. J., Hill, R. D. 1965. Environmental influence on light and dark CO_2 fixation by *Kalanchoë daigremontiana. Can. J. Bot.* 53:1132–38

104. Neales, T. F. 1973. Effect of night temperature on the assimilation of carbon dioxide by mature pineapple plants *Ananas comosus* (L.) Merr *Aust. J. Biol. Sci.* 26:539–46

105. Neales, T. F. 1973. The effect of night temperature on CO_2 assimilation, transpiration and water use efficiency in *Agave americana* L. *Aust. J. Biol. Sci.* 26:705–14

106. Neales, T. F. 1975. The gas exchange patterns of CAM plants. See Ref. 90, pp. 299–310

107. Neales, T. F., Hartney, V. J., Patterson, A. A. 1968. Physiological adaptation to drought in the carbon assimilation and water loss of xerophytes. *Nature* 219:469–72

108. Neales, T. F., Hew, C. S. 1975. Two types of carbon fixation in tropical orchids. *Planta* 123:303–6

109. Nishida, K. 1963. Studies on stomatal movement of crassulacean plants in relation to the acid metabolism. *Physiol. Plant.* 16:281–98

110. Nishida, K., Sanada, Y. 1977. Carbon dioxide fixation in chloroplasts isolated

from CAM plants. *Plant Cell Physiol.* Spec. Issue 3:341–46

111. Nobel, P. S. 1976. Water relations and photosynthesis of a desert CAM plant, *Agave deserti. Plant Physiol.* 58:576–82

112. Nobel, P. S. 1977. Water relations and photosynthesis of a barrel cactus, *Ferocactus acanthodes* in the Colorado desert. *Oecologia* 27:117–33

113. Nuernbergk, E. L. 1961. Endogener Rhythmus und CO_2-Stoffwechsel bei Pflanzen mit diurnalem Säurerhythmus. *Planta* 56:28–70

114. Osmond, C. B. 1974. Carbon reduction and photosystem II deficiency in leaves of C_4 plants. *Aust. J. Plant Physiol.* 1:41–50

115. Osmond, C. B. 1975. Environmental control of photosynthetic options in crassulacean plants. See Ref. 90, pp. 311–21

116. Osmond, C. B. 1976. Ion uptake and carbon metabolism in cells of higher plants. In *Encyclopedia of Plant Physiology,* new ser., ed. U. Lüttge, M. G. Pitman, 2a:345–72. Berlin: Springer. 400 pp.

117. Osmond, C. B. 1976. CO_2 assimilation and dissimilation in the light and dark in CAM plants. See Ref. 26, pp. 217–33

118. Osmond, C. B., Allaway, W. G. 1974. Pathways of CO_2 fixation in the CAM plant *Kalanchoë daigremontiana* I. Patterns of CO_2 fixation in the light. *Aust. J. Plant Physiol.* 1:503–11

119. Osmond, C. B., Allaway, W. G., Sutton, B. G., Troughton, J. H., Queiroz, O., Lüttge, U., Winter, K. 1973. Carbon isotope discrimination in photosynthesis of CAM plants. *Nature* 246:41–42

120. Osmond, C. B., Bender, M. M., Burris, R. H. 1976. Pathways of CO_2 fixation in the CAM plant *Kalanchoë daigremontiana* III. Correlation with $\delta^{13}C$ value during growth and water stress. *Aust. J. Plant Physiol.* 3:787–99

121. Osmond, C. B., Björkman, O. 1975. Pathways of CO_2 fixation in the CAM plant *Kalanchoë daigremontiana* II. Effects of O_2 and CO_2 concentration on light and dark CO_2 fixation. *Aust. J. Plant Physiol.* 2:155–62

122. Osmond, C. B., Laties, G. G. 1969. Compartmentation of malate in relation to ion absorption in beet. *Plant Physiol.* 44:7–14

123. Osmond, C. B., Ziegler, H., Stichler, W., Trimborn, P. 1975. Carbon isotope discrimination in alpine succulent plants supposed to be capable of crass-

ulacean acid metabolism (CAM). *Oecologia* 18:209–17

124. Pucher, G. W., Leavenworth, C. S., Ginter, W. D., Vickery, H. B. 1947. Studies on the metabolism of crassulacean plants: the effect upon the composition of *Bryophyllum calycinum* of the form in which nitrogen is supplied. *Plant Physiol.* 22:205–27

125. Queiroz, O. 1965. Sur le métabolisme acide des Crassulacées. Action à long terme de la température de nuit sur la synthèse d'acide malique par *Kalanchoë blossfeldiana* "Tom Thum" placée en jours courts. *Physiol. Vég.* 3:203–13

126. Queiroz, O. 1967. Recherche d'un modèle enzymatique pour le déterminisme de la désacidification diurne chez les Crassulacées. *C. R. Acad. Sci. Paris. Ser. D* 265:1928–31

127. Queiroz, O. 1968. Sur le métabolisme acide des Crassulacées. III. Variations d'activité enzymatique sous l'action du photopériodisme et du thermopériodisme. *Physiol. Vég.* 6:117–36

128. Queiroz, O. 1974. Circadian rhythms and metabolic patterns. *Ann. Rev. Plant Physiol.* 25:115–34

129. Queiroz, O. 1977. CAM: rhythms of enzyme capacity and activity as adaptive control mechanisms. In *Encyclopedia of Plant Physiology: Photosynthesis,* Vol. 2, ed. M. Gibbs, E. Latzko. Berlin: Springer. In press

130. Queiroz, O., Morel, C. 1974. Photoperiodism and enzyme activity. Towards a model for the control of circadian metabolic rhythms in the crassulacean acid metabolism. *Plant Physiol.* 54:596–602

131. Ranson, S. L., Thomas, M. 1960. Crassulacean acid metabolism. *Ann. Rev. Plant Physiol.* 11:81–110

132. Rouhani, I., Vines, H. M., Black, C. C. 1973. Isolation of mesophyll cells from *Sedum telephium* leaves. *Plant Physiol.* 51:97–103

133. Schulze, E.-D., Ziegler, H., Stichler, W. 1976. Environmental control of crassulacean acid metabolism in *Welwitschia mirabilis* Hook Fil. in its natural range of distribution in the Namib Desert. *Oecologia* 24:323–34

134. Smith, F. A., Raven, J. A. 1976. H^+ transport and regulation of cell pH. In *Encyclopedia of Plant Physiology* new ser., ed. U. Lüttge, M. G. Pitman. IIa:315–46. Berlin: Springer. 400 pp.

135. Somers, G. F. 1951. The influence of light, temperature and some enzyme poisons on the total organic acid content of leaf tissue of *Kalanchoë dai-*

gremontiana (Hamet et Perrier). *Plant Physiol.* 26:1–18

136. Sugiyama, T., Laetsch, W. M. 1975. Occurrence of pyruvate orthophosphate dikinase in the succulent plant, *Kalanchoë daigremontiana* Hamet et Perr. *Plant Physiol.* 56:605–7

137. Sutton, B. G. 1975. The path of carbon in CAM plants at night. *Aust. J. Plant Physiol.* 2:377–87

138. Sutton, B. G. 1975. Glycolysis in CAM plants. *Aust. J. Plant Physiol.* 2:389–402

139. Sutton, B. G. 1975. Kinetic properties of phosphorylase and phosphofructokinase of *Kalanchoë daigremontiana* and *Atriplex spongiosa.* *Aust. J. Plant Physiol.* 2:403–11

140. Sutton, B. G., Osmond, C. B. 1972. Dark fixation of CO_2 by Crassulacean plants: evidence for a single carboxylation step. *Plant Physiol.* 50:360–65

141. Sutton, B. G., Ting, I. P., Troughton, J. H. 1976. Seasonal effects on carbon isotope composition of cactus in a desert environment. *Nature* 261:42–43

142. Szarek, S. R., Johnson, H. B., Ting, I. P. 1973. Drought adaptation in *Opuntia basilaris.* Significance of recycling carbon through crassulacean acid metabolism. *Plant Physiol.* 52:539–41

143. Szarek, S. R., Ting, I. P. 1974. Seasonal patterns of acid metabolism and gas exchange in *Opuntia basilaris.* *Plant Physiol.* 54:76–81

144. Szarek, S. R., Ting, I. P. 1975. Photosynthetic efficiency of CAM plants in relation to C_3 and C_4 plants. See Ref. 90, pp. 289–97

145. Szarek, S. R., Ting, I. P. 1975. Physiological responses to rainfall in *Opuntia basilaris* (Cactaceae). *Am. J. Bot.* 62:602–9

146. Szarek, S. R., Ting, I. P. 1977. The occurrence of crassulacean acid metabolism among plants. *Photosynthetica.* In press

147. Ting, I. P. 1971. Nonautotrophic CO_2 fixation and crassulacean acid metabolism. See Ref. 52, pp. 169–85

148. Ting, I. P. 1975. Crassulacean acid metabolism in natural ecosystems in relation to annual CO_2 uptake patterns and water utilization. See Ref. 26, pp. 251–68

149. Ting, I. P., Dugger, W. M. 1968. Nonautotrophic carbon dioxide metabolism in cacti. *Bot. Gaz.* 129:9–15

150. Ting, I. P., Hanscom, Z. 1977. Induction of acid metabolism in *Portulacaria afra. Plant Physiol.* 59:511–14

151. Ting, I. P., Johnson, H. B., Szarek, S. R. 1972. Net CO_2 fixation in crassulacean acid metabolism plants. In *Net Carbon Dioxide Assimilation in Higher Plants,* ed. C. C. Black, pp. 26–53. Mobile: South. Sect. Am. Soc. Plant Physiol./ Cotton

152. Ting, I. P., Osmond, C. B. 1973. Activation of plant P-enolpyruvate carboxylase by glucose-6-phosphate: a particular role in crassulacean acid metabolism. *Plant Sci. Lett.* 1:123–28

153. Treichel, S. 1975. Crassulaceensäurestoffwechsel bei einem salztoleranten Vertreter der Aizoaceae: *Apentia cordifolia. Plant Sci. Lett.* 4:141–44

154. Treichel, S., Bauer, P. 1974. Unterschiedliche NaCl-Abhängigkeit des tagesperiodischen CO_2-Gaswechsels bei einigen halisch wachsenden Küstenpflanzen. *Oecologia* 17:87–93

155. Troughton, J. H. 1971. Aspects of the evolution of the photosynthetic carboxylation reaction in plants. See Ref. 52 pp. 124–29

156. Troughton, J. H., Mooney, H. A., Berry, J. A., Verity, D. 1977. Variable carbon isotope ratios of *Dudleya* species growing in natural habitats. *Oecologia* 30:307–12

157. Troughton, J. H., Wells, P. V., Mooney, H. A. 1974. Photosynthetic mechanisms and paleoecology from carbon isotope ratios in ancient specimens of C_4 and CAM plants. *Science* 185: 610–12

158. Vieweg, G. H., De Fekete, M. A. R. 1977. Tagesgang der Amylasenaktivität in Blatt von *Kalanchoë daigremontiana. Z. Pflanzenphysiol.* 81:74–79

159. Von Willert, D. J., Treichel, S., Kirst, G. O., Curdts, E. 1976. Environmentally controlled changes of phosphoenolpyruvate carboxylases in *Mesembryanthemum. Phytochemistry* 15: 1435–36

160. Walker, D. A. 1962. Pyruvate carboxylation and plant metabolism. *Biol. Rev.* 37:215–56

161. Walker, D. A. 1976. Plastids and intracellular transport. In *Encyclopedia of Plant Physiology,* new ser., ed. C. R. Stocking, U. Heber 3:85–136. Berlin: Springer. 517 pp.

162. Welch, W. R. 1938. Water relations of *Bryophyllum calycinum* subjected to severe drying. *Plant Physiol.* 13:469–87

163. Whelan, T., Sackett, W. M., Benedict, C. R. 1973. Enzymatic fractionation of carbon isotopes by phosphoenolpyru-

vate carboxylase from C_4 plants. *Plant Physiol.* 51:1051–54

164. Wiebe, H. H., Al-Saadi, H. A. 1976. Matric bound water of water tissue from succulents. *Physiol. Plant.* 36: 47–51

165. Wilkins, M. B. 1959. An endogenous rhythm in the rate of carbon dioxide output of *Bryophyllum* I. Some preliminary experiments. *J. Exp. Bot.* 10: 377–90

166. Wilkins, M. B. 1967. An endogenous rhythm in the rate of carbon dioxide output in *Bryophyllum* V. The dependence of rhythmicity upon aerobic metabolism. *Planta* 72:66–77

167. Wilkinson, M. J., Smith, H. 1976. Properties of phosphoenolpyruvate carboxylase from *Bryophyllum fedtschenkoi* leaves and fluctuations in carboxylase activity during the endogenous rhythm of carbon dioxide output. *Plant Sci. Lett.* 6:319–24

168. Winter, J., Kandler, O. 1976. Misleading data on isotope distribution in malate-^{14}C from CAM plants caused by fumarase activity of *Lactobacillus plantarum*. *Z. Pflanzenphysiol.* 78:103–12

169. Winter, K. 1973. CO_2-Fixieringsreaktionen bei der Salzpflanze *Mesembryanthemum crystallinum* unter variierten Aussenbedingungen. *Planta* 114: 75–85

170. Winter, K. 1974. Evidence for the significance of crassulacean acid metabolism as an adaptive mechanism to water stress. *Plant Sci. Lett.* 3:279–81

171. Winter, K. 1974. Einfluss von Wasserstress auf die Aktivität der Phosphoenolpyruvat-Carboxylase bei *Mesembryanthemum crystallinum*. *Planta* 121: 147–53

172. Winter, K. 1974. NaCl-induzierter Crassulaceen-Säurestoffwechsel bei der Salzpflanze *Mesembryanthemum crystallinum*. Abhängigkeit des CO_2-Gaswechsels von der Tag/Nacht Temperatur und von der Wasserversorgung der Pflanzen. *Oecologia* 15:383–92

173. Winter, K., Lüttge, U. 1976. Balance between C_3 and CAM pathway of photosynthesis. In *Water and Plant Life,* ed. O. L. Lange, L. Kappen, E.-D. Schulze, pp. 321–33. Berlin: Springer. 536 pp.

174. Winter, K., Von Willert, D. J. 1972. NaCl-induzierter Crassulaceensäurestoffwechsel bei *Mesembryanthemum crystallinum*. *Z. Pflanzenphysiol.* 267: 166–70

175. Winter, K., Troughton, J. H. 1978. Photosynthetic pathways in plants of coastal and inland habitats of Israel and the Sinai. *Flora* 167:1–34

176. Wolf, J. 1960. Der diurnale Säurerhythmus. In *Encyclopedia of Plant Physiology,* ed. W. Ruhland, 12(2):809–89. Berlin: Springer. 1421 pp.

177. Wong, S. C., Hew, C. S. 1976. Diffusive resistance, titratable acidity and CO_2 fixation in two tropical epiphytic ferns. *Am. Fern J.* 66:121–24

Ann. Rev. Plant Physiol. 1978. 29:415–36
Copyright © 1978 by Annual Reviews Inc. All rights reserved

REGULATORY MECHANISMS IN MEIOTIC CROSSING-OVER

✦7657

Herbert Stern and Yasuo Hotta

Department of Biology, University of California, San Diego, La Jolla, California 92093

CONTENTS

INTRODUCTION AND BACKGROUND

Meiosis is the seat of genetic recombination and of the reductional division of chromosome sets. In the case of plants it is also the channel leading into the gametophyte stage during which gametes are produced. Each of these aspects of the reproductive process imposes its special metabolic and structural requirements on the meiotic cell. The course of metabolism in a meiocyte giving rise to an embryo sac is therefore different from one giving rise to pollen. The megaspore develops a large cytoplasm designed to meet the needs of the embryo sac; the microspore initiates its haploid life with a fresh metabolic apparatus that develops the necessary reserves for pollen grain germination and growth. For those interested in comparative biology it is instructive to compare the late meiotic metabolism in a microsporocyte with that in a spermatocyte. On the whole, the metabolic activity of a microsporocyte declines during meiotic prophase whereas that of a spermatocyte rises, showing a very high rate of RNA synthesis during pachytene (10, 41). Microsporocytes have no need to anticipate all postmeiotic needs because their products have active haploid genomes; by contrast, spermatocytes must do so because the genomes of the postmeiotic spermatids are rendered inactive until after fertilization. To do justice to the full span of meiotic metabolism in this review would be

415

0066-4154/78/0701-0415$01.00

impossible. Our aim is to assess the available information on the topic of meiotic crossing-over. It is one function of a meiotic cell that lends itself to generalizations spanning both plant and animal kingdoms.

Recombination is currently a subject of high interest because of recently developed techniques for inserting DNA segments into heterologous genomes. The success achieved with microbial systems coupled with the evidence that viral sequences may be naturally present in some eukaryotic genomes (7) have generated the hope that genetic recombination may be achieved, especially in plants, without the normal channels of sexual reproduction. Whether the techniques prove as feasible for genetic manipulations in higher plants as in bacteria remains to be seen. Molecular mechanisms for joining or inserting DNA fragments are probably universal, but the conditions under which these mechanisms operate vary with genomic complexity. The meiocyte of a flowering plant is specialized for crossing-over and is appropriately programmed for the purpose, a programming that is absent from all other cells in the plant. Only in meiocytes are the genes essential to the meiotic process coordinately expressed. Within that process, recombinational mechanisms identified in microbial organisms constitute an essential but insufficient system for crossing-over.

In achieving crossing-over, meiocytes of higher eukaryotes display the following characteristics: 1. Chromosomes rarely interlock in the course of contraction and pairing despite their relatively tight packing within a nucleus. 2. Crossing-over is an infrequent event at any particular site in a chromosome. It is also unevenly distributed along a chromosome; heterochromatic regions rarely undergo crossing-over. 3. When two or more crossovers occur in a chromosome their position relative to each other is not random. A crossover in one region of a chromosome precludes the occurrence of a second in its immediate vicinity.

The textbook impression that crossovers somehow occur randomly along chromosomes is dimmed by the evidence for a stringent organization of the meiotic process. It is now apparent from studies of both lilies and mice that the metabolism of a meiocyte is rigorously programmed and that specific elements of the chromosome are involved in the programming (22). Using *Lilium* as a model, the program may be summarized as follows: there are three intervals of DNA synthesis in a meiocyte—an attenuated S-phase, a delayed replication associated with chromosome pairing during zygotene, and a repair synthesis during pachytene. The details of these various intervals have been discussed recently, and the interested reader is referred to a number of highly informative articles prepared for a Royal Society symposium (49, 56). This review is directed at the nature and regulation of those mechanisms that directly support crossing-over.

THE MOLECULAR SETTING FOR CROSSING-OVER

(Note: Crossovers are generally identified by genetic analysis as a recombination between linked genes. A less precise and also less rigorous method for identifying crossovers is by cytological analysis of chiasma formation. The latter method has been widely used in plant studies, especially where there is a dearth of genetic markers. *Zea mays* is an outstanding example of an organism in which the two methods have been used in combination, and it is the best source of cytogenetic information on meiosis. In this review we will not distinguish between the two methods; the absence of chiasmata will be interpreted as an absence of crossing-over.)

A simplified definition of a crossover is a reciprocal exchange of precisely corresponding segments between two homologous chromatids. Where detailed genetic analysis of a crossover region has proved feasible, as is the case for tetrad analysis in yeast and other fungi, the event has been found to be more complex than what is suggested by the simplified definition. Single-strand breakage, heteroduplex formation, excision, and resynthesis of the excised DNA over distances up to 2000 nucleotides have been implicated by the genetic evidence (13). The pattern of resynthesis has been and continues to be a crucial issue in constructing molecular models of recombination. If the respective DNA sequences of chromosomes are heterozygous at the crossover site, pairing of complementary strands from the different chromosomes would result in heteroduplex formation. If excision occurs in the heteroduplex region, resynthesis of the excised strand would result in a sequence complementary to the intact one and thus different from the original one, a phenomenon that has long been recognized as "gene conversion." A wealth of information on the characteristics of conversion has accumulated in recent years, but the material is beyond the scope of this review. Although the precise relationship between gene conversion and reciprocal crossing-over is still unsettled, current molecular models of recombination are designed to accommodate both (18, 37).

The diagram in Figure 1 illustrates the kinds of molecular events that probably accompany recombination. The scheme is not intended to summarize the present state of the field, but rather to serve as background for readers who are unfamiliar with current deliberations on the molecular aspects of recombination. Crossing-over in eukaryotes probably involves many, if not all, of the events depicted in the figure; the problem is to determine how they are organized in more complex genomes. Molecular studies of meiosis in higher eukaryotes are mainly addressed to the nature of the organization, emphasis being given to supportive processes rather than to the ultimate steps in recombination.

THE INTRODUCTION OF CHROMOSOME BREAKS

Crossing-over, as shown in Figure 1, requires and probably begins with a breakage of DNA. It is generally assumed that such breaks are single-stranded, a condition that retains the intact strand to serve as template for restoring the broken one and thus to preserve the linear integrity of the chromosome. This assumption is sustained by observations of DNA behavior during meiosis. A significant number of double-stranded cuts has not been detected in physical analyses of DNA from different stages of meiosis (24). By contrast, strong evidence has been adduced for the transient occurrence of single-stranded nicks during meiosis in yeast, lilies, and mice (6, 21, 28, 56). In lilies and also in mice it has been found that nicking of DNA is temporally regulated and occurs at pachytene after completion of chromosome pairing. Some overlapping between pairing and nicking may occur, but analytical procedures are not precise enough to establish such a relation. When single-strand sedimentation profiles from different meiotic stages are compared, the distinctiveness of pachytene is apparent. Those from pachytene are bimodal, whereas those from other stages are unimodal (24). The slower sedimenting component in the pachytene profiles has a molecular weight of about 48×10^6 daltons or 160 kilobases (kb). It is interesting, though possibly coincidental, that the mean size of the slower sedimenting fragments should be the same in lily and mouse even though their

Mechanisms in Recombination

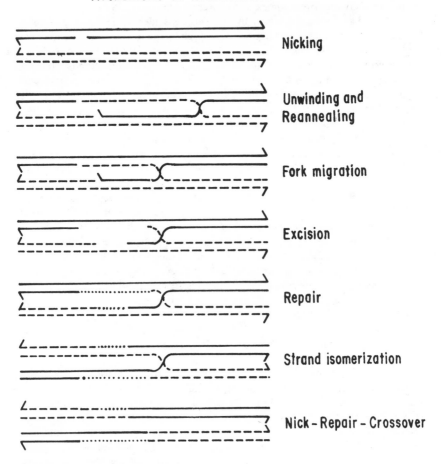

Figure 1   The various diagrams of molecular mechanisms are intended only to provide a perspective on the kinds of events that must ultimately occur in chromosomes to achieve crossing-over. Many excellent discussions of models are available (18, 37).

genome sizes differ by a factor of 17. It would appear that the average distance between nicks is approximately fixed and that meiocytes with smaller genomes have a smaller number of total nicks.

The nicking of DNA at pachytene most probably furnishes substrate for the crossing-over process. Presumably, accumulation of accidentally generated nicks is inadequate for assuring the regularity of meiotic crossing-over. It is unlikely, however, that the inadequacy is a function of the number of nicks formed. If four single-strand breaks are required per crossover, a *Lilium* microsporocyte would need approximately one nick for every 30×10^8 nucleotides to form 36 chiasmata. So low a frequency of breaks would be difficult to establish experimentally, and could probably be achieved in most cells at any given time by inhibiting repair mechanisms. The fact that the actual number of nicks exceeds the required number by about 10^4 suggests a much more extensive arrangement for crossing-over than could be provided by randomly generated nicks.

Nicking is effected by an endonuclease which, on the basis of in vitro measurements, begins to increase at the time that chromosome pairing begins, and reaches a maximum at the end of zygotene or beginning of pachytene (27). The enzyme acts only on double-stranded DNA (ds-DNA) and produces only single-strand nicks having 3'-phosphoryl and 5'-hydroxyl termini. Analyses of terminal residues in DNA isolated at different meiotic stages show that only at pachytene do the numbers of 5'-OH termini exceed the 5'-P ones; the ratio is reversed at all other stages as it is in somatic tissues (56). Only if pachytene cells are irradiated does the DNA have 5'-OH/5'-P ratios similar to those found at other stages. The evidence is thus fairly compelling that the increased endonuclease activity measured in vitro is the agent of nick formation observed in vivo.

It is difficult to be precise about the fraction of DNA attacked by endonuclease because rapidly repaired nicks would escape detection. Indeed, most of the single-stranded interruptions detected are gaps rather than nicks (Figure 2). If nicks alone were the source of the slower sedimenting ss-DNA, they would disappear after treating pachytene nuclei with ligase alone rather than with ligase in the presence of DNA polymerase. The widespread occurrence of gaps at pachytene indicates that endonuclease must be accompanied by exonuclease activity. Since the endonuclease is known to form 3'-P termini, and since the gaps in pachytene DNA have a preponderance of such termini, it is probable that the nicks are converted into gaps by an exonuclease which excises in a 5'-3' direction.

THE REGULATION OF DNA BREAKAGE

If the occurrence of DNA nicking at pachytene is determined by the time of endonuclease synthesis, enzyme formation would have to be coordinated with the process of homolog pairing. That such coordination exists is patent, but certain studies show that the time of endonuclease formation is not sufficient to determine the occurrence of nicking. The action of endonuclease in vivo seems to be governed by the achievement of effective pairing between homologous chromosomes. In the absence of such pairing, nicking activity is low or absent. The relationship is revealed by studies of the achiasmatic lily hybrid "Black Beauty" (24). As is true for many hybrids, failure to form chiasmata is attributable to insufficient homology for pairing between parental chromosomes. However, the aspect of pairing affected by non-homology is uncertain. Pairing can and frequently does occur between nonhomologous chromosomes and between nonhomologous regions of otherwise homologous chromosomes. Such heterologous pairing has been fully documented in cytological analyses of corn microsporocytes (31, 32). It may be argued that heterologous pairing is not normal, and this may indeed be the case. However, electron microscope analyses of such paired regions reveal no structural abnormalities in the synaptonemal complex (15, 47). Since inadequate homology leads to chiasma failure, even under conditions of apparently normal pairing, we prefer to assign the failure to a lack of "effective pairing," a term that was coined many years ago (46). We thus avoid specifying a particular aspect of the pairing process that leads to an absence of nicking, while retaining the specific functional relationships between homology, nicking, and chiasma formation.

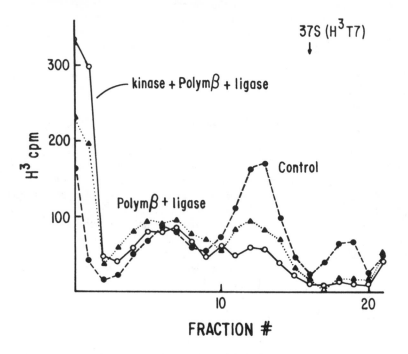

Figure 2 Sedimentation behavior of ss-DNA after treating isolated pachytene nuclei in the following ways: DNA ligase alone; ligase + nuclear DNA β-polymerase; ligase + polymerase + polynucleotide kinase. The "control" curve applies to nuclei incubated with and without DNA ligase. Ligase alone has no significant action in reducing the lower molecular weight component as would occur if nicks were sealed. DNA from T7 bacteriophage serves as marker in the upper region of the gradient. Except for meiotic stage, the experiment is identical with the one demonstrating a presence of gaps in Z-DNA (26).

The near absence of pachytene nicking in achiasmatic microsporocytes is evident from ss-DNA sedimentation profiles which show 1/10th of the usual amount of slow sedimenting component, a value that is commensurate with the low frequency of chiasma formation (24). Since all chromosomes pair and form chiasmata in the amphidiploid of Black Beauty (12), we presume that general nicking occurs once the homology for effective pairing is provided. If so, effectiveness of pairing must control either formation of the enzyme or its activity in vivo. That question has been resolved by assaying for endonuclease activity in the microsporocytes of the achiasmatic hybrid. The levels of in vitro activity, including the cyclical pattern, are essentially the same for achiasmatic and chiasmatic forms (unpublished).

The transient formation of endonuclease activity would thus seem to be an invariant feature of the meiotic program. It is timed to coincide with chromosome pairing but is unaffected by whether or not pairing occurs. It may be concluded that under in vivo conditions chromosomal DNA becomes susceptible to endonuclease action only if the chromosomes are effectively paired. The concept of effectively paired chromosomes having a different enzyme susceptibility from unpaired ones is fundamental. Regardless of the mechanism involved, the relationship implies that certain structural interactions associated with pairing can regulate metabolic interactions. If so, the pairing of chromosomes to facilitate crossing-over by juxtaposing homologous segments would be only one function of the paired state; a second function would be to permit effective interactions between chromosomes and enzymes essential to the occurrence of crossing-over. Whether the effective interactions precede or follow synaptonemal complex formation is beyond the reach of current biochemical studies, but it is an important issue that bears on the criticisms raised by Maguire and others concerning the common assumption that crossing-over follows completion of chromosome pairing (32, 33).

Recently the relationship between endonuclease action and chromosome pairing was further studied in a collaborative effort (with Michael Bennett from the Plant Breeding Institute at Cambridge, England, and Luis Antonio Toledo from the Faculdade de Ciencias Medicas e Biologicas de Botucato, Sao Paulo, Brazil). The aim of the study was to determine directly whether promotion of effective chromosome pairing in the achiasmatic diploid hybrid would lead to DNA nicking. The approach used was to double the number of chromosomes in the microsporocytes by administering colchicine to flower buds of Black Beauty in situ during premeiotic mitosis. Chromosomes in tetraploid microsporocytes would be expected to form chiasmata and, if the proposed relationship between chromosome pairing and DNA nicking is correct, pachytene DNA should be nicked even though microsporocytes are housed in a diploid plant. Despite the fact that colchicine abolishes chiasmata if applied after premeiotic mitosis to normally chiasmatic forms, unambiguous results were obtained (53). Tetraploid microsporocytes which had chiasmatic meioses also showed nicking at pachytene. The level of nicking was similar to that observed in chiasmatic varieties. There is thus little doubt that pairing itself can govern a key metabolic interaction in meiocytes.

If chromosome pairing determined susceptibility to DNA nicking at pachytene, it follows that susceptibility is determined separately for each chromosome pair, and perhaps also for each paired region within a bivalent. The presence of occasional chiasmatic bivalents in otherwise achiasmatic microsporocytes of diploid Black Beauty is compatible with the postulated relationship. The mechanism by which pairing renders chromosomes susceptible to endonuclease action remains obscure. It is even possible that an exonuclease rather than the endonuclease is the key enzyme since nicks formed without gaps might be difficult to detect. Such uncertainties, however, do not alter the essential conclusion relating chromosome pairing to metabolic regulation. Comparable relationships exist in other types of situations. A recessive mutant has been described in the plant *Hypochoeris radicata* ($2n = 8$) which, when present in the homozygous state, results in three rather than four normal bivalents at meiosis (45). The same pair of chromosomes is affected in about 90% of the cells. In plants heterozygous for the mutant gene, none of the chromosomes is affected. Moreover, when examined with the light microscope, the affected chromosomes appear to be normally paired during pachytene and so point to an event following the achievement of pairing that is responsible for lack of chiasma formation. A similar situation has been reported for an experimental population of *Crepis capillaris* ($2n = 6$). Three types of recessive mutations have been found, each mutation causing a variable degree of chiasma failure in one particular chromosome pair (58). In *Crepis* it is clear that desynapsis occurs prematurely after pairing. Whether endonuclease activity has any role in these phenomena is unknown. What is evident is the autonomy of chromosome pairs in determining their own crossing-over, a relationship that is consistent with the observations on nicking and pairing.

The invariance of endonuclease appearance and disappearance during meiosis is compatible with the enzyme having a critical role in crossing-over. It would seem, however, that to coordinate nicking activity with completion of chromosome pairing, and to prevent it from occurring in the absence of pairing, a regulatory device is superimposed on the enzyme cycle. Regulation is achieved by making substrate susceptibility a function of the effectively paired state of the chromosomes. The implications of such a regulatory relationship are apparent, even though the nature of effective pairing remains unresolved. Almost certainly, an apparently normal synaptonemal complex does not necessarily represent a paired condition adequate to permit DNA nicking.

THE REPAIR OF CHROMOSOME BREAKS

Chromosome breaks must be repaired to maintain normal cell function and, like other cell types, microsporocytes have adequate DNA repair mechanisms. Cells at any stage of meiosis, except perhaps at metaphase, respond to breakage of their DNA by initiating repair synthesis. However, if irradiated at pachytene, meiotic cells manifest a much higher capacity for repair synthesis than do meiocytes at other stages. The relatively high increase in DNA synthesis at pachytene following radiation or chemical induction of DNA lesions has been demonstrated in animal spermatogenesis (30, 52). A similar situation prevails in the microsporocytes of *Lilium* (Figure 3). The apparently rapid repair of damaged DNA during pachytene is, like endonuclease activity, a fixed feature of meiotic metabolism, being equally pronounced in chiasmatic and achiasmatic forms.

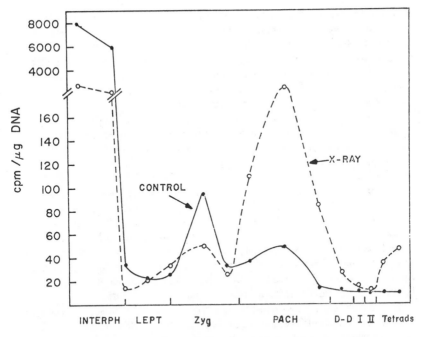

Figure 3 The relatively high capacity of pachytene microsporocytes to repair X-ray–induced lesions in DNA. A dose of 200 rads was used at each meiotic stage (unpublished).

The basis for the heightened response of pachytene cells to DNA damage is unknown. Synthesis, whether induced endogenously or exogenously, is entirely of the repair type as demonstrated by its resistance to hydroxyurea and by the incorporation of labeled precursor into both DNA strands (56). Although the in vitro activities of enzymes such as DNA polymerase, DNA ligase, and polynucleotide kinase vary during meiosis, the activities are not highest at pachytene and are therefore unlikely to account for the level of repair synthesis in pachytene cells (27). It is significant, nevertheless, that the stage at which DNA lesions are produced endogenously is also the stage at which the capacity to repair lesions is highest. Rapid repair may be essential in the sequence of reactions that lead from DNA nicking ultimately to crossing-over.

SITES OF DNA SYNTHESIS DURING MEIOTIC PROPHASE

Commonly the frequency of crossing-over between two genes is treated as a function of the distance between them. This implies that crossing-over is equally probable at any point along a chromosome. A direct proportionality between physical distance and frequency of crossing-over is a simplification which, though useful, obscures the fact that the position of a crossover is not entirely random. Two categories of meiotic behavior bear on this point. The first is the phenomenon of positive interference, in which the occurrence of a crossover in one region of a chromosome precludes the occurrence of a second one within a relatively large distance from it. Thus, if two or more crossovers occur in a chromosome arm, their positions relative to each other are not random. The second category of nonrandom behavior concerns inequalities in frequency of crossing-over between different regions of a chromosome. At one extreme in this category are the heterochromatic regions of chromosomes in which crossing-over is virtually absent. Two genes separated by a long stretch of heterochromatin rarely cross-over, behaving as though they were close neighbors (50). At the other extreme are situations in which frequency of crossing-over or, more correctly, of conversion within a gene, is affected by as little as a single base substitution (42).

Between these extremes are numerous examples in plant meiosis where several kinds of factors are known to influence sites of crossing-over. The rye genome has been studied extensively with respect to regulation of chiasma frequency and distribution. In some genotypes, chiasmata are concentrated toward the region distal from the centromere; in some genotypes the distribution is randomized; in still other genotypes, the normal distal localization of chiasmata is maintained, but the frequency is significantly altered (29). Other examples of nonrandom distribution have been reported in cases where a decrease in chiasmata in one arm of a chromosome, or in one pair of chromosomes, results in compensatory increases elsewhere (48). Data based on chiasma position are subject to some uncertainty because of difficulties in proving that the observed position of a chiasma is necessarily the position at which the crossover occurred. Nevertheless, given the general concordance between the cytological data obtained in some organisms and the genetic data obtained in others, it would be difficult to avoid the conclusion that both types of evidence relate to the selective occurrence of crossover regions. This being so, it is highly unlikely that the site of a crossover depends solely on randomly positioned DNA lesions; randomness is almost certainly a factor within particular chromosomal regions.

The pattern of DNA synthesis during meiotic prophase is consistent with the involvement of nonrandomly distributed factors in positioning of crossover sites. The two intervals of prophase synthesis, one at zygotene and the other at pachytene, each occur in specific segments of DNA. Their occurrence during meiotic prophase strongly suggests at least an indirect role in crossing-over. Several correlations point to zygotene DNA synthesis (Z-DNA) being involved in homolog pairing (25, 26), and if so, it is probable that Z-DNA regions influence crossover positions. Despite their close temporal association, the contrast in respective characteristics of Z-DNA and P-DNA (DNA synthesized during pachytene) adds emphasis to the general observation that the process of crossing-over is dependent on activities in preselected DNA regions.

In *Lilium*, Z-DNA consists of segments which are 5–10,000 base pairs (bp) long and which are mainly of the "unique" type. P-DNA consists of segments that are of the order of 200 bp in length and are repeated 700–2000 times per genome (25, 55). Z-DNA replicates semiconservatively at zygotene, but not completely. Short gaps at either end of the newly synthesized Z-DNA strands persist until about the time of chromosome disjunction (26). While nicks and gaps in P-DNA are removed by repair synthesis, Z-DNA gaps are unavailable to the repair system. The contrast in the respective responses of Z-DNA and P-DNA to the DNA metabolizing enzymes of the meiotic nucleus offers strong circumstantial evidence that chromosomes are equipped with specific segments to transact specific meiotic activities. We speculate that Z-DNA is essential to chromosome matching at early prophase, and to some aspect of chromosome disjunction at or after late prophase, whereas P-DNA is essential to the recombination process. The relative distribution of P-DNA and Z-DNA segments within the chromosomes remains to be determined.

The distinctive sequence organizations of Z-DNA and P-DNA segments are apparent from the C_0t profiles of DNA synthesized during S-phase zygotene, and pachytene (Figure 4). DNA synthesized during S-phase has the same C_0t profile as total nuclear DNA. As expected, the S-phase synthesis is uniformly distributed over the genome. Z-DNA, on the other hand, reassociates mainly in the unique region of the genome, whereas P-DNA reassociates at the region of intermediate repeats (25, 55). Mouse spermatocytes have a similar P-DNA pattern, thus indicating that preferential localization of pachytene repair synthesis in a moderate repeat component is probably universal for higher eukaryotes (22). The localization of pachytene synthesis is not a general characteristic of repair. Exogenously induced repair synthesis is indistinguishable by C_0t analysis from S-phase synthesis. Intrachromosomal sites of endogenously induced repair synthesis are probably determined by the selective distribution of nicks and gaps originating from the action of meiotic endonuclease.

P-DNA can be resolved into two fractions (30, 56). Thirty percent of P-DNA consists of sequences which have a low repeat number and thus are not part of the moderate repeat component. Preliminary analyses indicate that the two fractions of

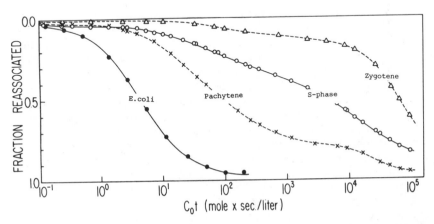

Figure 4 C_0t analysis of DNA synthesized at different stages of meiosis. Reproduced from Hotta & Stern (25).

P-DNA are separated by less than about 1000 bp, and if so, are not randomly positioned with respect to each other. The reassociation curve of moderate repeats, although not that of a second order reaction, is close enough to one to indicate a limited degree of heterogeneity in the repeat numbers of the different sequences within the component. It is possible to calculate the approximate number of families within the repeat component if it is assumed that the total P-DNA per genome is 10^8 bp (0.1% of 10^{11} bp) and that each sequence is repeated 1000 times. On the basis of these assumptions, the entire repeat component has a complexity of 10^5 bp. If the length and complexity of each repeat site is estimated at 200 bp, it follows that there are 500 different families in the component. Since *Lilium* has 12 chromosome pairs, each chromosome would have 20–50 families of P-DNA repeats; less than 20 is very unlikely.

The role that P-DNA plays in crossing-over is a matter of conjecture. The sequences might serve only as sites for nicking and, depending on their intra-chromosomal distribution, thus determine the frequency of possible crossovers in different chromosome regions. P-DNA could have a role in processes other than crossing-over by functioning in a manner similar to the insertion sequences currently being studied in microorganisms (43). That genetic elements can be shifted about within the genome of higher eukaryotes has been long and firmly established for the "controlling elements" in *Zea mays* (35). There is thus the possibility that the transfer of chromosomal segments, be they in translocations, inversions, or insertions are mediated by P-DNA sequences. The joining of nonhomologous chromosome fragments, such as occurs after breakage by irradiation, probably requires a prior complementary matching between single-strand tails from each of the fragments. It is unlikely, however, that such complementarity would exist between the ends of randomly broken fragments from nonhomologous chromosomes. P-DNA sequences, if appropriately distributed, could provide the needed complementary tails.

In considering the possible roles of P-DNA (or Z-DNA) in crossing-over, it is important to distinguish between absolute requirements and facilitation. We doubt that P-DNA is absolutely required for a crossover, but we speculate that it facilitates its occurrence. Facilitation might seem to be superfluous in situations which have very few crossovers per DNA nucleotide, but low frequency of crossing-over in large-sized genomes poses special problems in regulation. Outside of meiosis, cells in a flowering plant or a mammal are probably organized to prevent crossing-over rather than to facilitate it. In heterozygous organisms, somatic crossing-over would lead to homozygosity in undesirable recessive genes; it is not surprising that it occurs rarely if at all. Even in *Drosophila,* which has somatic pairing, crossing-over is a million times rarer in somatic cells than in meiotic ones, about 5×10^{-6} exchanges per mitotic division (B. Baker, private communication) compared with 5.6 per meiotic one. Despite the overwhelming difference in frequency, the number of nucleotides involved in exchanges in a single meiotic cell of *Drosophila* is exceedingly small, about one in 6×10^7 bp. The regularity of such crossing-over in meiocytes can only be achieved by an elaborately organized mechanism.

THE TRANSITION FROM NICKING TO CROSSING-OVER

The strategy of gametogenesis in very many organisms may be described as overproduction and limited utilization. This may seem unjust to flowering plants where a prolific production of pollen is required to overcome the hazards of achieving cross-fertilization, but it is a strategy nevertheless. The strategy is strikingly illustrated in a most shielded reproductive system, that of mammals. No more than about $1/10^4$ oocytes in a human fetus ever develop into mature eggs, and about 10^7–10^8 sperm are deposited in the uterus to achieve a single fertilization. Whether the apparent wastefulness is wasteful is a subject unto itself, but it may be noted that in assessing biological efficiency, wastefulness of overproduction should be matched against the complexity of organization which would be required to avoid waste. In many cases, the seeming inefficiency of biological processes is more apparent than real. Nicking activity at pachytene may be yet another example of efficient inefficiency.

There is a large disparity between the number of nicked regions repaired in a meiocyte and the number of crossovers. In discussing the nicking process, it was pointed out that in *Lilium* microsporocytes, the ratio of nicks formed to nicks utilized in a crossover is about 10^4. In purely arithmetic terms, the disparity between production and utilization is striking, and it raises the question of whether there is any real relationship between the nick-repair process and crossing-over. The possibility that there may be none should be kept in mind. We view the possibility as unlikely, mainly because of the temporal and cytological correlations between nick-repair activity and crossing-over, and partly because adherence to the viewpoint of a meiotically functional P-DNA provides a logical direction for further study.

If it is assumed that nick-repair events constitute a necessary step in the achievement of crossing-over, there should be, at the very least, two routes for resolution of the nicking process, one of which leads to crossovers and the other to a restoration of the original state. The simplest physiological model by which such resolution could be effected is that of a branched pathway in which only $1/10^4$ lesions are shunted in the direction of crossing-over. The problem is to identify mechanisms which might make a model of progressive elimination of potential crossover sites seem reasonable.

Various lines of evidence indicate that many of the proteins required to repair damaged DNA are also required for DNA recombination (3). To this extent at least, a relationship exists between pachytene DNA repair-synthesis and recombination. Enzymes such as DNA polymerase, DNA ligase, and polynucleotide kinase are commonly involved in the repair of gaps and are probably also involved in the immediate support of recombinational activity. In fact, such enzymes are present in virtually all types of cells. The relationship of exonucleases to repair and recombination is more difficult to define. In some cases the same enzyme has been shown to function in both. Thus enzymes which excise dimers might also excise DNA in heteroduplex regions. But whether all kinds of exonucleases function both in repair and recombination is undetermined. What is evident from studies of repair synthesis in meiocytes is that they are programmed for elevated repair capacity during pachy-tene, but such elevation sheds no light on the selective process for achieving cross-ing-over.

Using the diagram in Figure 1 as a guide, it may be argued that the mechanisms unique to crossing-over, and hence uninvolved in repair, are those that separate DNA duplexes into single strands and those that facilitate their reannealing. Strand separation is presumably also required in semiconservative replication, but repair synthesis requires neither separation ("unwinding") nor reannealing. Experimental evidence on the specific roles of proteins which unwind or anneal DNA in the process of recombination is uneven. All of the evidence comes from studies of microbial systems, mainly those infected with phage, and in virtually all of them semiconservative replication occurs together with recombination. The best studied protein is the gene-32 protein which is required for replication and recombination in T4 infected cells (2). It facilitates reassociation of ss-DNA in vitro and, under given conditions, it also promotes DNA unwinding. Of the two activities affecting secondary DNA structure, it is the unwinding process that has been generally emphasized, possibly because of its apparent relevance to replication and recombi-nation.

Proteins which affect secondary and tertiary structure of DNA have been studied in many eukaryotic organisms. Indeed, the histones themselves can and do alter tertiary DNA structure by causing a supercoiling when combined with DNA under appropriate conditions (60). Enzymes in mammalian cells which can remove super-coils from circular DNA have been described (59) and corresponding enzymes, including some which can introduce supercoils, have been identified in bacteria (14). Proteins affecting tertiary DNA configurations most probably meet different physio-logical requirements from those affecting secondary structure, although some rela-tionship does appear to exist between supercoiling of DNA and capacity for recombination (39). As yet there is no information on the involvement of proteins affecting tertiary DNA structure in the meiotic process, and further discussion of the possibilities would be premature.

In meiocytes of *Lilium,* and also of rodents, a protein has been identified which facilitates reannealing of ss-DNA and may therefore be regarded as affecting second-ary structure (23, 34). Proteins of this type fall into the broad category of DNA-binding proteins, and as such they have been widely sought among eukaryotes, particularly mammalian cells. The extent to which this protein and one other to be discussed are also present in somatic tissues is an open question. If present, however, they are at levels close to the limits of detection. Certain DNA binding proteins have been thoroughly studied in mammalian tissues such as thymus, and although they do have some effect on secondary DNA structure, their action is not nearly as pronounced as those found in meiocytes (17). Possibly the evolutionary course of the proteins among eukaryotes has been toward a separation of replicative and recombinational functions. If so, it is the latter function which is prominent in prophase meiocytes and which is essential to the pathway leading from the initial step of endogenous nicking to the ultimate event of crossing-over.

Of the two proteins that have been identified in lily microsporocytes and in rodent spermatocytes, one unwinds DNA duplexes into single strands and will be referred to as "U-protein" (*Biochemistry*, in press); the other, which facilitates reannealing, will be referred to as "R-protein" (22, 56). Both proteins have their counterparts in microbial systems. In microbial studies, the term "unwinding protein" has been retained for those proteins that promote a separation of duplex strands, usually in the presence of ATP (1). Proteins which facilitate reannealing, like the gene-32 protein, have been referred to as "binding proteins" (51), and most recently the term "helix-destabilizing protein" has been proposed (2a). We have continued to use the term "reassociation protein" because its capacity to reanneal DNA and its localization within the nuclear membrane point to a function in chromosome pairing (56; Y. Hotta, H. Stern, *Biochemistry*, in press).

During zygotene and pachytene a DNA-binding protein, which may be assayed as a DNA-dependent ATPase, increases prominently in activity (*Biochemistry*, in press). The activity is difficult to detect during premeiotic S-phase and also at other stages either before or after zygotene and pachytene. In terms of temporal behavior, the activity of the protein correlates with the meiotic phase of crossing-over. The relationship of the ATPase property to unwinding has not been resolved in any of the U-proteins examined, but since ATPase activity is highest in presence of ss-DNA, it must operate independently of unwinding (1). The U-protein of *Lilium* meiocytes differs in some respects from the bacterial U-proteins, but for this presentation it will be sufficient to consider the properties of the *Lilium* protein alone, even though studies are still at the beginning stage.

The two properties of the U-protein relevant to recombination are its mode of binding to duplex DNA and the nature of its unwinding activity. If the protein is mixed with intact DNA duplexes (those not having any internal nicks), the protein binds only at the ends of the duplexes. Nicks are also sites of binding; where gaps exist binding is even more obvious because of the presence of ss-DNA. The binding itself does not require ATP and in its absence no changes occur after formation of the complex. A characteristic of the binding which has been demonstrated for duplex ends is the requirement for a 3'OH terminus. 3'-phosphoryl termini prevent binding whereas 5'-phosphoryl termini have no effect. The 3'-OH terminus is probably a critical factor in selecting a lesion for repair or crossing-over since not only must DNA polymerase and U-protein compete for the same terminus, but the 3'-phosphoryl termini produced by meiotic endonuclease are unavailable to either protein. Presumably regulated phosphatase activity makes termini available.

When ATP is added to a U-protein/DNA complex, part of the DNA becomes single-stranded. A significant feature of such action is the limited degree of DNA unwinding, regardless of the amount of protein added. No more than 50–60 bp are unwound at an end and no more than 400–500 bp are unwound at a nick. The difference in unwinding at the two sites may be due to different proteins, but even so the essential feature of limited unwinding would remain unchanged. This feature is significant in terms of crossing-over since it makes available relatively short stretches of single-stranded DNA for duplex formation between members of homologous chromatids. Assuming that such action occurs, it is essential to have a mechanism for facilitating an annealing of the single strands formed. It would seem that the R-protein fulfills the required function.

Three characteristics of the R-protein point to its being a tightly regulated meiotic component (34). 1. It has a number of phosphorylatable sites which if phosphorylated abolish its ability to bind DNA and, as would be expected, also its ability to facilitate ss-DNA reassociation. If all phosphate residues are removed from the protein, it remains active in DNA binding but no longer facilitates reannealing. It is likely that this property functions in a regulatory capacity, but no direct evidence has yet been obtained. 2. Most of the R-protein occurs in association with a nuclear lipoprotein complex which increases markedly at the beginning of meiosis, and only a very small proportion is present in the soluble fraction of the cell homogenate (22, 23). The distribution is significant because Z-DNA synthesis, but not P-DNA repair synthesis, occurs in association with the lipoprotein complex (16). If the distribution of the protein reflects its relative availability to pairing and crossing-over, the amount available for crossing-over would be strongly limited. 3. The formation of active R-protein in hybrid plants is dependent on the presence of sufficient homology between the parent chromosome sets to permit effective chromosome pairing. This latter characteristic is striking inasmuch as formation or activation of the protein precedes, or at most is coincident with, chromosome pairing, the very process it is supposed to facilitate. It is different from the meiotic endonuclease, which is active but ineffective in the absence of chromosome pairing, and also from the U-protein which is equally active in chiasmatic and achiasmatic cells. The various regulatory factors affecting endonuclease and U- and R-proteins are depicted diagrammatically in Figure 5.

The unusual regulatory features of the R-protein have also been probed recently in the collaborative project referred to earlier. The diploid achiasmatic hybrid Black Beauty has a low level of R-protein and also of the nuclear lipoprotein fraction in which the R-protein is found. However, microsporocytes in the diploid plant which are converted to chiasmatic tetraploid cells by administration of colchicine in situ have levels of R-protein that are as high or higher than those of chiasmatic diploids. It is thus clear that the introduction of pairing homology into cells lacking homology for effective pairing is sufficient to cause formation of active R-protein. How pairing homology mediates the formation is puzzling because it begins to occur before zygotene. A possible explanation is that a prezygotene process of homolog matching is the critical event. Such dependence of R-protein on chromosome matching, coupled with its phosphorylation characteristics and its association with a meiotically distinctive nuclear lipoprotein, point to a key meiotic function.

The molecular properties of the R-protein are quite similar to those of the gene-32 protein found in T4-infected cells (2). In the presence of Mg^{2+} it facilitates the reassociation of ss-DNA regardless of source. In the case of T7-DNA (4×10^4 bp), over 90% reassociation is effected by the protein under conditions where no more than 10% would reanneal in its absence (23, 34). The extent of reassociation is smaller for complex genomes, but the effectiveness of the R-protein in promoting reassociation is unambiguous. If Mg^{2+} is absent from the medium, a relatively unstable condition for the duplex structure, R-protein promotes unwinding (34). In the case of the gene-32 protein, some evidence exists that the unwinding action is affected by a proteolytic product (20). This possibility has not been examined in the meiotic protein. Our interest, in any case, is not directed toward the unwinding action but rather at the reannealing property which could complement that action of the U-protein.

We have recently analyzed the behavior of duplex DNA in the presence of R-protein and U-protein (unpublished). Their interactions may be briefly described: the R-protein, as expected, neither binds to nor unwinds duplex DNA in the presence of Mg^{2+}; its behavior is unchanged if the Mg^{2+} concentration in the medium is reduced to 1 mM, the level required for U-protein activity. The combination of U-protein and R-protein in the absence of ATP is also without effect on the DNA duplex. If, however, ATP is added to the medium, entire molecules of T7 DNA are unwound, the ss-DNA becoming attached to R-protein. The success of the interaction in vitro depends upon control of the Mg^{2+} concentration. If it is raised from the original 1 mM concentration to 5 mM during the reaction, reannealing begins. If this is done early in the reaction, the unwound DNA is quickly restored to the duplex condition.

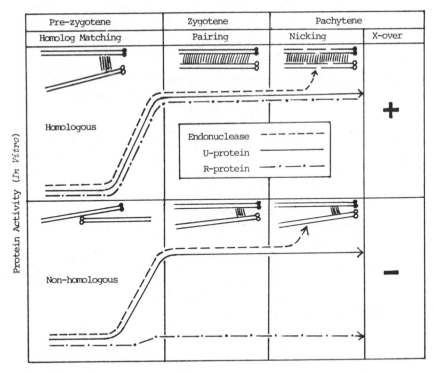

Figure 5 Effects of homology and pairing on protein activities during meiotic prophase.

The interactions between R- and U-protein are based entirely on in vitro behavior and therefore have only limited value in assessing in vivo regulatory mechanisms. The in vitro interactions are nevertheless suggestive of an in vivo function. The simultaneous and transient presence during meiotic prophase of two proteins that have complementing properties essential to recombination is strong presumptive evidence for an interacting role in that process. Although it is possible to argue against their having a major role in recombination, it is difficult to deny that their temporal behavior in meiocytes and their complementary effects on secondary DNA structure are strong arguments for their participation. They can be fitted readily into a scheme in which they are competitors for the nicks and gaps endogenously produced during pachytene. This property is more appropriately considered under the broad heading of "Speculations."

SPECULATIONS

In concluding this review we would like to put the various findings on the biochemistry of meiosis into a more meaningful, though necessarily incomplete, conceptual framework. In so summarizing the data, we can draw attention to those problems which we consider to be critical in developing an understanding of meiotic organization for achieving crossovers. Recombination in a meiotic cell involves not only the molecular mechanisms observed in prokaryotes, themselves not fully understood, but also a set of regulatory devices superimposed on the immediate molecular events of recombination. In plants and animals these devices are activated by a developmental process that leads to differentiation of meiocytes, male and female. In the meiocyte, there is a demonstrable coordination between the sequence of structural changes within the nucleus and the cyclical activities of various proteins. The structure of meiotic chromosomes and their DNA sequence organization affect the accessibility of specific chromosomal sites to the transient activities of enzymes and other proteins essential to crossing-over. It is the combination of protein activation by still unexplored regulatory mechanisms and specific chromosomal site availability that seem to be fundamental to meiotic development. The study of meiosis is not so much a question of identifying the molecular events essential to recombination, although the need is there, as of identifying the metabolic and structural conditions that make those molecular events effective.

The process of meiosis begins well before the cytological entry of a cell into meiosis, but where that beginning lies in the progression from archesporial tissue to meiocytes is difficult to define. For our purpose it will be useful to combine premeiosis with meiotic prophase and to divide the whole interval into phases I and II. We assign to phase I those processes that are prerequisites for the chromosomes to begin pairing, and to phase II those processes which follow the completion of pairing. The pairing stage, zygotene, is left unassigned because we are unable to be precise about the transitions from I to II in biochemical terms.

The regulatory pattern of meiosis may be treated as a dichotomously branched pathway, each branchpoint representing a critical turn in the direction of or away from crossing-over. The concept has been widely applied to a variety of developmental processes and also to the occurrence of meiosis in sporulating yeast cultures. At their S-phase, microsporocytes are well into the meiotic pathway. That S-phase is distinctive in its relatively long duration. For most, if not all, species it is the cell type with the longest S-phase (4, 19). The factors leading to S-phase prolongation are unknown and so too is the function. In *Lilium,* the first identifiable fork in the developmental pathway occurs near or just after the end of the S-phase (44). Until that point, microsporocytes can be induced to undergo a mitotic rather than a meiotic division. In sporulating yeast, a comparable situation has been defined as the point of "commitment" (54). In yeast, however, the capacity to undergo cross-ing-over at a meiotic rate precedes a commitment to meiotic segregation so that reversal to mitosis may be accompanied by a high rate of crossing-over. In higher eukaryotes, it may be assumed that the commitment following premeiotic S-phase initiates a set of activities which leads to chromosome pairing, crossing-over, and reductional segregation.

The influence of post S-phase events on meiosis is unambiguous even though there is as yet little direct study of the pre-pairing interval. Perturbations of meiocytes during this period (or slightly before it in the case of *Triticum*) have strong effects on subsequent chromosome behavior. Colchicine in wheat and lily (11, 53) and cold shock in *Ornithogalum* (9) significantly reduce pairing and/or crossing-over. That a structural counterpart exists to this physiological interval is becoming increasingly evident. The formation of "axial" or "lateral" elements along the chromosomes prior to the beginning of pairing has long been known from EM studies (40). In the case of wheat, synaptonemal complexes have been found to be present during premeiotic S-phase (36). EM evidence is also accumulating for a positioning of the chromosomes prior to the zygotene stage (8, 61). From the little physiological and biochemical information available, it is not unreasonable to propose the existence of a second critical interval following the establishment of a machinery for stable pairing during which the chromosomes may be directed toward the formation of components essential to crossing-over or fail to be so directed thereby resulting in an achiasmatic situation. We further propose that in normal meiocytes the critical factor is chromosome homology.

In the achiasmatic hybrid Black Beauty, the absence of sufficient homology for effective pairing results in a much reduced formation of nuclear meiotic lipoprotein and R-protein. In chiasmatic types, these two components begin to increase during leptotene so that their formation, or activation, is arrested either prior to or coinci-dent with the pairing process, or more precisely, with the process stabilizing pairing. It is the absence of homology rather than the absence of zygotene pairing that is responsible for failure of active R-protein formation. We suggest that some interac-tion between homologs must occur prior to zygotene and that an inadequate interac-tion signals the failure to form R-protein and its associated lipoprotein. Some form of homologous matching precedes homologous pairing and regulates the provision of agents for such pairing. We recall the proviso that the pairing we have in mind is "effective" pairing which is not necessarily identical with morphological pairing. We are still unable to separate experimentally the mechanisms leading to effective pairing from those stabilizing homolog association within the synaptonemal com-plex.

It is during phase II of the meiotic process that certain molecular consequences of ineffective pairing become apparent. A third developmental branchpoint becomes evident at the end of zygotene, and it determines whether or not the DNA in the chromosomes becomes susceptible to the action of meiotic endonuclease. Without effective pairing there is no nicking. It is important to note that whereas during phase I the branchpoints determine the direction of the cell as a whole, during phase II they apply to the direction of each pair of chromosomes. Presumably nicking activity occurs only in effectively paired chromosomes. R-protein is an extra-chromosomal component and its reduced formation is considered to be general for the meiocyte. By contrast, the endonuclease activity is not reduced but its effectiveness in vivo depends upon prior chromosome pairing.

Once chromosomal DNA is nicked, a new set of alternatives appear, the outcome of which affects a particular region of the chromosome rather than the chromosome as a whole. As discussed earlier, potential regions for crossing-over are not randomly determined and crossing-over is infrequent for any particular site within a region. Our speculation concerning the pathway of choices is summarized diagrammatically in Figure 6. It shows a progressive reduction in the number of possibilities for the occurrence of a crossover with meiotic development. We propose that the formation of 3'-phosphoryl termini by meiotic endonuclease action represents the first regulatory point in the final stage of the pathway. Although no specific phosphatase has been isolated from meiocytes, we assume that such an enzyme activity must exist in order to make the termini available to the action of the repair system or to binding with U-protein. We assume that most termini react with the repair complex to

PROGRESSIVE ELIMINATION OF NICKED REGIONS IN FORMATION OF A CROSSOVER

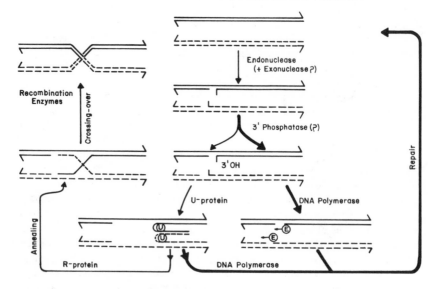

Figure 6 A speculative scheme for regulating crossovers in meiocytes with large genomes.

remove the lesions. The repaired sites are thus eliminated from the possibility of crossing-over. Termini interacting with U-protein remain potential sites for crossing-over, but in the absence of additional factors, no change occurs beyond the limited unwinding effected by the U-protein. Since we have found that U-protein does not inhibit the action of DNA polymerase, we consider it probable that most of the sites associated with U-protein are also repaired by the polymerase reaction.

We suggest that the critical factor is the availability of the R-protein for coupling with the U-protein–DNA complex. Its level is much more tightly regulated in accordance with pairing homology than the other proteins thus far identified. Its association with nuclear lipoprotein or some other nuclear structure such as the "recombination nodules" observed by electron microscopy (5) might impose additional restrictions on its availability for interaction during pachytene. In the absence of procedures for intracellular localization of the R-protein, any scheme involving its functioning as a limiting factor is entirely conjectural. Our emphasis is on the concept that the ultimate event of crossing-over is achieved through a series of elimination steps and not by the chance presence of all essential reactants at one among very many chromosomal sites.

The most striking feature of meiosis in flowering plants, and in higher eukaryotes generally, is the very small number of crossovers per DNA nucleotide per meiotic division and the very high regularity of its occurrence. The larger the genome, the lower is the frequency of exchange. The relative genome sizes of lily, mouse, and *Drosophila* are 330:20:1; their respective numbers of crossovers per meiotic division per 10^8 base pairs are 0.027, 0.3, and 1.7. The regularity of infrequent events is achieved by an elaborate structural and metabolic organization that serves as a framework within which the immediate mechanisms of recombination operate. At the molecular level we perceive a sequence organization in the chromosomal DNA which is specifically addressed to initiating sites for crossing-over. We also perceive a differentiated metabolic program designed to promote conditions for facilitating crossing-over. We further perceive a set of regulatory mechanisms operating between specific structural components of the chromosomes and preprogrammed metabolic activities. We believe it highly probable that it is these regulatory mechanisms which advance the meiotic process by stepwise elimination of potential sites for crossing-over. It is quite probable that the ultimate site of a crossover is already determined by structural factors in advance of the elimination process, a situation considered by various investigators (33, 38, 57). How homologous matching regulates the activation or synthesis of proteins essential to crossing-over and how DNA sequence organization governs the distribution of potential sites of crossing-over are problems to which further research on meiosis will be addressed.

Literature Cited

1. Abdel-Monem, M., Lauppe, H., Kartenbeck, J., Durwald, H., Hoffmann-Berling, H. 1977. *J. Mol. Biol.* 110: 667–85
2. Alberts, B. 1970. *Fed. Proc.* 29: 1154–63
2a. Alberts, B., Sternglanz, R. 1977. *Nature* 269:655–61

3. Boram, W. R., Roman, H. 1976. *Proc. Natl. Acad. Sci. USA* 73:2828–32
4. Callan, H. G. 1973. *Cold Spring Harbor Symp. Quant. Biol.* 38:195–204
5. Carpenter, A. T. C. 1975. *Proc. Natl. Acad. Sci. USA* 72:3186–89
6. Chandley, A. C., Hotta, Y., Stern, H. 1977. *Chromosoma* 62:243–53

7. Chilton, M. D., Drummond, M. H., Merlo, D. J., Sciaky, D., Montoya, A. L., Gordon, M. P., Nester, E. W. 1977. *Cell* 11:263–71

8. Church, K., Moens, P. B. 1976. *Chromosoma* 56:249–63

9. Church, K., Wimber, D. E. 1971. *Exp. Cell Res.* 64:119–24

10. Dickinson, H. G., Heslop-Harrison, J. 1977. *Philos. Trans. R. Soc. London Ser. B.* 277:185–89

11. Dover, G. A., Riley, R. 1973. *J. Cell Sci.* 12:143–61

12. Emsweller, S. L., Uhring, J. 1966. *Lily Yearb.* 29:1–3

13. Fogel, S., Mortimer, R. K. 1971. *Ann. Rev. Genet.* 5:219–36

14. Gellert, M., Mizuuchi, K., O'Dea, M. H., Nash, H. A. 1976. *Proc. Natl. Acad. Sci. USA* 73:3872–76

15. Gillies, C. B. 1973. *Chromosoma* 43:145–76

16. Hecht, N. B., Stern, H. 1971. *Exp. Cell Res.* 69:1–10

17. Herrick, G., Alberts, B. 1976. *J. Biol. Chem.* 251:2124–32

18. Holliday, R. 1964. *Genet. Res.* 5:282–304

19. Holm, P. B. 1977. *Carlsberg Res. Commun.* 42:249–81

20. Hosoda, J., Takacs, B., Brack, C. 1974. *FEBS Lett.* 47:338–42

21. Hotta, Y., Chandley, A. C., Stern, H. 1977. *Chromosoma* 62:255–68

22. Hotta, Y., Chandley, A. C., Stern, H. 1977. *Nature* 269:240–42

23. Hotta, Y., Stern, H. 1971. *Dev. Biol.* 26:87–99

24. Hotta, Y., Stern, H. 1974. *Chromosoma* 46:279–96

25. Hotta, Y., Stern, H. 1975. In *The Eukaryote Chromosome*, ed. W. J. Peacock, R. D. Brock, pp. 283–300. Aust. Natl. Univ. Press

26. Hotta, Y., Stern, H. 1976. *Chromosoma* 55:171–82

27. Howell, S. H., Stern, H. 1971. *J. Mol. Biol.* 55:357–78

28. Jacobson, G. K., Piñon, R., Esposito, R. E., Esposito, M. S. 1975. *Proc. Natl. Acad. Sci. USA* 72:1887–91

29. Jones, G. H. 1974. *Heredity* 32:375–87

30. Kofman-Alfaro, S., Chandley, A. C. 1971. *Exp. Cell Res* 69:33–44

31. Maguire, M. P. 1966. *Genetics* 53:1071–77

32. Maguire, M. P. 1972. *Genetics* 70:353–70

33. Maguire, M. P. 1977. *Philos. Trans. R. Soc. London B Ser.* 277:245–58

34. Mather, J., Hotta, Y. 1977. *Exp. Cell Res.* 109:181–89

35. McClintock, B. 1961. *Am. Nat.* 95:265–77

36. McQuade, H. A., Bassett, B. 1977. *Chromosoma* 63:153–59

37. Meselson, M. S., Radding, C. M. 1975. *Proc. Natl. Acad. Sci. USA* 72:358–61

38. Millington-Ward, A. M., Koops, F. B. J., van der Mark-Iken, C. 1971. *Genetica* 42:13–24

39. Mizuuchi, K., Nash, H. A. 1976. *Proc. Natl. Acad. Sci. USA* 73:3524–28

40. Moens, P. B. 1968. *Chromosoma* 23:418–51

41. Monesi, V. 1971. *J. Reprod. Fertil. Suppl.* 13:1–14

42. Moore, C., Sherman, F. 1977. *Genetics* 85:1–22

43. Nevers, P., Saedler, H. 1977. *Nature* 268:109–15

44. Ninnemann, H., Epel, B. 1973. *Exp. Cell Res.* 79:318–26

45. Parker, J. S. 1975. *Chromosoma* 49:391–406

46. Pritchard, R. H. 1960. *Genet. Res.* 1:1–24

47. Rasmussen, S. W. 1977. *Carlsberg Res. Commun.* 42:163–97

48. Rhoades, M. M., Dempsey, E. 1966. *Genetics* 53:989–1020

49. Riley, R. 1977. *Philos. Trans. R. Soc. London Ser. B* 277:183–376

50. Roberts, P. A. 1965. *Nature* 205:725–26

51. Scott, J. F., Eisenberg, S., Bertsch, L. L., Kornberg, A. 1977. *Proc. Natl. Acad. Sci. USA* 74:193–97

52. Sega, G. A. 1974. *Proc. Natl. Acad. Sci USA* 71:4955–59

53. Shepard, J., Boothroyd, E. R., Stern, H. 1974. *Chromosoma* 44:423–37

54. Simchen, G., Piñon, R., Salts, Y. 1972. *Exp. Cell Res.* 75:207–18

55. Smyth, D. R., Stern, H. 1973. *Nature New Biol.* 245:94–96

56. Stern, H., Hotta, Y. 1977. *Philos. Trans. R. Soc. London Ser. B* 277:277–93

57. Stern, H., Westergaard, M., von Wettstein, D. 1975. *Proc. Natl. Acad. Sci. USA* 72:961–65

58. Tease, C., Jones, G. H. 1976. *Chromosoma* 57:33–49

59. Vosberg, H. P., Grossman, L. I., Vinograd, J. 1975. *Eur. J. Biochem.* 55:79–93

60. Weintraub, H., Worcel, A., Alberts, B. 1976. *Cell* 9:409–17

61. Zickler, D. 1977. *Chromosoma* 61:289–316

Ann. Rev. Plant Physiol. 1978. 29:437–60
Copyright © 1978 by Annual Reviews Inc. All rights reserved

ENERGY COUPLING
FOR MEMBRANE TRANSPORT

♦7658

Ronald J. Poole

Biology Department, McGill University, Montreal, Quebec H3A 1B1, Canada

CONTENTS

0066-4154/78/0701-0437$01.00

INTRODUCTION: PRIMARY AND SECONDARY
TRANSPORT PROCESSES

Metabolic energy may be supplied to membrane transport processes either directly, by mechanisms which couple the "uphill" movement of, for instance, Na^+ or H^+ with a chemical reaction such as the hydrolysis of ATP, or indirectly, by mechanisms which couple the transport of other substances to the back-fluxes of Na^+ or H^+ down their electrochemical gradients (cf 124). Recent research has attempted to define more precisely the primary metabolic transport processes, and at the same time has revealed the great extent and importance of the secondary mechanisms of cotransport and countertransport [symport and antiport in the terminology of Mitchell (122, 123)]. Because the primary and secondary transport processes frequently interact with each other via the membrane potential, increasing attention is being paid to the role of the potential in energy coupling and to whether a given transport process is electrogenic, i.e. whether it contributes directly to the potential by transporting a net electric charge across the membrane.

In this review we will consider the nature and role of electrogenic H^+ efflux and other primary transport processes at the plasmalemma and, where possible, at the tonoplast of plant cells, and will discuss the mode of energy coupling to organic and inorganic transport substrates. Transport in animal cells and bacteria will be considered only briefly for comparative purposes. I will not attempt to review transport in chloroplasts and mitochondria. For reviews on transport in these organelles, see (55, 56, 129) on chloroplasts and (141, 187) on mitochondria. For further information on transport in bacteria see (53). Many other topics related to this review are discussed in the *Encyclopedia of Plant Physiology,* New Series (111).

Bacteria

The dominant transport process driven by ATP hydrolysis is the efflux of H^+ (53). This gives rise (122, 123) to the so-called proton-motive force (pmf) or electrochemical gradient of hydrogen ions across the membrane. The proton-motive force is created by the combined effects of the difference in pH and the difference in electrical potential between the solutions on either side of the membrane, and at room temperature is given by the equation:

$$pmf = -59 \, \Delta \, pH + \psi \qquad\qquad 1.$$

where ψ is the membrane potential, which has been variously designated by other authors as $\Delta\psi$, E, V, or PD. Skulachev (160) suggests that the pmf should be regarded as a biological energy source as fundamental and perhaps as widespread and versatile as the high-energy phosphate bond (cf 104). Just as the cycle of ATP synthesis and hydrolysis couples respiration or photosynthesis to various types of cell work, the circulation of protons across the membrane, forced against a gradient through one channel and flowing back "downhill" through another, enables energy to be transferred from redox reactions to phosphorylation reactions or vice versa, or from either of these to the transport of solutes or to other membrane events such as the rotation of bacterial flagella (52). The versatility of this system is increased by the fact that most of the proton pathways are freely reversible. Thus the bacterial ATPase will pump protons out of the cell if supplied with ATP, but it can also generate ATP if the proton gradient is sufficient to push protons inward through this channel.

The pmf is now widely accepted as a basic energy-coupling mechanism in bacteria as well as in chloroplasts and mitochondria. This acceptance is a result (53, 141, 173) of (a) the development of methods of measuring pH and potentials in these systems, (b) the purification and reconstruction in vitro of proton-translocating redox systems and proton-translocating ATPases, and (c) the demonstration that artificially applied gradients of pH and/or potential can drive phosphorylation or transport.

Animal Cells

The transport of H^+ does not seem to play a central role in energy coupling at the plasma membrane of animal cells. A number of different ATPases have been implicated in the transport of sodium and other ions (41, 79), and in some cases have been isolated and reconstituted and shown to perform ATP-driven transport activities in vitro (87). For the transport of organic substances, on the other hand, the direct involvement of ATP is questionable, and in many cases the transport of sugars and amino acids is coupled stoichiometrically to an influx of sodium and is influenced by the sodium gradient (57, 156). Thus the sodium gradient is analogous to the proton-motive force in bacteria: it is created by a primary ATP-dependent transport process, and it serves to energize a number of secondary transport processes at the plasma membrane. In both animal cells (41, 79, 87) and bacteria (52) there are also other primary transport processes which function more or less independently.

Plant Cells

Transport across the plasma membranes of fungi and green plants seems to have more in common with that in bacteria than that in animal cells. The prominence of H^+ movements has long been recognized (68, 69, 149). As a result of increasing evidence for electrogenic H^+ pumps and for proton-linked fluxes of other materials in plants (see below), it now appears that H^+ efflux is a major ATP-dependent transport process in most plant-cell membranes. Thus an evaluation of energy coupling for membrane transport is necessarily oriented around the role of this ion.

ELECTROGENIC H^+ EFFLUX: A PRIMARY TRANSPORT PROCESS

As a result of the pioneering work of N. Higinbotham, C. L. and C. W. Slayman, and others, it now appears that electrogenic pumps are a universal feature of plant cell membranes, including fungi, algae, bryophytes, and higher plants (59–61, 162). In most, but not all, cases they are believed to transport protons; the evidence for this is strong but always indirect. Thus the potential and conductivity of the membrane cannot always be accounted for by active or passive movements of other ions, the membrane potential can be very sensitive to pH, and in a number of cases membrane hyperpolarization has been shown to be closely correlated with the net efflux of H^+ against its electrochemical gradient (e.g. 139, 162). For a variety of higher plant cells, additional evidence for electrogenic H^+ efflux has been obtained by the use of the fungal toxin fusicoccin, which seems to have a specific activating effect on this transport process (118).

Generally the activity of electrogenic pumps can only be detected under conditions of high pH, low K^+, in the presence of Ca^{2+}, and sometimes only in the light (162, 174). There are a number of possible explanations for this. At low external pH the net efflux of protons through the pump is opposed by the gradient of pH across the membrane. In high K^+ and in the absence of Ca^{2+}, the passive ion conductivity may short-circuit the pump potential. The rate of transport through the pump may also be kinetically regulated by Ca^{2+} and light. In addition to these factors, which may mask or limit the effects of electrogenic pumps, there is also the possibility that under some conditions the pump may be able to operate in a nonelectrogenic or electrically neutral mode. In other words, it is not yet established whether electrogenic H^+ pumps in plants can also carry other ions such as K^+ which may balance the electric charge of the proton under some experimental conditions.

CHARACTERIZATION OF ELECTROGENIC PUMPS

In order to assess the role of electrogenic pumps in energy coupling it is necessary to develop methods of measuring them: techniques which can detect the circulation of H^+ or other ions in the absence of net fluxes and in the absence of large effects on the membrane potential. One-way fluxes of H^+ cannot be measured with a radioisotope (^3H) because of the high water permeability of the membrane. Therefore, a steady-state circulation of H^+ across the membrane would be invisible, except for its electrical properties. It is fortunate, therefore, from a technical point of view, that the H^+ pump can be detected by its electrogenic properties. Moreover, if H^+ is carried without any balancing ion being transported through the pump channel, the electric current through the pump will be a direct measure of the rate of H^+ transport.

Studies of current-voltage relationships of the membrane can therefore provide a powerful way of characterizing the proton circulation and thus the flow of energy from primary to secondary transport systems. The results of such studies are expressed in terms of equivalent circuits. This approach has some limitations (20) but nevertheless seems valuable at this stage. Figure 1 shows the simplest possible equivalent circuit for a membrane. The circuit can be extended to account for any number of parallel pathways through the membrane, and in principle all components of the circuit can be determined in order to give a full picture of energy coupling in the membrane. Thus the electrical potential of the H^+ pump is given by the equation:

$$\psi_1 = \Delta G_{\text{ATP}}/nF + 59\ \Delta pH. \qquad 2.$$

where ΔG_{ATP} is the change in free energy for the hydrolysis of 1 mole of ATP, and n is the stoichiometry of the pump. This is thought to be $2H^+$/ATP [but see (16)].

If the right hand side of the equivalent circuit represents K^+ diffusion, its potential would be given by the equation:

$$\psi_2 = -59 \log K_i/K_o. \qquad\qquad 3.$$

If the right-hand side represents a $1:1$ coupled proton-sugar cotransport system, then its potential would be given by the equation:

$$\psi_2 = 59 \, \Delta \, pH - 59 \log ([sugar]_{in}/ [sugar]_{out}). \qquad\qquad 4.$$

The various conductivities (g_1, g_2) can be determined from the current-voltage relationships of the membrane under various experimental conditions. From such a circuit one might deduce the total energy flow through the pump, the proportion of energy consumed by each transport process, and the overall effects of changes in ATP level, pH, or pump kinetics on the membrane system.

This approach also permits an assessment of the extent to which the flux is under "thermodynamic" control (responding to changes in ψ_1) versus kinetic control (responding to changes in g_1). It might be expected on the basis of Mitchell's hypothesis (122, 123) that the pump will have a high conductance and will be readily reversible. Reversibility of a bacterial H^+ pump has been demonstrated in a system reconstituted in vitro (173). Since the potential across various cell membranes (see below) appears to approach the equilibrium potential of the pump, it would seem that the conductance of the passive systems in these membranes must be low compared with that of the pump and that the pump is mainly under thermodynamic control. Under other circumstances, however, the pump seems to have a lower

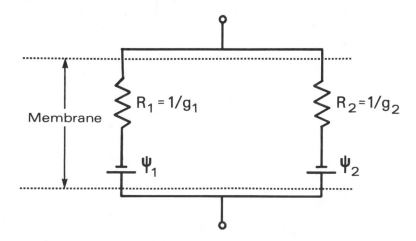

Figure 1   A simple equivalent circuit for a membrane. ψ_1, R_1, g_1, are the potential, resistance, and conductance for a primary transport process (metabolically coupled pump), and ψ_2, R_2, g_2 are the potential, resistance, and conductance for a secondary (cotransport) process, or for a diffusion or leak. Additional elements (ψ_3, R_3, g_3, etc) may be added in parallel to represent other transport processes.

conductance and to be under kinetic control (174). It is relevant that the protein complex composing the mitochondrial H^+-ATPase includes an inhibitory subunit which exerts kinetic control on the pump rate depending on the ATP/ADP balance (182). A similar inhibitory subunit is present in the H^+-ATPase of *Escherichia coli* (172).

Apart from the question of regulatory mechanisms, the pump conductance will also reflect the kinetics of the transport carrier. When the membrane potential is far from the equilibrium potential of the pump, the proton flux will reach a maximum due to the limited number of carrier molecules. A technical point here is that the change in current for a small change in potential (slope conductance) would be minimal when the carrier is operating at its maximal rate, even though the rate of proton circulation is maximal at this point. [For more rigorous theoretical treatments of the electrical properties of ion pumps, see (40, 143)].

Neurospora

In this fungus, Slayman et al (165) have demonstrated an impressive correlation between the membrane potential and the intracellular concentration of ATP, while the latter is changing with time as a result of respiratory inhibition. The relationship fits a Michaelis curve, with a K_m for ATP of 2 mM. The membrane potential before inhibition (about –180 mV) agrees closely with the thermodynamic equilibrium value calculated from Equation 2 above, assuming $2H^+$/ATP, especially if one includes a value of one for ΔpH (168). However, the membrane potential during inhibition (about –40 mV) is much less than that which would be in equilibrium with the remaining ATP, indicating kinetic rather than thermodynamic control, as might be expected from the Michaelis kinetics. These results have been extended by the work of Scarborough (153). After developing a method (152) for the preparation of (inside-out) plasma membrane vesicles, Scarborough (153) showed that a potential (monitored by uptake of SCN^-) was generated in the vesicles during ATP hydrolysis. This system should prove useful for further studies on the stoichiometry and other properties of the pump. Bowman & Slayman (15) and Scarborough (154) have now characterized the ATPase activity of the plasma membrane vesicles. The K_m for ATP is approximately 2 mM as predicted from the electrical potential data.

These various studies establish firmly that the electrogenic pump in *Neurospora* is driven by ATP. Its role in H^+ transport is inferred from a close correlation between the membrane potential and H^+ fluxes under various circumstances and a lack of correlation with any other ion fluxes which could generate the potential (162). The relevance of these studies to transport in green plants is suggested by the fact that the overall electrical (161) and transport (e.g. 166) properties of *Neurospora* are very similar to those of algae and higher plants (162). The enzymic properties of the ATPases (15, 154) are also similar (see below). In another study of *Neurospora* (164), the current-voltage curve for the pump was calculated by subtracting the membrane current-voltage curve in the presence of respiratory inhibitors from that measured before inhibition. The result suggested that the pump behaves as a constant current source with a high resistance and that it is insensitive to the membrane potential. This is difficult to reconcile with the previous conclusion (above) that the pump reaction comes close to equilibrium with the membrane potential. It seems possible that decreasing the ATP/ADP ratio with inhibitors may not abolish the conductance of the pump, and thus the subtraction procedure would not be valid. This possibility would affect another conclusion of Slayman et al (165): it was calculated that the ATP turnover to maintain the membrane potential with a measured membrane conductance of 1 S m^{-2} would require 27% of the total turnover of ATP in the cell. The measured membrane conductance represents both the pump (g_1) and the leak (g_2). If g_1 is not negligible, then the measured conductance will overestimate g_2 and hence overestimate the energy required to maintain the potential. Doubts have also been expressed (110) about the calculation of ATP turnover in this material. On the other hand, it may be noted that the figure of 27% for the cellular energy devoted to transport is not out of line with that estimated for animal cells (186).

Characean Cells

Spanswick (174) has shown that light can evoke a large hyperpolarization in *Nitella translucens,* together with an almost tenfold increase in conductance. Moreover, in the light both the potential and the conductance become very sensitive to temperature. The large temperature-sensitive conductance in the light was attributed to the pump, and it was suggested that under these conditions the membrane potential (up to –200 mV at pH 6) is in equilibrium with the metabolic reactions energizing the pump (cf Equation 2). The effects of inhibitors and 710 nm light (175) was thought to indicate the involvement of ATP. It has been found, however, that the ATP level is not affected by light (121), suggesting that the effect of light is on g_1 rather than ψ_1 (Figure 1), as is also indicated by the large change in membrane conductivity. Although the pump rate is reduced in the dark, it is not completely abolished, because the potential still retains some sensitivity to pH and temperature.

In a study of *Nitella* under different conditions, Vredenberg & Tonk (183) distinguished between a short-term effect of light on g_2 and a long-term effect on g_1. The current-voltage curves in this study seem to show that the total membrane conductance in a variety of energy states and external pH values is simply a function of the membrane potential. Bentrup (13) suggests that under these conditions, unlike Spanswick's, g_2 is not negligibly small compared with g_1. A clear separation of these parameters has not yet been achieved.

Richards & Hope (148) investigated the effect of external pH on the potential and conductance in *Chara corallina,* and considered that while an electrogenic H$^+$ pump operates at high pH, there is a large passive diffusion of H$^+$ at low pH. However, Walker & Smith (184) showed that in this species the membrane potential, over a wide range of pH (pH 5 to pH 8) and in both light and darkness, follows Equation 2 above, assuming 2H$^+$/ATP. There is therefore no need to invoke a passive flux of H$^+$, and indeed the membrane conductance in *Chara* was found to be temperature-sensitive over the whole range of external pH (148). Thus the electrical characteristics of *Chara,* even more than *Nitella,* are dominated by the H$^+$ pump.

Acetabularia

This marine alga differs from the other organisms discussed here in that its electrogenic pump is insensitive to pH and correlates with a large active influx of Cl^-, although active H^+ efflux is also believed to occur (151). By exploiting the temperature sensitivity of the pump, Gradmann & Klemke (49) and Gradmann (47, 48) have had some success in separating the electrical characteristics of the pump and leak pathways through the membrane. Essentially their procedure is to subtract the current-voltage curve at 5°C from that at 20°C, making some correction for the effect of temperature on the passive Cl^- channel. The resulting current-voltage curve for the pump indicates an equilibrium potential of −190 mV and shows the expected saturation of the pump conductance with large hyper- or de-polarizations. A slowly responding component of the pump current was attributed to adjustments in the ATP pool after sudden changes in pump activity. Again, the equilibrium potential of the pump corresponds with a stoichiometry of 2 ions/ATP, and the pump consumption appears to be of the order of 5% of the ATP turnover.

Riccia

In this aquatic liverwort, Felle & Bentrup (36) have conducted the most detailed investigation of current-voltage relations of a "higher plant." The potential responds (slowly) to light in a similar manner to that of *Nitella translucens* (above). In the light the potential, −215 mV at pH 5.5, is close to the calculated value for ψ_1 (Equation 2 above). Also, the conductance is higher in the light and the current-voltage curve is linear at potentials not too far from ψ_1 as expected for the pump. In the dark, the membrane potential is closer to the potassium equilibrium value and the current-voltage curve shows rectification as expected for K^+ diffusion. Like Richards & Hope (148), Felle & Bentrup assume a significant passive permeability to H^+. It is not clear why this is necessary in either study, since all responses to pH could be attributed to the pump (see above).

Higher Plant Cells

These cells pose several problems for direct measurements of current flow through the electrogenic pump. There is the question of electrical coupling with adjacent cells through the plasmodesmata, the difficulty of inserting more than one electrode, and the possibility of underestimating the resistance due to damage by the electrode. Using a single electrode method, Anderson et al (1) found that cell membrane resistance in *Pisum sativum* roots increased severalfold over a 30 min period after penetration of the electrode, although there was no change in the membrane potential. A similar result was obtained by Lin & Hanson (100) in roots of *Zea mays*. The increase in resistance may indicate a gradual repair of damage caused by the microelectrode. The constant membrane potential with changing resistance suggests that the electrogenic pump rate is regulated so as to stabilize the membrane potential (1). Jones et al (75) quote other data in support of this idea. It may be noted that it is not simply a question of the pump reactions coming to equilibrium according to Equation 2, since the potential is often constant over a considerable range of external pH (75, 100).

Anderson et al (2) found no change in resistance of pea root cells on inhibition of the electrogenic pump with carbon monoxide. As noted earlier, it is difficult to interpret such a result since it is not clear whether a change in the ATP/ADP ratio would affect g_1 or only ψ_1 (cf Figure 1). Unlike carbon monoxide, cyanide caused an increase in membrane resistance, but the response was complex and suggested that cyanide had a direct effect on the cell membrane as well as on the respiratory energy supply.

Summary

Although electrical studies such as the construction of current-voltage curves offer a promising approach to the study of the primary and secondary transport systems at the cell membrane, the results obtained so far are fragmentary. When treatments such as light or respiratory inhibitors are applied, it is often not clear which component of the equivalent circuit (Figure 1) is being affected. Perhaps substances such as diethylstilbestrol (10, 78) or fusicoccin (118) will provide more specific tools for the experimental control of pump activity. Even so, changes in one membrane activity are apt to affect many other processes through changes in $\Delta \psi$ or ΔpH, and the system cannot be analyzed unless these factors are controlled or accounted for. Despite these complexities, the above survey shows that the necessary methods are available, and we can expect further progress in this area.

TRANSPORT OF ORGANIC MOLECULES: COTRANSPORT WITH H⁺

Bacteria

A wide range of transport substrates in bacteria are now believed to be cotransported or countertransported with protons, and are thus energized by the proton-motive force (53). For example, the β-galactoside "permease" in *Escherichia coli*, which was previously believed to be driven by ATP hydrolysis (155) or by redox reactions (11), is now accepted to be proton-linked (43, 76). Thus (43) the accumulation ratio of thiomethylgalactoside (TMG) comes to thermodynamic equilibrium with the calculated proton-motive force according to the equation:

$$-59 \log (TMG)_{in}/ (TMG)_{out} = \psi - 59 \,\Delta pH \qquad\qquad 5.$$

The two components of the proton-motive force, ψ and ΔpH, can be controlled by the use of various uncouplers and antibiotics. Uncouplers such as carbonyl cyanide, m-chlorophenyl hydrazone (CCCP) cause a collapse of the total proton-motive force. Indeed, sensitivity to CCCP can provide a simple test for the dependence of a bacterial transport system on the proton-motive force (52). The antibiotic valinomycin, in contrast, promotes rapid flux of K^+ ions, thus bringing the potential to the K^+ equilibrium value. If the potential is reduced by valinomycin plus K^+, the pump tends to accelerate and to increase ΔpH. Conversely, nigericin promotes a neutral exchange of K^+ and H^+, thus collapsing ΔpH and allowing an increase in ψ.

As indicated above, the accumulation of β-galactosides depends on both ψ and ΔpH. By measuring transport while manipulating the pH and potential gradients across the membrane of *Staphylococcus aureus,* Niven & Hamilton (127) concluded that basic, neutral, and acidic amino acids are accumulated in response to ψ, total pmf, and ΔpH respectively. This corresponds to the idea that the three groups of amino acids are transported as positively charged molecules without H^+, positively charged complexes with H^+, and neutral complexes with H^+, respectively.

A further complication suggested by Kaback (76) concerns the way in which proton-dependent transport systems may be affected by external pH. In Kaback's system (membrane vesicles from *E. coli*) neither the membrane potential nor the internal pH are very sensitive to changes in external pH. It is clear therefore that the total pmf available to drive proton-dependent transport falls drastically with increasing external pH. It is proposed that the cell compensates for this by a change in the stoichiometry of the carrier with pH. Thus a decrease in energy available per proton at high external pH may be compensated by carrying two protons with each substrate molecule instead of one.

This by no means exhausts the possibilities of bacterial transport. It has been proposed that in some species the proton gradient energizes an efflux of sodium, and the sodium gradient in turn drives the transport of amino acids (92, 181). In addition to these transport systems depending directly or indirectly on the proton-motive force, there exist transport systems which are dependent on other energy sources entirely (52, 147).

Fungi

Slayman & Slayman (167, 168) have given evidence for a proton-dependent cotransport of sugars in *Neurospora.* If the uptake system is derepressed by starvation, addition of glucose or its nonmetabolizable analogue 3-O-methyl-D-glucose causes a large depolarization of the membrane as well as a brief net uptake of protons. The peak depolarization shows a saturation curve when plotted against external glucose concentration, with a half-maximal value at 42 μM, corresponding to the apparent K_m of the glucose transport system. The uptake of protons corresponds initially to an approximately 1 : 1 ratio of H^+ : sugar. Both the proton uptake and the depolarization decrease with time, presumably due to a speeding up of the H^+-efflux pump.

Various strains of *Saccharomyces* also show a stoichiometric uptake of protons with various sugars and amino acids when metabolism is inhibited (18, 22, 31, 157, 158). These systems are difficult to analyze, not only because information on the membrane potential is lacking, but also because there are a number of transport systems with overlapping specificities. These various transport systems apparently differ in the ratio of protons absorbed per molecule of substrate (158).

Algae

Komor, Tanner, and their co-workers have conducted an intensive series of investigations on sugar transport in *Chlorella.* As in *Neurospora,* there is a transient influx of protons (80) and depolarization (86) on addition of sugar. An initial stoichiometry of 1 H^+ : 1 glucose was found, and for a number of different sugars the concentration of sugar giving half-maximal proton uptake was the same as that giving half-maximal sugar uptake (84).

The total proton-motive force across the cell membrane of *Chlorella* was shown to be sufficient to drive the observed 1600-fold accumulation of 6-deoxyglucose (86). Uptake is strictly dependent on an energy supply, presumably to generate the pmf, but this energy can be provided by either respiration or cyclic photophosphorylation (29, 82). From the stimulation of respiration during transport, it was calculated that one ATP molecule was required for the uptake of one sugar molecule (28). On the other hand, a value of approximately one was also obtained for the quantum efficiency for sugar uptake in far-red light (82). Since the stoichiometry of phosphorylation in far-red light is believed to be 1 ATP/2 quanta (21), 1 sugar / quantum corresponds to 2 sugars/ATP, which seems more in line with the expected stoichiometry of $2H^+$/ATP for the proton pump. It has not yet been shown whether an artificially created proton-motive force will also drive transport in the absence of ATP.

Komor & Tanner (85) also showed that proton dissociation from the sugar-proton carrier occurs with a pK_a of 6.85. The protonated form has a 100-fold higher affinity for sugars, which accounts for an observed difference in K_m for influx versus efflux (81). The difference in affinity is not, however, enough to explain the 1600-fold accumulation, and it is postulated that the rate of translocation of free carrier across the membrane is affected by the membrane potential (81, 85).

Higher Plants

The case for electrogenic cotransport of H^+ and organic molecules in higher plants has not been as thoroughly documented as in the organisms discussed above. However, transient depolarizations (34, 75, 142) and proton influxes (83, 117, 142) have been observed on addition of sugars to various plant tissues. Depolarizations have also been demonstrated on addition of amino acids (34, 35, 177), and there seems to be a relation between the magnitude of the depolarization and the rate of amino acid transport (35). Uptake of sugars and amino acids also appears to be affected by factors controlling the proton-motive force (34, 35, 45, 46, 83, 117, 118, 177). Phloem sieve tubes, which have as their main function the transport of organic molecules, have several characteristics which would favor H^+-sugar cotransport. These include an alkaline sap, high K^+ content, high ATP and ATPase levels (46, 117).

It seems likely that for higher plants, as indeed for most organisms, cotransport with ions is the major mechanism of energy coupling for transport of organic molecules.

POTASSIUM TRANSPORT

The question of whether active uptake of K^+ occurs in plants has been reviewed by many authors (60, 65, 111, 116). Although there have been many cautions about the reliability of the various measurements involved, i.e. cytoplasmic activities, membrane potentials, plasmalemma fluxes, the general view is that K^+ can be actively transported across the plasmalemma of plant cells. Apart from kinetic evidence for carrier-mediated transport (33), there is the fact that the membrane potential usually falls short of that required for net passive K^+ uptake to an increasing extent as the external concentration of K^+ is decreased (e.g. 23), although net uptake is known to occur from very dilute external solutions. In one recent report (100) the observation that net K^+ uptake occurs against an electrochemical gradient is supported by the fact that addition of valinomycin causes a transient hyperpolarization.

Relation to H^+ Efflux

It is agreed that the energy source for cation transport is ATP (60, 65, 70, 96, 108, 132, 178) but the manner of energy coupling is not established. It seems very likely that K^+ uptake is in fact mediated directly or indirectly by the electrogenic H^+-efflux pump. This conclusion is based not only on the many observations of K^+/H^+ exchanges (e.g. 68, 69, 90, 149) but also on the fact that many treatments which affect the activity of the electrogenic pump have a parallel effect on K^+ uptake. These include specific wavelengths of light (175, cf 113), aging (99, 139), pH (139), hormones (119, 120), and fusicoccin (23, 120, 136, 137). This parallel activity of the electrogenic pump and K^+ uptake is found at low K^+ concentrations, where there is more evidence for carrier-mediated K^+ transport (see above), as well as at higher K^+ concentrations, where diffusion may play a larger role (137). In addition to a common dependence on the above factors, none of which appear to act through the energy supply, it has been noted above that both the electrogenic pump and the transport of K^+ are energized directly or indirectly by ATP. As discussed below, a K^+-activated ATPase located at the plasmalemma shows features which suggest its involvement in both H^+ and K^+ transport.

If it is accepted that K^+ uptake can be carrier-mediated and active, and that it is dependent on the electrogenic H^+-efflux pump, there is still a question as to whether K^+ is carried by the pump itself, neutralizing the H^+ efflux partially and perhaps to a variable extent (139), or whether a separate carrier is involved. For instance, a carrier which cotransports K^+ and H^+ inward in exchange for Na^+ outward has been suggested for *Neurospora* by Slayman (163). In a simple membrane system, it would be easy to test for the dependence of K^+ transport on the proton gradient by dissipating the proton gradient with a proton carrier such as CCCP (cf 52). Unfortunately, it is usually difficult to separate effects of CCCP on the cell membrane from its effects on ATP production by mitochondria. However, according to Slayman & Slayman (168), K^+ uptake is sensitive to uncouplers in a mutant of *Neurospora* in which the ATP level remains high. Felle & Bentrup (37) have recently reported that the effect of CCCP on the conductance of the cell membrane can be distinguished from its effect on ATP levels in the liverwort *Riccia fluitans*. This may allow a more direct test for dependence of various transport processes on the proton gradient.

K^+-ATPase

The identification of transport ATPases in plants is beset with difficulties such as the separation and identification of the plasma membrane, the large background component of ATPase which is not ion-stimulated, and the separation of cation versus anion effects. However, one ATPase component found in a number of higher plant species (42, 58, 95) has the following characteristics. It is probably located at the plasmalemma (e.g. 67). It is activated by Mg^{2+} and further stimulated by K^+. There is no synergistic effect of Na^++K^+. It shows little sensitivity to the inhibitors ouabain or oligomycin but is inhibited by N,N'-dicyclohexylcarbodiimide (DCCD) (94). All of these features are also found in the plasma membrane ATPases of *Neurospora* (15, 154) and of bacteria (51), although stimulation by K^+ is not found in all bacterial species (51). Additional common features of the K^+-ATPases of higher plants and *Neurospora* include a pH optimum between pH 6 and pH 7, a K_M for $Mg \cdot ATP$ of 1–2 mM, and sensitivity to *p*-chloromercuribenzoate (9, 15, 66, 94, 154). An ATPase from the yeast *Schizosaccharomyces pombe* (30) also shares most of the properties of these enzymes.

The plasma membrane ATPases of the above fungi and of bacteria have been implicated in the electrogenic transport of protons (44, 54, 162). A similar role for the cation-stimulated ATPase of higher plants has received recent support from the demonstration (12) that it is stimulated by fusicoccin (cf above). That this enzyme also has a role in K^+ uptake is suggested by correlations between K^+-stimulated ATPase activity and K^+ transport rates, when these are compared among various species (42) and over a wide range of concentrations (94, 180). The multiphasic kinetics (126) of K^+ transport and K^+-ATPase activity are remarkably similar (94). However, the significance of this observation is obscure, since anions (32, 125) and even sugars (103) show similar transport kinetics, although they are not known to activate the ATPase.

None of this evidence throws much light on the question of whether the cations are carried by the ATPase itself. Since the ATPase activity in higher plants has been measured in ostensibly closed vesicles (67, 179), it would be possible for ions to stimulate the ATPase indirectly by changing the potential or the proton-motive force across the membrane. However, with *Neurospora* ATPase, a similar cation stimulation was obtained using plasma membranes prepared as open sheets (15). Thus it seems likely that in *Neurospora,* stimulation occurs by direct binding of the ion to the ATPase. This is not to say that the bound ions are necessarily transported. In fact, as pointed out above, the sensitivity of K^+ uptake to CCCP (168) suggests that K^+ transport in *Neurospora* is dependent on the proton-motive force. Clearly, further investigation is needed to answer these questions.

SODIUM TRANSPORT

Na⁺ Efflux: Coupling with K⁺ or H⁺ Influx

Plant cells, like animal cells, typically maintain a high ratio of $K^+ : Na^+$ in the cytoplasm, and there is evidence that Na^+ is actively transported out of the cytoplasm at both the plasmalemma and the tonoplast (133, 135, 176). Na^+ efflux is usually increased in the presence of external K^+ (73, 115, 144, 145). Raven (145) showed that in *Hydrodictyon africanum,* Na^+ efflux and K^+ influx have similar apparent K_m values for external K^+. In addition (145, 146), both of these fluxes, in contrast to the active influx of Cl^-, are inhibited by ouabain (0.5–1.0 mM) and by CCCP (5×10^{-6} M), are relatively insensitive to the photosynthetic inhibitor dichlorophenyl-dimethylurea (DCMU), and are stimulated by red light (705–730 nm wavelength). These results suggest that there is a close coupling between the two fluxes.

Although there have been a few other reports of inhibition by ouabain at rather high concentrations (24, 27, 115), this specific inhibitor of the (Na^++K^+)-activated ATPase of animal cells is usually ineffective in plant material (e.g. 39, 64, 144, 159). In other respects also, the ATPases of plant cell membranes (see below) do not resemble those of animal cells. Moreover, Ratner & Jacoby (144) have shown that ^{22}Na efflux from barley root tips is enhanced by external K^+ only when K^+ uptake is associated with a net efflux of H^+. It was found in addition that low external pH itself enhances Na^+ efflux, even when the respiratory energy supply is inhibited. It is therefore proposed (144) that Na^+ efflux is achieved by means of an H^+/Na^+ antiport, driven by the proton-motive force across the cell membrane. A similar countertransport of Na^+ and H^+ has also been proposed for some bacteria (92, 181, 185), fungi (163), and blue-green algae (130).

Na+ Influx

In higher plants (71, 144) active efflux of Na^+ is more readily observed in the relatively nonvacuolated cells of root tips, whereas highly vacuolated cells may show a significant net influx of sodium which is dependent on metabolic energy. Both the Na^+ efflux from root tips and its influx into vacuolated cells are more prominent in the more salt-tolerant species (71). Na^+ influx is particularly large in tissue with a low salt content (134) and in some halophytes (e.g. 140). Na^+ influx at the cell membrane is always down an electrochemical gradient and often insensitive to metabolic inhibition (e.g. 144, 145), whereas Na^+ uptake into the vacuole is both against a gradient (see above) and dependent on metabolic energy (144).

(Na++K+)-ATPase

Kylin and his co-workers (50, 77, 88) have demonstrated some complex interactions between Na^+ and K^+ in the stimulation of membrane ATPase activities in sugar beet (*Beta vulgaris* L.) and the mangrove *Avicennia nitida* Jacq. It was thought that the effects of Na^+ and K^+ may have some physiological significance since both of these species are halophilic. Moreover, a study of various strains of sugar beet with differing capacities for Na^+ accumulation showed corresponding differences in the sensitivity of the ATPase activities to Na^+ and K^+ (89). Since the membrane fractions have not been characterized, the various observed ATPase activities cannot be ascribed to any particular locations in the cell. These (Na^++K^+)-ATPases could perhaps be responsible for Na^+ transport at either the plasmalemma or the tonoplast, or at both of these membranes. However, the evidence for their involvement in Na^+ transport at all is incomplete.

ANION TRANSPORT

ATP Versus Redox Energy

The energetics of Cl^- transport have been reviewed by MacRobbie (115, 116). Cl^- is actively transported toward the vacuole at both the plasmalemma and the tonoplast. The active influx of Cl⁻ at the plasmalemma has been thought to depend directly on redox energy rather than on ATP. This view is based largely on studies with *Nitella translucens* (113, 114) and *Hydrodictyon africanum* (e.g. 146). In these algae, both cation and Cl⁻ fluxes are stimulated by light, but only the cation fluxes are stimulated in far-red light or in the presence of DCMU. This suggested that ATP production by cyclic photophosphorylation can drive cation fluxes but not Cl⁻ uptake. Unfortunately, none of these studies included actual measurements of ATP concentrations. Miller & Spanswick (121) have now shown that, under aerobic conditions, ATP levels in *Nitella* are unchanged by light, as seems to be the case in many photosynthetic cells (46, 97, 108, 178). Since cation transport at least is still believed to be energized by ATP (see above), the stimulatory effects of light have nothing to do with the energy supply, but indicate some other regulatory effect on transport rates. The above experiments thus show that there are differences in the cellular regulation of Cl⁻ transport compared with that of K⁺ and Na⁺ transport, but give no evidence for differences in energy supply.

Other experiments on these same algae (see 115, 116) have shown differences between K⁺ and Cl⁻ uptake in their sensitivity to various inhibitors, and especially to uncouplers such as CCCP. The lower sensitivity of Cl⁻ uptake to CCCP again suggested that ATP is not required for Cl⁻ influx. Although ATP levels in *Nitella* are greatly affected by CCCP (121), there has been no quantitative comparison of the effects of CCCP on ATP levels and ion fluxes in these cells. There are therefore many possible explanations for the difference between cation and anion fluxes, since CCCP could affect proton gradients at the plasmalemma, or other unknown intracellular processes, before affecting ATP levels. Again, it must be concluded that, in the absence of further information, these experiments give little evidence for any particular mode of energy coupling to Cl⁻ transport in these cells. These comments also apply to some studies on leaves of higher plants, where the effects of DCMU and of CCCP have been interpreted in terms of coupling of Cl⁻ transport to electron flow (109, 128).

Claims for a linkage of transport to redox reactions rather than to ATP hydrolysis have also been made for storage tissue of higher plants. Thus Atkinson and coworkers (7, 8, 138) found no correlation between transport rates and ATP levels in carrot (*Daucus carota* L.) and beet (*Beta vulgaris* L.). However, similar studies on beet by Petraglia & Poole (132) gave opposite results. Both cation and anion influx at the plasmalemma showed a close correlation with ATP content in the presence of various inhibitors. Possible explanations for the discrepancy include both theoretical and technical factors. Thus Lin & Hanson (98) point out that an inhibitor such as L-ethionine may reduce ATP levels without reducing "energy charge" (6). On the other hand, it is difficult to measure ATP levels under N₂ since even a brief exposure of the tissue to air restores the ATP content to the aerobic level (132).

Another study on carrot storage tissue by Cram (25) showed that Cl⁻ influx at the plasmalemma was less sensitive to CCCP and oligomycin than was Cl⁻ influx at the tonoplast. However, the plasmalemma influx was inhibited under N₂. Studies on other tissues (4, 5, 93, 112) also suggest different effects of inhibitors at the plasmalemma and tonoplast. Again, ATP measurements are lacking, and interpretation in terms of redox coupling (25) remains speculative.

Most other investigations (see 60, 65, 115, 116), including studies of Cl^- transport in other species as well as studies of transport of other ions such as phosphate, have concluded that ATP is the probable energy source, although again few of these studies actually measured ATP content. Most studies in which ATP has been measured have found a correlation between ATP levels and transport rates for chloride (70, 74, 108, 131, 132), sulfate (131), and phosphate (14). In the case of phosphate transport in corn roots, Lin & Hanson (98) consider that ATP could be the energy source if the coupling is via a proton gradient. The same conclusion could be drawn from the data of Jeanjean (72) for phosphate uptake by *Chlorella*.

In conclusion, the current evidence, though it remains inadequate, probably favors ATP as the ultimate energy source for all anion transport.

Cotransport with H^+

The uptake of anions with H^+, or in exchange for OH^-, has frequently been proposed (e.g. 68, 69), although only more recently (169) has it been postulated that the proton gradient alone provides an adequate driving force. Thus Smith (169, 170) suggested that cotransport of Cl^- with H^+ could account for many of the phenomena observed in Characean cells, including some dramatic effects of amines on Cl^- uptake. On further investigation (107, 171, 184), the evidence for cotransport with H^+ was weakened, since it appears that even if Cl^- uptake is energized by the proton gradient, its rate is controlled by other factors. In addition, measurements of cytoplasmic pH (171, 184) show that the proton gradient is inadequate to drive Cl^- uptake at high external pH unless $2H^+$ are transported for each Cl^-. This would make Cl^- transport electrogenic, but the effect would not be detectable in *Chara* (171). A small depolarization is in fact observed in carrot cells on substitution of Cl^- for SO_4^{2-} (3, 26), but there is at present no evidence that this is correlated with Cl^- uptake.

Hyperpolarizing effects of Cl^- transport in *Acetabularia* (151) and in *Limonium* salt glands (62) suggest a direct linkage of Cl^- transport to metabolism in these cases. In addition, Lucas (105) has demonstrated in *Chara corallina* an extremely active uptake of HCO_3^-, which is not obligately linked to OH^- or H^+ fluxes (106), and thus presumably depends directly on metabolic energy. There is little evidence available for other anions, although phosphate uptake could perhaps be driven by the proton gradient [see above and (22)].

Anion-ATPases

The best example of an anion-stimulated ATPase, which shows a correlation with anion transport rates in a plant system, is the Cl^--ATPase of the *Limonium* salt gland (63). This ATPase is strongly stimulated by Cl^- ions, and its activity is induced in parallel with the induction of Cl^- transport when the tissue is loaded with salt. The induction is prevented by puromycin, which has no inhibitory effect on the activity of the induced enzyme. These observations support the idea of a direct coupling of Cl^- transport to ATPase activity, rather than to redox energy or H^+ fluxes.

There are also indications of anion-stimulated ATPase activity in other plant membrane preparations, both from the plasmalemma (19, 58) and the tonoplast (101, 102), as well as in uncharacterized membranes (150). None of these activities has yet been correlated with anion transport, although the vacuolar anion-ATPase activity is correlated with H^+ transport (101).

In summary, there has been little clear evidence so far, and little agreement, about energy coupling for anion transport. Nevertheless, there are indications that anion transport is dependent on ATP levels, that at least in some cases it is not proton-linked, and that there is anion-stimulated ATPase activity in plant membranes. Thus the evidence, at least for Cl^- and HCO_3^- transport at the plasmalemma, seems to favor a primary transport system linked to the hydrolysis of ATP.

SUMMARY AND OUTLOOK

It is perhaps characteristic of the progress of science that two membrane activities which have been somewhat neglected in classical plant physiology, namely, the transport of protons and of sugars, are now on their way to being the best understood, while energy coupling for transport of the intensively studied major ions, K^+ and Cl^-, is still in doubt. Recent advances owe much to concepts developed with simpler membrane systems from bacteria or from cell organelles, and call for further efforts to develop membrane vesicles from plant cells. At present the most promising subcellular systems are isolated vacuoles from higher plants (101, 102) and plasma membrane vesicles from *Neurospora* (153). A preparation of plasmalemma vesicles from higher plants (179) could not be shown to perform active transport, whereas other membrane vesicle preparations (91) have not yet been well characterized or shown to respond specifically to ATP. One study (29) has emphasized the need to control the release of free fatty acids during cell breakage to avoid damage to transport systems.

In addition to studies with membrane vesicles, electrical studies on intact cells can provide a unique approach not available for bacterial or subcellular systems. However, the complexities of regulation in intact cells, and the degree of interaction of transport events through the membrane potential or the cytoplasmic pH, emphasize the need for greater caution in interpreting effects of inhibitors or light on transport and the need to measure all relevant variables. There is still a lack of specific inhibitors for transport processes in plants, although fusicoccin (118) promises to be a most useful specific reagent.

Looking beyond our immediate need to ascertain the types of energy coupling involved in the transport of cations and anions, there are two other sets of problems waiting to be investigated. These are, on the one hand, the molecular mechanisms of transport across membranes, and on the other hand, the ways in which transport processes are integrated into the overall economy of the cell. The most promising system for a molecular approach is the H^+-sugar cotransport system of *Chlorella*, for which the inducible protein has been partially purified and characterized (38) although so far only in an inactive form. As for the integration of transport into the energy balance of the cell, I have said nothing about the classical problem of salt respiration (17) nor about the status of transport in the cell's priorities for energy utilization, and little about the proportion of cellular energy devoted to transport, or its efficiency of energy conversion. Only when these questions are also answered can we put membrane transport into perspective in the bioenergetics of the plant cell.

ACKNOWLEDGMENTS

I thank Dr. Sarah P. Gibbs and Dr. Gordon A. Maclachlan for their helpful comments on the manuscript.

Literature Cited

1. Anderson, W. P., Hendrix, D. L., Higinbotham, N. 1974. Higher plant cell membrane resistance by a single intracellular electrode method. *Plant Physiol.* 53:122–24
2. Anderson, W. P., Hendrix, D. L., Higinbotham, N. 1974. The effect of cyanide and carbon monoxide on the electrical potential and resistance of cell membranes. *Plant Physiol.* 54:712–16
3. Anderson, W. P., Robertson, R. N., Wright, B. J. 1977. Membrane potentials in carrot root cells. *Aust. J. Plant Physiol.* 4:241–52
4. Arisz, W. H. 1953. Active uptake, vacuole-secretion and plasmatic transport of chloride-ions in leaves of *Vallisneria spiralis. Acta Bot. Neerl.* 1:506–15
5. Arisz, W. H. 1958. Influence of inhibitors on the uptake and the transport of chloride ions in leaves of *Vallisneria spiralis. Acta Bot. Neerl.* 7:1–32
6. Atkinson, D. E. 1972. The adenylate energy charge in metabolic regulation. In *Horizons of Bioenergetics*, ed. A. San Pietro, H. Gest, pp. 83–96. New York: Academic
7. Atkinson, M. R., Eckerman, G., Grant, M., Robertson, R. N. 1966. Salt accumulation and adenosine triphosphate in carrot xylem tissue. *Proc. Natl. Acad. Sci. USA* 55:560–64
8. Atkinson, M. R., Polya, G. M. 1968. Effects of L-ethionine on adenosine triphosphate levels, respiration, and salt accumulation in carrot xylem tissue. *Aust. J. Biol. Sci.* 21:409–20
9. Balke, N. E., Hodges, T. K. 1975. Plasma membrane adenosine triphosphatase of oat roots. Activation and inhibition by Mg^{2+} and ATP. *Plant Physiol.* 55:83–86
10. Balke, N. E., Hodges, T. K. 1977. Inhibition of ion absorption by diethylstilbestrol. *Plant Physiol.* 59:Suppl. 78, p. 15

11. Barnes, E. M. Jr., Kaback, H. R. 1970. β-galactoside transport in bacterial membrane preparations: energy coupling via membrane-bound D-lactic dehydrogenase. *Proc. Natl. Acad. Sci. USA* 66:1190–98
12. Beffagna, N., Cocucci, S., Marré, E. 1977. Stimulating effect of fusicoccin on K-activated ATPase in plasmalemma preparations from higher plant tissues. *Plant Sci. Lett.* 8:91–98
13. Bentrup, F. W. 1975. Cell electrophysiology and membrane transport. *Progr. Bot.* 37:64–77
14. Bledsoe, C., Cole, C. V., Ross, C. 1969. Oligomycin inhibition of phosphate uptake and ATP labeling in excised maize roots. *Plant Physiol.* 44:1040–44
15. Bowman, B. J., Slayman, C. W. 1977. Characterization of plasma membrane adenosine triphosphatase of *Neurospora crassa. J. Biol. Chem.* 252:3357–63
16. Brand, M. D., Lehninger, A. L. 1977. H^+/ATP ratio during ATP hydrolysis by mitochondria: Modification of the chemiosmotic theory. *Proc. Natl. Acad. Sci. USA* 74:1955–59
17. Briggs, G. E., Hope, A. B., Robertson, R. N. 1961. *Electrolytes and Plant Cells.* Oxford: Blackwell. 217 pp.
18. Brocklehurst, R., Gardner, D., Eddy, A. A. 1977. The absorption of protons with α-methyl glucoside and α-thioethyl glucoside by the yeast N.C.Y.C. 240. *Biochem. J.* 162:591–99
19. Cambraia, J., Balke, N., Hodges, T. K. 1976. Cation- and anion-sensitive ATPases of the plasma membrane of oat roots. *Plant Physiol.* 57:Suppl. 434, p. 84
20. Caplan, S. R., Essig, A. 1977. A thermodynamic treatment of active sodium transport. *Curr. Top. Membr. Transp.* 9:145–76

21. Chain, R. K., Arnon, D. I. 1977. Quantum efficiency of photosynthetic energy conversion. *Proc. Natl. Acad. Sci. USA* 74:3377–81

22. Cockburn, M., Earnshaw, P., Eddy, A. A. 1975. The stoichiometry of the absorption of protons with phosphate and L-glutamate by yeasts of the genus *Saccharomyces. Biochem. J.* 146:705–12

23. Cocucci, M., Marré, E., Ballarin Denti, A., Scacchi, A. 1976. Characteristics of fusicoccin-induced changes of transmembrane potential and ion uptake in maize root segments. *Plant Sci. Lett.* 6:143–56

24. Cram, W. J. 1968. The effects of ouabain on sodium and potassium fluxes in excised root tissue of carrot. *J. Exp. Bot.* 19:611–16

25. Cram, W. J. 1969. Respiration and energy-dependent movements of chloride at plasmalemma and tonoplast of carrot root cells. *Biochim. Biophys. Acta* 173:213–22

26. Cram, W. J. 1975. Relationships between chloride transport and electrical potential differences in carrot root cells. *Aust. J. Plant Physiol.* 2:301–10

27. Cummins, J. T., Strand, J. A., Vaughan, B. E. 1966. Sodium transport in *Ulva. Biochim. Biophys. Acta* 126:330–37

28. Decker, M., Tanner, W. 1972. Respiratory increase and active hexose uptake of *Chlorella vulgaris. Biochim. Biophys. Acta* 266:661–69

29. Decker, M., Tanner, W. 1976. Rapid release of free fatty acids during cell breakage and their effects on a sugar-proton cotransport system in *Chlorella vulgaris. FEBS Lett.* 60:346–48

30. Delhez, J., Dufour, J. P., Goffeau, A. 1976. Comparaison des propriétés des ATPases mitochondriales et plasmiques chez la levure *Schizosaccharomyces pombe. Arch. Int. Physiol. Biochim.* 84:602–3

31. Eddy, A. A., Nowacki, J. A. 1971. Stoichiometrical proton and potassium ion movements accompanying the absorption of amino acids by yeast *Saccharomyces carlsbergensis. Biochem. J.* 122:701–11

32. Elzam, O. E., Rains, D. W., Epstein, E. 1964. Ion transport kinetics in plant tissue: Complexity of the chloride absorption isotherm. *Biochim. Biophys. Res. Commun.* 15:273–76

33. Epstein, E. 1976. Kinetics of ion transport and the carrier concept. See Ref. 111, 2B:70–94

34. Etherton, B., Nuovo, G. J. 1974. Rapid changes in membrane potentials of oat coleoptile cells induced by amino acids and carbohydrates. *Plant Physiol.* 53:Suppl. 277, p. 49

35. Etherton, B., Rubinstein, B. 1977. Evidence for amino acid-H$^+$ co-transport in oat coleoptiles. *Plant Physiol.* 59: Suppl. 639, p. 117

36. Felle, H., Bentrup, F. W. 1976. Effect of light upon membrane potential conductance and ion fluxes in *Riccia fluitans. J. Membr. Biol.* 27:153–70

37. Felle, H., Bentrup, F. W. 1977. A study of the primary effect of the uncoupler carbonyl cyanide *m*-chlorophenylhydrazone on membrane potential and conductance in *Riccia fluitans. Biochim. Biophys. Acta* 464:179–87

38. Fenzl, F., Decker, M., Haass, D., Tanner, W. 1977. Characterization and partial purification of an inducible protein related to hexose proton cotransport of *Chlorella vulgaris. Eur. J. Biochem.* 72:509–14

39. Findlay, G. P., Hope, A. B., Pitman, M. G., Smith, F. A., Walker, N. A. 1969. Ionic fluxes in cells of *Chara corallina. Biochim. Biophys. Acta* 183:565–76

40. Finkelstein, A. 1964. Carrier model for active transport of ions across a mosaic membrane. *Biophys. J.* 4:421–40

41. Finn, A. L. 1976. Changing concepts of transepithelial sodium transport. *Physiol. Rev.* 56:453–64

42. Fisher, J. D., Hansen, D., Hodges, T. K. 1970. Correlation between ion fluxes and ion-stimulated adenosine triphosphatase activity of plant roots. *Plant Physiol.* 46:812–14

43. Flagg, J. L., Wilson, T. H. 1977. A protonmotive force as the source of energy for galactoside transport in energy depleted *Escherichia coli. J. Membr. Biol.* 31:233–55

44. Foury, F., Boutry, M., Goffeau, A. 1976. Fonctions de transport de l'ATPase plasmique de *Schizosaccharomyces pombe. Arch. Int. Physiol. Biochim.* 84:618–19

45. Giaquinta, R. 1977. Possible role of pH gradient and membrane ATPase in the loading of sucrose into the sieve tubes. *Nature* 267:369–70

46. Giaquinta, R. 1977. Phloem loading of sucrose. pH dependence and selectivity. *Plant Physiol.* 59:750–55

47. Gradmann, D. 1975. Analog circuit of the *Acetabularia* membrane. *J. Membr. Biol.* 25:183–208

48. Gradmann, D. 1976. "Metabolic" action potentials in *Acetabularia*. *J. Membr. Biol.* 29:23–45
49. Gradmann, D., Klemke, W. 1974. Current-voltage relationship of the electrogenic pump in *Acetabularia mediterranea*. In *Membrane Transport in Plants*, ed. U. Zimmermann, J. Dainty, pp. 131–38. Berlin, Heidelberg, New York: Springer-Verlag. 473 pp.
50. Hansson, G., Kylin, A. 1969. ATPase activities in homogenates from sugarbeet roots, relation to Mg^{2+} and $(Na^+ + K^+)$-stimulation. *Z. Pflanzenphysiol.* 60:270–75
51. Harold, F. M. 1972. Conservation and transformation of energy by bacterial membranes. *Bacteriol. Rev.* 36:172–230
52. Harold, F. M. 1975. On the diversity of links between transport and metabolism in bacteria. In *Molecular Aspects of Membrane Phenomena*, ed. H. R. Kaback et al, pp. 266–77. Berlin: Springer-Verlag. 338 pp.
53. Harold, F. M. 1977. Membranes and energy transduction in bacteria. *Curr. Top. Bioenerg.* 6:83–149
54. Harold, F. M., Pavlasová, E., Baarda, J. R. 1970. A transmembrane pH gradient in *Streptococcus faecalis:* origin and dissipation by proton conductors and N,N'-dicyclohexylcarbodiimide. *Biochim. Biophys. Acta* 196:235–44
55. Hauska, G., Trebst, A. 1977. Proton translocation in chloroplasts. *Curr. Top. Bioenerg.* 6:151–220
56. Heber, U. 1974. Metabolite exchange between chloroplasts and cytoplasm. *Ann. Rev. Plant Physiol.* 25:393–421
57. Heinz, E., Geck, P., Pietrzyk, C. 1976. Driving forces of amino acid transport in animal cells. *Ann. NY Acad. Sci.* 264:428–41
58. Hendrix, D. L., Kennedy, R. M. 1977. Adenosine triphosphatase from soybean callus and root cells. *Plant Physiol.* 59:264–67
59. Higinbotham, N. 1970. Movement of ions and electrogenesis in higher plant cells. *Am. Zool.* 10:393–403
60. Higinbotham, N. 1973. The mineral absorption process in plants. *Bot. Rev.* 39:15–69
61. Higinbotham, N., Anderson, W. P. 1974. Electrogenic pumps in higher plant cells. *Can. J. Bot.* 52:1011–21
62. Hill, A. E., Hill, B. S. 1973. The electrogenic chloride pump of the *Limonium* salt gland. *J. Membr. Biol.* 12:129–44
63. Hill, B. S., Hill, A. E. 1973. ATP-driven chloride pumping and ATPase activity in the *Limonium* salt gland. *J. Membr. Biol.* 12:145–58
64. Hodges, T. K. 1966. Oligomycin inhibition of ion transport in plant roots. *Nature* 209:425–26
65. Hodges, T. K. 1973. Ion absorption by plant roots. *Adv. Agron.* 25:163–207
66. Hodges, T. K. 1976. ATPases associated with membranes of plant cells. See Ref. 111, 2A:260–83
67. Hodges, T. K., Leonard, R. T., Bracker, C. E., Keenan, T. W. 1972. Purification of an ion-stimulated adenosine triphosphatase from plant roots: Association with plasma membranes. *Proc. Natl. Acad. Sci. USA* 69:3307–11
68. Jackson, P. C., Adams, H. R. 1963. Cation-anion balance during potassium and sodium absorption by barley roots. *J. Gen. Physiol.* 46:369–86
69. Jacobson, L., Overstreet, R., King, H. M., Handley, R. 1950. A study of potassium absorption by barley roots. *Plant Physiol.* 25:639–47
70. Jacoby, B., Plessner, O. E. 1970. Oligomycin effect on ion absorption by excised barley roots and on their ATP content. *Planta* 90:215–21
71. Jacoby, B., Ratner, A. 1977. Metabolic sodium fluxes in roots of barley, corn, bean and vetch. *Plant Physiol.* 59:Suppl. 645, p. 118
72. Jeanjean, R. 1976. The effect of metabolic poisons on ATP level and on active phosphate uptake in *Chlorella pyrenoidosa*. *Physiol. Plant.* 37:107–10
73. Jeschke, W. D., Stelter, W. 1973. K^+-dependent net Na^+ efflux in roots of barley plants. *Planta* 114:251–58
74. Johansen, C., Lüttge, U. 1974. Respiration and photosynthesis as alternative energy sources for chloride uptake by *Tradescantia albiflora* leaf cells. *Z. Pflanzenphysiol.* 71:189–99
75. Jones, M. G. K., Novacky, A., Dropkin, V. H. 1975. Transmembrane potentials of parenchyma cells and nematode-induced transfer cells. *Protoplasma* 85:15–37
76. Kaback, H. R. 1976. Molecular biology and energetics of membrane transport. *J. Cell. Physiol.* 89:575–94
77. Karlsson, J., Kylin, A. 1974. Properties of Mg^{2+}-stimulated and $(Na^+ + K^+)$-activated adenosine-5'-triphosphatase from sugar beet cotyledons. *Physiol. Plant.* 32:136–42
78. Keifer, D., Spanswick, R. 1977. Membrane potential and resistance of *Chara australis*. *Plant Physiol.* 59:Suppl. 469, p. 85

79. Keynes, R. D. 1969. From frog skin to sheep rumen: a survey of transport of salts and water across multicellular structures. *Q. Rev. Biophys.* 2:177–281

80. Komor, E. 1973. Proton-coupled hexose transport in *Chlorella vulgaris. FEBS Lett.* 38:16–18

81. Komor, E., Haass, D., Komor, B., Tanner, W. 1973. The active hexose-uptake system of *Chlorella vulgaris. K_m-values* for 6-deoxyglucose influx and efflux and their contribution to sugar accumulation. *Eur. J. Biochem.* 39:193–200

82. Komor, E., Loos, E., Tanner, W. 1973. A confirmation of the proposed model for the hexose uptake system of *Chlorella vulgaris.* Anaerobic studies in the light and in the dark. *J. Membr. Biol.* 12:89–99

83. Komor, E., Rotter, M., Tanner, W. 1977. A proton-cotransport system in a higher plant: sucrose transport in *Ricinus communis. Plant Sci. Lett.* 9:153–62

84. Komor, E., Tanner, W. 1974. The hexose-proton symport system of *Chlorella vulgaris.* Specificity, stoichiometry and energetics of sugar-induced proton uptake. *Eur. J. Biochem.* 44:219–23

85. Komor, E., Tanner, W. 1974. The hexose-proton cotransport system of *Chlorella.* pH-dependent change in K_m values and translocation constants of the uptake system. *J. Gen. Physiol.* 64:568–81

86. Komor, E., Tanner, W. 1976. The determination of the membrane potential of *Chlorella vulgaris.* Evidence for electrogenic sugar transport. *Eur. J. Biochem.* 70:197–204

87. Korenbrot, J. I. 1977. Ion transport in membranes: incorporation of biological ion-translocating proteins in model membrane systems. *Ann. Rev. Physiol.* 39:19–49

88. Kylin, A., Gee, R. 1970. Adenosine triphosphatase activities in leaves of the mangrove *Avicennia nitida* Jacq. Influence of sodium to potassium ratios and salt concentrations. *Plant Physiol.* 45:169–72

89. Kylin, A., Hansson, G. 1971. Transport of sodium and potassium, and properties of (sodium + potassium)-activated adenosine triphosphatases: possible connection with salt tolerance in plants. In *Potassium in Biochemistry and Physiology.* Int. Potash Inst. Colloq., Skokloster, Sweden

90. Lado, P., Rasi-Caldogno, F., Colombo, R., De Michaelis, M. I., Marré, E. 1976. Effects of monovalent cations on IAA- and FC-stimulated proton-cation exchange in pea stem segments. *Plant Sci. Lett.* 7:199–209

91. Lai, Y. F., Thompson, J. E. 1972. Effects of germination on $Na^+ - K^+$-stimulated adenosine 5′-triphosphatase and ATP-dependent ion transport of isolated membranes from cotyledons. *Plant Physiol.* 50:452–57

92. Lanyi, J. K., Renthal, R., MacDonald, R. E. 1976. Light-induced glutamate transport in *Halobacterium halobium* envelope vesicles. II. Evidence that the driving force is a light-dependent sodium gradient. *Biochemistry* 15:1603–10

93. Laties, G. G. 1959. The generation of latent-ion-transport capacity. *Proc. Natl. Acad. Sci. USA* 45:163–72

94. Leonard, R. T., Hodges, T. K. 1973. Characterization of plasma membrane-associated adenosine triphosphatase activity of oat roots. *Plant Physiol.* 52:6–12

95. Leonard, R. T., Hotchkiss, C. W. 1976. Cation-stimulated adenosine triphosphatase activity and cation transport in corn roots. *Plant Physiol.* 58:331–35

96. Leonard, R. T., Mettler, I. J. 1977. Addition of ATP into isolated plant protoplasts and the effect on ion transport. *Plant Physiol.* 59:Suppl. 81, p. 15

97. Lilley, R. McC., Hope, A. B. 1971. Adenine nucleotide levels in cells of the marine alga, *Griffithsia. Aust. J. Biol. Sci.* 24:1351–54

98. Lin, W., Hanson, J. B. 1974. Phosphate absorption rates and adenosine 5′-triphosphate concentrations in corn root tissue. *Plant Physiol.* 54:250–56

99. Lin, W., Hanson, J. B. 1974. Increase in electrogenic membrane potential with washing of corn root tissue. *Plant Physiol.* 54:799–801

100. Lin, W., Hanson, J. B. 1976. Cell potentials, cell resistance, and proton fluxes in corn root tissue. Effects of dithioerythritol. *Plant Physiol.* 58:276–82

101. Lin, W., Wagner, G. J., Hind, G. 1977. The proton pump and membrane potential of intact vacuoles isolated from *Tulipa* petals. *Plant Physiol.* 59:Suppl. 471, p. 85

102. Lin, W., Wagner, G. J., Siegelman, H. W., Hind, G. 1977. Membrane-bound ATPase of intact vacuoles and tonoplasts isolated from mature plant tissue. *Biochim. Biophys. Acta* 465:110–17

103. Linask, J., Laties, G. G. 1973. Multiphasic absorption of glucose and 3-O-

methyl glucose by aged potato slices. *Plant Physiol.* 51:289–94

104. Lipmann, F. 1941. Metabolic generation and utilization of phosphate bond energy. *Adv. Enzymol.* 1:99–162

105. Lucas, W. J. 1975. Photosynthetic fixation of ¹⁴carbon by internodal cells of *Chara corallina. J. Exp. Bot.* 26:331–46

106. Lucas, W. J. 1976. Plasmalemma transport of HCO_3^- and OH^- in *Chara corallina:* Non-antiporter systems. *J. Exp. Bot.* 27:19–31

107. Lucas, W. J., Smith, F. A. 1976. Influence of irradiance on H^+ efflux and Cl^- influx in *Chara corallina:* an investigation aimed at testing two Cl^- transport models. *Aust. J. Plant Physiol.* 3:443–56

108. Lüttge, U., Ball, E. 1976. ATP levels and energy requirements of ion transport in cells of slices of greening barley leaves. *Z. Pflanzenphysiol.* 80:50–59

109. Lüttge, U., Pallaghy, C. K., Osmond, C. B. 1970. Coupling of ion transport in green cells of *Atriplex spongiosa* leaves to energy sources in the light and in the dark. *J. Membr. Biol.* 2:17–30

110. Lüttge, U., Pitman, M. G. 1976. Transport and energy. See Ref. 111, 2A:251–59

111. Lüttge, U., Pitman, M. G., eds. 1976. *Encyclopedia of Plant Physiology, New Series,* Vol. 2, Parts A, B. Berlin, Heidelberg, New York: Springer-Verlag. 2A, 400 pp.; 2B, 456 pp.

112. MacDonald, I. R., Laties, G. G. 1963. Kinetic studies of anion absorption by potato slices at 0°C. *Plant Physiol.* 38:38–44

113. MacRobbie, E. A. C. 1965. The nature of the coupling between light energy and active ion transport in *Nitella translucens. Biochim. Biophys. Acta* 94:64–73

114. MacRobbie, E. A. C. 1966. Metabolic effects on ion fluxes in *Nitella translucens.* I. Active influxes. *Aust. J. Biol. Sci.* 19:363–70

115. MacRobbie, E. A. C. 1970. The active transport of ions in plant cells. *Q. Rev. Biophys.* 3:251–94

116. MacRobbie, E. A. C. 1975. Ion transport in plant cells. *Curr. Top. Membr. Transp.* 7:1–48

117. Malek, F., Baker, D. A. 1977. Proton co-transport of sugars in phloem loading. *Planta* 135:297–99

118. Marré, E. 1977. Effects of fusicoccin and hormones on plant cell membrane activities: observations and hypotheses. In *Regulation of Cell Membrane Activities in Plants,* ed. E. Marré, O. Ciferri, pp. 185–202. Amsterdam, Oxford, New York: North Holland. 332 pp.

119. Marré, E., Lado, P., Ferroni, A., Ballarin Denti, A 1974. Transmembrane potential increase induced by auxin, benzyladenine and fusicoccin. Correlation with proton extrusion and cell enlargement. *Plant Sci. Lett.* 2:257–65

120. Marré, E., Lado, P., Rasi-Caldogno, F., Colombo, R., De Michaelis, M. I. 1974. Evidence for the coupling of proton extrusion to K^+ uptake in pea internode segments treated with fusicoccin or auxin. *Plant Sci. Lett.* 3:365–79

121. Miller, A. G., Spanswick, R. M. 1977. ATP, NADH and NADPH levels in *Chara* and *Nitella. Plant Physiol.* 59:Suppl. 470, p. 85

122. Mitchell, P. 1961. Coupling of phosphorylation to electron and hydrogen transfer by a chemi-osmotic type of mechanism. *Nature* 191:144–48

123. Mitchell, P. 1966. Chemiosmotic coupling in oxidative and photosynthetic phosphorylation. *Biol. Rev.* 41:445–502

124. Mitchell, P. 1967. Translocations through natural membranes. *Adv. Enzymol.* 29:33–87

125. Nissen, P. 1971. Uptake of sulfate by roots and leaf slices of barley: mediated by single, multiphasic mechanisms. *Physiol. Plant.* 24:315–24

126. Nissen, P. 1977. Ion uptake in higher plants and KCl stimulation of plasmalemma adenosine triphosphatase: comparison of models. *Physiol. Plant.* 40:205–14

127. Niven, D. F., Hamilton, W. A. 1974. Mechanisms of energy coupling to the transport of amino acids by *Staphylococcus aureus. Eur. J. Biochem.* 44:517–22

128. Nobel, P. S. 1969. Light-dependent potassium uptake by *Pisum sativum* leaf fragments. *Plant Cell Physiol.* 10:597–605

129. Packer, L., Murakami, S., Mehard, C. W. 1970. Ion transport in chloroplasts and plant mitochondria. *Ann. Rev. Plant Physiol.* 21:271–304

130. Paschinger, H. 1977. DCCD induced sodium uptake by *Anacystis nidulans. Arch. Microbiol.* 113:285–91

131. Penth, B., Weigl, J. 1971. Anionen-Influx, ATP-Spiegel and CO_2-Fixierung in *Limnophila gratioloides* und *Chara foetida. Planta* 96:212–23

132. Petraglia, T., Poole, R. J. 1977. Correlation between ion transport and ATP

levels in storage tissue of red beet. *Plant Physiol.* 59:Suppl. 82, p. 15

133. Pierce, W. S., Higinbotham, N. 1970. Compartments and fluxes of K^+, Na^+ and Cl^- in *Avena* coleoptile cells. *Plant Physiol.* 46:666–73

134. Pitman, M. G., Courtice, A. C., Lee, B. 1968. Comparison of potassium and sodium uptake by barley roots at high and low salt status. *Aust. J. Biol. Sci.* 21:871–81

135. Pitman, M. G., Saddler, H. D. W. 1967. Active sodium and potassium transport in cells of barley roots. *Proc. Natl. Acad. Sci. USA* 57:44–49

136. Pitman, M. G., Schaefer, N., Wildes, R. A. 1975. Stimulation of H^+ efflux and cation uptake by fusicoccin in barley roots. *Plant Sci. Lett.* 4:323–29

137. Pitman, M. G., Schaefer, N., Wildes, R. A. 1975. Relation between permeability to potassium and sodium ions and fusicoccin-stimulated hydrogen-ion efflux in barley roots. *Planta* 126:61–73

138. Polya, G. M., Atkinson, M. R. 1969. Evidence for a direct involvement of electron transport in the high-affinity ion accumulation system of aged beet parenchyma. *Aust. J. Biol. Sci.* 22:573–84

139. Poole, R. J. 1974. Ion transport and electrogenic pumps in storage tissue cells. *Can. J. Bot.* 52:1023–28

140. Poole, R. J. 1976. Transport in cells of storage tissue. See Ref. 111, 2A:229–48

141. Racker, E. 1976. *A New Look at Mechanisms in Bioenergetics.* New York, San Francisco, London: Academic. 197 pp.

142. Racusen, R. H., Galston, A. W. 1977. Electrical evidence for rhythmic changes in the cotransport of sucrose and hydrogen ions in *Samanea pulvini. Planta* 135:57–62

143. Rapoport, S. I. 1970. The sodium-potassium exchange pump: relation of metabolism to electrical properties of the cell. I. Theory. *Biophys. J.* 10:246–59

144. Ratner, A., Jacoby, B. 1976. Effect of K^+, its counter anion, and pH on sodium efflux from barley root tips. *J. Exp. Bot.* 27:843–52

145. Raven, J. A. 1967. Ion transport in *Hydrodictyon africanum. J. Gen. Physiol.* 50:1607–25

146. Raven, J. A. 1967. Light stimulation of active transport in *Hydrodictyon africanum. J. Gen. Physiol.* 50:1627–40

147. Rhoads, D. B., Epstein, W. 1977. Energy coupling to net K^+ transport in *Escherichia coli* K-12. *J. Biol. Chem.* 252:1394–1401

148. Richards, J. L., Hope, A. B. 1974. The role of protons in determining membrane electrical characteristics in *Chara corallina. J. Membr. Biol.* 16:121–44

149. Rothstein, A., Enns, L. H. 1946. The relationship of potassium to carbohydrate metabolism in baker's yeast. *J. Cell. Comp. Physiol.* 28:231–52

150. Rungie, J. M., Wiskich, J. T. 1973. Salt-stimulated adenosine triphosphatase from smooth microsomes of turnip. *Plant Physiol.* 51:1064–68

151. Saddler, H. D. W. 1970. The membrane potential of *Acetabularia mediterranea. J. Gen. Physiol.* 55:802–21

152. Scarborough, G. A. 1975. Isolation and characterization of *Neurospora crassa* plasma membranes. *J. Biol. Chem.* 250:1106–11

153. Scarborough, G. A. 1976. The *Neurospora* plasma membrane ATPase is an electrogenic pump. *Proc. Natl. Acad. Sci. USA* 73:1485–88

154. Scarborough, G. A. 1977. Properties of the *Neurospora crassa* plasma membrane ATPase. *Arch. Biochem. Biophys.* 180:384–93

155. Scarborough, G. A., Rumley, M. K., Kennedy, E. P. 1968. The function of adenosine 5'-triphosphate in the lactose transport system of *Escherichia coli. Proc. Natl. Acad. Sci. USA* 60:951–58

156. Schultz, S. G., Curran, P. F. 1970. Coupled transport of sodium and organic solutes. *Physiol. Rev.* 50:637–718

157. Seaston, A., Carr, G., Eddy, A. A. 1976. The concentration of glycine by preparations of the yeast *Saccharomyces carlsbergensis* depleted of adenosine triphosphate. Effects of proton gradients and uncoupling agents. *Biochem. J.* 154:669–76

158. Seaston, A., Inkson, C., Eddy, A. A. 1973. The absorption of protons with specific amino acids and carbohydrates by yeast. *Biochem. J.* 134:1031–43

159. Shieh, Y. J., Barber, J. 1971. Intracellular sodium and potassium concentrations and net cation movements in *Chlorella pyrenoidosa. Biochim. Biophys. Acta* 233:594–603

160. Skulachev, V. P. 1977. Transmembrane electrochemical H^+-potential as a convertible energy source for the living cell. *FEBS Lett.* 74:1–9

161. Slayman, C. L. 1965. Electrical properties of *Neurospora crassa.* Effects of external cations on the intracellular potential. *J. Gen. Physiol.* 49:69–92

162. Slayman, C. L. 1970. Movement of ions and electrogenesis in microorganisms. *Am. Zool.* 10:377–92

163. Slayman, C. L. 1974. Proton pumping and generalized energetics of transport: a review. See Ref. 49, pp. 107–19

164. Slayman, C. L., Gradmann, D. 1975. Electrogenic proton transport in the plasma membrane of *Neurospora. Biophys. J.* 15:968–71

165. Slayman, C. L., Long, W. S., Lu, C. Y.-H. 1973. The relationship between ATP and an electrogenic pump in the plasma membrane of *Neurospora crassa. J. Membr. Biol.* 14:305–38

166. Slayman, C. L., Slayman, C. W. 1968. Net uptake of potassium in *Neurospora.* Exchange for sodium and hydrogen ions. *J. Gen. Physiol.* 52:424–43

167. Slayman, C. L., Slayman, C. W. 1974. Depolarization of the plasma membrane of *Neurospora* during active transport of glucose: Evidence for a proton-dependent cotransport system. *Proc. Natl. Acad. Sci. USA* 71:1935–39

168. Slayman, C. W., Slayman, C. L. 1975. Energy coupling in the plasma membrane of *Neurospora:* ATP-dependent proton transport and proton-dependent sugar cotransport. See Ref. 52, pp. 233–48

169. Smith, F. A. 1970. The mechanism of chloride transport in Characean cells. *New Phytol.* 69:903–17

170. Smith, F. A. 1972. Stimulation of chloride transport in *Chara* by external pH changes. *New Phytol.* 71:595–601

171. Smith, F. A., Walker, N. A. 1976. Chloride transport in *Chara corallina* and the electrochemical potential difference for hydrogen ions. *J. Exp. Bot.* 27: 451–59

172. Smith, J. B., Sternweis, P. C. 1977. Purification of membrane attachment and inhibitory subunits of the proton translocating adenosine triphosphatase from *Escherichia coli. Biochemistry* 16:306–11

173. Sone, N., Yoshida, M., Hirata, H., Kagawa, Y. 1977. Adenosine triphosphate synthesis by electrochemical proton gradient in vesicles reconstituted from purified adenosine triphosphatase and phospholipids of thermophilic bacterium. *J. Biol. Chem.* 252:2956–60

174. Spanswick, R. M. 1972. Evidence for an electrogenic ion pump in *Nitella translucens.* I. The effects of pH, K^+, Na^+, light and temperature on the membrane potential and resistance. *Biochim. Biophys. Acta* 288:73–89

175. Spanswick, R. M. 1974. Evidence for an electrogenic ion pump in *Nitella translucens.* II. Control of the light-stimulated component of the membrane potential. *Biochim. Biophys. Acta* 332: 387–98

176. Spanswick, R. M., Williams, E. J. 1964. Electrical potentials and Na, K and Cl concentrations in the vacuole and cytoplasm of *Nitella translucens. J. Exp. Bot.* 15:193–200

177. Stebbins, N., Etherton, B. 1977. Amino acid induced depolarizations of membrane potentials in oat coleoptiles. *Plant Physiol.* 59:Suppl. 336, p. 61

178. Steinitz, B., Jacoby, B. 1974. Energetics of $^{22}Na^+$ absorption by bean leaf slices. *Ann. Bot.* 38:453–57

179. Sze, H., Hodges, T. K. 1976. Characterization of passive ion transport in plasma membrane vesicles of oat roots. *Plant Physiol.* 58:304–8

180. Sze, H., Hodges, T. K. 1977. Selectivity of alkali cation influx across the plasma membrane of oat roots. Cation specificity of the plasma membrane ATPase. *Plant Physiol.* 59:641–46

181. Tokuda, H., Kaback, H. R. 1977. Sodium-dependent methyl 1-thio-β-D-galactopyranoside transport in membrane vesicles isolated from *Salmonella typhimurium. Biochemistry* 16:2130–36

182. Van de Stadt, R. J., De Boer, B. L., Van Dam, K. 1973. The interaction between the mitochondrial ATPase (F_1) and the ATPase inhibitor. *Biochim. Biophys. Acta* 292:338–49

183. Vredenberg, W. J., Tonk, W. J. M. 1973. Photosynthetic energy control of an electrogenic ion pump at the plasmalemma of *Nitella translucens. Biochim. Biophys. Acta* 298:354–68

184. Walker, N. A., Smith, F. A. 1975. Intracellular pH in *Chara corallina* measured by DMO distribution. *Plant Sci. Lett.* 4:125–32

185. West, I. C., Mitchell, P. 1974. Proton-/sodium ion antiport in *Escherichia coli. Biochem. J.* 144:87–90

186. Whittam, R. 1964. The interdependence of metabolism and active transport. In *The Cellular Functions of Membrane Transport,* ed. J. F. Hoffman, pp. 139–54. Englewood Cliffs, NJ: Prentice-Hall. 291 pp.

187. Wiskich, J. T. 1977. Mitochondrial metabolite transport. *Ann. Rev. Plant Physiol.* 28:45–69

Ann. Rev. Plant Physiol. 1978. 29:461–86
Copyright © 1978 by Annual Reviews Inc. All rights reserved

SEXUAL PHEROMONES
IN ALGAE AND FUNGI

❖7659

Gary Kochert

Department of Botany, University of Georgia, Athens, Georgia 30602

CONTENTS

INTRODUCTION

Chemical communication involving such phenomena as smell and taste is of undoubted importance in highly evolved organisms such as insects and mammals. Less highly evolved organisms have counterparts to these processes which are just as fundamental to their survival. Chemical communication between unicellular organisms must have been occurring before the origin of multicellularity. It thus seems plausible that complicated phenomena such as taste, smell, and endocrine responses involving reception, transmission, and neurological processing were predated and had their origin in outwardly simpler processes such as the chemotactic behavior of flagellated gametes or zoospores. Accordingly, there should be mechanistic parallels, and the study of chemical communication in all organisms will eventually contribute to a unified concept of the whole spectrum of responses.

This review will concentrate on chemical communication involved in the sexuality of algae and fungi. Chemical communication implies a signal in the form of a chemical substance, transmission of that signal through a medium such as air or water, and reception by the target cell or organism. The terminology utilized to

461

describe these processes has not standardized and a brief explanation would appear in order.

Hormones were originally defined as products of internal secretion (10). By this original definition, then, hormones are produced in one part of the body of an organism and are transported to and affect another part of the body. To describe chemicals involved in communication between individual organisms the term "ecto-hormone" (a term contradictory within itself) was introduced (11). This term has now almost disappeared from the literature, having been largely replaced by the term "pheromone." A pheromone is a chemical compound secreted to the outside by one individual and received by a second individual of the same species where it causes a definite behavioral or developmental response (50). All the biologically active substances described in this article could thus be included in the definition of pheromone. The term pheromone has gained wide acceptance in the invertebrate animal literature (particularly insects), but it has been little used in algal and fungal reports. There the term "sex hormone" has been used extensively, following a precedent set in the extensive writings of Raper (86). Raper promoted a widening of the term "hormone" to include substances having a specific effect outside the body of the secreting organism, although he later considered sex hormones as one category of pheromones (87). In the German literature, chemicals involved in sexual reproduction are called "gamones" but the term has not been widely used in the American literature. The term "sex hormone" is so ingrained in the algal and fungal literature that it will not be easily displaced, but in this review all such substances will be termed pheromones.

Pheromones have been demonstrated which affect virtually all stages of the sexual process in algae and fungi. These stages include: gametogenesis or the differentiation of sexual organs, chemotaxis or chemotropism of differentiated gametes or sexual structures, and specific adhesion and fusion of gametes. This review will cover only those pheromones that are actually transmitted from one organism to another through an intervening medium. Sexual interactions requiring surface contact such as sexual agglutination in *Chlamydomonas* or *Hansenula* are thus excluded. An excellent review with the emphasis on cell surface interactions has recently appeared and can be consulted for an entry to this literature (29).

The present review treats pheromones whose effects may be classified into two broad categories. These were distinguished by Wilson & Bossert (119) as releaser effects and primer effects. Releaser effects are behavioral responses that occur almost immediately. An example would be the chemotactic response of a flagellated male gamete toward an egg. Primer effects are slower, longer lasting responses involving an alteration of the growth pattern or the differentiation of new structures. It is not always possible to distinguish between the two effects in a strictly dichotomous manner, but in general the distinction will hold. This review will concentrate on the more recent literature and on sexual systems in which the pheromones involved have been characterized to some degree. Table 1 summarizes the properties of some of these pheromones. The historical background to these systems and descriptions of other organisms where sexual pheromones can be inferred from their biological activity can be found in other recent reviews (18, 22, 29, 47, 87, 113).

Table 1 Properties of some algal and fungal pheromones

Organism	Pheromone name	Structure	General properties and function	Reference
Chlamydomonas moewusii var. *rotunda*	—	—	volatile, heat-stable small molecule, produced by (−) gametes, attracts (+) gametes	110, 111
Allomyces sp.	sirenin		produced by female gametes, attracts male gametes	63
Fucus serratus	fucoserraten		volatile, produced by female gametes, attracts male gametes	75
Ectocarpus siliculosis	ectocarpen		volatile, produced by female gametes, attracts male gametes	76
Cutleria multifida	multifidene		volatile, produced by female gametes, attracts male gametes	48
Oedogonium cardiacum	—	—	water-soluble, not volatile, produced by eggs, attracts sperm	41, 62
Oedogonium borisianum	—	—	produced by oogonial mother cell, attracts andro-spores	89
Achlya sp.	antheridiol		produced by female, induces antheridial branches, attracts antheridial branches	8
Achlya sp.	oogoniol		produced by male, induces differentiation of oogonia	66
Various Mucorales	trisporic acid (c)		induces differentiation of zygophores	112
Volvox carteri	—	—	glycoprotein, mol wt 30,000, induces differentiation of females	53, 98
Saccharomyces cerevisiae	α-factor	—	tridecapeptide, produced by α mating type, induces G1 arrest and shape changes in *a* mating type	100

Sexual Attractant Pheromones

Chemotactic and chemotropic systems are widespread in the algae and fungi. Only a few cases have been analyzed in detail; many have been superficially described, and doubtless many more remain to be discovered. For more detail about chemotactic and chemotropic responses not involved in sexuality, the reader is referred to the excellent recent review by Gooday (38).

Isogamous forms of algae and fungi seem to depend on chance encounter of the gametes to achieve fertilization. Indeed it is difficult to imagine how a chemotactic system would function where gametes of both mating types are actively motile. Reports of sexual chemotaxis in isogamous forms are rare. The evolutionary trend away from isogamy necessitated a parallel trend toward the utilization of sexual attractants. In nearly every case where one gamete is relatively immobile (customarily termed the female gamete) that gamete will be found to produce a pheromone which attracts the male gamete. A multitude of systems are available for analysis by experimental biologists. However, only a very few sexual pheromones have been isolated and chemically characterized. In general, the biologists who discover the system lack the necessary training in organic chemistry or biochemistry, and the chemists and biochemists either do not know the systems exist or lack the training required to produce the pheromones in culture. In the few cases where pheromone characterization has been successful, it has been through the combined efforts of biologists and chemists such as Machlis, Nutting & Rapoport (63) or Müller & Jaenicke [summarized in (46)]. The way is open for significant progress in several of these systems. It is up to the biologists to bring these systems to the attention of chemists and to actively seek their collaboration.

CHLAMYDOMONAS   One interesting possibility for future work is *Chlamydomonas moewusii* var. *rotunda*. This organism produces isogamous, flagellated gametes and is the only isogamous species of *Chlamydomonas* reported to produce a sexual attractant pheromone. Tsubo (110, 111) reported that the mating type (−) gametes release an attractant into the culture medium. Gametes of the (+) mating type are attracted into capillaries containing (−) gametes or (−) gamete conditioned medium. Synthesis of the attractant and the response to it were limited to gametes; vegetative cells neither produced nor responded to the attractant. The attractant has some degree of species-specificity since *C. reinhardi* gametes did not respond. Gametes of other varieties of *C. moewusii* and the very closely related *C. eugametos* did respond. Interestingly, in these other varieties both mating types were attracted. No sexual agglutination occurred in the interspecific combinations, showing that attraction and agglutination are separable processes. Not much information was gained about the chemical nature of the attractant, but it is apparently a low molecular weight, heat-stable, volatile substance. Hydrocarbons such as ethylene and ethane mimic the effect as they do in the *Fucus* system (see below), but one cannot tell the relative concentrations required from the data given. With every compound tested the (+) mating type of *C. moewusii* var. *rotunda* reacted in the same way as did both mating types of other varieties of *C. moewusii* and *C. eugametos*. The (−) mating type of *C. moewusii* var. *rotunda* did not respond positively to any of the compounds tested. This remains an interesting system in which no work has been reported in more than 15 years, and the original work of Tsubo has never been confirmed. Given the ease with which *Chlamydomonas* can be grown and induced to undergo sexual reproduction, it should be amenable to further investigation. Since the attractant is volatile, it should be possible to collect it with the same methods used by Müller and Jaenicke (46) to purify brown algal attractant pheromones. Tsubo also reported the isolation of ultraviolet-induced mutants which failed to produce the pheromone. Procedures for genetic analysis in *Chlamydomonas* are well established, and this system could thus be used to study the genetics of pheromone production and action. It is also interesting that the only reported sexual attractant pheromone in the genus *Chlamydomonas* occurs in *C. moewusii*. While the organism is isogamous, there is a behavioral difference between the gametes in that the (−) mating type gametes become nonmotile shortly after the initial stages of pair formation. These two observations may mean that *C. moewusii* is evolving toward anisogamy or oogamy. It would be interesting from this point of view to investigate some of the anisogamous and oogamous species of *Chlamydomonas* to determine whether they produce attractant pheromones. The strains of *Chlamydomonas* used by Tsubo are available from the University of Texas Culture Collection of Algae (31, 96).

ALLOMYCES   The first plant sex hormone to be chemically characterized was sirenin. Sirenin is produced by female gametes of the aquatic fungus *Allomyces*. In this organism gametophytic plants normally produce paired male and female gametangia. The male gametangia and the resultant male gametes contain elevated levels of carotene and are visibly orange in color. Female gametes are somewhat larger than males and are colorless. Machlis (56) presented the first evidence for a sexual attractant pheromone in *Allomyces*, although such a pheromone was earlier predicted by Raper (86). Female gametes of *Allomyces* are flagellated and can swim, but move rather sluggishly and tend to stop in the vicinity of the gametangium. Male gametes are attracted to the females and cluster around them. When one of the males fuses with a female, sirenin secretion rapidly stops. The resultant zygote develops into the diploid sporophytic plant after a period of motility.

Machlis (56, 61) showed that sirenin could be bioassayed by its ability to attract male gametes and cause them to attach to a dialysis membrane through which sirenin was diffusing. Machlis (64) also worked out the culture conditions necessary for the production of large amounts of sirenin. Wild-type *Allomyces* shows monoclonic sexual reproduction (sexual reproduction occurs in one clone) and male and female gametes are formed simultaneously. Male gametes inactivate sirenin and upon fusing with the females stop production of sirenin by the females. Thus wild-type cultures of *Allomyces* would not yield much sirenin and would become predominantly composed of nonsexual diploid plants from growth of the zygotes. The key to this effort was the utilization of predominantly female interspecies hybrids for the production of sirenin. Emerson & Wilson (36) had shown that some hybrids of *A. arbuscula* and *A. macrogynus* were almost unisexual. Machlis (56) selected several hybrids from such a cross and was able to select strains which produced almost exclusively either male or female gametes.

In collaboration with Nutting and Rapoport, the chemical structure of sirenin was elucidated and the structure confirmed by synthesis (63, 82). It is a bicyclic sesquiterpenediol (Table 1) of molecular weight 236. Pure synthetic sirenin shows activity at $10^{-10}M–10^{-5}M$ (23). The responding system appears to be very specific since of the isomers and analogs tested by Machlis, only l-sirenin was active (60). There is some indication that species-specific sirenins exist (57). When sirenin produced by the hybrid strain was assayed for chemotactic activity against the parent species, it was found that A. macrogynus male gametes responded well but A. arbuscula male gametes responded very poorly. This could indicate that species-specific sirenins are produced or it could simply mean that A. arbuscula gametes are much less sensitive to sirenin. Only a single concentration of sirenin was used in these experiments because it is very laborious to isolate manually the male gametangia from the hermaphroditic parent species.

Male gametes can be shown to take up or bind sirenin with first-order kinetics (60). Since efforts to reextract sirenin from treated male gametes were unsuccessful, it was concluded that male gametes metabolize sirenin to an inactive product. This would contribute to the maintenance of a concentration gradient. It was also demonstrated that male gametes can become "saturated" with sirenin and lose their ability to respond chemotactically. Full recovery requires about 45 min.

The Allomyces system is a fascinating one and offers great promise for future research. Very little has been done to analyze the mechanism of action of sirenin. A study in this area would be inherently interesting as well as potentially informative about general mechanisms of eucaryote chemotaxis. Allomyces produces five kinds of flagellated cells (male gametes, female gametes, zygotes, haploid zoospores, and diploid zoospores). Sirenin is produced only by female gametes and only the male gametes respond to it. However, the zoospores and the zygote respond chemotactically to certain amino acids or mixtures of amino acids (58, 101). It is very interesting that when the male gamete, which responds to sirenin, and the female gamete fuse, the resultant zygote very quickly acquires the ability to respond to amino acids and loses its response to sirenin. If the first step in chemotaxis is binding of the attractant to surface membrane receptors, then there must be a very rapid membrane change associated with fertilization. One might imagine that sirenin receptors are masked or inactivated and amino acid receptors become available. This interesting possibility could be investigated in several ways. One could do binding studies with radioactively labeled sirenin and amino acids to look for a rapid change in binding characteristics. It would probably prove preferable to do binding studies with isolated plasma membranes rather than whole cells. This would help separate binding of amino acids from uptake and incorporation into protein and might also eliminate the apparent degradation of sirenin carried out by male gametes. Another approach could involve surface labeling of cells with [125]iodine by the lactoperoxidase system (44). One could surface label the cells, isolate the membranes, and characterize the labeled components on sodium dodecyl sulfate polyacrylamide gels. Further studies might utilize amino acid or sirenin affinity columns in an attempt to isolate specific receptors.

The experimental approaches suggested should pose no great technical problems. No one has published a membrane isolation procedure for Allomyces, but it should be relatively straightforward since the flagellated cells have no cell wall and large quantities can be obtained. Labeled sirenin is not commercially available, but can be prepared synthetically. Again a collaboration between a chemist and a biologist would appear in order.

It is also interesting that no detailed study of the swimming patterns of *Allomyces* flagellated cells has been reported. As Wilson (117) very correctly points out:

> It follows that a first step in understanding the behavior of a given species is a thorough examination of the sensory physiology of the species. It is also axiomatic that as complete a repertory of behavioral acts as possible be catalogued—"the ethogram" and the functions of the acts as adaptions to the natural environment analyzed.

The only published observations on effects of sirenin on swimming behavior is that of Carlile & Machlis (23). This study is a good start, but does not enable one to tell what the basic swimming pattern is, what effect sirenin has on turning frequencies, or whether temporal changes in sirenin concentration are detected.

Pommerville (personal communication) has utilized photographic techniques to analyze certain of these questions. His observations indicate that *Allomyces* male gametes alternate smooth swimming (runs) with abrupt changes in direction (jerks). Gametes apparently do not revolve around their longitudinal axis, and all jerks in any one motility path result in turns in only one direction. The introduction of sirenin to male gametes causes a marked change in the frequency of jerks. Higher concentrations tend to suppress the jerks and lower concentrations increase the frequency of jerks. Pommerville also has made observations of the approach of male to female gametes. These seem to corroborate the observations with purified sirenin. Male gametes swam in long, slightly curved runs when swimming toward female gametes. When swimming away from the females, jerks were more frequent until the direction was rectified. The similarity of these results to those obtained from studies of bacterial chemotaxis (1) is striking and merits further detailed studies. It would be particularly interesting to determine whether *Allomyces* gametes respond to temporal gradients of sirenin as do bacteria (17).

As mentioned above, *Allomyces* has the distinct advantage as a model system for studies on eucaryotic chemotaxis of having both zoospores and gametes and having these respond to different compounds. Machlis has studied zoospore chemotaxis in some detail (58). Among the amino acids, only leucine, lysine, and proline were attractants. A mixture of leucine and lysine proved more active than either compound alone. The ecological reason for the attractive properties of these particular amino acids remains obscure. Genetic approaches have proved very helpful in the elucidation of mechanisms of bacterial chemotaxis, and it would be interesting to apply some of these approaches to the *Allomyces* system. It should be possible to isolate nonchemotactic mutants with some sort of a selection apparatus. It would be interesting to know whether one could isolate "generally" nonchemotactic mutants similar to those described in bacteria (1). Would single-step mutants of this type be deficient in both the zoospore response to amino acids and the gamete response to sirenin?

Unfortunately, *Allomyces* does not appear to be an ideal organism for genetic studies. The common laboratory strains appear to be polyploid; the gametes are diploid and sporophytes autotetroploid (36). However, it may be possible to reduce these to a normal haploid-diploid cycle by growth at high temperature or in the presence of amino acid analogs (L. W. Olson, personal communication).

BROWN ALGAE The only other algal or fungal gamete attractant pheromones to have been chemically characterized are those of three genera of marine brown algae. It had been known for some time that brown algae exhibited gamete chemotaxis. The first case analyzed was that of *Fucus*. This organism is oogamous and the large, nonmotile eggs are shed into the sea water. The male gametes in *Fucus*, as in most brown algae, are laterally biflagellate, with the flagellum which is directed toward the anterior being somewhat longer. The male gametes can be observed to cluster around the eggs prior to fertilization. Very shortly after fertilization male gametes are no longer attracted by the eggs.

Cook and collaborators (26, 27) were the first to make a systematic investigation of gamete chemotaxis in *Fucus*. They were able to show that eggs produce a volatile attractant pheromone. The attractant could be collected in a cold trap from a stream of hydrogen or nitrogen which had been bubbled through a suspension of eggs or oogonia. They could collect only very small amounts of the compound, and the methodology available at that time was not adequate for complete chemical characterization. They did suggest, however, that the attractant was a simple hydrocarbon. A large number of simple organic compounds were tested for biological activity and several hydrocarbons were found to be active. Of these, *n*-hexane, *n*-heptane, and *n*-octane seemed to most closely resemble the natural compound.

Species-specificity of the pheromone was also investigated by Cook and collaborators. It was shown that there was complete cross-reactivity among *F. vesiculosus, F. serratus,* and *F. spiralis*. Ripe eggs of each of these species attracted their own male gametes as well as those of the other two species.

The *Fucus* work was brought to fruition by Müller & Jaenicke (75). The attractant produced by *F. serratus* was obtained by bubbling air through suspensions of eggs and oogonia from plants collected from nature. The attractant could be extracted from the air stream by passing it through a liquid fluorocarbon or over droplets of Vaseline. Only 690 μg of an odoriferous, oily material was obtained from 250 kg of fresh material. When the extracted material was subjected to gas chromatography only a single homogeneous peak was obtained. The material was shown to be *trans, cis*-1,3,5-octatriene by analysis and synthesis. Müller & Jaenicke named the compound fucoserraten.

Ectocarpus siliculosus is also a marine brown alga. Its life cycle was thoroughly studied by Müller with cultured material (71). In this organism the male and female gametes appear to be identical when they are first released from the parent plant, but exhibit a behavioral difference. The female gametes soon cease swimming and attach themselves to a substrate. The male gametes are then attracted to the female gametes and cluster around each female in response to an attractant pheromone. As in the chemotactic systems cited, production of the attractant ceases very shortly after fertilization.

Using methods similar to those described above for *Fucus*, Müller et al were able to obtain about 92 mg of the *Ectocarpus* gamete attractant in 2 years of mass production. Again the gas chromatographic profiles gave essentially a single pure compound. Analysis by mass spectrometry and spectroscopy revealed a hydrocarbon with the composition $C_{11}H_{16}$, containing three nonconjugated double bonds and a seven-membered ring. The structure was confirmed by synthesis and named ectocarpen (76). Interestingly, the same compound had been isolated earlier as a component of the essential oil fraction of another marine brown alga, *Dictyopteris* (70).

Cutleria is the other brown alga which has been investigated by Müller, Jaenicke, and collaborators. Its pattern of sexuality is similar to that of *Ectocarpus* except that the flagellated female gametes are much larger than the males. Again a similar extraction procedure was used to obtain volatile extracts from suspensions of female gametes. Three compounds were present when the extracts were subjected to gas chromatography (48, 72). By mass spectroscopy all three gave the same formula, $C_{11}H_{16}$, and all contained three unconjugated double bonds and a ring. The major one appeared to be the biologically most active compound. When analyzed further, primarily by NMR spectroscopy, it proved to be 4 vinyl-5-(*cis*-1'-butenyl)-cyclopentene. The compound was named multifidene, after the species of *Culteria* used. The other two compounds were found to be a cyclohexene derivative which was named aucanten and, significantly, ectocarpen. These latter two compounds were also components of the essential oils of asexual plants of *Cutleria.*

Müller (74) has developed a method for quantitative measurement of chemotaxis with the marine brown algal systems and has measured threshold values and biological cross-reactivity of a wide variety of natural pheromones, isomers, and other compounds. Several interesting findings have emerged. Each of the brown algal components so far chemically characterized appears to be species-specific but only in the sense that the homologous attractant is effective at lower concentrations than the heterologous. For example, male gametes of *Cutleria* respond to ectocarpen, but the threshold concentration is tenfold higher. *Ectocarpus* male gametes respond to multifidene, but require threshold concentrations 310-fold higher than do *Cutleria* male gametes. Both *Ectocarpus* and *Cutleria* male gametes respond to aucanten and to *n*-hexane, but threshold concentrations are 31- and 310-fold higher respectively than the homologous natural pheromones. Direct observation of intergeneric combinations of female and male gametes confirmed the results obtained with the pure compounds. Female gametes of *Ectocarpus* do attract male gametes of *Cutleria* (and vice versa), but fusion of the gametes does not occur. Whether these interactions are of any biological significance is not clear.

Müller & Seferiadis (77) also investigated threshold concentrations for fucoserraten, 9 octatriene isomers, ectocarpen, and *n*-hexane in two species of *Fucus.* Male gametes of *F. serratus* and *F. vesiculosus* were equally sensitive to fucoserraten. Most of the other octatrienes were less effective by factors of 3.1–31. Ectocarpen and *n*-hexane showed rather weak activity with the threshold concentration for *n*-hexane being 3100 times higher than for fucoserraten. An interesting correlation was pointed out between the type of sexual reproduction present and the efficiency of the chemotactic process. The anisogamous and oogamous genera apparently have a more efficient system than the isogamous genus. This seems in order since anisogamous and oogamous forms produce fewer but larger female gametes than isogamous forms. Over a given area of dispersal, female gametes of anisogamous and oogamous forms would be more widely spaced and would require a more efficient chemotactic process.

The brown algal sex pheromones seem to fit the concept that pheromones were evolved as a result of "semanticization" and "ritualization" of ordinary secretion processes (118). According to this concept, regular excretory or secretory processes of an organism, which would have originally had an entirely different function, are modified during evolution into specific systems of chemical communication. Ordinary products of lipid metabolism might thus eventually become "ritualized" into specific attractant pheromones. The sex attractant of female rhesus monkeys, for example, is a mixture of several short-chain fatty acids which are ordinary products of lipid metabolism. It would appear that the brown algal attractant pheromones have been evolutionarily derived from essential oils. Ectocarpen is produced as an essential oil by vegetative thalli of *Dictyopteris* and *Cutleria* and is apparently not used as a sexual attractant by these organisms. In *Ectocarpus,* where it serves as a sexual attractant pheromone, ectocarpen is produced by female gametes and not vegetative thalli. Moreover, many of the intermediates used by Jaenicke in the chemical synthesis of brown algal attractants are present in the essential oil component of *Dictyopteris* (70). A biosynthetic pathway has been proposed in which all the brown algal organic compounds that now serve as the sex pheromones could be derived from C_{11} essential oil components (46, 70). The biological functions of essential oils in marine algae are not clear. They may be involved in buoyancy (46). Whatever their function in asexual thalli, it seems clear that the brown algal sex pheromones are evolutionary derivatives of essential oils.

At present little is known about the mechanism of action of the brown algal pheromones. Detailed studies of the swimming behavior of the male gametes have not been reported and this would seem to be a logical first step. Apparently the presence of an attractant causes the male gamete to deviate from its normal straight swimming pattern and to curve toward the female gamete in increasingly narrow circles. Male gametes also apparently become positively thigmotactic in the presence of the attractant pheromone (73). Radioactively labeled ectocarpen has been synthesized and used for preliminary binding studies (45). Male gametes very rapidly took up the label, reaching a peak after only 15 secs of exposure. With increasing time the labeling was greatly diminished. The reasons for this are obscure, but they might represent saturation of receptors coupled with removal of the side chain label by some metabolic process. Clearly more work is called for here. Some preliminary autoradiographic studies indicate that the initial binding of the attractant is over the long flagellum of the male gamete. Upon longer incubation, the label was found to be predominantly over the cell body. Again the significance of this is not clear, but it may indicate some rearrangement of membrane receptors which would be interesting to pursue. The same sort of approaches outlined above for *Allomyces* could be used to analyze pheromone receptors in *Ectocarpus.*

Ectocarpus would appear to represent a very favorable genus for further analysis of chemotaxis. It has the advantage of having diclonic sexual reproduction, and the male and female gametophytes can be separately maintained asexually for production of the attractant and the responding cells. There is then no danger of the culture becoming overgrown with diploid plants from zygotes as can happen in *Allomyces.*

Ectocarpus apparently has a true haploid-diploid life cycle although tetraploids are occasionally formed (36). Since there are apparently no serious problems with polyploidy, it might be profitable to undertake some genetic work. If mutants which do not respond to ectocarpen could be isolated, it would be interesting to see if these would retain the ability to respond to aucanten or *n*-hexane. Also, could generally nonchemotactic mutants be isolated which would fail to respond to any chemoattractant? Would this class of mutant retain the ability to bind labeled ectocarpen? Could one cross nonchemotactic mutants, perhaps by centrifuging the male and female gametes into contact? If so, it might be possible to genetically dissect the "pathway" of chemotaxis. Nothing has been described about chemotactic responses of *Ectocarpus* zoospores. If the zoospores show chemotaxis, it would be interesting to determine whether some mutants blocked in gamete chemotaxis would also be blocked in zoospore chemotaxis.

Ectocarpus is an interesting organism for doing genetic crosses. It has potential advantages and disadvantages. The zygotes grow directly into diploid plants, so there is an intervening generation before segregants can be analyzed. Mitosis occurs with meiosis in unilocular sporangia so that large numbers of clones would have to be analyzed. *Ectocarpus* does, however, have certain interesting features for genetic crosses. It is possible to maintain asexually both the haploid and diploid phases of the life cycle. Thus one only needs to isolate a single diploid plant from a cross to be able to completely analyze segregation patterns, since multiple meiotic events will occur in the various sporangia.

OEDOGONIUM   The systems cited above are the only ones in the algae and fungi in which the chemoattractant has been chemically characterized. Preliminary work has been done with two other systems, however, and these rate further investigation. One is the *Chlamydomonas* system discussed above. The general characteristics of the attractant suggest it will turn out to be similar to the *Allomyces* and brown algal systems. The other is the fresh-water, filamentous green alga *Oedogonium.* This organism produces a sperm attractant which from preliminary work appears to be different in chemical composition from the volatile pheromones described for the other algal groups.

Oedogonium cardiacum produces sperm and eggs in separate clones. In both cases, sexual structures can be induced by nitrogen starvation. The culture medium from female cultures then contains a species-specific sperm attractant which can be bioassayed by the usual methods (41, 62). The attractant appears to be highly water soluble (not extracted by methylene chloride, chloroform, benzene, butanol, or propanol) and not volatile, in distinct contrast to the brown algal attractants. The size of the molecule also appears to be somewhat larger. It is virtually nondialyzable and, based on gel filtration and ultrafiltration data, the attractant would appear to have a molecular weight of 500–1500. It always copurified with a yellow pigment. There was little absorption at 280 nm by purified extracts, and it was concluded the pheromone is probably not a peptide.

Some species of *Oedogonium* exhibit a more complex sort of life cycle. In these species an additional type of flagellated cell, the androspore, is produced. In *Oedogonium boriseanum,* the androspore shows a clear chemotactic attraction to oogonial mother cells (89). They swim to these, attach, and each grows into a dwarf male filament with only a few cells. Sperm are then formed in terminal cells of the dwarf male. Interestingly, the oogonial mother cell will not divide to form the oogonium until an androspore has attached. Thus some sort of contact reaction or chemical interaction is implicated. In turn, the direction of growth of the dwarf male filament appears to be controlled by its position on the oogonial mother cell. The sperm released from the dwarf male are kept close mechanically to the oogonium by a mass of mucilaginous material, but appear to also exhibit some chemotactic attraction. Thus this species of *Oedogonium* appears to exhibit quite a complex series of chemically coordinated steps. No progress has been reported on further characterization of any of these pheromones since they were first reported some 15 years ago.

The genus *Oedogonium* would appear to represent quite a fertile field for further research. Continued work on the *Oedogonium* sperm attractant could concentrate on purification and characterization, but it should be realized that purifying a water-soluble compound such as this one is inherently more difficult than purifying a volatile compound. The brown algal attractants were virtually pure after the first isolation step, when nearly all metabolites and cellular components are left behind in the aqueous phase. There are reported to be hundreds of species of *Oedogonium.* All are oogamous and one would suspect that all species must produce a sperm attractant. Does each of the many species produce a chemically different attractant? If so, are they all metabolically related? Alternatively, do several species produce the same attractant, but depend on other reactions such as surface-specific cell fusion to prevent interspecies fertilizations? *Oedogonium* could provide much data on the relationship between gamete attractants and speciation, but some relatively simple way to isolate and characterize the gamete attractants would have to be devised. There is also apparently a problem with culturing the organism for reproducible production of attractant pheromones (59).

It would also be interesting to analyze the swimming patterns exhibited by *Oedogonium* flagellated cells during chemotaxis. As discussed above, this is an essential first step toward understanding this behavioral response, but would also be interesting on a comparative basis. *Oedogonium* flagellated cells are quite different in structure from either *Allomyces* or brown algal flagellated cells in that they possess a ring of flagella around the anterior end of the cell. Their mechanical means of orienting to the attractant gradient may be quite different from the simpler forms. Unfortunately, to my knowledge, no one is now working on any of these questions.

A system similar to that in *Oedogonium* appears to be operative in *Sphaeroplea* (83). In this green alga, eggs and male gametes are formed in separate filaments. Pascher reported that filaments with eggs strongly attracted male gametes. A string also attracted male gametes after it had been soaked in medium containing female filaments.

Pheromones which Induce Sexual Differentiation

ACHLYA   *Achlya* is a filamentous fresh-water fungus which has been shown to produce "primer" type pheromones. Most species of *Achlya* produce antheridia and oogonia on the same thallus, but *A. bisexualis* and *A. ambisexualis* are almost completely unisexual, and these exhibit an interesting pheromonal interaction during sexual reproduction. The late John R. Raper clearly demonstrated the salient features of this interaction in a series of reports [summarized in (87)]. The female strain constitutively produces a pheromone which initiates sexual reproduction in the male. This pheromone was named "hormone A" by Raper, but is now called antheridiol. In the presence of antheridiol, the male thallus produces multiple, small antheridial branches. These grow chemotropically toward the source of the antheridiol. Concomitantly, the male begins production of oogoniol (Raper's hormone B), which induces the female to begin formation of oogonia. The antheridial branches make contact with the oogonia and nuclear transfer and fertilization follow. Raper originally postulated a hormone C which was produced by oogonial initials, served as the chemoattractant for the antheridial branches, and induced the differentiation of antheridia. The existence of hormone C was questioned by Barksdale (7, 8), who demonstrated that antheridiol absorbed on plastic spheres would chemotactically attract antheridial branches and that antheridial branches would differentiate antheridia in response to added antheridiol. For antheridiol to serve as the chemoattractant in vivo it would be necessary that oogonial initials produce more antheridiol than vegetative filaments. Experimental evidence for this has not been reported. The concentrations of antheridiol used by Barksdale were 10–100 times physiological concentrations (87), so it would appear that the existence of hormone C has not been rigorously demonstrated or disproved.

Raper & Haagen-Smit (88) apparently were able to purify antheridiol, but it was not possible to completely characterize the product at that time. McMorris & Barksdale have collaborated to establish the structure of both antheridiol and oogoniol as steroids (65, 66). Antheridiol is active at concentrations as low as 6×10^{-12} g/ml. The structural and stereochemical requirements for biological activity are quite strict (9). A wide variety of closely related sterols are essentially inactive even at higher concentrations, and stereoisomers of antheridiol are only 10^{-3}–10^{-6} as active as the nature compound.

Some progress has been made in deciphering the biochemical changes which accompany sexual induction. The first observable morphological effect of antheridiol action is the appearance of the antheridial initials. These lateral branches are visible 3–4 hours after addition of the pheromone. Several biochemical changes are evident before this time. Total RNA synthesis, as measured by uridine incorporation and RNA accumulation, shows an increase within 30 min. Apparently, increase in ribosomal RNA synthesis is the first detectable effect (43). An increased synthesis of poly-A–containing RNA occurs at about 3 hours after hormone treatment, just before the first detectable morphological effect. Increased synthesis of proteins is also detectable at about this time (95, 109).

Not much is known about specifically which proteins are synthesized in response to antheridiol. Probably many proteins are ultimately made. This is supported by the observations of Silver & Horgen (95) that a heterodisperse population of poly-A–containing RNAs appear in response to antheridiol. One specific protein may be cellulase. A prerequisite for lateral branch formation would be the production of a localized, limited hydrolysis of the cell wall through the production or activation of a hydrolytic enzyme. There are reports of a hormone-stimulated, cycloheximide-sensitive increase in cellulase activity (49, 107), and there is some evidence that Golgi vesicles which localize at the point of antheridial branch formation contain cellulase (78, 81). Groner et al studied the spectrum of proteins produced in response to antheridiol and reported that one protein of molecular weight 69,000 was synthesized in large amounts just prior to the appearance of the characteristic lateral branches, but the protein was not further identified (39).

The primary action of the *Achlya* steroid pheromones is thus still quite unknown. Antheridiol is apparently taken up from the medium and degraded by target mycelium (6, 79). Actinomycin D blocks any morphological manifestation of hormone action (109). This is not particularly surprising since the first detectable effect of antheridiol is a growth response (i.e. the formation of lateral branches). It is, of course, tempting to ascribe the mode of action to one similar to that demonstrated for steroid hormones in animal tissues (121). In these cases the hormone enters the target cell, binds to a specific protein receptor in the cytoplasm, enters the nucleus, and alters the pattern of transcription and subsequent translation. It would seem that something similar to this must occur in the *Achlya* system, but there is little direct evidence. Horgen reported that incubation of *Achlya* chromatin with antheridiol and cytosol fraction from male organisms increased the RNA synthetic capacity of the chromatin when incubated with either *E. coli* or endogeneous *Achlya* RNA polymerase (42). A similar cytosol fraction from a female strain (which does not react to antheridiol) showed little stimulatory effect. The stimulatory effect is apparently the result of an increased number of RNA polymerase binding and initiation sites (102). It would appear that most of the elements of a mammalian-type steroid hormone response are present in *Achlya*. Direct binding experiments designed to isolate a receptor protein have not yet been performed. These experiments have not been feasible because of the difficulty of synthesizing high specific activity antheridiol. Some progress has been made toward solving this problem so perhaps direct binding experiments can be expected soon (W. E. Timberlake, personal communication).

In animal tissue-culture systems some progress has been made toward a genetic dissection of the steroid hormone response (122). Genetic crosses cannot be made in these systems, however. Unfortunately, *Achlya* does not seem to be an ideal system for a genetic analysis of hormone action. The organism is diploid, which complicates selection of mutants, and the genetics of sexual inheritance and expression are poorly understood (54). A variety of strains have been isolated. They show a range of sexual expression from strongly male to strongly female. Intermediate strains can respond as males when paired with a "strong" female or as females when paired with a "strong" male. All strains appear to have the genetic capacity to form both male and female sexual organs and to produce both pheromones. While crosses can be made between strongly male and strongly female strains, the zygotes germinate erratically and usually in low percentage. When the progeny from such a cross are analyzed for sexual type a very confusing picture arises. The results do not fall into any pattern explainable by any simple gene or chromosome mechanism. Some epigenetic control of the expression of sexual phenotypes and pheromone production must be in effect, but this is not understood.

Sexual pheromone systems have been reported in two genera fairly closely related to *Achlya*. In both of these cases there is convincing evidence that a pheromonal system is operative, but no further information. Sherwood (94) reported that in *Dictyuchus*, oogonia could be induced by a filtrate from a mixed male and female culture. This would appear to represent an activity like that of oogoniol in *Achlya*, but there are no reports of oogoniol being tested on *Dictyuchus* and no reports of further work of any sort on the *Dictyuchus* pheromone.

Sapromyces is another aquatic fungus with a sexual morphology similar to that of *Achlya* and *Dictyuchus*. Bishop (12) showed that filtrates from female plants would induce antheridial hyphae on males. It also appeared that, in common with the *Achlya* system, production of oogonia and directional growth of antheridial branches were controlled by pheromones. This organism would appear also to merit further investigation.

MUCORALES A very interesting hormonal system occurs in members of the Mucorales. These fungi are filamentous forms. Both monoclonic (homothallic) and diclonic (heterothallic) species exist, but nearly all work has been done with diclonic forms. When these species are mated, special filaments (zygophores) intermediate in size between vegetative mycelia and asexual sporangiophores are formed. The zygophores curve toward one another, make contact, wall off their tips as gametangia, and fuse to form zygotes.

The importance of sexual hormones in this process was first shown by Burgeff (21). He demonstrated that cultures of compatible mating type would induce zygophores on one another even when separated by a collodion membrane. Plempel (84) extended these observations and provided evidence that each mating type produces a pheromone which stimulates zygophore formation in the opposite mating type. The natural assumption was that two compounds were involved. Instead, a single compound could be isolated which induced zygophore formation equally well in both mating types. This was an interesting observation not seen in other pheromones discovered to that time. The breakthrough in identification of this compound came from the study of a related phenomenon, carotenoid production in mated cultures. Mated cultures of Mucorales may produce 15–20 times more carotene than separate cultures of each mating type. The function of the elevated carotene levels is still not certain. The zygospore wall in these fungi is composed partially of sporopollenin. Beta-carotene is apparently oxidatively polymerized to sporopollenin in this system, and the higher carotene levels may simply function to elevate the specific precursor pool (37). Elevated carotene levels seem to be characteristic of many cell types which show sensitive chemotactic or chemotropic responses. Male gametes of *Allomyces* also contain elevated carotene levels, as do the male gametes of *Fucus* (27). Female gametes of these organisms, which do not show a chemotactic response, do not contain elevated carotene levels. In the Mucorales both mating types exhibit chemotropism during the mating process and both produce elevated carotene levels. It has also been reported that olfactory organs of higher animals also contain elevated carotene levels which may be important in chemoreception (91). There must be some fundamental mechanistic explanation for this correlation, but no convincing arguments have thus far been presented.

Prieto et al (85) showed that trisporic acids were present in extracts of mated cultures and that they stimulated carotenogenesis when added to unmated cultures of many of these organisms. Trisporic acids are derivatives of vitamin A and can be formed from β-carotene by a series of steps (4, 19).

It remained only for Van den Ende to show that trisporic acids also served to stimulate zygophore formation in both mating types of *Mucor mucedo* (112, 115). *Cis-trans* trisporic acid B appeared to be the most active form. It was subsequently found that trisporic acids stimulate zygophore formation and carotene synthesis is a wide variety of mucoraceous fungi. Labeling studies clearly demonstrated that both mating types synthesize trisporic acids in mated cultures (114). The interesting question posed was why individual mating types in diclonic strains did not produce trisporic acids and become sexual. (This is apparently just what happens in mono-clonic strains.) It first seemed probable that some factor or cofactor necessary for enzymatic synthesis of trisporic acids was diffusing between the isolated mating types. It now appears that the materials exchanged between mating partners are actually trisporic acid precursors (103, 105).

These mating-type-specific trisporic precursors have been isolated and character-ized in both *M. mucedo* and *Blakeslea trispora* (5, 20, 80). The (+) mating type forms 4-hydroxy methyltrisporates. These are biologically active when applied to minus strains where they induce zygophore formation, carotene synthesis, and serve as precursors of trisporic acids. They are volatile and can exert their action across an air barrier. Trisporols are formed by (−) mating type and show the same biologi-cal activities when applied to (+) strains.

Trisporic acids are thus produced by both mating types but by slightly different metabolic pathways, and each mating type requires a metabolite from the other strain to complete the pathway (Figure 1).

An interesting question then arises. Which is the active regulatory compound, the mating-type–specific precursor or trisporic acid itself? This has been a difficult question to answer conclusively. Both trisporic acids and the mating-type–specific precursors will induce zygosphore formation. Sutter has suggested that the precur-sors are the true regulatory compound and that trisporic acids are inactive end products (105). This suggestion is based on two sorts of evidence. Relatively large amounts of trisporic acids are required to induce sexuality in *Phycomyces blakes-leeanus* while small amounts of the precursors suffice. There are also mutants of (−) mating type *M. mucedo* which will not respond to added trisporic acids but will respond to the precursors. It is possible, however, that each of the cases merely reflects a lowered permeability to trisporic acids and that precursors are only active because they are converted to trisporic acids intracellularly.

What is needed to resolve this question is mutants which are unable to con-vert the mating-type–specific precursors to trisporic acids. If the mating reaction proceeds normally in these, a nonessential role would be indicated for trisporic acids.

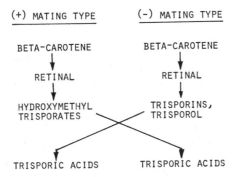

Figure 1 Trisporic acid biosynthesis in the Mucorales.

Very little has been reported about the molecular mode of action of these phero-mones. Trisporic acid stimulation of carotenogenesis is inhibited by cycloheximide (108). This has led to the suggestion that trisporic acid stimulates the synthesis of a limiting enzyme involved in the isoprenoid pathway. It also appears likely that trisporic acids also feed back and stimulate their own formation from β-carotene (116). This stimulation is also inhibited by cycloheximide and by 5-fluorouracil, but the exact site affected in the reaction sequence is not known. Whatever the pheromone receptor is in these systems, it must be fairly specific since the small chemical differences between the mating-type–specific precursors can be discrim-inated.

The mutants which have been isolated thus far in these mucoraceous fungi have been very helpful in dissecting the mating reaction. The *car* mutants of *Phycomyces* clearly implicated the role of carotenes as precursors to the sexual pheromones (104). A number of mutants with altered trisporic acid responses have been isolated in *Mucor.* No recombination analysis could be made in *Mucor,* however, in part because of very low zygospore germination frequencies (120). Indeed, genetic analy-sis is not straightforward in any members of the Mucorales. Complications are introduced by the fact that each gametangium contributes many nuclei to the zygospore. Segregation analysis thus becomes complex and it is difficult to insure that one is working with homocaryotic strains.

VOLVOX   The pheromonal systems discussed thus far have all involved relatively low molecular weight molecules. Higher organisms are known to produce a variety of peptide and glycoprotein hormones and these have counterparts in the algae and fungi. The genus *Volvox,* of the green algae, contains more than 20 species, all of which are spherical to spheroidal in shape (52, 97). Each individual, termed a spheroid, contains a few hundred to several thousand cells embedded in a transpar-ent extracellular matrix. The cells are of two types. Somatic cells are biflagellate and their coordinated beating propels the organism about. Somatic cells do not divide and die at the end of each generation. Reproductive cells are of several types. Asexual organisms contain asexual reproductive cells called gonidia, which divide and differentiate to form juvenile organisms.

It is not obvious from observations of material collected in the field that a pheromonal system is involved in *Volvox* sexual reproduction. For this reason, *Volvox* sexual pheromones were not discovered until detailed cultural studies were undertaken. The first *Volvox* sexual pheromones was discovered by Darden (32). He found that gonidia of *V. aureus* normally cleave to form asexual organisms like the parent. In older cultures, however, a few gonidia would form male spheroids rather than asexuals. Males can be easily distinguished because they produce bundles of sperm. Once a few males were formed, a cascade reaction appeared to take place and large numbers of males were produced. Cultures which were frequently transferred to fresh medium failed to produce males. Once a few males are produced, however, the culture rapidly "goes male." Darden subsequently showed that medium from cultures which had produced males contained a pheromone which induced the formation of males. Why the first male appears has still not been resolved. It could be that a low-level, constitutive synthesis of the pheromone by asexual organisms occurs and when a threshold level is reached a few males are induced. The males then produce large amounts of the pheromone and the culture "goes male." It is also possible that a transient release from repression occurs or that the first male is a result of mutation (97).

In *V. aureus* the sperm fertilize gonidia in young asexual organisms of the same clone. No morphologically differentiated females occur. Other species of *Volvox* are diclonic. Of these, *V. carteri* has been investigated the most extensively (52, 97). In this organism males and specialized females (containing eggs rather than gonidia) are formed in separate clones. Males produce a pheromone which stimulates male production and also induces the formation of females by gonidia in the female clone. Formation of females by wild-type female clones is dependent on the pheromone produced by males. Females apparently do not produce a pheromone.

The biological activity of the *Volvox* pheromones is thus to induce the formation of males or females by the gonidia. In the absence of the pheromone, gonidia form asexual individuals. The pheromones are active in very low concentrations, 10^{-16} M being sufficient for a partial response. Several species of *Volvox* are now known to produce sex pheromones and all are species- or even strain-specific.

All the *Volvox* pheromones reported appear to be proteins or glycoproteins. Only two have been purified and partially characterized. These were isolated from an American and a Japanese isolate of *V. carteri* (53, 98). The two do not show biological cross-reactivity but appear to be similar in general chemical and physical properties. Both are glycoproteins of about 30,000 molecular weight. The pheromone from the American isolate contains about 20% carbohydrate, the Japanese 40%. Several neutral sugars and n-acetylglucosamine are present in each, but the number of carbohydrate chains and the linkages involved are as yet unknown. Both pheromones have a very basic pI and are very resistant to destruction by heat or enzymatic hydrolysis. Of the enzymes tested, only generally acting proteases such as pronase have been shown to destroy the biological activity.

The pheromones are produced in fairly large quantities (up to 1 mg/l) and released into the culture medium by males. They can be isolated by a simple procedure and can be stored for long periods with no apparent loss of biological activity. It appears then that *Volvox* presents a favorable system for analysis of the mode of action of these pheromones.

In terms of chemical structure and biological function, the *Volvox* pheromones parallel the gonadotropic hormones found in higher animals. These have no known parallels in higher plants. Gonadotropic hormones are also glycoproteins of about 30,000 molecular weight and their function in animal systems is to control differentiation of the gametes. Gonadotropic hormones are believed to exert their effect by binding to a specific receptor present on the surface of target cells (24). Binding is specific, of high affinity, and reversible. The hormone-receptor complex then modulates some internal process with the hormone never actually entering the cell. There is some evidence that changes in cyclic AMP levels are involved, so the system is believed to conform to the classic "second-messenger" model (67).

The pheromone from *V. carteri* can be iodinated in vitro without apparent loss of biological activity, and some binding studies have been performed (G. Kochert, unpublished observations). Binding to whole organisms is apparently species-specific and is fully reversible. These observations parallel the known biological activity of the pheromone. Binding to isolated gonidia can also be demonstrated to be reversible and saturable. These observations are consistent with there being surface receptors for the pheromones, but no direct localization studies have been performed.

It is not known if there is a cyclic nucleotide regulation system in *Volvox,* but it seems reasonable that there would be since this has been demonstrated in the closely related alga *Chlamydomonas* (3). Added cyclic nucleotides, theobromine, or caffeine have no effect on the induction process, but direct experiments need to be performed.

One advantage that *Volvox* has over many other systems described here is its suitability for genetics. In *V. carteri,* males and females occur in separate haploid clones. Genetic crosses can be made easily, and a high percentage of zygospore germination is routinely obtained. Inheritance of sexuality shows a regular 1:1 segregation (51). Mutants of various sorts have been obtained and a genetic map is being constructed (93). The *Volvox* system thus has considerable potential for genetic analysis of sexual differentiation and sexual hormone action.

Not very much has been done on genetics of hormone action in any system. In animal tissue culture systems, mutants have been isolated which are resistant to steroid hormone-induced lethality (122). When they were analyzed, various aspects of the "pathway" of hormone action were found to be defective. Some showed decreased amounts of the hormone receptor, while others seemed to be defective in the nuclear transfer element. Other tissue culture lines have yielded mutants resistant to cyclic AMP-induced lethality (25). These animal systems are valuable for the insight they provide, but it is impossible to utilize formal genetic approaches with them. Mixing of cell extracts or cell fusion studies are the only possibilities. Also, these tissue culture cell lines are cancer cells with grossly altered phenotypes and variable chromosome numbers, and it is not certain that extrapolation to normal cells in vivo is justified.

Mutants of the sexual hormone system have been reported in *V. carteri.* These have been of several types. Meredith & Starr reported that isolates of male clones grown under identical conditions yield hormone preparations of varying potency (68). When crosses were made between high and low potency isolates, the progeny showed a range of potencies. The results apparently indicated that hormone potency was a polygenic trait. However, it is not known whether the differences in potency are caused by differences in the amount of hormone produced or by subtle qualitative differences in the hormone molecules produced by the different isolates.

Mutants of the female clone in *V. carteri* have also been reported. Mutant clones which form females in the absence of the sex pheromone arise spontaneously in fairly high frequency (97). This trait appears to segregate as a single allele unlinked to sexual type. Noninducible mutants can also be isolated. No temperature-sensitive mutants of this type have yet been reported, so it has not been possible to analyze these genetically. It would also be interesting to analyze these mutants in terms of their ability to bind radioactively labeled pheromone. If the *Volvox* sex pheromone acts by a second messenger mechanism, one might expect to find some noninducible mutants which show decreased binding because of an altered surface receptor, while others might bind normal amounts of hormone but be defective in some later step in the hormone sequence. The potential for this sort of combined biochemical and genetic approach is one of the greatest assets of the *Volvox* system.

ASCOMYCETES   Among the higher fungi there is convincing evidence for sexual pheromones in the ascomycetes. The system in yeasts is at present confusing, and the various reports have not been reconciled into a consistent picture. Haploid yeast cells are of two mating types, *a* and *α*. Two such cells in the proper stage of the life cycle (unbudded) which are in proximity will elongate toward each other and fuse at the point of contact to form a zygote. Although many pheromones have been postulated to be operative in this interaction, only one such factor has been purified. Cells of the *α* mating type constitutively produce and release a pheromone into the culture medium. This pheromone (the *α* factor) induces morphological and biochemical changes in *a* cells; the cells are arrested in G1 and deformed in shape. The effect is to arrest the cells in the life cycle stage when they can fuse and to cause changes in the cell wall which renders the cells able to fuse (the changes in cell shape are indicators of cell wall changes). The *α* factor has been purified and characterized (99, 100). It is a peptide containing 13 amino acids, the sequence of which was determined. Three other peptides, derived from the primary component by removal of the N-terminal amino acid and oxidation of the methionine residue, are present in the medium and are also biologically active. A peptide with comparable biological activity is also apparently produced by *a* cells. For a complete review of the mating system in yeasts the reader is referred to the work of Crandall and associates (29, 30). Preliminary results indicate that a similar sexual pheromonal system may be operative in the heterobasidiomycete *Tremella* (90).

Bistis and associates (13–16) provided convincing evidence of a pheromonal involvement in the sexuality of *Ascobolus stercorarius*. Two mating types, designated A and *a,* are present in this filamentous ascomycete. When compatible filaments approach, an ascogonial primordium is formed by one mating type. The primordium develops into an ascogonium with a slightly thinner filamentous appendage called the trichogyne. The trichogyne grows toward the other mating type, fuses with it, and receives one or more nuclei. After nuclear fusion, the ascogonium and adjacent filaments develop into the mature fruiting body. Each mating type can form ascogonial primordia and can serve as nuclear donors but they are self-incompatible.

Pheromones appear to be involved in several steps of this reaction, and the apparent sequence is as follows. Each mating type constitutively produces a pheromone which activates the other mating type to serve as a nuclear donor. The activated element then produces a pheromone which induces formation of ascogonial primordia. Finally, the trichogyne grows chemotropically toward the activated nuclear donor and fusion follows.

Nothing is known about the chemical nature of these pheromones. They are able to exert their effects through membrane filters. The pheromone which activates the nuclear donor can be collected by diffusion into agar blocks, but the pheromone which induces ascogonial primordia could not be obtained in this manner.

CONCLUDING REMARKS

The study of the origin and evolution of pheromones and hormones will always contain a liberal serving of speculation, but is fascinating nevertheless. It seems reasonable that pheromonal communication between unicellular organisms is the oldest form of communication. Development of multicellular organisms with internal communication and coordination by hormones would have been dependent on the development of such a system. The "ancestors" of present-day hormones would thus be pheromones of simpler organisms (40, 55). The origin of the pheromones themselves may have been from surface cell components which "leaked" into the surrounding medium and were subsequently recruited to serve as specific communicating agents. About the only sort of evidence which can be used to support this is chemical similarities between pheromones and structural components of cells. In the brown algae it seems clear that attractant pheromones evolved from essential oils. One of the main roles of sterols in eucaryotes seems to be as membrane structural components. The steroid hormones of *Achlya* may have evolved from membrane structural components. There is no evidence for this at present, but as membrane structural components become characterized it may be possible to see relationships. The glycoprotein pheromones of *Volvox* may be altered membrane structural components or altered components of the extracellular matrix. Again, chemical characterization of these components has not reached the point where meaningful comparisons can be made, but this is a direction that would be interesting to pursue.

This review has demonstrated that communication by pheromones is widespread in algal and fungal sexual systems. It will also have demonstrated the meager state of our present knowledge about pheromone structure and mode of action. Modern methods of chemical analysis utilizing small amounts of material have progressed to the point that they are no longer the limiting factor in pheromone structure studies. The limiting factor now appears to be primarily in the number of biologists willing to spend the time necessary to "domesticate" algal or fungal systems to the point where meaningful chemical analysis can be performed.

The analysis of pheromone function in these systems has barely begun. In chemotactic systems a variety of approaches need to be taken. Detailed studies of the swimming behavior of flagellated cells should be undertaken using photographic tracking techniques (33). Some progress has been made in this area since the pioneering study by Couch (28). Fungal flagellated cells appear to swim in linear, often spiral paths interrupted by rather abrupt turns (69, 92). Chemotactic agents can change the frequency of turning (2), and the situation in simple fungal zoospores may prove to be analogous to bacterial chemotaxis. Careful experiments need to be devised to determine whether these cells can respond to temporal gradients of attractants as do bacteria. It seems obvious that highly specific pheromone receptor molecules are involved in chemotactic responses, but there is little information (and not many ideas) about the way in which reception of the attractant is translated into an altered pattern of flagellar movement. Membrane depolarization and altered permeability to calcium ions has been demonstrated to affect the pattern of flagellar activity in the ciliate *Paramecium* (35). The requirement for calcium displayed by algal and fungal chemotaxis is suggestive of such a role and this could be tested with new methods for detection of membrane potential changes (34, 106).

Pheromones which function in a primer role are even more complex to analyze. It is difficult to distinguish primary and secondary responses and it is usually difficult to separate growth and developmental effects. Algal and fungal primer pheromones are chemically quite similar to hormones of metazoan animals, and present functional studies seem centered around efforts to show that the mechanisms of action are similar. This seems a reasonable approach for the present. Indeed, the simplicity of the algal and fungal systems and the potential of some for genetic approaches make it likely that the point of parity could soon be reached and we could soon be learning about hormonal mechanisms in metazoa from the study of pheromones in simpler forms.

ACKNOWLEDGMENTS

Preparation of this manuscript and the author's research has been supported by the National Science Foundation. This support is gratefully acknowledged.

Literature Cited

1. Adler, J. 1975. Chemotaxis in bacteria. See Ref. 22, pp. 91–100
2. Allen, R. N., Newhook, F. J. 1974. Suppression by ethanol of spontaneous turning activity in zoospores of *Phytophthora cinnamomi. Trans. Br. Mycol. Soc.* 63:383–85
3. Amrhein, N., Filner, P. 1973. Adenosine 3':5'-cyclic monophosphate in *Chlamydomonas reinhardii:* Isolation and characterization. *Proc. Natl. Acad. Sci. USA* 70:1099–1103
4. Austin, D. G., Bu'Lock, J. D., Winstanley, D. J. 1969. Trisporic acid biosynthesis and carotenogenesis in *Blakeslea trispora. Biochem. J.* 113:34
5. Austin, D. J., Bu'Lock, J. D., Drake, D. 1970. The biosynthesis of trisporic acids from β-carotene via retinal and trisporol. *Experientia* 26:348–49
6. Barksdale, A. W. 1963. The uptake of exogenous hormone A by certain strains of *Achlya. Mycologia* 55:164–71
7. Barksdale, A. W. 1963. The role of hormone A during sexual conjugation in *Achlya ambisexualis. Mycologia* 55: 627–32
8. Barksdale, A. W. 1967. The sexual hor-

mones of the fungus *Achlya. Ann. NY Acad. Sci.* 144:313–19

9. Barksdale, A. W., McMorris, T. C., Seshadri, R., Arunachalam, T., Edwards, J. A., Sundeen, J., Green, D. M. 1974. Response of *Achlya ambisexualis* E87 to the hormone antheridiol and certain other steroids. *J. Gen. Microbiol.* 82:295–99

10. Bayliss, W. M., Starling, E. 1904. The chemical regulation of the secretory process. *Proc. R. Soc. London Ser. B* 73:310–22

11. Bethe, A. 1932. Vernachlässigte Hormone. *Naturwissenschaften* 20:177–81

12. Bishop, H. 1940. A study of sexuality in *Sapromyces reinschii. Mycologia* 32:505–29

13. Bistis, G. 1956. Sexuality in *Ascobolus stercorarius.* I. Morphology of the ascogonium; plasmogamy; evidence for a sexual hormonal mechanism. *Am. J. Bot.* 43:389–94

14. Bistis, G. 1957. Sexuality in *Ascobolus stercorarius.* II. Primary experiments on various aspects of the sexual process. *Am. J. Bot.* 44:436–43

15. Bistis, G., Olive, L. S. 1968. Induction of antheridia in *Ascobolus stercorarius. Am. J. Bot.* 55:629–34

16. Bistis, G., Raper, J. R. 1963. Heterothallism and sexuality in *Ascobolus stercorarius. Am. J. Bot.* 50:880–91

17. Brown, D. A., Berg, H. C. 1974. Temporal stimulation of chemotaxis in *Escherichia coli. Proc. Natl. Acad. Sci. USA* 71:1388–92

18. Bu'Lock, J. D. 1976. Hormones in fungi. In *The Filamentous Fungi,* ed. J. E. Smith, D. R. Berry, 2:345–68. London: Arnold

19. Bu'Lock, J. D., Jones, B. E., Taylor, D., Winskill, N., Quarrie, S. A. 1974. Sex hormones in Mucorales. The incorporation of C_{20} and C_{18} precursors into trisporic acids. *J. Gen. Microbiol.* 80:301–6

20. Bu'Lock, J. D., Winskill, N., Jones, B. E. 1974. Structures of the mating type specific prohormones of Mucorales. *Chem. Commun.* 708–11

21. Burgett, H. 1924. Untersuchungen über Sexualität und Parasitismus bei Mucorineen. *Bot. Abh.* 4:1–135

22. Carlile, M. J., ed. 1975. *Primitive Sensory and Communication Systems.* New York: Academic. 258 pp.

23. Carlile, M. J., Machlis, L. 1965. The response of male gametes of *Allomyces* to the sexual hormone sirenin. *Am. J. Bot.* 52:478–83

24. Catt, K. J., Tsuruhara, T., Dufau, M. L. 1972. Gonadotropin binding sites of the rat testis. *Biochim. Biophys. Acta* 279:194–201

25. Coffino, P., Bourne, H. R., Friedrich, U., Hochman, J., Drisel, P. A., Lemaire, I., Melmon, K. L., Tomkins, G. M. 1976. Molecular mechanisms of cyclic AMP action: a genetic approach. *Recent Prog. Horm. Res.* 32:669–82

26. Cook, A. H., Elvidge, J. A. 1951. Fertilization in the Fucaceae: investigations on the nature of the chemotactic substance produced by eggs of *Fucus serratus* and *F. vesiculosus. Proc. R. Soc. London Ser. B* 138:97–114

27. Cook, A. H., Elvidge, J. A., Heilbron, I. 1948. Fertilization, including chemotactic phenomena in the Fucaceae. *Proc. R. Soc. London Ser. B* 135:293–301

28. Couch, J. N. 1941. The structure and action of the cilia in some aquatic phycomycetes. *Am. J. Bot.* 28:704–13

29. Crandall, M. 1977. Mating-type interactions in microorganisms. In *Receptors and Recognition,* Vol. 3, ed. P. Cuatrecasas, M. F. Greaves. New York: Chapman & Hall, In press

30. Crandall, M., Egel, R., MacKay, V. L. 1977. Physiology of mating in three yeasts. *Adv. Microb. Physiol.* 15:307–98

31. Culture collection of algae. 1976. *J. Phycol.* 12:467

32. Darden, W. H. 1966. Sexual differentiation in *Volvox aureus. J. Protozool.* 13:239–55

33. Davenport, D. 1973. Studies in microorganismal behavior by computerized television. In *Behavior of Microorganisms,* ed. A. Perez-Miravete, 106–16. New York: Plenum. 301 pp.

34. Doughty, M. J., Dodd, G. H. 1976. Fluorometric determination of the resting potential changes associated with the chemotactic response in *Paramecium. Biochim. Biophys. Acta* 451:592–603

35. Eckert, R. 1973. Electrical mechanisms controlling locomotion in the ciliated protozoa. See Ref. 33, pp. 117–26

36. Emerson, R., Wilson, C. M. 1954. Interspecific hybrids and the cytogenetics and cytotaxonomy of *Euallomyces. Mycologia* 46:393–434

37. Gooday, G. W. 1973. Differentiation in the Mucorales. *Symp. Soc. Gen. Microbiol.* 74:233–39

38. Gooday, G. W. 1975. Chemotaxis and chemotropism in fungi and algae. See Ref. 22, pp. 155–204

39. Groner, B., Hynes, N., Sippel, A. E., Schutz, G. 1976. Induction of specific proteins in hyphae of *Achlya ambisexualis* by the steroid hormone antheridiol. *Nature* 261:599–601

40. Haldane, J. B. S. 1955. Animal communication and the origin of human language. *Sci. Prog.* 43:385–401

41. Hoffman, L. R. 1960. Chemotaxis of *Oedogonium* sperms. *Southwest. Nat.* 5:111–16

42. Horgan, P. A. 1977. Cytosol-hormone stimulation of transcription in the aquatic fungus, *Achlya ambisexualis. Biochem. Biophys. Res. Commun.* 75:1022–28

43. Horgen, P. A., Smith, R., Silver, J. C., Craig, G. 1975. Hormonal stimulation of ribosomal RNA synthesis in *Achlya ambisexualis. Can. J. Biochem.* 53:1341–45

44. Hynes, R. O. 1976. Surface labelling techniques for eukaryotic cells. In *New Techniques in Biophysics and Cell Biology*, ed. R. H. Pain, B. J. Smith, 3:147–212. New York: Wiley

45. Jaenicke, L., ed. 1974. Chemical signal transmission by gamete attractants in brown algae. In *Biochemistry of Sensory Functions*, pp. 307–9. Heidelberg: Springer-Verlag. 641 pp.

46. Jaenicke, L. 1977. Sex hormones of brown algae. *Naturwissenschaften* 64:69–75

47. Jaenicke, L., Müller, D. G. 1973. Gametenlockstoffe bie niederen Pflanzen und Tieren. *Fortschr. Chem. Org. Naturst.* 30:61–100

48. Jaenicke, L., Müller, D. G., Moore, R. E. 1974. Multifidene and aucantene, C_{11} hydrocarbons in the male-attracting essential oil from the gynogametes of *Cutleria multifida* (Smith) Grev. (Phaeophyta). *J. Am. Chem. Soc.* 96:3224–25

49. Kane, B. E., Reiskind, J. B., Mullins, J. T. 1973. Hormonal control of sexual morphogenesis in *Achlya:* Dependence on protein and ribonucleic acid synthesis. *Science* 180:1192

50. Karlson, P., Luscher, M. 1959. 'Pheromones': a new term for a class of biologically active substances. *Nature* 183:55–56

51. Kochert, G. 1968. Differentiation of reproductive cells in *Volvox carteri. J. Protozool.* 15:438–52

52. Kochert, G. 1975. Developmental mechanisms in *Volvox* reproduction. *Symp. Soc. Dev. Biol.* 33:55–90

53. Kochert, G., Yates, I. 1974. Purification and partial characterization of a glycoprotein sexual inducer from *Volvox carteri. Proc. Natl. Acad. Sci. USA* 71:1211–14

54. Lasure, L., Griffin, D. H. 1975. Inheritance of sex in *Achlya bisexualis. Am. J. Bot.* 62:216–20

55. Levinson, J. A. 1972. Zur Evolution und Biosynthese der terpenoiden Pheromone und Hormone. *Naturwissenschaften* 59:477–84

56. Machlis, L. 1958. Evidence for a sexual hormone in *Allomyces. Physiol. Plant.* 11:181–92

57. Machlis, L. 1968. The response of wild type male gametes of *Allomyces* to sirenin. *Plant Physiol.* 43:1319–20

58. Machlis, L. 1969. Zoospore chemotaxis in the watermold *Allomyces. Physiol. Plant.* 22:126–39

59. Machlis, L. 1973. The effects of bacteria on the growth and reproduction of *Oedogonium cardiacum. J. Phycol.* 9:342–44

60. Machlis, L. 1973. The chemotactic activity of various sirenins and analogues and the uptake of sirenin by the sperm of *Allomyces. Plant Physiol.* 52:527–30

61. Machlis, L. 1973. Factors affecting the stability and accuracy of the bioassay for the sperm attractant sirenin. *Plant Physiol.* 52:524–26

62. Machlis, L., Hill, G. G. C., Steinback, E., Reed, W. 1974. Some characteristics of the sperm attractant from *Oedogonium cardiacum. J. Phycol.* 10:199–204

63. Machlis, L., Nutting, W. H., Rapoport, H. 1968. The structure of sirenin. *J. Am. Chem. Soc.* 90:1674–76

64. Machlis, L., Nutting, W. H., Williams, M. W., Rapoport, H. 1966. Production, isolation, and characterization of sirenin. *Biochemistry* 5:2147–52

65. McMorris, T. C., Barksdale, A. W. 1967. Isolation of a sex hormone from the water mold *Achlya bisexualis. Nature* 215:320–21

66. McMorris, T. C., Seshadri, R., Weihe, G. R., Aresenault, G. P., Barksdale, A. W. 1975. Structures of oogonial-1,-2, and -3, steroidal sex hormones of the water mold *Achlya. J. Am. Chem. Soc.* 97:2544–45

67. Mendelson, C., Dufau, M. L., Catt, K. J. 1975. Gonadotropin binding and stimulation of cyclic adenosine 3':5'-monophosphate and testosterone production in isolated Leydig cells. *J. Biol. Chem.* 250:8813–23

68. Meredith, R., Starr, R. C. 1975. The genetic bases of male potency in *Volvox carteri* f. nagariensis (Chlorophyceae). *J. Phycol.* 11:265–72

69. Miles, C. A., Holwill, M. E. J. 1969. Asymmetric flagellar movement in relation to the orientation of the spore of *Blastocladiella emersonii. J. Exp. Biol.* 50:683–87

70. Moore, R. E. 1977. Volatile compounds from marine algae. *Acc. Chem. Res.* 10:40–47

71. Müller, D. G. 1967. Generationswechsel, Kernphasenwechsel und Sexualitat der braunalge *Ectocarpus siliculosis* in Kulturversuch. *Planta* 75:39–54

72. Müller, D. G. 1974. Sexual reproduction and isolation of a sex attractant in *Cutleria multifida* (Smith) Grev. (Phaeophyta). *Biochem. Physiol. Pflanzen* 165:212–15

73. Müller, D. G. 1976. Sexual isolation between a European and an American population of *Ectocarpus siliculosis* (Phaeophyta). *J. Phycol.* 12:252–54

74. Müller, D. G. 1976. Quantitative evaluation of sexual chemotaxis in two marine brown algae. *Z. Pflanzenphysiol.* 80:120–30

75. Müller, D. G., Jaenicke, L. 1973. Fucoserraten, the female sex attractant of *Fucus serratus* L. *FEBS Lett.* 30: 137–39

76. Müller, D. G., Jaenicke, L., Donike, M., Akintobi, T. 1971. Sex attractant in brown alga: chemical structure. *Science* 171:815–17

77. Müller, D. G., Seferiadis, K. 1977. Specificity of sexual chemotaxis in *Fucus serratus* and *Fucus vesiculosis* (Phaeophyceae). *Z. Pflanzenphysiol.* 84:85–94

78. Mullins, J. T., Ellis, E. A. 1974. Sexual morphogenesis in *Achlya:* Ultrastructural basis for the hormonal induction of antheridial hyphae. *Proc. Natl. Acad. Sci. USA* 71:1347–50

79. Musgrave, A., Nieuwenhuis, D. 1975. Metabolism of radioactive antheridiol by *Achlya* species. *Arch. Microbiol.* 105:313–17

80. Nieuwenhuis, M., Van den Ende, H. 1975. Sex specificity of hormone synthesis in *Mucor mucedo. Arch. Mikrobiol.* 102:167–69

81. Nolan, R. A., Bal, A. K. 1974. Cellulase localization in hyphae of *Achlya ambisexualis. J. Bacteriol.* 117:840–43

82. Nutting, W. H., Rapoport, H., Machlis, L. 1968. The structure of sirenin. *J. Am. Chem. Soc.* 90:6434–38

83. Pascher, A. 1931. Über Gruppenbildung und Geschlechtwechsel bei den Gameten einer Chlamydomonadine (*Chlamydomonas paupera*). *Jarhb. Wiss. Bot.* 75:551–80

84. Plempel, M. 1963. Die chemischen Grundlagen der Sexualreaktion bei zygomyceten. *Planta* 59:509–20

85. Prieto, A., Spalla, C., Bianchi, M., Biffi, G. 1964. Biosynthesis of β-carotene by strains of Choanephoraceae. *Chem. Ind. London,* p. 551

86. Raper, J. R. 1952. Chemical regulation of sexual processes in the thallophytes. *Bot. Rev.* 18:447–545

87. Raper, J. R. 1970. Chemical ecology among lower plants. In *Chemical Ecology,* ed. E. Sondheimer, J. B. Simeone, pp. 21–42. New York: Academic. 336 pp.

88. Raper, J. R., Haagen-Smit, A. J. 1942. Sexual hormones in *Achlya.* IV. Properties of hormone A of *Achlya bisexualis. J. Biol. Chem.* 143:311–20

89. Rawitcher-Kunkel, E., Machlis, L. 1962. The hormonal integration of sexual reproduction in *Oedogonium. Am. J. Bot.* 49:177–83

90. Reid, I. D. 1974. Properties of conjugation hormones (erogens) from the basidiomycete *Tremella mesenterica. Can. J. Bot.* 52:521–24

91. Rosenberg, B., Misra, T. N., Switzer, R. 1968. Mechanism of olfactory transduction. *Nature* 217:423–27

92. Royle, D. J., Hickman, C. J. 1964. Analysis of factors governing *in vitro* accumulation of zoospores of *Pythium aphanidermatum* on roots I. Behavior of zoospores. *Can. J. Microbiol.* 10: 151–61

93. Sessoms, A. H., Huskey, R. J. 1973. Genetic control of development in *Volvox:* Isolation and characterization of morphogenetic mutants. *Proc. Natl. Acad. Sci. USA* 70:1335–38

94. Sherwood, W. A. 1966. Evidence for a sexual hormone in the water mold *Dictyuchus. Mycologia* 58:215–20

95. Silver, J. C., Horgen, P. A. 1974. Hormonal regulation of presumptive mRNA in the fungus *Achlya ambisexualis. Nature* 249:252–54

96. Starr, R. C. 1964. The culture collection of algae at Indiana University. *Am. J. Bot.* 51:1033–44

97. Starr, R. C. 1970. Control of differentiation in *Volvox. Dev. Biol. Suppl.* 4:59–100

98. Starr, R. C., Jaenicke, L. 1974. Purification and characterization of the hor-

mone initiating sexual morphogenesis in *Volvox carteri* f. nagariensis. *Proc. Natl. Acad. Sci. USA* 71:1050–54

99. Stötzler, D., Duntze, W. 1976. Isolation and characterization of four related peptides exhibiting α-factor activity from *Saccharomyces cerevisiae*. *Eur. J. Biochem.* 65:257–62

100. Stötzler, D., Kiltz, H., Duntze, W. 1976. Primary structure of α-factor peptides from *Saceharomyces cerevisiae*. *Eur. J. Biochem.* 69:397–400

101. Stumm, C., Hermans, J. M. H., Croes, A. F., Bucks, J. R. 1976. Chemotaxis and transport of amino acids in *Allomyces arbuscula*. *Antonie van Leeuwenhoek J. Microbiol. Serol.* 42:203–9

102. Sutherland, R. B., Horgen, P. A. 1977. The effects of the steroid sex hormone, antheridiol, on the initiation of RNA synthesis in the simple eukaryote, *Achlya ambisexualis*. *J. Biol. Chem.* In press

103. Sutter, R. P. 1970. Trisporic acid synthesis in *Blakeslea trispora*. *Science* 168:1590–92

104. Sutter, R. P. 1975. Mutations affecting sexual development in *Phycomyces*. *Proc. Natl. Acad. Sci. USA* 72:127–30

105. Sutter, R. P. 1977. Regulation of the first stage of sexual development in *Phycomyces blakesleeanus* and in other mucoraceous fungi. In *Eucaryotic Microbes as Model Developmental Systems*, ed. D. H. O'Day, P. A. Horgen, pp. 251–72. New York: Dekker. 440 pp.

106. Szmelcman, S., Adler, J. 1976. Change in membrane potential during bacterial chemotaxis. *Proc. Natl. Acad. Sci. USA* 73:4387–91

107. Thomas, D. des S., Mullins, J. T. 1969. Cellulase induction and wall extension in the water mold *Achlya ambisexualis*. *Physiol. Plant.* 22:347–53

108. Thomas, D. M., Goodwin, T. W. 1967. Studies on carotenogenesis in *Blakeslea trispora*. I. General observations on synthesis in mated and unmated strains. *Phytochemistry* 6:355–60

109. Timberlake, W. E. 1976. Alternations in RNA and protein synthesis associated with steroid hormone-induced

sexual morphogenesis in the water mold *Achlya*. *Dev. Biol.* 51:202–14

110. Tsubo, Y. 1957. On the mating reactions of a *Chalydomonas*, with special references to clumping and chemotaxis. *Bot. Mag.* 70:327–40

111. Tsubo, Y. 1961. Chemotaxis and sexual behavior in *Chlamydomonas*. *J. Protozool.* 8:114–21

112. Van den Ende, H. 1968. Relationships between sexuality and carotene synthesis in *Blakeslea trispora*. *J. Bacteriol.* 96:1298–1303

113. Van den Ende, H. 1976. *Sexual Interactions in Plants*. New York: Academic. 186 pp.

114. Van den Ende, H., Werkman, B. A., Van den Briel, M. L. 1972. Trisporic acid synthesis in mated cultures of the fungus *Blakeslea trispora*. *Arch. Mikrobiol.* 86:175–84

115. Van den Ende, H., Wiechmann, A. H. C. A., Reyngoud, D. J., Hendriks, T. 1970. Hormonal interactions in *Mucor mucedo* and *Blakeslea trispora*. *J. Bacteriol.* 101:423–28

116. Werkman, B. A., Van den Ende, H. 1973. Trisporic acid synthesis in *Blakeslea trispora*. Interaction between *plus* and *minus* mating types. *Arch. Mikrobiol.* 90:365–74

117. Wilson, E. O. 1971. *The Insect Societies*. Cambridge: Harvard. 548 pp.

118. Wilson, E. O. 1975. *Sociobiology*. Cambridge: Harvard. 697 pp.

119. Wilson, E. O., Bossert, W. H. 1963. Chemical communication among animals. *Recent Prog. Horm. Res.* 19:673–716

120. Wurtz, T., Jockusch, H. 1975. Sexual differentiation in *Mucor:* Trisporic acid response mutants and mutants blocked in zygospore development. *Dev. Biol.* 43:213–20

121. Yamamoto, K. R., Alberts, B. M. 1976. Steroid receptors: Elements for modulation of eukaryotic transcription. *Ann. Rev. Biochem.* 45:721–46

122. Yamamoto, K. R., Gehring, U., Stampfer, M. R., Sibley, C. H. 1976. Genetic approaches to steroid hormone action. *Recent Prog. Horm. Res.* 32:3–32

Ann. Rev. Plant Physiol. 1978. 29:487–510

DEVELOPMENT
OF CELL POLARITY

❖7660

Ralph S. Quatrano

Department of Botany and Plant Pathology, Oregon State University,
Corvallis, Oregon 97331

CONTENTS

INTRODUCTION

Although much emphasis has been placed on analyzing the temporal and quantitative regulation of gene activity as the basis for understanding plant cell development, relatively little attention has been devoted to spatial controls. A characteristic of many different plant cells, from egg cells to those highly specialized cell types such as root hair cells, is the localization of subcellular components in specific regions of the cytoplasm. Cells that possess an axis with structurally or physiologically different ends are termed polar. To explain the basis of cell polarity, one must understand how external environments can interact with genetic mechanisms to direct the accumulation of specific cellular components to precise locations within the cell. Subsequent segregation of nuclei into these polar regions of cytoplasm results in different microenvironments for each of the genetically identical nuclei. The ensuing nucleocytoplasmic interactions have been shown in both plant and animal cells to be the basis for selective gene expression in different regions of cells, the developing embryo, and in mature tissues (6, 20, 29, 43). Thus the divergence

487

0066-4154/78/0701-0487$01.00

of gene expression in different regions of the embryo and in different cells of mature tissue is initiated by the unequal distribution of cytoplasmic components. The widespread occurrence of polar cells in plants and their relationship to subsequent cell specialization led Bünning to state "Ohne polarität keine differenzierung" (9).

Although early observations and descriptions of polarity in plants extend back into the eighteenth century (cf 4, 93), Vöchting in the late 1800s introduced the term polarity into the plant literature with his classical experiments on excised willow twigs (101). At the turn of the twentieth century Goebel, Janse, Sachs, Pfeffer, Klebs, and Winkler had extended the experimental and theoretical aspects of polarity (cf 93). It was Vöchting, however, who proposed that the polar characteristics of tissues and organs were relatively stable and irreversible and that these bipolar, axial structures were the result of a polarity expressed by individual cells. Although difficult to prove by isolating single cells from higher plant organs, histological studies of cellular differentiation in angiosperms indicated the presence of a "polar cytoplasm" in the region of a cell which would later differentiate into a specific cell type (cf 8, 93).

The most striking demonstrations of a stable polar axis in individual cells have been reported in the filamentous algae. Unlike the angiosperm cells which exhibit an easily discernible polar cytoplasm, many of these algal cells have no conspicuous accumulation of cellular inclusions. Yet they possess a stable polar axis. For example, when individual cells were removed from filaments of *Griffithsia* (90, 104, 105) and *Cladophora* (47), the isolated cells regenerated shoot cells from the apical end and rhizoid cells from the basal end. In the case of *Cladophora*, the polarity was retained even after the isolated cell was plasmolyzed, thereby severing any connections between the plasma membrane and cell wall (47). A structural basis for the polar axis was suggested by experiments in the early 1900s. Applied external forces, such as centrifugation and electrical currents, to *Griffithsia* cells could alter the polarity; shoot cells at the centrifugal pole (90) and rhizoids toward the positive pole (89). Studies such as these and many others led to a general hypothesis stating that within the cytoplasm a stable cytoskeletal framework exists which is initially oriented with respect to some extracellular gradient. This "polar protoplasmic structure" provides the structural basis upon which a chemical or particle gradient can be maintained for subsequent differentiation. The hypothesis was clearly stated by Bünning (8) 26 years ago:

It may therefore be concluded that polar molecules situated in the peripheral strata of the protoplasm are forced by external factors, e.g., light, gravity, spermatozoa, etc., to orient themselves in a particular direction; these molecules are then firmly anchored in this orientation pattern. This asymmetry may then lead to electrical potential differences and to chemical gradients which in their turn are of importance for anatomical and morphological differentiation. It is known from experiments with model non-living membranes that structural asymmetries may lead to polar transport of matter and to electrical potentials.

Although this hypothesis was supported by extensive descriptive and experimental evidence accumulated during this century, a firm cytological and biochemical basis is lacking.

A number of lengthy reviews have been compiled on the subject of polarity in plants (4, 8, 9, 19, 29, 32, 49, 53, 54, 88, 93), and for the most part these will not be repeated in this relatively brief review. My purpose is not to describe the very interesting examples of polarity in a large number of plant systems, nor to document its expression at levels of organization other than at the cell level. This has been accomplished adequately in the above-mentioned reviews. However, one system, zygotes of the brown alga *Fucus,* has been used for almost 90 years as a model to study how a cell becomes polar (66, 87). During the last decade, a considerable amount of experimentation with this system has been aimed at trying to understand the mechanism of cytoplasmic localization. I will focus my discussion on *Fucus* and on data not treated extensively in other excellent reviews of this system (35–38, 80, 113). By discussing recent approaches and hypotheses dealing with the fucoid egg, models can be constructed, tested, and applied to other plant systems. By determining the applicability and universality of the *Fucus* results to other plants, we should have a more complete understanding of polarity.

FUCUS DEVELOPMENT

Zygotes of the Fucales have been used recently to probe the biochemical, cytological, and biophysical basis of polar axis determination (80). The pattern of polar development during embryogenesis in *Fucus* is similar to many different plant embryos including angiosperms (107). In addition, many higher plant cells undergo a pattern of differentiation similar to that of the first two cells in the *Fucus* embryo (i.e. polarity followed by an unequal cell division). Therefore, this system can be used to propose and analyze mechanisms of differentiation operative at stages in higher plant development that are very difficult to analyze experimentally (cf 93, 107). The relative ease in obtaining synchronous single-celled cultures of *Fucus* zygotes that can be grown aseptically in a defined media and free of accessory cells (80, 81) has great potential for the experimental study of cell polarity, cell differentiation, and plant embryogenesis.

Within 8–14 hours after fertilization, the fucoid zygotes form a localized protuberance or rhizoid which represents the first sign of an asymmetric development. Within the cytoplasm of the rhizoid, one can detect the accumulation of subcellular components which are the earliest signs of polarity in the previously apolar, homogeneous cytoplasm of the spherical zygote (7, 78). When the rhizoid and its unique contents are separated from the remaining zygote by the first cell plate, the resulting two cells of the embryo are different from one another in structure, biochemical composition, and developmental fate (7, 80, 113). The rhizoid and its progeny contribute to the holdfast portion of the mature plant while the thallus cell and its derivatives form the frond. Hence the polarity acquired by the zygote is the basis for cellular differentiation in the two-celled embryo and the developmental axis of the entire plant.

In analyzing the underlying basis of polarity as a mechanism of differentiation, the main advantages of the fucoid embryos are: (*a*) the structural and biochemical polarity exhibited in the zygote occurs in a previously homogeneous egg cytoplasm; (*b*) the cytoplasmic site of the localizations can be experimentally determined and controlled by a variety of externally applied gradients. Thus, in a synchronously developing unicellular system, one can describe and analyze the cytological and biochemical changes occurring at a cytoplasmic site which was predetermined by an extracellular gradient.

A wide variety of external gradients can orient the polar axis (cf 35). For example, rhizoids form on the shaded side of a unilateral light gradient (80, 113), the low end of a pH gradient (113), the positive pole of a voltage gradient (70), and the more concentrated side of a Ca^{2+} or K^+ gradient (35, 86). The polar axis remains labile until a few hours before rhizoid formation, and each vector is perceived by the zygote at different but overlapping periods after fertilization (35). Hence an axis oriented by unilateral light at one time can be reoriented at a later time by light (or by another vector) from a different direction (79).

However, none of the above gradients are *required* for a polar zygote to form. Once fertilized, zygotes of a number of fucoid species become polar in a gradient-free environment (51, 80, 97, 113). Knapp (40) has shown in the brown alga *Cytoseira* that sperm entry, in the absence of other gradients, determines the site of rhizoid formation. Although Overton (68) reported the parthenogenic development of eggs into polar embryos, a number of laboratories including mine, have not been able to repeat his result. Since no quantitative data was given, Overton's observation could be explained by a very small number of eggs that were already fertilized. Therefore, sperm entry appears to be required, and the point of entry is the subsequent site of polar development unless a subsequent vector is imposed across the cell. This data and the elegant demonstration by Jaffe (33) that polarized light produces bipolar embryos, argues strongly for a polar axis which is initially labile and "arises in some more epigenetic manner than through the directed rotation of some preformed asymmetric structure." Postfertilization RNA and protein synthesis (72, 77), as well as the acquisition of a sufficient pressure potential for rhizoid elongation (3, 80), are also required for polar embryo formation.

POLAR CELL FORMATION

Processes involved with polar cell formation in *Fucus* can be divided into those events responsible for (*a*) the irreversible fixation of a polar axis originally determined by sperm entry or by some external gradient imposed on the zygote after fertilization, and (*b*) the localization along this axis of material needed for cell wall expansion at the rhizoid pole and thallus-specific functions at the opposite pole.

Polar Axis Fixation

Unfortunately, polar axis fixation and the localized accumulation of macromolecules experimentally directed by light or other gradients cannot be separated in time from each other or from cell division, even in synchronously developing cultures of zygotes (50). For example, the time course of these events in a population of *F. distichus* zygotes is between 11–16 hr for the fixation or irreversible determination of a cytoplasmic site for rhizoid formation, and between 14–18 hr for the actual formation of the rhizoid or a polar cell. Although the timing of these events may vary for different species and genera of the Fucales under different culture conditions (81), light-induced axis fixation always precedes and overlaps by 2–4 hr, the expression of a polar cell.

Some success in separating fixation from rhizoid formation was achieved by Torrey & Galun (98). They demonstrated in *F. vesiculosus* that zygotes grown in a seawater-sucrose medium and unilaterally illuminated formed spherical, multicellular embryos with no apparent localizations. When these apolar embryos were removed from the hypertonic medium and placed in seawater, rhizoids were formed *only* from the shaded hemisphere. Since unilateral light was applied continuously from one direction, two possibilities existed concerning a fixed polar axis: (*a*) it may have been present in the spherical embryos long before rhizoid emergence, or (*b*) an axis could have been fixed just before or concurrent with rhizoid emergence. Even if separation was achieved (*a*), only a portion of the cells in the multicellular embryo population would possess a fixed axis (those cells in shaded hemisphere) and the time of fixation could not be precisely determined. Hence the biochemical and biophysical basis of the fixation process would be difficult to discern.

A recent approach appears to have been successful in separating these events from each other in a synchronously developing single cell population of *F. distichus* zygotes. By treating zygotes exposed to unilateral light with reversible inhibitors of rhizoid formation, Quatrano (79) temporarily inhibited the localization processes and asked whether fixation was likewise delayed or if these two processes could be uncoupled. To determine if fixation had occurred in treated cultures, the source of orienting light was rotated 90° after controls established a fixed axis. The second direction of unilateral light would not be effective in orienting rhizoid growth if the inhibitor failed to affect the fixation process. If the second light source oriented treated populations of zygotes, fixation was delayed and most likely not separated in time from the localization events. When cycloheximide (CH), an inhibitor of protein synthesis in *Fucus* (77), or sucrose, which prevents water uptake into the zygote by lowering the potential of the external solution, was added during the fixation process, no effect was observed on fixation but rhizoid formation was delayed by 8 hr. Although CH has been reported to block fixation (60), we have been unable to repeat that observation. Thus, when either CH or sucrose is present from 9–15 hr after fertilization, the *entire* population of single cells has a fixed polar axis by 16 hr with no observable localizations at the rhizoid site until several hours later. The sucrose result would predict that the spherical, multicellular embryos observed by Torrey and Galun possessed a stable, fixed polar axis long before rhizoid formation.

However, when cytochalasin B (CB), which is known to disrupt microfilaments and affect membrane function (30), was present during the same time, fixation was prevented, i.e. the polar axis remained labile. CB has several other interesting effects on polar axis induction by light. If CB is present only during one unilateral light pulse of 60 min, the resulting rhizoids are randomly oriented (56, 79). When CB is introduced for 4 hr *after* the single light pulse, rhizoids are oriented with respect to the light. Thus, although CB prevents axis establishment and axis fixation by light, it does not disrupt the orientation of a previously induced axis (79).

Use of these inhibitors will allow one to isolate a population of cells undergoing fixation separate from localization and to determine if a biochemical or cytological event is directly associated with either process by its susceptibility to CB. For example, enzymatic sulfation of a fucose polymer occurs at the same time as axis fixation (82). In attempting to determine the relationship between this biochemical event and fixation, one can ask whether this biochemical event behaves like the fixation process when perturbated by such inhibitors. It appears reasonably clear that this does not happen. Sulfation is completely inhibited by CH (82) and is not affected by CB (60), just the opposite of the effects exhibited by fixation when treated with these compounds. Likewise, colchicine (an inhibitor of microtubule assembly) prevents spindle formation, karyokinesis, and cell plate formation while having no effect on fixation, rhizoid formation, or the ability of zygotes to orient to unilateral light (79). Whether all microtubules were disrupted [e.g. the preprophase band of microtubules (30) found in the cortical cytoplasm] was not determined by electron microscopy. By using these "handles" one can begin to discard those physiological processes (e.g. spindle formation, sulfation) that are not essential for a particular development phenomena (e.g. fixation) and begin to order the subcellular events occurring at this time.

Care must be taken in interpreting these observations since their basis rests primarily on inhibitor data. However, several observations in addition to their reversible effects suggest that these inhibitors are relatively selective in their action. CH prevents protein synthesis (77) while at the same concentration has no effect on the timing or number of cells undergoing axis fixation (79). The timing and amount of sulfation as well as the incorporation of the sulfated fucan into the cell wall is unaffected by CB (60). However, the location of the sulfated fucan deposition is affected by CB and will be discussed later (60).

At a time when the axis is fixed and before the localizing events associated with rhizoid formation, is there any structural change occurring at the presumptive rhizoid pole that can be associated with the fixation process? If zygotes are grown in an orienting gradient (e.g. light) and embedded for sectioning so that the presumptive site of rhizoid formation is known, events occurring at this location before and during fixation and localization can be observed by electron microscopy. Quatrano (78) demonstrated an accumulation of osmiophilic bodies and some undefined extracellular material in the cell wall of the future rhizoid in light-oriented, spherical zygotes of *F. vesiculosus* that possessed a fixed polar axis. If a true median section was viewed, the perinuclear region was highly polarized, with fingerlike projections radiating toward the site of rhizoid initiation. Numerous membranous extensions from the nuclear envelope were observed on the rhizoid side of the nucleus. There was a heavy concentration of mitochondria, ribosomes, osmiophilic bodies, densely fibrillar vesicles, and what appears to be Golgi-derived vesicles filled with finely fibrillar material in this region. Only mitochondria and Golgi bodies are subsequently accumulated in the rhizoid cell (7). Although these changes occur at the same time as fixation, they most likely represent an *expression* of a fixed axis or the beginnings of localizations necessary for rhizoid extension. Treatment of zygotes with CH, CB, and sucrose should help clarify the relationships of these observations to the fixation and localization process.

In a similar study using *F. vesiculosus,* Vreugdenhil et al (103) were able to predict the site of rhizoid formation using the "group effect" (113). When the presumptive rhizoid hemisphere was observed with the electron microscope, they did not report the cytoplasmic polarization but did describe the cell wall localization in only the rhizoid area. It consisted of an inner fibrillar layer and an amorphous outer layer that exhibited the characteristic color of sulfated polysaccharides when stained (cf 45). The localization of sulfated polysaccharides (fucoidin) in this region was initially reported almost a decade ago (45) and has been confirmed recently in isolated cell walls (61). An electrophoretically distinct sulfated fucan (F_2) can be identified at the time when the localized stain appears at the rhizoid site. F_2 has been isolated and is being characterized (31, 84). In order to determine if the extracellular deposition of this polysaccharide is part of the fixation process independent of rhizoid formation, Vreugdenhil et al (103) grew zygotes in seawater/sucrose. The localized deposition of F_2 occurred in the apolar, multicellular embryos, indicating that this process is independent of wall extension and the development of an osmotic pressure potential. It also demonstrates that spherical embryos with a fixed axis possess a morphological expression of the polarity as predicted from the experimental studies with light-induced fixation in the presence of sucrose (79). However, in this study there was no indication that the morphological marker would be present *coincident with* fixation. They observed the cell wall localization in multicellular, spherical embryos that were 42 hr old. To select the key structural event directly associated with fixation, one could predict from the inhibitor studies that it should be present by 16 hr when zygotes are treated with CH or sucrose from 9–15 hr after fertilization, but absent when treated in the same way with CB. This experiment has not as yet been reported.

There is some indirect evidence to suggest that deposition of F_2 into the cell wall is not the fixation event but one of the earliest expressions of a stable polar axis. If cell walls are isolated after 16 hr and treated with Toluidine Blue O (TBO) at a pH below 2 (specific stain for sulfated polysaccharides), only a localized region of the wall is stained, that area forming the rhizoid (61). Walls isolated prior to 8 hr do not stain with TBO, indicating that very little if any sulfated polysaccharide is present in the wall by that time. This has recently been confirmed (84). When walls from 16 hr embryos incubated with CB were stained, the sulfated polysaccharides were not localized, but the stain was evenly distributed throughout the wall surface (60). Hence, CB does not interfere with the process of sulfation, secretion, or incorporation in the cell wall, but apparently uncouples these processes from the directed deposition of F_2 to the fixed site, i.e. prevents axis fixation.

An excellent study by Nuccitelli (62) helps further order several other events with respect to fixation. His conclusions support the view that a local influx of ions and the accumulation and secretion of some material in the cytoplasm of the rhizoid region actually occurs prior to the irreversible determination of the rhizoid site. *Pelvetia fastigiata* zygotes grown in normal seawater exhibit both an accumulation of cytoplasmic vesicles and a clear area between the plasma membrane and cell wall at the rhizoid pole several hours prior to rhizoid emergence. This "cortical clearing" is most likely material for cell wall formation accumulating intracellularly and being secreted. Consistent with the latter point, Peng & Jaffe (69) have described by freeze-fracture techniques the deposition of new membrane patches ($\sim$30 μm) covering the rhizoid region at the time of cortical clearing. By moving the source of unilateral light 180° just after the first signs of clearing appeared, Nuccitelli observed a second cortical clearing area 180° from the first. *Both* areas persisted for a few hours, with the rhizoid finally emerging from the region of the latest formed area. This points to a slightly later event, not cortical clearing, that fixes a particular site for subsequent rhizoid extension. It also demonstrates that localizations such as the accumulation of cell wall vesicles appear prior to the irreversible commitment of the cytoplasmic site to which they are drawn.

In addition to cortical clearing, local fluxes of ions moving inward clearly precede rhizoid formation in *Pelvetia*. They can be localized in the plasma membrane regions of the presumptive rhizoid site before axis fixation. Also, in hydrated pollen of lily, the local region of largest inward current predicts the germination site and precedes germination by a few hours (108, 109). A similar phenomena can be demonstrated at the site of cap regeneration in *Acetabularia* (58, 59). In the *Pelvetia* and lily systems an ultrasensitive vibrating probe (cf 37) was utilized to detect currents entering and leaving various surface regions. This instrument allows one to measure very small currents (0.1 m A/cm^2) with a spatial resolution of about 30 μm accompanied by little if any disturbance to the living system. Using the probe, Nuccitelli (62) demonstrated that shortly after fertilization the spatial current pattern around the *Pelvetia* zygote shifts between several inward current regions. However, as the time of fixation approaches, these inward currents were concentrated at the presumptive site of rhizoid formation. Using the same material, he then observed cortical clearing occurring at this site and always at the region of largest inward current. If the orienting light was reversed, the spatial current pattern changed with an inward current on the new dark side within 40 min, followed in about an hour by a second region of cortical clearing at the new site of inward current. If the light reversal occurred after fixation, neither the reversal of the inward current nor the second clearing area was observed. The main points of this important study seem clear: (*a*) the appearance of a second cortical clearing was preceded by a local inward current, (*b*) both events occur prior to fixation and predict the final site of rhizoid formation, and (*c*) only when the electrical polarity was reversed did the cortical clearing and localized growth change. The polar plasmolysis in *Fucus* reported 38 years ago by Whitaker (113) may be related to the cortical clearing and these localized membrane changes reported by Nuccitelli.

The transcellular current in zygotes is characterized in part by relatively large pulses (63) of current mostly accounted for by Cl$^-$ efflux stimulated by Ca^{2+} entry. Recent studies also indicate that a small ($\sim$5%) but developmentally significant portion of the current is carried by Ca^{2+}. When zygotes of *Pelvetia* are placed in a Ca^{2+} gradient, rhizoids tend to form from the side of highest Ca^{2+} influx (86). Robinson & Jaffe (85) directly demonstrated that Ca^{2+} preferentially enters the rhizoid hemisphere during axis fixation, then decreases from a five-fold difference to virtually no difference between the rhizoid and thallus hemispheres at the time of rhizoid formation. Also, the inward current as measured by the vibrating probe is increased when treatments are given to promote Ca^{2+} influx, i.e. raising external

Ca^{2+} and decreasing external Na^+ (62). This current carried by Ca^{2+} appears to be produced by leaks at the rhizoid site and pumps at the thallus site (38). However, the fact that the total Ca^{2+} efflux and influx remain constant over this period of development argues that the light gradient, and perhaps other orienting vectors, influence polarity by redistributing sections of membrane responsible for transporting ions inward. The mechanism for such directed movements of membrane components in the light gradient is not known.

When summarized, these results lead to the following time course of events within the zygote:

1. Fertilization and the detection of randomly located membrane patches directing ions inward.
2. These membrane components being localized toward the presumptive site of rhizoid formation by an external gradient.
3. Accumulation and secretion of vesicles containing cell wall material (cortical clearing) at this site.
4. A process sensitive to CB and insensitive to CH and sucrose which fixes this site of Ca^{2+} accumulation and vesicle secretion for subsequent localizations of particles and organelles needed for wall extension.
5. The incorporation of F_2 and other polysaccharide material into the rhizoid wall.

Given the above information, what can be proposed as a model or working hypothesis for the fixation process (step 4)? The primary role of the plasma membrane components directing ions inward in determining the site of rhizoid formation suggests that their stabilization within the membrane or to the underlying cytoplasm is the critical event. The lability of the polar axis during the period between 6–10 hr after fertilization in *Fucus* can be interpreted best with Nuccitelli's data as the mobility of these patches within the lipid bilayer of the plasma membrane (57) in response to the changing light direction. Orientation of the polar axis by other gradients such as ions, pH, and electrical fields may act as forces localizing membrane components. The observation that rhizoids form toward the positive pole when cultured in a steady voltage gradient (70) could be explained by the "lateral electrophoresis" (37) of negatively charged membrane components responsible for the inward directing current. Membrane receptors of the lectin Concanavalin A (Con A) in cultured muscle cells of *Xenopus* can be redistributed by extracellular electrical fields (75). The accumulation of fluorescein-labeled Con A at the negative side of the cell by fields as low as 1.2 mV for 30 min indicates that Con A receptors are free to move within the fluid matrix of the membrane in response to electrical vectors. Once the rhizoid or growth-essential membrane components are localized in response to an orienting gradient (e.g. light, electrical), could their stabilization (immobility) at that site be thought of as the equivalent of fixation?

Although no direct information is available in *Fucus* or other plant systems on the stabilization of membrane components, an extensive literature is available implicating microtubules and/or microfilaments in restricting the movement of membrane components in animal cells (23, 57, 74). Plant cells do contain microfilaments

(30) as well as actin filaments in the ectoplasm/endoplasm interface of *Chara* (39) and in the spindle apparatus of *Haemanthus* endosperm cells (26). *Fucus* zygotes also contain microfilaments (7), and a protein has been isolated in our laboratory which migrates upon electrophoresis with f-actin from muscle. The fact that CB reversibly prevents polar axis fixation in *Fucus* could be used as indirect evidence implicating a plasma membrane/microfilament association as the basis for fixation. Attachment of microfilaments to the sol-gel interface in *Nitella* is prevented by CB (13). Great care must be used in linking CB effects to microfilaments without direct evidence (cf 30), but in view of the information now available (primarily from animal cells), it could be helpful to propose a model using this association as a basis to stimulate and focus future thinking and testing.

Several recent reviews summarize evidence supporting the hypothesis that microtubules and microfilaments control the mobility, stabilization, and topographical distribution of cell membrane and surface components (23, 57, 74). A form of membrane flow known as "capping" is demonstrated by a variety of fluorescent labeled polyvalent ligands such as certain antibodies or lectins (57). The cross-linking of membrane receptors imbedded in the plasma membrane by these ligands grow to form patches, clusters, and then a "cap" at one end of the cell, while the other membrane components flow in the opposite direction. A variety of environmental factors and drugs interfere with cap formation. , including low temperature, respiratory inhibitors, local anesthetics, colchicine, and CB (57). Colchicine promotes the redistribution of receptors for the lectin Con A (65), while CB can prevent or reverse Con A-induced cap formation in a number of animal cells (99). Results with these two compounds have implicated microtubules and microfilaments in receptor movement and stabilization.

Recent findings that actin copurifies with isolated plasma membranes (28) and morphological evidence for associations between microtubules (2) or microfilaments (73) and the plasma membrane are supportive of these findings. A number of studies have demonstrated coordinate changes in the cytoplasmic distribution of microtubules and microfilaments during cap formation (1, 2). Albertini & Clark (2) have shown that Con A-induced capping in rabbit ovarian granulosa cells results in the accumulation of microtubules and colchicine binding proteins in the cytoplasm beneath the cap. The translocation of Con A receptors is prevented by CB and points to an active role of microfilaments in this redistribution. In addition, a subplasmalemma accumulation of microfilaments in the capped region has been reported (1). These investigators suggest that the capped region is a preferred site of microtubule polymerization or that microtubules are passively pulled into this region by Con A receptor translocation. It is interesting to note that Hepler & Palevitz (30) pointed to a key role of "microtubule organizing centers" in controlling the plane of cell division in plant cells. They suggested that these centers in the cortical cytoplasm, possibly attached to the plasma membrane, can give rise to the preprophase band of microtubules which controls the plane of cell division. In view of the above discussion, could the relationship between an extracellular gradient and the orientation of the plane of cell division be linked to microfilaments and their stabilization of redistributed membrane components?

When one considers the above findings in light of what is known about the induction and fixation of a polar axis in *Fucus,* a hypothetical model can be proposed for further testing. Membrane components in *Fucus* involved in transporting ions (e.g. Ca^{2+}) inward are translocated to the dark side of the light gradient. This movement is mediated by a CB-sensitive process. As a result of this local increase in intracellular Ca^{2+} caused by the localized membrane patches in the rhizoid region, many cellular processes including enzyme activation (24), vesicle secretion (15; cf 62), and microtubule assembly could be regionally activated or supressed, thereby amplifying the existing polarization. For nonmuscle cells both salt (e.g. Mg^{2+}, Ca^{2+}, KCl) concentrations and actin-associated proteins are involved with control of the contractile properties and formation of actin filaments from the monomer units (14, 74). The accumulation of these membrane patches at the presumptive rhizoid site are stabilized in the membrane or to the underlying cytoplasm by a cytoskeletal component, possibly microfilaments. This corresponds to polar axis fixation. The microfilaments and/or other cytoskeletal components (e.g. microtubules) may serve to provide a "track" for the accumulation of vesicles needed for cell wall extension, and serve as a point to organize and orient the spindle apparatus. Such processes in this region may be further modified by the local increase of specific ions caused by the accumulation of specific membrane components directing inward current fluxes. The same could be said for events occurring at the opposite pole. Certain parts of this model are testable: Can microfilaments, actin bundles, microtubules, and/or colchicine binding proteins be localized at the fixed site of rhizoid formation? Are they associated with the plasma membrane, and is their structure or polymerization influenced by ions such as Ca^{2+}? Are membrane patches directing ions inward prevented from becoming localized in the presence of CB (like the deposition of fucoidin and the polar axis)? Are the vesicles which are localized in the rhizoid region associated with any cytoskeletal component?

Polarity Expression

Once a stable polar axis has been determined, what is the nature of the cellular components which are localized, and what is the mechanism whereby they become sequestered at the fixed site? In numerous plant systems one can detect morphological and cytochemical differences in the cytoplasm or cell wall in one region of the cell. This "polar cytoplasm" will subsequently become part of a differentiated cell type, usually by being segregated from the rest of the parent cell by an unequal cell division (4, 53, 93). The molecules or particles accumulated in the one cell could be of two types: (*a*) cell-specific components which immediately distinguish the new cell from its parent, or (*b*) components of a more "determinative" nature which would commit the new cell and possibly its progeny to a particular developmental pathway, ultimately leading to the expression of a specific cell or tissue type.

Subcellular particles of an undefined nature are found localized in the cytoplasm of a wide variety of plant cells including progenitor cells of pollen grains (9), root hairs (92), guard cells of certain monocots (93), and the egg cell of the liverwort *Fegatella* (102). Cytochemistry, autoradiography, and vital staining can distinguish a polar cytoplasm in the region of the presumptive rhizoid in *Equisetum* spores (52) and rhizoid tips of the fern *Polypodium* (94). Accumulation of acidic polysaccharides, basic proteins, and RNA can be detected in apical regions of the red alga *Polysiphonia* (111) and in the region of cap regeneration in the single-celled *Acetabularia* (112). In *Cladophora,* one can observe the incorporation of ^{35}S and ^{32}P into macromolecules localized in the rhizoid-forming region (91). Although these examples demonstrate an expression of a polar axis, they tell us little about the specific nature of the localized components, how they are sequestered into a particular region of the cell, and what genetic controls are involved. If one can chemically define what macromolecules are distributed unequally, the latter two questions can be approached. Table 1 outlines in general terms the levels where controls may be imposed to account for the expression of cell polarity, i.e. the intracellular localization of macromolecules. Three examples of plant cells in which specific molecules have been localized will be discussed in more detail.

CAP REGENERATION IN ACETABULARIA   Cap differentiation in *Acetabularia* depends upon the release of "morphogenetic substances" (believed to be RNA) from the nucleus. It does not require the presence of the nucleus for expression. Anucleated stalks can form the species-specific cap as well as regulate the levels of certain enzymes (29, 96). In view of this, long-lived or stable mRNA has been implicated in the genetic control of this localized differentiation (cf 5, 76). One feature of the new cap structure is that the cell wall in this region of the unicell contains rhamnose and large quantities of glucose and galactose, unlike the cell wall composition of stalks and rhizoids (114). Several studies have focused attention on enzymes that may play a role in this localized alteration in the cell wall, for example, UDPG-pyrophosphorylase (phosphorylase).

A close temporal correlation was observed by Zetsche et al (114) between a three- to four-fold increase in enzyme activity and the appearance of the cap. Inhibitor experiments indicate that (*a*) new protein synthesis is required for phosphorylase activity, (*b*) nuclear RNA synthesis but not chloroplast RNA synthesis is required, and (*c*) nuclear RNA synthesis inhibitors have no effect on enzyme activity in

Table 1 Possible mechanisms to account for the localization of gene products and cell-specific molecules distributed at random within a cell

Random	Mechanism	Localized
I. RNA Template	transport	RNA Template
	local *translation*	
II. Polypeptide	transport	Polypeptide
	local *activation*	
III. Active enzyme	transport	Active enzyme
	local *accumulation*	
IV. Product	transport	Product

anucleated cells. To determine if a similar spatial correlation exists between the phosphorylase and site of cap initiation, Zetsche et al (114) found that although the activity of this enzyme is not limited to the apical region of the stalk, a clear apico-basal distribution does exist. If normal cells are sectioned into three pieces containing identical protein concentrations, the apical region has roughly twice as much phosphorylase activity as the stalk and four times the activity of the rhizoid section. This apico-basal distribution of enzyme is maintained and amplified four-fold during cap formation. Differences in activity that may be caused by the polar distribution of enzyme inhibitors, activators, and localized enzyme destruction have been excluded (114). It appears that the polar distribution of activity is most probably the result of different amounts of enzyme, although this has not been directly determined.

Is the distribution of enzyme a result of preferential synthesis of the enzyme in the apical region of the stalk? This appears to be the case when one couples the data above with the following experiment. If the same three sections (apical, stalk, rhizoid) from capless cells are incubated separately, only the apical section forms a cap. Each of the other sections exhibits normal increases in length. However, the increase in phosphorylase activity beginning at 16 days and doubling by 31 days occurs only in apical segments. No significant increase is observed after 16 days in the stalk or rhizoid portions. In terms of the framework outlined in Table 1, it appears that the localization of phosphorylase activity is either the result of more template-specific RNA in the apical region (Level I) or a greater rate of translation in the apical region of equally distributed RNA template for phosphorylase (Level II). Although an apico-basal distribution of RNA has been reported for *Acetabularia* (55, 112), this most probably represents nontemplate RNA and differences in turnover rates. Before mechanisms are sought for the transport of template RNA to the apical region or the translation of cap-specific template RNA in that region, more direct evidence should be obtained to further substantiate the interesting results reported on the intracellular distribution of this enzyme.

SEPTUM FORMATION IN YEAST   During vegetative growth in yeasts, cell division occurs by budding. At a specific time in the cell cycle a protuberance, the bud, appears on the cell surface and begins to enlarge. Organelles from the mother cell migrate into the bud, followed by a thickening of the cell wall at the constriction between mother and daughter cells. At this site, localized growth of a thin disk, the primary septum, occurs which separates the cytoplasms of the two cells. This thin cross-wall between the two cells is further reinforced by material laid down from both the mother and daughter cells, the secondary septa. When the two cells detach, the mother cell retains the primary septum as a component of the bud scar. The daughter cell retains only the secondary septum, the birth scar.

The bud scar and the primary septum are composed primarily of hexosamine (chitin), whereas the yeast cell wall is composed mainly of glucans and mannans. Cabib and co-workers have utilized this system to investigate the mechanism whereby the synthesis of chitin is localized to a particular region of the cell (primary septum) and at a specific time in the cell cycle (budding). Their excellent studies have been reviewed in detail elsewhere and will only be summarized briefly in this article (10, 12).

A particulate enzyme, chitin synthetase (CS), is responsible for chitin formation via the following generalized reaction:

$$\text{UDP-N-acetyglucosamine} + \text{acceptor} \xrightarrow{\text{CS}} \text{UDP} + \text{(N-acetylglucosamine-acceptor)}.$$

The antibiotic Polyoxin D is a powerful inhibitor of CS, and if budding yeast cells are grown in the presence of Polyoxin D, abnormalities are seen in the region of the septum while the rest of the cell wall is normal in appearance. Experiments with Polyoxin D and temperature-sensitive mutants have established that chitin synthesis is not necessary for emergence and growth of the bud. Chitin synthesis is necessary for completion of the septum, in the absence of which most cells eventually die (11).

If CS is prepared from a yeast protoplast lysate, it is present as an inactive or zymogen form and attached to the internal surface of the plasma membrane (PM) (22). In order to isolate the PM intact, Cabib used Con A to coat the PM prior to rupture and then showed that the CS zymogen is associated with the purified PM. Activation of CS can be accomplished by proteolytic treatment (100).

The activity of CS is apparently controlled by specific inhibitor and activating factors found in the yeast cytoplasm. The activating factor is associated with a vesicle or vacuole fraction and has been purified to homogeneity (100). It is a protease identical to an enzyme previously known as proteinase B, with a molecular weight of 44,000. The inhibitor appears to be a small (8000–9000 mol wt), heat stable protein, and since it is found in the soluble fraction of the cell lysate, it is probably located free in the cytosol (10). The inhibitor acts by blocking the proteolytic activity of the activation factor, thereby preventing CS activity (12). Cabib has proposed that when vesicles containing the activating factor fuse with the PM, the CS zymogen is activated at that site.

What directs the vesicles (vacuole) to the specific site of primary septum formation has not been elucidated. However, it is possible that as these vesicles pass the narrow constriction between the mother cell and the newly forming bud, contact of the vesicle membrane and the PM is confined to this site. Therefore, activation of CS would occur at a specific site, the constriction, and during the time of budding. The localization of chitin deposition would then be accomplished. The role of the inhibitor in the activation step is unclear. Possibly it acts as a safety mechanism to trap any activating factor released into the cytoplasm and thus prevents chitin synthesis at other locations on the cell surface.

The hypothesis proposed to account for the localized synthesis of chitin involves at least two mechanisms: 1. the sequestering of molecules (activator) into vesicles in order to confine activation to a particular area of the cell, and 2. the use of zymogens (CS) to initiate synthetic events at a specific time in the cell cycle. Both of these mechanisms can account for the temporal and spatial distribution CS activity without concomitant gene activation, and would fit into Level II (localized enzyme activation) of the scheme in Table 1. Whether these mechanisms are applicable to other cells which display localizations remains to be determined.

RHIZOID FORMATION IN FUCUS   In a previous section the deposition of a sulfated polysaccharide (F_2) into a unique cell wall layer in only the rhizoid cell wall was discussed as one of the first events associated with the expression of a stable polar axis in *Fucus* zygotes. This polysaccharide, known as fucoidin, is an α-1,2-linked fucan with ester-linked sulfate groups located primarily on the C-4 of fucose (71). Although fucose is the primary sugar, xylose, glucose, galactose, mannose, and glucuronic acid are also found in fucoidin polymer. Fucoidin comprises about 20% of the polysaccharides found in the cell wall at 4 hr after fertilization and remains at that level throughout early development (84). Isolated cell walls from 4-hour zygotes have a relatively low ratio of fucose to xylose and little sulfate when compared to walls from older embryos. When extracts of walls from 4-hr zygotes are subjected to cellulose acetate electrophoresis at pH 7, a single fucan (F_1) can be detected. By 12 hr the developing wall acquires the F_2 fucan which appears heavily sulfated due to its rate of migration in an electric field and upon staining with TBO. The color and timing coincide precisely with the cytochemical detection of a sulfated polysaccharide at the rhizoid site. The fact that this new electrophoretic component is incorporated into the wall coincident with a change in sugar composition of the wall toward higher fucose levels argues against F_1, at a greater degree of sulfation, accounting for the new electrophoretic species of fucan (84). We have also found that purified F_2 has two to three times more fucose than purified F_1, indicating that these two fucans are probably different sugar polymers.

How does fucoidin (F_2) become localized at the rhizoid site? Several possibilities exist that might account for the localization of the TBO-stained material (fucoidin) in the rhizoidal region. Since TBO is staining the negatively charged sulfate groups in fucoidin under the conditions employed, the appearance of localized stain may be the result of (*a*) unmasking of sulfate groups already attached to preexisting fucoidin, (*b*) the biochemical attachment of sulfate to a previously synthesized fucan, or (*c*) the de novo synthesis of the entire molecule. Whether one of these possibilities occurs throughout the cell at random (with the resulting product transported to the site of rhizoid formation), or whether a specific localized region is the site of de novo synthesis, sulfation, or unmasking of fucoidin is the critical question (Table 1).

A considerable amount of data (cf 80, 82) supports the conclusion that there does not appear to be de novo synthesis of the entire molecule nor the unmasking of the sulfate groups on fucoidin, but rather the sulfation of a previously existing fucan. By using the stain TBO cytochemically and $^{35}SO_4$ autoradiographically, McCully (45) first detected the appearance of a sulfated polymer at the time of rhizoid formation. The macromolecule is initially localized around the rhizoid half of the nucleus radiating toward the site of rhizoid initiation, and eventually becomes incorporated in the region of the cell wall protuberance. This same pattern and timing has been described for certain organelles and inclusions (78). During rhizoid elongation and after the first cell division, most if not all of the sulfated polysaccharide is cytochemically detected only in the rhizoid cell, including the extracellular region of the rhizoid tip where it is presumably involved with the adhesion of the two-celled embryo to the substratum (17, 61).

When zygotes were pulsed with $^{35}SO_4$ for 60 min at different times after fertilization, the enzymatic sulfation of fucoidin was initiated at 10 hr after fertilization (82), the same time this polymer was detected in the rhizoid region by cytochemical and autoradiographic studies (45, 83). The pattern of sulfate accumulation into fucoidin cannot be accounted for on the basis of changes in the pool size or permeability of the zygotes to sulfate. Sulfation is apparently dependent upon new protein synthesis as judged by the ability of CH to prevent incorporation of ^{35}S into fucoidin (82).

Previous autoradiographic and cytochemical evidence cited above indicated that sulfation occurs during rhizoid formation, and the sulfated fucoidin becomes sequestered in the rhizoid cell, specifically in the cell wall. However, because of the long pulses (several hours) of $^{35}SO_4$ used in the autoradiographic experiments (45), it could not be determined if sulfation was initially random and then localized or if the sulfating system was unevenly distributed initially, i.e. polar. In other words, is the cell-specific rhizoid product (fucoidin) transported to a predetermined intracellular site or is it sulfated only at the site? Using zygotes of *Fucus distichus* exposed to 5-min pulses of $^{35}SO_4$ followed by various chase periods, we recently found (83) that at the time of rhizoid initiation, cytoplasmic sulfation of the fucoidin was initially random as evidenced by a random secretion of the ^{35}S-polysaccharide into the cell wall. During subsequent chase periods, the ^{35}S-polysaccharide was transported and secreted selectively into the rhizoid wall. In more developmentally advanced embryos, sites of sulfation appeared sequestered into the rhizoid area since short pulses resulted in secretion of the ^{35}S-polysaccharide preferentially into the rhizoid wall. These results are consistent with the hypothesis that the sulfating sites of fucoidin [shown by Evans and collaborators (25) to be the Golgi] are randomly distributed in the cytoplasm at the time of rhizoid formation and gradually transported to the rhizoidal area during rhizoid development.

Crayton et al (17) reported that zygotes grown in seawater without sulfate but containing methionine do not appreciably sulfate fucoidin but still form rhizoids. Under these conditions, no localization of fucoidin in the rhizoid cell wall was observed when cells were stained with TBO. This result suggests that although sulfation is not required for rhizoid formation, it may be required for localization of fucoidin. However, since TBO depends upon the presence of negatively charged groups (i.e. sulfate) on the polymer, the unsulfated polymer might still be localized but not detected by this stain. One can then ask if the enzymatic modification of the polymer by the addition of sulfate is required for its localization in the rhizoid wall.

To answer this question, a specific stain for both the sulfated and desulfated fucoidin was required. We approached this problem by determining if certain proteins or glycoproteins that bind specifically to certain sugar moieties in polysaccharides (i.e. lectins) could be used as a tag for fucoidin. It was shown recently that fluorescein isothiocyanate (FITC) conjugated soybean lectin bound to a localized patch of the cell wall of *Rhizobium japonicum* (41). We demonstrated in vitro that the lectin, ricin (RCA$_I$), complexed with both sulfated and desulfated fucoidin but not with other brown algal polysaccharides. The binding of RCA$_I$ to fucoidin was inhibited by galactose, indicating that the complex is formed through terminal galactose units on the fucoidin. Mian & Percival (46) have demonstrated by chemical means that certain fucan fractions contain terminal galactose units.

With the in vitro specificity of RCA_I for fucoidin demonstrated, we conjugated this lectin with FITC to determine if it could be used as a cytological marker for fucoidin in vivo. The two-celled *Fucus* embryo grown in artificial seawater containing sulfate demonstrated a very intense fluorescence at the rhizoid tip after treatment with the $FITC-RCA_I$, suggesting the localization of the fucoidin polymer in this region of the embryo wall (83). Under these conditions, the rhizoid wall stains metachromatically with TBO at pH 1.5, indicating the presence of a sulfated polymer. This same localization of the fluorescent conjugate was observed in the two-celled embryos desulfated with methanolic-HCl. However, no metachromatic staining was observed in these desulfated embryos. This indicated that if an unsulfated fucoidin was incorporated into the wall, the $FITC-RCA_I$ complex would bind (as predicted by the in vitro results) whereas the TBO would not detect the unsulfated fucoidin. However, when embryos grown in the absence of sulfate are treated with $FITC-RCA_I$ or with TBO, no localization of the markers is evident at the rhizoid tip. If unsulfated fucoidin had been incorporated into the rhizoid wall, localized fluorescence would have been evident. Extracts from zygotes grown in the absence of sulfate had the same amount of fucoidin and RCA_I binding material as extracts from sulfate-grown zygotes (unpublished observations).

These results suggest that the enzymatic sulfation of the fucan is necessary for its localization and/or incorporation into the rhizoid wall. The lack of fucoidin in the rhizoid wall when grown in the absence of sulfate also points to a role of the sulfated fucans in adhesion. It has been shown that embryos grown without sulfate but containing methionine form rhizoids but do not adhere to the substratum (17). When sulfate is added to the medium, the sulfated polysaccharide is detected in the rhizoid wall (by TBO staining and $FITC-RCA_I$ binding) and the embryos adhere to the substratum.

In summary, sulfation of fucoidin was dependent on new protein synthesis, as evidenced by its inhibition with CH (Level III, Table 1). Fucoidin was not initially localized in the rhizoid area of the *Fucus* zygote but as rhizoid development proceeded, the sulfated fucoidin and the enzymatic sites for sulfation (Golgi) appeared to be transported to the rhizoid wall. The enzymatic sulfation of the fucan was in some way required for the transport to and/or incorporation into the rhizoid cell wall.

Mechanism of Transport

It is clear in *Fucus* and possibly in *Acetabularia* that certain particles and macromolecules are synthesized throughout the cell and then redistributed to some predetermined site specified by the polar axis. Two possible mechanisms could control this type of segregation: (*a*) a cytoplasmic electrical potential gradient or field which could segregate particles/molecules on the basis of their net charge (*electrophoretic*), and (*b*) a mechanical, contractile mechanism involving actin and microfilaments (*contractile*).

CONTRACTILE   Numerous reviews (e.g. 14, 74) have focused on the relationship between movement and a contractile system involving actin/myosin and associative proteins organized into a structure such as actin cables (21) or microfilaments (23, 57). This subject has also been reviewed recently for plant cells (30). Actin and myosin-like molecules isolated from nonmuscle cells can interact in vitro with the appropriate actin or myosin from muscle cells (which are known to generate force for movement in vivo), indicating that they are likely to interact in vivo to cause movement (cf 14). Polar actin filaments must be oriented in one direction for movement (contraction). Such an orientation can be visualized in vivo by the arrowhead configuration when heavy meromyosin (HMM) binds to actin. Kersey et al (39) have demonstrated in *Nitella* and *Chara* that the arrowhead complexes are pointing in the direction opposite to the direction of cytoplasmic streaming (the same relationship was found between actin polarity and contraction in muscle). Similar results were found in the mitotic spindle of the endosperm cells of *Haemanthus* (i.e. most arrowheads pointed toward the chromosomes). Actin in this location may possibly play a role in chromosome movement (26). Condeelis (16) has found actin filaments in pollen tubes of *Amaryllis,* and microfilamentous material was located between the generative cell and vegetative nucleus in *Petunia* pollen tubes (18), as well as in *Clivia* and *Lilium* (27). It has been suggested that these filaments are involved with the movement of these elements during pollen development and tube growth.

In a previous section the possible role of microfilaments in polar axis fixation in *Fucus* was discussed in terms of directing and stabilizing components within the fluid matrix of the membrane. In view of the above studies, microfilaments may also play a role in the directional transport of subcellular particles via a contractile mechanism. In *Fucus* zygotes (which contain microfilaments and actin) the directed deposition of fucoidin into the rhizoid cell wall is prevented by CB (60). Attachment of secretory granules (67) and organelles, including chloroplasts of *Nitella* (39) and *Mougeotia* (106), to actin filaments arranged in a polar or undirectional manner has been documented. Mollenhauer & Morré (48) have shown in maize root tips that a CB-sensitive subcellular component "is involved with the vectorial movement of secretory vesicles from sites of formation at dictyosomes to sites of fusion at the cell surface."

All of these studies are at best suggestive that a mechanism of intracellular transport may involve the interaction of vesicle binding to filamentous structures that possess contractile properties. However, with present techniques and methodology, the following approaches can be undertaken: (*a*) Is a contractile mechanism operative during the expression of polarity in *Fucus* or *Acetabularia?* (*b*) If so, is it localized at the fixed site of rhizoid or cap formation? (*c*) Are vesicles which contain the localized macromolecules and have been shown to be transported to the fixed site bound to filamentous structures?

ELECTROPHORETIC   It was shown earlier that the *Fucus* zygote (37) as well as *Acetabularia* (58, 59) drive an electrical current through their cytoplasms. The demonstrated gradient of electrical potential in these systems may serve to orient a cytoskeletal component such as microfilaments. Nuccitelli et al (64) have shown in amebas that an endogenous membrane-driven current is associated with the polarity of microfilament-dependent ameboid streaming. These currents may also be the driving force to localize charged components. Several investigators (42, 95), including Went (110), suggested in the early to mid-1900s that electrophoretic phenomena may play a pivotal role in the establishment and maintenance of polarity. Jaffe's (34) elegant demonstration over a decade ago of an electrical current passing through the *Fucus* zygote rekindled interest in this as a mechanism for subcellular localization. He proposed in *Fucus* that "in traversing the cytoplasm the current will generate a field that may significantly localize negatively-charged molecules or particles toward the growth point (or, if there are any, positively charged ones toward its antipode)."

The rhizoid pole of the current (positive) represents the site of entering cations such as Ca^{2+}. The magnitude of an electrical field generated is in large part dependent upon the ions carrying the current. If the entering cations have a low cytoplasmic mobility and are immobilized locally by an anionic gel in the cytoplasm, local binding would initiate a fixed charged gradient and thus a field. Jaffe has calculated, based on the current measurements and the fact that Ca^{2+} carries at least a portion of the current, that a field on the order of 100 mV/cm could be generated across the *Fucus* zygote (38). This is sufficient, even in view of the leveling action of diffusion, to localize large macromolecules and small particles. Is there any evidence that negatively charged elements are localized in the rhizoid area? As was previously discussed, we have shown that fucoidin must be sulfated in order to be localized in the rhizoid cell wall. This enzymatic addition of sulfate to fucoidin results in a net negative charge on the polymer. We also demonstrated that the amount of enzymatic sulfation in vivo is proportional to its electrophoretic mobility in vitro (82). Although the electrical potential gradient is sufficient to account for the localization of *free* fucoidin, most of the sulfated molecules in the cytoplasm are found in Golgi-derived vesicles. Secretory vesicles which have been isolated from other systems are found to be negatively charged (44, 102). It is not known whether the enzymatic sulfation that occurs within the Golgi apparatus of *Fucus* results in an increase in the net negative charge on the vesicles that accumulate at the rhizoid pole.

Since these vesicles that are localized in the rhizoid region can be isolated (unpublished observations), the surface and electrophoretic properties can now be investigated before and after sulfation. Similarly, the distribution of Golgi and fucoidin vesicles in the rhizoid and thallus regions are being monitored by electronmicroscopy before and after sulfation. We hope these approaches will lead us to a more direct determination of the role of electrical fields in localizing macromolecules at predetermined sites within the zygote.

CONCLUSIONS

Although I have reviewed the subject of polarity in plants, my emphasis has been on the cellular and molecular levels, using the *Fucus* zygote as a model. Because

Fucus has many advantages for polarity studies, as well as being quite extensively studied, I have focused on this system in order to propose models and hypotheses to be tested further in *Fucus* and explored in other systems.

After the apolar zygote of *Fucus* is placed in any one of a number of external gradients for several hours, its polar axis is labile, i.e. still able to be oriented with another or the same gradient from a different direction. However, several hours later the polar axis is irreversibly determined, followed by accumulation of intracellular particles at this fixed site of rhizoid formation. Evidence was presented showing that various inhibitors can separate the overlapping processes of polar axis fixation, intracellular localizations at the rhizoid site, and cell division, which are all essential for cellular differentiation in the two-celled embryo. CB affected the orientation and delayed the fixation of a light-induced polar axis with no qualitative effect on cell division. Disruption of the mitotic apparatus and microtubules by colchicine had no influence on the localizations or on the photopolarization of the developmental axis. The CB-sensitive process necessary for axis fixation was postulated to be microfilament assembly or stability. Both microfilaments and actin have been found in the zygote at the time of rhizoid initiation, although neither have yet been localized in the rhizoid.

During the period of a labile polarity, external gradients such as light have been shown to direct membrane patches to the shaded side of the cell. These membrane components are involved with directing ions inward to the cytoplasm and when localized can generate an electrical potential gradient across the cell. It was suggested that these membrane patches in the rhizoid region that are responsible for the first detectable localization (i.e. a Ca^{2+} influx) are stabilized to the underlying cytoplasm by microfilaments. Once these membrane components are stabilized, the polar axis is fixed and the local influx of ions at this site could serve to initiate other processes (e.g. enzyme activation, vesicle secretion for wall growth, spindle orientation, etc) to amplify the intracellular polarity. These filaments may then serve as a cytoskeletal transport track for the vesicles carrying rhizoid cell wall material (e.g. fucoidin). The driving force for these accumulations could be the electrical potential gradient caused in part by the Ca^{2+} influx or a contractile mechanism involving actin. The demonstration that enzymatic sulfation of fucoidin (which results in a net negative charge on the polymer) is required for its transport to the positive (rhizoid) pole of the electrical gradient is consistent with an electrophoretic mechanism.

ACKNOWLEDGMENTS

I would like to thank Patricia T. Stevens for her help in parts of this review. Research cited from my laboratory was supported by grants from the NSF and PHS.

Literature Cited

1. Albertini, D. F., Anderson, E. 1977. Microtubule and microfilament rearrangements during capping of concanavalin A receptors on cultured ovarian granulosa cells. *J. Cell Biol.* 73:111–27
2. Albertini, D. F., Clark, J. I. 1975. Membrane-microtubule interactions: concanavalin A capping induced redistribution of cytoplasmic microtubules and colchicine binding proteins. *Proc. Natl. Acad. Sci. USA* 72:4976–80
3. Allen, R. D., Jacobsen, L., Joaquin, J., Jaffe, L. F. 1972. Ionic concentrations in developing *Pelvetia* eggs. *Dev. Biol.* 27:538–45
4. Bloch, R. 1965. Polarity and gradients in plants: A survey. In *Encyclopedia of Plant Physiology*, ed. W. Ruhland, 15(1):234–74. New York: Springer-Verlag. 1645 pp.
5. Brachet, J., Bonotto, S., eds. 1970. *Biology of Acetabularia.* New York: Academic. 300 pp.
6. Brachet, J., Lang, A. 1965. The role of the nucleus and the nucleo-cytoplasmic interactions in morphogenesis. See Ref. 4, 15(1):1–40
7. Brawley, S. H., Quatrano, R. S., Wetherbee, R. 1977. Fine-structural studies of the gametes and embryo of *Fucus vesiculosus* L. (Phaeophyta) III. Cytokinesis and the multicellular embryo. *J. Cell Sci.* 24:275–94
8. Bünning, E. 1952. Morphogenesis in plants. *Surv. Biol. Prog.* 2:105–40
9. Bünning, E. 1953. *Entwicklungs-und Bewegungsphysiologie der Pflanze.* Berlin: Springer-Verlag. 539 pp.
10. Cabib, E. 1975. Molecular aspects of yeast morphogenesis. *Ann. Rev. Microbiol.* 29:181–214
11. Cabib, E., Bowers, B. 1975. Timing and function of chitin synthesis in yeast. *J. Bacteriol.* 124:1586–93
12. Cabib, E., Ulane, R., Bowers, B. 1974. A molecular model for morphogenesis: The primary septum of yeast. *Curr. Top. Cell Regul.* 8:1–32
13. Chen, C. W. 1973. Observations of protoplasmic behavior and mobile protoplasmic fibrils in cytochalasin B treated *Nitella* rhizoid. *Protoplasma* 77:427–35
14. Clarke, M., Spudich, J. A. 1977. Nonmuscle contractile proteins: The role of actin and myosin in cell motility and shape determination. *Ann. Rev. Biochem.* 46:797–822
15. Cochrane, D. E., Douglas, W. W. 1974. Calcium-induced extrusion of secretory granules (exocytosis) in mast cells exposed to 48/80 or the ionophore A-23187 and X-537A. *Proc. Natl. Acad. Sci. USA* 71:408–12
16. Condeelis, J. S. 1974. The identification of F actin in the pollen tube and protoplast of *Amaryllis belladonna. Exp. Cell Res.* 88:435–39
17. Crayton, M. A., Wilson, E., Quatrano, R. S. 1974. Sulfation of fucoidan in *Fucus* embryo. II. Separation from initiation of polar growth. *Dev. Biol.* 39:164–67
18. Cresti, M., Van Went, J. L., Willemse, M. T. W., Pacini, E. 1976. Fibrous masses and cell and nucleus movement in the pollen tube of *Petunia hybrida. Acta Bot. Neerl.* 25:381–83
19. Dahl, A. L. 1971. Development, form and environment in the brown alga *Zonaria farlowii* (Dictyotales). *Bot. Mar.* 14:76–112
20. Davidson, E. H. 1976. *Gene Activity in Early Development.* New York: Academic. 452 pp. 2nd ed.
21. De Rosier, D., Mandelkow, E., Silliman, A., Tilney, L., Kane, R. 1977. Structure of actin-containing filaments from two types of non-muscle cells. *J. Mol. Biol.* 113:679–95
22. Duran, A., Bowers, B., Cabib, E. 1975. Chitin synthetase zymogen is attached to the yeast plasma membrane. *Proc. Natl. Acad. Sci. USA* 72:3952–55
23. Edelman, G. M. 1976. Surface modulation in cell recognition and cell growth. *Science* 192:218–26
24. Evans, H. J., Sorger, G. J. 1966. Role of mineral elements with emphasis on the univalent cations. *Ann. Rev. Plant Physiol.* 17:47–76
25. Evans, L. V., Simpson, M., Callow, M. E. 1974. Polysaccharide sulfation in *Laminaria. Planta* 117:93–95
26. Forer, A., Jackson, W. T. 1976. Actin filaments in the endosperm mitotic spindles in a higher plant, *Haemanthus katherinae* Baker. *Cytobiology* 12:199–214
27. Franke, W. W., Herth, W., van der Woude, W. J., Mooré, D. J. 1972. Tubular and filamentous structures in pollen tubes: possible involvement as guide elements in protoplasmic streaming and vectorial migration of secretory vesicles. *Planta* 105:317–41

28. Gruenstein, E., Rich, A., Weihing, R. R. 1975. Actin associated with membranes from 3T3 mouse fibroblast and HeLa cells. *J. Cell Biol.* 64:223–34
29. Hemmerling, J. 1963. Nucleocytoplasmic interactions in *Acetabularia* and other cells. *Ann. Rev. Plant Physiol.* 14:65–92
30. Hepler, P. K., Palevitz, B. A. 1974. Microtubules and microfilaments. *Ann. Rev. Plant Physiol.* 25:309–62
31. Hogsett, W. E., Quatrano, R. S. 1975. Isolation of polysaccharides sulfated during early embryogenesis in *Fucus. Plant Physiol.* 55:25–29
32. Jaffe, L. F. 1958. Morphogenesis in lower plants. *Ann. Rev. Plant Physiol.* 9:359–84
33. Jaffe, L. F. 1958. Tropistic responses of zygotes of the Fucaceae to polarized light. *Exp. Cell Res.* 15:282–99
34. Jaffe, L. F. 1966. Electrical currents through the developing *Fucus* egg. *Proc. Natl. Acad. Sci. USA* 56:1102–9
35. Jaffe, L. F. 1968. Localization in the developing *Fucus* egg and the general role of localizing currents. *Adv. Morphog.* 7:295–328
36. Jaffe, L. F. 1970. On the centripetal course of development, the *Fucus* egg, and self-electrophoresis. *Dev. Biol. Suppl.* 3:83–111
37. Jaffe, L. F., Nuccitelli, R. 1977. Electrical controls of development. *Ann. Rev. Biophys. Bioeng.* 6:445–76
38. Jaffe, L. F., Robinson, K. R., Nuccitelli, R. 1974. Local cation entry and self-electrophoresis as an intracellular localization mechanism. *Ann. NY Acad. Sci.* 238:372–89
39. Kersey, Y. M., Hepler, P. K., Palevitz, B. A., Wessells, N. K. 1976. Polarity of actin filaments in Characean algae. *Proc. Natl. Acad. Sci. USA* 73:165–67
40. Knapp, E. 1931. Entwicklungsphysiologische Untersuchungen an Fucaceen-Eiern. *Planta* 14:731–51
41. Law, I. J., Strijdom, B. W. 1977. Some observations on plant lectins and *Rhizobium* specificity. *Soil Biol. Biochem.* 9:79–84
42. Lund, E. J. 1923. Electrical control of organic polarity in the egg of *Fucus. Bot. Gaz.* 76:288–301
43. Mather, K. 1965. Genes and cytoplasm in development. See Ref. 4, 15(1):41–73
44. Mathews, E. K., Evans, R. J., Dean, P. M. 1972. The ionogenic nature of the secretory-granule membrane. *Biochem. J.* 130:825–32

45. McCully, M. E. 1970. The histological localization of the structural polysaccharides of seaweeds. *Ann. NY Acad. Sci.* 175:702–11
46. Mian, A. J., Percival, E. 1973. Carbohydrates of the brown seaweeds *Himanthalia lorea* and *Bifurcaria bifurcata.* II. Structural studies of the "fucans". *Carbohydr. Res.* 26:146–61
47. Miehe, H. 1905. Wachstum, Regeneration und Polaritat isolierter Zellen. *Ber. Dtsch. Bot. Ges.* 23:257–64
48. Mollenhauer, H. H., Morré, D. J. 1976. Cytochalasin B, but not colchicine, inhibits migration of secretory vesicles in root tips of maize. *Protoplasma* 87:39–48
49. Moss, B. 1974. Morphogenesis. In *Algal Physiology and Biochemistry,* ed. W. D. P. Stewart, pp. 788–813. Berkeley: Univ. California Press. 989 pp.
50. Murphy, T. M., Kahn, A., Lang, A. 1970. Stabilization of the polarity axis in the zygotes of some Fucaceae. *Planta* 90:97–108
51. Nakazawa, S. 1956. Development mechanics of Fucaceous algae. I. The preexistent polarity in *Coccophora* eggs. *Sci. Rep. Tohoku Imp. Univ. Ser. 4* 22:175–79
52. Nakazawa, S. 1956. The latent polarity in *Equisetum* spores. *Bot. Mag.* 69:506–9
53. Nakazawa, S. 1960. Nature of protoplasmic polarity. *Protoplasma* 52:274–94
54. Nakazawa, S. 1962. Polarity. In *Physiology and Biochemistry of Algae,* ed. R. Lewin, pp. 653–61. New York; Academic. 929 pp.
55. Naumova, L. P., Pressman, E. K., Sandakchiev, L. S. 1976. Gradient of RNA distribution in the cytoplasm of *Acetabularia mediterranea. Plant Sci. Lett.* 6:231–35
56. Nelson, D. R., Jaffe, L. F. 1973. Cells without cytoplasmic movements respond to cytochalasin. *Dev. Biol.* 30:206–8
57. Nicolson, G. L. 1976. Transmembrane control of the receptors on normal and tumor cells. I. Cytoplasmic influence over cell surface components. *Biochim. Biophys. Acta* 457:57–108
58. Novák, B., Bentrup, F. W. 1972. An electrophysiological study of regeneration in *Acetabularia mediterranea.* Planta 108:227–44
59. Novák, B., Sironval, C. 1975. Inhibition of regeneration of *Acetabularia mediterranea* enucleated posterior stalk seg-

ments by electrical isolation. *Plant Sci. Lett.* 5:183–88

60. Novotny, A. M., Forman, M. 1974. The relationship between changes in cell wall composition and the establishment of polarity in *Fucus* embryos. *Dev. Biol.* 40:162–73

61. Novotny, A. M., Forman, M. 1975. The composition and development of cell walls of *Fucus* embryos. *Planta* 122:67–78

62. Nuccitelli, R. 1978. Oöplasmic segregation and secretion in the *Pelvetia* egg is accompanied by a membrane-generated electrical current. *Dev. Biol.* 62:13–33

63. Nuccitelli, R., Jaffe, L. F. 1976. The ionic components of the current pulses generated by developing fucoid eggs. *Dev. Biol.* 49:518–31

64. Nuccitelli, R., Poo, M.-M., Jaffe, L. F. 1977. Relations between ameboid movement and membrane-controlled electrical currents. *J. Gen. Physiol.* 69:743–63

65. Oliver, J. M., Zurier, R. B., Berlin, R. D. 1975. Concanavalin A cap formation on polymorphonuclear leukocytes of normal and beige (Chediak-Higashi) mice. *Nature* 253:471–73

66. Oltmanns, F. 1889. Beitrage zur Kenntnis der Fucaceen. *Bild. Bot.* 14:1889

67. Ostlund, R. E., Leung, J. T., Kipnis, D. M. 1977. Muscle actin filaments bind pituitary secretory granules *in vitro. J. Cell Biol.* 73:78–87

68. Overton, J. B. 1913. Artificial parthenogenesis in *Fucus. Science* 37:841–44

69. Peng, H. B., Jaffe, L. F. 1976. Cell-wall formation in *Pelvetia* embryos. A freeze-fracture study. *Planta* 133:57–71

70. Peng, H. B., Jaffe, L. F. 1976. Polarization of fucoid eggs by steady electrical fields. *Dev. Biol.* 53:277–84

71. Percival, E., McDowell, R. H. 1967. *Chemistry and Enzymology of Marine Algal Polysaccharides.* New York: Academic. 219 pp.

72. Peterson, D. M., Torrey, J. G. 1968. Amino acid incorporation in developing *Fucus* embryos. *Plant Physiol.* 43: 941–47

73. Pollard, T. D., Korn, E. D. 1973. Electron microscopic identification of actin associated with isolated amoeba plasma membranes. *J. Biol. Chem.* 248:448–50

74. Pollard, T. D., Wiehing, R. R. 1974. Actin and myosin and cell movement. *CRC Rev. Biochem.* 2:1–65

75. Poo, M.-M., Robinson, K. R. 1977. Electrophoresis of concanavalin A

76. Puiseux-Dao, S. 1970. *Acetabularia and Cell Biology.* New York: Springer-Verlag. 162 pp.

77. Quatrano, R. S. 1968. Rhizoid formation in *Fucus* zygotes: Dependence on protein and ribonucleic acid syntheses. *Science* 162:468–70

78. Quatrano, R. S. 1972. An ultrastructural study of the determined site of rhizoid formation in *Fucus* zygotes. *Exp. Cell Res.* 70:1–12

79. Quatrano, R. S. 1973. Separation of processes associated with differentiation of two-celled *Fucus* embryos. *Dev. Biol.* 30:209–13

80. Quatrano, R. S. 1974. Developmental biology: Development in marine organisms. In *Experimental Marine Biology,* ed. R. Mariscal, pp. 303–46. New York: Academic. 373 pp.

81. Quatrano, R. S. 1978. Gamete release, fertilization and embryogenesis in the Fucales. In *Handbook of Phycological Methods,* Vol. 2. Cytological and Developmental Methods. Cambridge: Cambridge Univ. Press. In press

82. Quatrano, R. S., Crayton, M. A. 1973. Sulfation of fucoidan in *Fucus* empryos. I. Possible role in localization. *Dev. Biol.* 30:29–41

83. Quatrano, R. S., Hogsett, W. E., Roberts, M. 1978. Localization of a sulfated polysaccharide in the rhizoid wall of *Fucus distichus* (Phaeophyta) zygotes. *Proc. Int. Seaweed Symp., 9th, 1977, Santa Barbara.* In press

84. Quatrano, R. S., Stevens, P. T. 1976. Cell wall assembly in *Fucus* zygotes. I. Characterization of the polysaccharide components. *Plant Physiol.* 58:224–31

85. Robinson, K. R., Jaffe, L. F. 1975. Polarizing fucoid eggs drive a calcium current through themselves. *Science* 187:70–72

86. Robinson, K. R., Jaffe, L. F. 1976. Calcium gradients and egg polarity. *J. Cell Biol.* 70:37a

87. Rosenvinge, M. L. 1889. Influence des agents exterieurs sur l'organisation polaire et dorsiventrale des plantes. *Rev. Gen. Bot.* 1:53–62, 123–27

88. Round, F. E. 1973. Physiology: Polarity and morphogenesis. In *The Biology of the Algae,* pp. 199–204. New York: St. Martin's. 278 pp. 2nd ed.

89. Schechter, V. 1934. Electrical control of rhizoid formation in the red alga, *Griffithsia borneriana. J. Gen. Physiol.* 18:1–21

90. Schechter, V. 1935. The effect of centrifuging on the polarity of an alga, *Griffithsia bornetiana*. *Biol. Bull.* 68:172–79

91. Schoser, G. 1956. Uber die Regeneration bei den Cladophoraceen. *Protoplasma* 47:103–34

92. Schumacher, W. 1936. Üntersuchungen Uber die Wanderung des Fluoresceins in den Haaren von *Cucurbita Pepo*. *Jahrb. Wiss. Bot.* 82:507–33

93. Sinnott, E. W. 1960. *Plant Morphogenesis*. New York: McGraw-Hill. 550 pp.

94. Smith, D. L. 1972. Staining and osmotic properties of young gametophytes of *Polypodium vulgare* L. and their bearing on rhizoid function. *Protoplasma* 74:465–79

95. Spek, J. 1930. Zustandsänderungen der Plasmakolloide bei Befruchtung und Entwicklung des *Nereis*-Eies. *Protoplasma* 9:370–427

96. Spencer, T., Harris, H. 1964. Regulation of enzyme synthesis in an enucleate cell. *Biochem. J* 91:282–86

97. Sussex, I. M. 1967. Polar growth of *Hormosira banksii* zygotes in shake culture. *Am. J. Bot.* 54:505–10

98. Torrey, J. G., Galun, E. 1970. Apolar embryos of *Fucus* resulting from osmotic and chemical treatment. *Am. J. Bot.* 57:111–19

99. Ukena, T., Borysenko, J. Z., Karnovsky, M. J., Berlin, R. D. 1974. Effects of colchicine, cytochalasin B, and 2-deoxyglucose on the topographical organization of surface-bound concanavalin A in normal and transformed fibroblasts. *J. Cell Biol.* 61:70–82

100. Ulane, R. E., Cabib, E. 1976. The activating system of chitin synthetase from *Saccharomycess cerevisiae*. *J. Biol. Chem.* 251:3367–74

101. Vöchting, H. 1878. *Über Organbildung in Pflanzenreich*. Bonn: Cohen. 258 pp.

102. Vos, J., Kurizama, K., Roberts, E. 1968. Electrophoretic mobilities of brain subcellular particles. *Brain Res.* 9:224–30

103. Vreugdenhil, D., Dijkstra, M. L., Libbenga, K. R. 1976. The ultrastructure of the cell wall of normal and apolar embryos of *Fucus vesiculosus*. *Protoplasma* 88:305–14

104. Waaland, S. D. 1975. Evidence for a species-specific cell fusion hormone in red algae. *Protoplasma* 86:253–61

105. Waaland, S. D., Cleland, R. 1972. Development in the red alga, *Griffthsia pacifica*: control by internal and external factors. *Planta* 105:196–204

106. Wagner, G., Haupt, W., Laux, A. 1972. Reversible inhibition of chloroplast movement by cytochalasin B in the green alga *Mougeotia*. *Science* 176: 808–9

107. Wardlaw, C. W. 1968. *Morphogenesis in Plants*. London: Methuen. 451 pp.

108. Weisenseel, M. H., Jaffe, L. F. 1976. The major growth current through lily pollen tubes enters as K+ and leaves as H+. *Planta* 133:1–7

109. Weisenseel, M. H., Nuccitelli, R., Jaffe, L. F. 1975. Large electrical currents traverse growing pollen tubes. *J. Cell Biol.* 66:556–67

110. Went, F. W. 1932. Eine botanische Polaritätstheorie. *Jahrb. Wiss. Bot.* 76:528–54

111. Werz, G. 1961. Über Anreicherungen von Ribonukleinsäure, speziellem Protein und anionischem Polysaccharid in jungen Zellen von *Polysiphonia* spec. *Naturwissenschaften* 48:221–22

112. Werz, G. 1965. Determination and realization of morphogenesis in *Acetabularia*. *Brookhaven Symp. Biol.* 18:185–203

113. Whitaker, D. M. 1940. Physical factors of growth. *Growth* Suppl.:75–90

114. Zetsche, K., Grieninger, G. E., Anders, J. 1970. Regulation of enzyme activity during morphogenesis of nucleate and anucleate cells of *Acetabularia*. See Ref. 5, pp. 87–110

Ann. Rev. Plant Physiol. 1978. 29:511–66

THE PHYSIOLOGY OF METAL TOXICITY IN PLANTS[1]

❖7661

C. D. Foy

Plant Stress Laboratory, Plant Physiology Institute, ARS-USDA, Beltsville, Maryland 20705

R. L. Chaney

Biological Waste Management and Soil Nitrogen Laboratory, Agricultural Environmental Quality Institute, ARS-USDA, Beltsville, Maryland 20705

M. C. White

Maryland Environmental Service, Annapolis, Maryland 21401

CONTENTS

[1]Joint contribution from the Plant Stress Laboratory and the Biological Waste Management and Soil Nitrogen Laboratory.

511

0066-4294/78/0601-0511$01.00

INTRODUCTION

Metal toxicity in plants was last reviewed in this series in 1963, 1964, and 1966 (44, 54, 126, 153); however, more recent reviews have been published elsewhere (56, 57, 73, 134–136). Current emphasis on soil, water, and air pollution, food quality, and food and energy shortages in certain parts of the world make it desirable to reexamine the role of excess metals in plant growth. The objective of this paper is to update our knowledge concerning the physiology of some important metal toxicities in plants, with particular emphasis on the mechanisms of differential tolerances among plant species and among cultivars within the same species.

Toxic levels of metals in soils may be caused by natural soil properties or by agricultural, manufacturing, mining, and waste disposal practices (56, 57, 71, 137, 184, 229). Aluminum toxicity is an important growth limiting factor for plants in many acid soils below pH 5.0 but can occur at pH levels as high as 5.5 (135). This problem is particularly serious in strongly acid subsoils that are difficult to lime (114), and it is being intensified by heavy applications of acid-forming nitrogenous fertilizers. Strong subsoil acidity (Al toxicity) reduces plant rooting depth, increases susceptibility to drought, and decreases the use of subsoil nutrients. Aluminum toxicity in cotton and wheat is aggravated by high temperature (247, 316, 351). Manganese toxicity is a problem in some strongly acid soils and mine spoils (below pH 5.5) whose parent materials are sufficiently high in total Mn (134); however, it can also occur at high pH levels in soils under reducing conditions created by flooding, compaction, or organic matter accumulation. Gupta & Chipman (163) reported Mn toxicity of carrots in a sphagnum peat at pH 7.8–8.1. In this instance the toxicity was attributed to an increased solubility of a humic fraction of peat which rendered Mn more available to the plants. Steam sterilization or drying (of high Mn soils) can greatly increase Mn solubility and toxicity (287, 335). Soil microorganisms appear to play a major role in determining soil levels of reduced Mn^{2+} which is absorbed by plants, especially at the higher soil pH levels (115, 333). Iron toxicity apparently is involved in physiological disorders of rice under flooded conditions and also in sugarcane, macadamia nut, and other crops under nonflooded conditions (90, 414). In mine spoils and other waste land, excesses of Zn, Cu, Ni, Cd, or other mineral elements may limit plant growth, particularly in acid soils, but sometimes even in neutral pH soils; toxicities of Mg and Ni have been reported in serpentine soils (73).

Metal toxicities can also appear on previously productive cropland that has been treated repeatedly with metal-containing pesticides and fertilizers (57, 73). For example, Fe deficiency chlorosis of citrus seedlings in Florida has been partially attributed to the accumulation of excess Cu resulting from repeated spray and fertilizer applications. Excess Mn levels have been reported in certain Florida citrus soils. Excess Zn in old peach orchard soils of South Carolina has reduced the growth of peach trees, cotton, and soybeans. This occurred on a site treated with Zn oxysulfate to control bacterial spot disease in peach trees. In some instances excess metals in soils and plants are the result of airborne pollutants from industrial installations.

Any productive soil can be damaged by an imbalance of essential mineral elements (56, 57, 73, 229). For example, excess fertilization with NH_4^+ or K can induce Mg or Ca deficiencies in plants. Excess Cu, Ni, Zn, and P can induce Fe-deficiency chlorosis. Conversely, excess Fe can intensify Zn deficiency (7, 8). Such plant nutritional imbalances can occur in soils that have been fertilized indiscriminately, in soils treated with sewage sludge of high metal content and perhaps also in waste disposal fields near animal feedlots or food processing plants (73).

ALUMINUM TOXICITY

General Effects

PLANT SYMPTOMS   The symptoms of Al injury are not always easily identifiable. In some plants, the foliar symptoms resemble those of P deficiency (overall stunting; small, dark green leaves and late maturity; purpling of stems, leaves, and leaf veins; yellowing and death of leaf tips). In others, Al toxicity appears as an induced Ca deficiency or reduced Ca transport problem (curling or rolling of young leaves and collapse of growing points or petioles). Aluminum-injured roots are characteristically stubby and brittle. Root tips and lateral roots become thickened and turn brown. The root system as a whole is corraloid in appearance, with many stubby lateral roots but lacking in fine branching. Such roots are inefficient in absorbing nutrients and water. In general, young seedlings are more susceptible to Al than older plants (420).

PHYSIOLOGICAL EFFECTS   Much of the physiological research on the mechanism of Al toxicity has involved a single plant species or variety. In general, Al has been shown to: interfere with cell division in plant roots, fix P in less available forms in the soil and in or on plant roots, decrease root respiration, interfere with certain enzymes governing the deposition of polysaccharides in cell walls, increase cell wall rigidity (by cross-linking pectins), and interfere with the uptake, transport, and use of several elements (Ca, Mg, P, K) and water by plants (135, 136, 383). Metal ions such as Al are known to form strong complexes and to precipitate nucleic acids; in fact, they are used to complex and isolate polynucleotides from leaves (429).

Differential Aluminum Tolerance in Plants

Plant species and varieties vary widely in tolerance to excess Al in the growth medium (135). In several species, these differences are genetically controlled (369). Closely related genotypes (preferably near-isogenic lines) are valuable tools for studying the physiological mechanisms of toxicity or tolerance.

Epstein (125) pointed out that an element present in excess can interfere with metabolism through competition for uptake, inactivation of enzymes, displacement of essential elements from functional sites, or alteration of the structure of water. Many of these effects probably involve modification of membrane structure and function.

The exact physiological mechanisms of Al toxicity or tolerance are still debated; these may well be different in different plant species and varieties and be controlled by different genes through different biochemical pathways. Obviously Al tolerant plants must be able to prevent the absorption of excess Al or detoxify the Al after it has been absorbed. Some of the plant physiological factors associated with differential Al tolerance are discussed below.

pH CHANGES IN ROOT ZONES   Certain Al-tolerant cultivars of wheat, barley, rice, peas, and corn (inbreds) increase the pH of their nutrient solutions and thus decrease the solubility and toxicity of Al (85, 86, 135, 139, 201, 239, 323; C. D. Foy, unpublished data). In contrast, Al-sensitive cultivars of the same species decrease or have no effect on the pH of their nutrient cultures and thus are exposed to higher concentrations of Al for longer periods. In certain wheat genotypes, these differential pH changes have also been demonstrated in thin layers of soil removed directly from plant roots and even in the bulk of soil pot cultures (135; C. D. Foy, unpublished data). Thus, within limits, plants can alter their environments to their own benefit or detriment.

Wilkinson (463, 464) and Barber (22) listed possible causes of pH lowering in plant root zones. These include H ion release resulting from excess cation over anion absorption, release and hydrolysis of CO_2, release of H ions from carboxyl groups of polygalacturonic acid residues of pectic acid, and excretion of protons from microorganisms associated with the roots. See also Raven & Smith (367).

Dodge & Hiatt (111) found that differential pH-changing abilities among Al tolerant and sensitive wheat cultivars were associated with differential anion-cation uptake. They postulated that the differential pH changes were due to differences in NO_3^- absorption and that these differences might result from cultivar differences in

NO_3^- metabolism. Treatment with NH_4^+-N (the uptake of which lowers the pH of the medium) decreased nitrate reductase activity. Mugwira & Patel (323) found that in solutions containing only KNO_3 and $Ca(NO_3)_2$ the anion-cation uptake difference accounted for the solution pH change by Al tolerant and sensitive wheat cultivars. However, in complete nutrient solutions the relationship between excess cation or anion uptake appears less direct (A. L. Fleming, unpublished data). In some cases, elemental analyses of plant materials do not account for the direction or magnitude of the pH changes observed in nutrient solutions. The pH changes often appear more closely related to the nutritional status of roots than to differential ionic uptake. Root zone pH changes by Al tolerant and sensitive wheat cultivars are associated with the presence of well-developed lateral and adventitious roots.

Differential Al tolerances between certain cultivars of soybean and snap bean do not appear related to differential pH changes in root zones (135, 141). Henning (182) concluded that pH changes associated with differential Al tolerance between wheat varieties are merely consequences of differential death of root meristems. Whether the pH changes are primary causes of initial differential Al toxicity or simply the results of differential growth under Al stress is not known; however, once they occur, there can be no doubt about their effects on the subsequent solubility and toxicity of Al.

NH_4^+ vs NO_3^- NUTRITION   In strongly acid soils, nitrification is inhibited and NH_4^+ is an important source of N for plants (367). Many plants that are adapted to such soils and hence tolerant to Al also tolerate NH_4^+ levels that are toxic to other plants, and in some cases seem to prefer NH_4^+-N to NO_3^--N. Examples are cranberry, sugarcane, birch (*Betula verucosa*), *Deschampsia flexuosa,* certain grasses like *Paspalum notatum* and *Lolium rigidum,* and blueberries (135, 160, 303, 359, 384, 428, 438, 469). Both highbush and lowbush blueberries use NH_4^+ effectively, but NO_3^--N is toxic. Nitrate toxicity in lowbush blueberry coincides with a lack of nitrate reductase activity in its leaves and roots (428).

Havill and co-workers (175) noted that certain calcifuge species, notably members of the Ericaceae, had low nitrate reductase activities and restricted abilities to use NO_3^-. However, he found that NO_3^- is an important N source for other calcifuges and all calcicoles on at least some acid soils of pH 3.7–4.0. Gigon & Rorison (154) concluded that Al tolerance and NH_4^+ tolerance of *Deschampia flexuosa* did not coincide with a lack of nitrate reductase activity. Rorison (384, 385) recently classified several plant species according to their responses to nitrogen source with and without Al. Gigon & Rorison (154) and Kotze, Shear & Faust (248) have suggested that NH_4^+ toxicity be considered as a possible growth-limiting factor in acid soils. See (147) for NH_4^+-nitrate reductase interactions in apple roots. Both NH_4^+ and Al reduce the uptake of several essential nutrients (135, 384). Adding $CaCO_3$ (0.5 g/l) to nutrient solutions has alleviated NH_4^+ toxicity by enhancing the metabolism of tomato plants (355). The ratio between NO_3^- and NH_4^+ in the nutrient solution determines the rate and direction of plant-induced pH changes in the presence or absence of Al. Aluminum tolerance in certain wheat cultivars is characterized by the ability to use NO_3^- efficiently in the presence of NH_4^+ and to increase the pH of the growth medium (139).

ALUMINUM UPTAKE AND TRANSLOCATION   With respect to Al concentrations in plant tops, Al-tolerant plants may be divided into at least three groups. In the first group, Al concentrations in tops are not consistently different from those in Al-sensitive plants, but the roots of tolerant plants often contain less Al than those of sensitive plants. Plants in this category include several cultivars of wheat, barley, soybean, and snap bean (135). In such cases, tolerance is apparently related to an Al exclusion mechanism. In a second group of plants, Al tolerance is associated with lower Al levels in tops and entrapment of excess Al in roots. Examples are azalea (281), cranberry (303), rice (201), triticale and rye (322), and alfalfa clones (348). In a third group of plants, Al tolerance is directly associated with Al accumulation by the tops. Chenery & Sporne (80) defined Al accumulator plants as those containing $>$ 1000 ppm Al in their tops. They found that 37 of the 259 dicot families studied contained Al-accumulating members. The ability to accumulate Al was statistically correlated with seven primitive traits. For example, with few exceptions, the Al accumulators were arborescent and were especially common among tropical rain forest families. Examples of Al-accumulator plants are tea (292, 293), certain Hawaiian grasses (313), *Atriplex hastata* (222), pine trees (412), and mangrove (183).

The tea plant appears to protect itself against Al injury, at least in part, by trapping most of the excess Al in older leaves. These may contain 20,000 ppm Al or more (396), whereas young leaves may contain only 100 ppm and buds as little as 50 ppm Al. Matsumoto et al (293) reported that old tea leaves contained 30,000 ppm Al and that the Al was localized in epidermal cells having distinctly thickened walls.

Several investigators have studied the location of Al in plant roots and suggested possible physiological mechanisms of tolerance or sensitivity. Using dyes that combined with Al or flouresced when chelated with Al, Henning (182) found that much of the Al absorbed by wheat roots penetrated the boundary between root apex and root cap and accumulated in the nuclei and cytoplasm of cells adjacent to this zone. Some Al passed through the epidermis and cortex, but considerable amounts were retained in cortical cells. Although the endodermis seemed to prevent movement of Al into the central cylinder, Henning suggested that some Al may have bypassed the endodermis by entering the root apex and passing through meristematic cells of the central cylinder. Henning also found that the Al-tolerant Atlas 66 wheat cultivar required 100–200 times as much Al in the medium as did the Al-sensitive Brevor before Al penetrated the plasmalemma of meristematic root cells. However, once inside the cells, Al was equally harmful to sensitive and tolerant wheat cultivars. From this evidence he concluded that Al tolerance in wheat is due to Al exclusion at the root cell plasmalemma and that cultivar differences in Al tolerance are due to differences in the molecular construction of this membrane. Moore (315) suggested that a dominant allele in Al-tolerant wheat varieties may add or further complete a protein network of the plasmalemma that reduces permeability to Al.

From respiration inhibitor studies with DNP, Rhue (376) concluded that Al uptake was not an active process but rather the result of passive diffusion across the plasmalemma. He suggested that the role of metabolism in Al uptake is in the maintenance of root membrane structure and integrity. Klimashevskii & Dedov

(241) found that Al which moved in elongating segments of pea roots reduced cell wall plasticity and almost completely inhibited root cell growth. They suggested that levels of free hydroxy groups in elongating cell walls and the corresponding induction of the extracellular pH by growing cells can determine the genotype specific susceptibility to Al. Matsumoto et al (295) speculated that plant differences in Al tolerance may depend upon differences in structural properties of cell walls, particularly in the extent of methylation of galacturonic acid; however, he found no positive interaction between Al and uronic acids in Al-treated pea roots. He suggested that the precipitation of large amounts of Al on the root cell surface was associated with the polymerization of the absorbed monomeric Al due to pH increase in the root.

Klimashevskii et al (242, 243) concluded that the genotype specificity of plant reaction to toxic Al ions is due to the chemical and ion exchangeable properties of the pecto-cellulose cell walls and differences in the absorption and localization of Al in root tissues. Aluminum entered the root cell of Al-susceptible pea cultivars more readily, and the strength of Al fixation to cell walls was far less than that in Al-tolerant genotypes. Aluminum accumulation in the roots and certain cell structures of susceptible plants were attributed to disturbances in membrane permeability. Gonik & Klimashevskii (156) found that Al in nutrient cultures decreased the content of SH groups in root homogenates of an Al-sensitive pea cultivar but increased them in an Al-resistant cultivar. Kuznetsova et al (250) reported that Al decreased the total concentrations of free radicals to a greater degree in the roots of an Al-sensitive pea variety (Spartanets) than in those of an Al-tolerant variety (Uspekh).

CALCIUM NUTRITION   Aluminum tolerance in certain cultivars of wheat, barley, soybean, and snap bean has been associated with the ability to resist Al-induced Ca deficiency or reduced Ca transport (135, 136, 141). For example, in the presence of Al, the Al-tolerant Dade snap bean cultivar produced more stem exudate, and the exudate contained higher Ca concentrations than did that of the Al-sensitive Romano cultivar. This higher Ca uptake by the Al-tolerant cultivar was also found in whole plant tops and in the cell wall, mitochondrial, and supernatant fractions of root homogenates when plants were grown with Al. In the absence of Al, the Al-sensitive Romano contained as much or more Ca in these fractions than the Al-tolerant Dade. Rhue & Grogan (377) reported that increasing the Ca concentrations of nutrient solutions decreased Al tolerance differences among corn inbred lines.

Awad, Edwards & Milhain (18) concluded that the yield-reducing effects of Al toxicity per se and Al-induced Ca deficiency could not be separated in an experiment involving Kikuyu grass (*Pennisetum clandestinum,* Hochst) on an acid soil at pH 4.36. Aluminum-induced interference in Ca uptake has also been reported in peaches (198) and apple trees (248).

PHOSPHORUS NUTRITION   In many plants Al tolerance appears to be closely associated with P-use-efficiency. For example, in certain cultivars of wheat and tomato and inbred lines of corn, Al tolerance coincides with the ability to tolerate low P levels in nutrient solutions, either in the presence or absence of Al (85, 135, 143). Aluminum tolerance in certain pea cultivars has been associated with higher P concentrations in plant roots (242). Andrew & Vanderberg (14) found that Al increased P concentrations in the tops of Al-tolerant legume species but decreased those of Al-sensitive species. Aluminum markedly increased the redox potential of root tissues, decreased contents of high bond energy P, and increased contents of mineral P in the roots of peas (102). These effects were more pronounced in the roots of Al-susceptible cv. Tulunskii Zelenyi than in the Al-resistant cv. Uspekh. Many others have noted that the close association between Al injury and P nutrition (60, 440).

Aluminum tends to accumulate in the roots of many sensitive plants, often in close association with P. Hutchinson et al (206) concluded that sugar beet treated with Al formed an insoluble phosphate in the cortex of the roots, thereby creating a P deficiency for plant growth. Aluminum toxicity was attributed to inhibited cell division and immobilization of P within plant roots. Subsequent studies with an electron microscope (232, 233) confirmed that an Al-phosphate precipitated in meristematic zones of primary and lateral roots of Al-sensitive sugar beet cultivars but not in those of Al-tolerant cultivars. The precipitate occurred mainly in the cortex, endodermis, and lateral roots, but some Al penetrated to the stele. McCormick & Borden (298, 299) showed an interaction between Al and P in the root cap and in epidermal and cortical regions of barley (*Hordeum vulgare*) and poplar (*Poplus species*) root extending back from the root tips for 1–5 mm. The Al-P interaction appeared to be located in the cell walls and cytoplasmic membranes. Results also suggested that Al absorbed by root surfaces or that in intercellular free spaces may immobilize the P present in root tissue or external substrate. Stryker, Gilliam & Jackson (411) reported that Al in roots may extract P from adjacent root cells and tissues and thus serve as a sink for plant P absorbed from other sites. McCormick & Borden (299), using a transmitting electron microscope and molybdenum as an electron dense stain (combined with P and Al in plant roots), concluded that $AlPO_4$ precipitated in barley roots. The precipitate occurred in scattered globules in mucilaginous layers along root surfaces and in the intercellular regions of the root tips. Some precipitate also appeared in the cytoplasm of root cells. Others who have reported similar Al X P interactions in plant roots include Rasmussen (365) and Waisel et al (443).

Naidoo et al (331) used an electron microscope equipped with an X-ray emission detector to locate sites of Al injury in roots of Al-tolerant Dade and Al-sensitive Romano snap bean and in Al-sensitive Hancock cotton cultivars that had been grown with 20 ppm Al at pH 4.6 for 12 days. Linear scans across root sections indicated that Al and P precipitated together in or on the outer cells of the root cap. In spot analyses of nuclei, cytoplasm, and cell walls, the major elements detected were Al, P, S, and Ca. Highest Al concentrations were in the nucleus. The authors suggested that Al was bound to esteric P in nucleic acids and to membrane lipids and that it reduced or inhibited cell division by alteration of nucleic acid molecules. Nuclei of the Al-tolerant Dade snap bean tended to have higher Al:P ratios in meristematic cells than did those of the Al-sensitive Romano cultivar. On the basis of such evidence, Naidoo & associates speculated that Al-resistant plants can tolerate more Al associated with their nuclear P before metabolism is totally inhibited.

In pea roots, Al was localized in the epidermis and regions where cells were actually dividing, such as root tips and differentiating lateral roots (294, 295). Within the cells Al accumulated mainly in the nuclei and cell walls. Molecular sieving (Sephadex G-25) chromatography indicated that Al^{3+} in nucleic acids associated preferentially with DNA. Clarkson & Sanderson (89) suggested that Al prevented DNA replication in onion roots by cross-linking of polymers, which increased the rigidity of the DNA double helix. In contrast, Henning (182) found no evidence that Al altered DNA in wheat roots. He concluded that Al inhibited the entire mitotic cycle and not just the late stage of the S-period; as reported by Clarkson (86) for onion roots.

Clarkson (87) found that most of the P^{32} absorbed by Al-injured barley roots was inorganic and was exchangeable with nonlabeled P. Andrew & Vandenberg (14) found that Al-injured legume roots lost P to the solution. Aluminum is reported to decrease hexose phosphorylation. Clarkson (87, 88) showed further that Al citrate reduced the activity of a purified yeast hexokinase, reduced the rate of sugar phosphorylation by crude mitochondrial extracts from barley roots, and increased concentrations of ATP in barley roots. Woolhouse (471) noted that Al inhibited the activities of ATPase in plants. From this evidence Clarkson (88) concluded that Al acts directly or indirectly to prevent the use of ATP in glucose phosphorylation. Similar evidence has been obtained for peas (33, 35).

In apparent contrast to some of the work cited above, Klimashevskii & associates (239, 240) and Bernatskaya (35) reported that Al increased the activities of ATPase and acid phosphatases in pea roots. They concluded that Al injured the cell walls by activating polygalacturonase, which hydrolyzes pectins and thereby promotes faster Al penetration. The increased activity of acid phosphatase was interpreted as an indication of damage to membranes which leads to liberation of enzymes from lysosomes, mitochondria, and other phosphate-containing cell structures. Differential Al tolerance in two cultivars of peas was attributed to the differential effects of Al on ATPase activity more than in an Al-tolerant variety. They found further that Al penetrated cell walls and accumulated in greatest concentrations in mitochondria, nuclei, and other structures of root cells. An Al-sensitive pea cultivar fixed 2–4 times as much Al in cell walls, nuclei, and mitochondria as did a resistant cultivar. There was a direct correlation between Al absorption and activity of acid phosphatases in roots.

Certain Al-tolerant wheat varieties (132) and corn inbred lines (82) have higher activities of root phosphatases than Al-sensitive genotypes of the same species. Woolhouse (471) found that the ATPase activity of cell wall preparations from roots of an acid soil ecotype of *Agrostis tenuis* was inhibited less by Al than was that of a preparation from a calcareous soil ecotype of the same species. He suggested that structural changes in these enzymes might be responsible for differential Al tolerance of the ecotypes studied. Bieleski (39) suggested that low P levels in root zones induce the activity of acid phosphatases in roots and enable plants to extract P from organic sources in soils. Perhaps the $H_2PO_4^-$ ions, assumed to be absorbed by plants, originate from the breakdown of organic P forms. In strongly acid soils most of the P (Fe and Al forms) may be largely unavailable to plants without the intervention of soil microorganisms. In such cases, the root phosphatase activity of plant genotypes may correlate with Al tolerance because the enzyme is necessary to release P from microbial forms. Phosphatases may also function in metabolizing P in roots containing high levels of Al; however, no specific mechanisms have been proposed.

ORGANIC ALUMINUM COMPLEXES IN PLANTS   Jones (222) suggested that organic acids (oxalic and citric) in the roots of Al-tolerant species chelated Al and thus prevented the Al-P precipitation that would normally occur at physiological pH values. According to Small (399), the acidiphilous plants generally have strong organic acid buffer systems in their cells, in contrast to the alkaphiles in which phosphate buffers dominate the system. Grime & Hodgson (161) suggested that Al resistance of certain calcifuge species is due to a chelating mechanism which also has an affinity for Fe. Bartlett & Reigo (24) noted that Al complexed by citrate, EDTA, or soil organic matter extract was detoxified for maize, whereas ionic Al severely injured the roots and decreased the Ca and Mn contents of roots and the P, Ca, and Mn contents of tops.

The tea plant contains appreciable amounts of organic acids and polyphenols which could detoxify Al by chelation and account for the Al tolerance of the species (396). Flavenols and quercetin haempherol-flavenols with free 5 or 3OH groups apparently form strong complexes with Al. It was suggested that at a soil pH of 3.9, Al^{3+} and $H_2PO_4^-$ ions form complexes (with a ratio of 1:1) having less charge, or even neutral molecules (with or without organic acids) which move passively into the tea plant.

Jayman & Sivasubramaniam (213) found that root exudates of young tea plants contain appreciable quantities of malic acid which solubilize P, Fe, and Al from rock phosphate fertilizer. Reagent malic acid solubilized the same elements when incubated with a tea soil. It was suggested that in tea soils, where most of the P added as rock phosphate is immobilized by Fe and Al, malic acid may be useful in chelating these elements and so releasing P for plant growth. Malic acid could also reduce the direct toxicities of Al or Fe to more sensitive species by the same mechanism.

Thawornwong & van Diest (420) found that 0.5 to 2 ppm of ionic Al was lethal to rice seedlings in nutrient solutions, but 2 ppm Al in chelated form was not harmful. Aluminum at 2 ppm was not harmful to rice past the seedling stage.

White, Tiffin & Taylor (460) reported that polymeric complexes of Al and P form in dilute solutions, reaching a maximum at pH 5.0. These have 3 moles of P to 4 moles of Al. At pH 4.5 such complexes can stay in metastable equilibrium for months or years, and may affect interactions of Al and P in plant growth.

White (459) reported that alfalfa roots absorbed 3 to 4 times as much Al at pH 5.0 as at pH 4.5, but plant injury was less. The low toxicity of a high internal Al was attributed to the passive uptake of polymeric Al phosphate having a low net charge density. It was suggested that such complexes may serve as internal P reserves when external supplies are limited.

UPTAKE OF FE, MG, SI, K, AND OTHER MINERAL ELEMENTS   Otsuka (347) found that in nutrient cultures at pH 4.1, Al decreased the growth of acid soil-sensitive wheat and barley varieties and induced a Fe deficiency chlorosis when low Fe levels were used. At high Fe levels in solution, the Al-induced chlorosis was alleviated. At low Fe levels, Al added at 0.9 or 1.8 ppm induced a more severe Fe chlorosis than that caused by Cu (0.17 ppm) or Co (0.80 ppm). The Al treatment also reduced Fe concentrations in the plant shoots, and even an Al pretreatment decreased Fe concentrations of plants subsequently grown without Al.

Davis, McCauley & Byers (101) showed that Al (0.5 ppm) in solution interfered with Fe incorporation by a mutant strain (SK 11) of *Bacillus megaterium* but not by the normal strain (ATCC 192/13). The superior Al resistance of the latter strain to Al-induced Fe deficiency was attributed to its ability to produce a secondary hydroxamate (skizokinen) which rendered Fe more available, either by solubilizing Fe or permitting the uptake of a ferric hydroxamate chelate by an alternate route. It was concluded that the mutant strain had lost the ability to produce skizokinen.

Jones & Jones (227) associated the poor health of peach trees with unfavorable Fe/Al ratios (1:1 or less) in plant tissues. Weaver, Dowler & Nesmith (453) concluded that accumulation (during dormancy) of several elements in peach trees (Al, K, Mg, Ca, Sr, B, Zn) may be an indication that trees have been predisposed to the short life syndrome. Hoffer & Trost (192) associated the accumulation of Al and Fe in nodal tissue of corn with increased susceptibilities to certain strains of root rot. The accumulation of Fe and Al by plants was affected both by soil conditions and plant genotype.

Acid soil sensitivity in certain wheat and barley cultivars has been associated with Al-induced Fe deficiency in nutrient solutions at pH 4.1 (347). Foliar symptoms in soybean and sorghum on acid, Al-toxic Bladen soil have sometimes resembled Fe deficiency chlorosis [C. D. Foy, unpublished data; Brown & Jones, (57–59)].

Lee (257) suggested that greater Al tolerance in certain cultivars of Irish potato is associated with the ability of plants to absorb K and Mg. In certain inbred lines of corn, Al tolerance coincides with greater Mg efficiency (83). Ali (5) reported that Al toxicity in wheat could be completely overcome by increasing the concentrations of Ca, Mg, K, or Na in the medium, either individually or collectively. The Al tolerance rankings of corn inbreds can be altered by changing Mg concentrations of nutrient solutions (377). Ratner et al (366) noted that Mo counteracted the harmful effects of 1–3 ppm Al on alfalfa root tips at pH 3.8 and even protected plants against injury during a second exposure to Al in the absence of Mo.

Ota (346) associated Al tolerance in rice cultivars with high levels of Si in the epidermal cells of leaves. Silicon is known to reduce the internal toxicity of Mn in barley leaves (466) and may play a similar role in detoxifying Al. Silicon may also precipitate Al in soil solution and reduce its toxicity to plants. Mattson & Hester (296) showed that the addition of silicate to strongly acid soils lowered the soil pH at which plants were injured.

Berezovskii & Klimashevskii (33) found that 2 ppm Al in nutrient cultures sharply decreased NO_3^- uptake by pea roots, the incorporation of N into organic compounds, and translocation of N^{15} to stems and leaves. These effects were greater in the Al-susceptible Tulunski Zelenyi cv. than in the Al-resistant Uspekh cv.

Beneficial Effects of Aluminum

Aluminum is not generally regarded as an essential element for plant growth, but under some conditions, low concentrations can increase growth or produce other desirable effects (135). Plants that have shown positive growth responses to Al in nutrient cultures include rice (3 ppm), tropical legumes (0.5 ppm), eucalyptus (1 ppm), tea (27 ppm added at pH 6.0), peach (17.5 ppm), sugar beet (1 ppm), corn inbreds (3.5 ppm), and wheat (3 ppm) (14, 83, 135, 201, 233, 293, 327). When added Al was beneficial to rice cultivars classified as Al-tolerant or sensitive, the growth stimulus was greater in Al-tolerant cultivars (201). In wheat, an Al concentration (3 ppm Al at initial pH 4.5) which was highly detrimental to Sonora 63 (Mexico) was markedly beneficial to BH 1146 (Brazil) (139).

The mechanisms by which small quantities of Al benefit plant growth or other qualities are not always clear and may be different for different plant genotypes and growth media (139); these responses do not necessarily result from Al effects on plants per se. Possible explanations include: increasing Fe solubility and availability in calcareous soils (or in slightly acid, neutral, or alkaline nutrient solutions by the hydrolysis of Al and a pH decrease); correcting or preventing internal Fe deficiency by displacing Fe from bound, metabolically inactive sites in calcicolous plants (*Scabiosa columbaria*); blocking negative charges on cell wall sites and thereby promoting P uptake (eucalyptus); correcting or preventing P toxicity (Al-tolerant corn inbreds); delaying root deterioration in low Ca solutions by slowing growth and preventing depletion of Ca from the medium (sunflower); altering the distribution of growth regulators in roots (peach); preventing toxicities of Cu (citrus) and Mn (atriplex); serving as a fungicide; and reducing undesirable top growth in N-rich nursery stock (84, 135, 161, 328; C. D. Foy and J. W. Schwartz, unpublished data) (See also 46, 119, 244, 267, 269, 368).

Matsumoto et al (293) speculated that Al has a physiological role in accelerating root formation and might be transferred to leaves and epidermal cells of the tea plant as waste material. He noted beneficial effects of Al on root growth after 20 days and on top growth after 50 days.

Millikan (311) found that Al markedly reduced or prevented Fe chlorosis caused by excess Zn or Mn in flax. Vickers, Zak & Odurukwe (439) reported that 5 ppm Al in solution stimulated root elongation in milk vetch (*Astragalus cicer* L. cv Lutana), but 15 ppm Al was toxic. This species was not particularly sensitive to Al and a soil pH of 4.2. The lime response (pH 4.2–5.4) was attributed to increased Ca and P uptake and a decline of excess soluble Al and Mn in the soil, allowing root penetration.

Genetic Control of Aluminum Tolerance

Al tolerance in certain barley populations is controlled by one major, dominant gene (369). At least one degree of Al tolerance in certain wheat populations is also reportedly under single gene control (231). However, preliminary studies with other wheat populations indicated that two or possibly three genes, plus modifiers, are involved in wheat (251; H. N. Lafever and L. G. Campbell, unpublished data). In Atlas 66 wheat an Al tolerance factor has been located on chromosome 5D (360). Lopez et al (278) found that the diploid and tetraploid wheats tested to date are highly sensitive to Al (0.4 ppm in solution); the hexaploid wheats differ widely in tolerance, but all were injured by 25 ppm Al in solution; and rye cultivars varied from sensitivity to 1 ppm Al to tolerance to 30 ppm Al in solution.

Slootmaker (398) suggested that the inclusion of a rye chromosome in triticale (a wheat X rye cross) makes it tolerant to high soil acidity and presumably Al. This conclusion is supported by the data of Mugwira, Patel & Rao (324), who found that on five acid soils in Alabama the lime responses of wheat, triticale, and rye were 87, 31, and 20% respectively. Abruzzi rye had lower lime requirements than the triticales 6TA 131 and 6TA 385 and Arthur wheat. The average increase in dry matter in limed soils was 90% for triticale 6TA 385, 54% for 6TA 131, and only 20% for Trail blazer triticale and Abruzzi rye. Under comparable conditions the lime response of Al-sensitive Arthur wheat was about 100%.

Differential Al tolerance of barley and wheat cultivars, demonstrated in greenhouse and growth chamber experiments (soil and nutrient solution), have been confirmed by grain yields in field plots of acid, Al-toxic soils (251, 370). There is no evidence to date that Al tolerance in barley or wheat is necessarily associated with low yield potential in the absence of Al.

There is also evidence that Al tolerance in alfalfa is genetically controlled (106, 107); however, specific genes responsible for tolerance have not been identified.

MANGANESE TOXICITY

General Effects

PLANT SYMPTOMS   Unlike Al, excess Mn generally affects plant tops more severely than roots. In addition, Mn produces more definitive symptoms in plant tops than does Al, and for a given plant, Mn accumulates in the foliage somewhat in proportion to injury (134, 139). However, the symptoms of Mn toxicity are quite diverse among plant species (11–13, 226). Plant symptoms of Mn toxicity include marginal chlorosis and necrosis of leaves (alfalfa, rape, kale, lettuce), leaf puckering (cotton, soybean, snap bean), and necrotic spots on leaves (barley, lettuce, soybeans) (134, 139). Specific plant physiological disorders associated with excess Mn include "crinkle leaf" of cotton (1), "stem streak necrosis" of potato (378), and "internal bark necrosis" (IBN) of apple trees (121, 129). In severe cases of Mn toxicity, plant roots turn brown, usually after the tops have been severely injured.

Plant symptoms of Mn toxicity are often detectable at stress levels which produce little or no reduction in vegetative growth. By contrast, Al toxicity can greatly reduce yields (by root damage) without producing clearly identifiable symptoms in plant tops. Hence, in acid soils containing high levels of both Al and Mn, the plant growth reduction observed may be erroneously attributed to Mn toxicity when Al toxicity is the more important of the two factors (138, 139).

PHYSIOLOGICAL AND BIOCHEMICAL EFFECTS   Manganese toxicity has been associated with the destruction of auxin (indole acetic acid-IAA) in cotton (318, 319) and Japanese morning glory (408), a possible amino acid imbalance in potato (378), and reduced leaf cell number and volume and reduced leaf and root dry weights of sugar beets (419). In cotton the disorder has been related to elevated activities of peroxidase and polyphenol oxidase, lower activities of catalase, ascorbic acid oxidase, glutathione oxidase, lower ATP contents, and lower respiration rates. Morgan et al (319) found that either Mn excess or Mn deficiency markedly increased the in vitro destruction of auxin by increasing IAA oxidase activity in cotton. Typical symptoms of auxin deficiency, regarding growth, IAA oxidase activity, leaf abscission, and internode length were manipulated in both directions by raising or lowering the Mn supply from optimum to toxic or deficient levels. Meudt (304) reported that Mn enhances the sulfite-induced chain reaction during the enzyme auto-oxidation of IAA. Manganese ions were believed to function in electron transfer between sulfite ions and IAA free radicals. Bhatt et al (38) found that 36 ppm Mn as $MnCL_2$ reversed the growth inhibition of sorghum roots caused by 100 ppm of gibberellic acid (GA), which is known to enhance auxin production in many plants. The inhibition of root growth induced by GA was explained on the basis of raising the auxin to inhibitory levels for roots and stimulatory levels for tops. Excess Mn is known to promote the oxidation of auxin; hence, it was suggested that the promotion of root growth by Mn was due to the oxidation product of auxin. The authors suggested that the mechanism of GA action is auxin-mediated and that the oxidation product of auxin is essential for its physiology. It was suggested further that the enhanced production of auxin by GA and its oxidation by Mn was causing growth stimulation in both tops and roots—in tops by supplying needed auxin and in roots by preventing excesses (supplying the necessary oxidation product of IAA). Higher than normal levels of Mn (1900 ppm) in *Scopolia sinensis* (host of the potato spindle tuber virus) increased the replication of the virus RNA (395). Thus excess Mn may predispose plants to certain diseases. Under some conditions the addition of Si, Fe, Ca, or P alleviates Mn toxicity.

Juang (228) found evidence that in high Mn soils higher Zn levels were required for optimum growth of sugarcane. Wilson (468) reported that Mn added to a Leesville soil (pH 6.9) (1000 $\mu g/g$) completely inhibited nitrification in soybeans during the first 5 weeks of growth, but nitrification was resumed after the 6th week.

Manganese concentrations of 432–540 ppm induced the development of erythromycin-resistant mitochondrial mutations in yeast (21, 364). Manganese was the only one of 11 divalent cations tested which produced this effect. These investigators cited the work of others showing that many Mn-induced mitochondrial mutations are up to 4500 base pairs long. Manganese apparently acts as an error-producing factor during mitochondrial DNA replication; 90% of total protein synthesis was inhibited, but mitochondrial protein synthesis was less strongly inhibited. Manganese uptake associated with mutations in yeast was promoted by glucose and decreased by Mg to a greater degree than by Zn. The process was also delayed by cycloheximide. Nuclear DNA replication was strongly inhibited by excess Mn. Mitochondrial

DNA replication was only weakly inhibited during the first 3 hr of labeling. Thus Mn seems to belong to a small group of mutagens capable of producing mutations but no recombination. There is no evidence that Mn really induced gene conversion.

Differential Manganese Tolerances In Plants

Plant species and cultivars within species differ widely in tolerance to excess soluble or exchangeable Mn (34, 134, 139, 140). Tolerance to excess Mn may or may not coincide with tolerance to excess Al. Atlas 66 wheat from North Carolina is more tolerant to Al than Monon from Indiana, but Monon is more tolerant to excess Mn than Atlas 66 (142). On the other hand, preliminary studies indicate that Al-tolerant Dayton (Ohio) barley is also more tolerant to excess Mn than Al-sensitive Kearney (Kansas) barley (C. D. Foy and P. S. Baenziger, unpublished data).

Manganese tolerance in certain plants has been attributed to reduced absorption, less translocation of excess Mn to plant tops, and/or greater tolerance to high Mn levels within plant tissues (134, 139).

MANGANESE UPTAKE AND TRANSPORT Waterlogging of soil promotes the reduction of Mn to the divalent (available) form, and there is considerable evidence that tolerances of some plant species to certain wet soils coincide with their tolerances to excess Mn in nutrient cultures. Graven, Attoe & Smith (158) suggested that the wet soil sensitivity of alfalfa might be due in part to Mn sensitivity. Dionne & Pesant (109) found that alfalfa was more sensitive to Mn toxicity and poor soil aeration (associated with soil waterlogging) than was birdsfoot trefoil. Certain other pasture species that are most tolerant to waterlogging (130, 300) are generally also more tolerant to high Mn concentrations in nutrient solutions (185, 320). Robson & Loneragan (379) noted that the Mn-tolerant *Trifolium subterraneum* (cv. Geraldton) was more tolerant to waterlogging than the Mn-sensitive *Medicago truncatula*. The superior Mn tolerance of rice (compared with soybean) coincides with greater oxidizing power of its roots (112, 124). Doi (112) found that soybean was injured in paddy soil when planted alone, but this injury was reduced when soybean was planted with rice. The beneficial effect could have been due, at least in part, to the oxidation and detoxification of Mn by rice roots which would have protected the more sensitive soybean.

In nutrient solution about 20 times as much Mn was required to produce toxicity in corn as in peanut (31). High Mn sensitivity in peanut was associated with the accumulation of Mn in its leaves but little or no accumulation in roots, stems, or petioles, except during the early growth stage. The superior Mn tolerance of corn (compared with peanut) was associated with reduced transport of Mn from roots and stems to leaves (31, 32). The superior Mn tolerance of Siam 29 rice (compared with Pebifun) was attributed to a lower Mn absorption (276). Greater Mn tolerance of *Trifolium subterraneum* (compared with *Medicago truncatula*) was associated with a lower rate of Mn absorption and greater retention of excess Mn in roots (379). Andrew & Hegarty (10) concluded that the relative tolerances of either tropical or temperate legume species depend in part on the retention of excess Mn within the root system. Ouellette & Dessureaux (348) reached a similar conclusion regarding alfalfa clones that differed in Mn tolerance.

Munns, Johnson & Jacobson (329), who studied Mn deficiency rather than toxicity, concluded that oat cultivar differences in shoot Mn contents were due to variations in the size and turnover rates of a labile fraction of Mn in the roots. Variations in root Mn content were attributed largely to variations in the size of the nonlabile fraction. The nonlabile root fraction was increased by increasing the pH or decreasing the temperature of the medium; this effect was much greater in the Mn-inefficient Algerian than in the Mn-efficient Sun II. Conversion of Mn into the nonlabile form had no effect on the transport into shoots. A similar compartmentalization of Mn (physical and/or chemical) may also be involved in differential tolerances to excess Mn in some crop cultivars.

INTERNAL TOLERANCE TO EXCESS MANGANESE   Plant species and cultivars differ widely in tolerance to a given level of Mn within their tops (134, 139). For example, Andrew & Hegarty (10) found that toxicity levels associated with symptoms in plant tops ranged from 380 ppm Mn in *Medicago sativa* to 1600 in *Centrosema pubescens*. White (461) reported that Mn toxicity was associated with concentrations of 1000, 500, and 200 ppm in the tops of beans, peas, and barley, respectively. Manganese concentrations of > 2600 ppm were found in carrot tops showing Mn toxicity symptoms (bronzing), and yields were reduced when the foliage contained 7100–9600 ppm Mn (164). Bragg soybean showed Mn toxicity (leaf crinkling and chlorotic speckling) when blade 3 (most recently matured leaf) of the tops contained > 160 ppm Mn (340). Tea and tomato are more tolerant to high internal levels of Mn than many other species (105, 476). Ward (452) estimated that internal Mn concentrations required for toxicity in the tops of tomato were 450–500 ppm for young leaves and 900–1000 ppm for old leaves. Dennis (105) found that tomatoes grown on steam-sterilized soils at initial pH 5.3–5.4 had Mn toxicity when the tops contained 2808–5240 ppm, coupled with low N and high P contents. The cultivar "Potentate" was more susceptible than V548 and Ware Cross, two other standard New Zealand cultivars.

In addition to its ability to oxidize Mn from the divalent (available) to the tetravalent (unavailable) form (and thereby reduce uptake), the rice plant must also have high internal tolerance to excess Mn because its leaves accumulate 5 to 10 times as much Mn as those of many other grasses such as oats, barley, wheat, and ryegrass (441). For example, Mn concentrations in old leaves of rice were 6000–7000 ppm whereas those in oats, wheat, and barley ranged from 800–1200, and ryegrass was lowest with 600–900 ppm Mn. Unlike the other grasses studied, rice accumulated more Mn in its tops than in its roots.

In some Mn-induced disorders, such as leaf speckling in barley, internal bark necrosis in apple, and leaf marginal chlorosis in mustard, the toxicity is related to localized accumulations of Mn rather than high overall Mn concentrations in plant tops (131, 466, 467). For example, Williams et al (467) found that the yellow leaf margins of mustard affected by Mn toxicity contained 2300 ppm Mn compared with

570 ppm for green portions of the same leaves. Highest levels were in old leaves. Leaves of normal plants on limed plots did not exceed 200 ppm. Fertilizers increased Mn concentrations of plants in the order $(NH_4)_2SO_4 > NH_4NO_3 > Ca(NO_3)_2$; this coincided with the order of soil acidification by the different fertilizers. There were no symptoms above a soil pH of 5.5, and yields were inversely correlated with Mn in plants.

Some cultivars of wheat, cotton, soybean, and lettuce tolerate higher levels of Mn in their tops than others (58, 134, 140, 142, 178, 179, 402). Winterhalder (470) showed that seedlings of *Eucalyptus saligna* were more tolerant to excess soil Mn that those of *Eucalyptus gummifera,* although the leaves of the former contained higher Mn concentrations. On a Mn toxic Richland soil at pH 5.2, Brown & Jones (58) found that the higher Mn tolerance of Lee soybean (compared with Bragg and Forrest) was associated with a higher internal Mn tolerance. Iron nutrition did not seem to be involved in differential Mn tolerance, since the Mn-sensitive cultivars included Fe-efficient Bragg and Fe-inefficient Forrest. In fact, Fe toxicity was suspected as a yield-limiting factor for the Fe-inefficient Bragg cultivar. Thus, contrary to some evidence in the literature, susceptibility to Mn toxicity and Fe toxicity seem to coincide in these two soybeans.

The relative tolerances of plants to excess Mn are affected by climatic factors such as temperature and light intensity (134). For example, at 21°C day and 18°C night, Bragg soybean was much more sensitive to excess Mn in nutrient solution than Lee. But raising the temperature to 33°C day and 28°C night completely prevented Mn toxicity in both cultivars, even though the higher temperature increased Mn uptake (179). Grafting experiments showed that Mn tolerance was controlled by the genotype of the shoot (58, 178, 179). Additional details concerning critical Mn levels in soils and plants are given in earlier reviews (134, 139).

INTERACTIONS OF MN WITH FE, SI, P, AND OTHER MINERAL ELEMENTS Excess Mn has induced Fe deficiency in potatoes grown in nutrient culture and produced Mn/Fe ratios of 18 or more in plant tops (258). Aluminum counteracted these effects by increasing Fe content of plants and decreasing Mn/Fe ratios. Chelated Fe decreased Mn uptake and toxicity of lettuce grown on steam-sterilized soils (403). Iron sprays also corrected Mn toxicity in eucalyptus (470). Leach & Taper (256) concluded that the optimun Fe/Mn ratios in plants ranged from 1.5 to 3.0 for kidney beans and from 0.5 to 5.0 for tomato. Iron deficiency developed at lower ratios and Mn toxicity at higher ratios. Similar Fe/Mn uptake antagonisms were observed for tomato and onion. Ohki (340) noted reciprocal Fe/Mn relationships in cotton; Mn concentrations of 4 and 247 ppm in plant tops were associated with Fe concentrations of 270 and 51 ppm respectively. Beaton (29) cited evidence that Mn toxicity limits the growth of Douglas fir in one area of Northeastern Washington, apparently by inducing Fe deficiency. This species is known to be responsive to Fe applications.

Tanaka & Navasero (416, 417) concluded that Mn toxicity symptoms and Fe deficiency symptoms are different in rice and that the range within which Fe toxicity can be remedied by Mn applications is narrow. Millikan (311) reported that excess Mn induced an Fe deficiency chlorosis which was prevented or cured by additions of Fe, Al, or Mo, or by P deficiency.

Agarwala (2, 3) described two types of Mn toxicity in chickpeas and found that genotypes differed in sensitivity to both types. The specific effects of Mn toxicity, characterized by a yellowing of leaf margins and brown necrotic spots on leaflets of middle and young leaves, was more severe in genotype T-1 than in T-3. But the Mn-induced Fe deficiency chlorosis was more severe in genotype T-3; Mn treatment of this genotype (T-3) also decreased Fe concentrations of young leaves more markedly than in genotype T-1. In chlorotic plants the reduction of chlorophyll by excess Mn was counteracted by high Fe. Low P levels increased Fe uptake. Excess Mn decreased soluble protein levels only in Fe-deficient plants. With low P, excess Mn decreased the catalase activity of T-3 (Fe-chlorosis susceptible) but not of the T-1 (chlorosis resistant) genotype. With low P levels, excess Mn depressed leaf levels of peroxidase in Fe-sufficient leaves of T-3 (Fe-chlorosis susceptible). Manganese was more effective than Co in suppressing Fe uptake by chickpeas. The differential Fe efficiency in the T-1 and T-3 genotypes was attributed to differential Fe uptake.

Osawa & Ikeda (345) also described two types of plant injury induced by excess Mn. The first type, characterized by interveinal chlorosis on upper leaves, was apparently identical to Fe deficiency and was observed in spinach, tomato, pepper, and bean. The second type of Mn toxicity, characterized by marginal chlorosis of lower leaves, often with brown, necrotic spots, was observed in lettuce, celery, and cabbage. Eggplant and Welsh onion did not show either symptom. In general, increasing the Fe supply prevented or reduced the severity of the interveinal chlorosis, but Fe additions had little or no effect in reducing the marginal chlorosis of celery and cabbage; iron treatment was somewhat effective with lettuce. Leaf analyses indicated that the Mn-induced interveinal leaf chlorosis is due to Fe deficiency. In contrast, the marginal chlorosis of leaves seemed due to accumulation of excess Mn. The abilities of Fe to reduce the detrimental effects of Mn on plant growth varied widely with plant species. It was remarkably effective in spinach, and some benefit was noted in tomato, pepper, lettuce, and eggplant. Iron had almost no effect in preventing yield depressions due to Mn toxicity in celery, cabbage, and Welsh onion. Iron concentrations of 30 ppm in solution caused Fe toxicity (growth inhibition) in pepper, lettuce, and eggplant. In spinach the Fe/Mn ratio in nutrient solution was closely related to normal growth. Decreasing this ratio gave Mn-induced chlorosis and decreased growth. However, in tomato, pepper, bean, and eggplant, both Fe/Mn ratio and Mn concentration in nutrient solution affected plant growth and/or occurrence of Mn-induced chlorosis. In celery, cabbage, and Welsh onion the absolute Mn concentration appeared to be the dominant factor. There was a close relationship between the Fe/Mn ratio in leaves and plant growth, except for the 30 ppm Fe level which produced Fe toxicity. A decrease in this ratio was associated with reduced growth. However, growth inhibition by excess Fe (30 ppm) could not be explained by the increase in this ratio.

Manganese absorption in tomatoes is influenced by interactions between Fe, Mn, and Mo (237). Added Fe counteracted the yield depressive effects of added Mn, but the amount of Fe needed for maximum yield was increased as the Mo supply increased. At low Fe levels Mo decreased yields. At higher Fe levels Mo increased yields.

Brown & Jones (58) suggested that high Fe levels in the tops of Fe-inefficient, Mn-sensitive, Bragg soybean may accentuate Mn toxicity or create Fe toxicity per se. They also speculated that high K levels in the tops of Mn-tolerant Lee soybean alleviate the harmful effects of high internal Mn concentrations.

Increased Ca levels in the growth medium often decrease Mn uptake and toxicity (178, 379, 391). Bortner (47) suggested that P may reduce the toxicity of excess Mn by rendering it inactive within the plant. Heintze (180) concluded that P detoxifies Mn by precipitation within plant roots.

There is abundant evidence that a soluble source of Si in the growth medium can protect plants against Mn toxicity. Lewin & Reimann (266) reported that Si-deficient plants accumulated higher Mn concentrations than Si-sufficient plants. Okuda & Takahashi (342) found that Mn oxidation was greater in rice plants supplied with Si than in Si-deficient plants. Silicon decreased excessive uptake of both Mn and Fe. Silicon prevents the formation of necrotic spots of high Mn concentrations in barley leaves without reducing the overall Mn concentrations of plant tops (466). Peaslee & Frink (352) reported that treating an acid soil with H_2SiO_3 significantly decreased both Mn and Al concentrations in tissues of plants grown in a greenhouse. However, Si did not affect the uptake of Cu or Zn. Higher uptake of Si by monocots than dicots may help to explain the generally higher Mn tolerance of the former.

Bowen (49) reported that Mn at 1 ppm reduced the growth of Sudan grass in nutrient solutions. The addition of Si at 5 ppm decreased accumulations of Mn, Cu, Fe, and Zn in plant tissues; in fact, Si induced a Mn deficiency in plants receiving 0.5 ppm Mn or less in the nutrient solution. It was concluded that under these conditions one function of Si was to reduce Mn toxicity. Bowen doubted that Si is essential for Sudan grass, but concluded that if it is essential, the requirement is less than 0.025 ppm in solution.

Alyxia rubricaulis (apocynaceae) and several species of *Maytenus* (Celastraceae) accumulate very high Mn concentrations in their leaves, up to 32,000 ppm in *Maytenus bureaviana*. Alyxis accumulates high Mn concentrations only in acid soils, but Maytenus accumulates high levels of Mn even on basic hypermagnesium soils. In Maytenus species, Mn accumulation depends on the total Mn in the soil and is reportedly independent of pH (211). Such results point out the fact that plants modify soil chemistry within their root zones.

From the foregoing evidence it appears that the toxicity of a given level of soluble Mn in the growth medium or even within the plant depends upon interactions between Mn and several other mineral elements, particularly Fe and Si. Such interactions may account for the wide variety of plant symptoms and different growth reductions produced by excess Mn in different plant species and cultivars.

ORGANIC MN COMPLEXES IN PLANTS   There is little published information on organic Mn complexes in plants, especially under phytotoxic conditions. Rapid uptake and translocation of available Mn by all species indicates a mobility unaffected by binding to insoluble organic ligands in the roots. In vitro electrophoretic studies have shown no organic Mn binding to soluble compounds in tomato xylem exudate, even though Mn concentration of the exudate was increased 18-fold (423). Apparently in this system the stability constants of Mn for the organic components are too low to compete with other cations. Hofner (193), however, reported a close association between Mn and an amino acid and carbohydrate fraction of sunflower stem exudate. He used gel filtration to fractionate the exudate into three associated components with molecular weights below 1500. Bremner & Knight (53) and Bremner (52) concluded that in ryegrass Mn existed as a single, cationic and perhaps noncomplexed form, but several anionic Cu and Zn complexes occurred in closely related forms. Soluble, low molecular weight compounds evidently can bind or chelate Mn in the exudate fluid, but their function under both normal and phytotoxic conditions is unclear.

In related studies, Van Goor & Wiersma (436, 437) examined the phloem sap of castorbean for evidence of Mn binding. They observed only limited Mn binding to the organic constituents of the sap. Gel filtration and electrophoresis showed that 60–70% of the Mn behaved as a simple cation. The bound Mn was associated with compounds having molecular weights between 1000 and 5000. Sutcliffe (413) had suggested earlier that organic complexes can reduce the transport of Mn to plant tops.

Although high stability binding is infrequent for Mn, it can occur. A protein-Mn complex with a molecular weight of 56,300 and with one atom of Mn has been isolated from peanut seed. Its function is unknown (108). Thus, from the available evidence, Mn binding or chelation does not seem to be an important mechanism for detoxifying excess levels of Mn within plants.

MANGANESE IN RELATION TO RHIZOBIA   Dobereiner (110) suggested that the sensitivity of many legumes to acid soils could be explained by a specific Mn toxicity to the N-fixing process. When plants depended upon symbiotic N fixation, Mn concentrations of 25 ppm in sand culture decreased the total N contents of bean plants by 30% to 60%; where plants were adequately supplied with mineral N, the corresponding reduction was only 13%. Under a mild Mn toxicity, the reduction in nodule numbers or efficiency of N fixation in beans was compensated by an increase in nodule size. Effects of manganese toxicity varied with inoculated strains of *Rhizobium phaseoli*. In an acid subsoil having a pH of 4.4 but a low level of available Mn, nodulation in beans was vigorous. Souto & Dobereiner (403) reported that Mn markedly decreased nodulation in tropical legumes and that Mn toxicity varied among varieties.

Dobereiner (110) suggested that contradictions in the literature concerning the response of legumes to lime might be due to variable soluble Mn concentrations in acid soils and variation in tolerance to high Mn concentration among plant and rhizobium strains. Kliewer (238) found that 20 ppm Mn in nutrient solutions reduced the number of nodulated alfalfa plants to 50% but did not affect the nodulation of birdsfoot trefoil. In nutrient cultures at pH 4.6–4.7, 50 ppm Mn almost prevented nodulation of snap beans over a 30 day period; 5 ppm Mn delayed the initiation of the process, but nodulation was fair; and 0.5 ppm Mn permitted good nodulation (J. E. Ambler, personal communication). Freire (146) pointed out the need for rhizobial strains that are tolerant to low pH and to high concentrations of Al and Mn for use in areas of low input agriculture. He found that soybean varieties with low tolerance to excess Mn showed a higher response to lime, absorbed more Mn and less Ca, and had lower nodule numbers and weights than Mn-tolerant varieties. The ratio between Ca and Mn seemed to be important in nodulation and Mn tolerance. Aluminum in nutrient solution increased Mn uptake and toxicity symptoms in soybeans.

Holding & Lowe (196) reported that 900 ppm Mn in an agar medium significantly reduced the effectiveness of 10 rhizobial strains, but much of the effectiveness was restored after 20 weeks. They suggested that Mn replaced Mg in an enzyme system associated with rhizobial effectiveness. Complexes of Mn (II) with ligands containing P and N were said to be isomorphous with the corresponding Mg (II) complexes. These investigators concluded that Mn affects symbiosis by reducing N fixation but also delays nodule appearance by an unknown mechanism.

Genetic Control of Manganese Tolerance

Manganese tolerance in alfalfa has been attributed to additive genes having little or no dominance (106). Eenink (120) reported that lettuce genotypes differed greatly in tolerance to exchangeable Mn in steam-sterilized soils. He studied the inheritance of Mn tolerance by intercrossing five lettuce genotypes. These were *Latuca sativa* cv. "Neptune" (Mn-sensitive); Plenos, Troppo, and Celtuce (Mn-tolerant); plus an accession of *Latuca serricola* (Mn-tolerant). Studies of the progenies indicated that Mn tolerance was determined by different numbers of genes in the parents, varying from one gene in Plenos and Troppo, two genes in *L. serricola,* to possibly four genes in *L. sativa* cv. Celtuce. In the first three parents the genes were linked in repulsion phase; their locations were indicated on a chromosome map.

IRON TOXICITY

General Occurrence and Importance

Iron toxicity is believed to be involved in several extremely complicated physiological diseases of rice under flooded conditions. These include "bronzing" in Sri Lanka and elsewhere, "Alkagare Type" disorder in Japan, and "Akiochi" in Korea (4, 200, 358, 414, 418, 421). Excess ferrous Fe also apparently contributes to "freckle leaf" of sugarcane in Hawaii, along with excess Al, Mn, and Zn (90).

Ponnamperuma (358) associated a bronzing disorder in rice with high concentrations of reduced products, particularly Fe^{2+}, in the soil solution. The condition was improved by drainage, delayed submergence, or the addition of reduction retardants such as MnO_2. The addition of MnO_2 at 0.4% by weight to the soil corrected a physiological disorder of rice and improved the growth of rice on three acid soils of pH 3.6 to 5.8. The beneficial effects of MnO_2 were attributed to an increase in the redox potential and reduced concentrations of Fe^{2+} and organic reduction products. Nhung & Ponnamperuma (336) noted that even after submergence, the pH levels of some acid soils do not rise above 6.0. At pH levels below 6.0 a reduced soil can contain 5000 ppm Fe^{2+} in the soil solution if the important solid phase is $Fe_3(OH)_8$; if FeS is the major solid phase, the concentration of Fe^{2+} depends on the pH and H_2S levels. In acid soils at pH 3.6 the death of rice seedlings was attributed to high concentrations of Al (68 ppm) and Fe^{2+} (490 ppm) in the soil solution at planting time, two weeks after submergence. Aluminum at 25 ppm and $Fe^{2+} > 500$ ppm are highly toxic to rice. Ferrous Fe concentrations > 400 ppm during most of the season were associated with toxicity. High salt (NaCl) concentrations aggravated the Fe toxicity disorder by causing physiological drought (336). Iron toxicity was overcome by liming to pH 5.0–5.5 at planting, to give a pH of 6.0 a few weeks after flooding. Application of MnO_2 counteracted Fe toxicity by decreasing the concentration of Fe^{2+} in solution. The addition of $Fe(OH)_3$ aggravated Fe toxicity. Ferrous Fe concentrations of 730 ppm in an acid soil solution killed rice plants one day after transplanting; 365 ppm of water-soluble Fe^{2+} at planting or 655 ppm 11 weeks after planting produced toxicity symptoms. However, water-soluble Mn concentrations as high as 1530 ppm at planting did not harm rice in the vegetative stage.

Iron toxicity (foliar injury) has been produced in cigar wrapper tobacco by sprinkler irrigation with pond water containing > 1.5 ppm Fe (363, 375). The excess ferrous Fe in the pond water was attributed to the reducing conditions created by excess growth of aquatic plants. Wallace & Bhan (444) suggested that some plants grow poorly in acid soils because of excess Fe absorption. Yields of hemp, mustard, asparagus, cucumber, spinach, squash, and alfalfa were subnormal for reasons other than, or in addition to, Al toxicity. Rogers (381) reported an Fe-induced Mn deficiency in Elberta peach. Brown & Jones (58) suggested that Fe toxicity limited the growth of Bragg soybean on an acid Richland soil at pH 5.2. Olsen (344) attributed the poor growth of hemp and mustard to Fe toxicity in certain acid soils (below pH 6.0).

SYMPTOMS OF FE TOXICITY   Symptoms of Fe toxicity are expressed differently in different plants. Millikan (311) noted that excess Fe in flax produced dark green foliage and stunted top and root growth. Roots were thickened and showed large accumulations of inorganically bound phosphate. Phosphate deficiency intensified the dark green color and excess P reduced it. These symptoms are very similar to those often described for Al toxicity. However, Skeen (397) maintained that Fe and Al were quite different in their effects on the roots of lupine and bean; he found that root tips were flabby with excess Fe and brittle with excess Al. In rice, Fe toxicity has been characterized by brown spots starting from the tips of lower leaves (414). The spots spread over these leaves, then progress to upper leaves. Eventually the lower leaves turn gray or white. Symptoms differ widely with age of plant, nutritional state, and cultivar. Iron toxicity is frequently difficult to identify by plant symptoms alone (414). In tobacco excess Fe produces brittle, tender, dark brown to purple leaves which have poor burning qualities and flavor (353, 375). In navy bean Fe toxicity associated with Zn deficiency produced black spots on the foliage (7, 8).

PHYSIOLOGY OF FE TOXICITY   In general, Fe toxicity is associated with increased Fe uptake and translocation by plant tops (58, 81, 90, 353, 375, 414, 418). For example, Rhoads (375) found that in tobacco plants injured by Fe toxicity, leaf strength decreased with increasing Fe content between 450 and 1126 ppm. Such leaves also contained lower Mn concentrations than normal (353). Tanaka & Yoshida (418) reported that the "bronzing" disease of rice was associated with accumulation of Fe in necrotic spots on leaves. "Freckle leaf" in sugarcane has also been associated with localized accumulations of Fe in leaves (90). High Mn/SiO_2 ratios in plant tissues seem to be associated with the disorder. Macadamia leaf chlorosis in acid soils of Hawaii has been related to high Fe and/or low Ca concentrations in plants. "Maui leaf freckling" of sugarcane has been associated with the accumulations of Fe, Al, and Mn and with low levels of SiO_2 in leaves (90). Apparently, plants high in Ca and SiO_2 can tolerate higher internal levels of Fe, Al, and Mn, perhaps by preventing localization into toxic spots. Clements (90) concluded that Si functions primarily as a detoxifier and is not essential for sugarcane if toxic factors are absent. Howeler (200) attributed bronzing in flooded rice to Fe-induced deficiencies of several essential elements, mainly P, K, Ca, and Mg on an oxisol. Aluminum contents were also higher in affected leaves, but there was no clear-cut relationship between Al concentration and degree of bronzing. Inaka (cited in 414) found that bronzed leaves of rice contained Fe concentrations that were 3–6 times as high as those of healthy leaves. The soils involved in producing bronzing in rice showed lower concentrations of K, Mn, and Si, and higher total sulfides, especially H_2S, in their solutions than did normal soils.

Mulleriyawa (326) indicated that Fe toxicity may cause bronzing, especially when the soil K level is low. He also suggested that excess H_2S could predispose plants to bronzing by reducing or inhibiting root respiration.

Tanaka et al (416, 417) stated that in the presence of high Fe concentrations in the medium, the rice root oxidizes Fe and deposits it on root surfaces. Root tips accumulate considerable amounts of Fe and translocate it to lower leaves if critical concentrations are exceeded. Cutting the roots increases Fe uptake and the degree of toxicity. The lowest Fe concentration found to produce Fe toxicity was 100 ppm at pH 3.7, but sometimes 500 ppm are required, depending upon many factors. Much less Fe is required to injure young seedlings than older plants. Root damage by H_2S may aggravate or predispose plant roots to Fe toxicity by destroying their oxidizing powers. The Fe contents of bronzed plants are usually high but not always. Even in nutrient solutions the critical Fe levels required to cause bronzing are difficult to determine. Susceptibility to bronzing is influenced by age, nutritional status, and form of Fe added. Diagnosis of Fe toxicity by Fe contents of plants is also difficult. Iron toxicity is more severe when K levels are low in the growth medium. Several of the physiological disorders in rice such as "bronzing" and "Alkagare 1" may have common causes. Differences in symptoms may be due to differences in varietal expressions of the toxicity (416, 417). Tadano (414) reported that Fe-intoxicated rice roots were higher in Fe and lower in K. Treatment with NaCl increased the Fe contents of rice shoots. This was attributed to a decrease in Fe retaining power (decreased oxidizing ability) of roots and not to Fe exclusion.

Differential Tolerance of Plants to Fe Toxicity

Plant species and genotypes within species differ in tolerance to Fe toxicity. For example, Skeen (396) found that *Lupinus alba* was three times as resistant to excess Fe and Al as *Phaseolus vulgaris*. Olsen (343) concluded that *Deschampsia flexuosa* and rye (*Secale cereale*) were more resistant to Fe toxicity than hemp, either in a soil at pH 4.0 or in nutrient solutions at pH 4.0 with low Ca levels. Greater Fe sensitivity in hemp was attributed to a more rapid Fe absorption rate. Moorman (317) noted that bananas and rice were more tolerant to excesses of both Fe and Al than sugarcane.

As might be expected, tolerance to Fe toxicity appears to coincide with tolerance to waterlogging in soils. Jones & Etherington (220) found that *Erica tetralix* was more tolerant to waterlogging than *Erica cinera*, L. The latter absorbed more Fe, and its cut shoots were more severely injured by ferric KEDTA than those of *E. tetralix*. Hence, the greater wet soil sensitivity of *E. cinera* was attributed to a greater sensitivity to Fe toxicity. Bartlett (23) obtained evidence that the roots of plant species tolerant to wet soil oxidized Fe more effectively and reduced its transport to plant tops more effectively than plants sensitive to wet soil. Alfalfa, which is sensitive to waterlogging, showed no ability to oxidize Fe. Reed canary grass and rice, which tolerate wet soils, were efficient oxidizers of Fe. Bartlett (23) suggested that wet-loving plants lower the toxicity of reduced substances such as Fe^{2+} by oxidation in the root zone.

Rice cultivars differ in resistance to Fe toxicity, and in general the upland cultivars are more sensitive to salinity, alkalinity, P deficiency, Zn deficiency, and reduction products, such as Fe^{2+}, than lowland cultivars (209). Nagai & Matono (330) showed a positive correlation between the weight of ferrous coating, total root weight, and root CEC in rice varieties that were resistant to soil-reducing conditions.

Singh (394) found that lines of navy bean (*Phaseolus vulgaris*, L.) differed in susceptibility to an Fe-induced Mn deficiency chlorosis. The Fe-tolerant (nonchlorotic) lines exuded less sap, and the sap contained higher Fe concentrations than those of Fe-susceptible (chlorotic) lines. However, the Fe-tolerant lines absorbed less total Fe than Fe-sensitive lines. Hence Fe/Mn ratios were lower in the sap of the Fe-tolerant (nonchlorotic) lines. It was concluded that the Fe-tolerant lines adjusted the ionic imbalance (between Fe and Mn) by reducing the total Fe transport through reducing the delivery rate of sap which is at the same time more concentrated in Mn. Odurukwe & Maynard (339) reported that the corn inbred line Ind. Wf 9 was more susceptible to Fe toxicity than Oh. 40B. Greater sensitivity of the Ind. Wf 9 was attributed to a higher concentration of available Fe within its tissues, as indicated by higher Fe:P and Fe:Mn ratios.

Bragg soybean was more susceptible to Fe toxicity in nutrient solutions than Forrest, Lee, and T203 cultivars (58, 59). Greater susceptibility of Bragg was associated with greater accumulation of Fe by plant tops (1320 ppm for Bragg versus 112 ppm for Forrest). The tops of Bragg soybean also accumulated higher concentrations of Fe than those of Forrest on a Mn-toxic Richland soil at pH 5.2 (249 vs 58 ppm) and on an Al-toxic Bladen soil at pH 4.3 (353 vs 54 ppm Fe). It was suggested that excessive Fe uptake limited growth of the Fe-efficient Bragg cultivar on the acid Richland soil. There was also evidence that high Fe concentrations within the tops of Bragg soybean intensified the Mn toxicity symptoms on this high Mn soil. Okamoto et al (341) reported that a strain of *Penicillium ochrochloron* having a high tolerance to excess Fe was also tolerant to Cu, Zn, Pb, and Cd, but sensitive to Hg, Ni, and Co.

Tadano (414) concluded that rice plants may escape Fe toxicity by lowering the Fe^{2+} concentration in the growth medium, excluding Fe^{2+} from the roots, and/or preventing Fe translocation from roots to tops. Rice roots can increase the Eh (reduction potential) of the soil solution and thereby decrease the concentrations of Fe^{2+}; however, this effect is partly offset by the fact that growing plants lower the pH of the medium. Plant-induced increases in Eh can be enhanced by K fertilization. Kumada (cited in 416) reported that rice roots secrete O_2 and oxidize Fe^{2+} to Fe^{3+}, and thereby prevent its penetration of critical root zones. Normal rice plants exclude excess Fe, and respiration inhibitors increase Fe uptake by roots. Salts (NaCl) reportedly reduce the power of excised roots to oxidize Fe^{2+} absorbed by roots. Salt treatments also decreased water uptake and increased Fe concentrations in shoots; total Fe absorption decreased, but the percentage of Fe translocated increased (414). Tolerance of plants to Fe toxicity is influenced by many factors, including age of plant, nutritional status, and plant genotype. Young plants are more susceptible than older plants (5 days vs 95 days). If plants are subjected to high Fe levels for long periods, Fe accumulates gradually in shoots. The ability to exclude excess Fe is lower in plants that are deficient in Ca, Mg, P, Mn, and especially K. The translocation rate of Fe is lower in N-deficient plants and higher in plants deficient in Mg, Mn, K, and Ca than in normal plants. Rice plants that are deficient in K, Ca, Mg, Mn thus accumulate more Fe in their shoots and are more susceptible to Fe toxicity than plants adequately supplied with these elements.

OTHER METAL TOXICITIES

Occurrence and Importance

Although any of the heavy metals can be toxic to plants at some level of solubility, only a few have been generally observed to cause phytotoxicity in soils. In soils, most heavy metals occur as inorganic compounds or are bound to organic matter, clays, or hydrous oxides of Fe, Mn, and Al (6, 123, 188, 214, 230, 270). Because of this precipitation and sorption of most metals by soils, only Zn, Cu, and Ni toxicities have occurred frequently. Toxicities of Pb, Co, Be, As, and Cd occur only under very unusual conditions. Other elements may be toxic in solution cultures but are not phytotoxic in soils, even at very high levels (e.g. Cr, Ag, Sn, Ga, and Ge). Lead and Cd are of interest not because of phytotoxicity, but because plant uptake moves them into the food chain (51, 284, 435). Thus most research on toxicity of heavy metals has involved Zn, Cu, Ni, Cd, and Pb.

NATURAL OCCURRENCE   Toxic metals occur naturally in soils because the parent materials contained the metals. Geochemical studies over ore deposits have shown many patterns of metal residues because of the nature of ore deposition and soil formation processes (6, 48, 188, 249). The science of biogeochemistry and the art of biogeochemical prospecting are based on the observations that plants and soils are often enriched in a metal over or near an ore deposit (64).

Phytotoxic levels of Zn have been studied in natural soils in several areas. Wallace & Hewitt (449) found Zn toxicity of cereal crops on calcareous soils in England. Several workers (63, 406, 407) reported Zn phytotoxicity to many crops growing on an acid peat deposit that is enriched in Zn, Cd, and Pb by geochemical processes.

High levels of Cu were found in a neutral pH peat swamp (117). Phytotoxicity occurred when the peat became aerobic, allowing CuS to be oxidized and Cu to become plant available (145). Nickel toxicity occurs naturally in some soils developed from serpentinite rocks (9, 168, 204, 462). Although most serpentine soils also cause a Mg/Ca imbalance in plants (361), those which have high Ni, adequate Ca, and low pH have caused Ni toxicity in the field.

In each of these cases (Zn, Cu, and Ni enriched soils), the diversity of plant species is severely restricted, and often edaphic ecotypes have evolved which are tolerant of the specific metal present in excess in the soil (15).

AIR AND WATER POLLUTION AS METAL SOURCES   Metals can impact soils and biota by deposition from polluted air. Many studies have been conducted on stack emissions of Zn, Cd, Cu, Pb, Ni, etc (17, 30, 61, 67, 113, 155, 207, 215, 216, 254, 275). Plants can become heavily contaminated by surface particulates. Generally, most metals are deposited within a few kilometers of the stack; however, significant depositions have been found as far away as 100 km. Automobile Pb emissions are generally restricted to 30 meters, but some automotive Pb is deposited beyond the Arctic circle (253, 255). Metal smelters, foundaries, steel mills, coal-fired power plants, and incinerators are demonstrated air emission sources for Cd, Pb, Zn, and Cu. Mine spoil, ore tailings, and transported ores can become fugitive dusts and move short distances through the air (113, 181, 253).

Water can become enriched in dissolved or suspended metals by natural processes or by man's activities. The Cd problem "Itai-Itai" disease (human) developed where stored ore tailings were released to a stream during storms; suspended particles then entered rice paddies downstream (245, 475). Huge amounts of Cd and Ni accumulated near a discharge pipe from a battery manufacturer at Foundry Cove, New York (45). Many dredge spoils are enriched in metals (as high as 1% Zn) because of water-borne sources (197, 261); subsequent deposition of the spoils on land leads to high metal contents and potential impact on plants (261).

AGRICULTURAL CHEMICALS AND URBAN WASTES AS METAL SOURCES Many materials ordinarily used in agriculture (fertilizers, pesticides, manure, limestone) as well as urban wastes (sewage sludge, refuse, fly ash, fluidized bed material, and composted sludge or refuse) contain significant quantities of heavy metals, much higher than levels in normal soils. Phytotoxicity or food chain impacts could result if metal-contaminated materials were applied, or if improper management subsequently occurred. Copper toxicity developed in Florida (373, 456) and elsewhere (104) when excessive Cu was applied to perennial citrus, banana, or grape orchards as both Cu fertilizer and pesticide (e.g. Bordeaux mixture). Similarly, Zn toxicity developed in soybean (259) and cotton (260) where Zn oxysulfate pesticide was sprayed on peach orchards.

Phosphorus fertilizers contain Cd at 2–200 ppm (148, 263, 321, 372, 465). Some mineralized limestone deposits contain Zn and Cd at ore-grade levels. Swine and poultry manures can contain high levels of Cu and Zn if Cu is added to replace antibiotics (19, 100). Sewage sludges often contain potentially toxic levels of metals and pose a considerable environmental metal risk if their use is unregulated (20, 36, 68, 73, 148, 149, 274, 297, 349, 455). Composted refuse and fly ash may produce metal toxicities or harmful levels of salinity or B (363). Rubber wastes can cause Zn toxicity (305). Burned tires and copper wire leave Zn and Cu residues (353). Other wastes can also supply metals to soils and crops (41, 52, 350).

An important consideration is the rate of metal addition to soils. Some processes add only very small amounts yearly (e.g. fertilizers); others (e.g. sewage sludge) can increase soil metals over 100-fold in one year. Some metal sources impact huge areas (fertilizer, pesticides, limestone); others impact only a small area each year (sludge).

Phytotoxicity

To evaluate meaningful physiological and biochemical effects of toxic metals, one must examine conditions (metal species and concentrations) relevant to phytotoxicity in nature (93). Much research reported was not based on proved relevant concentrations and species of metals. To assist the reader in evaluating or selecting metal concentrations and metal species used for phytotoxicity studies, the first part of this section reviews information on metal levels and species, metal movement from soil to root, and metal absorption and translocation.

SOIL FACTORS AFFECTING METAL TOXICITY   Plant availability of a metal in soil depends on soil adsorption strength as well as plant effectors such as root exudates for metal chelation or reduction. Concepts of metal equilibrium in soil, and of metal movement from soil to root, have been developing for many years.

Metal equilibria in soils   Lindsay and others (188, 189, 270–272, 389, 409) have developed models for the chemical activity of metal ions in soil. Activity is usually so dependent on pH that equilibrium activity (pMe) vs pH diagrams are used (the activity of divalent cations should be 100 times higher for each unit decrease in pH). The activity of the metal in question (pMe), which would be in equilibrium with specific inorganic compounds, is calculated from solubility data. The effect of changes in redox potential of the soil or in CO_2 concentration can be estimated: low redox potential allows sulfide compounds to form, CO_2 concentration affects metal carbonate equilibria, and phosphate concentrations and sorbing phases control metal phosphate equilibria.

Studies on Zn, Cu, and Cd have shown several complications for this chemical equilibrium model. First, metals sorbed by organic matter, clays, and hydrous oxides of Fe, Mn, and Al cause the metal activity to be considerably lower than equilibrium values for known inorganic compounds. If crystalline inorganic compounds are formed from heavy metals added to soils, the metals would be less plant-available because only surface metals are influenced by root processes. Second, soluble low-molecular weight chelates of the metals are formed in soil solution; this keeps the free metal ion activity low (in equilibrium with strongly bound adsorbed metal ions), but increases the soluble metal concentration manyfold. Most soluble Cu, Zn (152, 190, 191) and Cd (409) are chelated (up to 99 + %). Both adsorption and chelation are strongly affected by soil pH; at acid pH, soil metals are naturally much more plant available although they may not be in nutrient solutions. Most surface-bound metals remain in equilibrium with the chelated soluble metals in the soil solution (available to plants in the "labile pool") (157, 427).

Several other soil factors play a role in metal binding, although these are much less important than pH. The organic matter, clay, and hydrous oxides can adsorb metals (123, 349); soils with higher metal sorption capacity have lower potential for plant uptake of metals (306–308).

Movement of metals from soil to plant roots   Metal phytotoxicity can result only if metals can move from the soil to plant roots. Several authors (22, 72, 272, 277, 464) have summarized the movement process. Barber (22) has described a model for this movement by using metals, while most other models have been applied only to macronutrients (62). Metals in the soil solution (free ions, ion pairs, or chelates) can move with the soil water (convection or mass-flow) as the plant absorbs water for transpiration. If the rate of plant absorption of metals exceeds the rate of arrival by convection, a depletion zone is created at the root and the concentration gradient promotes diffusion from the soil to the root. Hodgson (189), Lindsay (272), and Elgawharry et al (122) have noted the importance of low molecular-weight soluble chelating compounds in both convection and diffusion of metals. For some metals, inorganic Cl^- can promote complex formation (150, 166); chloride salts of added metals or fertilizers can then cause artifacts (65, 173, 309). Besides the role of chelators (which could be formed during decomposition of organic wastes used as fertilizers, of crop residues, or of organic materials released by growing roots), numerous other factors affect metal diffusion: soil pH; metal concentration and strength of absorption; soil texture; soil bulk density; soil moisture content; and concentration of other nutrients and cations. Growing roots can cause local pH and bulk density changes which affect metal convection and diffusion rates. Roots can alter the pH of the soil in the "rhizocylinder" as much as several pH units (400). As noted above, changes in soil pH near the root can strongly affect metal movement to the root. Root release of reducing polyphenols or chelators can release metals from Fe, Mn, and Al oxide surfaces (55).

Another important concept is the "labile pool" (157). Metals in the labile pool are in equilibrium with those being absorbed by plants from the soil solution. The metals Zn, Cu, Ni, and Cd appear to remain in the labile pool for extended periods rather than forming crystalline, insoluble compounds. However, crystalline inorganic compounds appear to be formed in calcareous soils that have low organic matter and low cation exchange capacity (409).

Metals may interact with macronutrients and other metals in both the adsorption equilibria and the diffusion/convection process. Very little study of metal movement to roots has been reported for high to toxic levels of soil metals.

METAL ABSORPTION   Metals may be actively absorbed, absorbed via passive diffusion due to ion activity gradients, or even inadvertently accumulated by an active mechanism by which a macronutrient cation is generally absorbed. Nearly all study to date has been conducted at low to deficient metal supply; active processes specific for individual metals are likely to be less important in metal absorption at high than at low metal supply.

The results of single salt uptake studies seem especially irrelevant in studies of metal toxicity. If in soil solution nearly all soluble metals are chelated, the plant would have to compete with chelators for the metal, or the intact metal chelate would have to enter the root. This has been a very controversial area of study. Chelators added to nutrient solutions reduce metal activity and metal uptake dramatically (103, 116, 144, 169, 170). Chelators have been used to estimate the affinity for metals of the metal uptake system in plant roots. If the activity of Zn is $10^{-10.6}$ M (170) or the activity of Cu is 10^{-13} M (116) in complete nutrient solutions, corn can obtain adequate amounts of Zn and Cu for full growth rates. At lower activities (obtained by increasing chelator:metal ratio) corn was deficient in Zn or Cu even though the total supply was nominally adequate. On the other hand, chelators added to soils can increase soluble metals manyfold and promote metal convection and diffusion and hence potential for uptake and toxicity (272, 338, 447). The levels of Cu, Co, and Cd in snap beans reported by Wallace et al (446–448) for plants grown on metal- and chelator-amended soils were so high that uptake of metal chelates seemed a reasonable explanation (increased diffusion and convection rates seem equally explanatory).

Competition among metals both for chelation (272, 338), and hence movement to the root, and for uptake at the root (314, 315, 344) have been reported. Further interactions occur between metals and nutrients and metals and soluble salts. Interactions could vary with crop and soil. If metal toxicity inhibited root growth, absorption of elements like P, K, and Fe could be reduced because they are mostly absorbed by diffusion; this is an indirect interaction, and as discussed below, may be an important mechanism in metal phytotoxicity.

METAL TRANSLOCATION   Translocation of metals from roots to tops remains poorly characterized. Perhaps the most important process, release from root cells to the xylem, is so difficult to study that little is known about release to the xylem of even macronutrient cations. However, experiments have shown some characteristics of metal translocation relevant to the physiology of metal toxicity.

The most characterized phenomenon is chemical species of metals appearing in the flowing xylem sap. Tiffin (425, 426) has reviewed this research. Briefly, a model of chelation equilibria among cations and low molecular weight chelators (organic and amino acids) has been developed (169, 425, 426). Citrate binds all Fe in xylem exudate (425). Other metals having lower stability constants with natural xylem sap chelators, or with lower metal/Ca stability constant ratios (e.g. Zn, Mn, Co), generally do not form insoluble chelates. Exchange rates of the components of metal chelates limit analysis by electrophoretic or chromatographic separation. However, because metal chelates are formed between organic and amino acids and Zn, Mn, and Co, chelate species can be predicted based on stability constants, competing cations, activities, etc [see Halvorsen & Lindsay (169)]. Alternatively, Tiffin (423, 425) demonstrated Zn chelation by observing the electrophoretic mobility of $^{65}Zn^{2+}$ in xylem exudates vs neutral salt electrolytes. Anionic species predominated in the exudate electrolyte, while in the absence of the natural chelators only a cation was seen in the salt electrolyte. The concentration of organic and amino acids in flowing xylem sap should always be high enough to hold metals soluble under normal conditions. However, plant species vary widely in levels of specific natural chelating compounds. Furthermore, the effects of phytotoxic levels of metals on this process have not been evaluated for Zn, Mn, Co, or Cd.

Translocation of Cu and Ni now appears to involve a specific chelator (424–426). Unidentified nonaromatic polyaminopolycarboxylic acids carried all of the Cu (even under phytotoxic conditions) and most of the Ni in the xylem exudate of tomato and perhaps other species. Work is progressing on the chemistry of these compounds (422, 426), but their physiology needs study too. What factors control release of metal ions, metal chelates, and chelators to the xylem under both normal and phytotoxic conditions? What is the fate of natural metal chelates in the soil solution in relation to plant uptake and translocation? Tiffin found that with excessive Cu supply, all xylem Cu was bound to the unknown chelator; however, with excessive Ni supply, tomato xylem sap contained insufficient amounts of this chelator to carry all the Ni (424, 425). The Ni would then be chelated by other organic and amino acids. If excessive Cu or Ni were supplied in soils, what would the translocated metal species be? Although much knowledge has accumulated in this area in the last decade, we still lack a fundamental knowledge of the chemistry and physiology of metal translocation—especially under metal toxicity conditions.

Jarvis et al (212) found that the roots of some crops (lettuce, cress, etc) released much more of their absorbed Cd for translocation to the shoots than other crops (ryegrass, orchardgrass, timothy, parsnip). The chemistry and physiology of these species differences are unclear. Is greater translocation due to active transport or to lack of metal sorption to fixed or soluble chelators in the root? Or is it perhaps due to exchange with the Ca, Mn, and Zn moving through the roots (215)?

Translocation of Pb also reveals a complicated interaction among nutrients and plant metabolism. Plants growing on nutrient-deficient Pb mine spoils and waste heaps can have extremely high foliar Pb (218, 219). In fertile soils, huge amounts of added Pb had little effect on foliar Pb (25). Precipitation of Pb phosphates, especially in phosphate-rich organelles, seemed an obvious explanation to this fertility difference (285); higher soil phosphate fertility reduced foliar Pb in corn (306), but was unrelated to foliar Pb in soybean (309). Besides the "obvious" but inconsistent effect of phosphate on foliar Pb levels, an important role of sulfate status has been reported (223, 224); although sulfate would logically seem to have its effect through sulfur-containing amino acids (and in protein), this relationship remains untested.

Besides the effects of soil sorption differences (306, 307), soil pH, phosphate, and sulfate status, a seasonal effect on Pb translocation has been observed. During late fall and winter, foliar Pb is considerably increased (up to tenfold) in orchardgrass and clover (312) and fescue (177). Although this seasonal increase is consistently observed, its physiology remains unexplained in terms of uptake or translocation processes.

Chemical species of other elements in the translocation system are also being characterized. Plants fed ^{51}Cr-chromate translocated only chromate (282); however, in both roots and leaves chromic compounds accumulated, predominantly trisoxalatochromium (III) (283). Chromium species in other plants may be very different from those in this Cr-accumulator crop.

SYMPTOMS OF PHYTOTOXICITY AND THEIR INTERACTIONS WITH NUTRIENT ELEMENTS   Ideally, each metal causing phytotoxicity would cause some characteristic symptom that would allow its diagnosis; further, the symptom would be apparent before substantial economic or ecologic damage occurred. Unfortunately, this is not the case.

The most general symptoms are stunting and chlorosis. The chlorosis may appear to be Fe-deficiency chlorosis, and the interactions of toxic metals and Fe have been studied for many years. Chlorosis from excess Zn, Cu, Ni, and Cd appears to be due to a direct or an indirect interaction with foliar Fe. For these and other elements, painting chlorotic leaves with $FeSO_4$ alleviates the chlorosis (78, 162, 185, 186); Fe chelates have been used to correct Cu toxicity in Florida (265, 275). Analysis of chlorotic, young foliage (after careful washing to remove soil contamination) showed low foliar Fe when soils or solutions contained toxic Cu (401), Ni, or Co (337), Cu or Ni (388), or Cd (165). Excessive Zn and Cu added in sludge cause similar chlorosis (75, 280). When Zn and possibly when Cd cause phytotoxicity, chlorosis is observed only at low pH (76), or when neutral soils have low plant-available Fe (57); young, symptom-bearing leaves usually have Fe concentrations much higher than those normally considered adequate (382, 386, 457). This result indicates that the chlorosis is not always a simple, Zn-induced inhibition of Fe translocation from roots to tops, although this inhibition can be demonstrated (8). Still, the chlorosis can be alleviated by painting the leaves with Fe. Root et al (382) felt that Cd-induced chlorosis might be due to changes in Fe:Zn ratios in corn leaves.

White et al (458) observed that increased soil Zn greatly increased translocation of Mn to soybean tops. They hypothesized that the Zn and Mn interfere with Fe utilization in the leaves for chlorophyll synthesis. Furthermore, a Zn-induced Mn-toxicity symptom (crinkle leaf) was seen in soybean (1, 458).

The Fe deficiency induced by excess toxic metals is affected by (a) climatic and soil conditions other than those which affect metal toxicity (279); (b) phosphorus status of the soil and plants (57, 405); and (c) Fe status of the soil (57, 373). Excess Cu caused severe chlorosis in Florida on Lakeland sand low in Fe (374, 405), whereas phytotoxic levels of Cu did not cause any visual symptoms on Plainfield sand in Wisconsin (451). When ground rubber tires caused Zn-toxicity-induced chlorosis, the chlorosis was corrected by adding Fe (305). On soils low in Mn, Zn excess can contribute to Mn deficiency (264, 430).

However, Zn toxicity does not always cause chlorosis. Working with Fe-sufficient neutral pH soils, Boawn & Rasmussen (43) and Boawn (42) failed to see chlorosis in any of 20 crops studied. They thought they found Zn-induced P deficiency (43). Although cereals suffered severe Fe-deficiency chlorosis on Zn-toxic calcareous soils (449), rye was not chlorotic when severely injured by Zn, Cu, and Mn on an acid soil (236).

Specific symptoms for individual metals have been reported. A unique pattern of chlorosis and necrosis in oat is caused by excess Ni (205); oat has been used repeatedly as a Ni toxicity indicator crop (9, 168) even though it is not extremely sensitive to Ni (204). These specific symptoms have recently been found to interact strongly with soil Mg level (362). An accumulation of a purple pigment, specific for Cd toxicity, starting at the pulvini of soybean leaves, has been reported (77). Additionally, a Cd-induced curling of stems of red kidney bean was reported (208). Other general aspects of symptoms have been described by Chapman (79) and Hewitt (187).

The stunting commonly observed with metal toxicity can be due to a specific toxicity of the metal to the crop, antagonism with other nutrients in the crop, or inhibition of root penetration in the soil. For most of the metals considered, toxicity is first experienced in the root tips. Lateral root development is severely restricted (50, 98). If root length is restricted, then nutrients such as P, K, Fe, etc [which are generally absorbed by diffusion rather than convection (22)] could fall to growth-limiting levels. Furthermore, all these observations are subject to climatic effects which can intensify or lessen symptoms (279), e.g. seasonal soil temperature and moisture content patterns.

Symptoms may be masked or enhanced by other factors. Crop cultivars differing in susceptibility to Fe deficiency show different responses to excessive Zn and Cu; these differential responses were exhibited by soybean, corn, tomato, and sorghum cultivars (55, 59, 60). Navy bean cultivars differentially showed Fe-deficiency chlorosis when excessive Zn or Cu was supplied (357). Spring growth may be green and the leaves later become chlorotic (371). A more general pattern is severe chlorosis of seedling leaves when the seed Fe stores are depleted; subsequently, if roots reach subsoils with adequate available Fe, the plant recovers from chlorosis. Usually metal tolerance of the seedling is critical to survival.

Air pollutants may induce similar symptoms and/or interact synergistically with toxic metals to reduce yields. Czuba & Ormrod (96) reported on interactions of ozone with Cd and Zn. Similar interactions are found for SO_2 with Ni or Cu. With the air pollutant $\times$ metal interactions, symptoms are severe at concentrations of ozone or metals that would have caused little or no symptoms in the absence of the other factor.

Interactions between soil Fe, soil P, and added Cu are observed in Cu-induced chlorosis of citrus (405). At low P, severe stunting but little chlorosis resulted; at high P, stunting was largely corrected, but chlorosis was severe. Brown & Jones (60) discussed the potential impact of high annual P fertilizer applications on soils with low available Fe for crops like sorghum; if metal toxicity stress were superimposed on existing P-Fe interactions, chlorosis would result.

PHYSIOLOGY AND BIOCHEMISTRY OF METAL PHOTOTOXICITY   Studies on the physiology of metal toxicity are difficult. Not only are concentrations of soluble metals in cell cytoplasm unknown, but the activity of a given metal in the cytoplasm is affected by chelating carboxylic and amino acids, by cations other than the metal in question, and by pH. Experiments that do not account for these important factors cannot be considered physiologically relevant. This is why the above information on soil-plant interactions in the movement of metals to the plant was included in this general review. These are constraints on physiologically meaningful experiments. The physiology of metal toxicity begins with increased metal supply to the roots and proceeds to a failure of a clearly defined "essential-to-life" plant process.

Unfortunately, very little work has been conducted to identify which "essential-to-life" processes are sensitive to metals. Most knowledge on metal toxicity has been achieved by studying the physiology of ecotypic tolerance of metals (see below). Most other work has involved nonphysiological conditions and study of organelles. Although the study of isolated organelles has led to a better understanding of physiological processes, achieving realistic metal levels, chemical species, and ion activity in buffer solutions has proved too difficult.

Failure to reach physiological conditions has been most severe in studies of Pb toxicity. As noted above, Pb is strongly sorbed by soils, forms insoluble crystalline compounds in soils (389), and hence seldom reaches high levels in leaves or roots. One exception is P-deficient Pb mine soils (219). Freshly added Pb salts are more readily available to plants (306, 307, 309), but high levels of Pb from long-term automobile Pb deposition (173, 252) or Pb sprays (221) have little effect on Pb uptake by plants. If the P status of a soil is adequate for normal plant growth, plants do not accumulate Pb (25); phosphate forms insoluble Pb compounds in soils and roots.

With this background, how does one conduct a Pb toxicity study? Many workers have supplied Pb and P in culture solutions on alternating days to avoid precipitation of Pb. By using dilute flowing nutrient solutions, Jones et al (223, 224) avoided the Pb precipitation problem; comparing these results with those of soil solutions is difficult. Since Pb toxicity occurs only in Pb mine soils, their soil solutions should be compared with those of normal soils.

Some researchers have studied Pb toxicity and uptake by plants after adding $PbCl_2$ to soils (65, 174, 246, 306, 307). Unfortunately, Pb forms a soluble chloride complex (166); adding the chloride influences soil solution Pb concentrations and alters the distribution of chemical species of Pb in the soil solution. In short-term experiments, this should be expected to lead to increased plant uptake and even to Pb phytotoxicity. But this toxicity remains nonphysiological.

Malone et al (285) observed the formation of Pb-rich deposits in dictyosome vesicles of corn exposed to high levels of Pb. No deposits were found in mitochondria, plastids, or nuclei; mitochondria accumulate huge amounts of Pb if exposed in vitro (40). The apparent removal of Pb from cells via dictyosome vesicles could be an important Pb excretion process; further study under physiological conditions seems warranted. Hampp et al (172) reported on the effects of Pb on enzymes of the reductive pentose phosphate pathway; others have reported on the effects of Pb on transpiration, nodulation, gas exchange, photosynthesis, respiration, etc (26, 28, 40, 66, 202). Whether specific effects of Pb on these processes will be observed under environmentally and physiologically relevant conditions is unknown.

The same problems exist for study of most metals; study of Cd is especially subject to problems. Cadmium availability is strongly influenced by soil pH, Eh, presence of chelators, presence of Cl⁻, etc (74, 150, 166, 409, 415). Because of the need to protect the food chain from excessive Cd, Cd phytotoxicity will seldom be allowed to result from man's activities. Although ecotypic Cd tolerance has been observed (393), it occurred jointly with Zn and Pb tolerances because of the natural joint occurrence of these metals in ore deposits. Although many physiological studies have been reported (27, 93, 171, 202, 246, 262, 310), their relevance is uncertain. Cadmium appears to be absorbed passively (95) and translocated freely (212). Chelators in nutrient solutions confound Cd uptake (144). Pronounced interactions occur between Zn and Cd and Ca and Cd in Cd uptake and translocation (74, 77, 217, 253). Apparently, part of Cd toxicity is a result of Cd interference in a Zn-dependent process (128, 383). Certainly, study at chronic toxic levels is more meaningful than work only at acute toxic levels (91, 94).

The physiology and biochemistry of Zn, Cu, and Ni toxicity have received little study beyond the responses of intact plants. Generally these elements cause chlorosis (3, 79); Cu and Ni cause an actual Fe deficiency by inhibiting translocation of Fe from roots to tops (70, 273, 445). While Zn inhibits Fe translocation in some cases (8), young Zn-toxic chlorotic leaves generally contain more than 100 ppm Fe; true Fe deficiency generally occurs at $\leq$ 40 ppm Fe in young leaves. While most crops develop Fe deficiency from excess Cu, others show wilting and other root injury effects first; Cu and Ni phytotoxicity strongly influence root development and metabolism (97–99, 167, 325, 404, 410). Few details of the biochemistry of these systems are understood. If soils contain high available Fe when Cu is supplied in excess, Fe can be translocated to leaves in substantial amounts. Whether or not Cu in leaves interferes with photosynthesis (69) etc is unclear. Copper is so strongly chelated that it seems unlikely that foliar Cu would cause direct toxicity. However, root Cu can become extremely high before foliar Cu is increased substantially. Poor nutrient absorption and translocation can reduce crop yields when root growth is so strongly inhibited.

Some interesting interactions have been noted: because added Ni causes a physiological Zn deficiency, small amounts of Zn counteract low-level Ni toxicity (37); Cd and Cu interfere with Zn uptake and translocation (176). Because Fe stress causes plants to increase their potential for uptake and translocation of Fe manyfold, plants subjected to intermediate toxic levels of Zn and Ni have increased uptake of ^{59}Fe from ^{59}Fe chelates; at higher metal levels, the toxicity also interferes with the Fe-stress response.

Several important experimental approaches to the physiology of metal toxicity have remained untried. By examining the effect of metal supply on the metabolism of specifically labeled organic compounds, one can characterize whether certain pathways are inhibited by a metal in vivo. By determining levels of specific compounds in the leaves, one can assess the metabolic state of the leaf in relation to metal supply. Chemical species and compartmentalization of metals at toxic levels are largely unknown.

Our understanding of competitive inhibition of metalloenzymes will increase as they are characterized in plants and studied in vivo for the effects of metal toxicity on their activity (e.g. displacement of the metal activator). The recent identification of a Ni metalloenzyme (356), urease, illustrates how little is now known about plant metalloenzymes and their physiology.

Differential Plant Tolerance to Heavy Metals

Evolution of plants tolerant to heavy metals has become an increasingly studied topic. Although much information has been accumulated, most applies only to ecotypic species. Little information is available on crop plants.

DIFFERENTIAL TOLERANCE AMONG CULTIVARS OF CROP PLANTS   Earley (118) reported that soybean cultivars responded differentially to toxic Zn in sand culture. The plants suffered Fe deficiency, with tolerant strains less injured than susceptible strains. The nutrient solution he used supplied little available Fe, and Earley actually characterized differential susceptibility to Zn effects on Fe-stress response (8, 57, 457). White (457) characterized these cultivar differences further, and found that they were associated with differences in susceptibility to Zn-induced Fe deficiency, Zn uptake and translocation, and susceptibility to toxicity unrelated to Fe deficiency. Reciprocal grafts have also shown that shoots confer tolerance to Zn excess (457), in contrast to Fe-inefficient cultivars which differ in Zn effect on root phenomena. Polson & Adams (357) also found that shoots conferred Zn tolerance to navy bean cultivars. In these studies, Zn and Mn translocation and interactions also differed; however, shoot differences clearly predominated in controlling Zn tolerance. Little is known of the biochemistry of differential tolerance of any metals in crop plants.

DIFFERENTIAL TOLERANCE OF METALS AMONG ECOTYPES

Characteristics   Within many plant species, individuals tolerant to high substrate metal levels have evolved. This phenomenon has been studied extensively for Zn, Cu, Ni, and Pb (15, 16, 64, 159, 390, 391, 442). Ecotype tolerance has even been found for As (380) and Cd (393). Usually the plants have developed tolerance to only the metals present in excess; one apparent exception is the co-tolerance of Ni by Zn-tolerant bentgrasses (159). On Zn and Pb mine soils, most Zn- and Pb-tolerant ecotypes were also Cd-tolerant (393), but Cd is usually present in substantial amounts in these soils.

Tolerant individuals generally display a range of tolerance. Tolerance usually is well correlated with available metals in the soils where the plants occur. Recently tolerance without ecotype development has been suggested (301, 472). Little information on available metal levels was provided in these studies, and soil factors were often antagonistic to toxicity. The preceding sections on plant availability of metals in soils should provide a background on how important the soil pH, organic matter, and phosphate status are in controlling metal phytotoxicity.

For example, tolerance developed only in individuals on strongly acid soils near a Cu ore roasting area (194, 195). One species may require tolerant ecotypes to colonize a toxic soil, while another species may not (286). If researchers would use a named cultivar of a crop plant for comparison studies, and do pH adjustment and nutrient factorial studies with suspected tolerant crops, the role of apparent tolerance to soluble metal salts in nutrient solution would be much clearer.

Ecotypes can develop very rapidly; Wu & Bradshaw (473) found ecotypes in areas polluted for fewer than 20 years. Ecotypes tolerant to Pb developed along a roadside (472), and ecotypes tolerant to Zn developed under galvanized fences, etc. The sharpness of boundaries between tolerant and nontolerant individuals is especially interesting. Under fences, Zn-tolerant individuals continued to exist in a 20 cm band on either side of the fence; a few centimeters away nontolerant individuals thrived (15). McNeilly (302) reported on Cu tolerance on a small Cu mine soil area; the boundary was very sharp upwind, but tolerant seed were produced 100 meters downwind. Walley et al (450) found that "common" seed of colonial bentgrass produced individuals fully Cu-tolerant and nearly fully Zn-tolerant as compared with mine soil ecotypes; the inherited tolerance was independent because only a very low percentage of Cu-tolerant plants were also Zn-tolerant. Gartside & McNeilly (151) found that Cu tolerance was not present in all crops; agronomically important crops either developed only intermediate Cu-tolerance or failed to develop tolerance. Although "common" seed of colonial bentgrass contained Zn-tolerant plants, a named variety did not (203).

One beneficial use of these metal-tolerant crops would be revegetation of metal-toxic mine wastes and other areas polluted by man's activities. Several helpful reports are available on successful use of metal-tolerant ecotypes in this way (203, 216). Usually coupling metal-tolerant seed with proper pH adjustment and fertilization results in rapid revegetation. Metal-tolerant legumes are needed to make this a long-term successful practice.

Physiological and biochemical mechanisms of tolerance   Mechanisms of metal tolerance by plants have been studied for some time. At first, exclusion from roots seemed a likely mechanism because root cell walls bound metals. The extent of binding by the cell wall was related to the degree of tolerance to a specific metal (354, 431–434). Jones et al (225) even isolated a Zn complex from roots of Zn-tolerant bentgrass after digesting the roots with cellulase. Although binding metals to root cell walls may contribute to metal tolerance, it is not sufficient to enable the plants to prevent metal transport to their leaves (219, 442). In fact, copper flower may transport Cu from its roots to its tops to protect its roots from excess Cu (199, 371).

Transport to a compartment where toxic metals are removed from cell cytoplasm may be a protective device. Nickel accumulates to 25% of the dry weight of the latex of a New Caledonian Ni accumulator (210). Ernst (127) and Mathys (288) favor the compartmentalization hypothesis and suggest that malate may chelate Zn in the vacuoles of tolerant plants (289–291). However, data supporting this physical distribution of a metal are lacking. It is hoped that electron microprobe studies on ecotypes of several species, conducted along with chemical measurements and several levels of metal supply, will clarify the importance of these hypotheses. The fact that high malate, Zn-tolerant ecotypes are not tolerant of Cu is difficult to understand since malate would be expected to bind Cu much more strongly than it does Zn.

Differential metal tolerance of enzymes from ecotypes has also been studied. Soluble acid phosphatases did not differ in sensitivity to Zn (92); however, cell wall-bound acid phosphatases in tolerant and nontolerant ecotypes differed considerably in sensitivity to metals. A detailed consideration of improved methods to conduct these comparisons was presented by Wainwright & Woolhouse (442). Organelle-related processes should also differ in metal tolerance (474). Mathys (289) and Ernst (127) have reported the most detailed studies to date on metal tolerance of enzymes from tolerant and nontolerant ecotypes. They found no differences in metal tolerance of enzymes in in vitro studies, i.e. no "resistant enzymes." However, in in vivo studies, the activities of several enzymes were maintained at normal levels in tolerant ecotypes as metal supply increased, but activities fell markedly in nontolerant ecotypes. This confirms that tolerant plants were able to maintain normal processes when subjected to metal stress which severely interfered with the metabolism of nontolerant plants. Mathys and Ernst believed this resulted from compartmentalization of absorbed metals which protected the cytoplasm.

Studies on mechanisms of tolerance of higher plant ecotypes should benefit by knowledge generated in studies of microbes. Ashida (16) and Ross (387) considered tolerance mechanisms of fungi. Some precipitate Cu at their cell wall by generating sulfide (16, 234, 235). Furthermore, these cells seem to produce a Cu-binding thionein protein similar to metallotheoneins in animals (332).

Other cells adapt to metal stress by excluding toxic metals. *Chlorella* that exclude Cu were reported by Foster (133). Bacteria appear to develop resistance to Ni and Co by reducing their Mg carrier activity; this is indirect evidence that these metals ordinarily enter on the Mg carrier when supplied in toxic doses (334, 454). These two metals may not form the sulfides that protect fungi (341). The role of intranuclear metal-binding proteins in protecting organisms is an exciting new observation (392); this could protect the cells from interference in metabolic and genetic processes. However, vacuolar compartmentalization may be sufficiently effective for higher plants.

CONCLUSIONS

Metal toxicities in plants are often not clearly identifiable entities; instead, they may be the results of complex interactions of the major toxic ions in question with other essential or nonessential ions and with other environmental factors.

Although excesses of various metals may produce some common effects on plants in general, there are many cases of specific differential effects of individual metals on different plant genotypes. Such occurrences must be recognized in approaching any problem of metal toxicity. It now seems likely that the phytotoxic mechanisms of a given metal ion involve different biochemical pathways in different plant species and varieties.

Once the genetic control mechanisms of metal tolerance are identified, it may be possible to combine metal tolerance with other desirable traits to produce plants that are better adapted to high metal soils. Such problems are often not economically correctable with conventional fertilization and liming practices. Furthermore, the selection of near-isogenic lines may provide valuable tools for studying specific biochemical mechanisms of tolerance. Once these mechanisms are better understood, it may be possible to select or breed, even more precisely, those plants having greatest tolerance to a particular metal toxicity. Such biochemical knowledge concerning metal tolerance mechanisms could also lead to the development of improved chemical (fertilization, liming, organic matter, etc) and physical (tillage, drainage, etc) management practices for problem soils.

In the past, much of the research on the physiological mechanisms of ion uptake and use have been confined to a single plant genotype or species. We suggest that this approach should be replaced with comparative physiological studies between closely related genotypes (near isogenic lines, if possible) of the same species which differ widely in tolerance to a given metal toxicity.

Differential cultivar tolerances to metal toxicity almost certainly involve differences in the structure and function of membranes. But such differences are extremely difficult to measure in living plants. Any fractionation, extraction, or tissue fixation procedure used will introduce the possibility of measuring only artifacts. Electron microscope procedures involving the use of X-ray emission can determine the physical location of metal ions (having an atomic weight of 24 or above) in root sections, provided that membranes have not been disturbed during tissue preparation. Other promising approaches in studying metal toxicity in tolerant and sensitive plant genotypes include determining the chemical compartmentalization of metals in various plant fractions, levels and kinds of organic and amino acids which may act as metal chelators and detoxifiers, NH_4^+ vs NO_3^- tolerance or preference (in relation to pH change and metal ion activities in root zones and plant fractions), levels and forms of enzymes, and changes in root permeabilities to ions and molecules.

The research proposed above requires close collaboration between soil scientists, plant breeders, plant physiologists, plant biochemists, and perhaps pathologists. Until recently such cooperation has been rare in both state and federal institutions concerned with agricultural research. A multi-disciplinary approach is now essential if world food needs are to be met.

Literature Cited

1. Adams, F., Wear, J. I. 1957. Manganese toxicity and soil acidity in relation to crinkle leaf of cotton. *Soil Sci. Soc. Am. Proc.* 21:305–8

2. Agarwala, S. C. 1977. Absorption, translocation and utilization of iron and molybdenum in plants. *Final Rep. US P.L. 480 Proj. A7-SWC-75*

3. Agarwala, S. C., Bisht, S. S., Sharma, C. P. 1977. Relative effectiveness of certain heavy metals in producing toxicity and symptoms of iron deficiency in barley. *Can. J. Bot.* 55:1299–1307

4. Aizer, R. S., Rajagopel, C. K., Money, N. S. 1975. Available zinc, copper, iron, and manganese status of the acid rice soils of Kuttanad, Kerala State. *Agric. Res. J. Kerala* 13:15–19

5. Ali, S. M. E. 1973. *Influence of cations on aluminum toxicity in wheat (Triticum aestivum, Vill. Host).* PhD thesis. Oregon State Univ. Corvallis, Ore.

6. Allaway, W. H. 1968. Agronomic controls over the environmental cycling of trace elements. *Adv. Agron.* 20:235–74

7. Ambler, J. E., Brown, J. C. 1969. Cause of differential susceptibility to zinc deficiency in two varieties of navy beans (*Phaseolus vulgaris* L.). *Agron. J.* 61: 41–43

8. Ambler, J. E., Brown, J. C., Gauch, H. G. 1970. Effect of zinc on translocation of iron in soybean plants. *Plant Physiol.* 46:320–23

9. Anderson, A. J., Meyer, D. R., Mayer, F. K. 1973. Heavy metal toxicities: levels of nickel, cobalt, and chromium in the soil and plants associated with visual symptoms and variation in growth of an oat crop. *Aust. J. Agric. Res.* 24:557–71

10. Andrew, C. S., Hegarty, M. P. 1969. Comparative responses to manganese excess of eight tropical and four temperate pasture legume species. *Aust. J. Agric. Res.* 20:687–96

11. Andrew, C. S., Johnson, A. D., Sandland, R. L. 1973. Effect of aluminum on the growth and chemical composition of some tropical and temperate pasture legumes. *Aust. J. Agric. Res.* 24:325–39

12. Andrew, C. S., Pieters, W. H. J. 1970. Manganese toxicity symptoms of one temperate and seven tropical pasture legumes. *Tech. Pap. Div. Trop. Pastures* 4:2–8 (Trop. Abstr. 1971, No. 377).

13. Andrew, C. S., Pieters, W. H. J. 1976. Foliar symptoms of mineral disorders in *Glycine wightii. CSIRO Aust. Div. Trop. Agron. Tech. Pap.* 18:1–12

14. Andrew, C. S., Vandenberg, P. J. 1973. The influence of aluminum on phosphate sorption by whole plants and excised roots of some pasture legumes. *Aust. J. Agric. Res.* 24:341–51

15. Antonovics, J., Bradshaw, A. D., Turner, R. G. 1971. Heavy metal tolerance in plants. *Adv. Ecol. Res.* 7:1–85

16. Ashida, J. 1965. Adaptation of fungi to metal toxicants. *Ann. Rev. Phytopathol.* 3:153–74

17. Ashton, W. M. 1972. Nickel pollution. *Nature* 237:46–47

18. Awad, A. S., Edwards, D. G., Milhain, P. J. 1976. Effect of pH and phosphate on soluble soil aluminum and on growth and composition of Kikuyu grass. *Plant Soil* 45:531–42

19. Baker, D. E. 1974. Copper: Soil, water, plant relationships. *Fed. Proc.* 33: 1188–93

20. Baker, D. E., Chesnin, L. 1976. Chemical monitoring of soils for environmental quality and animal and human health. *Adv. Agron.* 27:305–74

21. Baranowska, H., Ejchart, A., Putrament, A. 1977. Manganese mutagenesis in yeast. V. On mutation and conversion induction in nuclear DNA. *Mutat. Res.* 42:343–45

22. Barber, S. A. 1974. Influence of the plant root on ion movement in soil. In *The Plant Root and Its Environment,* ed. E. W. Carson, pp. 525–64. Charlottesville: Univ. Press Virginia

23. Bartlett, R. J. 1960. Iron oxidation proximate to plant roots. *USDA, ARS, SWC, East. Soil Water Manage. Res. Branch Field Location Ann. Rep.* Burlington, Vt., pp. 15–16

24. Bartlett, R. J., Riego, D. C. 1972. Effect of chelation on the toxicity of aluminum. *Plant Soil* 37:419–23

25. Baumhardt, G. R., Welch, L. F. 1972. Lead uptake and corn growth with soil-applied lead. *J. Environ. Qual.* 1:92–94

26. Bazzaz, F. A., Carlson, R. W., Rolfe, G. L. 1974. The effect of heavy metals on plants: Part I. Inhibition of gas exchange in sunflower by Pb, Cd, Ni, and Ti. *Environ. Pollut.* 7:241–46

27. Bazzaz, F. A., Rolfe, G. L., Carlson, R. W. 1974. Effect of cadmium on photosynthesis and transpiration of excised leaves of corn and sunflower. *Physiol. Plant.* 32:373–76

28. Bazzaz, F. A., Rolfe, G. L., Windle, P. 1974. Differing sensitivity of corn and soybean photosynthesis and transpiration to lead contamination. *J. Environ. Qual.* 3:156–58

29. Beaton, J. D. 1973. Fertilizer methods and applications to forestry practice. Forest Fert. Symp. Proc., *USDA For. Serv. Gen. Tech. Rep. NE-3, 55-71*

30. Beavington, F. 1975. Heavy metal contamination of vegetables and soil in domestic gardens around a smelting complex. *Environ. Pollut.* 9:211–17

31. Benac, R. 1976. Effect of manganese concentration in the nutrient solution on groundnuts (*Arachis hypogaea (L.) Oleagineax* 31:539–43 (Fr:Eng)

32. Benac, R. 1976. Response of a sensitive (*Arachis hypogaea*) and a tolerant (*Zea mays*) species to different concentrations of manganese in the environment. *Cah. ORSTOM Ser.* 11:43–51, (Fr:Eng)

33. Berezovskii, K. K., Klimashevskii, E. L. 1975. Assimilation of nitrogen by two pea cultivars differing in their sensitivity to Al³⁺. *Sib. Vestn. Skh. Nauki* 4:22–26 (Russ:Eng)

34. Berg, W. A., Vogel, W. G. 1973. Toxicity of acid coal-mine spoils to plants. In *Ecology and Reclamation of Disturbed Lands,* ed. R. J. Hutnik, G. Davis, 1:57–68. New York: Gordon & Breach

35. Bernatskaya, M. L., Klimashevskii, E. L., Lapteva, T. I., Shmulevskaya, T. A. 1976. Effect of aluminum on respiration activity of surface phosphatases in growing parts of pea roots. *Fiziol. Biokhim. Kul't. Rast.* 8:25–29 (Russ:Eng)

36. Berrow, M. L., Webber, J. 1972. Trace elements in sewage sludges. *J. Sci. Food Agric.* 23:93–100

37. Berry, W. L. 1976. The effects of zinc on the dose response curve of seedling lettuce to acute Ni toxicity. *Agron. Abstr.* 1976:20

38. Bhatt, K. C., Vaishnav, P. P., Singh, Y. D., Chinoy, J. J. 1976. Reversal of gibberellic acid-induced inhibition of root growth by manganese *Biochem. Physiol. Pflanz.* 170:453–55

39. Bieleski, R. L. 1971. Enzyme changes in plants following changes in their mineral nutrition. *Plant Anal. Fert. Probl. Abstr. 6th Int. Colloq. Tel Aviv., Israel,* pp. 143–53

40. Bittell, J. E., Koeppe, D. E., Miller, R. J. 1974. Sorption of heavy metal cations by corn mitochondria and the effects on electron and energy transfer reactions. *Physiol. Plant.* 30:226–30

41. Blood, J. W. 1963. Problems of toxic elements in crop husbandry. NAAS *Q. Rev.* 14(59):97–100

42. Boawn, L. C. 1971. Zinc accumulation characteristics of some leafy vegetables. *Commun. Soil Sci. Plant Anal.* 2:31–36

43. Boawn, L. C., Rasmussen, P. E. 1971. Crop response to excessive zinc fertilization of alkaline soil. *Agron. J.* 63:874–76

44. Bollard, E. G., Butler, G. W. 1966. Mineral nutrition of plants. *Ann. Rev. Plant Physiol.* 17:77–112

45. Bondietti, E. A., Sweeton, F. H., Tamura, T., Perhac, R. M., Hulett, L. D., Kneip, T. J. 1974. Characterization of cadmium and nickel contaminated sediments from Foundry Cove, New York. *Proc. 1st Ann. NSF Trace Contam. Conf.,* pp. 211–24

46. Borkenhagen, J. E., Iyer, J. G. 1972. Aluminum sulfate as a stabilizer of nursery stock development. *J. For.* 70:33–34

47. Bortner, C. 1935. Manganese toxicity in tobacco. *Soil Sci.* 39:15–33

48. Bowen, H. J. M. 1966. *Trace Elements in Biochemistry.* New York: 241 pp.

49. Bowen, J. E. 1972. Manganese-silicon interaction and its effect on growth of sudan grass. *Plant Soil* 37:577–88

50. Brams, E. A., Fiskell, J. G. A. 1971. Copper accumulation in citrus roots and desorption with acid. *Soil Sci. Soc. Am. Proc.* 35:772–75

51. Braude, G. L., Jelinek, C. F., Corneliussen, P. 1975. FDA's review of the potential health hazards associated with the land application of municipal waste water sludges. *Proc. Natl. Conf. Munic. Sludge Manage. Disposal,* pp. 214–17. Rockville, Md: Information Transfer

52. Bremner, I. 1974. Heavy-metal toxicities. *Q. Rev. Biophys.* 7:75–124

53. Bremner, I., Knight, A. H. 1970. The complexes of zinc, copper, and manganese present in ryegrass. *Br. J. Nutr.* 24:279–89

54. Brown, J. C. 1963. Interactions involving nutrient elements. *Ann. Rev. Plant Physiol.* 14:93–106

55. Brown, J. C., Ambler, J. E. 1973. "Reductants" released by roots of Fe-deficient soybeans. *Agron. J.* 65:311–14

56. Brown, J. C., Ambler, J. E., Chaney, R. L., Foy, C. D. 1972. Differential responses of plant genotypes to micronutrients. In *Micronutrients in Agriculture,* ed. J. J. Mortvedt, P. M. Giordano, W. L. Lindsay, pp. 389–418. Madison, Wis: Soil Sci. Soc. Am.

57. Brown, J. C., Jones, W. E. 1975. Heavy metal toxicity in plants. 1. A crisis in embryo. *Commun. Soil Sci. Plant Anal.* 6:421–38
58. Brown, J. C., Jones, W. E. 1977. Manganese and iron toxicities dependent on soybean variety. *Commun. Soil Sci. Plant Anal.* 8:1–15
59. Brown, J. C., Jones, W. E. 1977. Fitting plants nutritionally to soils. I. Soybeans. *Agron. J.* 69:399–404
60. Brown, J. C., Jones, W. E. 1977. Fitting plants nutritionally to soils, III. Sorghum. *Agron. J.* 69:410–14
61. Buchauer, M. J. 1973. Contamination of soil and vegetation near a zinc smelter by zinc, cadmium, copper, and lead. *Environ. Sci. Technol.* 7:131–35
62. Claassen, N., Barber, S. A. 1976. Simulation model for nutrient uptake from soil by a growing plant root system. *Agron. J.* 68:961–64
63. Cannon, H. L. 1955. Geochemical relations of zinc-bearing peat to the Lockport dolomite, Orleans County, New York. *Geol. Surv. Bull.* 1000-D:119–85
64. Cannon, H. L. 1960. Botanical prospecting for ore deposits. *Science* 132: 591–98
65. Carlson, R. W., Bazzaz, F. A. 1977. Growth reduction of American sycamore (*Plantanus occidentalis* L.) caused by Pb-Cd interaction. *Environ. Pollut.* 12:243–53
66. Carlson, R. W., Bazzaz, F. A., Rolfe, G. L. 1975. The effect of heavy metals on plants: Part II. Net photosynthesis and transpiration of whole corn and sunflower plants treated with Pb, Cd, Ni, and Ti. *Environ. Res.* 10:113–20
67. Cartwright, B., Merry, R. H., Tiller, K. G. 1976. Heavy metal contamination of soils around a lead smelter at Port Pirie, South Australia. *Aust. J. Soil Res.* 15:69–81
68. CAST. 1976. Application of sewage sludge to cropland: Appraisal of potential hazards of the heavy metals to plants and animals. *Counc. Agric. Sci. Technol., Ames, Iowa, Rep. 64.* 63 pp.
69. Cedeno-Maldonade, A. J., Swader, J. A., Heath, R. L. 1972. The cupric ion as an inhibitor of photosynthetic electron transport in isolated chloroplasts. *Plant Physiol.* 508:698–701
70. Chaney, R. L. 1970. *Effect of nickel on iron metabolism by soybean.* PhD thesis. Purdue Univ., Lafayette, Ind. 192 pp. *Diss. Abstr. Int.* 31:1692–93
71. Chaney, R. L. 1973. Crop and food chain effects of toxic elements in sludges

and effluents. In *Recycling Municipal Sludges and Effluents on Land,* pp. 129–41. Washington, DC: Natl. Assoc. State Univ. Land Grant Coll.
72. Chaney, R. L. 1975. Metals in plants-absorption mechanisms, accumulation, and tolerance. *Proc. Symp. Metals Biosphere,* pp. 79–99. Guelph, Ontario: Dep. Land Resource Sci., Univ. Guelph
73. Chaney, R. L., Giordano, P. M. 1977. Microelements as related to plant deficiencies and toxicities. In *Soils for Management and Utilization of Organic Wastes and Waste Waters,* ed. L. F. Elliot, F. J. Stevenson, pp. 233–80. Madison, Wis: Am. Soc. Agron., Soil Sci. Soc. Am. 672 pp.
74. Chaney, R. L., Hornick, S. B. 1978. Accumulation and effects of cadmium on crops. In *Proc. 1st Int. Cadmium Conf. Metals Bull.* (London), pp. 125–40
75. Chaney, R. L., Hundeman, P. T. 1977. The influence of application rate of a leached high-metal sewage sludge, soil pH, and crop species on phytotoxicity and crop metal contents. *Agron. Abstr.* p. 23
76. Chaney, R. L., White, M. C., Simon, P. W. 1975. Plant uptake of heavy metals from sewage sludge applied to land. In *Proc. 2nd Natl. Conf. Munic. Sludge Manage.,* pp. 167–78. Rockville, Md: Information Transfer
77. Chaney, R. L., White, M. C., van Tienhoven, M. 1976. Interaction of Cd and Zn in phytotoxicity and uptake by soybean. *Agron. Abstr.* 1976:21
78. Chapman, H. D. 1966. Diagnostic criteria for plants and soils. Riverside: Univ. California, Div. Agric. Sci. 793 pp.
79. Chapman, H. D., Liebig, G. F. Jr., Vanselow, A. P. 1939. Some nutritional relationships as revealed by a study of mineral deficiency and excess symptoms on citrus. *Soil Sci. Soc. Am. Proc.* 4:196–200
80. Chenery, E. M., Sporne, K. R. 1976. A note on the evolutionary status of aluminum accumulation among dicotyledons. *New Phytol.* 76:551–54
81. Chin, T. F. 1966. Iron and manganese absorption by rice plants. *Soils Fert. Taiwan,* 1–6
82. Clark, R. B. 1975. Characterization of phosphatase in intact maize roots. *Agric. Food. Chem.* 23:458–60
83. Clark, R. B. 1975. Differential magnesium efficiency in corn inbreds. I. Dry matter yields and mineral element composition. *Soil Sci. Soc. Am. Proc.* 39: 488–91

84. Clark, R. B. 1977. Effect of aluminum on growth and mineral elements of Al-tolerant and Al-intolerant corn. *Plant Soil* 47:653–62

85. Clark, R. B., Brown, J. C. 1974. Differential phosphorus uptake by phosphorus stressed corn inbreds. *Crop Sci.* 14:505–8

86. Clarkson, D. T. 1965. The effect of aluminum and some trivalent metal cations on cell division in the root apices of *Allium cepa*. *Ann. Bot.* 29:309–51

87. Clarkson, D. T. 1966. Effect of aluminum on the uptake and metabolism of phosphorus by barley seedlings. *Plant Physiol.* 41:165–72

88. Clarkson, D. T. 1969. Metabolic aspects of aluminum toxicity and some possible mechanisms for resistance. In *Ecological Aspects of the Mineral Nutrition of Plants*, ed. I. H. Rorison, pp. 381–97. Oxford, Edinburg: Blackwell

89. Clarkson, D. T., Sanderson, J. Jr. 1969. The uptake of a polyvalent cation and its distribution in the root apices of *Allium cepa*. Tracer and autoradiographic studies. *Planta* 89:136–54

90. Clements, H. F., Putnam, E. W., Suehisa, R. H., Yee, G. L. N., Wehling, M. L. 1974. Soil toxicities as causes of sugarcane leaf freckle, macadamia leaf chlorosis (Keaau) and Maui sugarcane growth failure. *Hawaii Agric. Exp. Stn. Tech. Bull. 88.* 52 pp.

91. Collins, F. W., Cunningham, L. M., Hutchinson, T. C. 1976. Physiological and biochemical aspects of cadmium toxicity in soybean. Part II. Toxicity, bioaccumulation, and subcellular fractionation of cadmium in soybean grown at subchronic to acute cadmium levels. In *Trace Substances in Environmental Health*, ed. D. D. Hemphill, 10:145–66. Columbia: Univ. Missouri

92. Cox, R. M., Thurman, D. A., Brett, M. 1976. Some properties of the soluble acid phosphatases of roots of zinc-tolerant and non-tolerant clones of *Anthoxanthum odoratum*. *New Phytol.* 77:547–52

93. Cunningham, J. D., Keeney, D. R., Ryan, J. A. 1975. Phytotoxicity and uptake of metals added to soils as inorganic salts or in sewage sludge. *J. Environ. Qual.* 4:460–62

94. Cunningham, L. M., Collins, F. W., Hutchinson, T. C. 1976. Physiological and biochemical aspects of cadmium toxicity in soybean. Part I. Toxicity symptoms and autoradiographic distribution of cadmium in roots, stems, and leaves. *Proc. Int. Conf. Heavy Metals in Environ.* 2(1):97–120

95. Cutler, J. M., Rains, D. W. 1974. Characterization of cadmium uptake by plant tissue. *Plant Physiol.* 54:67–71

96. Czuba, M., Ormrod, D. P. 1974. Effects of cadmium and zinc on ozone-induced phototoxicity in cress and lettuce. *Can. J. Bot.* 52:645–49

97. Daniels, R. R., Struckmeyer, B. E. 1973. Copper toxicity in *Phaseolus vulgaris* L. as influenced by iron nutrition. III. Partial alleviation by sucinnic acid 2,2-dimethyl hydrazide. *J. Am. Soc. Hortic. Sci.* 98:449–52

98. Daniels, R. R., Struckmeyer, B. E., Peterson, L. A. 1972. Copper toxicity in *Phaseolus vulgaris* L. as influenced by iron nutrition. I. An anatomical study. *J. Am. Soc. Hortic. Sci.* 97:249–54

99. Daniels, R. R., Struckmeyer, B. E., Peterson, L. A. 1973. Copper toxicity in *Phaseolus vulgaris* L. as influenced by iron nutrition. II. Elemental and electron microprobe analysis. *J. Am. Soc. Hortic. Sci.* 98:31–34

100. Davis, G. K. 1974. High-level copper feeding of swine and poultry and the ecology. *Fed. Proc.* 33:1194–96

101. Davis, W. B., McCauley, M. J., Byers, B. R. 1971. Iron requirements and aluminum sensitivity of hydroxamic acid requiring strain of *Bacillus megaterium*. *J. Bacteriol.* 105:589–94

102. Dedov, V. M., Klimashevskii, E. L. 1976. On the mechanism of genotypic resistance of plants to Al^{3+}. 2. Effect of Al ions on pH redox potential and the content of high energy phosphorus in root tissues of peas. *Sib. Vestn. Skh. Nauki* 3:13–16 (Russ:Eng)

103. DeKock, P. C., Mitchell, R. L. 1957. Uptake of chelated metals by plants. *Soil Sci.* 84:55–62

104. Delas, J. 1963. The toxicity of copper accumulating in soils. *Agrochimica* 7:258–88

105. Dennis, D. 1968. Manganese toxicity in tomatoes. *NZ J. Agric.* 117:118–19

106. Dessureaux, L. 1959. Heritability of tolerance to manganese toxicity in lucerne. *Euphytica* 8:260–65

107. Devine, T. E., Foy, C. D., Fleming, A. L., Hanson, C. H., Campbell, T. A., McMurtrey, J. E. III, Schwartz, J. W. 1976. Development of alfalfa strains with differential tolerance to aluminum toxicity. *Plant Soil* 44:73–79

108. Dieckert, J. W., Rozacky, E. 1969. Isolation and partial characterization of manganin, a new manganoprotein from

peanut seeds. *Arch. Biochem. Biophys.* 134:473–77

109. Dionne, J. L., Pesant, A. R. 1976. Effects of pH and water regime on the yield and Mn content of lucerne and birdsfoot trefoil grown in the glasshouse. *Can. J. Plant Sci.* 56:919–28 (Fr:Eng)

110. Dobereiner, J. 1966. Manganese toxicity effects on nodulation and fixation in beans (*Phaseolus vulgaris,* L.) in acid soils. *Plant Soil* 24:153–66

111. Dodge, C. D., Hiatt, A. J. 1972. Relationship of pH to ion uptake imbalance by varieties of wheat (*Triticu n vulgare,* L.) *Agron. J.* 64:476–77

112. Doi, Y. 1952. Studies on the oxidizing power of roots of crop plants. 1. The differences of crop plants and wild grasses. 2. Interrelation between paddy rice and soybean. *Proc. Crop Sci. Soc. Jpn* 21:12–13, 14–15 (Jap:Eng)

113. Dorn, C. R., Pierce, J. O., Chase, G. R., Phillips, P. E. 1975. Environmental contamination by lead, cadmium, zinc, and copper in a new lead-producing area. *Environ. Res.* 9:159–72

114. Doss, B. D., Lund, Z. F. 1975. Subsoil pH effects on growth and yield of cotton. *Agron. J.* 67:193–96

115. Douka, C. E. 1977. Study of bacteria from manganese concentrations, precipitation of manganese by whole cells and cell free extracts of isolated bacteria. *Soil Biol. Biochem.* 9:89–97

116. Dragun, J., Baker, D. E., Risius, M. L. 1976. Growth and element accumulation by two single-cross corn hybrids as affected by copper in solution. *Agron. J.* 68:446–70

117. Dykeman, W. R., de Sousa, A. S. 1966. Natural mechanisms of copper tolerance in a copper swamp forest. *Can. J. Bot.* 44:871–78

118. Earley, E. B. 1943. Minor element studies with soybeans. I. Varietal reactions to concentrations of zinc in excess of the nutritional requirement. *J. Am. Soc. Agron.* 35:1012–23

119. Edwards, J. H., Horton, B. D., Kirkpatrick, H. C. 1976. Aluminum toxicity symptoms in peach seedlings. *J. Am. Soc. Hortic. Sci.* 101:139–42

120. Eenink, A. H., Garretsen, G. 1977. Inheritance of insensitivity of lettuce to a surplus of exchangeable manganese in steam sterilized soils. *Euphytica* 26: 47–53

121. Eggert, D. A., Hayden, R. A. 1970. Histochemical relationship of manganese

to internal bark necrosis of apple. *J. Am. Soc. Hortic. Sci.* 95:715–19

122. Elgawhary, S. M., Lindsay, W. L., Kemper, W. D. 1970. Effect of complexing agents and acids on the diffusion of zinc to a simulated root. *Soil Sci. Soc. Am. Proc.* 34:211–14

123. Ellis, B. G., Knezek, B. D. 1972. Adsorption reactions of micronutrients in soils. See Ref. 56, pp. 59–78

124. Engler, R. M., Patrick, W. H. 1975. Stability of sulfides of manganese, iron, zinc, copper, and mercury in flooded and non-flooded soil. *Soil Sci.* 119: 217–21

125. Epstein, E. 1969. Mineral metabolism of halophytes. See Ref. 88, pp. 345–53

126. Epstein, E., Jeffries, R. L. 1964. The genetic basis of selective ion transport in plants. *Ann. Rev. Plant Physiol.* 15: 169–84

127. Ernst, W. H. O. 1977. Physiology of heavy metal resistance in plants. See Ref. 94, 2(1):121–36

128. Falchuk, K. H., Fawcett, D. W., Vallee, B. L. 1975. Competitive antagonism of cadmium and zinc in the morphology and cell division of *Euglena gracilis. J. Submicrosc. Cytol.* 7:139–52

129. Ferree, D. C., Thompson, A. H. 1970. Internal bark necrosis of the apple as influenced by calcium placement and soil manganese. *Univ. Maryland Agric. Exp. Stn. Bull. A-166*

130. Finn, I. J., Bourget, S. H., Nielson, K. F., Dow, B. K. 1961. Effects of different soil moisture tensions on grass and legume species. *Can. J. Soil Sci.* 41: 16–23

131. Fisher, A. G., Eaton, G. W., Porritt, S. W. 1977. Internal bark necrosis of Delicious apple in relation to soil pH and leaf manganese. *Can. J. Plant Sci.* 57: 297–99

132. Fleming, A. L. 1975. *Characterization of acid phosphatase activity in wheat varieties differing in P efficiency.* ASA Abstr. Ann. Meet., p. 70

133. Foster, P. L. 1977. Copper exclusion as a mechanism of heavy metal tolerance in a green alga. *Nature* 269:322–23

134. Foy, C. D. 1973. Manganese and plants. In *Manganese,* pp. 51–76. Washington, DC: Natl. Acad. Sci., Nat. Res. Counc. 191 pp.

135. Foy, C. D. 1974. Effects of aluminum on plant growth. See Ref. 22, pp. 601–42

136. Foy, C. D. 1974. Effects of soil calcium on plant growth. See Ref. 22, pp. 565–600

137. Foy, C. D. 1978. Acid soil toxicity. Effect of nutrient deficiencies and toxicities in plants. In *Handbook of Nutrition and Food.* Chemical Rubber Co. Press. In press

138. Foy, C. D. 1977. General principles involved in screening plants for aluminum and manganese tolerance. In *Plant Adaptation to Mineral Stress in Problem Soils,* ed. M. J. Wright, S. A. Ferrari, pp. 255–67. Special Publ. Cornell Univ. Agric. Exp. Stn., Ithaca, NY. 420 pp.

139. Foy, C. D., Fleming, A. L. 1978. *The physiology of plant tolerance to excess available aluminum and manganese in acid soils.* Presented at symp. on *Crop Tolerance to Sub-optimal Land Conditions.* ASA Meet., Houston, 1976. In press

140. Foy, C. D., Fleming, A. L., Armiger, W. H. 1969. Differential tolerance of cotton varieties to excess manganese. *Agron. J.* 61:690–94

141. Foy, C. D., Fleming, A. L., Gerloff, G. C. 1972. Differential aluminum tolerance in two snapbean varieties. *Agron. J.* 64:815–18

142. Foy, C. D., Fleming, A. L., Schwartz, J. W. 1973. Opposite aluminum and manganese tolerances in two wheat varieties. *Agron. J.* 65:123–26

143. Foy, C. D., Gerloff, G. C., Gabelman, W. H. 1973. Differential effects of aluminum on the vegetative growth of tomato cultivars in acid soil and nutrient solution. *J. Am. Soc. Hortic. Sci.* 98:427–32

144. Francis, C. W., Rush, S. G. 1974. Factors affecting uptake and distribution of cadmium in plants. See Ref. 91, 7:75–81

145. Fraser, D. C. 1961. A syngenetic copper deposit of recent age. *Econ. Geol.* 56:951–62

146. Freire, J. R. 1977. Inoculation of soybeans. In *Exploiting the Legume-Rhizobium Symbiosis in Tropical Agriculture,* ed. J. M. Vincent, A. S. Whitney, J. Bose, pp. 335–80. Coll. Trop. Agric. Misc. Publ. 145. Dep. Agron. Soil Sci. Univ. Hawaii, Kahului, Maui, Hawaii

147. Frith, G. J. T. 1972. Effect of ammonium-nutrition on the activity of nitrate reductase in the roots of apple seedlings. *Plant Cell Physiol.* 13:1085–90

148. Fulkerson, W., Goeller, H. E. 1973. *Cadmium—The Dissipated Element.* NTIS No. ORNL-NSF-EP-21. 473 pp.

149. Furr, A. K., Kelly, W. C., Bache, C. A., Gutenmann, W. H., Lisk, D. J. 1976. Multi-element absorption by crops grown in pots on municipal sludge-amended soil. *J. Agric. Food Chem.* 24:889–92

150. Garcia-Miragaya, J., Page, A. L. 1976. Influence of ionic strength and inorganic complex formation on the sorption of trace amounts of Cd by montmorillonite. *Soil Sci. Soc. Am. J.* 40:658–63

151. Gartside, D. W., McNeilly, T. 1974. The potential for evolution of heavy metal tolerance in plants. II. Copper tolerance in normal populations of different plant species. *Heredity* 32:335–48

152. Geering, H. R., Hodgson, J. F. 1969. Micronutrient cation complexes in soil solution: III. Characterization of soil solution ligands and their complexes with Zn^{2+} and Cu^{2+}. *Soil Sci. Soc. Am. Proc.* 33:54–59

153. Gerloff, G. C. 1963. Comparative mineral nutrition of plants. *Ann. Rev. Plant Physiol.* 14:107–24

154. Gigon, A., Rorison, I. H. 1972. The response of some ecologically distinct plant species to nitrate and to ammonium nitrogen. *J. Ecol.* 60:93–102

155. Gingell, S. M., Campbell, R., Martin, M. H. 1976. The effect of zinc, lead, and cadmium pollution on the leaf surface microflora. *Environ. Pollut.* 11:25–37

156. Gonik, S. A., Klimashevskii, E. L. 1974–1975. Effect of Al ions on contents of SH and SS groups in roots of two pea cultivars. *Biologiya* 1 (1975) 4 G196:1974 269–77

157. Graham, E. R. 1973. Selective distribution and labile pools of micronutrient elements as factors affecting plant uptake. *Soil Sci. Soc. Am. Proc.* 37:70–74

158. Graven, E. H., Attoe, O. J., Smith, D. 1965. Effects of liming and flooding on manganese toxicity in alfalfa. *Soil Sci. Soc. Am. Proc.* 29:702–6

159. Gregory, R. P. G., Bradshaw, A. D. 1965. Heavy metal tolerance in populations of *Agrostis tenuis* Sibth. and other grasses. *New Phytol.* 64:131–43

160. Greidamus, T., Peterson, L. A., Schrader, L. E., Dana, M. S. 1972. Essentiality of ammonium for cranberry nutrition. *J. Am. Soc. Hortic. Sci.* 97:272–77

161. Grime, J. P., Hodgson, J. G. 1969. An investigation of the significance of lime chlorosis by means of large scale comparative experiments. See Ref. 88, pp. 67–99

162. Guest, P. L., Chapman, H. D. 1944. Some effects of pH on the growth of

citrus in sand and solution cultures. *Soil Sci.* 58:455–65

163. Gupta, U., Chipman, E. W. 1976. Influence of iron and pH on the yield and iron, manganese, zinc and sulfur concentrations of carrots grown on sphagnum peat soil. *Plant Soil* 44:559–66

164. Gupta, U., Chipman, E. W., MacKay, D. C. 1970. Influence of manganese and pH on chemical composition, bronzing of leaves, and yield of carrots grown on acid sphagnum peat soil. *Soil Sci. Soc. Am. Proc.* 34:762–64

165. Haghiri, F. 1973. Cadmium uptake by plants. *J. Environ. Qual.* 2:93–96

166. Hahne, H. C. H., Kroontje, W. 1973. Significance of pH and chloride concentration on behavior of heavy metal pollutants: mercury (II), cadmium (II), zinc (II), and lead (II). *J. Environ. Qual.* 2:444–50

167. Hallsworth, E. G., Yates, M. G., Cansfield, P. E., Saul, J. T. 1965. Studies in the nutrition of the forage legumes. V. The effects of variation of copper supply on the concentrations of copper, manganese and iron present in *T. Subterraneum* grown in sand culture. *Plant Soil* 23:323–36

168. Halstead, R. L. 1968. Effect of different amendments on yield and composition of oats grown on a soil derived from serpentine materials. *Can. J. Soil Sci.* 48:301–5

169. Halvorsen, A. D., Lindsay, W. L. 1972. Equilibrium relationships of metal chelates in hydroponic solutions. *Soil Sci. Soc. Am. Proc.* 36:755–61

170. Halvorsen, A. D., Lindsay, W. L. 1977. The critical Zn^{2+} concentration for corn and the nonabsorption of chelated zinc. *Soil Sci. Soc. Am. J.* 41:531–34

171. Hampp, R., Beulich, K., Ziegler, H. 1976. Effects of zinc and cadmium on photosynthetic CO_2 fixation and Hill activity of isolated spinach chloroplasts. *Z. Pflanzenphysiol.* 77:336–44

172. Hampp, R., Ziegler, H., Ziegler, I. 1973. Influence of lead ions on the activity of enzymes of the reductive pentose phosphate pathway. *Biochem. Physiol. Pflanzen* 164:588–95

173. Hassett, J. J., Miller, J. E. 1977. Uptake of lead by corn from roadside samples. *Commun. Soil Sci. Plant Anal.* 8: 49–55

174. Hassett, J. J., Miller, J. E., Koeppe, D. E. 1976. Interaction of lead and cadmium on maize root growth and uptake of lead and cadmium by roots. *Environ. Pollut.* 11:297–302

175. Havill, D. C., Lee, J. A., Stewart, G. R. 1974. Nitrate utilization by species from acidic and calcareous soils. *New Phytol.* 73:122–23

176. Hawf, L. R., Schmid, W. E. 1967. Uptake and translocation of zinc by intact plants. *Plant Soil* 27:249–60

177. Haye, S. N., Horvath, D. J., Bennett, O. L., Singh, R. 1976. A model of seasonal increase of lead in a food chain. See Ref. 91, 9:387–93

178. Heenan, D. P., Carter, O. G. 1976. Tolerance of soybean cultivars to manganese toxicity. *Crop Sci.* 16:389–91

179. Heenan, D. P., Carter, O. G. 1977. Influence of temperature on the expression of manganese toxicities by two soybean varieties. *Plant Soil* 47:219–27

180. Heintze, J. G. 1968. Manganese phosphate reactions in aqueous systems and the effects of application of monocalcium phosphate on the availability of manganese to oats in alkaline fan soil. *Plant Soil* 24:407–23

181. Hemphill, D. D., Marienfeld, C. J., Reddy, R. S., Heilage, W. D., Pierce, J. O. 1973. Toxic heavy metals in vegetables and forage grasses in the Missouri Lead Belt. *J. Assoc. Off. Anal. Chem.* 56:994–98

182. Henning, S. J. 1975. *Alumium toxicity in the primary meristem of wheat roots.* PhD thesis. Oregon State Univ., Corvallis, Ore.

183. Hesse, P. R. 1963. Phosphorus relationships in mangrove swamp mud with particular reference to aluminum toxicity. *Plant Soil* 19:205–18

184. Hewitt, E. J. 1948. The resolution of factors in soil acidity. IV. The relative effects of aluminum and manganese toxicities on some farm and market garden crops. *Ann. Rep. Long Ashton Agric. Hortic. Res. Stn.,* pp. 58–65

185. Hewitt, E. J. 1948. Relation of manganese and some other metals to the iron status of plants. *Nature* 101: 489–90

186. Hewitt, E. J. 1953. Metal interrelationships in plant nutrition. 1. Effects of some metal toxicities on sugar beet, tomato, oat, potato, and narrowstem kale grown in sand cultures. *J. Exp. Bot.* 4:59–64

187. Hewitt, E. J. 1966. Sand and water culture methods used in the study of plant nutrition. *Commonw. Bur. Hortic. Plant Crops (Gr. Br.) Tech. Commun. 22.* 547 pp. 2nd ed.

188. Hodgson, J. F. 1963. Chemistry of the micronutrient elements in soil. *Adv. Agron.* 15:119–59

189. Hodgson, J. F. 1969. Contribution of metal-organic complexing agents to the transport of metals to roots. *Soil Sci. Soc. Am. Proc.* 33:68–75

190. Hodgson, J. F., Geering, H. R., Norvell, W. A. 1965. Micronutrient cation complexes in soil solution: I. Partition between complexed and uncomplexed forms by solvent extraction. *Soil Sci. Soc. Am. Proc.* 29:665–69

191. Hodgson, J. F., Lindsay, W. L., Trierweiler, J. F. 1966. Micronutrient cation complexing in soil solution: II. Complexing of zinc and copper in displaced solution from calcareous soils. *Soil Sci. Soc. Am. Proc.* 30:723–26

192. Hoffer, G. N., Trost, J. F. 1923. The accumulation of Fe and Al compounds and its probable relation to root rot. *Agron. J.* 15:233–30

193. Hofner, W. 1970. Elsen und manganhatlige verbindungen in blutungssaft von *Helianthus annuus*. *Physiol. Plant.* 23:673–77

194. Hogan, G. D., Courtin, G. M., Ravser, W. E. 1977. Copper tolerance in clones of *Agrostis gigantae* from a mine waste site. *Can. J. Bot.* 55:1043–50

195. Hogan, G. D., Courtin, G. M., Ravser, W. E. 1977. The effects of soil factors on the distribution of *Agrostis gigantea* on a mine waste site. *Can. J. Bot.* 55:1038–42

196. Holding, A. J., Lowe, J. F. 1971. Some effects of acidity and heavy metals on the rhizobium-leguminous plant association. *Plant Soil,* Spec. vol., pp. 153–66

197. Holmes, C. W., Slade, E. A., McLerran, C. J. 1974. Migration and redistribution of zinc and cadmium in marine estuarine systems. *Environ. Sci. Technol.* 3:255–59

198. Horton, B. D., Kirkpatrick, H. C. 1976. Aluminum toxicity symptoms in peach trees. *J. Am. Soc. Hortic. Sci.* 101:139–42

199. Howard-Williams, C. 1972. Factors influencing copper tolerance in *Becium homblei. Nature* 237:171

200. Howeler, R. H. 1973. Iron-induced oranging disease of rice in relation to physiochemical changes in a flooded oxisol. *Soil Sci. Soc. Am. Proc.* 37:898–903

201. Howeler, R. H., Cadavid, L. F. 1976. Screening of rice cultivars for tolerance to Al-toxicity in nutrient solutions as compared with a field screening method. *Agron. J.* 68:551–55

202. Huang, C.-Y., Bazzaz, F. A., Vanderhoef, L. N. 1974. The inhibition of soybean metabolism by cadmium and lead. *Plant Physiol.* 54:122–24

203. Humphreys, M. O., Bradshaw, A. D. 1977. Genetic potentials for solving problems of soil mineral stress: heavy metal toxicities. See Ref. 138, pp. 95–105

204. Hunter, J. G., Vergnano, O. 1952. Nickel toxicity in plants. *Ann. Appl. Biol.* 39:279–84

205. Hunter, J. G., Vergnano, O. 1953. Trace-element toxicities in oat plants. *Ann. Appl. Biol.* 40:761–77

206. Hutchinson, F. E., Newbauer, B. F., Verrill, D. B., Kesar, M. 1971. The influence of aluminum and manganese ions on the growth of sugar beets grown in solution and soil culture. *Proj. Completion Rep., Maine Agric. Exp. Stn. Crops Res. Div., ARS, USDA, Beltsville, MD.*

207. Hutchinson, T. C., Whitby, L. M. 1974. Heavy-metal pollution in the Sudbury mining and smelting region of Canada, I. Soil and vegetation contamination by nickel, copper, and other metals. *Environ. Conserv.* 1:123–32

208. Imai, I., Siegel, S. M. 1973. A specific response to toxic cadmium levels in red kidney bean embryos. *Physiol. Plant.* 29:118–20

209. International Rice Research Institute Annual Report. 1973. See pp. 100–4. Los Banos, Laguna, Philippines

210. Jaffre, T., Brooks, R. R., Lee, J., Reeves, R. D. 1976. *Sebertia acuminata:* A hyperaccumulator of nickel from New Caledonia. *Science* 193:579–80

211. Jaffre, T., Heim, R. 1977. Accumulation du manganese par des especes associees aux terrain ultrabasiqaes de nouvelle-celedonie. *C. R. Acad. Sci. D.* 284:1573–75

212. Jarvis, S. C., Jones, L. H. P., Hopper, M. J. 1976. Cadmium uptake from solution by plants and its transport from roots to shoots. *Plant Soil* 44:179–91

213. Jayman, T. C. Z., Sivasubramaniam, S. 1975. Release of bound iron and aluminum from soils by the root exudates of tea (*Camellia sinensis*) plants. *J. Sci. Food Agric.* 26:1895–98

214. Jenne, E. A. 1968. Controls on Mn, Fe, Co, Ni, Cu, and Zn concentrations in soils and water: The significant role of hydrous Mn and Fe oxides. *Adv. Chem.* 73:337–87

215. John, M. K. 1976. Interrelationships between plant cadmium and uptake of some other elements from culture solu-

tions by oats and lettuce. *Environ. Pollut.* 11:85–95

216. John, M. K., Chuah, H. H., VanLaerhoven, C. J. 1972. Cadmium contamination of soil and its uptake by oats. *Environ. Sci. Technol.* 6:555–57

217. John, M. K., VanLaerhoven, C. J., Bjerring, J. H. 1976. Effect of a smelter complex on the regional distribution of cadmium, lead, and zinc in litters and soil horizons. *Arch. Environ. Contam. Toxicol.* 4:456–68

218. Johnson, M. S., McNeilly, T., Putwain, P. O. 1977. Revegetation of metalliferous mine spoil contaminated by lead and zinc. *Environ. Pollut.* 12:261–77

219. Johnson, W. R., Proctor, J. 1977. A comparative study of metal levels in plants from two contrasting lead-mine sites. *Plant Soil* 46:251–57

220. Jones, H. E., Etherington, J. R. 1970. Comparative studies on plant growth and distribution in relation to waterlogging. I. The survival of *Erica cinera,* L. and *Erica tetralix* and its apparent relationship to iron and manganese uptake in waterlogged soil. *J. Ecol.* 58:487–96

221. Jones, J. S., Hatch, M. B. 1945. Spray residues and crop assimilation of arsenic and lead. *Soil. Sci.* 60:277–88

222. Jones, L. H. 1961. Aluminum uptake and toxicity in plants. *Plant Soil* 13:292–310

223. Jones, L. H. P., Clement, C. R., Hopper, M. J. 1973. Lead uptake from solution by perennial ryegrass and its transport from roots to shoots. *Plant Soil* 38:403–14

224. Jones, L. H. P., Jarvis, S. C., Cowling, D. W. 1973. Lead uptake from soils by perennial ryegrass and its relation to the supply of an essential element (sulphur). *Plant Soil* 38:605–19

225. Jones, R. G. W., Sutcliffe, M., Marshall, C. 1971. Physiological and biochemical basis for heavy metal tolerance in clones of *Agrostis tenuis.* In *Recent Advances in Plant Nutrition,* ed. 2:575–81. New York: Gordon & Breach

226. Jones, R. K., Clay, H. J. 1976. Foliar symptoms of nutrient disorders in Townsville stylo (*Stylosanthes humilis*). *CSIRO Aust. Div. Trop. Agron. Tech. Pap. No.* 19:1–11

227. Jones, T. L., Jones, U. S. 1974. Influence of soil pH, aluminum and sulfur on short life peach trees growing on loamy sands in Southeastern United States. *Fla. State Hortic. Proc.* 87:367–71

228. Juang, T.-C. 1973. Nutrient balance involving zinc, iron and manganese in sugarcane. (*Soil Fert. Taiwan* 1:25–34)

229. Kamprath, E. J., Foy, C. D. 1971. Lime-fertilizer-plant interactions in acid soils. In *Fertilizer, Technology and Use,* ed. R. A. Olson et al, pp. 105–51. Madison, Wis: Soil Sci. Soc. Am. 611 pp. 2nd ed.

230. Keeney, D. R., Wildung, R. E. 1977. Chemical properties of soils. See Ref. 73, pp. 74–97

231. Kerridge, P. C., Kronstad, W. E. 1968. Evidence of genetic resistance to aluminum toxicity in wheat (*Triticum aestivum* Vill. Host.) *Agron. J.* 60:710–11

232. Kesar, M., Benedict, F., Hutchinson, F. E., Verrill, D. B. 1977. Differential aluminum tolerance of sugarbeet cultivars as evidenced by anatomical structure. *Agron. J.* 69:347–50

233. Kesar, M., Benedict, F., Newbauer, F., Hutchinson, F. E. 1975. Influence of aluminum ions on developmental morphology of sugarbeet roots. *Agron. J.* 67:84–88

234. Kikuchi, T. 1965. Production of hydrogen sulfide from sulfite by a copper-adapted yeast. *Plant Cell Physiol.* 6:37–46

235. Kikuchi, T. 1965. Studies on the pathway of sulfide production in a copper-adapted yeast. *Plant Cell Physiol.* 6:195–210

236. King, L. D., Morris, H. D. 1972. Land disposal of liquid sewage sludge II. The effect on soil pH, manganese, zinc, and growth and chemical composition of rye (*Secale cereale* L.) *J. Environ. Qual.* 1:425–29

237. Kirsch, R. K., Howard, M. E., Peterson, R. G. 1960. Interrelationships among iron, manganese, and molybdenum in the growth and nutrition of tomato grown in nutrient solution. *Plant Soil* 12:259–75

238. Kliewer, W. M. 1961. *The effects of varying combinations of molybdenum, aluminum, manganese, phosphorus, nitrogen, calcium, hydrogen ion concentrations, lime, and rhizobium strain on growth, composition, and nodulation of several legumes.* PhD thesis. Cornell Univ., Ithaca, NY

239. Klimashevskii, E. L., Berezovskii, K. K. 1973. Genetic resistance of plants to ionic toxicity in the root zone. *Sov. Plant Physiol.* 20:51–54

240. Klimashevskii, E. L., Bernatskaya, M. L. 1973. Activity of ATPase and acid phosphatase in growth zones of the roots of two varieties of peas having

different sensitivity to Al-ion toxicity. *Sov. Plant Physiol.* 20:201–4

241. Klimashevskii, E. L., Dedov, V. M. 1975. Localization of growth inhibiting action of aluminum ions in elongating cell walls (Russ: Eng) *Fiziol. Rast.* 22:1183–90

242. Klimashevskii, E. L., Dedov, V. M. 1977. Precipitation of Al³⁺ by the root tissues. One reason for the genotypic specificity of plant resistance to toxicity. *Dokl. Vses. Ordena Lenina Akad. Skh. Nauk Imeni V. K. Lenina* 1:8–10 (Russ:Eng)

243. Klimashevskii, E. L., Markova, Yu. A., Zyabkina, S. M., Zirenki, G. K., Zolotukhin, T. E., Pavolova, S. E. 1976. Aluminum absorption and localization in root tissues of different pea varieties. *Fiziol. Biokhim. Kul't. Rast.* 8(4):396–401 (Russ:Eng)

244. Ko, W. H., Hora, F. K. 1972. Identification of an Al ion as a soil fungotoxin. *Soil Sci.* 113:42–45

245. Kobayashi, J. 1970. Relation between the "itai-itai" disease and the pollution of river water by cadmium from a mine. *Proc. 5th Int. Water Pollut. Res. Conf. San Francisco* I-25:1-7

246. Koeppe, D. E., Miller, R. J., Root, R. A., Bittell, J. E., Malone, C. 1975. Uptake and some physiological effects of cadmium on corn. *Proc. 1st Ann. NSF Trace Contam. Conf.*, pp. 533–63

247. Konzak, C. F., Polle, E., Kittrick, J. A. 1977. Screening several crops for aluminum tolerance. See Ref. 138, pp. 311–27

248. Kotze, W. A., Shear, C. B., Faust, M. 1976. Effect of nitrogen source and the presence or absence of aluminum on the growth and calcium nutrition of apple seedlings. *J. Am. Soc. Hortic. Sci.* 101:305–9

249. Kubota, J., Allaway, W. H. 1972. Geographic distribution of trace element problems. See Ref. 56, pp. 525–54

250. Kuznetsova, N. N., Kreier, K. G., Kononets, V. A. 1975. Effects of Al on the content of free radicals in the roots of plants with different tolerances to Al. *Biologiya* 3:143–45 (Russ:Eng)

251. Lafever, H. M., Campbell, L. G., Foy, C. D. 1977. Differential response of wheat cultivars to Al. *Agron. J.* 69:563–68

252. Lagerwerff, J. V. 1972. Lead, mercury, and cadmium as environmental contaminants. See Ref. 56, pp. 593–636

253. Lagerwerff, J. V., Biersdorf, G. T. 1972. Interactions of zinc with uptake and translocation of cadmium in radish. See Ref. 92, 5:515–22

254. Lagerwerff, J. V., Brower, D. L., Biersdorf, G. T. 1973. Accumulation of cadmium, copper, lead, and zinc in soil and vegetation in the proximity of a smelter. See Ref. 91, 6:71–78

255. Lagerwerff, J. V., Specht, A. W. 1970. Contamination of roadside soil and vegetation with cadmium, nickel, lead, and zinc. *Environ. Sci. Technol.* 4:583–86

256. Leach, W., Taper, C. D. 1954. Studies in plant mineral nutrition. II. The absorption of Fe and Mn by dwarf kidney beans, tomato, and onion from culture solutions. *Can. J. Bot.* 32:561–70

257. Lee, C. R. 1971. Influence of aluminum on plant growth and mineral nutrition of potatoes. *Agron. J.* 63:604–8

258. Lee, C. R. 1972. Interrelationships of aluminum and manganese on the potato plant. *Agron. J.* 64:546–49

259. Lee, C. R., Craddock, G. R. 1969. Factors affecting plant growth in high-zinc medium: II. Influence of soil treatments on growth of soybeans on strongly acid soil containing zinc from peach sprays. *Agron. J.* 61:565–67

260. Lee, C. R., Page, N. R. 1967. Soil factors influencing the growth of cotton following peach orchards. *Agron. J.* 59:237–40

261. Lee, C. R., Sturgis, T. C., Landin, M. C. 1976. A hydroponic study of heavy metal uptake by selected marsh plant species. *US Army Eng. Waterways Exp. Stn. Tech. Rep. D-76-5.* 63 pp.

262. Lee, K. C., Cunningham, B. A., Paulsen, G. M., Liang, G. H., Moore, R. B. 1976. Effects of cadmium on respiration rate and activities of several enzymes in soybean seedlings. *Physiol. Plant* 36:4–6

263. Lee, K. W., Keeney, D. R. 1975. Cadmium additions to Wisconsin soils by commercial fertilizer and waste-water sludge applications. *Water, Air, Soil Pollut.* 5:109–12

264. Leeper, G. W. 1972. *Reactions of Heavy Metals with Soil with Special Regard to Their Application in Sewage Wastes.* Dep. Army, Corps Eng., contract No. DACW73-73-C-0026. 70 pp.

265. Leonard, C. D., Stewart, I. 1952. Correction of iron chlorosis in citrus with chelated iron. *Proc. Fla. State Hortic. Soc.* 65:20–24

266. Lewin, J., Reimann, B. E. F. 1969. Silicon and plant growth. *Ann. Rev. Plant Physiol.* 20:289–304

267. Lewis, W. E. 1973. Effects of mineral salts on *Aphanomyces enteiches* and aphanomyces root rot of peas. *Phytopathology* 63:989–93
268. Li, E. H., Miles, C. D. 1975. Effects of cadmium on photoreaction II of chloroplasts. *Plant Sci. Lett.* 5:33–40
269. Liebig, G. F., Vaneslow, A. P., Chapman, H. D. 1942. Effects of Al on Cu toxicity as revealed by solution culture and spectrographic studies of citrus. *Soil Sci.* 53:341–57
270. Lindsay, W. L. 1972. Inorganic phase equilbria of micronutrients in soils. See Ref. 56, pp. 41–57
271. Lindsay, W. L. 1973. Inorganic reactions of sewage wastes with soils. *Proc. Joint Conf. Recycling Municipal Sludges and Effluents on Land,* pp. 91–96
272. Lindsay, W. L. 1974. Role of chelation in micronutrient availability. See Ref. 22, pp. 508–24
273. Lingle, J. C., Tiffin, L. O., Brown, J. C. 1963. Iron uptake-translocation of soybean as influenced by other cations. *Plant Physiol.* 38:71–76
274. Lisk, D. J. 1972. Trace metals in soils, plants, and animals. *Adv. Agron.* 24:267–325
275. Little, P., Martin, M. H. 1972. A survey of zinc, lead, and cadmium in soil and natural vegetation around a smelting complex. *Environ. Pollut.* 3:241–43
276. Lockard, R. G. 1959. *Bull. 108, Dep. Agric. Malaya. F. M. S.,* p. 418
277. Loneragan, J. F. 1975. The availability and absorption of trace elements in soil-plant systems and their relation to movement and concentrations of trace elements in plants. In *Trace Elements in Soil-Plant-Animal Systems,* Ed. D. J. D. Nicholas, A. R. Egan, pp. 109–34. New York: Academic
278. Lopez, A., Metzger, R., Konzak, W. E., Moore, D. P. 1976. Reaction to differential levels of aluminum concentrations in wheat, rye, and their contributions to tolerance in triticale. *Crop. Sci.* Abstr., West. Soc., p. 11
279. Lucas, R. E., Knezek, B. D. 1972. Climatic and soil conditions promoting micronutrient deficiencies in plants. See Ref. 56, pp. 265–88
280. Lunt, H. A. 1953. The case for sludge as a soil improver with emphasis on value of pH control and toxicity of minor elements. *Water & Sewage Works* 100:295–301
281. Lunt, O. R., Kofranek, A. M. 1970. Manganese and aluminum tolerance of

azalea (cv. Sweetheart Supreme). *Plant Anal. Fert. Probl. Abstr. 6th Int. Colloq. Tel Aviv, Israel,* pp. 559–73
282. Lyon, G. L., Peterson, P. J., Brooks, R. R. 1969. Chromium - 51 transport in the xylem sap of *Leptospermum scoparium* (Manuka). *NZ J. Sci.* 2:541–45
283. Lyon, G. L., Peterson, P. J., Brooks, R. R. 1969. Chromium - 51 distribution in tissues and extracts of *Leptospermum scoparium.* *Planta* 88:282–87
284. Mahaffey, K. R., Corneliussen, P. E., Jelinek, C. F., Fiorino, J. A. 1975. Heavy metal exposure from foods. *Environ. Health Perspect.* 12:63–69
285. Malone, C., Koeppe, D. E., Miller, R. J. 1974. Localization of lead accumulated by corn plants. *Plant Physiol.* 53:388–94
286. Maschmeyer, J. R., Quinn, J. A. 1976. Copper tolerance in New Jersey populations of *Agrostis stolonifera* and *Paronychia fastigiata. Bull. Torrey Bot. Club* 103:244–51
287. Masui, M., Ishida, A. 1975. Studies on manganese excess in muskmelon. IV. Manganese excess in relation to steam sterilization, soil pH, and organic matter. *J. Jpn. Soc. Hortic. Sci.* 44:41–46
288. Mathys, W. 1973. Comparative investigations of the uptake of zinc by resistant and sensitive populations of *Agrostis tenuis* Sibth. *Flora* 162:492–99
289. Mathys, W. 1975. Enzymes of heavy-metal-resistant and non-resistant populations of *Silene cucubalus* and their interaction with some heavy metals *in vitro* and *in vivo. Physiol. Plant* 33:161–65
290. Mathys, W. 1977. The role of malate, oxalate, and mustard oil glucosides in the evolution of zinc-resistance in herbage plants. *Physiol. Plant.* 40:130–36
291. Mathys, W. 1977. The role of malate in zinc tolerance. See Ref. 94
292. Matsumoto, H., Hirasawa, F., Morimura, S., Takahashi, E. 1976. Localization of alumunum in tea leaves. *Plant Cell Physiol.* 17:890–95
293. Matsumoto, H., Hirasawa, F., Morimura, S., Takahashi, E. 1976. Localization of aluminum in tea leaves. *Plant Cell Physiol.* 17:627–31
294. Matsumoto, H., Hirasawa, F., Torikai, H., Takahashi, E. 1976. Localization of absorbed aluminum in pea root and its binding to nucleic acids. *Plant Cell Physiol.* 17:127–37
295. Matsumoto, H., Morimura, S., Takahashi, E. 1977. Less involvement of pectin

in the precipitation of aluminum in pea root. *Plant Cell Physiol.* 18:325–35

296. Mattson, S., Hester, J. B. 1933. The laws of soil colloidal behavior. XII. The amphoteric nature of soils in relation to aluminum toxicity. *Soil Sci.* 36:229–44

297. McCalla, T. M., Peterson, J. R. 1977. Properties of agricultural and municipal wastes. See Ref. 73, pp. 10–43

298. McCormick, L. H., Borden, F. Y. 1972. Phosphate fixation by aluminum in plant roots. *Soil Sci. Soc. Amer. Proc.* 36:779–802

299. McCormick, L. H., Borden, F. Y. 1974. The occurrence of aluminum phosphate precipitate in plant roots. *Soil Sci. Soc. Am. Proc.* 38:931–34

300. McKenzie, R. E. 1951. Ability of forages to survive early spring flooding *Sci. Agric.* 31:358–67

301. McNaughton, S. J., Folsom, T. C., Lee, T., Park, F., Price, C., Roeder, D., Schmitz, J., Stockwill, C. 1974. Heavy metal tolerance in *Typha latifolia* without the evolution of tolerant races. *Ecology* 55:1163–65

302. McNeilly, T. 1968. Evolution in closely adjacent plant populations. III. *Agrostis tenuis* on a small copper mine. *Heredity* 23:99–108

303. Medappa, K. C., Dana, M. N. 1970. Tolerance of cranberry plants to Mn, Fe, and Al. *J. Am. Soc. Hortic. Sci.* 95:107–10

304. Meudt, W. J. 1971. Interactions of sulfite and manganeous ion with peroxidase oxidation products of indole-3-acetic acid. *Phytochemistry* 10:2103–9

305. Milbocker, D. C. 1974. Zinc toxicity to plants grown in media containing polyrubber. *Hortscience* 9:545–46

306. Miller, J. E., Hassett, J. J., Koeppe, D. E. 1975. The effect of soil lead sorption capacity on the uptake of lead by corn. *Commun. Soil Sci. Plant Anal.* 6: 349–58

307. Miller, J. E., Hassett, J. J., Koeppe, D. E. 1975. The effect of soil properties and extractable lead levels on lead uptake by soybeans. *Commun. Soil Sci. Plant Anal.* 6:339–47

308. Miller, J. E., Hassett, J. J., Koeppe, D. E. 1976. Uptake of cadmium by soybeans as influenced by soil cation exchange capacity, pH, and available phosphorus. *J. Environ. Qual.* 5:157–60

309. Miller, J. E., Hassett, J. J., Koeppe, D. E. 1977. Interactions of lead and cadmium on metal uptake and growth of corn plants. *J. Environ. Qual.* 6:18–20

310. Miller, R. J., Bittell, J. E., Koeppe, D. E. 1973. The effect of cadmium on electron and energy transfer reactions in corn mitochondria. *Physiol. Plant.* 28:166–71

311. Millikan, C. R. 1949. Effects on flax of a toxic concentration of boron iron, molybdenum, aluminum, copper, zinc, manganese, cobalt, or nickel in the nutrient solution. *R. Soc. Victoria Proc.* 61:25–42

312. Mitchell, R. L., Reith, J. W. S. 1966. The lead content of pasture herbage. *J. Sci. Food Agric.* 17:437–40

313. Moomaw, J. C., Nakamura, M. T., Sherman, G. D. 1959. Aluminum in some Hawaiian plants. *Pac. Sci.* 13(1): 335–41

314. Moore, D. P. 1972. Mechanisms of micronutrient uptake by plants. See Ref. 56, pp. 171–98

315. Moore, D. P. 1974. Physiological effects of pH on roots. See Ref. 22, pp. 135–51

316. Moore, D. P., Kronstad, W. E., Metzger, R. J. 1977. Screening wheat for aluminum tolerance. See Ref. 138, pp. 287–95

317. Moorman, F. R. 1963. Acid sulfate soils (cat clays) of the tropics. *Soil Sci.* 95:271–75

318. Morgan, P. W., Joham, H. E., Amin, J. V. 1966. Effect of manganese toxicity on the indole-acetic acid oxidase system of cotton. *Plant Physiol.* 41:718–24

319. Morgan, P. W., Taylor, D. M., Joham, H. E. 1976. Manipulations of IAA-oxidase activity and auxin deficiency symptoms in intact cotton plants with manganese nutrition. *Physiol. Plant* 37: 149–56

320. Morris, H. D., Pierre, W. H. 1949. Minimum concentrations of manganese necessary for injury to various legumes in culture solution. *Agron. J.* 41:107–12

321. Mortvedt, J. J., Giordano, P. M. 1977. Crop uptake of heavy metal contaminants in fertilizers. In *Biological Implications of Metals in the Environment. Proc. 15th Ann. Hanford Life Sci. Sym. Richland, Wash.* In press

322. Mugwira, L. M., Elgawhary, S. M., Patel, K. I. 1976. Differential tolerances of triticale, wheat, rye, and barley to aluminum in nutrient solution. *Agron. J.* 68:782–87

323. Mugwira, L. M., Patel, S. V. 1977. Root zone pH changes and ion uptake imbalances by triticale, wheat and rye. *Agron. J.* 69:719–22

324. Mugwira, L. M., Patel, K. I., Rao, P. V. 1976. Lime requirement for triticale

in relation to other small grains. *Acta Agron. Acad. Sci. Hung.* 25:365–80

325. Mukherji, S., Gupta, B. D. 1972. Characterization of copper toxicity in lettuce seedlings. *Physiol. Plant.* 27:126

326. Mulleriyawa, R. P. 1966. *Some factors influencing bronzing, a physiological disease of rice in Ceylon.* MS thesis, Coll. Agric., Univ. Philippines

327. Mullette, K. J. 1975. Stimulation of growth in *Eucalyptus* due to aluminum. *Plant Soil* 42:495–99

328. Mullette, K. J., Hannon, N. J., Elliott, A. G. L. 1974. Insoluble phosphorus usage by eucalyptus. *Plant Soil* 41:199–205

329. Munns, D. N., Johnson, C. M., Jacobson, L. 1963. Uptake and distribution of manganese in oat plants. III. An analysis of biotic and environmental effects. *Plant Soil* 19:285–95

330. Nagai, T., Matono, T. 1959. Cultivated rice varieties viewed from root characters. IV. Interrelationships among root activity, ferrous coating formations, and cation exchange capacity. *Proc. Crop. Sci. Soc. Japan* 28:208–10

331. Naidoo, G., Stewart, J. McD., Lewis, R. J. 1976. *Sites of accumulation of aluminum in snap beans and cotton roots.* PhD thesis. Univ. Tennessee, Knoxville, Tenn.

332. Naiki, N., Yamagata, S. 1976. Isolation and some properties of copper-binding proteins found in a copper-resistant strain of yeast. *Plant Cell Physiol.* 17:1281–95

333. Nambier, E. K. S. 1975. Mobility and plant uptake of micronutrients in relation to soil water content. See Ref. 277, pp. 151–63

334. Nelson, D. L., Kennedy, E. P. 1971. Magnesium transport in *Escherichia coli.* Inhibition by cobaltous ion. *J. Biol. Chem.* 246:3042–49

335. Nelson, L. E. 1977. Changes in water soluble Mn due to soil sample preparation and storage. *Commun. Soil. Sci. Plant Anal.* 8:479–87

336. Nhung, Mai-Thi-My, Ponnamperuma, F. N. 1966. Effects of calcium carbonate, manganese dioxide, ferric hydroxide, and prolonged flooding, chemical and electrochemical changes and growth of rice in a flooded, acid sulfate soil. *Soil. Sci.* 102:29–41

337. Nicholas, D. J. D., Lloyd-Jones, C. P., Fisher, D. J. 1957. Some problems associated with determining iron in plants. *Plant Soil* 8:367–77

338. Norvell, W. A. 1972. Equilibria of metal chelates in soil solution. See Ref. 56, pp. 115–38

339. Odurukwe, S. O., Maynard, D. N. 1969. Mechanisms of the differential response of Wf9 and Oh40B corn seedlings to iron nutrition. *Agron. J.* 61:694–97

340. Ohki, K. 1975. Mn and B effects on micronutrients and P in cotton. *Agron. J.* 67:204–7

341. Okamoto, K., Suzuki, M., Fukami, M., Toda, S., Fuwa, K. 1977. Heavy metal tolerance of *Penicillium ochro-chloron*. II. Uptake of heavy metals by copper tolerant fungus *Penicillium ochro-chloron. Agric. Biol. Chem.* 41:17–22

342. Okuda, A., Takahashi, E. 1965. The role of silicon. *Int. Grass. Res. Inst., Los Banos, P.I.,* pp. 123–46

343. Olsen, C. 1958. Iron absorption in different plant species as a function of the pH value of the solution. *C. R. Lab. Carlsberg* 31(4):41–59

344. Olsen, S. R. 1972. Micronutrient interactions. See Ref. 56, pp. 243–64

345. Osawa, T., Ikeda, H. 1976. Heavy metal toxicities in vegetable crops. I. The effect of iron concentrations in the nutrient solution on manganese toxicities in vegetable crops. *J. Jpn. Soc. Hortic. Sci.* 45:50–58

346. Ota, 1968. Studies on the physiological disease of rice called "bronzing." *Bull. Natl. Inst. Agric. Sci. Nishigahara, Tokyo, Japan, Ser. D. (Plant Physiology, Genetics, Crops in General, No. 18)* (Jap:Eng)

347. Otsuka, K. 1970. Aluminum induced Fe chlorosis. Aluminum and manganese toxicities for plants. IV. *Soil Sci. Plant Nutr.* 16:140, Abstr. 2

348. Ouellette, G. J., Dessureaux, L. 1958. Chemical composition of alfalfa as related to degree of tolerance to manganese and aluminum. *Can. J. Plant Sci.* 38:206–14

349. Page, A. L. 1974. Fate and effects of trace elements in sewage sludge when applied to agricultural lands. A literature review study. *US Environ. Prot. Agency Rep. No. EPA-670/2-74-005.* 108 pp.

350. Patterson, J. B. E. 1971. Metal toxicities arising from industry. In *Trace Elements in Soils and Crops. Ministry Agric. Fish Food, Tech. Bull.* 21:193–207

351. Pearson, R. W., Ratliff, L. F., Taylor, H. M. 1970. Effect of soil temperature, strength, and pH on cotton seedling root elongation. *Agron J.* 62:243–46

352. Peaslee, D. E., Frink, G. R. 1969. Influence of silicic acid on uptake on Mn, Al, Zn, and Cu by tomato (*Lycoperiscon esculentum*) grown on an acid soil. *Soil Sci. Soc. Am. Proc.* 33:569–71

353. Perkins, H. F., Gibson, E. J., Bertrand, A. R. 1972. Influence of iron content on quality of cigar wrapper tobacco. *Commun. Soil Sci. Plant Anal.* 3:459–66

354. Peterson, P. J. 1969. The distribution of zinc-65 in *Agrostis tenuis* Sibth. and *A. stolonifera* L. tissues. *J. Exp. Bot.* 20: 863–75

355. Pierpont, R. A., Minotti, P. L. 1977. Effects of calcium carbonate on ammonium assimilation by tomato seedlings. *J. Am. Soc. Hortic. Sci.* 102:20–23

356. Polacco, J. C. 1977. Nitrogen metabolism in soybean tissue culture. II. Urea utilization and urease synthesis require Ni. *Plant Physiol.* 59:827–30

357. Polson, D. E., Adams, M. W. 1970. Differential response of navy beans to zinc. I. Differential growth and elemental composition at excessive zinc levels. *Agron. J.* 62:557–60

358. Ponnamperuma, F. N. 1955. Physiological diseases of rice attributed to iron toxicity. *Nature* 175:265

359. Presad, M. 1976. Nitrogen nutrition and yield of sugarcane as affected by N-Serve. *Agron. J.* 68:343–46

360. Prestes, A. M., Konzak, C. F., Hendrix, J. W. 1975. An improved seedling culture method for screening wheat for tolerance to toxic levels of aluminum. *Agron Abstr.,* p. 60

361. Proctor, J. 1971. The plant ecology of serpentine. II. Plant response to serpentine soils. *J. Ecol.* 59:397–410

362. Proctor, J., McGowan, I. D. 1976. Influence of magnesium on nickel toxicity. *Nature* 260:134

363. Purves, D. 1972. Consequences of trace-element contamination of soils. *Environ. Pollut.* 3:17–24

364. Putrament, A., Baranowska, H., Ejchart, A., Jachymczyk, W. 1977. Manganese mutagenesis in yeast.VI.Mn^{2+} uptake, mitochondrial DNA replication and E^r induction comparison with other divalent cations. *Mol. Gen. Genet.* 151: 69–76

365. Rasmussen, H. P. 1968. Entry and distribution of aluminum in *Zea mays:* Electron microprobe X-ray analysis. *Planta* 81:28–37

366. Ratner, E. I., Smirnoy, A. M., Kuan, K. H. 1962. Importance of molybdenum for growth of isolated roots of lucerne depending on the acidity of the medium and its content of Al. *Friziol. Rast.* 9:279–88

367. Raven, J. A., Smith, F. A. 1976. Nitrogen assimilation and transport in vascular land plants in relation to intracellular pH regulation. *New Phytol.* 76: 415–31

368. Rees, W. J., Sidrak, G. M. 1961. Interrelationship of aluminum and manganese toward plants. *Plant Soil* 14: 101–17

369. Reid, D. A. 1971. Genetic control of reaction to aluminum in winter barley. In *Barley Genetics II - Proc. 2nd Int. Barley Genetics Symp. Pullman, Wash., 1969,* ed. R. A. Nilan, pp. 409–13. Washington State Univ. Press.

370. Reid, D. A., Jones, G. D., Armiger, W. H., Foy, C. D., Koch, E. J., Starling, T. M. 1969. Differential aluminum tolerance of winter barley varieties and selections in associated greenhouse and field experiments. *Agron. J.* 61:218–22

371. Reilly, A., Reilly, C. 1973. Copper-induced chlorosis in *Becium homblei* (De Wild.) Duvign and Plancke. *Plant Soil* 38:671–74

372. Reuss, J., Dooley, H. L., Griffis, W. 1976. Plant uptake of cadmium from phosphate fertilizer. *Ecol. Res. Ser.* EPA-600/3-76-053. 43 pp.

373. Reuther, W., Smith, P. F. 1954. Toxic effects of accumulated copper in Florida soils. *Soil Sci. Soc. Fla. Proc.* 14:17–23

374. Reuther, W., Smith, P. F., Scudder, G. K. Jr. 1953. Relation of pH and soil type to toxicity of copper to citrus seedlings. *Fla. State Hortic. Soc. Proc.* 66:73–80

375. Rhoads, F. M. 1971. Relations between Fe in irrigation water and leaf quality of cigar wrapper tobacco. *Agron. J.* 63: 938–40

376. Rhue, R. D. 1976. *The time concentration interaction of Al toxicity in wheat root meristems.* PhD thesis. Oregon State Univ., Corvallis, Ore.

377. Rhue, R. D., Grogan, C. O. 1977. Screening corn for aluminum tolerance. See Ref. 138, pp. 297–310

378. Robinson, D. B., Hodgson, W. A. 1961. The effect of some amino acids on manganese toxicity in potato. *Can. J. Plant Sci.* 41:436–37

379. Robson, A. D., Loneragan, J. F. 1970. Sensitivity of annual *Medicago* species to manganese toxicity as affected by calcium and pH. *Aust. J. Agric. Res.* 21:223–32

380. Rocovich, S. E., West, D. A. 1975. Arsenic tolerance in a population of the

grass *Andropogon scoparius* Michx. *Science* 188:263–64

381. Rogers, E. 1973. Iron-induced manganese deficiency in 'July Elberta' peach trees. *J. Am. Soc. Hortic. Sci.* 98:19

382. Root, R. A., Miller, R. J., Koeppe, D. E. 1975. Uptake of cadmium—its toxicity and effect on the iron-to-zinc ratio in hydroponically grown corn. *J. Environ. Qual.* 4:473–76

383. Rorison, I. H. 1965. The effect of aluminum on the uptake and incorporation of phosphate by excised sanfoin roots. *New Phytol.* 63:23–27

384. Rorison, I. H. 1972.The effect of extreme soil acidity on the nutrient uptake and physiology of plants. *Int. Inst. Land Reclam. Improv. Publ.* 18:223–54. *Acid sulphate soils, Proc. Int. Symp. Wageningen*, pp. 13–20. I. Introducing papers and bibliography

385. Rorison, I. H. 1975. Nitrogen source and metal toxicity. *J. Sci. Food Agric.* 26:1426

386. Rosen, J. A., Pike, C. S., Golden, M. L. 1977. Zinc, iron, and chlorophyll metabolism in zinc-toxic corn. *Plant Physiol.* 59:1085–87

387. Ross, I. S. 1975. Some effects of heavy metals on fungal cells. *Trans. Br. Mycol. Soc.* 64:175–93

388. Roth, J. A., Wallihan, E. F., Sharpless, R. G. 1971. Uptake by oats and soybeans of copper and nickel added to a peat soil. *Soil Sci.* 112:338–42

389. Santillian-Medrano, J., Jurinak, J. J. 1975. The chemistry of lead and cadmium in soil: solid phase formation. *Soil Sci. Soc. Am. Proc.* 39:851–56

390. Schiller, W. 1974. Studies on the resistance to copper of two ecotypes of *Silene cucubalus* Wif. *Flora* 163:327–41

391. Shuman, L. M., Anderson, O. E. 1976. Interactions of manganese with other ions in wheat and soybeans. *Commun. Soil Sci. Plant Anal.* 7:547–57

392. Silverberg, B. A., Stokes, P. M., Ferstenberg, L. B. 1976. Intranuclear complexes in a copper-tolerant green alga. *J. Cell Biol.* 69:210–14

393. Simon, E. 1977. Cadmium tolerance in populations of *Agrostis tenuis* and *Festuca ovina. Nature* 265:328–30

394. Singh, K. K. 1977. Exudate delivery and iron and manganese transport determining differential responses of navy bean lines (*Phaseolus vulgaris, L.*) to iron-induced manganese chlorosis. *Abstr., Seminar on Recent Adv. Plant Sci.,* Assoc. Adv. Plant Sci. in collaboration with Bidkan Chandra Krishi Viskwa Uidyalaya Kalgani, p. 48 (Reg. Res. Lab.) Jorhat 785006

395. Singh, R. P., Lee, C. R., Clark, M. C. 1974. Manganese effect on the local lesion symptoms of potato spindle tuber virus in *Scopolia sinensis. Phytopathology* 64:1015–18

396. Sivasubramaniam, S., Talibudeen, O. 1972. Effects of aluminum on the growth of tea (*Camellia sinensis*) and its uptake of potassium and phosphorus. *Tea* 43:4–13

397. Skeen, J. R. 1929. The tolerance limit of seedlings for aluminum and the antagonism of calcium. *Soil Sci.* 27:69–80

398. Slootmaker, L. A. J. 1974. Tolerance to high soil acidity in wheat related species, rye and triticale. *Euphytica* 23:505–13

399. Small, J. 1946. *pH and Plants.* London: Bailliere, Tindall & Cox

400. Smiley, R. W. 1974. Rhizosphere pH as influenced by plants, soils, and nitrogen fertilizers. *Soil Sci. Soc. Am. Proc.* 38:795–99

401. Smith, P. F., Reuther, W., Specht, A. W. 1950. Mineral composition of chlorotic orange leaves and some observations on the relation of sample preparation technique to the interpretation of results. *Plant Physiol.* 25:496–506

402. Sonneveld, C., Voogt, S. J. 1975. Studies on the manganese uptake of lettuce on steam-sterilized glasshouse soils. *Plant Soil* 42:49–64

403. Souto, S. M., Dobereiner, J. 1971. Manganese toxicity in tropical forage legumes. *Pesq. Agropec Bras.* 4:128–38. Soils and Fertilizers 34, 3, No. 2546

404. Sowell, W. F., Rouse, R. D., Wear, J. I. 1957. Copper toxicity of the cotton plant in solution cultures. *Agron. J.* 49:206–7

405. Spencer, W. F. 1966. Effect of copper on yield and uptake of phosphorus and iron by citrus seedlings grown at various phosphorus levels. *Soil Sci.* 102:296–99

406. Staker, E. V. 1942. Progress report on the control of zinc toxicity in peat soils. *Soil Sci. Soc. Am. Proc.* 7:387–92

407. Staker, E. V., Cummings, R. W. 1941. The influence of zinc on the productivity of certain New York peat soils. *Soil Sci. Soc. Am. Proc.* 6:207–14

408. Stonier, T., Rodriguez-Tormes, F., Yoneda, Y. 1968. Studies on auxin protectors. IV. The effect of manganese on auxin protector I of the Japanese morning glory. *Plant Physiol.* 43:69–72

409. Street, J. J., Lindsay, W. L., Sabey, B. R. 1977. Solubility and plant uptake of cadmium in soils amended with cadmium and sewage sludge. *J. Environ. Qual.* 6:72–77

410. Struckmeyer, B. E., Peterson, L. A., Tai, F. H. M. 1969. Effects of copper on the composition and anatomy of tobacco. *Agron. J.* 61:932–36

411. Stryker, R. B., Gilliam, J. W., Jackson, W. A. 1974. Non-uniform transport of phosphorus from single roots to the leaves of *Zea mays. Physiol. Plant.* 30:231–39

412. Suchting, H. 1948. Investigations on nutrition conditions in the forest. X. The effect of soluble Al on pines in two forest soils. 2. *Pflernahr. Dung.* 42:193–218

413. Sutcliffe, J. F. 1962. *Mineral Salts Absorption in Plants.* New York: Pergamon McMillan

414. Tadano, T. 1975. Devices of rice roots to tolerate high iron concentrations in growth media. *Jpn. Agric. Res. Q.* 9:34–39

415. Takijima, Y., Katsumi, F., Tabezawa, K. 1973. Cadmium contamination of soils and rice plants caused by zinc mining. II. Soil conditions of contaminated paddy fields which influence heavy metal contents in rice. *Soil Sci. Plant Nutr.* 19:173–82

416. Tanaka, A., Loe, R., Navasero, S. A. 1966. Some mechanisms involved in the development of iron symptoms in the rice plant. *Soil Sci. Plant Nutr.* 12:32–38

417. Tanaka, A., Navasero, S. A. 1966. Interaction between iron and manganese in the rice plant. *Soil Sci. Plant Nutr.* 12:29–33

418. Tanaka, A., Yoshida, S. 1970. Nutritional disorders of the rice plant in Asia. *Int. Rice. Res. Inst. Tech. Bull. 10.* Makati, Rizal, P. I. 51 pp.

419. Terry, N., Evans, P. S., Thomas, D. E. 1975. Manganese toxicity effects on leaf cell multiplication and expansion and on dry matter yield of sugar beets. *Crop Sci.* 15:205–8

420. Thawornwong, N., Van Diest, A. 1974. Influences of high acidity and aluminum on the growth of lowland rice. *Plant Soil* 41:141–59

421. Thenabadu, M. W. 1974–1975. Iron in the nutrition of the rice plant. *J. Natl. Agric. Soc. Ceylon* 11/12:87–102

422. Thompson, J. F., Tiffin, L. O. 1974. Fractionation of nickel complexing compounds of peanut seeds with ion exchange resins. *Plant Physiol.* 53 Suppl. Abstr. 125

423. Tiffin, L. O. 1967. Translocation of manganese, iron, cobalt, and zinc in tomato. *Plant Physiol.* 42:1427–32

424. Tiffin, L. O. 1971. Translocation of nickel in xylem exudate of plants. *Plant Physiol.* 48:273–77

425. Tiffin, L. O. 1972. Translocation of micronutrients in plants. See Ref. 56, pp. 199–229

426. Tiffin, L. O. 1977. The form and distribution of metals in plants: An overview. In *Biological Implications of Metals in the Environment,* pp. 315–34. *Proc. 15th Ann. Hanford Life Sci. Symp.* ERDA-TIC-Conf. No. 750929, Oak Ridge, Tenn.

427. Tiller, K. G., Honeysett, J. L., de Vries, M. P. C. 1972. Soil zinc and its uptake by plants. II. Soil chemistry in relation to prediction of availability. *Aust. J. Soil Res.* 10:165–82

428. Townsend, J. R., Blatt, C. R. 1966. Lowbush blueberry: Evidence for the absence of a nitrate reducing system. *Plant Soil* 25:456–59

429. Trim, A. R. 1959. Metal ions as precipitants for nucleic acids and their use in the isolation of polynucleotides from leaves. *Biochem. J.* 73:298–304

430. Trocmé, S., Barbier, G., Chabannes, J. 1950. Chlorosis, caused by lack of manganese, of crops irrigated with filtered water from Paris sewers. *Ann. Agron. Ser. A* 1:663–85. (In French)

431. Turner, R. G. 1970. The subcellular distribution of zinc and copper within the roots of metal-tolerant clones of *Agrostis tenuis* Sibth. *New Phytol.* 69:725–31

432. Turner, R. G., Gregory, R. P. G. 1967. The use of radioisotopes to investigate heavy metal tolerance in plants. In *Isotopes in Plant Nutrition and Physiology,* pp. 493–508. Austria: I.A.E.A

433. Turner, R. G., Marshall, C. 1971. The accumulation of ^{65}Zn by root homogenates of zinc-tolerant and non-tolerant clones of *Agrostis tenuis* Sibth. *New Phytol.* 70:539–45

434. Turner, R. G., Marshall, C. 1972. The accumulation of zinc by subcellular fractions of roots of *Agrostis tenuis* Sibth. in relation to zinc tolerance. *New Phytol.* 71:671–76

435. Vallee, B. L., Ulmer, D. D. 1972. Biochemical effects of mercury, cadmium, and lead. *Ann. Rev. Biochem.* 41:91–128

436. Van Goor, B. J., Wiersma, D. 1974. Redistribution of potassium, calcium,

magnesium and manganese in the plant. *Physiol. Plant.* 31:163–68

437. Van Goor, B. J., Wiersma, D. 1976. Chemical forms of manganese and zinc in phloem exudates. *Physiol. Plant.* 36:213–16

438. Van Tuil, H. D. W. 1965. Organic salts in plants in relation to nutrition and growth. *Agric. Res. Rep. 657. Inst. Biol. Chem. Res. Field Crops and Herbage, Wageningen, The Netherlands.*

439. Vickers, J. C., Zak, J. M., Odurukwe, S. O. 1977. Effects of pH and Al on the growth and chemical composition of cicer milkvetch. *Agron. J.* 69:511–13

440. Villigarcia, S. 1974. *Aluminum tolerance in the Irish potato (Solanum tuberosum) and the influence of substrate aluminum on growth and mineral nutrition of potatoes.* PhD thesis. North Carolina State Univ., Raleigh, NC. *Diss. Abstr. Int.* 8:1974. 34:9:4157B-4158B

441. Vlamis, J., Williams, D. E. 1967. Manganese and silicon interactions in the Gramineae. *Plant Soil* 28:131–40

442. Wainwright, S. J., Woolhouse, H. W. 1976. Physiological mechanisms of heavy metal tolerance. In *The Ecology of Resource Degradation and Renewal,* ed. M. J. Chadwicks, G. T. Goodman. *Br. Ecol. Soc. Symp.* 15:231–57. Oxford: Blackwell

443. Waisel, Y., Hoffen, A., Eshel, A. 1970. The localization of aluminum in the cortex cells of bean and barley roots by X-ray microanalysis. *Physiol Plant.* 23:75–9

444. Wallace, A. Bhan, K. C. 1962. Plants that do poorly in acid soils. In *A Decade of Synthetic Chelating Agents in Inorganic Plant Nutrition,* ed. A. Wallace, pp. 36–38

445. Wallace, A., DeKock, P. C. 1966. Translocation of iron in tobacco, sunflower and bush bean plants. In *Current Topics in Plant Nutrition,* ed. A. Wallace, pp. 3–9. Ann Arbor: Edward Bros.

446. Wallace, A., Mueller, R. T. 1973. Effects of chelated and non-chelated cobalt and copper on yields and microelement composition of bush beans grown on calcareous soil in a glasshouse. *Soil Sci. Soc. Am. Proc.* 37:907–8

447. Wallace, A., Mueller, R. T., Cha, J. W., Alexander, G. V. 1974. Soil pH, excess lime, and chelating agent on micronutrients in soybeans and bush beans. *Agron. J.* 66:698–700

448. Wallace, A., Romney, E. M., Alexander, G. V., Soufi, S. M., Patel, P. M.

1977. Some interactions in plants among cadmium, other heavy metals, and chelating agents. *Agron. J.* 69:18–20

449. Wallace, T., Hewitt, E. J. 1946. Studies in iron deficiency of crops. 1. Problems of iron deficiency and the interrelationships of mineral elements in iron nutrition. *J. Pomol. Hortic. Sci.* 22:153–61

450. Walley, K. A., Khan, M. S. I., Bradshaw, A. D. 1974. The potential for evolution of heavy metal tolerance in plants. I. Copper and zinc tolerance in *Agrostis tenuis. Heredity* 32:309–19

451. Walsh, L. M., Erhardt, W. H., Seibel, H. D. 1972. Copper toxicity in snapbeans (*Phaseolus vulgaris* L.). *J. Environ. Qual.* 1:197–200

452. Ward, G. M. 1977. Manganese deficiency and toxicity in greenhouse tomatoes. *Can. J. Plant Sci.* 57:107–15

453. Weaver, D. J., Dowler, W. M., Nesmith, W. C. 1976. Association between elemental content of dormant peach trees and susceptibility to short life. *J. Am. Soc. Hortic. Sci.* 101:486–89

454. Webb, M. 1970. The mechanism of acquired resistance to Co^{2+} and Ni^{2+} in gram-positive and gram-resistant bacteria. *Biochim. Biophys. Acta* 222:440–46

455. Webber, J. 1972. Effects of toxic metals in sewage on crops. *Water Pollut. Control* 71:404–13

456. Westgate, P. J. 1952. Preliminary report on copper toxicity and iron chlorosis in old vegetable fields. *Proc. Fla. State Hortic. Sci.* 65:143–46

457. White, M. C. 1976. *Differential varietal tolerance in soybean (Glycine max L.) to phytotoxic levels of zinc in a Sassafras sandy loam.* MS thesis, Univ. Maryland, College Park, Md. 196 pp.

458. White, M. C., Chaney, R. L., Decker, A. M. 1974. Differential varietal tolerance in soybean to toxic levels of zinc in Sassafras sandy loam. *Agron. Abstr.* 1974:144–45

459. White, R. E. 1976. Studies on the mineral ion absorption by plants. III. The interaction of aluminum phosphate and pH on the growth of *Medicago sativa. Plant Soil* 46:195–208

460. White, R. E., Tiffin, L. O., Taylor, A. W. 1976. The existence of polymeric complexes in dilute solutions of aluminum and orthophosphate. *Plant Soil* 45:521–29

461. White, R. P. 1970. Effects of lime upon soil and plant manganese levels in an

acid soil. *Soil Sci. Soc. Am. Proc.* 34:625–29

462. Wild, H. 1970. Geobotanical anomalies in Rhodesia. 3. The vegetation of nickel-bearing soils. *Kirkia* 7, Suppl.: 1–62

463. Wilkinson, H. F. 1970. *Nutrient movement in the vicinity of plant roots.* PhD thesis. Univ. West. Australia, Perth

464. Wilkinson, H. F. 1972. Movement of micronutrients to plant roots. See Ref. 56, pp. 139–69

465. Williams, C. H., David, D. J. 1973. The effect of superphosphate on the cadmium content of soils and plants. *Aust. J. Soil Res.* 11:43–56

466. Williams, D. E., Vlamis, J. 1957. The effect of silicon on yield and Mn^{54} uptake and distribution in the leaves of barley plants grown in culture solution. *Plant Physiol.* 32:404–9

467. Williams, D. E., Vlamis, J., Hall, H., Gowans, K. D. 1971. Urbanization, fertilization and manganese toxicity in Alameda mustard. *Calif. Agric.* 25:8

468. Wilson, D. O. 1977. Influence of added manganese on nitrification in a low Mn soil. *Plant Soil* 46:687–90

469. Wiltshire, G. H. 1973. Response of grasses to nitrogen source. *J. Appl. Ecol.* 10:429–35

470. Winterhalder, E. K. 1963. Differential resistance of two species of *Eucalyptus* to toxic soil manganese levels. *Aust. J. Sci.* 25:363–64

471. Woolhouse, H. W. 1969. Differences in the properties of the acid phosphatases of plant roots and their significance in the evolution of edaphic ecotypes. See Ref. 88, pp. 357–80

472. Wu, L., Antonovics, J. 1976. Experimental ecological genetics in *Plantago* II. Lead tolerance in *Plantago lanceolata* and *Cynodon dactylon* from a roadside. *Ecology* 57:205–8

473. Wu, L., Bradshaw, A. D. 1972. Aerial pollution and the rapid evolution of copper tolerance. *Nature* 238:167–69

474. Wu, L., Thurman, D. A., Bradshaw, A. D. 1975. The uptake of copper and its effects upon respiratory processes of roots of copper-tolerant and non-tolerant clones of *Agrostis stolonifera*. *New Phytol.* 75:225–29

475. Yamagata, N., Shigematsu, I. 1970. Cadmium pollution in perspective. *Bull. Inst. Public Health* 19:1–27

476. Yoshida, K., Imanishi, M., Kitagawa, Y. 1976. Studies on the inorganic components of tea. II. Luxurious absorption of manganese in tea soil originated from Syenite. *Chagyo Kenkyu Hoko* B9 44:39–45

AUTHOR INDEX

A

Abdel-Monem, M., 429
Abdullaev, Kh. A., 219, 220, 232
Abdurakhmanova, Z. N., 218, 223
Abelson, P. H., 76
Abramsky, T., 106
Acevedo, E., 278, 301, 304, 309
Ackerman, T. L., 299, 301
Adamova, N. P., 61
Adams, B., 173, 182
Adams, D. G., 337
Adams, F., 523, 541
Adams, H. R., 439, 448, 452
Adams, M. W., 542, 545
Adesnik, M., 35
Adler, I., 240, 241
Adler, J., 467, 482
Adolph, K. W., 322
Afting, E.-G., 208
Agarwala, S. C., 528, 544
Aghion, P., 249
Agro, A. F., 37
Ahmad, N., 132, 133
Aizer, R. S., 531
Akazawa, T., 69
Akhmedov, Yu. D., 232
Akhmedova, L. R., 232
Akhtar, M., 99, 166, 174
Akintobi, T., 463, 469
Akoyunoglu, G., 98
Aksenova, N. P., 249
Albersheim, P., 79
Alberte, R. S., 326, 327
Albertini, D. F., 496
Alberts, B., 428-30
Alberts, B. M., 474
Albertsson, P.-Å., 36
Albrecht, S. L., 265, 266
Albright, L. J., 27, 30, 34
Aleem, M. I. H., 74
Alessi, J., 282, 286, 304, 306
Alexander, G. V., 539
Alexander, K., 174
Alexandrov, V. Ya., 25, 31, 33
Ali, S. M. E., 521
Aliev, K. A., 217, 220, 224
Allaway, W. G., 381, 384, 386, 387, 390, 391, 401, 402, 405
Allaway, W. H., 535, 536
Allen, L. H. Jr., 293, 294
Allen, M. M., 326
Allen, R. D., 490
Allen, R. L., 115
Allen, R. N., 482
Allsopp, A., 245, 250
Al-Saadi, H. A., 385
Altenburg, L. C., 31, 36

Altman, K. I., 102
Alves, L. M., 162
Amalric, F., 27-29
Amann, H., 348
Ambler, J. E., 512, 513, 532, 538, 541, 542, 544, 545
Amin, J. V., 524
Amrhein, N., 479
Anders, J., 498, 499
ANDERSEN, K., 263-76; 264-69
Andersen, K. S., 230
Anderson, A. J., 536, 542
Anderson, C. D., 296
Anderson, E., 496
Anderson, J. D., 155
Anderson, J. M., 225, 226
Anderson, L., 69-71
Anderson, O. E., 529, 545
Anderson, W. P., 439, 444, 445, 452
Andresen, H. A., 26
Andrew, C. S., 518, 519, 522, 523, 525, 526
Andrews, D. M., 138
Andrews, T. J., 232, 391
Angelocci, L. R., 299
Angus, J. F., 298
Antonovics, J., 536, 545, 546
Apel, K., 220, 225
Apirion, D., 30, 37
Appel, W., 348
Appleby, C. A., 272
Apte, S. K., 328
Arca, M., 32
Aresenault, G. P., 463, 473
Arigoni, D., 166, 174
Arisz, W. H., 451
Armiger, W. H., 523, 525, 527
Armstrong, J. B., 37
Armstrong, J. J., 224
Arndt, S., 30, 33, 36, 37
Arnold, L. M., 34
Arnold, W., 47, 48, 58-61
Arnon, D. I., 69-72, 447
Arnon, I., 278-80, 283, 284, 286, 297
Arnstein, H. R. V., 34
Arpin, M., 31
Arron, G. P., 115
Arsenault, G. P., 164, 166
Arthur, W. E., 48
Artus, C. S., 38
Arunachalam, T., 473
Asahi, T., 207
Asakawa, Y., 171
Ashida, J., 545, 547
Ashton, F. M., 194
Ashton, W. M., 536

Ashwood-Smith, M. J., 26
Aspinall, D., 302
Astaurova, O. B., 29
Atkinson, D. E., 451
Atkinson, M. R., 451
Atlan, H., 29
Attoe, O. J., 525
Aurich, O., 171, 176, 181, 225
Austin, B., 391
Austin, D. G., 476
Austin, D. J., 476
Austin, S. M., 321, 325, 329, 330, 332
Ausubel, F., 263, 265, 266, 332
Ausubel, F. M., 263
Avadhani, P. N., 391
Avivi-Bleiser, N., 115
Avron, M., 60, 61, 127, 132, 133
Awad, A. S., 517
Axelrod, D., 38
Azzi, J., 48, 58, 59, 61
Azzi, J. R., 48, 49, 59, 60

B

Baarda, J. R., 449
Babcock, G. T., 56, 57
Bache, C. A., 537
Bachofen, R., 70
Badger, M. R., 391
Baertschi, P., 81
Bagdasarian, M., 103
Bahr, J. A., 381, 402
Baier, W., 280, 282
Bajer, A. S., 38
Baker, D. A., 447
Baker, D. E., 537, 539
Baker, D. N., 227
Bakker, H. J., 179
Bal, A. K., 474
Balke, N. E., 445, 449, 453
Ball, E., 205, 244, 396, 397, 399, 401, 448, 451, 452
Ballade, P., 257
Ballarin Denti, A., 448
Bamberg, S. A., 299, 301
Banfalvi, Z., 274
Baranowska, H., 524
Barber, J., 51, 61, 347, 450
Barber, J. T., 248
Barber, L., 272, 273
Barber, S. A., 514, 538, 542
Barbier, G., 542
Barbieri, G., 54, 57
Barbour, M. G., 285, 300
Barendse, G. W. M., 150
Barker, R. E., 292, 293
Barksdale, A. W., 463, 473, 474

567

SUBJECT INDEX

SUBJECT INDEX

CUMULATIVE INDEXES

CONTRIBUTING AUTHORS, VOLUMES 25-29

CHAPTER TITLES, VOLUMES 25-29